Beginning & Intermediate ALGEBRA

Fourth Edition

Julie Miller
Daytona State College

Molly O'Neill
Daytona State College

Nancy Hyde
Broward College—Professor Emeritus

MAT 094/136

Special Edition for Norwalk Community College

Mc Graw Hill Education

1 2 3 4 5 6 7 8 9 0 BKM BKM 19 18 17 16

ISBN-13: 978-1-260-02253-7
ISBN-10: 1-260-02253-6

Solutions Program Manager: Nicole Schmitt
Project Manager: Lynn Nagel
Cover Photo Credits:
(student/diagram) © Hemera Technologies
(background) © Hemera Technologies

Letter from the Authors

Dear Colleagues,

We originally embarked on this textbook project because we were seeing a lack of student success in our developmental math sequence. In short, we were not getting the results we wanted from our students with the materials and textbooks that we were using at the time. The primary goal of our project was to create teaching and learning materials that would get better results.

At Daytona State College, our students were instrumental in helping us develop the clarity of writing; the step-by-step examples; and the pedagogical elements, such as Avoiding Mistakes, Concept Connections, and Problem Recognition Exercises, found in our textbooks. They also helped us create the content for the McGraw-Hill lecture videos and dynamic Flash animations that accompany this text.

This project has been a true collaboration with our Board of Advisors and colleagues in developmental mathematics around the country. We are sincerely humbled by those of you who have used our books and by the over 400 colleagues around the country who have partnered with us providing valuable suggestions through reviews, symposia, focus groups, and being on our Board of Advisors. You partnered with us to create materials that will help students get better results. For that we are immeasurably grateful.

As an author team, we have an ongoing commitment to provide the best possible text materials for instructors and students. With your continued help and suggestions we will continue the quest to help all of our students get better results.

Sincerely,

Julie Miller
julie.miller.math@gmail.com

Molly O'Neill
molly.s.oneill@gmail.com

Nancy Hyde
nhyde@montanasky.com

About the Authors

Julie Miller is from Daytona State College, where she has taught developmental and upper-level mathematics courses for 20 years. Prior to her work at Daytona State College, she worked as a software engineer for General Electric in the area of flight and radar simulation. Julie earned a bachelor of science in applied mathematics from Union College in Schenectady, New York, and a master of science in mathematics from the University of Florida. In addition to this textbook, she has authored several course supplements for college algebra, trigonometry, and precalculus, as well as several short works of fiction and nonfiction for young readers.

"My father is a medical researcher, and I got hooked on math and science when I was young and would visit his laboratory. I can remember using graph paper to plot data points for his experiments and doing simple calculations. He would then tell me what the peaks and features in the graph meant in the context of his experiment. I think that applications and hands-on experience made math come alive for me and I'd like to see math come alive for my students."

—Julie Miller

Molly O'Neill is also from Daytona State College, where she has taught for 22 years in the School of Mathematics. She has taught a variety of courses from developmental mathematics to calculus. Before she came to Florida, Molly taught as an adjunct instructor at the University of Michigan–Dearborn, Eastern Michigan University, Wayne State University, and Oakland Community College. Molly earned a bachelor of science in mathematics and a master of arts and teaching from Western Michigan University in Kalamazoo, Michigan. Besides this textbook, she has authored several course supplements for college algebra, trigonometry, and precalculus and has reviewed texts for developmental mathematics.

"I differ from many of my colleagues in that math was not always easy for me. But in seventh grade I had a teacher who taught me that if I follow the rules of mathematics, even I could solve math problems. Once I understood this, I enjoyed math to the point of choosing it for my career. I now have the greatest job because I get to do math every day and I have the opportunity to influence my students just as I was influenced. Authoring these texts has given me another avenue to reach even more students."

—Molly O'Neill

Nancy Hyde served as a full-time faculty member of the Mathematics Department at Broward College for 24 years. During this time she taught the full spectrum of courses from developmental math through differential equations. She received a bachelor of science degree in math education from Florida State University and a master's degree in math education from Florida Atlantic University. She has conducted workshops and seminars for both students and teachers on the use of technology in the classroom. In addition to this textbook, she has authored a graphing calculator supplement for *College Algebra*.

"I grew up in Brevard County, Florida, where my father worked at Cape Canaveral. I was always excited by mathematics and physics in relation to the space program. As I studied higher levels of mathematics I became more intrigued by its abstract nature and infinite possibilities. It is enjoyable and rewarding to convey this perspective to students while helping them to understand mathematics."

—Nancy Hyde

Dedication

To Our Students

Julie Miller ⚘ Molly O'Neill ⚘ Nancy Hyde

Contents

Study Tips 1

Chapter 1 The Set of Real Numbers 5

1.1 Fractions 6
1.2 Introduction to Algebra and the Set of Real Numbers 21
1.3 Exponents, Square Roots, and the Order of Operations 35
1.4 Addition of Real Numbers 45
1.5 Subtraction of Real Numbers 54
Problem Recognition Exercises: Addition and Subtraction of Real Numbers 62
1.6 Multiplication and Division of Real Numbers 63
Problem Recognition Exercises: Adding, Subtracting, Multiplying, and Dividing Real Numbers 74
1.7 Properties of Real Numbers and Simplifying Expressions 75
Group Activity: Evaluating Formulas Using a Calculator 88
Chapter 1 Summary 89
Chapter 1 Review Exercises 94
Chapter 1 Test 96

Chapter 2 Linear Equations and Inequalities 99

2.1 Addition, Subtraction, Multiplication, and Division Properties of Equality 100
2.2 Solving Linear Equations 112
2.3 Linear Equations: Clearing Fractions and Decimals 121
Problem Recognition Exercises: Equations vs. Expressions 128
2.4 Applications of Linear Equations: Introduction to Problem Solving 128
2.5 Applications Involving Percents 139
2.6 Formulas and Applications of Geometry 146
2.7 Mixture Applications and Uniform Motion 156
2.8 Linear Inequalities 165
Group Activity: Computing Body Mass Index (BMI) 180
Chapter 2 Summary 181
Chapter 2 Review Exercises 187
Chapter 2 Test 190
Chapter 1–2 Cumulative Review Exercises 191

Chapter 3 Graphing Linear Equations in Two Variables 193

3.1 Rectangular Coordinate System 194
3.2 Linear Equations in Two Variables 203
3.3 Slope of a Line and Rate of Change 218
3.4 Slope-Intercept Form of a Linear Equation 232
Problem Recognition Exercises: Linear Equations in Two Variables 242
3.5 Point-Slope Formula 243

3.6 Applications of Linear Equations and Modeling 251
Group Activity: Modeling a Linear Equation 259
Chapter 3 Summary 260
Chapter 3 Review Exercises 265
Chapter 3 Test 269
Chapters 1–3 Cumulative Review Exercises 271

Chapter 4 Systems of Linear Equations 273
4.1 Solving Systems of Equations by the Graphing Method 274
4.2 Solving Systems of Equations by the Substitution Method 284
4.3 Solving Systems of Equations by the Addition Method 294
Problem Recognition Exercises: Systems of Equations 304
4.4 Applications of Linear Equations in Two Variables 305
4.5 Systems of Linear Equations in Three Variables 314
4.6 Applications of Systems of Linear Equations in Three Variables 323
Group Activity: Creating Linear Models from Data 327
Chapter 4 Summary 329
Chapter 4 Review Exercises 335
Chapter 4 Test 338
Chapters 1–4 Cumulative Review Exercises 339

Chapter 5 Polynomials and Properties of Exponents 341
5.1 Multiplying and Dividing Expressions with Common Bases 342
5.2 More Properties of Exponents 352
5.3 Definitions of b^0 and b^{-n} 357
Problem Recognition Exercises: Properties of Exponents 366
5.4 Scientific Notation 367
5.5 Addition and Subtraction of Polynomials 373
5.6 Multiplication of Polynomials and Special Products 382
5.7 Division of Polynomials 392
Problem Recognition Exercises: Operations on Polynomials 403
Group Activity: The Pythagorean Theorem and a Geometric "Proof" 404
Chapter 5 Summary 405
Chapter 5 Review Exercises 408
Chapter 5 Test 411
Chapters 1–5 Cumulative Review Exercises 412

Chapter 6 Factoring Polynomials 415
6.1 Greatest Common Factor and Factoring by Grouping 416
6.2 Factoring Trinomials of the Form $x^2 + bx + c$ 426
6.3 Factoring Trinomials: Trial-and-Error Method 432
6.4 Factoring Trinomials: AC-Method 441

6.5 Difference of Squares and Perfect Square Trinomials 448
6.6 Sum and Difference of Cubes 454
Problem Recognition Exercises: Factoring Strategy 461
6.7 Solving Equations Using the Zero Product Rule 462
Problem Recognition Exercises: Polynomial Expressions Versus Polynomial Equations 469
6.8 Applications of Quadratic Equations 470
Group Activity: Building a Factoring Test 477
Chapter 6 Summary 478
Chapter 6 Review Exercises 483
Chapter 6 Test 485
Chapters 1–6 Cumulative Review Exercises 486

Chapter 7 Rational Expressions and Equations 487
7.1 Introduction to Rational Expressions 488
7.2 Multiplication and Division of Rational Expressions 498
7.3 Least Common Denominator 505
7.4 Addition and Subtraction of Rational Expressions 511
Problem Recognition Exercises: Operations on Rational Expressions 521
7.5 Complex Fractions 522
7.6 Rational Equations 530
Problem Recognition Exercises: Comparing Rational Equations and Rational Expressions 540
7.7 Applications of Rational Equations and Proportions 541
Group Activity: Computing Monthly Mortgage Payments 552
Chapter 7 Summary 553
Chapter 7 Review Exercises 558
Chapter 7 Test 560
Chapters 1–7 Cumulative Review Exercises 561

Chapter 8 Relations and Functions 563
8.1 Introduction to Relations 564
8.2 Introduction to Functions 573
8.3 Graphs of Functions 585
Problem Recognition Exercises: Characteristics of Relations 597
8.4 Algebra of Functions and Composition 598
8.5 Variation 605
Group Activity: **Deciphering a Coded Message** 614
Chapter 8 Summary 615
Chapter 8 Review Exercises 618
Chapter 8 Test 621
Chapters 1–8 Cumulative Review Exercises 623

Chapter 9 More Equations and Inequalities 625

9.1 Compound Inequalities 626
9.2 Polynomial and Rational Inequalities 638
9.3 Absolute Value Equations 649
9.4 Absolute Value Inequalities 656
Problem Recognition Exercises: Equations and Inequalities 666
9.5 Linear Inequalities and Systems of Linear Inequalities in Two Variables 667
Group Activity: **Recognizing Inequality Types** 680
Chapter 9 Summary 681
Chapter 9 Review Exercises 686
Chapter 9 Test 689
Chapters 1–9 Cumulative Review Exercises 690

Chapter 10 Radicals and Complex Numbers 693

10.1 Definition of an nth Root 694
10.2 Rational Exponents 706
10.3 Simplifying Radical Expressions 713
10.4 Addition and Subtraction of Radicals 720
10.5 Multiplication of Radicals 726
Problem Recognition Exercises: Simplifying Radical Expressions 734
10.6 Division of Radicals and Rationalization 734
10.7 Solving Radical Equations 744
10.8 Complex Numbers 754
Group Activity: Margin of Error of Survey Results 764
Chapter 10 Summary 766
Chapter 10 Review Exercises 772
Chapter 10 Test 775
Chapters 1–10 Cumulative Review Exercises 776

Chapter 11 Quadratic Equations and Functions 779

11.1 Square Root Property and Completing the Square 780
11.2 Quadratic Formula 790
11.3 Equations in Quadratic Form 804
Problem Recognition Exercises: Quadratic and Quadratic Type Equations 809
11.4 Graphs of Quadratic Functions 810
11.5 Vertex of a Parabola: Applications and Modeling 824
Group Activity: Creating a Quadratic Model of the Form $y = a(x - h)^2 + k$ 834
Chapter 11 Summary 836
Chapter 11 Review Exercises 840
Chapter 11 Test 843
Chapters 1–11 Cumulative Review Exercises 844

Chapter 12 Exponential and Logarithmic Functions and Applications 847

12.1 Inverse Functions 848
12.2 Exponential Functions 857
12.3 Logarithmic Functions 867
Problem Recognition Exercises: Identifying Graphs of Functions 880
12.4 Properties of Logarithms 881
12.5 The Irrational Number e and Change of Base 889
Problem Recognition Exercises: Logarithmic and Exponential Forms 902
12.6 Logarithmic and Exponential Equations and Applications 903
Group Activity: Creating a Population Model 915
Chapter 12 Summary 917
Chapter 12 Review Exercises 921
Chapter 12 Test 924
Chapters 1–12 Cumulative Review Exercises 926

Chapter 13 Conic Sections 929

13.1 Distance Formula, Midpoint Formula, and Circles 930
13.2 More on the Parabola 941
13.3 The Ellipse and Hyperbola 950
Problem Recognition Exercises: Formulas and Conic Sections 959
13.4 Nonlinear Systems of Equation in Two Variables 960
13.5 Nonlinear Inequalities and Systems of Inequalities 967
Group Activity: Investigating the Graphs of Conic Sections on a Calculator 976
Chapter 13 Summary 977
Chapter 13 Review Exercises 982
Chapter 13 Test 985
Chapters 1–13 Cumulative Review Exercises 987

Chapter 14 Binomial Expansions, Sequences, and Series 989

14.1 Binomial Expansions 990
14.2 Sequences and Series 996
14.3 Arithmetic Sequences and Series 1005
14.4 Geometric Sequences and Series 1011
Problem Recognition Exercises: Identifying Arithmetic and Geometric Sequences 1019
Group Activity: Investigating Mean and Standard Deviation 1020
Chapter 14 Summary 1021
Chapter 14 Review Exercises 1024
Chapter 14 Test 1025
Chapters 1–14 Cumulative Review Exercises 1027

Additional Topics Appendix A-1

A.1 Additional Factoring A-1
A.2 Mean, Median, and Mode A-6
A.3 Introduction to Geometry A-15
A.4 Solving Systems of Linear Equations by Using Matrices A-31
A.5 Determinants and Cramer's Rule A-41

Student Answer Appendix SA-1

Online Appendix B (www.mhhe.com/moh)

B.1 Transformations of Graphs and Piecewise-Defined Functions
B.2 Fundamentals of Counting
B.3 Introduction to Probability
B.4 Review of the Set of Real Numbers
B.5 Review of Linear Equations and Linear Inequalities
B.6 Review of Graphing
B.7 Review of Systems of Linear Equations in Two Variables
B.8 Review of Polynomials and Properties of Exponents
B.9 Review of Factoring Polynomials and Solving Quadratic Equations
B.10 Review of Rational Expressions

Index I-1

Appendix B B-30

How Will Miller/O'Neill/Hyde Help Your Students *Get Better Results?*

Better Clarity, Quality, and Accuracy!

Julie Miller, Molly O'Neill, and Nancy Hyde know what students need to be successful in mathematics. Better results come from clarity in their exposition, quality of step-by-step worked examples, and accuracy of their exercises sets; but it takes more than just great authors to build a textbook series to help students achieve success in mathematics. Our authors worked with a strong mathematical team of instructors from around the country to ensure that the clarity, quality, and accuracy you expect from the Miller/O'Neill/Hyde series was included in this edition.

"The most complete text at this level in its thoroughness, accuracy, and pedagogical soundness. The best developmental mathematics text I have seen."
—Frederick Bakenhus, *Saint Phillips College*

Better Exercise Sets!

Comprehensive sets of exercises are available for every student level. Julie Miller, Molly O'Neill, and Nancy Hyde worked with a board of advisors from across the country to offer the appropriate depth and breadth of exercises for your students. **Problem Recognition Exercises** were created to improve student performance while testing.

Practice exercise sets help students progress from skill development to conceptual understanding. Student tested and instructor approved, the Miller/O'Neill/Hyde exercise sets will help your students *get better results*.

- **Problem Recognition Exercises**
- **Skill Practice Exercises**
- **Study Skills Exercises**
- **Mixed Exercises**
- **Expanding Your Skills Exercises**
- **Vocabulary and Key Concepts Exercises**

"This series was thoughtfully constructed with students' needs in mind. The Problem Recognition section was extremely well designed to focus on concepts that students often misinterpret."
—Christine V. Wetzel-Ulrich, *Northampton Community College*

Better Step-By-Step Pedagogy!

Beginning and Intermediate Algebra provides enhanced step-by-step learning tools to help students *get better results.*

- **Worked Examples** provide an "easy-to-understand" approach, clearly guiding each student through a step-by-step approach to master each practice exercise for better comprehension.
- **TIPs** offer students extra cautious direction to help improve understanding through hints and further insight.
- **Avoiding Mistakes** boxes alert students to common errors and provide practical ways to avoid them. Both of these learning aids will help students get better results by showing how to work through a problem using a clearly defined step-by-step methodology that has been class tested and student approved.

"The book is designed with both instructors and students in mind. I appreciate that great care was used in the placement of 'Tips' and 'Avoiding Mistakes' as it creates a lot of teachable moments in the classroom."
—Shannon Vinson, *Wake Tech Community College*

Get Better Results

Formula for Student Success

Step-by-Step Worked Examples

- Do you get the feeling that there is a disconnection between your students' class work and homework?
- Do your students have trouble finding worked examples that match the practice exercises?
- Do you prefer that your students see examples in the textbook that match the ones you use in class?

Miller/O'Neill/Hyde's *Worked Examples* offer a clear, concise methodology that replicates the mathematical processes used in the authors' classroom lectures!

Example 4 Solving an Application Involving Consecutive Integers

The sum of two consecutive odd integers is -188. Find the integers.

Solution:

In this example we have two unknown integers. We can let x represent either of the unknowns.

Step 1: Read the problem.

...presents the first odd integer. **Step 2:** Label the unknowns.

...sents the second odd integer.

$\begin{pmatrix}\text{second}\\ \text{integer}\end{pmatrix} = (\text{total})$ **Step 3:** Write a verbal model.

$(x + 2) = -188$ **Step 4:** Write a mathematical equation.

$+ (x + 2) = -188$

$2x + 2 = -188$ **Step 5:** S...

$x + 2 - 2 = -188 - 2$

$2x = -190$

$\frac{2x}{2} = \frac{-190}{2}$

$x = -95$

The first integer is $x = -95$. **Step 6:** I...

The second integer is $x + 2 = -95 + 2 = -93$.

The two integers are -95 and -93.

"As always, MOH's Worked Examples are so clear and useful for the students. All steps have wonderfully detailed explanations written with wording that the students can understand. MOH is also excellent with arrows and labels making the Worked Examples extremely clear and understandable."
—Kelli Hammer, *Broward College–South*

"Easy to read step-by-step solutions to sample textbook problems. The 'why' is provided for students, which is invaluable when working exercises without available teacher/tutor assistance."
—Arcola Sullivan, *Copiah-Lincoln Community College*

Example 3 Solving a System of Linear Equations by Graphing

Solve the system by the graphing method.

$$x - 2y = -2$$
$$-3x + 2y = 6$$

30. $x + y = -1$

$2x - y = -5$

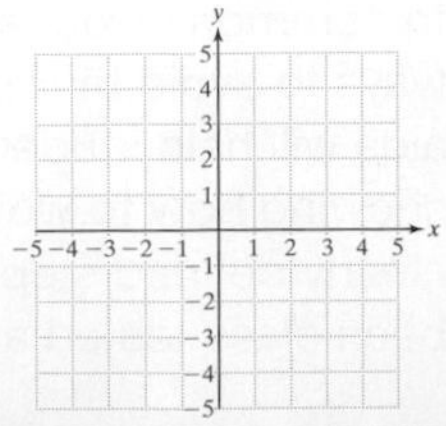

Classroom Examples

To ensure that the classroom experience also matches the examples in the text and the practice exercises, we have included references to even-numbered exercises to be used as Classroom Examples. These exercises are highlighted in the Practice Exercises at the end of each section.

Better Learning Tools

Chapter Openers

Tired of students not being prepared? The Miller/O'Neill/Hyde *Chapter Openers* help students get better results through engaging *Puzzles and Games* that introduce the chapter concepts and ask "Are You Prepared?"

Chapter 6

This chapter is devoted to factoring polynomials for the purpose of solving equations.

Are You Prepared?

Along the way, we will need the skill of recognizing perfect squares and perfect cubes. A perfect square is a number that is a square of a rational number. For example, 49 is a perfect square because $49 = 7^2$. We also will need to recognize perfect cubes. A perfect cube is a number that is a cube of a rational number. For example, 125 is a perfect cube because $125 = 5^3$.

To complete the puzzle, first answer the questions and fill in the appropriate box. Then fill the grid so that every row, every column, and every 2×3 box contains the digits 1 through 6.

A. What number squared is 1?
B. What number squared is 16?
ber cubed is 1?
ber squared is 36?
ber squared is 25?
ber cubed is 64?
ber cubed is 8?
ber cubed is 27?
ber squared is 4?
ber squared is 9?

			A		B
	C			D	E
F		1		G	H
I		5			
1	4				2
	5		J		

"I really like the chapter openers in MOH. The problems are a nice way to begin a class, and with the 'message' at the end, students can self check, and at some point can guess the answer similar to *Wheel of Fortune.* The activity is easy enough so that students feel confident, but at the same time, gives a nice review."
—Leonora Smook, *Suffolk County Community College*

TIP and Avoiding Mistakes Boxes

TIP and **Avoiding Mistakes** boxes have been created based on the authors' classroom experiences—they have also been integrated into the **Worked Examples.** These pedagogical tools will help students get better results by learning how to work through a problem using a clearly defined step-by-step methodology.

Example 2 Multiplying Rational Expressions

Multiply. $\dfrac{3c - 3d}{6c} \cdot \dfrac{2}{c^2 - d^2}$

Solution:

$\dfrac{3c - 3d}{6c} \cdot \dfrac{2}{c^2 - d^2}$

$= \dfrac{3(c - d)}{2 \cdot 3 \cdot c} \cdot \dfrac{2}{(c - d)(c + d)}$ Factor.

$= \dfrac{\cancel{3}(\cancel{c - d})}{\cancel{2} \cdot \cancel{3} \cdot c} \cdot \dfrac{\cancel{2}}{(\cancel{c - d})(c + d)}$ Simplify.

$= \dfrac{1}{c(c + d)}$ Multiply remaining factors.

Avoiding Mistakes

If all the factors in the numerato reduce to a ratio of 1, a factor o 1 is left in the numerator.

Skill Practice Multiply.

2. $\dfrac{4x - 8}{x + 6} \cdot \dfrac{x^2 + 6x}{2x}$

Answers

1. $\dfrac{5}{2a}$ **2.** $2(x - 2)$

Avoiding Mistakes Boxes

Avoiding Mistakes boxes are integrated throughout the textbook to alert students to common errors and how to avoid them.

"MOH presentation of reinforcement concepts builds students' confidence and provides easy to read guidance in developing basic skills and understanding concepts. I love the visual clue boxes 'Avoiding Mistakes.' Visual clue boxes provide tips and advice to assist students in avoiding common mistakes."
—Arcola Sullivan, *Copiah-Lincoln Community College*

TIP Boxes

Teaching tips are usually revealed only in the classroom. Not anymore! TIP boxes offer students helpful hints and extra direction to help improve understanding and provide further insight.

TIP: The acronym, FOIL (first outer inner last) can be used as a memory device to multiply the two binomials.

Outer terms, First terms, Inner terms, Last terms — First, Outer, Inner, Last

$(3y + 2)(7y - 6) = (3y)(7y) + (3y)(-6) + (2)(7y) + (2)(-6)$

$= 21y^2 - 18y + 14y - 12$

$= 21y^2 - 4y - 12$

Note: It is important to realize that the acronym FOIL may only be used when finding the product of two *binomials*.

Get Better Results

Better Exercise Sets! Better Practice! Better Results!

- Do your students have trouble with problem solving?
- Do you want to help students overcome math anxiety?
- Do you want to help your students improve performance on math assessments?

Problem Recognition Exercises

Problem Recognition Exercises present a collection of problems that look similar to a student upon first glance, but are actually quite different in the manner of their individual solutions. Students sharpen critical thinking skills and better develop their "solution recall" to help them distinguish the method needed to solve an exercise—an essential skill in developmental mathematics.

Problem Recognition Exercises were tested in the authors' developmental mathematics classes and were created to improve student performance on tests.

"The PREs are an excellent source of additional mixed problem sets. Frequently students have questions/comments like 'Where do I start?' or 'I know what to do once I get started, but I have trouble getting started.' Perhaps with these PREs, students will be able to overcome this obstacle."
—Erika Blanken, *Daytona State College*

Problem Recognition Exercises

Equations and Inequalities

For Exercises 1–24, identify the category for each equation or inequality (choose from the list here). Then solve the equation or inequality. Express the solution in interval notation where appropriate.

- Linear
- Quadratic
- Polynomial (degree greater than 2)
- Rational
- Absolute value

1. $z^2 + 10z + 9 > 0$ **2.** $5a - 2 = 6(a + 4)$ **3.** $\frac{x - 4}{2x + 4} \geq 1$

4. $4x^2 - 7x = 2$ **5.** $|3x - 1| + 4 < 6$ **6.** $2t^2 - t + 1 < 0$

7. $\frac{1}{2}p - \frac{2}{3} < \frac{1}{6}p - 4$ **8.** $p^2 + 3p \leq 4$ **9.** $3y^2 + y - 2 \geq 0$

10. $\frac{x + 6}{x + 4} = 7$ **11.** $3(2x - 4) \geq 1 - (x - 3)$ **12.** $|6x + 5| + 3 = 2$

13. $(x - 3)(2x + 1)(x + 5) \geq 0$ **14.** $-x^2 - x - 3 \leq 0$ **15.** $\frac{-6}{y - 2} < 2$

18. $x^2 - 36 < 0$

21. $5b - 10 - 3b = 3(b - 2) - 4$

24. $4x(x - 5)^2(2x + 3) < 0$

"These are so important to test whether a student can recognize different types of problems and the method of solving each. They seem very unique—I have not noticed this feature in many other texts or at least your presentation of the problems is very organized and unique."
—Linda Kuroski, *Erie Community College*

Student Centered Applications!

The Miller/O'Neill/Hyde Board of Advisors partnered with our authors to bring the *best applications* from every region in the country! These applications include real data and topics that are more relevant and interesting to today's student.

47. A boat in distress, 21 nautical miles from a marina, travels toward the marina at 3 knots (nautical miles per hour). A coast guard cruiser leaves the marina and travels toward the boat at 25 knots. How long will it take for the boats to reach each other?

48. An air traffic controller observes a plane heading from New York to San Francisco traveling at 450 mph. At the same time, another plane leaves San Francisco and travels 500 mph to New York. If the distance between the airports is 2850 mi, how long will it take for the planes to pass each other?

Group Activities!

Each chapter concludes with a Group Activity to promote classroom discussion and collaboration—helping students not only to solve problems but to explain their solutions for better mathematical mastery. Group Activities are great for both full-time and adjunct instructors—bringing a more interactive approach to teaching mathematics! All required materials, activity time, and suggested group sizes are provided in the end-of-chapter material.

Group Activity

Computing Monthly Mortgage Payments

Materials: A calculator

Estimated Time: 15–20 minutes

Group Size: 3

When a person borrows money to buy a house, the bank usually requires a down payment of between 0% and 20% of the cost of the house. The bank then issues a loan for the remaining balance on the house. The loan to buy a house is called a *mortgage*. Monthly payments are made to pay off the mortgage over a period of years.

A formula to calculate the monthly payment, P, for a loan is given by the complex fraction:

$$P = \frac{\frac{Ar}{12}}{1 - \frac{1}{\left(1 + \frac{r}{12}\right)^{12t}}}$$

where
P is the monthly payment
A is the original amount of the mortgage
r is the annual interest rate written as a decimal
t is the term of the loan in years

Suppose a person wants to buy a $200,000 house. The bank requires a down payment of 20%, and the loan is issued for 30 years at 7.5% interest for 30 years.

1. Find the amount of the down payment. ___________

2. Find the amount of the mortgage. ___________

ent). ___________

stion 3 by the total number of months
xt of the problem.

n for the house? ___________

(include the down payment). ___________

"This is one part of the book that would have me adopt the MOH book. I am very big on group work for *Beginning Algebra* and many times it is difficult to think of an activity. I would conclude the chapter doing the group activity in the class. Many books just have problems for this, but the MOH book provides an actual activity."
—Sharon Giles, *Grossmont College*

"MOH's group activity involves true participation and interaction; fun with fractions!"
—Monika Bender, *Central Texas College*

Get Better Results

Dynamic Math Animations

The Miller/O'Neill/Hyde author team has developed a series of Flash animations to illustrate difficult concepts where static images and text fall short. The animations leverage the use of on-screen movement and morphing shapes to enhance conceptual learning.

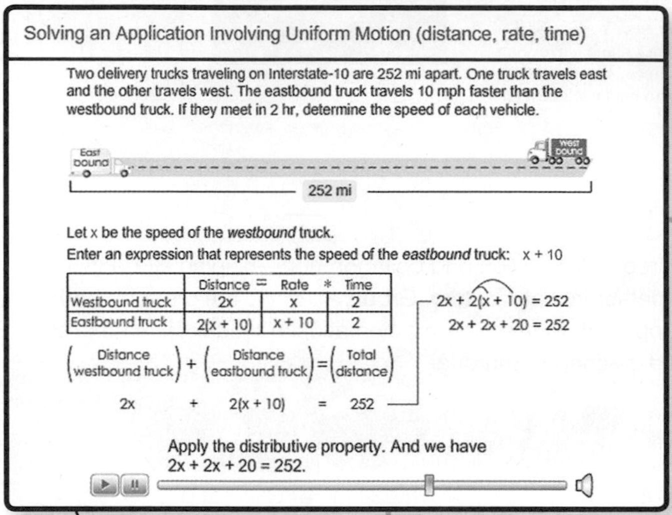

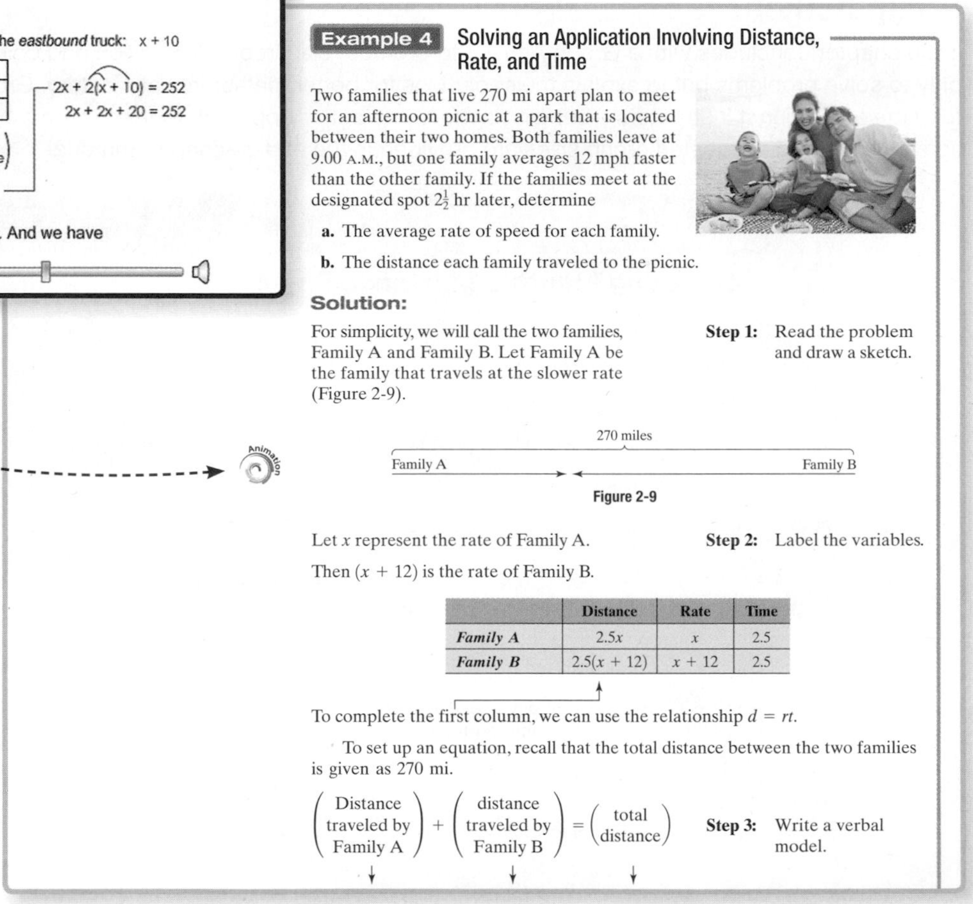

Example 4 Solving an Application Involving Distance, Rate, and Time

Two families that live 270 mi apart plan to meet for an afternoon picnic at a park that is located between their two homes. Both families leave at 9.00 A.M., but one family averages 12 mph faster than the other family. If the families meet at the designated spot $2\frac{1}{2}$ hr later, determine

a. The average rate of speed for each family.

b. The distance each family traveled to the picnic.

Solution:

For simplicity, we will call the two families, Family A and Family B. Let Family A be the family that travels at the slower rate (Figure 2-9). — **Step 1:** Read the problem and draw a sketch.

Family A → ← Family B (270 miles)

Figure 2-9

Let x represent the rate of Family A. — **Step 2:** Label the variables.

Then $(x + 12)$ is the rate of Family B.

	Distance	Rate	Time
Family A	$2.5x$	x	2.5
Family B	$2.5(x + 12)$	$x + 12$	2.5

To complete the first column, we can use the relationship $d = rt$.

To set up an equation, recall that the total distance between the two families is given as 270 mi.

$$\begin{pmatrix}\text{Distance}\\ \text{traveled by}\\ \text{Family A}\end{pmatrix} + \begin{pmatrix}\text{distance}\\ \text{traveled by}\\ \text{Family B}\end{pmatrix} = \begin{pmatrix}\text{total}\\ \text{distance}\end{pmatrix}$$

Step 3: Write a verbal model.

Through their classroom experience, the authors recognize that such media assets are great teaching tools for the classroom and excellent for online learning. The Miller/O'Neill/Hyde animations are interactive and quite diverse in their use. Some provide a virtual laboratory for which an application is simulated and where students can collect data points for analysis and modeling. Others provide interactive question-and-answer sessions to test conceptual learning. For word problem applications, the animations ask students to estimate answers and practice "number sense."

The animations were created by the authors based on over 75 years of combined teaching experience! To facilitate the use of the animations, the authors have placed icons in the text to indicate where animations are available. Students and instructors can access these assets online in either the ALEKS 360 Course product or Connect Math Hosted by ALEKS.

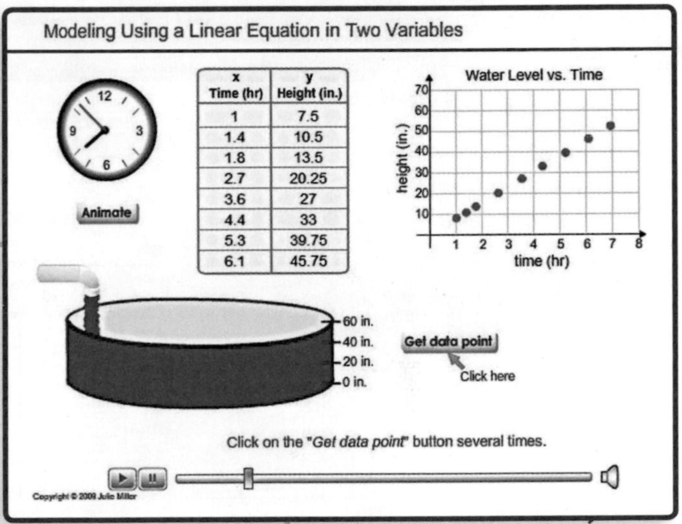

2. Writing a Linear Model Using Observed Data Points

Example 2 Writing a Linear Model from Observed Data Points

The monthly sales of hybrid cars sold in the United States are given for a recent year. The sales for the first 8 months of the year are shown in Figure 3-35. The value $x = 0$ represents January, $x = 1$ represents February, and so on.

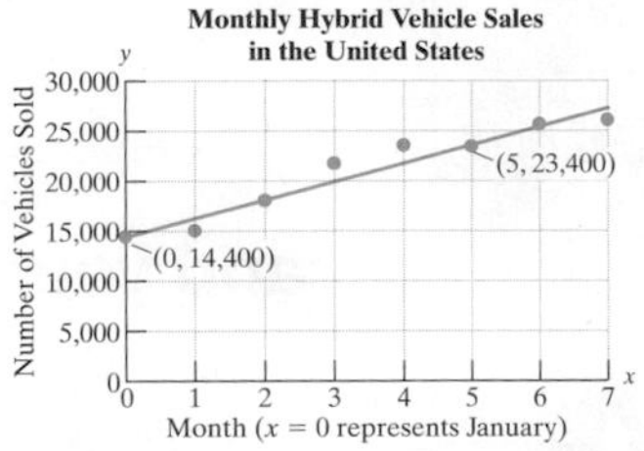

Figure 3-35

a. Use the data points from Figure 3-35 to find a linear equation that represents the monthly sales of hybrid cars in the United States. Let x represent the month number and let y represent the number of vehicles sold.

b. Use the linear equation in part (a) to estimate the number of hybrid vehicles sold in month 7 (August).

Solution:

a. The ordered pairs (0, 14,400) and (5, 23,400) are given in the graph. Use these points to find the slope.

(0, 14,400) (x_1, y_1) and (5, 23,400) (x_2, y_2) — Label the points.

$$m = \frac{y_2 - y_1}{x_2 - x_1} = \frac{23{,}400 - 14{,}400}{5 - 0}$$

$$= \frac{9000}{5}$$

$$= 1800$$

The slope is 1800. This indicates that sales increased by approximately 1800 per month during this time period.

With $m = 1800$, and the y-intercept given as (0, 14,400), we have the following linear equation in slope-intercept form.

$$y = 1800x + 14{,}400$$

b. To approximate the sales in month number 7, substitute $x = 7$ into the equation from part (a).

Quality Content For Today's Online Learners

Online Exercises were carefully selected and developed to provide a seamless transition from textbook to technology.

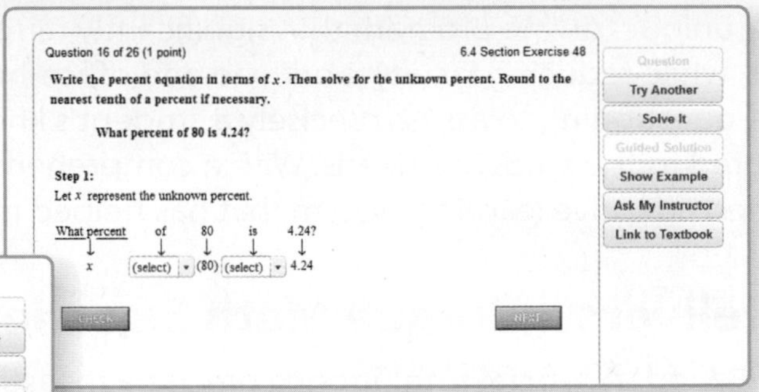

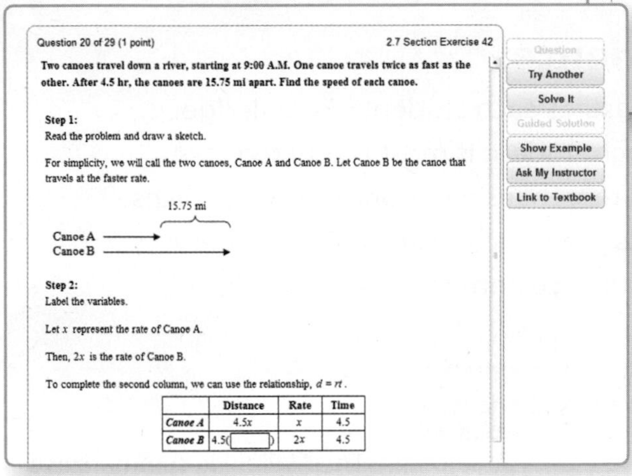

For consistency, the guided solutions match the style and voice of the original text as though the author is guiding the students through the problems.

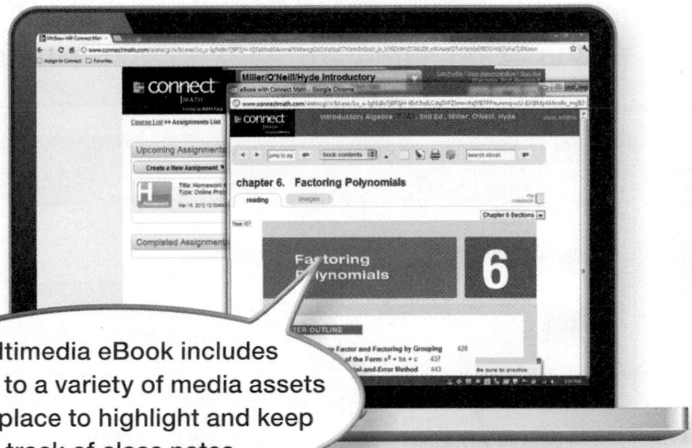

Multimedia eBook includes access to a variety of media assets and a place to highlight and keep track of class notes

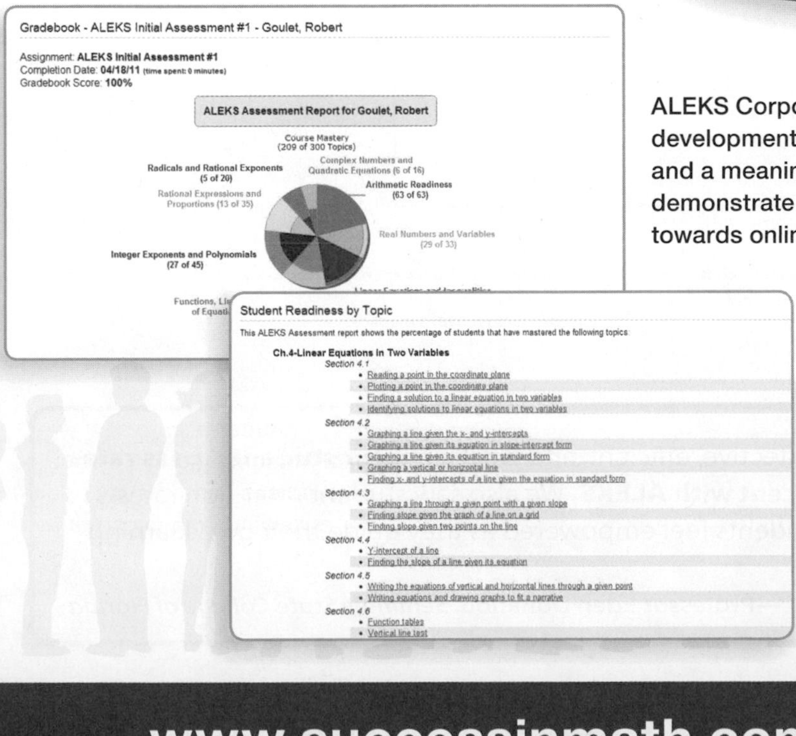

ALEKS Corporation's experience with algorithm development ensures a commitment to accuracy and a meaningful experience for students to demonstrate their understanding with a focus towards online learning.

The ALEKS® Initial Assessment is an artificially intelligent (AI), diagnostic assessment that identifies precisely what a student knows. Instructors can then use this information to make more informed decisions on what topics to cover in more detail with the class.

www.successinmath.com

Mc Graw Hill connect plus+ MATH

Hosted by **ALEKS Corp.**

ALEKS®

ALEKS is a unique, online program that significantly raises student proficiency and success rates in mathematics, while reducing faculty workload and office-hour lines. ALEKS uses artificial intelligence and adaptive questioning to assess precisely a student's knowledge, and deliver individualized learning tailored to the student's needs. With a comprehensive library of math courses, ALEKS delivers an unparalleled adaptive learning system that has helped millions of students achieve math success.

ALEKS Delivers a Unique Math Experience:

- **Research-Based, Artificial Intelligence** precisely measures each student's knowledge
- **Individualized Learning** presents the exact topics each student is most **ready to learn**
- **Adaptive, Open-Response Environment** includes comprehensive tutorials and resources
- **Detailed, Automated Reports** track student and class progress toward course mastery
- **Course Management Tools** include textbook integration, custom features, and more

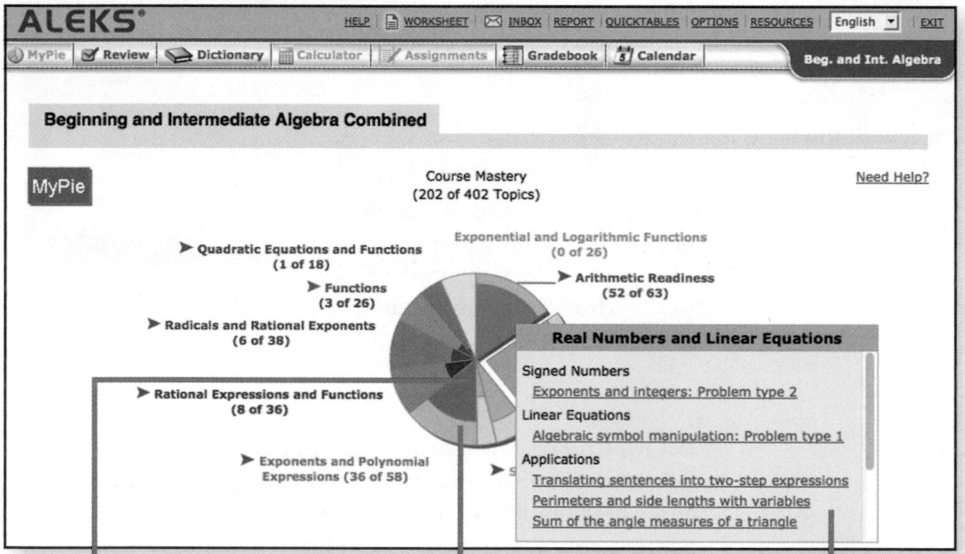

The ALEKS Pie summarizes a student's current knowledge, then delivers an individualized learning path with the exact topics the student is most ready to learn.

Dark portion represents what the student knows.

Light portion represents what the student still has to learn.

Ready to Learn topics appear in pop-up boxes when the student scrolls over a pie slice.

"My experience with ALEKS has been effective, efficient, and eloquent. **Our students' pass rates improved from 49 percent to 82 percent with ALEKS.** We also saw student retention rates increase by 12% in the next course. Students feel empowered as they guide their own learning through ALEKS."

—**Professor Eden Donahou, *Seminole State College of Florida***

To learn more about ALEKS, please visit: **www.aleks.com/highered/math**

ALEKS® Prep Products

ALEKS Prep products focus on prerequisite and introductory material, and can be used during the first six weeks of the term to ensure student success in math courses ranging from Beginning Algebra through Calculus. ALEKS Prep quickly fills gaps in prerequisite knowledge by assessing precisely each student's preparedness and delivering individualized instruction on the exact topics students are most ready to learn. As a result, instructors can focus on core course concepts and see improved student performance with fewer drops.

> "ALEKS is wonderful. It is a professional product that takes very little time as an instructor to administer. Many of our students have taken Calculus in high school, but they have forgotten important algebra skills. ALEKS gives our students an opportunity to review these important skills."
>
> —**Professor Edward E. Allen, *Wake Forest University***

ALEKS® 360 A Total Course Solution

With **eBook** Integration

A cost-effective total course solution: fully integrated, interactive eBook combined with the power of ALEKS adaptive learning and assessment.

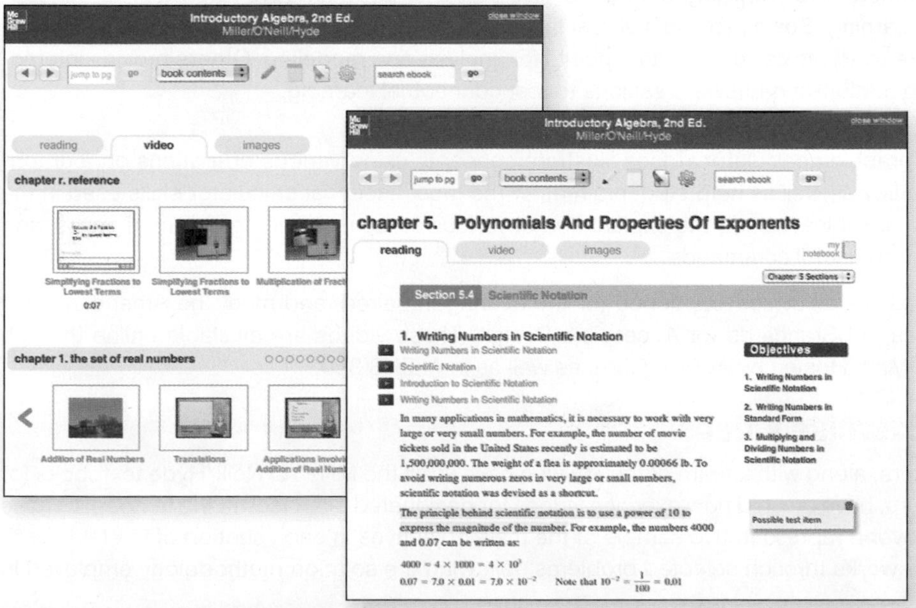

Students can easily access the full eBook content, multimedia resources, and their notes from within their ALEKS Student Accounts.

To learn more about ALEKS, please visit: **www.aleks.com/highered/math**

Additional Supplements

Student Resource Manual

The *Student Resource Manual (SRM),* created by the authors, is a printable, electronic supplement available to students through Connect Math Hosted by ALEKS Corp. Instructors can also choose to customize this manual and package with their course materials. With increasing demands on faculty schedules, this resource offers a convenient means for both full-time and adjunct faculty to promote active learning and success strategies in the classroom.

This manual supports the series in a variety of different ways:

- Discovery-based classroom activities written by the authors for each section
- Worksheets for extra practice written by the authors
- Lecture Notes designed to help students organize and take notes on key concepts
- Materials for a student portfolio

NEW Lecture Videos Created by the Authors

Julie Miller began creating these lecture videos for her own students to use when they were absent from class. The student response was overwhelmingly positive, prompting the author team to create the lecture videos for their entire developmental math book series. In these new videos, the authors walk students through the learning objectives using the same language and procedures outlined in the book. Students learn and review right alongside the author! Students can also access the written notes that accompany the videos.

- **Dynamic Math Animations**
  The authors have constructed a series of Flash animations to illustrate difficult concepts where static images and text fall short. The animations leverage the use of on-screen movement and morphing shapes to give students an interactive approach to conceptual learning. Some provide a virtual laboratory for which an application is simulated and where students can collect data points for analysis and modeling. Others provide interactive question-and-answer sessions to test conceptual learning.
- **Graphing Calculator Videos**
  The graphing calculator videos illustrate concepts using various operations on a graphing utility as well as help students master the most essential calculator skills used in the course. Topics include the explanation of various screens, avoiding common errors, and applying useful commands.

The videos are all closed-captioned for the hearing-impaired, and meet the Americans with Disabilities Act Standards for Accessible Design. These videos are available online through Connect Math Hosted by ALEKS Corp. as well as in ALEKS 360.

NEW Exercise Videos

The authors, along with a team of faculty who have used the Miller/O'Neill/Hyde textbooks for many years, have created new exercise videos for designated exercises in the textbook. These videos cover a representative sample of the main objectives in each section of the text. Each presenter works through selected problems, following the solution methodology employed in the text.

The video series is available online as part of Connect Math Hosted by ALEKS Corp. as well as in ALEKS 360. The videos are closed-captioned for the hearing impaired, and meet the Americans with Disabilities Act Standards for Accessible Design.

Annotated Instructor's Edition

In the *Annotated Instructor's Edition* (*AIE*), answers to all exercises appear adjacent to each exercise in a color used *only* for annotations. The *AIE* also contains Instructor Notes that appear in the margin. These notes offer instructors assistance with lecture preparation. In addition, there are Classroom Examples referenced in the text that are highlighted in the Practice Exercises. Also found in the *AIE* are icons within the Practice Exercises that serve to guide instructors in their preparation of homework assignments and lessons.

Powerpoints

The Powerpoints present key concepts and definitions with fully editable slides that follow the textbook. An instructor may project the slides in class or post to a website in an online course.

McGraw-Hill Connect Math Hosted by ALEKS Corp.

Connect Math Hosted by ALEKS Corp. is an exciting new assignment and assessment ehomework platform. Instructors can assign an AI-driven ALEKS Asssessment to identify the strengths and weaknesses of each student at the beginning of the term rather than after the first exam. Assignment creation and navigation is efficient and intuitive. The gradebook, based on instructor feedback, has a straightforward design and allows flexibility to import and export additional grades.

ALEKS Prep for Developmental Mathematics

ALEKS Prep for Beginning Algebra and Prep for Intermediate Algebra focus on prerequisite and introductory material for *Beginning Algebra* and *Intermediate Algebra*. These prep products can be used during the first 3 weeks of a course to prepare students for future success in the course and to increase retention and pass rates. Backed by two decades of National Science Foundation funded research, ALEKS interacts with students much like a human tutor, with the ability to precisely asses a student's preparedness and provide instruction on the topics the student is most likely to learn.

ALEKS Prep Course Products Feature:

- Artificial Intelligence Targeting Gaps in Individual Student's Knowledge
- Assessment and Learning Directed Toward Individual Student's Needs
- Open Response Environment with Realistic Input Tools
- Unlimited Online Access—PC and Mac Compatible

Free trial at www.aleks.com/free_trial/instructor

Instructor's Solutions Manual

The *Instructor's Solutions Manual* provides comprehensive, worked-out solutions to all exercises in the Chapter Openers, the Practice Exercises, the Problem Recognition Exercises, the end-of-chapter Review Exercises, the Chapter Tests, and the Cumulative Review Exercises.

Student's Solutions Manual

The *Student's Solutions Manual* provides comprehensive, worked-out solutions to the odd-numbered exercises in the Practice Exercise sets, the Problem Recognition Exercises, the end-of-chapter Review Exercises, the Chapter Tests, and the Cumulative Review Exercises. Answers to the Chapter Opener Puzzles are also provided.

Instructor's Test Bank

Among the supplements is a computerized test bank utilizing algorithm-based testing software to create customized exams quickly. Hundreds of text-specific, open-ended, and multiple-choice questions are included in the question bank. Sample chapter tests are also provided.

Get Better Results

Our Commitment to Market Development and Accuracy

McGraw-Hill's Development Process is an ongoing, never-ending, market-oriented approach to building accurate and innovative print and digital products. We begin developing a series by partnering with authors that desire to make an impact within their discipline to help students succeed. Next, we share these ideas and manuscript with instructors for review for feedback and to ensure that the authors' ideas represent the needs within that discipline. Throughout multiple drafts, we help our authors adapt to incorporate ideas and suggestions from reviewers to ensure that the series carries the same pulse as today's classrooms. With any new series, we commit to accuracy across the series and its supplements. In addition to involving instructors as we develop our content, we also utilize accuracy checks through our various stages of development and production. The following is a summary of our commitment to market development and accuracy:

1. 2 drafts of author manuscript
2. 2 rounds of manuscript review
3. 2 focus groups
4. 1 consultative, expert review
5. 2 accuracy checks
6. 2 rounds of proofreading and copyediting
7. Toward the final stages of production, we are able to incorporate additional rounds of quality assurance from instructors as they help contribute toward our digital content and print supplements

This process then will start again immediately upon publication in anticipation of the next edition. With our commitment to this process, we are confident that our series has the most developed content the industry has to offer, thus pushing our desire for quality and accurate content that meets the needs of today's students and instructors.

Acknowledgments and Reviewers

Paramount to the development of *Beginning and Intermediate Algebra* was the invaluable feedback provided by the instructors from around the country that reviewed the manuscript or attended a market development event over the course of the several years the text was in development.

AMATYC 2011 Focus Group

Shanna Goff, *Grand Rapids Community College*
Betsy McKinney, *Grand Rapids Community College*
Michelle Hempton, *Lansing Community College*
Linda Schott, *Ozarks Technical Community College*
Jessica Lopez, *Saint Philips College*
Lorraine Lopez, *San Antonio College*
Peter Georgakis, *Santa Barbara City College*

NADE 2012 Focus Group

Beth Rountree, *Brevard College*
Kelly Jackson, *Camden Community College*
Sharonlyn Moses-Polk, *Central Carolina Technical College*
Sharhonda Elmore-Rivers, *Central Carolina Technical College*
Elizabeth Valentine, *Charleston Southern University*
Joseph Hernandez, *Delta College*
Randall Nicols, *Delta College*
Thomas Wells, *Delta College*
Teresa Hasenauer, *Indian River State College*
Tiffany Lewis, *Indian River State College*
Rita Lindsay, *Indian River State College*
Deanna Voehl, *Indian River State College*
Jennifer Manor, *Pierpont Community and Technical College*
Eden Donahou, *Seminole State College of Florida*
Dave DelRossi, *Tallahassee Community College*
Natalie Johnson, *Tarrant County College*
Claudia Martinez, *Valencia College*

Reviewers of Miller/O'Neill/Hyde Developmental Mathematics Series

Maryann Faller, *Adirondack Community College*
Albert Miller, *Ball State University*
Debra Pearson, *Ball State University*
Patricia Parkison, *Ball State University*
Robin Rufatto, *Ball State University*
Melanie Walker, *Bergen Community College*
Robert Fusco, *Bergen Community College*
Latonya Ellis, *Bishop State Community College*
Ana Leon, *Bluegrass Community College & Technical College*
Kaye Black, *Bluegrass Community College & Technical College*
Barbara Elzey, *Bluegrass Community College & Technical College*
Cheryl Grant, *Bowling Green State University*
Beth Rountree, *Brevard College*
Juliet Carl, *Broward College*
Lizette Foley, *Broward College*
Angie Matthews, *Broward College*
Mitchel Levy, *Broward College*
Jody Harris, *Broward College*
Michelle Carmel, *Broward College*
Antonnette Gibbs, *Broward College*
Elizabeth Valentine, *Charleston Southern University*
Adedoyin Adeyiga, *Cheyney University of Pennsylvania*
Dot French, *Community College of Philadelphia*
Brad Berger, *Copper Mountain College*
Donna Troy, *Cuyamaca College*
Brianna Kurtz, *Daytona State College–Daytona Beach*
Jennifer Walsh, *Daytona State College–Daytona Beach*
Marc Campbell, *Daytona State College–Daytona Beach*
Richard Rupp, *Del Mar College*
Joseph Hernandez, *Delta College*
Randall Nichols, *Delta College*
Thomas Wells, *Delta College*
Paul Yun, *El Camino College*
Catherine Bliss, *Empire State College–Saratoga Springs*
Laurie Davis, *Erie Community College*
Linda Kuroski, *Erie Community College*
David Usinski, *Erie Community College*
Ron Bannon, *Essex County College*
David Platt, *Front Range Community College*
Alan Dinwiddie, *Front Range Community College*
Shanna Goff, *Grand Rapids Community College*
Betsy McKinney, *Grand Rapids Community College*
Cathy Gardner, *Grand Valley State University*
Jane Mays, *Grand Valley State University*
John Greene, *Henderson State University*
Fred Worth, *Henderson State University*
Ryan Baxter, *Illinois State University*
Angela Mccombs, *Illinois State University*
Elisha Van Meenen, *Illinois State University*
Teresa Hasenauer, *Indian River State College*
Tiffany Lewis, *Indian River State College*
Deanna Voehl, *Indian River State College*
Joe Jordan, *John Tyler Community College*

Get Better Results

Reviewers of the Miller/O'Neill/Hyde Developmental Mathematics Series

Sally Copeland, *Johnson County Community College*
Nancy Carpenter, *Johnson County Community College*
Susan Yellott, *Kilgore College*
Kim Miller, *Labette Community College*
Michelle Hempton, *Lansing Community College*
Michelle Whitmer, *Lansing Community College*
Kuen Lee, *Los Angeles Trade Tech*
Nic Lahue, *MCC-Longview Community College*
Jason Pallett, *MCC-Longview Community College*
Janet Wyatt, *MCC-Longview Community College*
Rene Barrientos, *Miami Dade College—Kendall*
Nelson De La Rosa, *Miami Dade College—Kendall*
Jody Balzer, *Milwaukee Area Technical College*
Shahla Razavi, *Mt. San Jacinto College*
Shawna Bynum, *Napa Valley College*
Tammy Ford, *North Carolina A & T University*
Ebrahim Ahmadizadeh, *Northampton Community College*
Christine Wetzel-Ulrich, *Northampton Community College*
Sharon Totten, *Northeast Alabama Community College*
Rodolfo Maglio, *Northeastern Illinios University*
Christine Copple, *Northwest State Community College*
Sumitana Chatterjee, *Nova Community College*
Charbel Fahed, *Nova Community College*
Ken Hirschel, *Orange County Community College*
Linda K. Schott, *Ozarks Technical Community College*
Matthew Harris, *Ozarks Technical Community College*
Daniel Kopsas, *Ozarks Technical Community College*
Andrew Aberle, *Ozarks Technical Community College*
Alan Papen, *Ozarks Technical Community College*
Angela Shreckhise, *Ozarks Technical Community College*
Jacob Lewellen, *Ozarks Technical Community College*
Marylynne Abbott, *Ozarks Technical Community College*
Jeffrey Gervasi, *Porterville College*
Stewart Hathaway, *Porterville College*
Lauran Johnson, *Richard Bland College*
Matthew Nickodemus, *Richard Bland College*
Cameron English, *Rio Hondo College*
Lydia Gonzalez, *Rio Hondo College*
Mark Littrell, *Rio Hondo College*
Matthew Pitassi, *Rio Hondo College*
Wayne Lee, *Saint Philips College*
Paula Looney, *Saint Philips College*
Fred Bakenhus, *Saint Philips College*
Lydia Casas, *Saint Philips College*
Gloria Guerra, *Saint Philips College*
Sounny Slitine, *Saint Philips College*
Jessica Lopez, *Saint Philips College*
Lorraine Lopez, *San Antonio College*
Peter Georgakis, *Santa Barbara City College*
Sandi Nieto-Navarro, *Santa Rosa Junior College*
Steve Drucker, *Santa Rosa Junior College*
Jean-Marie Magnier, *Springfield Tech Community College*
Dave Delrossi, *Tallahassee Community College*
Natalie Johnson, *Tarrant County College South*
Marilyn Peacock, *Tidewater Community College*
Yvonne Aucoin, *Tidewater Community College*
Cynthia Harris, *Triton College*
Jennifer Burkett, *Triton College*
Christyn Senese, *Triton College*
Jennifer Dale, *Triton College*
Patricia Hussey, *Triton College*
Glenn Jablonski, *Triton College*
Myrna La Rosa, *Triton College*
Michael Maltenfort, *Truman College*
Abdallah Shuaibi, *Truman College*
Marta Hidegkuti, *Truman College*
Sandra Wilder, *University of Akron*
Sandra Jovicic, *University of Akron*
Edward Migliore, *University of California–Santa Cruz*
Carolann Van Galder, *University of Wisconsin—Rock County*
Claudia Martinez, *Valencia College*
Stephen Toner, *Victor Valley Community College*
David Cooper, *Wake Tech Community College*
Karlata Elliott, *Wake Tech Community College*
Laura Kalbaugh, *Wake Tech Community College*
Kelly Vetter, *Wake Tech Community College*
Jacqui Fields, *Wake Tech Community College*
Jennifer Smeal, *Wake Tech Community College*
Shannon Vinson, *Wake Tech Community College*
Kim Walaski, *Wake Tech Community College*
Maziar Ouliaeinia, *Western Iowa Tech Community College*
Keith McCoy, *Wilbur Wright College*

Also, a special thanks to all instructors who have reviewed previous editions of this series.

Acknowledgments

The author team most humbly would like to thank all the people who have contributed to this project.

Special thanks to our team of digital authors for their thousands of hours of work: Jody Harris, Linda Schott, Lizette Hernandez Foley, Michael Larkin, Alina Coronel, and to the masters of ceremonies in the digital world: Donna Gerken, Nicole Lloyd, and Steve Toner. We also offer our sincerest appreciation to the video talent: Jody Harris, Alina Coronel, Didi Quesada, Tony Alfonso, and Brianna Kurtz. You folks are the best! To Mitchel Levy our exercise consultant, thank you for your watchful eye fine-tuning the exercise sets and for your ongoing valuable feedback. To Gene Rumann, thank you so much for ensuring accuracy in our manuscripts.

Finally, we greatly appreciate the many people behind the scenes at McGraw-Hill without whom we would still be on page 1. To Emily Williams, the best developmental editor in the business and steady rock that has kept the train on the track. To Mary Ellen Rahn, our executive editor and overall team leader. We're forever grateful for your support and innovative ideas. To our copy editor Pat Steele who has watched over our manuscript for many years and has been a long-time mentor for our writing. You're amazing. To the marketing team Alex Coleman, Peter Vaneria, Tim Cote, John Osgood, and Cheryl Sowa, thank you for your creative ideas in making our books come to life in the market. To the directors of digital content team, Emilie Berglund and Nicole Lloyd, we are most grateful for your long hours of work and innovation in a world that changes day-to-day. And many thanks to the team at ALEKS that oversees quality control in the digital content. To the production team Peggy Selle, Sherry Kane, Laurie Janssen, and Carrie Burger for making the manuscript beautiful and bringing it all together. And finally to Dawn Bercier, Ryan Blankenship, Marty Lange, and Kurt Strand, thank you for supporting our projects over the years and for the confidence you've always shown in us.

Most importantly, we give special thanks to the students and instructors who use our series in their classes.

New and Updated Content for Miller, O'Neill, and Hyde's *Beginning and Intermediate Algebra*, Fourth Edition:

Updates throughout the Text:

- New Vocabulary and Key Concept Exercises
- New Tips and Avoiding Mistakes boxes
- Updated Applications and Data in all instances where appropriate

Chapter by Chapter Changes:

BIA Chapter 1

- 54 new exercises
- 39 new vocabulary exercises
- 47 new PRE exercises
- 5 new examples
- Chapter R content is no longer labeled as a separate chapter. It still appears before Chapter 1.
- Rewrote narrative in Section 1.2: Introduction to Algebra and the Set of Real Numbers to include an objective on Variables and Expressions.
- Reorganized narrative in Section 1.3: Exponents, Square Roots, and the Order of Operations to not include objective on Evaluating Algebraic Expressions.
- New narrative written in Section 1.3: Exponents, Square Roots, and the Order of Operations about the objective on Translations.

BIA Chapter 2

- 41 new exercises
- 21 new vocabulary exercises
- 2 new PRE exercises
- 8 new examples
- Revised definition of a Linear Equation, Literal Equation, and Linear Inequality in One Variable.
- Revised narrative on Conditional Equations, Contradictions, and Identities.
- Included Set Builder Notation in the exercise set on Linear Inequalities.

BIA Chapter 3

- 30 new exercises
- 24 new vocabulary exercises
- 1 new example

BIA Chapter 4

- 12 new exercises
- 11 new vocabulary exercises
- 4 new PRE exercises
- 1 new example
- Reorganized Section 4.1: Solving Systems of Equations by the Graphing Method so that Dependent and Inconsistent Systems of Linear Equations are not a separate objective.
- Changed terminology from dependent system of linear equations to system of dependent equations throughout Section 4.5.

BIA Chapter 5

- 42 new exercises
- 23 new vocabulary exercises
- 18 new PRE exercises
- 2 new examples
- Revised definition of b^0.
- Reorganized chapter so that Problem Recognition Exercises: Properties of Exponents comes before Section 5.4: Scientific Notation.
- Revised narrative on writing polynomials in descending order.

BIA Chapter 6

- 23 new exercises
- 32 new vocabulary exercises
- 2 new examples

BIA Chapter 7

- 33 new exercises
- 14 new vocabulary exercises
- 2 new examples
- New chapter title to better reflect content.
- New narrative on finding the restricted values of a rational expression.
- Revised narrative on complex fractions.
- Revised Definition of Ratio and Proportion.

BIA Chapter 8

- 13 new exercises
- 22 new vocabulary exercises
- new PRE exercises
- Updated definition of Composition of Functions.

BIA Chapter 9

- 14 new exercises
- 23 new vocabulary exercises
- 2 new example
- Changed title of Section 9.5 to Linear Inequalities and Systems of Linear Inequalities in Two Variables. Also updated Objective 3 title to Systems of Linear Inequalities in Two Variables.
- New Procedure Box on solving a compound inequality. Broke apart into two boxes, 'And' and 'Or'.
- Reworked Procedure Box on Graphing a Linear Inequality in Two Variables.
- Updated examples and exercises in Section 9.5 to reflect a System of Linear Inequalities in Two Variables rather than a Compound Linear Inequality.

BIA Chapter 10

- 43 new exercises
- 48 new vocabulary exercises
- 6 new examples
- Additional explanation provided in Examples of Section 10.1, in the Definition Box of an *nth* Root.
- Reworked Property Box on $\sqrt[n]{a}$ and the explanation following.
- Split Example 4 into two separate Examples in Section 10.3.
- Rewrote narrative and Procedure Box on a radical equation with extraneous solutions.
- Rewrote Definition of $\sqrt{-b}$ for $b > 0$.

BIA Chapter 11

- 16 new exercises
- 39 new vocabulary exercises
- 4 new examples
- Rewrote narrative introducing the square root property, vertical shift, and horizontal shift.

BIA Chapter 12

- 10 new exercises
- 43 new vocabulary exercises
- 1 new example
- Included additional images and narrative to explain a One-to-One Function.
- New narrative on verifying if two functions are inverses.
- New definition on an Inverse Function.
- Reorganized Section 12.1 so that Introduction to the Inverse of a Function appears before finding the equation of the inverse of a function.

BIA Chapter 13

- 7 new exercises
- 17 new vocabulary exercises
- 2 new PRE exercises
- 3 new examples
- Provides the standard form of a circle, an ellipse at the beginning of the explanation for each example where appropriate.
- New narrative on graphing an ellipse and a hyperbola at the origin and on the introduction to nonlinear inequalities in two variables.

BIA Chapter 14

- 26 new exercises
- 21 new vocabulary exercises
- 4 new PRE exercises
- 4 new examples
- New Calculator Connections Box.
- Rewrote explanation on common difference.

BIA Additional Topics Appendix A

- 8 new exercises
- 8 new vocabulary exercises
- 1 new section on Additional Factoring
- Changed terminology from Dependent Systems to a System of Dependent Equations.

BIA Additional Topics Appendix B

- 3 new exercises
- 1 new example

Study Tips

In taking a course in algebra, you are making a commitment to yourself, your instructor, and your classmates. Following some or all of the study tips presented here can help you be successful in this endeavor. The features of this text that will assist you are printed in blue.

Concepts

1. Before the Course
2. During the Course
3. Preparation for Exams
4. Where to Go for Help

1. Before the Course

1. Purchase the necessary materials for the course before the course begins or on the first day.
2. Obtain a three-ring binder to keep and organize your notes, homework, tests, and any other materials acquired in the class. We call this type of notebook a portfolio.
3. Arrange your schedule so that you have enough time to attend class and to do homework. A common rule is to set aside at least 2 hours for homework for every hour spent in class. That is, if you are taking a 4-credit-hour course, plan on at least 8 hours a week for homework. A 6-credit-hour course will then take *at least* 12 hours each week—about the same as a part-time job. If you experience difficulty in mathematics, plan for more time.
4. Communicate with your employer and family members the importance of your success in this course so that they can support you.
5. Be sure to find out the type of calculator (if any) that your instructor requires.

2. During the Course

1. Read the section in the text *before* the lecture to familiarize yourself with the material and terminology. It is recommended that you read your math book with paper and pencil in hand. Write a one-sentence preview of what the section is about.
2. Attend every class, and be on time. Be sure to bring any materials that are needed for class such as graph paper, a ruler, or a calculator.
3. Take notes in class. Write down all of the examples that the instructor presents. Read the notes after class, and add any comments to make your notes clearer to you. Use a tape recorder to record the lecture if the instructor permits the recording of lectures.
4. Ask questions in class.
5. Read the section in the text *after* the lecture, and pay special attention to the Tip boxes and Avoiding Mistakes boxes.
6. After you read an example, try the accompanying Skill Practice problem. The skill practice problem mirrors the example and tests your understanding of what you have read.
7. Do homework every day. Even if your class does not meet every day, you should still do some work every day to keep the material fresh in your mind.
8. Check your homework with the answers that are supplied in the back of this text. Correct the exercises that do not match, and circle or star those that you cannot correct yourself. This way you can easily find them and ask your instructor, tutor, online tutor, or math lab staff the next day.

9. Be sure to do the Vocabulary and Key Concepts exercises found at the beginning of the Practice Exercises.
10. The Problem Recognition Exercises are located in all chapters. These provide additional practice distinguishing among a variety of problem types. Sometimes the most difficult part of learning mathematics is retaining all that you learn. These exercises are excellent tools for retention of material.
11. Form a study group with fellow students in your class, and exchange phone numbers. You will be surprised by how much you can learn by talking about mathematics with other students.
12. If you use a calculator in your class, read the Calculator Connections boxes to learn how and when to use your calculator.
13. Ask your instructor where you might obtain extra help if necessary.

3. Preparation for Exams

1. Look over your homework. Pay special attention to the exercises you have circled or starred to be sure that you have learned that concept.
2. Begin preparations for exams on the first day of class. As you do each homework assignment, think about how you would recognize similar problems when they appear on a test.
3. Read through the Summary at the end of the chapter. Be sure that you understand each concept and example. If not, go to the section in the text and reread that section.
4. Give yourself enough time to take the Chapter Test uninterrupted. Then check the answers. For each problem you answered incorrectly, go to the Review Exercises and do all of the problems that are similar.
5. To prepare for the final exam, complete the Cumulative Review Exercises at the end of each chapter, starting with Chapter 2. If you complete the cumulative reviews after finishing each chapter, then you will be preparing for the final exam throughout the course. The Cumulative Review Exercises are another excellent tool for helping you retain material.

4. Where to Go for Help

1. At the first sign of trouble, see your instructor. Most instructors have specific office hours set aside to help students. Don't wait until after you have failed an exam to seek assistance.
2. Get a tutor. Most colleges and universities have free tutoring available. There may also be an online tutor available.
3. When your instructor and tutor are unavailable, use the Student Solutions Manual for step-by-step solutions to the odd-numbered problems in the exercise sets.
4. Work with another student from your class.
5. Work on the computer. Many mathematics tutorial programs and websites are available on the Internet, including the website that accompanies this text.

Group Activity

Becoming a Successful Student

Materials: Computer with Internet access

Estimated Time: 15 minutes

Group Size: 4

Good time management, good study skills, and good organization will help you be successful in this course. Answer the following questions and compare your answers with your group members.

1. To motivate yourself to complete a course, it is helpful to have clear reasons for taking the course. List your goals for taking this course and discuss them with your group.

2. For the following week, write down the times each day that you plan to study math.

Monday	Tuesday	Wednesday	Thursday	Friday	Saturday	Sunday

3. Write down the date of your next math test. ____________

4. Taking 12 credit-hours is the equivalent of a full-time job. Often students try to work too many hours while taking classes at school.

a. Write down the number of hours you work per week and the number of credit-hours you are taking this term.

Number of hours worked per week ____________

Number of credit-hours this term ____________

b. The table gives a recommended limit to the number of hours you should work for the number of credit-hours you are taking at school. (Keep in mind that other responsibilities in your life such as your family might also make it necessary to limit your hours at work even more.) How do your numbers from part (a) compare to those in the table? Are you working too many hours?

Number of Credit-Hours	Maximum Number of Hours of Work per Week
3	40
6	30
9	20
12	10
15	0

5. Discuss with your group members where you can go for extra help in math. Then write down three of the suggestions.

____

____

____

6. Do you keep an organized notebook for this class? Can you think of any suggestions that you can share with your group members to help them keep their materials organized?

7. Look through Chapter 2 and find the page number corresponding to each feature in that chapter. Discuss with your group members how you might use each feature.

Problem Recognition Exercises: page ___________

Chapter Summary: page ___________

Chapter Review Exercises: page ___________

Chapter Test: page ___________

Cumulative Review Exercises: page ___________

8. Look at the Skill Practice exercises. For example, find Skill Practice exercises 1 and 2 in Section 1.1. Where are the answers to these exercises located? Discuss with your group members how you might use the Skill Practice exercises.

9. Do you think that you have math anxiety? Read the following list for some possible solutions. Check the activities that you can realistically try to help you overcome this problem.

_____ Read a book on math anxiety.

_____ Search the Web for tips on handling math anxiety.

_____ See a counselor to discuss your anxiety.

_____ Talk with your instructor to discuss strategies to manage math anxiety.

_____ Evaluate your time management to see if you are trying to do too much. Then adjust your schedule accordingly.

10. Some students favor different methods of learning over others. For example, you might prefer:

- Learning through listening and hearing.
- Learning through seeing images, watching demonstrations, and visualizing diagrams and charts.
- Learning by experience through a hands-on approach.
- Learning through reading and writing.

Most experts believe that the most effective learning comes when a student engages in *all* of these activities. However, each individual is different and may benefit from one activity more than another. You can visit a number of different websites to determine your "learning style." Try doing a search on the Internet with the key words "*learning styles assessment.*" Once you have found a suitable website, answer the questionnaire and the site will give you feedback on what method of learning works best for you.

11. As you read through Chapter 1, try to become familiar with the features of this textbook. Then match the feature in column B with its description in column A.

Column A

1. Allows you to check your work as you do your homework
2. Shows you how to avoid common errors
3. Provides an online tutorial and exercise supplement
4. Outlines key concepts for each section in the chapter
5. Provides exercises that allow you to distinguish between different types of problems
6. Offers helpful hints and insight
7. Offers practice exercises that go along with each example

Column B

a. Tips
b. ConnectMath
c. Skill Practice exercises
d. Problem Recognition Exercises
e. Answers to odd exercises
f. Chapter Summary
g. Avoiding Mistakes

The Set of Real Numbers

1

CHAPTER OUTLINE

1.1 Fractions 6

1.2 Introduction to Algebra and the Set of Real Numbers 21

1.3 Exponents, Square Roots, and the Order of Operations 35

1.4 Addition of Real Numbers 45

1.5 Subtraction of Real Numbers 54

Problem Recognition Exercises: Addition and Subtraction of Real Numbers 62

1.6 Multiplication and Division of Real Numbers 63

Problem Recognition Exercises: Adding, Subtracting, Multiplying, and Dividing Real Numbers 74

1.7 Properties of Real Numbers and Simplifying Expressions 75

Group Activity: Evaluating Formulas Using a Calculator 88

Chapter 1

In Chapter 1, we present operations on fractions and real numbers. The skills that you will learn in this chapter are particularly important as you continue in algebra.

Are You Prepared?

This puzzle will refresh your skills with whole numbers and the order of operations. Fill in each blank box with one of the four basic operations, +, −, ×, or ÷ so that the statement is true both going across and going down. Pay careful attention to the order of operations.

18		2		10	=	30
3	×	4		7	=	5
2	×	0		6	=	6
=		=		=		=
4	+	6	−	9	=	1

Section 1.1 Fractions

Concepts

1. Basic Definitions
2. Prime Factorization
3. Simplifying Fractions to Lowest Terms
4. Multiplying Fractions
5. Dividing Fractions
6. Adding and Subtracting Fractions
7. Operations on Mixed Numbers

1. Basic Definitions

The study of algebra involves many of the operations and procedures used in arithmetic. Therefore, we begin this text by reviewing the basic operations of addition, subtraction, multiplication, and division on fractions and mixed numbers.

We begin with the numbers used for counting:

the **natural numbers**: 1, 2, 3, 4, . . .

and

the **whole numbers**: 0, 1, 2, 3, . . .

Whole numbers are used to count the number of whole units in a quantity. A fraction is used to express part of a whole unit. If a child gains $2\frac{1}{2}$ lb, the child has gained two whole pounds plus a portion of a pound. To express the additional half pound mathematically, we may use the fraction, $\frac{1}{2}$.

A Fraction and Its Parts

Fractions are numbers of the form $\frac{a}{b}$, where $\frac{a}{b} = a \div b$ and b does not equal zero.

In the fraction $\frac{a}{b}$, the **numerator** is a, and the **denominator** is b.

The denominator of a fraction indicates how many equal parts divide the whole. The numerator indicates how many parts are being represented. For instance, suppose Jack wants to plant carrots in $\frac{2}{5}$ of a rectangular garden. He can divide the garden into five equal parts and use two of the parts for carrots (Figure 1-1).

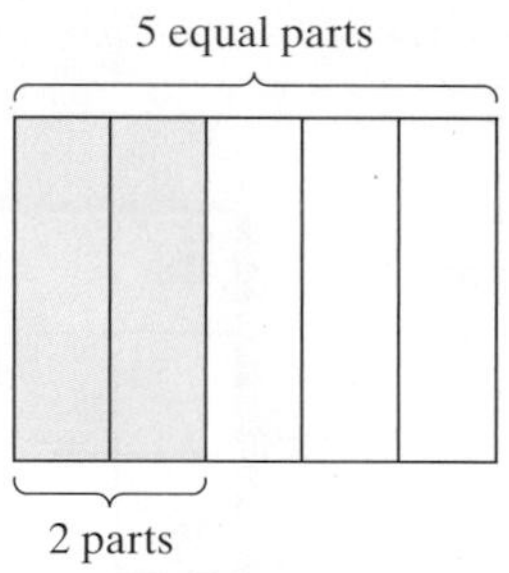

The shaded region represents $\frac{2}{5}$ of the garden.

Figure 1-1

Proper Fractions, Improper Fractions, and Mixed Numbers

1. If the numerator of a fraction is less than the denominator, the fraction is a **proper fraction**. A proper fraction represents a quantity that is less than a whole unit.
2. If the numerator of a fraction is greater than or equal to the denominator, then the fraction is an **improper fraction**. An improper fraction represents a quantity greater than or equal to a whole unit.
3. A **mixed number** is a whole number added to a proper fraction.

Proper Fractions: $\frac{3}{5}$ 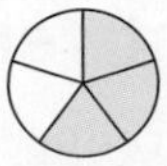 $\frac{1}{8}$ 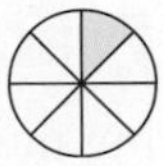

Improper Fractions: $\frac{7}{5}$ 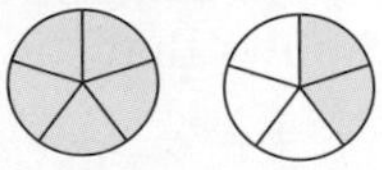 $\frac{8}{8}$ 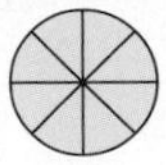

Mixed Numbers: $1\frac{1}{5}$ 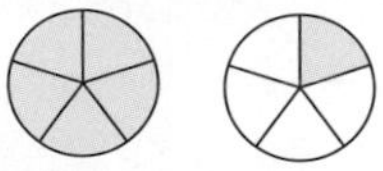 $2\frac{3}{8}$ 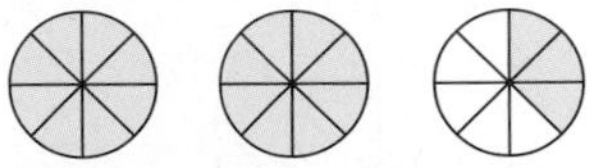

2. Prime Factorization

To perform operations on fractions it is important to understand the concept of a factor. For example, when the numbers 2 and 6 are multiplied, the result (called the **product**) is 12.

$$2 \times 6 = 12$$

(2 and 6: factors; 12: product)

The numbers 2 and 6 are said to be **factors** of 12. (In this context, we refer only to natural number factors.) The number 12 is said to be factored when it is written as the product of two or more natural numbers. For example, 12 can be factored in several ways:

$$12 = 1 \times 12 \qquad 12 = 2 \times 6 \qquad 12 = 3 \times 4 \qquad 12 = 2 \times 2 \times 3$$

A natural number greater than 1 that has only two factors, 1 and itself, is called a **prime number**. The first several prime numbers are 2, 3, 5, 7, 11, and 13. A natural number greater than 1 that is not prime is called a **composite number**. That is, a composite number has factors other than itself and 1. The first several composite numbers are 4, 6, 8, 9, 10, 12, 14, 15, and 16.

Avoiding Mistakes

The number 1 is neither prime nor composite.

Example 1 Writing a Natural Number as a Product of Prime Factors

Write each number as a product of prime factors.

a. 12 **b.** 30

Solution:

a. $12 = 2 \times 2 \times 3$

Divide 12 by prime numbers until the result is also a prime number.

$$\begin{array}{r} 2\overline{)12} \\ 2\overline{)6} \\ 3 \end{array}$$

Or use a factor tree

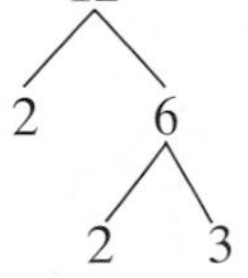

b. $30 = 2 \times 3 \times 5$

$$\begin{array}{r} 2\overline{)30} \\ 3\overline{)15} \\ 5 \end{array}$$

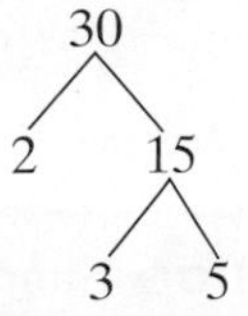

Skill Practice Write the number as a product of prime factors.

1. 40 **2.** 72

Answers

1. $2 \times 2 \times 2 \times 5$
2. $2 \times 2 \times 2 \times 3 \times 3$

3. Simplifying Fractions to Lowest Terms

The process of factoring numbers can be used to reduce or simplify fractions to lowest terms. A fractional portion of a whole can be represented by infinitely many fractions. For example, Figure 1-2 shows that $\frac{1}{2}$ is equivalent to $\frac{2}{4}$, $\frac{3}{6}$, $\frac{4}{8}$, and so on.

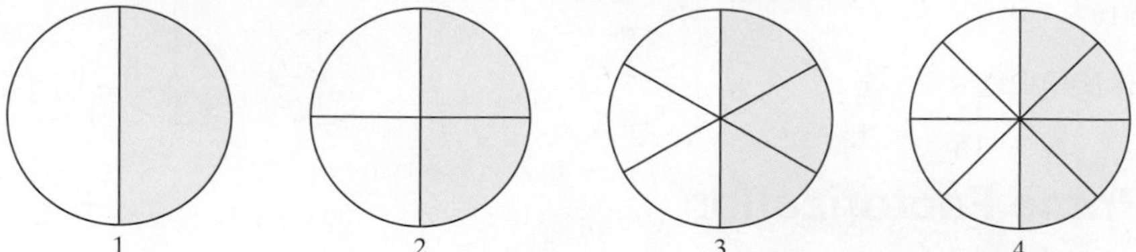

Figure 1-2

The fraction $\frac{1}{2}$ is said to be in **lowest terms** because the numerator and denominator share no common factor other than 1.

To simplify a fraction to lowest terms, we use the following important principle.

Fundamental Principle of Fractions

Suppose that a number, c, is a common factor in the numerator and denominator of a fraction. Then

$$\frac{a \times c}{b \times c} = \frac{a}{b} \times \frac{c}{c} = \frac{a}{b} \times 1 = \frac{a}{b}$$

To simplify a fraction, we begin by factoring the numerator and denominator into prime factors. This will help identify the common factors.

Example 2 Simplifying a Fraction to Lowest Terms

Simplify $\frac{45}{30}$ to lowest terms.

Solution:

$\frac{45}{30} = \frac{3 \times 3 \times 5}{2 \times 3 \times 5}$	Factor the numerator and denominator.
$= \frac{3}{2} \times \frac{3}{3} \times \frac{5}{5}$	Apply the fundamental principle of fractions.
$= \frac{3}{2} \times 1 \times 1$	Any nonzero number divided by itself is 1.
$= \frac{3}{2}$	Any number multiplied by 1 is itself.

Skill Practice Simplify to lowest terms.

3. $\frac{20}{50}$

Answer

3. $\frac{2}{5}$

In Example 2, we showed numerous steps to reduce fractions to lowest terms. However, the process is often simplified. Notice that the same result can be obtained by dividing out the greatest common factor from the numerator and denominator. (The **greatest common factor** is the largest factor that is common to both numerator and denominator.)

$\frac{45}{30} = \frac{3 \times 15}{2 \times 15}$ The greatest common factor of 45 and 30 is 15.

$= \frac{3 \times \overset{1}{\cancel{15}}}{2 \times \underset{1}{\cancel{15}}}$ The symbol ⁄ is often used to show that a common factor has been divided out.

$= \frac{3}{2}$ Notice that "dividing out" the common factor of 15 has the same effect as dividing the numerator and denominator by 15. This is often done mentally.

$\frac{\overset{3}{\cancel{45}}}{\underset{2}{\cancel{30}}} = \frac{3}{2}$ ⟵ 45 divided by 15 equals 3. ⟵ 30 divided by 15 equals 2.

Example 3 Simplifying a Fraction to Lowest Terms

Simplify $\frac{14}{42}$ to lowest terms.

Solution:

$\frac{14}{42} = \frac{1 \times 14}{3 \times 14}$ The greatest common factor of 14 and 42 is 14.

$= \frac{1 \times \overset{1}{\cancel{14}}}{3 \times \underset{1}{\cancel{14}}}$

$= \frac{1}{3}$ $\frac{\overset{1}{\cancel{14}}}{\underset{3}{\cancel{42}}} = \frac{1}{3}$ ⟵ 14 divided by 14 equals 1. ⟵ 42 divided by 14 equals 3.

Avoiding Mistakes

In Example 3, the common factor 14 in the numerator and denominator simplifies to 1. It is important to remember to write the factor of 1 in the numerator. The simplified form of the fraction is $\frac{1}{3}$.

Skill Practice Simplify to lowest terms.

4. $\frac{32}{12}$

4. Multiplying Fractions

Multiplying Fractions

If b is not zero and d is not zero, then

$$\frac{a}{b} \times \frac{c}{d} = \frac{a \times c}{b \times d}$$

To multiply fractions, multiply the numerators and multiply the denominators.

Answer

4. $\frac{8}{3}$

Example 4 Multiplying Fractions

Multiply the fractions: $\frac{1}{4} \times \frac{1}{2}$

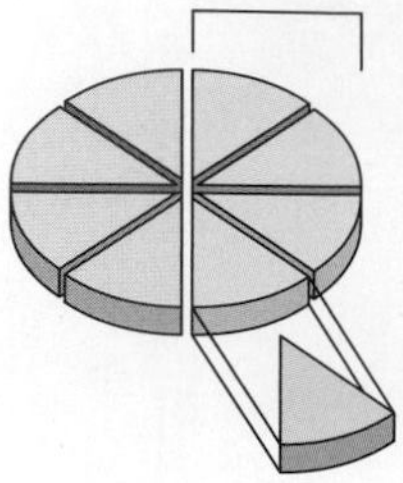

Figure 1-3

Solution:

$$\frac{1}{4} \times \frac{1}{2} = \frac{1 \times 1}{4 \times 2} = \frac{1}{8}$$ Multiply the numerators. Multiply the denominators.

Notice that the product $\frac{1}{4} \times \frac{1}{2}$ represents a quantity that is $\frac{1}{4}$ of $\frac{1}{2}$. Taking $\frac{1}{4}$ of a quantity is equivalent to dividing the quantity by 4. One-half of a pie divided into four pieces leaves pieces that each represent $\frac{1}{8}$ of the pie (Figure 1-3).

Skill Practice Multiply.

5. $\frac{2}{7} \times \frac{3}{4}$

Example 5 Multiplying Fractions

Multiply the fractions.

a. $\frac{7}{10} \times \frac{15}{14}$ **b.** $\frac{2}{13} \times \frac{13}{2}$ **c.** $5 \times \frac{1}{5}$

Solution:

a. $\frac{7}{10} \times \frac{15}{14} = \frac{7 \times 15}{10 \times 14}$ Multiply the numerators. Multiply the denominators.

$= \frac{\overset{1}{\cancel{7}} \times \overset{3}{\cancel{15}}}{\underset{2}{\cancel{10}} \times \underset{2}{\cancel{14}}}$ Divide out the common factors.

$= \frac{3}{4}$ Multiply.

TIP: The same result can be obtained by dividing out common factors *before* multiplying.

$$\frac{\overset{1}{\cancel{7}}}{\underset{2}{\cancel{10}}} \times \frac{\overset{3}{\cancel{15}}}{\underset{2}{\cancel{14}}} = \frac{3}{4}$$

b. $\frac{2}{13} \times \frac{13}{2} = \frac{2 \times 13}{13 \times 2} = \frac{\overset{1}{\cancel{2}} \times \overset{1}{\cancel{13}}}{\underset{1}{\cancel{13}} \times \underset{1}{\cancel{2}}} = \frac{1}{1} = 1$

Multiply $1 \times 1 = 1$.

Multiply $1 \times 1 = 1$.

c. $5 \times \frac{1}{5} = \frac{5}{1} \times \frac{1}{5}$ The whole number 5 can be written as $\frac{5}{1}$.

$= \frac{\overset{1}{\cancel{5}} \times 1}{1 \times \underset{1}{\cancel{5}}} = \frac{1}{1} = 1$ Divide out the common factors and multiply.

Skill Practice Multiply.

6. $\frac{8}{9} \times \frac{3}{4}$ **7.** $\frac{4}{5} \times \frac{5}{4}$ **8.** $10 \times \frac{1}{10}$

Answers

5. $\frac{3}{14}$ **6.** $\frac{2}{3}$ **7.** 1 **8.** 1

5. Dividing Fractions

Before we divide fractions, we need to know how to find the reciprocal of a fraction. Notice from Example 5 that $\frac{2}{13} \times \frac{13}{2} = 1$ and $5 \times \frac{1}{5} = 1$. The numbers $\frac{2}{13}$ and $\frac{13}{2}$ are said to be reciprocals because their product is 1. Likewise the numbers 5 and $\frac{1}{5}$ are reciprocals.

The Reciprocal of a Number

Two nonzero numbers are **reciprocals** of each other if their product is 1. Therefore, the reciprocal of the fraction

$$\frac{a}{b} \text{ is } \frac{b}{a} \qquad \text{because} \qquad \frac{a}{b} \times \frac{b}{a} = 1$$

Number	Reciprocal	Product
$\frac{2}{15}$	$\frac{15}{2}$	$\frac{2}{15} \times \frac{15}{2} = 1$
$\frac{1}{8}$	$\frac{8}{1}$ (or equivalently 8)	$\frac{1}{8} \times 8 = 1$
$6\left(\text{or equivalently } \frac{6}{1}\right)$	$\frac{1}{6}$	$6 \times \frac{1}{6} = 1$

To understand the concept of dividing fractions, consider a pie that is half-eaten. Suppose the remaining half must be divided among three people, that is, $\frac{1}{2} \div 3$. However, dividing by 3 is equivalent to taking $\frac{1}{3}$ of the remaining $\frac{1}{2}$ of the pie (Figure 1-4).

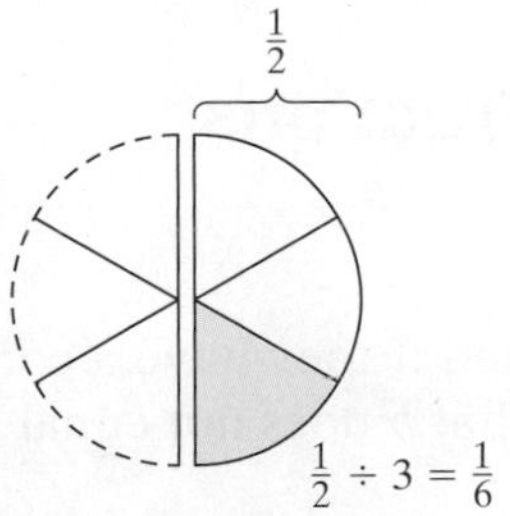

$$\frac{1}{2} \div 3 = \frac{1}{2} \cdot \frac{1}{3} = \frac{1}{6}$$

Figure 1-4

This example illustrates that dividing two numbers is equivalent to multiplying the first number by the reciprocal of the second number.

Dividing Fractions

Let a, b, c, and d be numbers such that b, c, and d are not zero. Then,

multiply

$$\frac{a}{b} \div \frac{c}{d} = \frac{a}{b} \times \frac{d}{c}$$

reciprocal

To divide fractions, multiply the first fraction by the reciprocal of the second fraction.

Example 6 **Dividing Fractions**

Divide the fractions.

a. $\frac{8}{5} \div \frac{3}{10}$ **b.** $\frac{12}{13} \div 6$

Solution:

a. $\frac{8}{5} \div \frac{3}{10} = \frac{8}{5} \times \frac{10}{3}$ Multiply by the reciprocal of $\frac{3}{10}$, which is $\frac{10}{3}$.

$= \frac{8 \times \overset{2}{\cancel{10}}}{\underset{1}{\cancel{5}} \times 3} = \frac{16}{3}$ Divide out the common factors and multiply.

b. $\frac{12}{13} \div 6 = \frac{12}{13} \div \frac{6}{1}$ Write the whole number 6 as $\frac{6}{1}$.

$= \frac{12}{13} \times \frac{1}{6}$ Multiply by the reciprocal of $\frac{6}{1}$, which is $\frac{1}{6}$.

$= \frac{\overset{2}{\cancel{12}} \times 1}{13 \times \underset{1}{\cancel{6}}} = \frac{2}{13}$ Divide out the common factors and multiply.

Avoiding Mistakes

Always check that the final answer is in lowest terms.

Skill Practice Divide.

9. $\frac{12}{25} \div \frac{8}{15}$ **10.** $\frac{1}{4} \div 2$

6. Adding and Subtracting Fractions

Adding and Subtracting Fractions

Two fractions can be added or subtracted if they have a common denominator. Let a, b, and c be numbers such that b does not equal zero. Then,

$$\frac{a}{b} + \frac{c}{b} = \frac{a+c}{b} \quad \text{and} \quad \frac{a}{b} - \frac{c}{b} = \frac{a-c}{b}$$

To add or subtract fractions with the same denominator, add or subtract the numerators and write the result over the common denominator.

Example 7 **Adding and Subtracting Fractions with the Same Denominator**

Add or subtract as indicated.

a. $\frac{1}{12} + \frac{7}{12}$ **b.** $\frac{13}{5} - \frac{3}{5}$

Answers

9. $\frac{9}{10}$ **10.** $\frac{1}{8}$

Solution:

a. $\frac{1}{12} + \frac{7}{12} = \frac{1+7}{12}$ Add the numerators.

$= \frac{8}{12}$

$= \frac{2}{3}$ Simplify to lowest terms.

b. $\frac{13}{5} - \frac{3}{5} = \frac{13-3}{5}$ Subtract the numerators.

$= \frac{10}{5}$ Simplify.

$= 2$ Simplify to lowest terms.

Skill Practice Add or subtract as indicated.

11. $\frac{2}{3} + \frac{5}{3}$ **12.** $\frac{5}{8} - \frac{1}{8}$

TIP: The sum $\frac{1}{12} + \frac{7}{12}$ can be visualized as the sum of the pink and blue sections of the figure.

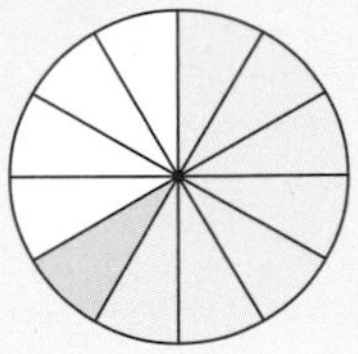

In Example 7, we added and subtracted fractions with the same denominators. To add or subtract fractions with different denominators, we must first become familiar with the idea of a least common multiple between two or more numbers. The **least common multiple (LCM)** of two numbers is the smallest whole number that is a multiple of each number. For example, the LCM of 6 and 9 is 18.

multiples of 6: 6, 12, 18, 24, 30, 36, ...

multiples of 9: 9, 18, 27, 36, 45, 54, ...

Listing the multiples of two or more given numbers can be a cumbersome way to find the LCM. Therefore, we offer the following method to find the LCM of two numbers.

Animation

Finding the LCM of Two Numbers

Step 1 Write each number as a product of prime factors.

Step 2 The LCM is the product of unique prime factors from *both* numbers. Use repeated factors the maximum number of times they appear in *either* factorization.

Example 8 Finding the LCM of Two Numbers

Find the LCM of 9 and 15.

Solution:

	3's	5's
9 =	(3 × 3)	
15 =	3 ×	(5)

For the factors of 3 and 5, we circle the greatest number of times each occurs. The LCM is the product.

$\text{LCM} = 3 \times 3 \times 5 = 45$

Skill Practice Find the LCM.

13. 10 and 25

Answers

11. $\frac{7}{3}$ or $2\frac{1}{3}$ **12.** $\frac{1}{2}$ **13.** 50

Example 11 Operations on Mixed Numbers

Subtract. $5\frac{1}{3} - 2\frac{1}{4}$

Solution:

$5\frac{1}{3} - 2\frac{1}{4}$

$= \frac{16}{3} - \frac{9}{4}$ Write the mixed numbers as improper fractions.

$= \frac{16 \times 4}{3 \times 4} - \frac{9 \times 3}{4 \times 3}$ The LCD is 12. Multiply numerators and denominators by the missing factors from the denominators.

$= \frac{64}{12} - \frac{27}{12}$

$= \frac{37}{12}$ or $3\frac{1}{12}$ Subtract the fractions.

Skill Practice Subtract.

17. $2\frac{3}{4} - 1\frac{1}{3}$

TIP: An improper fraction can also be written as a mixed number. Both answers are acceptable. Note that

$$\frac{37}{12} = \frac{36}{12} + \frac{1}{12} = 3 + \frac{1}{12}, \text{ or } 3\frac{1}{12}$$

This can easily be found by dividing.

$$\frac{37}{12} \rightarrow 12\overline{)37} \quad \text{quotient } 3, \quad -36, \quad \text{remainder } 1 \quad \rightarrow 3\frac{1}{12}$$

quotient
remainder
divisor

Example 12 Operations on Mixed Numbers

Divide. $7\frac{1}{2} \div 3$

Solution:

$7\frac{1}{2} \div 3$

$= \frac{15}{2} \div \frac{3}{1}$ Write the mixed number and whole number as fractions.

$= \frac{\overset{5}{\cancel{15}}}{2} \times \frac{1}{\underset{1}{\cancel{3}}}$ Multiply by the reciprocal of $\frac{3}{1}$, which is $\frac{1}{3}$.

$= \frac{5}{2}$ or $2\frac{1}{2}$ The answer may be written as an improper fraction or as a mixed number.

Avoiding Mistakes

Remember that when dividing (or multiplying) fractions, a common denominator is not necessary.

Answer

17. $\frac{17}{12}$ or $1\frac{5}{12}$

Skill Practice Divide.

18. $5\frac{5}{6} \div 3\frac{2}{3}$

Answer

18. $\frac{35}{22}$ or $1\frac{13}{22}$

Section 1.1 Practice Exercises

Study Skills Exercise

To enhance your learning experience, we provide study skills that focus on eight areas: learning about your course, using your text, taking notes, doing homework, taking an exam (test and math anxiety), managing your time, recognizing your learning style, and studying for the final exam.

Each activity requires only a few minutes and will help you pass this course and become a better math student. Many of these skills can be carried over to other disciplines and help you become a model college student. To begin, write down the following information:

a. Instructor's name

b. Instructor's office number

c. Instructor's telephone number

d. Instructor's e-mail address

e. Instructor's office hours

f. Days of the week that the class meets

g. The room number in which the class meets

h. Is there a lab requirement for this course? How often must you attend lab and where is it located?

Vocabulary and Key Concepts

1. a. A ____________ is the result of multiplying two or more numbers.

b. The numbers being multiplied in a product are called ____________.

c. Given a fraction $\frac{a}{b}$ with $b \neq 0$, the value a is the ____________ and ________ is the denominator.

d. A fraction is said to be in ____________ terms if the numerator and denominator share no common factor other than 1.

e. The fraction $\frac{4}{4}$ can also be written as the whole number ________, and the fraction $\frac{4}{1}$ can be written as the whole number ________.

f. Two nonzero numbers $\frac{a}{b}$ and $\frac{b}{a}$ are ____________ because their product is 1.

g. The least common multiple (LCM) of two numbers is the smallest whole number that is a ____________ of both numbers.

h. The ____________ common denominator of two or more fractions is the LCM of their denominators.

Concept 1: Basic Definitions

For Exercises 2–10, identify the numerator and denominator of each fraction. Then determine if the fraction is a proper fraction or an improper fraction.

2. $\frac{7}{8}$

3. $\frac{2}{3}$

4. $\frac{9}{5}$

5. $\frac{5}{2}$

6. $\frac{6}{6}$

7. $\frac{4}{4}$

8. $\frac{12}{1}$

9. $\frac{5}{1}$

10. $\frac{6}{7}$

For Exercises 81–84, find the least common multiple for each list of numbers. **(See Example 8.)**

81. 6, 15

82. 12, 30

83. 20, 8, 4

84. 24, 40, 30

For Exercises 85–100, add or subtract as indicated. **(See Examples 9–10.)**

85. $\frac{1}{8}+\frac{3}{4}$

86. $\frac{3}{16}+\frac{1}{2}$

87. $\frac{11}{8}-\frac{3}{10}$

88. $\frac{12}{35}-\frac{1}{10}$

89. $\frac{7}{26}-\frac{2}{13}$

90. $\frac{25}{24}-\frac{5}{16}$

91. $\frac{7}{18}+\frac{5}{12}$

92. $\frac{3}{16}+\frac{9}{20}$

93. $\frac{5}{4}-\frac{1}{20}$

94. $\frac{7}{6}-\frac{1}{24}$

95. $\frac{5}{12}+\frac{5}{16}$

96. $\frac{3}{25}+\frac{8}{35}$

97. $\frac{1}{6}+\frac{3}{4}-\frac{5}{8}$

98. $\frac{1}{2}+\frac{2}{3}-\frac{5}{12}$

99. $\frac{4}{7}+\frac{1}{2}+\frac{3}{4}$

100. $\frac{9}{10}+\frac{4}{5}+\frac{3}{4}$

101. For his famous brownie recipe, Chef Alfonso combines $\frac{2}{3}$ cup granulated sugar with $\frac{1}{4}$ cup brown sugar. What is the total amount of sugar in his recipe?

102. Chef Alfonso eats too many of his brownies and his waistline increased by $\frac{3}{4}$ in. during one month and $\frac{3}{8}$ in. the next month. What was his total increase for the 2-month period?

103. Currently, two of the most popular smartphones are the Apple iPhone and the LG Vortex. The thickness of the Vortex is $\frac{1}{2}$ in. while the iPhone measures $\frac{9}{25}$ in. How much thicker is the Vortex than the iPhone?

104. The diameter of a penny is $\frac{3}{4}$ in. while the dime is $\frac{7}{10}$ in. How much larger is the penny than the dime?

Concept 7: Operations on Mixed Numbers

For Exercises 105–118, perform the indicated operations. **(See Examples 11–12.)**

105. $3\frac{1}{5}\times 2\frac{7}{8}$

106. $2\frac{1}{2}\times 1\frac{4}{5}$

107. $1\frac{2}{9}\div 7\frac{1}{3}$

108. $2\frac{2}{5}\div 1\frac{2}{7}$

109. $1\frac{2}{9}\div 6$

110. $2\frac{2}{5}\div 2$

111. $2\frac{1}{8}+1\frac{3}{8}$

112. $1\frac{3}{14}+1\frac{1}{14}$

113. $3\frac{1}{2}-1\frac{7}{8}$

114. $5\frac{1}{3}-2\frac{3}{4}$

115. $1\frac{1}{6}+3\frac{3}{4}$

116. $4\frac{1}{2}+2\frac{2}{3}$

117. $1-\frac{7}{8}$

118. $2-\frac{3}{7}$

119. A board $26\frac{3}{8}$ in. long must be cut into three pieces of equal length. Find the length of each piece.

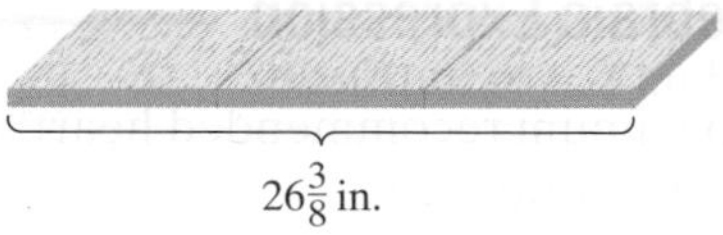

120. A futon, when set up as a sofa, measures $3\frac{5}{6}$ ft wide. When it is opened to be used as a bed, the width is increased by $1\frac{3}{4}$ ft. What is the total width of this bed?

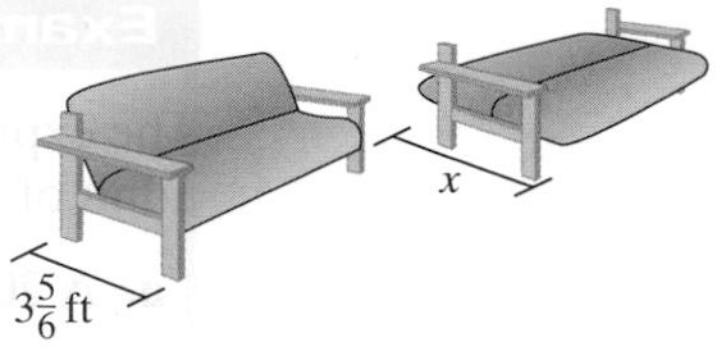

121. A plane trip from Orlando to Detroit takes $2\frac{3}{4}$ hr. If the plane traveled for $1\frac{1}{6}$ hr, how much time remains for the flight?

122. Silvia manages a sub shop and needs to prepare smoked turkey sandwiches. She has $3\frac{3}{4}$ lb of turkey in the cooler, and each sandwich requires $\frac{3}{8}$ lb of turkey. How many sandwiches can she make?

123. José's catering company plans to prepare two different shrimp dishes for an upcoming event. One dish requires $1\frac{1}{2}$ lb of shrimp and the other requires $\frac{3}{4}$ lb of shrimp. How much shrimp should José order for the two dishes?

124. Ayako took a trip to the store $5\frac{1}{2}$ mi away. If she rode the bus for $4\frac{5}{6}$ mi and walked the rest of the way, how far did she have to walk?

125. If Tampa, Florida, averages $6\frac{1}{4}$ in. of rain during each summer month, how much total rain would be expected in June, July, August, and September?

126. Pete started working out and found that he lost approximately $\frac{3}{4}$ in. off his waistline every month. How much would he lose around his waist in 6 months?

Introduction to Algebra and the Set of Real Numbers — Section 1.2

Concepts

1. Variables and Expressions
2. The Set of Real Numbers
3. Inequalities
4. Opposite of a Real Number
5. Absolute Value of a Real Number

1. Variables and Expressions

Doctors promote daily exercise as part of a healthy lifestyle. Aerobic exercise is exercise for the heart. During aerobic exercise, the goal is to maintain a heart rate level between 65% and 85% of an individual's maximum recommended heart rate. The maximum recommended heart rate, in beats per minute, for an adult of age a is given by:

$$\text{Maximum recommended heart rate} = 220 - a$$

In this example, value a is called a **variable**. This is a symbol or letter, such as x, y, z, a, and the like, that is used to represent an unknown number that is subject to change. The number 220 is called a **constant**, because it does not vary. The quantity $220 - a$ is called an algebraic expression. An algebraic **expression** is a collection of variables and constants under algebraic operations. For example, $\frac{3}{x}$, $y + 7$, and $t - 1.4$ are algebraic expressions.

The symbols used in algebraic expressions to show the four basic operations are shown here:

Addition $a + b$

Subtraction $a - b$

Multiplication $a \times b$, $a \cdot b$, $(a)b$, $a(b)$, $(a)(b)$, ab

(*Note:* We rarely use the notation $a \times b$ because the symbol $\times$ may be confused with the variable x.)

Division $a \div b$, $\frac{a}{b}$, a/b, $b\overline{)a}$

Skill Practice Plot the numbers on the real number line.

4. $\{-1, \frac{3}{4}, -2.5, \frac{10}{3}\}$

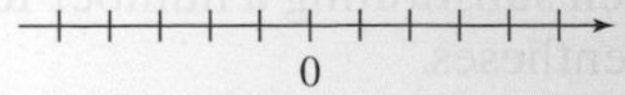

TIP: The natural numbers are used for counting. For this reason, they are sometimes called the "counting numbers."

In mathematics, a well-defined collection of elements is called a **set**. "Well-defined" means the set is described in such a way that it is clear whether an element is in the set. The symbols { } are used to enclose the elements of the set. For example, the set {A, B, C, D, E} represents the set of the first five letters of the alphabet.

Several sets of numbers are used extensively in algebra and are *subsets* (or part) of the set of real numbers.

Natural Numbers, Whole Numbers, and Integers

The set of **natural numbers** is $\{1, 2, 3, \ldots\}$

The set of **whole numbers** is $\{0, 1, 2, 3, \ldots\}$

The set of **integers** is $\{\ldots -3, -2, -1, 0, 1, 2, 3, \ldots\}$

Notice that the set of whole numbers includes the natural numbers. Therefore, every natural number is also a whole number. The set of integers includes the set of whole numbers. Therefore, every whole number is also an integer.

Fractions are also among the numbers we use frequently. A number that can be written as a fraction whose numerator is an integer and whose denominator is a nonzero integer is called a *rational number*.

Rational Numbers

The set of **rational numbers** is the set of numbers that can be expressed in the form $\frac{p}{q}$, where both p and q are integers and q does not equal 0.

We also say that a rational number $\frac{p}{q}$ is a *ratio* of two integers, p and q, where q is not equal to zero.

Example 4 Identifying Rational Numbers

Show that the following numbers are rational numbers by finding an equivalent ratio of two integers.

a. $\dfrac{-2}{3}$ **b.** -12 **c.** 0.5 **d.** $0.\overline{6}$

Solution:

a. The fraction $\frac{-2}{3}$ is a rational number because it can be expressed as the ratio of -2 and 3.

b. The number -12 is a rational number because it can be expressed as the ratio of -12 and 1, that is, $-12 = \frac{-12}{1}$. In this example, we see that an integer is also a rational number.

Answer

4.

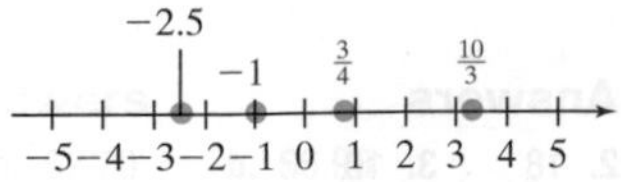

c. The terminating decimal 0.5 is a rational number because it can be expressed as the ratio of 5 and 10, that is, $0.5 = \frac{5}{10}$. In this example, we see that a terminating decimal is also a rational number.

d. The numeral $0.\overline{6}$ represents the nonterminating, repeating decimal 0.6666666 . . . . The number $0.\overline{6}$ is a rational number because it can be expressed as the ratio of 2 and 3, that is, $0.\overline{6} = \frac{2}{3}$. In this example, we see that a repeating decimal is also a rational number.

Skill Practice Show that each number is rational by finding an equivalent ratio of two integers.

5. $\frac{3}{7}$ **6.** -5 **7.** 0.3 **8.** $0.\overline{3}$

TIP: A rational number can be represented by a terminating decimal or by a repeating decimal.

Some real numbers, such as the number π, cannot be represented by the ratio of two integers. These numbers are called irrational numbers and in decimal form are nonterminating, nonrepeating decimals. The value of π, for example, can be approximated as $\pi \approx 3.1415926535897932$. However, the decimal digits continue forever with no repeated pattern. Another example of an irrational number is $\sqrt{3}$ (read as "the positive square root of 3"). The expression $\sqrt{3}$ is a number that when multiplied by itself is 3. There is no rational number that satisfies this condition. Thus, $\sqrt{3}$ is an irrational number.

Irrational Numbers

The set of **irrational numbers** is a subset of the real numbers whose elements cannot be written as a ratio of two integers.

Note: An irrational number cannot be written as a terminating decimal or as a repeating decimal.

The set of real numbers consists of both the rational and the irrational numbers. The relationship among these important sets of numbers is illustrated in Figure 1-6:

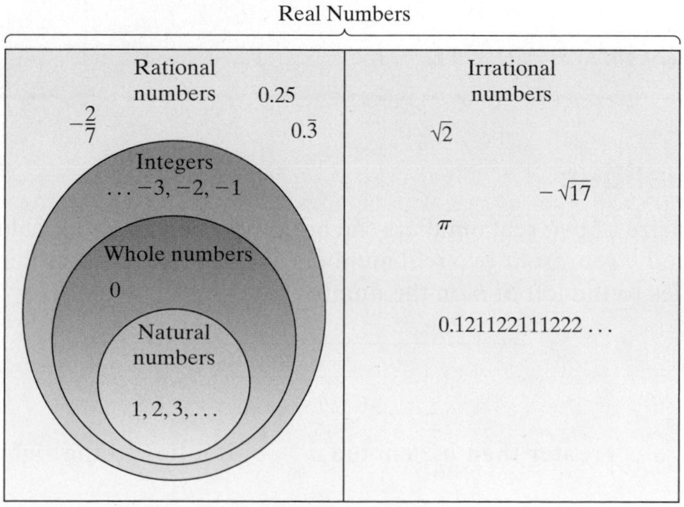

Figure 1-6

Answers

5. Ratio of 3 and 7
6. Ratio of −5 and 1
7. Ratio of 3 and 10
8. Ratio of 1 and 3

Example 5 Classifying Numbers by Set

Check the set(s) to which each number belongs. The numbers may belong to more than one set.

	Natural Numbers	Whole Numbers	Integers	Rational Numbers	Irrational Numbers	Real Numbers
5						
$\frac{-47}{3}$						
1.48						
$\sqrt{7}$						
0						

Solution:

	Natural Numbers	Whole Numbers	Integers	Rational Numbers	Irrational Numbers	Real Numbers
5	✔	✔	✔	✔ (ratio of 5 and 1)		✔
$\frac{-47}{3}$				✔ (ratio of −47 and 3)		✔
1.48				✔ (ratio of 148 and 100)		✔
$\sqrt{7}$					✔	✔
0		✔	✔	✔ (ratio of 0 and 1)		✔

Skill Practice Identify the sets to which each number belongs. Choose from: natural numbers, whole numbers, integers, rational numbers, irrational numbers, real numbers.

9. -4 **10.** $0.\overline{7}$ **11.** $\sqrt{13}$ **12.** 12 **13.** 0

3. Inequalities

The relative size of two real numbers can be compared using the real number line. Suppose a and b represent two real numbers. We say that a is less than b, denoted $a < b$, if a lies to the left of b on the number line.

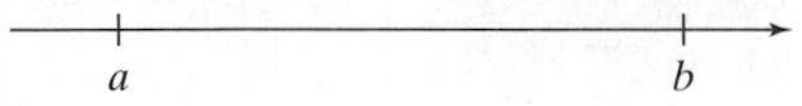

$a < b$

We say that a is greater than b, denoted $a > b$, if a lies to the right of b on the number line.

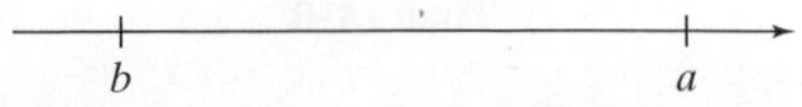

$a > b$

Answers

9. Integers, rational numbers, real numbers
10. Rational numbers, real numbers
11. Irrational numbers, real numbers
12. Natural numbers, whole numbers, integers, rational numbers, real numbers
13. Whole numbers, integers, rational numbers, real numbers

Table 1-1 summarizes the relational operators that compare two real numbers a and b.

Table 1-1

Mathematical Expression	Translation	Example
$a < b$	a is less than b.	$2 < 3$
$a > b$	a is greater than b.	$5 > 1$
$a \leq b$	a is less than or equal to b.	$4 \leq 4$
$a \geq b$	a is greater than or equal to b.	$10 \geq 9$
$a = b$	a is equal to b.	$6 = 6$
$a \neq b$	a is not equal to b.	$7 \neq 0$
$a \approx b$	a is approximately equal to b.	$2.3 \approx 2$

The symbols $<, >, \leq, \geq$, and $\neq$ are called *inequality signs*, and the statements $a < b, a > b, a \leq b, a \geq b$, and $a \neq b$ are called **inequalities**.

Example 6 Ordering Real Numbers

The average temperatures (in degrees Celsius) for selected cities in the United States and Canada in January are shown in Table 1-2.

Table 1-2

City	Temp (°C)
Prince George, British Columbia	−12.5
Corpus Christi, Texas	13.4
Parkersburg, West Virginia	−0.9
San Jose, California	9.7
Juneau, Alaska	−5.7
New Bedford, Massachusetts	−0.2
Durham, North Carolina	4.2

Plot a point on the real number line representing the temperature of each city. Compare the temperatures between the following cities, and fill in the blank with the appropriate inequality sign: $<$ or $>$.

Solution:

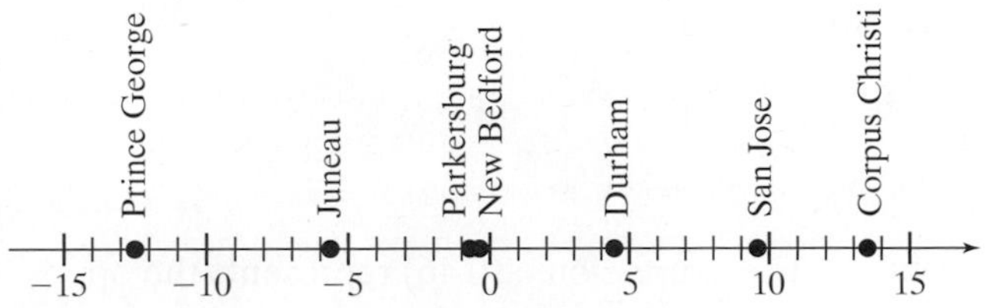

a. Temperature of San Jose $\boxed{<}$ temperature of Corpus Christi

b. Temperature of Juneau $\boxed{>}$ temperature of Prince George

c. Temperature of Parkersburg $\boxed{<}$ temperature of New Bedford

d. Temperature of Parkersburg $\boxed{>}$ temperature of Prince George

Skill Practice Fill in the blanks with the appropriate inequality sign: $<$ or $>$.

14. -11 ______ 20 **15.** -3 ______ -6

16. 0 ______ -9 **17.** -6.2 ______ -1.8

4. Opposite of a Real Number

To gain mastery of any algebraic skill, it is necessary to know the meaning of key definitions and key symbols. Two important definitions are the *opposite* of a real number and the *absolute value* of a real number.

The Opposite of a Real Number

Two numbers that are the same distance from 0 but on opposite sides of 0 on the number line are called **opposites** of each other. Symbolically, we denote the opposite of a real number a as $-a$.

Example 7 Finding the Opposite of a Real Number

a. Find the opposite of 5. **b.** Find the opposite of $-\frac{4}{7}$.

Solution:

a. The opposite of 5 is -5. **b.** The opposite of $-\frac{4}{7}$ is $\frac{4}{7}$.

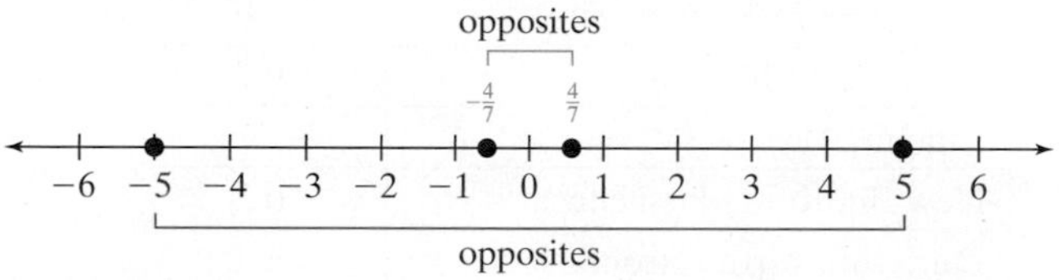

Skill Practice Find the opposite.

18. 224 **19.** -3.4

Example 8 Finding the Opposite of a Real Number

Evaluate each expression.

a. $-(0.46)$ **b.** $-\left(-\frac{11}{3}\right)$

Solution:

a. $-(0.46) = -0.46$ The expression $-(0.46)$ represents the opposite of 0.46.

b. $-\left(-\frac{11}{3}\right) = \frac{11}{3}$ The expression $-\left(-\frac{11}{3}\right)$ represents the opposite of $-\frac{11}{3}$.

Skill Practice Evaluate.

20. $-(2.8)$ **21.** $-\left(-\frac{1}{5}\right)$

Answers

14. $<$ **15.** $>$ **16.** $>$
17. $<$ **18.** -224 **19.** 3.4
20. -2.8 **21.** $\frac{1}{5}$

5. Absolute Value of a Real Number

The concept of absolute value will be used to define the addition of real numbers in Section 1.4.

Informal Definition of the Absolute Value of a Real Number

The **absolute value** of a real number a, denoted $|a|$, is the distance between a and 0 on the number line.

Note: The absolute value of any real number is positive or zero.

For example, $|3| = 3$ and $|-3| = 3$.

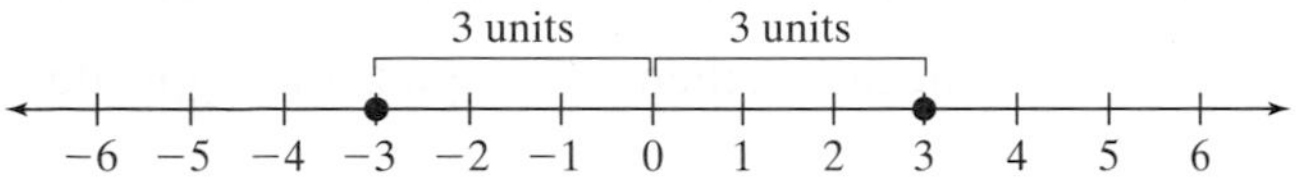

Example 9 **Finding the Absolute Value of a Real Number**

Evaluate the absolute value expressions.

a. $|-4|$ **b.** $\left|\frac{1}{2}\right|$ **c.** $|-6.2|$ **d.** $|0|$

Solution:

a. $|-4| = 4$ -4 is 4 units from 0 on the number line.

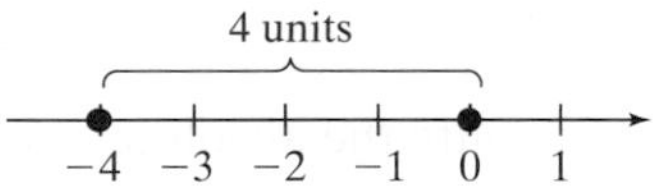

b. $\left|\frac{1}{2}\right| = \frac{1}{2}$ $\frac{1}{2}$ is $\frac{1}{2}$ unit from 0 on the number line.

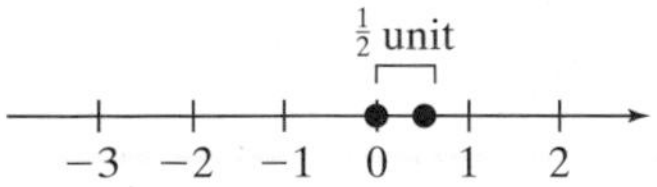

c. $|-6.2| = 6.2$ -6.2 is 6.2 units from 0 on the number line.

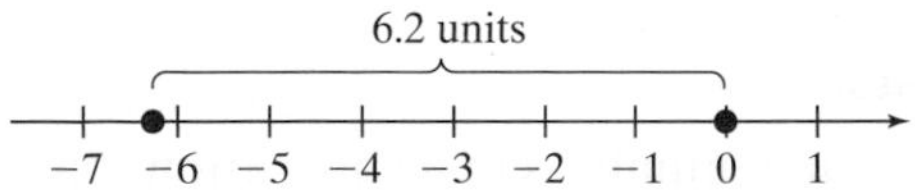

d. $|0| = 0$ 0 is 0 units from 0 on the number line.

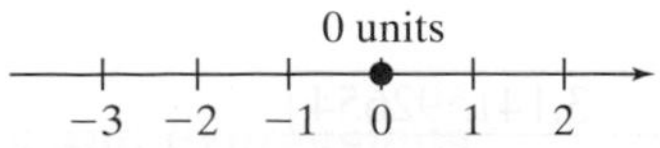

Skill Practice Evaluate.

22. $|-99|$ **23.** $\left|\frac{7}{8}\right|$ **24.** $|-1.4|$ **25.** $|1|$

Answers

22. 99 **23.** $\frac{7}{8}$

24. 1.4 **25.** 1

11. $c - 2 - d$ when $c = 15.4$, $d = 8.1$

12. $1.1 + t + s$ when $t = 93.2$, $s = 11.5$

13. abc when $a = \frac{1}{10}$, $b = \frac{1}{4}$, $c = \frac{1}{2}$

14. $x - y - z$ when $x = \frac{7}{8}$, $y = \frac{1}{2}$, $z = \frac{1}{4}$

15. The cost of downloading songs from iTunes can be represented by the expression $1.29s$, where s is the number of songs downloaded. Calculate the cost of downloading:

a. 3 songs **b.** 8 songs **c.** 10 songs

16. The number of calories burned by a 150-lb person by walking 2 mph can be represented by the expression $240h$, where h represents the number of hours spent walking. Calculate the number of calories burned by walking:

a. 4 hr **b.** $2\frac{1}{2}$ hr **c.** $1\frac{1}{4}$ hr

17. Aly is trying to limit her calorie intake for breakfast and lunch to 850 calories. The number of calories that she can consume for lunch is given by the expression $850 - b$, where b is the number of calories consumed for breakfast. Determine the number of calories allowed for lunch assuming that she had the following number of calories at breakfast:

a. 475 calories **b.** 220 calories **c.** 580 calories

18. Lorenzo knows that the gas mileage on his Subaru is about 25 miles per gallon. The number of gallons needed to travel a certain distance is given by the expression $\frac{d}{25}$, where d is the distance traveled. Find the number of gallons of fuel needed if Lorenzo drives:

a. 200 mi **b.** 450 mi **c.** 180 mi

Concept 2: The Set of Real Numbers

19. Plot the numbers on the real number line: $\{1, -2, -\pi, 0, -\frac{5}{2}, 5.1\}$ **(See Example 3.)**

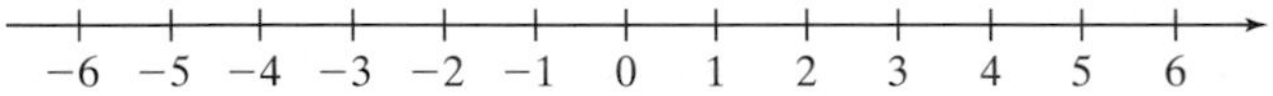

20. Plot the numbers on the real number line: $\{3, -4, \frac{1}{8}, -1.7, -\frac{4}{3}, 1.75\}$

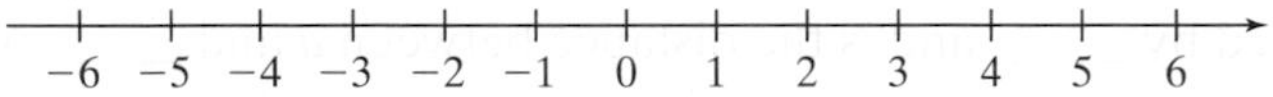

For Exercises 21–36, describe each number as (a) a terminating decimal, (b) a repeating decimal, or (c) a nonterminating, nonrepeating decimal. Then classify the number as a rational number or as an irrational number. **(See Example 4.)**

21. 0.29 **22.** 3.8 **23.** $\frac{1}{9}$ **24.** $\frac{1}{3}$

25. $\frac{1}{8}$ **26.** $\frac{1}{5}$ **27.** 2π **28.** 3π

29. -0.125 **30.** -3.24 **31.** -3 **32.** -6

33. $0.\overline{2}$ **34.** $0.\overline{6}$ **35.** $\sqrt{6}$ **36.** $\sqrt{10}$

37. List three numbers that are real numbers but not rational numbers.

38. List three numbers that are real numbers but not irrational numbers.

39. List three numbers that are integers but not natural numbers.

40. List three numbers that are integers but not whole numbers.

41. List three numbers that are rational numbers but not integers.

For Exercises 42–48, let $A = \{-\frac{3}{2}, \sqrt{11}, -4, 0.\overline{6}, 0, \sqrt{7}, 1\}$ **(See Example 5.)**

42. Are all of the numbers in set A real numbers?

43. List all of the rational numbers in set A.

44. List all of the whole numbers in set A.

45. List all of the natural numbers in set A.

46. List all of the irrational numbers in set A.

47. List all of the integers in set A.

48. Plot the real numbers from set A on a number line. (*Hint:* $\sqrt{11} \approx 3.3$ and $\sqrt{7} \approx 2.6$)

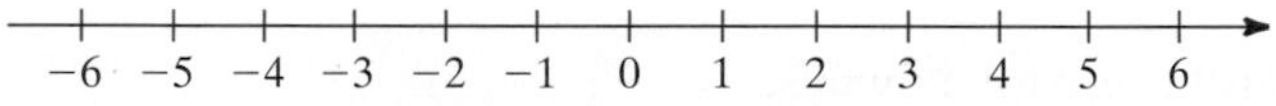

Concept 3: Inequalities

49. The LPGA Samsung World Championship of women's golf scores for selected players are given in the table. Compare the scores and fill in the blank with the appropriate inequality sign: $<$ or $>$. **(See Example 6.)**

LPGA Golfers	Final Score with Respect to Par
Annika Sorenstam	7
Laura Davies	−4
Lorie Kane	0
Cindy McCurdy	3
Se Ri Pak	−8

a. Kane's score ______ Pak's score.

b. Sorenstam's score ______ Davies's score.

c. Pak's score ______ McCurdy's score.

d. Kane's score ______ Davies's score.

50. The elevations of selected cities in the United States are shown in the figure. Compare the elevations and fill in the blank with the appropriate inequality sign: $<$ or $>$. (A negative number indicates that the city is below sea level.)

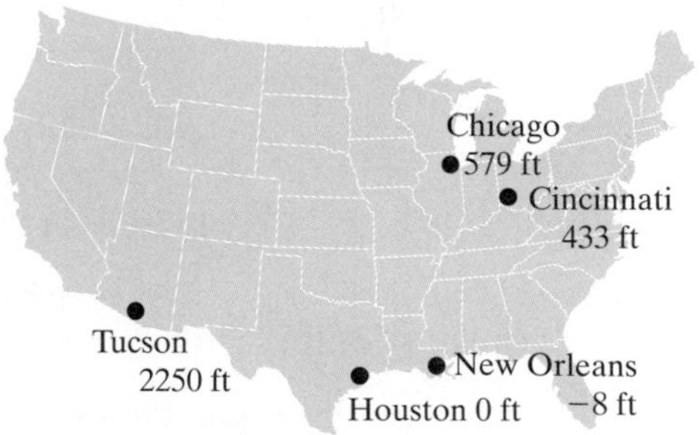

a. Elevation of Tucson ______ elevation of Cincinnati.

b. Elevation of New Orleans ______ elevation of Chicago.

c. Elevation of New Orleans ______ elevation of Houston.

d. Elevation of Chicago ______ elevation of Cincinnati.

Concept 4: Opposite of a Real Number

For Exercises 51–58, find the opposite of each number. **(See Example 7.)**

51. 18

52. 2

53. −6.1

54. −2.5

55. $-\frac{5}{8}$

56. $-\frac{1}{3}$

57. $\frac{7}{3}$

58. $\frac{1}{9}$

The opposite of a is denoted as $-a$. For Exercises 59–66, simplify. **(See Example 8.)**

59. $-(-3)$ **60.** $-(-5.1)$ **61.** $-\left(\frac{7}{3}\right)$ **62.** $-(-7)$

63. $-(-8)$ **64.** $-(36)$ **65.** $-(72.1)$ **66.** $-\left(\frac{9}{10}\right)$

Concept 5: Absolute Value of a Real Number

For Exercises 67–78, simplify. **(See Example 9.)**

67. $|-2|$ **68.** $|-7|$ **69.** $|-1.5|$ **70.** $|-3.7|$

71. $-|-1.5|$ **72.** $-|-3.7|$ **73.** $\left|\frac{3}{2}\right|$ **74.** $\left|\frac{7}{4}\right|$

75. $-|10|$ **76.** $-|20|$ **77.** $-\left|-\frac{1}{2}\right|$ **78.** $-\left|-\frac{11}{3}\right|$

For Exercises 79–80, answer true or false. If a statement is false, explain why.

79. If n is positive, then $|n|$ is negative. **80.** If m is negative, then $|m|$ is negative.

For Exercises 81–104, determine if the statements are true or false. Use the real number line to justify the answer. **(See Example 10.)**

81. $5 > 2$ **82.** $8 < 10$ **83.** $6 < 6$ **84.** $19 > 19$

85. $-7 \geq -7$ **86.** $-1 \leq -1$ **87.** $\frac{3}{2} \leq \frac{1}{6}$ **88.** $-\frac{1}{4} \geq -\frac{7}{8}$

89. $-5 > -2$ **90.** $6 < -10$ **91.** $8 \neq 8$ **92.** $10 \neq 10$

93. $|-2| \geq |-1|$ **94.** $|3| \leq |-1|$ **95.** $\left|-\frac{1}{9}\right| = \left|\frac{1}{9}\right|$ **96.** $\left|-\frac{1}{3}\right| = \left|\frac{1}{3}\right|$

97. $|7| \neq |-7|$ **98.** $|-13| \neq |13|$ **99.** $-1 < |-1|$ **100.** $-6 < |-6|$

101. $|-8| \geq |8|$ **102.** $|-11| \geq |11|$ **103.** $|-2| \leq |2|$ **104.** $|-21| \leq |21|$

Expanding Your Skills

105. For what numbers, a, is $-a$ positive? **106.** For what numbers, a, is $|a| = a$?

Exponents, Square Roots, and the Order of Operations

Section 1.3

Concepts

1. Exponential Expressions
2. Square Roots
3. Order of Operations
4. Translations

1. Exponential Expressions

In algebra, repeated multiplication can be expressed using exponents. The expression $4 \cdot 4 \cdot 4$ can be written as

exponent

$$4^3$$

base

In the expression 4^3, 4 is the base, and 3 is the exponent, or power. The exponent indicates how many factors of the base to multiply.

Definition of b^n

Let b represent any real number and n represent a positive integer. Then,

$$b^n = \underbrace{b \cdot b \cdot b \cdot b \cdot \ldots b}_{n \text{ factors of } b}$$

b^n is read as "b to the nth power."

b is called the **base**, and n is called the **exponent**, or **power**.

b^2 is read as "b squared," and b^3 is read as "b cubed."

The exponent, n, is the number of times the base, b, is used as a factor.

TIP: A number or variable with no exponent shown implies that there is an exponent of 1. That is, $b = b^1$.

Example 1 Evaluating Exponential Expressions

Translate the expression into words and then evaluate the expression.

a. 2^5 **b.** 5^2 **c.** $\left(\frac{3}{4}\right)^3$ **d.** 1^6

Solution:

a. The expression 2^5 is read as "two to the fifth power."
$2^5 = (2)(2)(2)(2)(2) = 32$

b. The expression 5^2 is read as "five to the second power" or "five, squared."
$5^2 = (5)(5) = 25$

c. The expression $(\frac{3}{4})^3$ is read as "three-fourths to the third power" or "three-fourths, cubed."

$$\left(\frac{3}{4}\right)^3 = \left(\frac{3}{4}\right)\left(\frac{3}{4}\right)\left(\frac{3}{4}\right) = \frac{27}{64}$$

d. The expression 1^6 is read as "one to the sixth power."
$1^6 = (1)(1)(1)(1)(1)(1) = 1$

Skill Practice Evaluate.

1. 4^3 **2.** 2^4 **3.** $\left(\frac{2}{3}\right)^2$ **4.** $(1)^7$

Answers

1. 64 **2.** 16 **3.** $\frac{4}{9}$ **4.** 1

2. Square Roots

If we reverse the process of squaring a number, we can find the square roots of the number. For example, finding a square root of 9 is equivalent to asking "what number(s) when squared equals 9?" The symbol, $\sqrt{\ }$ (called a **radical sign**), is used to find the *principal* square root of a number. By definition, the principal square root of a number is nonnegative. Therefore, $\sqrt{9}$ is the nonnegative number that when squared equals 9. Hence, $\sqrt{9} = 3$ because 3 is nonnegative and $(3)^2 = 9$.

Example 2 Evaluating Square Roots

Evaluate the square roots.

a. $\sqrt{64}$ **b.** $\sqrt{121}$ **c.** $\sqrt{0}$ **d.** $\sqrt{\frac{4}{9}}$

Solution:

a. $\sqrt{64} = 8$ Because $(8)^2 = 64$

b. $\sqrt{121} = 11$ Because $(11)^2 = 121$

c. $\sqrt{0} = 0$ Because $(0)^2 = 0$

d. $\sqrt{\frac{4}{9}} = \frac{2}{3}$ Because $\frac{2}{3} \cdot \frac{2}{3} = \frac{4}{9}$

Skill Practice Evaluate.

5. $\sqrt{81}$ **6.** $\sqrt{100}$ **7.** $\sqrt{1}$ **8.** $\sqrt{\frac{9}{25}}$

A perfect square is a number whose square root is a rational number. If a number is not a perfect square, its square root is an irrational number that can be approximated on a calculator.

TIP: To simplify square roots, it is advisable to become familiar with the following perfect squares and square roots.

$0^2 = 0 \longrightarrow \sqrt{0} = 0$	$7^2 = 49 \longrightarrow \sqrt{49} = 7$
$1^2 = 1 \longrightarrow \sqrt{1} = 1$	$8^2 = 64 \longrightarrow \sqrt{64} = 8$
$2^2 = 4 \longrightarrow \sqrt{4} = 2$	$9^2 = 81 \longrightarrow \sqrt{81} = 9$
$3^2 = 9 \longrightarrow \sqrt{9} = 3$	$10^2 = 100 \longrightarrow \sqrt{100} = 10$
$4^2 = 16 \longrightarrow \sqrt{16} = 4$	$11^2 = 121 \longrightarrow \sqrt{121} = 11$
$5^2 = 25 \longrightarrow \sqrt{25} = 5$	$12^2 = 144 \longrightarrow \sqrt{144} = 12$
$6^2 = 36 \longrightarrow \sqrt{36} = 6$	$13^2 = 169 \longrightarrow \sqrt{169} = 13$

3. Order of Operations

When algebraic expressions contain numerous operations, it is important to evaluate the operations in the proper order. Parentheses ( ), brackets [ ], and braces { } are used for grouping numbers and algebraic expressions. It is important

Answers

5. 9 **6.** 10 **7.** 1 **8.** $\frac{3}{5}$

to recognize that operations must be done within parentheses and other grouping symbols first. Other grouping symbols include absolute value bars, radical signs, and fraction bars.

Applying the Order of Operations

Step 1 Simplify expressions within parentheses and other grouping symbols first. These include absolute value bars, fraction bars, and radicals. If imbedded parentheses are present, start with the innermost parentheses.

Step 2 Evaluate expressions involving exponents, radicals, and absolute values.

Step 3 Perform multiplication or division in the order that they occur from left to right.

Step 4 Perform addition or subtraction in the order that they occur from left to right.

Example 3 Applying the Order of Operations

Simplify the expressions.

a. $17 - 3 \cdot 2 + 2^2$ **b.** $\frac{1}{2}\left(\frac{5}{6} - \frac{3}{4}\right)$

Solution:

a. $17 - 3 \cdot 2 + 2^2$

$= 17 - 3 \cdot 2 + 4$ Simplify exponents.

$= 17 - 6 + 4$ Multiply before adding or subtracting.

$= 11 + 4$ Add or subtract from left to right.

$= 15$

b. $\frac{1}{2}\left(\frac{5}{6} - \frac{3}{4}\right)$ Subtract fractions within the parentheses.

$= \frac{1}{2}\left(\frac{10}{12} - \frac{9}{12}\right)$ The least common denominator is 12.

$= \frac{1}{2}\left(\frac{1}{12}\right)$

$= \frac{1}{24}$ Multiply fractions.

Skill Practice Simplify the expressions.

9. $14 - 3 \cdot 2 + 3^2$

10. $\frac{13}{4} - \frac{1}{4}(10 - 2)$

Answers

9. 17 **10.** $\frac{5}{4}$

Solution:

a. $\frac{x}{5}$ or $x \div 5$ The quotient of x and 5

b. $p - \sqrt{q}$ The difference of p and the square root of q

c. $n - 7$ Seven less than n

d. $7 - n$ Seven less n

e. $|w| + 8$ Eight more than the absolute value of w

f. $18 - x$ x subtracted from 18

Avoiding Mistakes

Recall that "a less than b" is translated as $b - a$. Therefore, the statement "seven less than n" must be translated as $n - 7$, not $7 - n$.

Skill Practice Translate each English phrase to an algebraic expression.

15. The product of 6 and y
16. The difference of the square root of t and 7
17. Twelve less than x
18. Twelve less x
19. One more than two times x
20. Five subtracted from the absolute value of w

Example 7 Writing English Phrases as Algebraic Expressions

Translate each English phrase into an algebraic expression. Then evaluate the expression for $a = 6$, $b = 4$, and $c = 20$.

a. The product of a and the square root of b

b. Twice the sum of b and c

c. The difference of twice a and b

Solution:

a. The product of a and the square root of b

$a\sqrt{b}$

$= (\quad)\sqrt{(\quad)}$ Use parentheses to substitute a number for a variable.

$= (6)\sqrt{(4)}$ Substitute $a = 6$ and $b = 4$.

$= 6 \cdot 2$ Simplify the radical first.

$= 12$ Multiply.

b. Twice the sum of b and c

$2(b + c)$ To compute "twice the sum of b and c," it is necessary to take the sum first and then multiply by 2. To ensure the proper order, the sum of b and c must be enclosed in parentheses. The proper translation is $2(b + c)$.

$= 2((\quad) + (\quad))$ Use parentheses to substitute a number for a variable.

$= 2((4) + (20))$ Substitute $b = 4$ and $c = 20$.

$= 2(24)$ Simplify within the parentheses first.

$= 48$ Multiply.

Answers

15. $6y$ **16.** $\sqrt{t} - 7$
17. $x - 12$ **18.** $12 - x$
19. $2x + 1$ **20.** $|w| - 5$

c. The difference of twice a and b

$2a - b$	
$= 2(\quad) - (\quad)$	Use parentheses to substitute a number for a variable.
$= 2(6) - (4)$	Substitute $a = 6$ and $b = 4$.
$= 12 - 4$	Multiply first.
$= 8$	Subtract.

Skill Practice Translate each English phrase to an algebraic expression. Then evaluate the expression for $x = 3, y = 9, z = 10$.

21. The quotient of the square root of y and x

22. One-half the sum of x and y

23. The difference of z and twice x

Answers

21. $\frac{\sqrt{y}}{x}$; 1 **22.** $\frac{1}{2}(x + y)$; 6

23. $z - 2x$; 4

Calculator Connections

Topic: Evaluating Exponential Expressions on a Calculator

On a calculator, we enter exponents greater than the second power by using the key labeled [y^x] or [^]. For example, evaluate 2^4 and 10^6:

Scientific Calculator:

Enter: 2 [y^x] 4 [=] **Result:** 16

Enter: 10 [y^x] 6 [=] **Result:** 1000000

Graphing Calculator:

```
2^4
                16
10^6
           1000000
```

Topic: Applying the Order of Operations on a Calculator

Most calculators also have the capability to enter several operations at once. However, it is important to note that fraction bars and radicals require user-defined parentheses to ensure that the proper order of operations is followed. For example, evaluate the following expressions on a calculator:

a. $130 - 2(5 - 1)^3$ **b.** $\dfrac{18 - 2}{11 - 9}$ **c.** $\sqrt{25 - 9}$

Scientific Calculator:

Enter: 130 [−] 2 [×] [(] 5 [−] 1 [)] [y^x] 3 [=] **Result:** 2

Enter: [(] 18 [−] 2 [)] [÷] [(] 11 [−] 9 [)] [=] **Result:** 8

Enter: [(] 25 [−] 9 [)] [√] **Result:** 4

67. $[4^2 \cdot (6 - 4) \div 8] + [7 \cdot (8 - 3)]$

68. $(18 \div \sqrt{4}) \cdot \{[(9^2 - 1) \div 2] - 15\}$

69. $48 - 13 \cdot 3 + [(50 - 7 \cdot 5) + 2]$

70. $80 \div 16 \cdot 2 + (6^2 - |-2|)$

71. $\dfrac{7 + 3(8 - 2)}{(7 + 3)(8 - 2)}$

72. $\dfrac{16 - 8 \div 4}{4 + 8 \div 4 - 2}$

73. $\dfrac{15 - 5(3 \cdot 2 - 4)}{10 - 2(4 \cdot 5 - 16)}$

74. $\dfrac{5(7 - 3) + 8(6 - 4)}{4[7 + 3(2 \cdot 9 - 8)]}$

75. A person's debt-to-income ratio is the sum of all monthly installment payments (credit cards, loans, etc.) divided by monthly take-home pay. This number is often considered when one is applying for a loan. Each month, Monica makes credit card payments of \$52 and \$20, a student loan payment of \$65, and a payment for furniture of \$43. Her monthly take-home pay is \$1500.

a. Determine Monica's debt-to-income ratio.

b. To obtain a car loan, Monica's debt-to-income ratio must be less than 0.20. Does she meet this criteria?

76. Each month, Jared makes credit card payments of \$115, \$63, and \$95. He also makes a student loan payment of \$77 and another loan payment of \$100. His monthly take-home pay is \$2000.

a. Use the definition given in Exercise 75 to determine Jared's debt-to-income ratio.

b. To obtain a loan for a new home theater system his debt-to-income ratio must be less than 0.15. Does he meet this criteria?

77. The area of a rectangle is given by $A = lw$, where l is the length of the rectangle and w is the width. Find the area for the rectangle shown.

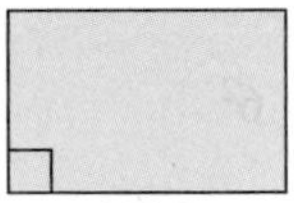

78. The perimeter of a rectangle is given by $P = 2l + 2w$. Find the perimeter for the rectangle shown.

79. The area of a trapezoid is given by $A = \frac{1}{2}(b_1 + b_2)h$, where b_1 and b_2 are the lengths of the two parallel sides and h is the height. A window is in the shape of a trapezoid. Find the area of the trapezoid with dimensions shown in the figure.

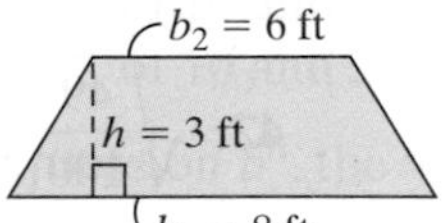

80. The volume of a rectangular solid is given by $V = lwh$, where l is the length of the box, w is the width, and h is the height. Find the volume of the box shown in the figure.

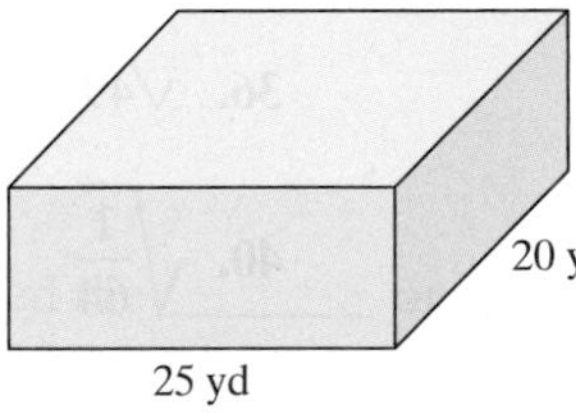

Concept 4: Translations

For Exercises 81–92, write each English phrase as an algebraic expression. **(See Example 6.)**

81. The product of 3 and x

82. The sum of b and 6

83. The quotient of x and 7

84. Four divided by k

85. The difference of 2 and a

86. Three subtracted from t

87. x more than twice y

88. Nine decreased by the product of 3 and p

89. Four times the sum of x and 12

90. Twice the difference of x and 3

91. Q less than 3

92. Fourteen less than t

For Exercises 93–100, write the English phrase as an algebraic expression. Then evaluate each expression for $x = 4$, $y = 2$, and $z = 10$. **(See Example 7.)**

93. Two times y cubed

94. Three times z squared

95. The absolute value of the difference of z and 8

96. The absolute value of the difference of x and 3

97. The product of 5 and the square root of x

98. The square root of the difference of z and 1

99. The value x subtracted from the product of y and z

100. The difference of z and the product of x and y

Expanding Your Skills

For Exercises 101–104, use the order of operations to simplify each expression.

101. $\dfrac{\sqrt{\frac{1}{9}} + \frac{2}{3}}{\sqrt{\frac{4}{25}} + \frac{3}{5}}$

102. $\dfrac{5 - \sqrt{9}}{\sqrt{\frac{4}{9}} + \frac{1}{3}}$

103. $\dfrac{|-2|}{|-10| - |2|}$

104. $\dfrac{|-4|^2}{2^2 + \sqrt{144}}$

105. Some students use the following common memorization device (mnemonic) to help them remember the order of operations: the acronym PEMDAS or **P**lease **E**xcuse **M**y **D**ear **A**unt **S**ally to remember **P**arentheses, **E**xponents, **M**ultiplication, **D**ivision, **A**ddition, and **S**ubtraction. The problem with this mnemonic is that it suggests that multiplication is done before division and similarly, it suggests that addition is performed before subtraction. Explain why following this acronym may give incorrect answers for the expressions:

a. $36 \div 4 \cdot 3$

b. $36 - 4 + 3$

106. If you use the acronym **P**lease **E**xcuse **M**y **D**ear **A**unt **S**ally to remember the order of operations, what must you keep in mind about the last four operations?

107. Explain why the acronym **P**lease **E**xcuse **D**r. **M**ichael **S**mith's **A**unt could also be used as a memory device for the order of operations.

Addition of Real Numbers

Section 1.4

Concepts

1. **Addition of Real Numbers and the Number Line**
2. **Addition of Real Numbers**
3. **Translations**
4. **Applications Involving Addition of Real Numbers**

1. Addition of Real Numbers and the Number Line

Adding real numbers can be visualized on the number line. To do so, locate the first addend on the number line. Then to add a positive number, move to the right on the number line. To add a negative number, move to the left on the number line. The following example may help to illustrate the process.

On a winter day in Detroit, suppose the temperature starts out at 5 degrees Fahrenheit (5°F) at noon, and then drops 12° two hours later when a cold front passes through. The resulting temperature can be represented by the expression $5° + (-12°)$. On the number line, start at 5 and count 12 units to the left (Figure 1-7). The resulting temperature at 2:00 P.M. is -7°F.

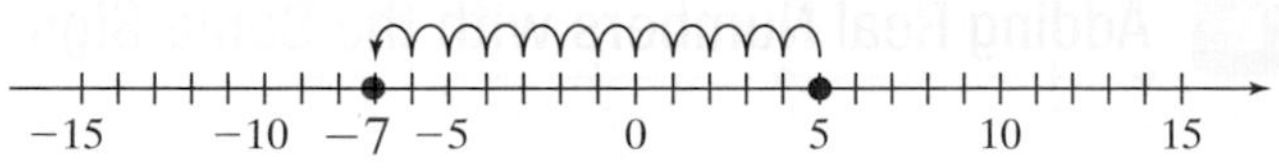

Figure 1-7

Adding Numbers with *Different* Signs

To add two numbers with *different* signs, subtract the smaller absolute value from the larger absolute value. Then apply the sign of the number having the larger absolute value.

Example 3 Adding Real Numbers with Different Signs

Add.

a. $12 + (-17)$ **b.** $-8 + 8$

Solution:

a. $12 + (-17)$ — First find the absolute value of the addends. $|12| = 12$ and $|-17| = 17$.

The absolute value of -17 is greater than the absolute value of 12. Therefore, the sum is negative.

$= -(17 - 12)$ — Next, subtract the smaller absolute value from the larger absolute value.

Apply the sign of the number with the larger absolute value.

$= -5$

b. $-8 + 8$ — First find the absolute value of the addends. $|-8| = 8$ and $|8| = 8$.

$= (8 - 8)$

$= 0$ — The absolute values are equal. Therefore, their difference is 0. The number zero is neither positive nor negative.

Skill Practice Add.

7. $-15 + 16$ **8.** $6 + (-6)$

Example 4 Adding Real Numbers with Different Signs

Add.

a. $-10.6 + 20.4$ **b.** $\frac{2}{15} + \left(-\frac{4}{5}\right)$

Solution:

a. $-10.6 + 20.4$ — First find the absolute value of the addends. $|-10.6| = 10.6$ and $|20.4| = 20.4$.

The absolute value of 20.4 is greater than the absolute value of -10.6. Therefore, the sum is positive.

$= +(20.4 - 10.6)$ — Next, subtract the smaller absolute value from the larger absolute value.

Apply the sign of the number with the larger absolute value.

$= 9.8$

Answers

7. 1 **8.** 0

b. $\frac{2}{15} + \left(-\frac{4}{5}\right)$ The least common denominator is 15.

$= \frac{2}{15} + \left(-\frac{4 \cdot 3}{5 \cdot 3}\right)$ Write each fraction with the LCD.

$= \frac{2}{15} + \left(-\frac{12}{15}\right)$ Find the absolute value of the addends.

$\left|\frac{2}{15}\right| = \frac{2}{15}$ and $\left|-\frac{12}{15}\right| = \frac{12}{15}$.

The absolute value of $-\frac{12}{15}$ is greater than the absolute value of $\frac{2}{15}$. Therefore, the sum is negative.

$= -\left(\frac{12}{15} - \frac{2}{15}\right)$ Next, subtract the smaller absolute value from the larger absolute value.

Apply the sign of the number with the larger absolute value.

$= -\frac{10}{15}$ Subtract.

$= -\frac{2}{3}$ Simplify to lowest terms.

Skill Practice Add.

9. $27.3 + (-18.1)$ **10.** $-\frac{9}{10} + \frac{2}{5}$

3. Translations

Example 5 Translating Expressions Involving the Addition of Real Numbers

Write each English phrase as an algebraic expression. Then simplify the result.

a. The sum of $-12, -8, 9$, and -1 **b.** Negative three-tenths added to $-\frac{7}{8}$

c. The sum of -12 and its opposite

Solution:

a. The sum of $-12, -8, 9$, and -1

$-12 + (-8) + 9 + (-1)$

$= -20 + 9 + (-1)$ Apply the order of operations by adding from left to right.

$= -11 + (-1)$

$= -12$

b. Negative three-tenths added to $-\frac{7}{8}$

$-\frac{7}{8} + \left(-\frac{3}{10}\right)$

$= -\frac{35}{40} + \left(-\frac{12}{40}\right)$ The common denominator is 40.

$= -\frac{47}{40}$ The numbers have the same signs. Add their absolute values and keep the common sign. $-\left(\frac{35}{40} + \frac{12}{40}\right)$

Answers

9. 9.2 **10.** $-\frac{1}{2}$

TIP: The sum of any number and its opposite is 0.

c. The sum of -12 and its opposite

$-12 + (12)$

$= 0$ Add.

Skill Practice Write as an algebraic expression, and simplify the result.

11. The sum of $-10, 4$, and -6

12. Negative 2 added to $-\frac{1}{2}$

13. -60 added to its opposite

4. Applications Involving Addition of Real Numbers

Example 6 Adding Real Numbers in Applications

a. It is common for newborn infants to fluctuate in weight. Elise and Benjamin's baby lost 7 oz the first week and gained 10 oz the second week. Write a mathematical expression to describe this situation and then simplify the result.

b. A student has \$120 in her checking account. After depositing her paycheck of \$215, she writes a check for \$255 to cover her portion of the rent and another check for \$294 to cover her car payment. Write a mathematical expression to describe this situation and then simplify the result.

Solution:

a. $-7 + 10$ A loss of 7 oz can be interpreted as -7 oz.

$= 3$ The infant had a net gain of 3 oz.

b. $\underbrace{120 + 215} + (-255) + (-294)$ Writing a check is equivalent to adding a negative amount to the bank account.

$= \underbrace{335 + (-255)} + (-294)$ Use the order of operations. Add from left to right.

$= 80 + (-294)$

$= -214$ The student has overdrawn her account by \$214.

Skill Practice

14. A stock was priced at \$32.00 per share at the beginning of the month. After the first week, the price went up \$2.15 per share. At the end of the second week it went down \$3.28 per share. Write a mathematical expression to describe the price of the stock and find the price of the stock at the end of the 2-week period.

Answers

11. $-10 + 4 + (-6); -12$

12. $-\frac{1}{2} + (-2); -\frac{5}{2}$

13. $60 + (-60); 0$

14. $32.00 + 2.15 + (-3.28)$; \$30.87 per share

Section 1.4 Practice Exercises

Study Skills Exercise

It is very important to attend class every day. Math is cumulative in nature, and you must master the material learned in the previous class to understand today's lesson. Because this is so important, many instructors have an attendance policy that may affect your final grade. Write down the attendance policy for your class.

Vocabulary and Key Concepts

1. a. If a and b are both negative, then $a + b$ will be (choose one: positive or negative).

b. If a and b have different signs, and if $|b| > |a|$, then the sum will have the same sign as (choose one: a or b).

Review Exercises

Plot the points in set A on a number line. Then for Exercises 2–7 place the appropriate inequality (<, >) between the numbers.

$$A = \left\{-2, \frac{3}{4}, -\frac{5}{2}, 3, \frac{9}{2}, 1.6, 0\right\}$$

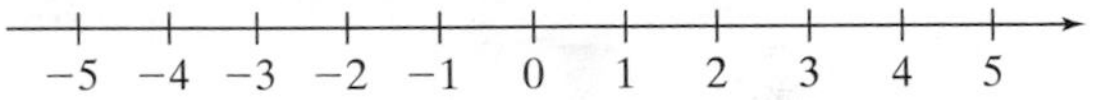

2. $-2 \square 0$

3. $\frac{9}{2} \square \frac{3}{4}$

4. $-2 \square -\frac{5}{2}$

5. $0 \square -\frac{5}{2}$

6. $\frac{3}{4} \square 1.6$

7. $\frac{3}{4} \square -\frac{5}{2}$

8. Evaluate the expressions.

a. $-(-8)$ **b.** $-|-8|$

Concept 1: Addition of Real Numbers and the Number Line

For Exercises 9–16, add the numbers using the number line. **(See Example 1.)**

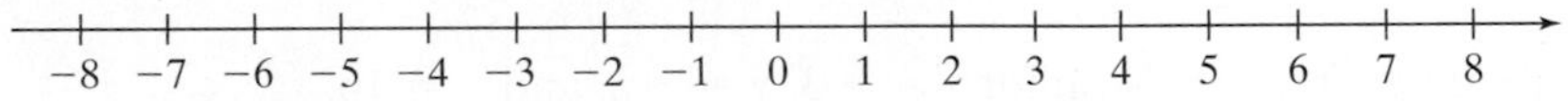

9. $-2 + (-4)$

10. $-3 + (-5)$

11. $-7 + 10$

12. $-2 + 9$

13. $6 + (-3)$

14. $8 + (-2)$

15. $2 + (-5)$

16. $7 + (-3)$

Concept 2: Addition of Real Numbers

For Exercises 17–70, add. **(See Examples 2–4.)**

17. $-19 + 2$

18. $-25 + 18$

19. $-4 + 11$

20. $-3 + 9$

21. $-16 + (-3)$

22. $-12 + (-23)$

23. $-2 + (-21)$

24. $-13 + (-1)$

25. $0 + (-5)$

26. $0 + (-4)$

27. $-3 + 0$

28. $-8 + 0$

29. $-16 + 16$

30. $11 + (-11)$

31. $41 + (-41)$

32. $-15 + 15$

33. $4 + (-9)$

34. $6 + (-9)$

35. $7 + (-2) + (-8)$

36. $2 + (-3) + (-6)$

37. $-17 + (-3) + 20$

38. $-9 + (-6) + 15$

39. $-3 + (-8) + (-12)$

40. $-8 + (-2) + (-13)$

41. $-42 + (-3) + 45 + (-6)$

42. $36 + (-3) + (-8) + (-25)$

43. $-5 + (-3) + (-7) + 4 + 8$

44. $-13 + (-1) + 5 + 2 + (-20)$

45. $23.81 + (-2.51)$

46. $-9.23 + 10.53$

47. $-\frac{2}{7} + \frac{1}{14}$

48. $-\frac{1}{8} + \frac{5}{16}$

49. $\frac{2}{3} + \left(-\frac{5}{6}\right)$

50. $\frac{1}{2} + \left(-\frac{3}{4}\right)$

51. $-\frac{7}{8} + \left(-\frac{1}{16}\right)$

52. $-\frac{1}{9} + \left(-\frac{4}{3}\right)$

53. $-\frac{1}{4} + \frac{3}{10}$

54. $-\frac{7}{6} + \frac{7}{8}$

55. $-2.1 + \left(-\frac{3}{10}\right)$

56. $-8.3 + \left(-\frac{9}{10}\right)$

57. $\frac{3}{4} + (-0.5)$

58. $-\frac{3}{2} + 0.45$

59. $8.23 + (-8.23)$

60. $-7.5 + 7.5$

61. $-\frac{7}{8} + 0$

62. $0 + \left(-\frac{21}{22}\right)$

63. $-\frac{3}{2} + \left(-\frac{1}{3}\right) + \frac{5}{6}$

64. $-\frac{7}{8} + \frac{7}{6} + \frac{7}{12}$

65. $-\frac{2}{3} + \left(-\frac{1}{9}\right) + 2$

66. $-\frac{1}{4} + \left(-\frac{3}{2}\right) + 2$

67. $-47.36 + 24.28$

68. $-0.015 + (0.0026)$

69. $-0.000617 + (-0.0015)$

70. $-5315.26 + (-314.89)$

71. State the rule for adding two numbers with different signs.

72. State the rule for adding two numbers with the same signs.

For Exercises 73–80, evaluate each expression for $x = -3$, $y = -2$, and $z = 16$.

73. $x + y + \sqrt{z}$

74. $2z + x + y$

75. $y + 3\sqrt{z}$

76. $-\sqrt{z} + y$

77. $|x| + |y|$

78. $z + x + |y|$

79. $-x + y$

80. $x + (-y) + z$

Concept 3: Translations

For Exercises 81–90, write each English phrase as an algebraic expression. Then simplify the result. **(See Example 5.)**

81. The sum of -6 and -10

82. The sum of -3 and 5

83. Negative three increased by 8

84. Twenty-one increased by 4

85. Seventeen more than -21

86. Twenty-four more than -7

87. Three times the sum of -14 and 20

88. Two times the sum of 6 and -10

89. Five more than the sum of -7 and -2

90. Negative six more than the sum of 4 and -1

Concept 4: Applications Involving Addition of Real Numbers

91. The temperature in Minneapolis, Minnesota, began at $-5°$F (5° below zero) at 6:00 A.M. By noon, the temperature had risen 13°, and by the end of the day, the temperature had dropped 11° from its noontime high. Write an expression using addition that describes the change in temperatures during the day. Then evaluate the expression to give the temperature at the end of the day.

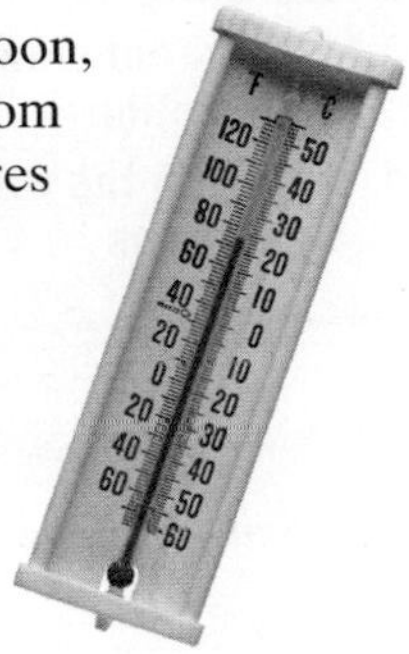

92. The temperature in Toronto, Ontario, Canada, began at 4°F. A cold front went through at noon, and the temperature dropped 9°. By 4:00 P.M., the temperature had risen 2° from its noontime low. Write an expression using addition that describes the changes in temperature during the day. Then evaluate the expression to give the temperature at the end of the day.

93. For 4 months, Amara monitored her weight loss or gain. Her records showed that she lost 8 lb, gained 1 lb, gained 2 lb, and lost 5 lb. Write an expression using addition that describes Amara's total loss or gain and evaluate the expression. Interpret the result. **(See Example 6.)**

94. Alan just started an online business. His profit/loss records for the past 5 months show that he had a profit of \$200, a profit of \$750, a loss of \$340, a loss of \$290, and a profit of \$900. Write an expression using addition that describes Alan's total profit or loss and evaluate the expression. Interpret the result.

95. Yoshima has \$52.23 in her checking account. She writes a check for groceries for \$52.95. **(See Example 6.)**

a. Write an addition problem that expresses Yoshima's transaction.

b. Is Yoshima's account overdrawn?

96. Mohammad has \$40.02 in his checking account. He writes a check for a pair of shoes for \$40.96.

a. Write an addition problem that expresses Mohammad's transaction.

b. Is Mohammad's account overdrawn?

97. The table gives the golf scores for Aree Song for five rounds of the LPGA Final Qualifying Tournament. Find her total score.

Aree Song	
Round 1	-5
Round 2	0
Round 3	-1
Round 4	-1
Round 5	$+1$

98. A company that has been in business for 5 years has the following profit and loss record.

a. Write an expression using addition to describe the company's profit/loss activity.

b. Evaluate the expression from part (a) to determine the company's net profit or loss.

Year	Profit/Loss (\$)
1	$-50{,}000$
2	$-32{,}000$
3	$-5{,}000$
4	13,000
5	26,000

Section 1.5 Subtraction of Real Numbers

Concepts

1. Subtraction of Real Numbers
2. Translations
3. Applications Involving Subtraction
4. Applying the Order of Operations

1. Subtraction of Real Numbers

In Section 1.4, we learned the rules for adding real numbers. Subtraction of real numbers is defined in terms of the addition process. For example, consider the following subtraction problem and the corresponding addition problem:

$$6 - 4 = 2 \quad \Leftrightarrow \quad 6 + (-4) = 2$$

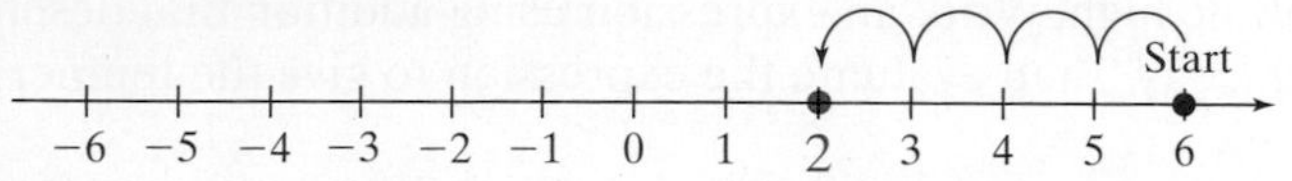

In each case, we start at 6 on the number line and move to the left 4 units. That is, adding the opposite of 4 produces the same result as subtracting 4. This is true in general. To subtract two real numbers, add the opposite of the second number to the first number.

Subtracting Real Numbers

If a and b are real numbers, then $a - b = a + (-b)$.

$$\left.\begin{aligned} 10 - 4 &= 10 + (-4) = 6 \\ -10 - 4 &= -10 + (-4) = -14 \end{aligned}\right\} \quad \text{Subtracting 4 is the same as adding } -4.$$

$$\left.\begin{aligned} 10 - (-4) &= 10 + (4) = 14 \\ -10 - (-4) &= -10 + (4) = -6 \end{aligned}\right\} \quad \text{Subtracting } -4 \text{ is the same as adding 4.}$$

Example 1 Subtracting Integers

Subtract the numbers.

a. $4 - (-9)$ **b.** $-6 - 9$ **c.** $-11 - (-5)$ **d.** $7 - 10$

Solution:

a. $4 - (-9)$

$= 4 + (9) = 13$

Take the opposite of −9.
Change subtraction to addition.

b. $-6 - 9$

$= -6 + (-9) = -15$

Take the opposite of 9.
Change subtraction to addition.

c. $-11 - (-5)$

$= -11 + (5) = -6$

Take the opposite of −5.
Change subtraction to addition.

d. $7 - 10$

$= 7 + (-10) = -3$

Take the opposite of 10.
Change subtraction to addition.

Skill Practice Subtract.

1. $1 - (-3)$ **2.** $-2 - 2$ **3.** $-6 - (-11)$ **4.** $8 - 15$

Answers

1. 4 **2.** −4 **3.** 5 **4.** −7

Example 2 Subtracting Real Numbers

a. $\frac{3}{20} - \left(-\frac{4}{15}\right)$ **b.** $-2.3 - 6.04$

Solution:

a. $\frac{3}{20} - \left(-\frac{4}{15}\right)$ The least common denominator is 60.

$= \frac{9}{60} - \left(-\frac{16}{60}\right)$ Write equivalent fractions with the LCD.

$= \frac{9}{60} + \left(\frac{16}{60}\right)$ Rewrite subtraction in terms of addition.

$= \frac{25}{60}$ Add.

$= \frac{5}{12}$ Simplify by dividing the numerator and denominator by the GCF of 5.

b. $-2.3 - 6.04$

$-2.3 + (-6.04)$ Rewrite subtraction in terms of addition.

-8.34 Add.

Skill Practice Subtract.

5. $\frac{1}{6} - \left(-\frac{7}{12}\right)$ **6.** $-7.5 - 1.5$

2. Translations

Example 3 Translating Expressions Involving Subtraction

Write an algebraic expression for each English phrase and then simplify the result.

a. The difference of -7 and -5

b. 12.4 subtracted from -4.7

c. -24 decreased by the sum of -10 and 13

d. Seven-fourths less than one-third

Solution:

a. The difference of -7 and -5

$-7 - (-5)$

$= -7 + (5)$ Rewrite subtraction in terms of addition.

$= -2$ Simplify.

Answers

5. $\frac{3}{4}$ **6.** -9

TIP: Recall that "b subtracted from a" is translated as $a - b$. In Example 3(b), -4.7 is written first and then 12.4.

TIP: Parentheses must be used around the sum of -10 and 13 so that -24 is decreased by the entire quantity $(-10 + 13)$.

b. 12.4 subtracted from -4.7

$-4.7 - 12.4$

$= -4.7 + (-12.4)$ Rewrite subtraction in terms of addition.

$= -17.1$ Simplify.

c. -24 decreased by the sum of -10 and 13

$-24 - (-10 + 13)$

$= -24 - (3)$ Simplify inside parentheses.

$= -24 + (-3)$ Rewrite subtraction in terms of addition.

$= -27$ Simplify.

d. Seven-fourths less than one-third

$\frac{1}{3} - \frac{7}{4}$

$= \frac{1}{3} + \left(-\frac{7}{4}\right)$ Rewrite subtraction in terms of addition.

$= \frac{4}{12} + \left(-\frac{21}{12}\right)$ The common denominator is 12.

$= -\frac{17}{12}$

Skill Practice Write an algebraic expression for each phrase and then simplify.

7. 8 less than -10

8. -7.2 subtracted from -8.2

9. 10 more than the difference of -2 and 3

10. Two-fifths decreased by four-thirds

3. Applications Involving Subtraction

Example 4 Using Subtraction of Real Numbers in an Application

During one of his turns on *Jeopardy*, Harold selected the category "Show Tunes." He got the \$200, \$600, and \$1000 questions correct, but he got the \$400 and \$800 questions incorrect. Write an expression that determines Harold's score. Then simplify the expression to find his total winnings for that category.

Solution:

$200 + 600 + 1000 - 400 - 800$

$= 200 + 600 + 1000 + (-400) + (-800)$ Add the positive numbers. Add the negative numbers.

$= 1800 + (-1200)$

$= 600$ Harold won \$600.

Skill Practice

11. During Harold's first round on *Jeopardy*, he got the \$100, \$200, and \$400 questions correct but he got the \$300 and \$500 questions incorrect. Determine Harold's score for this round.

Answers

7. $-10 - 8; -18$

8. $-8.2 - (-7.2); -1$

9. $(-2 - 3) + 10; 5$

10. $\frac{2}{5} - \frac{4}{3}; -\frac{14}{15}$

11. -100, Harold lost \$100.

Example 5 **Using Subtraction of Real Numbers in an Application**

The highest recorded temperature in North America was 134°F, recorded on July 10, 1913, in Death Valley, California. The lowest temperature of −81°F was recorded on February 3, 1947, in Snag, Yukon, Canada.

Find the difference between the highest and lowest recorded temperatures in North America.

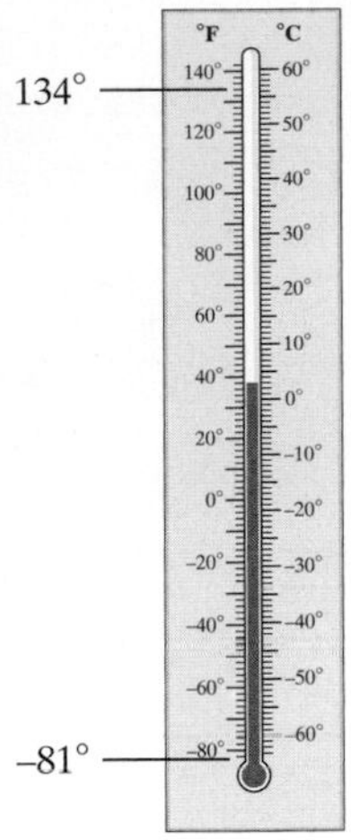

Solution:

$134 - (-81)$

$= 134 + (81)$ Rewrite subtraction in terms of addition.

$= 215$ Add.

The difference between the highest and lowest temperatures is 215°F.

Skill Practice

12. The record high temperature for the state of Montana occurred in 1937 and was 117°F. The record low occurred in 1954 and was −70°F. Find the difference between the highest and lowest temperatures.

4. Applying the Order of Operations

Example 6 **Applying the Order of Operations**

Simplify the expressions.

a. $-6 + \{10 - [7 - (-4)]\}$ **b.** $5 - \sqrt{35 - (-14)} - 2$

Solution:

a. $-6 + \{10 - [7 - (-4)]\}$ Simplify inside the inner brackets first.

$= -6 + \{10 - [7 + (4)]\}$ Rewrite subtraction in terms of addition.

$= -6 + \{10 - (11)\}$ Simplify the expression inside brackets.

$= -6 + \{10 + (-11)\}$ Rewrite subtraction in terms of addition.

$= -6 + (-1)$ Add within the braces.

$= -7$ Add.

b. $5 - \sqrt{35 - (-14)} - 2$ Simplify inside the radical first.

$= 5 - \sqrt{35 + (14)} - 2$ Rewrite subtraction in terms of addition.

$= 5 - \sqrt{49} - 2$ Add within the radical sign.

$= 5 - 7 - 2$ Simplify the radical.

$= 5 + (-7) + (-2)$ Rewrite subtraction in terms of addition.

$= -2 + (-2)$ Add from left to right.

$= -4$

Skill Practice Simplify the expressions.

13. $-11 - \{8 - [2 - (-3)]\}$ **14.** $(12 - 5)^2 + \sqrt{4 - (-21)}$

Answers

12. 187°F **13.** −14 **14.** 54

Example 7 Applying the Order of Operations

Simplify the expressions.

a. $\left(-\frac{5}{8} - \frac{2}{3}\right) - \left(\frac{1}{8} + 2\right)$ **b.** $-6 - |7 - 11| + (-3 + 7)^2$

Solution:

a. $\left(-\frac{5}{8} - \frac{2}{3}\right) - \left(\frac{1}{8} + 2\right)$ Simplify inside the parentheses first.

$= \left[-\frac{5}{8} + \left(-\frac{2}{3}\right)\right] - \left(\frac{1}{8} + 2\right)$ Rewrite subtraction in terms of addition.

$= \left[-\frac{15}{24} + \left(-\frac{16}{24}\right)\right] - \left(\frac{1}{8} + \frac{16}{8}\right)$ Get a common denominator in each parentheses.

$= \left(-\frac{31}{24}\right) - \left(\frac{17}{8}\right)$ Add fractions in each parentheses.

$= \left(-\frac{31}{24}\right) + \left(-\frac{17}{8}\right)$ Rewrite subtraction in terms of addition.

$= -\frac{31}{24} + \left(-\frac{51}{24}\right)$ Get a common denominator.

$= -\frac{82}{24}$ Add.

$= -\frac{41}{12}$ Simplify to lowest terms.

b. $-6 - |7 - 11| + (-3 + 7)^2$ Simplify within absolute value bars and parentheses first.

$= -6 - |7 + (-11)| + (-3 + 7)^2$ Rewrite subtraction in terms of addition.

$= -6 - |-4| + (4)^2$

$= -6 - (4) + 16$ Simplify absolute value and exponent.

$= -6 + (-4) + 16$ Rewrite subtraction in terms of addition.

$= -10 + 16$ Add from left to right.

$= 6$

Skill Practice Simplify the expressions.

15. $\left(-1 + \frac{1}{4}\right) - \left(\frac{3}{4} - \frac{1}{2}\right)$

16. $4 - 2|6 + (-8)| + (4)^2$

Answers

15. −1 **16.** 16

Calculator Connections

Topic: Operations with Signed Numbers on a Calculator

Most calculators can add, subtract, multiply, and divide signed numbers. It is important to note, however, that the key used for the negative sign is different from the key used for subtraction. On a scientific calculator, the [+/-] key or [+○-] key is used to enter a negative number or to change the sign of an existing number. On a graphing calculator, the [(-)] key is used. These keys should not be confused with the [−] key which is used for subtraction. For example, try simplifying the following expressions.

a. $-7 + (-4) - 6$ **b.** $-3.1 - (-0.5) + 1.1$

Scientific Calculator:

Enter: 7 [+○-] [+] [(] 4 [+○-] [)] [−] 6 [=] **Result:** −17

Enter: 3.1 [+○-] [−] [(] 0.5 [+○-] [)] + 1.1 [=] **Result:** −1.5

Graphing Calculator:

```
-7+(-4)-6
              -17
-3.1-(-0.5)+1.1
             -1.5
```

Calculator Exercises

Simplify the expression without the use of a calculator. Then use the calculator to verify your answer.

1. $-8 + (-5)$

2. $4 + (-5) + (-1)$

3. $627 - (-84)$

4. $-0.06 - 0.12$

5. $-3.2 + (-14.5)$

6. $-472 + (-518)$

7. $-12 - 9 + 4$

8. $209 - 108 + (-63)$

Section 1.5 Practice Exercises

Study Skills Exercise

Some instructors allow the use of calculators. What is your instructor's policy regarding calculators in class, on the homework, and on tests?

Helpful Hint: If you are not permitted to use a calculator on tests, it is a good idea to do your homework in the same way, without a calculator.

Vocabulary and Key Concepts

1. a. The expression $a - b$ is equal to $a +$ ______.

b. If a is positive and b is negative, then the difference $a - b$ will be (choose one: positive or negative).

Review Exercises

For Exercises 2–5, write each English phrase as an algebraic expression.

2. The square root of 6

3. The square of x

4. Negative seven increased by 10

5. Two more than $-b$

For Exercises 6–8, simplify the expression.

6. $4^2 - 6 \div 2$

7. $1 + 36 \div 9 \cdot 2$

8. $14 - |10 - 6|$

Concept 1: Subtraction of Real Numbers

For Exercises 9–14, fill in the blank to make each statement correct.

9. $5 - 3 = 5 +$ ________

10. $8 - 7 = 8 +$ ________

11. $-2 - 12 = -2 +$ ________

12. $-4 - 9 = -4 +$ ________

13. $7 - (-4) = 7 +$ ________

14. $13 - (-4) = 13 +$ ________

For Exercises 15–60, simplify. **(See Examples 1–2.)** Animation

15. $3 - 5$

16. $9 - 12$

17. $3 - (-5)$

18. $9 - (-12)$

19. $-3 - 5$

20. $-9 - 12$

21. $-3 - (-5)$

22. $-9 - (-5)$

23. $23 - 17$

24. $14 - 2$

25. $23 - (-17)$

26. $14 - (-2)$

27. $-23 - 17$

28. $-14 - 2$

29. $-23 - (-23)$

30. $-14 - (-14)$

31. $-6 - 14$

32. $-9 - 12$

33. $-7 - 17$

34. $-8 - 21$

35. $13 - (-12)$

36. $20 - (-5)$

37. $-14 - (-9)$

38. $-21 - (-17)$

39. $-\frac{6}{5} - \frac{3}{10}$

40. $-\frac{2}{9} - \frac{5}{3}$

41. $\frac{3}{8} - \left(-\frac{4}{3}\right)$

42. $\frac{7}{10} - \left(-\frac{5}{6}\right)$

43. $\frac{1}{2} - \frac{1}{10}$

44. $\frac{2}{7} - \frac{3}{14}$

45. $-\frac{11}{12} - \left(-\frac{1}{4}\right)$

46. $-\frac{7}{8} - \left(-\frac{1}{6}\right)$

47. $6.8 - (-2.4)$

48. $7.2 - (-1.9)$

49. $3.1 - 8.82$

50. $1.8 - 9.59$

51. $-4 - 3 - 2 - 1$

52. $-10 - 9 - 8 - 7$

53. $6 - 8 - 2 - 10$

54. $20 - 50 - 10 - 5$

55. $10 + (-14) + 6 - 22$

56. $-3 - (-8) + (-11) - 6$

57. $-112.846 + (-13.03) - 47.312$

58. $-96.473 + (-36.02) - 16.617$

59. $0.085 - (-3.14) + 0.018$

60. $0.00061 - (-0.00057) + 0.0014$

Concept 2: Translations

For Exercises 61–70, write each English phrase as an algebraic expression. Then evaluate the expression. **(See Example 3.)**

61. Six minus -7

62. Eighteen minus -1

63. Eighteen subtracted from 3

64. Twenty-one subtracted from 8

65. The difference of -5 and -11

66. The difference of -2 and -18

67. Negative thirteen subtracted from -1

68. Negative thirty-one subtracted from -19

69. Twenty less than -32

70. Seven less than -3

Concept 3: Applications Involving Subtraction

71. On the game, *Jeopardy*, Jasper selected the category "The Last." He got the first four questions correct (worth \$200, \$400, \$600, and \$800) but then missed the last question (worth \$1000). Write an expression that determines Jasper's score. Then simplify the expression to find his total winnings for that category. **(See Example 4.)**

72. On Courtney's turn in *Jeopardy*, she chose the category "Birds of a Feather." She already had \$1200 when she selected a Double Jeopardy question. She wagered \$500 but guessed incorrectly (therefore she lost \$500). On her next turn, she got the \$800 question correct. Write an expression that determines Courtney's score. Then simplify the expression to find her total winnings for that category.

73. In Ohio, the highest temperature ever recorded was 113°F and the lowest was −39°F. Find the difference between the highest and lowest temperatures. (*Source: Information Please Almanac*) **(See Example 5.)**

74. On a recent winter day at the South Pole, the temperature was −52°F. On the same day in Springfield, Missouri, it was a pleasant summer temperature of 75°F. What was the difference in temperature?

75. The highest mountain in the world is Mt. Everest, located in the Himalayas. Its height is 8848 meters (m). The lowest recorded depth in the ocean is located in the Marianas Trench in the Pacific Ocean. Its "height" relative to sea level is −11,033 m. Determine the difference in elevation, in meters, between the highest mountain in the world and the deepest ocean trench. (*Source: Information Please Almanac*)

76. The lowest point in North America is located in Death Valley, California, at an elevation of −282 ft. The highest point in North America is Mt. McKinley, Alaska, at an elevation of 20,320 ft. Find the difference in elevation, in feet, between the highest and lowest points in North America. (*Source: Information Please Almanac*)

Concept 4: Applying the Order of Operations

For Exercises 77–96, perform the indicated operations. **(See Examples 6–7.)**

77. $6 + 8 - (-2) - 4 + 1$

78. $-3 - (-4) + 1 - 2 - 5$

79. $-1 - 7 + (-3) - 8 + 10$

80. $13 - 7 + 4 - 3 - (-1)$

81. $2 - (-8) + 7 + 3 - 15$

82. $8 - (-13) + 1 - 9$

83. $-6 + (-1) + (-8) + (-10)$

84. $-8 + (-3) + (-5) + (-2)$

85. $-4 - \{11 - [4 - (-9)]\}$

86. $15 - \{25 + 2[3 - (-1)]\}$

87. $-\frac{13}{10} + \frac{8}{15} - \left(-\frac{2}{5}\right)$

88. $\frac{11}{14} - \left(-\frac{9}{7}\right) - \frac{3}{2}$

89. $\left(\frac{2}{3} - \frac{5}{9}\right) - \left(\frac{4}{3} - (-2)\right)$

90. $\left(-\frac{9}{8} - \frac{1}{4}\right) - \left(-\frac{5}{6} + \frac{1}{8}\right)$

91. $\sqrt{29 + (-4)} - 7$

92. $8 - \sqrt{98 + (-3) + 5}$

93. $|10 + (-3)| - |-12 + (-6)|$

94. $|6 - 8| + |12 - 5|$

95. $\dfrac{3 - 4 + 5}{4 + (-2)}$

96. $\dfrac{12 - 14 + 6}{6 + (-2)}$

For Exercises 97–104, evaluate each expression for $a = -2$, $b = -6$, and $c = -1$.

97. $(a + b) - c$

98. $(a - b) + c$

99. $a - (b + c)$

100. $a + (b - c)$

101. $(a - b) - c$

102. $(a + b) + c$

103. $a - (b - c)$

104. $a + (b + c)$

Problem Recognition Exercises

Addition and Subtraction of Real Numbers

1. State the rule for adding two negative numbers.

2. State the rule for adding a negative number to a positive number.

For Exercises 3–10, perform the indicated operations.

3. **a.** $14 + (-8)$ **b.** $-14 + 8$ **c.** $-14 + (-8)$ **d.** $14 - (-8)$ **e.** $-14 - 8$

4. **a.** $-5 - (-3)$ **b.** $-5 + (-3)$ **c.** $-5 - 3$ **d.** $-5 + 3$ **e.** $5 - (-3)$

5. **a.** $-25 + 25$ **b.** $25 - 25$ **c.** $25 - (-25)$ **d.** $-25 - (-25)$ **e.** $-25 + (-25)$

6. **a.** $\frac{1}{2} + \left(-\frac{2}{3}\right)$ **b.** $-\frac{1}{2} + \left(\frac{2}{3}\right)$ **c.** $-\frac{1}{2} + \left(-\frac{2}{3}\right)$ **d.** $\frac{1}{2} - \left(-\frac{2}{3}\right)$ **e.** $-\frac{1}{2} - \frac{2}{3}$

7. **a.** $3.5 - 7.1$ **b.** $3.5 - (-7.1)$ **c.** $-3.5 + 7.1$ **d.** $-3.5 - (-7.1)$ **e.** $-3.5 + (-7.1)$

8. **a.** $6 - 1 + 4 - 5$ **b.** $6 - (1 + 4) - 5$ **c.** $6 - (1 + 4 - 5)$ **d.** $(6 - 1) - (4 - 5)$

9. **a.** $-100 - 90 - 80$ **b.** $-100 - (90 - 80)$ **c.** $-100 + (90 - 80)$ **d.** $-100 - (90 + 80)$

10. **a.** $-8 - (-10) + 20^2$ **b.** $-8 - (-10 + 20)^2$ **c.** $[-8 - (-10) + 20]^2$ **d.** $[-8 - (-10)]^2 + 20$

Multiplication and Division of Real Numbers

Section 1.6

Concepts

1. Multiplication of Real Numbers
2. Exponential Expressions
3. Division of Real Numbers
4. Order of Operations

1. Multiplication of Real Numbers

Multiplication of real numbers can be interpreted as repeated addition. For example:

$3(4) = 4 + 4 + 4 = 12$ Add 3 groups of 4.

$3(-4) = -4 + (-4) + (-4) = -12$ Add 3 groups of -4.

These results suggest that the product of a positive number and a negative number is *negative.* Consider the following pattern of products.

$$\begin{aligned} 4 \cdot 3 &= 12 \\ 4 \cdot 2 &= 8 \\ 4 \cdot 1 &= 4 \\ 4 \cdot 0 &= 0 \\ 4 \cdot (-1) &= -4 \\ 4 \cdot (-2) &= -8 \\ 4 \cdot (-3) &= -12 \end{aligned}$$

The pattern decreases by 4 with each row.

Thus, the product of a positive number and a negative number must be *negative* for the pattern to continue.

Now suppose we have a product of two negative numbers. To determine the sign, consider the following pattern of products.

$$\begin{aligned} -4 \cdot 3 &= -12 \\ -4 \cdot 2 &= -8 \\ -4 \cdot 1 &= -4 \\ -4 \cdot 0 &= 0 \\ -4 \cdot (-1) &= 4 \\ -4 \cdot (-2) &= 8 \\ -4 \cdot (-3) &= 12 \end{aligned}$$

The pattern increases by 4 with each row.

Thus, the product of two negative numbers must be *positive* for the pattern to continue.

From the first four rows, we see that the product increases by 4 for each row. For the pattern to continue, it follows that the product of two negative numbers must be *positive.*

We now summarize the rules for multiplying real numbers.

Multiplying Real Numbers

- The product of two real numbers with the *same* sign is positive.

  Examples: $(5)(6) = 30$
  $(-4)(-10) = 40$

- The product of two real numbers with *different* signs is negative.

  Examples: $(-2)(5) = -10$
  $(4)(-9) = -36$

- The product of any real number and zero is zero.

  Examples: $(8)(0) = 0$
  $(0)(-6) = 0$

Example 1 **Multiplying Real Numbers**

Multiply the real numbers.

a. $-8(-4)$ **b.** $-2.5(-1.7)$ **c.** $-7(10)$

d. $\frac{1}{2}(-8)$ **e.** $0(-8.3)$ **f.** $-\frac{2}{7}\left(-\frac{7}{2}\right)$

Solution:

a. $-8(-4) = 32$ *Same* signs. Product is positive.

b. $-2.5(-1.7) = 4.25$ *Same* signs. Product is positive.

c. $-7(10) = -70$ *Different* signs. Product is negative.

d. $\frac{1}{2}(-8) = -4$ *Different* signs. Product is negative.

e. $0(-8.3) = 0$ The product of any real number and zero is zero.

f. $-\frac{2}{7}\left(-\frac{7}{2}\right) = \frac{14}{14}$ *Same* signs. Product is positive.

$= 1$ Simplify.

Skill Practice Multiply.

1. $-9(-3)$ **2.** $-1.5(-1.5)$ **3.** $-6(4)$

4. $\frac{1}{3}(-15)$ **5.** $0(-4.1)$ **6.** $-\frac{5}{9}\left(-\frac{9}{5}\right)$

Observe the pattern for repeated multiplications.

$(-1)(-1) = 1$

$(-1)(-1)(-1) = (1)(-1) = -1$

$(-1)(-1)(-1)(-1) = (1)(-1)(-1) = (-1)(-1) = 1$

$(-1)(-1)(-1)(-1)(-1) = (1)(-1)(-1)(-1) = (-1)(-1)(-1) = (1)(-1) = -1$

The pattern demonstrated in these examples indicates that

- The product of an even number of negative factors is positive.
- The product of an odd number of negative factors is negative.

2. Exponential Expressions

Recall that for any real number b and any positive integer, n:

$$b^n = \underbrace{b \cdot b \cdot b \cdot b \cdot \ldots b}_{n \text{ factors of } b}$$

Be particularly careful when evaluating exponential expressions involving negative numbers. An exponential expression with a negative base is written with parentheses around the base, such as $(-2)^4$.

Answers

1. 27 **2.** 2.25 **3.** −24
4. −5 **5.** 0 **6.** 1

To evaluate $(-2)^4$, the base -2 is used as a factor four times:

$$(-2)^4 = (-2)(-2)(-2)(-2) = 16$$

If parentheses are *not* used, the expression -2^4 has a different meaning:

- The expression -2^4 has a base of 2 (not -2) and can be interpreted as $-1 \cdot 2^4$.

$$-2^4 = -1(2)(2)(2)(2) = -16$$

- The expression -2^4 can also be interpreted as the opposite of 2^4.

$$-2^4 = -(2 \cdot 2 \cdot 2 \cdot 2) = -16$$

TIP: The following expressions are translated as:
$-(-3)$: opposite of negative 3
-3^2: opposite of 3 squared
$(-3)^2$: negative 3, squared

Example 2 Evaluating Exponential Expressions

Simplify.

a. $(-5)^2$ **b.** -5^2 **c.** $(-0.4)^3$ **d.** -0.4^3 **e.** $\left(-\frac{1}{2}\right)^3$

Solution:

a. $(-5)^2 = (-5)(-5) = 25$ Multiply two factors of -5.

b. $-5^2 = -1(5)(5) = -25$ Multiply -1 by two factors of 5.

c. $(-0.4)^3 = (-0.4)(-0.4)(-0.4) = -0.064$ Multiply three factors of -0.4.

d. $-0.4^3 = -1(0.4)(0.4)(0.4) = -0.064$ Multiply -1 by three factors of 0.4.

e. $\left(-\frac{1}{2}\right)^3 = \left(-\frac{1}{2}\right)\left(-\frac{1}{2}\right)\left(-\frac{1}{2}\right) = -\frac{1}{8}$ Multiply three factors of $-\frac{1}{2}$.

Avoiding Mistakes

The negative sign is not part of the base unless it is in parentheses with the base. Thus, in the expression -5^2, the exponent applies only to 5 and not to the negative sign.

Skill Practice Simplify.

7. $(-7)^2$ **8.** -7^2 **9.** $\left(-\frac{2}{3}\right)^3$ **10.** -0.2^3

3. Division of Real Numbers

Two numbers are *reciprocals* if their product is 1. For example, $-\frac{2}{7}$ and $-\frac{7}{2}$ are reciprocals because $-\frac{2}{7}(-\frac{7}{2}) = 1$. Symbolically, if a is a nonzero real number, then the reciprocal of a is $\frac{1}{a}$ because $a \cdot \frac{1}{a} = 1$. This definition also implies that a number and its reciprocal have the same sign.

The Reciprocal of a Real Number

Let a be a nonzero real number. Then, the **reciprocal** of a is $\frac{1}{a}$.

Recall that to subtract two real numbers, we add the opposite of the second number to the first number. In a similar way, division of real numbers is defined in terms of multiplication. To divide two real numbers, we multiply the first number by the reciprocal of the second number.

Answers

7. 49 **8.** -49
9. $-\frac{8}{27}$ **10.** -0.008

Division of Real Numbers

Let a and b be real numbers such that $b \neq 0$. Then, $a \div b = a \cdot \frac{1}{b}$.

Consider the quotient $10 \div 5$. The reciprocal of 5 is $\frac{1}{5}$, so we have

$$10 \div 5 = 2 \qquad \text{or equivalently,} \qquad 10 \cdot \frac{1}{5} = 2$$

(multiply; reciprocal)

Because division of real numbers can be expressed in terms of multiplication, then the sign rules that apply to multiplication also apply to division.

Dividing Real Numbers

- The quotient of two real numbers with the *same* sign is positive.

  Examples: $24 \div 4 = 6$
  $-36 \div -9 = 4$

- The quotient of two real numbers with *different* signs is negative.

  Examples: $100 \div (-5) = -20$
  $-12 \div 4 = -3$

Example 3 Dividing Real Numbers

Divide the real numbers.

a. $200 \div (-10)$ **b.** $\dfrac{-48}{16}$ **c.** $\dfrac{-6.25}{-1.25}$ **d.** $\dfrac{-9}{-5}$

Solution:

a. $200 \div (-10) = -20$ *Different* signs. Quotient is negative.

b. $\dfrac{-48}{16} = -3$ *Different* signs. Quotient is negative.

c. $\dfrac{-6.25}{-1.25} = 5$ *Same* signs. Quotient is positive.

d. $\dfrac{-9}{-5} = \dfrac{9}{5}$ *Same* signs. Quotient is positive.

Because 5 does not divide into 9 evenly the answer can be left as a fraction.

TIP: If the numerator and denominator of a fraction are both negative, then the quotient is positive. Therefore, $\frac{-9}{-5}$ can be simplified to $\frac{9}{5}$.

Skill Practice Divide.

11. $-14 \div 7$ **12.** $\dfrac{-18}{3}$ **13.** $\dfrac{-7.6}{-1.9}$ **14.** $\dfrac{-7}{-3}$

Answers

11. -2 **12.** -6 **13.** 4 **14.** $\frac{7}{3}$

Example 4 Dividing Real Numbers

Divide the real numbers.

a. $15 \div -25$ **b.** $-\frac{3}{14} \div \frac{9}{7}$

Solution:

a. $15 \div -25$ *Different* signs. Quotient is negative.

$= \frac{15}{-25}$

$= -\frac{3}{5}$

b. $-\frac{3}{14} \div \frac{9}{7}$ *Different* signs. Quotient is negative.

$= -\frac{3}{14} \cdot \frac{7}{9}$ Multiply by the reciprocal of $\frac{9}{7}$ which is $\frac{7}{9}$.

$= -\frac{\overset{1}{\cancel{3}}}{\underset{2}{\cancel{14}}} \cdot \frac{\overset{1}{\cancel{7}}}{\underset{3}{\cancel{9}}}$ Divide out common factors.

$= -\frac{1}{6}$ Multiply the fractions.

Skill Practice Divide.

15. $12 \div (-18)$ **16.** $\frac{3}{4} \div \left(-\frac{9}{16}\right)$

TIP: If the numerator and denominator of a fraction have opposite signs, then the quotient will be negative. Therefore, a fraction has the same value whether the negative sign is written in the numerator, in the denominator, or in front of the fraction.

$$\frac{-3}{5} = \frac{3}{-5} = -\frac{3}{5}$$

Multiplication can be used to check any division problem. If $\frac{a}{b} = c$, then $bc = a$ (provided that $b \neq 0$). For example:

$$\frac{8}{-4} = -2 \rightarrow \underline{\text{Check}}: \quad (-4)(-2) = 8 \checkmark$$

This relationship between multiplication and division can be used to investigate division problems involving the number zero.

1. The quotient of 0 and any nonzero number is 0. For example:

$$\frac{0}{6} = 0 \qquad \text{because } 6 \cdot 0 = 0 \checkmark$$

2. The quotient of any nonzero number and 0 is undefined. For example:

$$\frac{6}{0} = ?$$

Finding the quotient $\frac{6}{0}$ is equivalent to asking, "What number times zero will equal 6?" That is, $(0)(?) = 6$. No real number satisfies this condition. Therefore, we say that division by zero is undefined.

3. The quotient of 0 and 0 cannot be determined. Evaluating an expression of the form $\frac{0}{0} = ?$ is equivalent to asking, "What number times zero will equal 0?" That is, $(0)(?) = 0$. Any real number will satisfy this requirement; however, expressions involving $\frac{0}{0}$ are usually discussed in advanced mathematics courses.

Answers

15. $-\frac{2}{3}$ **16.** $-\frac{4}{3}$

Division Involving Zero

Let a represent a nonzero real number. Then,

1. $\frac{0}{a} = 0$ **2.** $\frac{a}{0}$ is undefined

4. Order of Operations

Example 5 Applying the Order of Operations

Simplify. $-8 + 8 \div (-2) \div (-6)$

Solution:

Animation

$-8 + 8 \div (-2) \div (-6)$	
$= -8 + (-4) \div (-6)$	Perform division before addition.
$= -8 + \frac{4}{6}$	The quotient of -4 and -6 is positive $\frac{4}{6}$ or $\frac{2}{3}$.
$= -\frac{8}{1} + \frac{2}{3}$	Write -8 as a fraction.
$= -\frac{24}{3} + \frac{2}{3}$	Get a common denominator.
$= -\frac{22}{3}$	Add.

Skill Practice Simplify.

17. $-36 + 36 \div (-4) \div (-3)$

Example 6 Applying the Order of Operations

Simplify. $\dfrac{24 - 2[-3 + (5 - 8)]^2}{2|-12 + 3|}$

Solution:

$\dfrac{24 - 2[-3 + (5 - 8)]^2}{2\|-12 + 3\|}$	Simplify numerator and denominator separately.
$= \dfrac{24 - 2[-3 + (-3)]^2}{2\|-9\|}$	Simplify within the inner parentheses and absolute value.
$= \dfrac{24 - 2[-6]^2}{2(9)}$	Simplify within brackets, [ ]. Simplify the absolute value.
$= \dfrac{24 - 2(36)}{2(9)}$	Simplify exponents.
$= \dfrac{24 - 72}{18}$	Perform multiplication before subtraction.
$= \dfrac{-48}{18}$ or $-\dfrac{8}{3}$	Simplify to lowest terms.

Answer

17. -33

Skill Practice Simplify.

18. $\dfrac{100 - 3[-1 + (2 - 6)^2]}{|20 - 25|}$

Example 7 Evaluating Algebraic Expressions

Given $y = -6$, evaluate the expressions.

a. y^2 **b.** $-y^2$

Solution:

a. y^2

$= (\quad)^2$	When substituting a number for a variable, use parentheses.
$= (-6)^2$	Substitute $y = -6$.
$= 36$	Square -6, that is, $(-6)(-6) = 36$.

b. $-y^2$

$= -(\quad)^2$	When substituting a number for a variable, use parentheses.
$= -(-6)^2$	Substitute $y = -6$.
$= -(36)$	Square -6.
$= -36$	Multiply by -1.

Skill Practice Given $a = -7$, evaluate the expressions.

19. a^2 **20.** $-a^2$

Answers

18. 11 **19.** 49 **20.** −49

Calculator Connections

Topic: Evaluating Exponential Expressions with Positive and Negative Bases

Be particularly careful when raising a negative number to an even power on a calculator. For example, the expressions $(-4)^2$ and -4^2 have different values. That is, $(-4)^2 = 16$ and $-4^2 = -16$. Verify these expressions on a calculator.

Scientific Calculator:

To evaluate $(-4)^2$

Enter: [( ] 4 [+○-] [ )] [x^2] **Result:** 16

To evaluate -4^2 on a scientific calculator, it is important to square 4 first and then take its opposite.

Enter: 4 [x^2] [+○-] **Result:** −16

Graphing Calculator:

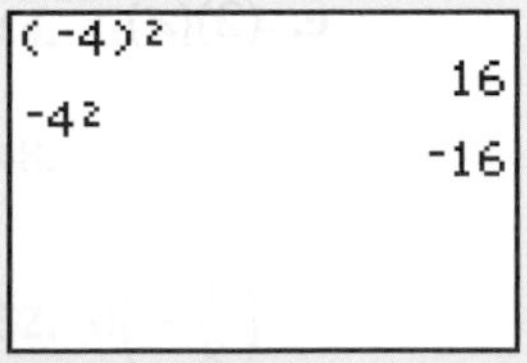

55. $\dfrac{-9}{6}$ **56.** $\dfrac{-15}{10}$ **57.** $\dfrac{-30}{-100}$ **58.** $\dfrac{-250}{-1000}$

59. $\dfrac{26}{-13}$ **60.** $\dfrac{52}{-4}$ **61.** $1.72(-4.6)$ **62.** $361.3(-14.9)$

63. $-0.02(-4.6)$ **64.** $-0.06(-2.15)$ **65.** $\dfrac{14.4}{-2.4}$ **66.** $\dfrac{50.4}{-6.3}$

67. $\dfrac{-5.25}{-2.5}$ **68.** $\dfrac{-8.5}{-27.2}$ **69.** $(-3)^2$ **70.** $(-7)^2$

71. -3^2 **72.** -7^2 **73.** $\left(-\dfrac{4}{3}\right)^3$ **74.** $\left(-\dfrac{1}{5}\right)^3$

75. $(-6.8) \div (-0.02)$ **76.** $(-12.3) \div (-0.03)$ **77.** $\left(-\dfrac{7}{8}\right) \div \left(-\dfrac{9}{16}\right)$ **78.** $\left(-\dfrac{22}{23}\right) \div \left(-\dfrac{11}{3}\right)$

Concept 4: Order of Operations

For Exercises 79–110, perform the indicated operations. **(See Examples 5–6.)**

79. $(-2)(-5)(-3)$ **80.** $(-6)(-1)(-10)$ **81.** $(-8)(-4)(-1)(-3)$

82. $(-6)(-3)(-1)(-5)$ **83.** $100 \div (-10) \div (-5)$ **84.** $150 \div (-15) \div (-2)$

85. $-12 \div (-6) \div (-2)$ **86.** $-36 \div (-2) \div 6$ **87.** $\dfrac{2}{5} \cdot \dfrac{1}{3} \cdot \left(-\dfrac{10}{11}\right)$

88. $\left(-\dfrac{9}{8}\right) \cdot \left(-\dfrac{2}{3}\right) \cdot \left(1\dfrac{5}{12}\right)$ **89.** $\left(1\dfrac{1}{3}\right) \div 3 \div \left(-\dfrac{7}{9}\right)$ **90.** $-\dfrac{7}{8} \div \left(3\dfrac{1}{4}\right) \div (-2)$

91. $12 \div (-2)(4)$ **92.** $(-6) \cdot 7 \div (-2)$ **93.** $\left(-\dfrac{12}{5}\right) \div (-6) \cdot \left(-\dfrac{1}{8}\right)$

94. $10 \cdot \dfrac{1}{3} \div \dfrac{25}{6}$ **95.** $8 - 2^3 \cdot 5 + 3 - (-6)$ **96.** $-14 \div (-7) - 8 \cdot 2 + 3^3$

97. $-(2 - 8)^2 \div (-6) \cdot 2$ **98.** $-(3 - 5)^2 \cdot 6 \div (-4)$ **99.** $\dfrac{6(-4) - 2(5 - 8)}{-6 - 3 - 5}$

100. $\dfrac{3(-4) - 5(9 - 11)}{-9 - 2 - 3}$ **101.** $\dfrac{-4 + 5}{(-2) \cdot 5 + 10}$ **102.** $\dfrac{-3 + 10}{2(-4) + 8}$

103. $-4 - 3[2 - (-5 + 3)] - 8 \cdot 2^2$ **104.** $-6 - 5[-4 - (6 - 12)] + (-5)^2$ **105.** $-|-1| - |5|$

106. $-|-10| - |6|$ **107.** $\dfrac{|2 - 9| - |5 - 7|}{10 - 15}$ **108.** $\dfrac{|-2 + 6| - |3 - 5|}{13 - 11}$

109. $\dfrac{6 - 3[2 - (6 - 8)]^2}{-2|2 - 5|}$ **110.** $\dfrac{12 - 4[-6 - (5 - 8)]^2}{4|6 - 10|}$

For Exercises 111–116, evaluate the expression for $x = -2$, $y = -4$, and $z = 6$. **(See Example 7.)**

111. $-x^2$

112. x^2

113. $4(2x - z)$

114. $6(3x + y)$

115. $\dfrac{3x + 2y}{y}$

116. $\dfrac{2z - y}{x}$

117. Is the expression $\dfrac{10}{5x}$ equal to $10/5x$? Explain.

118. Is the expression $10/(5x)$ equal to $\dfrac{10}{5x}$? Explain.

For Exercises 119–126, write each English phrase as an algebraic expression. Then evaluate the expression.

119. The product of -3.75 and 0.3

120. The product of -0.4 and -1.258

121. The quotient of $\frac{16}{5}$ and $\left(-\frac{8}{9}\right)$

122. The quotient of $\left(-\frac{3}{14}\right)$ and $\frac{1}{7}$

123. The number -0.4 plus the quantity 6 times -0.42

124. The number 0.5 plus the quantity -2 times 0.125

125. The number $-\frac{1}{4}$ minus the quantity 6 times $-\frac{1}{3}$

126. Negative five minus the quantity $\left(-\frac{5}{6}\right)$ times $\frac{3}{8}$

127. For 3 weeks, Jim pays \$2 a week for lottery tickets. Jim has one winning ticket for \$3. Write an expression that describes his net gain or loss. How much money has Jim won or lost?

128. Stephanie pays \$2 a week for 6 weeks for lottery tickets. Stephanie has one winning ticket for \$5. Write an expression that describes her net gain or loss. How much money has Stephanie won or lost?

129. Lorne sells ads for the local newspaper and has a quota for the number of ads he must sell each week. For the first two days of the week, Lorne was 5 above his daily quota. For the last three days of the week, Lorne was 3 below his daily quota. Write an expression that describes the net amount he was above or below his quota. Interpret the result.

130. Valerie trades stocks each day and analyzes her results at the end of the week. The first day of the week she had a profit of \$650. The next two days she had a loss of \$400 each day and the last two days she had a loss of \$150 each day. Write an expression that describes Valerie's profit or loss for the week. Interpret the result.

131. A pediatrician analyzed the effect of a special baby food on five toddlers. He recorded the amount of weight lost or gained (in ounces) by each child for one month as shown in the table.

Baby	A	B	C	D	E
Gain/Loss (oz)	12	−15	4	−9	3

Write an expression to calculate the average gain or loss in weight of the children and then simplify. Interpret your answer. (*Hint:* See Appendix A.1 for the formula for *average* (or mean).)

132. At the end of a 2-month class, a personal trainer analyzed the effect of her new exercise routine by recording the gain or loss (in inches) in waist measurements of her clients. The results are shown in the table.

Client	A	B	C	D	E	F
Gain/Loss (in.)	−1.5	−2	1.5	2.5	−3	−0.5

Write an expression to calculate the average gain or loss in waist measurement and then simplify. Interpret your answer.

Example 2 **Applying the Commutative Property of Addition**

Rewrite the expression in terms of addition. Then apply the commutative property of addition.

a. $5a - 3b$ **b.** $z^2 - \frac{1}{4}$

Solution:

a. $5a - 3b$

$= 5a + (-3b)$ Rewrite subtraction as addition of $-3b$.

$= -3b + 5a$ Apply the commutative property of addition.

b. $z^2 - \frac{1}{4}$

$= z^2 + \left(-\frac{1}{4}\right)$ Rewrite subtraction as addition of $-\frac{1}{4}$.

$= -\frac{1}{4} + z^2$ Apply the commutative property of addition.

Skill Practice Rewrite each expression in terms of addition. Then apply the commutative property of addition.

3. $8m - 2n$ **4.** $\frac{1}{3}x - \frac{3}{4}$

Example 3 **Applying the Commutative Property of Multiplication**

Use the commutative property of multiplication to rewrite each expression.

a. $12(-6)$ **b.** $x \cdot 4$

Solution:

a. $12(-6) = -6(12)$

b. $x \cdot 4 = 4 \cdot x$ (or simply $4x$)

Skill Practice Use the commutative property of multiplication to rewrite each expression.

5. $-2(5)$ **6.** $y \cdot 6$

2. Associative Properties of Real Numbers

The associative property of real numbers states that the manner in which three or more real numbers are grouped under addition or multiplication will not affect the outcome. For example:

$$(5 + 10) + 2 = 5 + (10 + 2) \quad \text{and} \quad (5 \cdot 10)2 = 5(10 \cdot 2)$$
$$15 + 2 = 5 + 12 \qquad\qquad (50)2 = 5(20)$$
$$17 = 17 \qquad\qquad 100 = 100$$

Answers

3. $8m + (-2n)$; $-2n + 8m$

4. $\frac{1}{3}x + \left(-\frac{3}{4}\right)$; $-\frac{3}{4} + \frac{1}{3}x$

5. $5(-2)$ **6.** $6y$

Associative Properties of Real Numbers

If a, b, and c represent real numbers, then

1. $(a + b) + c = a + (b + c)$ **associative property of addition**
2. $(ab)c = a(bc)$ **associative property of multiplication**

Example 4 **Applying the Associative Property**

Use the associative property of addition or multiplication to rewrite each expression. Then simplify the expression if possible.

a. $(y + 5) + 6$ **b.** $4(5z)$ **c.** $-\frac{3}{2}\left(-\frac{2}{3}w\right)$

Solution:

a. $(y + 5) + 6$

$= y + (5 + 6)$ Apply the associative property of addition.

$= y + 11$ Simplify.

b. $4(5z)$

$= (4 \cdot 5)z$ Apply the associative property of multiplication.

$= 20z$ Simplify.

c. $-\frac{3}{2}\left(-\frac{2}{3}w\right)$

$= \left[-\frac{3}{2}\left(-\frac{2}{3}\right)\right]w$ Apply the associative property of multiplication.

$= 1w$ Simplify.

$= w$

Note: In most cases, a detailed application of the associative property will not be shown. Instead, the process will be written in one step, such as

$$(y + 5) + 6 = y + 11, \quad 4(5z) = 20z, \quad \text{and} \quad -\frac{3}{2}\left(-\frac{2}{3}w\right) = w$$

Skill Practice Use the associative property of addition or multiplication to rewrite each expression. Simplify if possible.

7. $(x + 4) + 3$ **8.** $-2(4x)$ **9.** $\frac{5}{4}\left(\frac{4}{5}t\right)$

3. Identity and Inverse Properties of Real Numbers

The number 0 has a special role under the operation of addition. Zero added to any real number does not change the number. Therefore, the number 0 is said to be the *additive identity* (also called the *identity element of addition*). For example:

$$-4 + 0 = -4 \qquad 0 + 5.7 = 5.7 \qquad 0 + \frac{3}{4} = \frac{3}{4}$$

Answers

7. $x + (4 + 3)$; $x + 7$
8. $(-2 \cdot 4)x$; $-8x$
9. $\left(\frac{5}{4} \cdot \frac{4}{5}\right)t$; t

The number 1 has a special role under the operation of multiplication. Any real number multiplied by 1 does not change the number. Therefore, the number 1 is said to be the *multiplicative identity* (also called the *identity element of multiplication*). For example:

$$(-8)1 = -8 \qquad 1(-2.85) = -2.85 \qquad 1\left(\frac{1}{5}\right) = \frac{1}{5}$$

Identity Properties of Real Numbers

If a is a real number, then

1. $a + 0 = 0 + a = a$ **identity property of addition**
2. $a \cdot 1 = 1 \cdot a = a$ **identity property of multiplication**

The sum of a number and its opposite equals 0. For example, $-12 + 12 = 0$. For any real number, a, the opposite of a (also called the *additive inverse* of a) is $-a$ and $a + (-a) = -a + a = 0$. The inverse property of addition states that the sum of any number and its additive inverse is the identity element of addition, 0. For example:

Number	Additive Inverse (Opposite)	Sum
9	-9	$9 + (-9) = 0$
-21.6	21.6	$-21.6 + 21.6 = 0$
$\frac{2}{7}$	$-\frac{2}{7}$	$\frac{2}{7} + \left(-\frac{2}{7}\right) = 0$

If b is a nonzero real number, then the reciprocal of b (also called the *multiplicative inverse* of b) is $\frac{1}{b}$. The inverse property of multiplication states that the product of b and its multiplicative inverse is the identity element of multiplication, 1. Symbolically, we have $b \cdot \frac{1}{b} = \frac{1}{b} \cdot b = 1$. For example:

Number	Multiplicative Inverse (Reciprocal)	Product
7	$\frac{1}{7}$	$7 \cdot \frac{1}{7} = 1$
3.14	$\frac{1}{3.14}$	$3.14\left(\frac{1}{3.14}\right) = 1$
$-\frac{3}{5}$	$-\frac{5}{3}$	$-\frac{3}{5}\left(-\frac{5}{3}\right) = 1$

Inverse Properties of Real Numbers

If a is a real number and b is a nonzero real number, then

1. $a + (-a) = -a + a = 0$ **inverse property of addition**
2. $b \cdot \frac{1}{b} = \frac{1}{b} \cdot b = 1$ **inverse property of multiplication**

4. Distributive Property of Multiplication over Addition

The operations of addition and multiplication are related by an important property called the **distributive property of multiplication over addition**. Consider the expression $6(2 + 3)$. The order of operations indicates that the sum $2 + 3$ is evaluated first, and then the result is multiplied by 6:

$$\begin{aligned} &6(2 + 3) \\ &= 6(5) \\ &= 30 \end{aligned}$$

Notice that the same result is obtained if the factor of 6 is multiplied by each of the numbers 2 and 3, and then their products are added:

$$\begin{aligned} &6(2 + 3) && \text{The factor of 6 is distributed to the numbers 2 and 3.} \\ &= 6(2) + 6(3) \\ &= 12 + 18 \\ &= 30 \end{aligned}$$

The distributive property of multiplication over addition states that this is true in general.

TIP: The mathematical definition of the distributive property is consistent with the everyday meaning of the word *distribute*. To distribute means to "spread out from one to many." In the mathematical context, the factor a is distributed to both b and c in the parentheses.

Distributive Property of Multiplication over Addition

If a, b, and c are real numbers, then

$$a(b + c) = ab + ac \quad \text{and} \quad (b + c)a = ab + ac$$

Example 5 **Applying the Distributive Property**

Apply the distributive property: $2(a + 6b + 7)$

Solution:

$$\begin{aligned} &2(a + 6b + 7) \\ &= 2(a + 6b + 7) \\ &= 2(a) + 2(6b) + 2(7) && \text{Apply the distributive property.} \\ &= 2a + 12b + 14 && \text{Simplify.} \end{aligned}$$

Skill Practice Apply the distributive property.

10. $7(x + 4y + z)$

Answer

10. $7x + 28y + 7z$

Because the difference of two expressions $a - b$ can be written in terms of addition as $a + (-b)$, the distributive property can be applied when the operation of subtraction is present within the parentheses. For example:

$5(y - 7)$

$= 5[y + (-7)]$ Rewrite subtraction as addition of -7.

$= 5[y + (-7)]$ Apply the distributive property.

$= 5(y) + 5(-7)$

$= 5y + (-35)$, or $5y - 35$ Simplify.

Example 6 Applying the Distributive Property

Use the distributive property to rewrite each expression.

a. $-(-3a + 2b + 5c)$ **b.** $-6(2 - 4x)$

Solution:

a. $-(-3a + 2b + 5c)$

$= -1(-3a + 2b + 5c)$ The negative sign preceding the parentheses can be interpreted as taking the opposite of the quantity that follows or as $-1(-3a + 2b + 5c)$

$= -1(-3a + 2b + 5c)$

$= -1(-3a) + (-1)(2b) + (-1)(5c)$ Apply the distributive property.

$= 3a + (-2b) + (-5c)$ Simplify.

$= 3a - 2b - 5c$

TIP: Notice that a negative factor preceding the parentheses changes the signs of all the terms to which it is multiplied.

$-1(-3a + 2b + 5c)$
$= +3a - 2b - 5c$

b. $-6(2 - 4x)$

$= -6[2 + (-4x)]$ Change subtraction to addition of $-4x$.

$= -6[2 + (-4x)]$

$= -6(2) + (-6)(-4x)$ Apply the distributive property. Notice that multiplying by -6 changes the signs of all terms to which it is applied.

$= -12 + 24x$ Simplify.

Skill Practice Use the distributive property to rewrite each expression.

11. $-(12x + 8y - 3z)$ **12.** $-6(-3a + 7b)$

Note: In most cases, the distributive property will be applied without as much detail as shown in Examples 5 and 6. Instead, the distributive property will be applied in one step.

$2(a + 6b + 7)$ 1 step $= 2a + 12b + 14$

$-(3a + 2b + 5c)$ 1 step $= -3a - 2b - 5c$

$-6(2 - 4x)$ 1 step $= -12 + 24x$

Answers

11. $-12x - 8y + 3z$
12. $18a - 42b$

5. Algebraic Expressions

A **term** is a constant or the product or quotient of constants and variables. An algebraic expression is the sum of one or more terms. For example, the expression

$$-7x^2 + xy - 100 \quad \text{or} \quad -7x^2 + xy + (-100)$$

consists of the terms $-7x^2$, xy, and -100.

The terms $-7x^2$ and xy are **variable terms** and the term -100 is called a **constant term**. It is important to distinguish between a term and the factors within a term. For example, the quantity xy is one term, and the values x and y are factors within the term. The constant factor in a term is called the *numerical coefficient* (or simply **coefficient**) of the term. In the terms $-7x^2$, xy, and -100, the coefficients are -7, 1, and -100, respectively.

Terms are ***like* terms** if they each have the same variables and the corresponding variables are raised to the same powers. For example:

***Like* Terms**	**Unlike Terms**	
$-3b$ and $5b$	$-5c$ and $7d$	(different variables)
$9p^2q^3$ and p^2q^3	$4p^2q^3$ and $8p^3q^2$	(different powers)
$5w$ and $2w$	$5w$ and 2	(different variables)

Example 7 Identifying Terms, Factors, Coefficients, and *Like* Terms

a. List the terms of the expression $5x^2 - 3x + 2$.

b. Identify the coefficient of the term $6yz^3$.

c. Which of the pairs are *like* terms: $8b, 3b^2$ or $4c^2d, -6c^2d$?

Solution:

a. The terms of the expression $5x^2 - 3x + 2$ are $5x^2$, $-3x$, and 2.

b. The coefficient of $6yz^3$ is 6.

c. $4c^2d$ and $-6c^2d$ are *like* terms.

Skill Practice

13. List the terms in the expression. $4xy - 9x^2 + 15$

14. Identify the coefficients of each term in the expression. $2a - b + c - 80$

15. Which of the pairs are *like* terms? $5x^3, 5x$ or $-7x^2, 11x^2$

Two terms can be added or subtracted only if they are *like* terms. To add or subtract *like* terms, we use the distributive property as shown in Example 8.

Answers

13. $4xy, -9x^2, 15$
14. $2, -1, 1, -80$
15. $-7x^2$ and $11x^2$ are *like* terms.

Example 8 **Using the Distributive Property to Add and Subtract *Like* Terms**

Add or subtract as indicated.

a. $7x + 2x$ **b.** $-2p + 3p - p$

Solution:

a. $7x + 2x$

$= (7 + 2)x$ Apply the distributive property.

$= 9x$ Simplify.

b. $-2p + 3p - p$

$= -2p + 3p - 1p$ Note that $-p$ equals $-1p$.

$= (-2 + 3 - 1)p$ Apply the distributive property.

$= (0)p$ Simplify.

$= 0$

Skill Practice Simplify by adding *like* terms.

16. $8x + 3x$ **17.** $-6a + 4a + a$

Although the distributive property is used to add and subtract *like* terms, it is tedious to write each step. Observe that adding or subtracting *like* terms is a matter of adding or subtracting the coefficients and leaving the variable factors unchanged. This can be shown in one step, a shortcut that we will use throughout the text. For example:

$$7x + 2x = 9x \qquad -2p + 3p - 1p = 0p = 0 \qquad -3a - 6a = -9a$$

Example 9 **Combining *Like* Terms**

Simplify by combining *like* terms.

a. $3yz + 5 - 2yz + 9$ **b.** $1.2w^3 + 5.7w^3$

Solution:

a. $3yz + 5 - 2yz + 9$

$= 3yz - 2yz + 5 + 9$ Arrange *like* terms together. Notice that constants such as 5 and 9 are *like* terms.

$= 1yz + 14$ Combine *like* terms.

$= yz + 14$

b. $1.2w^3 + 5.7w^3$

$= 6.9w^3$ Combine *like* terms.

Skill Practice Simplify by combining *like* terms.

18. $4pq - 7 + 5pq - 8$ **19.** $8.3x^2 + 5.1x^2$

Answers

16. $11x$ **17.** $-a$

18. $9pq - 15$ **19.** $13.4x^2$

When we apply the distributive property, the parentheses are removed. Sometimes this is referred to as *clearing parentheses*. In Examples 10 and 11, we clear parentheses and combine *like* terms.

Example 10 Clearing Parentheses and Combining *Like* Terms

Simplify by *clearing parentheses* and combining *like* terms. $5 - 2(3x + 7)$

Solution:

$5 - 2(3x + 7)$ The order of operations indicates that we must perform multiplication before subtraction.

It is important to understand that a factor of -2 (not 2) will be multiplied to all terms within the parentheses. To see why this is so, we may rewrite the subtraction in terms of addition.

$= 5 + (-2)(3x + 7)$	Change subtraction to addition.
$= 5 + (-2)(3x + 7)$	A factor of -2 is to be distributed to terms in the parentheses.
$= 5 + (-2)(3x) + (-2)(7)$	Apply the distributive property.
$= 5 + (-6x) + (-14)$	Simplify.
$= 5 + (-14) + (-6x)$	Arrange *like* terms together.
$= -9 + (-6x)$	Combine *like* terms.
$= -9 - 6x$	Simplify by changing addition of the opposite to subtraction.

Skill Practice Clear the parentheses and combine *like* terms.

20. $9 - 5(2x - 7)$

Example 11 Clearing Parentheses and Combining *Like* Terms

Simplify by clearing parentheses and combining *like* terms.

a. $\frac{1}{4}(4k + 2) - \frac{1}{2}(6k + 1)$ **b.** $-(4s - 6t) - (3t + 5s) - 2s$

Solution:

a. $\frac{1}{4}(4k + 2) - \frac{1}{2}(6k + 1)$

$= \frac{4}{4}k + \frac{2}{4} - \frac{6}{2}k - \frac{1}{2}$	Apply the distributive property. Notice that a factor of $-\frac{1}{2}$ is distributed through the second parentheses and changes the signs.
$= k + \frac{1}{2} - 3k - \frac{1}{2}$	Simplify fractions.
$= k - 3k + \frac{1}{2} - \frac{1}{2}$	Arrange *like* terms together.
$= -2k + 0$	Combine *like* terms.
$= -2k$	

Answer

20. $-10x + 44$

b. $-(4s - 6t) - (3t + 5s) - 2s$

$= -1(4s - 6t) - 1(3t + 5s) - 2s$	Notice that a factor of -1 is distributed through each parentheses.
$= -4s + 6t - 3t - 5s - 2s$	Apply the distributive property.
$= -4s - 5s - 2s + 6t - 3t$	Arrange *like* terms together.
$= -11s + 3t$	Combine *like* terms.

Skill Practice Clear the parentheses and combine *like* terms.

21. $\frac{1}{2}(8x + 4) + \frac{1}{3}(3x - 9)$ **22.** $-4(x + 2y) - (2x - y) - 5x$

Example 12 Clearing Parentheses and Combining *Like* Terms

Simplify by clearing parentheses and combining *like* terms.

$$-7a - 4[3a - 2(a + 6)] \quad 4$$

Solution:

$-7a - 4[3a - 2(a + 6)] - 4$

$= -7a - 4[3a - 2a - 12] - 4$	Apply the distributive property to clear the innermost parentheses.
$= -7a - 4[a - 12] - 4$	Simplify within brackets by combining *like* terms.
$= -7a - 4a + 48 - 4$	Apply the distributive property to clear the brackets.
$= -11a + 44$	Combine *like* terms.

Avoiding Mistakes

First clear the innermost parentheses and combine *like* terms within the brackets. Then use the distributive property to clear the brackets.

Skill Practice Clear the parentheses and combine *like* terms.

23. $6 - 5[-2y - 4(2y - 5)]$

Answers

21. $5x - 1$ **22.** $-11x - 7y$
23. $50y - 94$

Section 1.7 Practice Exercises

Study Skills Exercise

Write down the page number(s) for the Chapter Summary for this chapter. Describe one way in which you can use the Summary found at the end of each chapter.

Vocabulary and Key Concepts

1. a. Given the expression $12y + ab - 2x + 18$, the terms $12y$, ab, and $-2x$ are variable terms, whereas 18 is a __________ term.

b. The constant factor in a term is called the __________.

c. Given the expression x, the value of the coefficient is __________, and the exponent is __________.

d. Terms that have the same variables, with corresponding variables raised to the same powers, are called __________ terms.

Review Exercises

For Exercises 2–14, perform the indicated operations.

2. $(-6) + 14$ **3.** $(-2) + 9$ **4.** $-13 - (-5)$ **5.** $-1 - (-19)$

6. $18 \div (-4)$ **7.** $-27 \div 5$ **8.** $-3 \cdot 0$ **9.** $0(-15)$

10. $\frac{1}{2} + \frac{3}{8}$ **11.** $\frac{25}{21} - \frac{6}{7}$ **12.** $\left(-\frac{3}{5}\right)\left(\frac{4}{27}\right)$ **13.** $\left(-\frac{11}{12}\right) \div \left(-\frac{5}{4}\right)$

14. $25 \cdot \left(-\frac{4}{5}\right)$

Concept 1: Commutative Properties of Real Numbers

For Exercises 15–22, rewrite each expression using the commutative property of addition or the commutative property of multiplication. **(See Examples 1 and 3.)**

15. $5 + (-8)$ **16.** $7 + (-2)$ **17.** $8 + x$ **18.** $p + 11$

19. $5(4)$ **20.** $10(8)$ **21.** $x(-12)$ **22.** $y(-23)$

For Exercises 23–26, rewrite each expression using addition. Then apply the commutative property of addition. **(See Example 2.)**

23. $x - 3$ **24.** $y - 7$ **25.** $4p - 9$ **26.** $3m - 12$

Concept 2: Associative Properties of Real Numbers

For Exercises 27–38, use the associative property of addition or multiplication to rewrite each expression. Then simplify the expression if possible. **(See Example 4.)**

27. $(x + 4) + 9$ **28.** $-3 + (5 + z)$ **29.** $-5(3x)$ **30.** $-12(4z)$

31. $\frac{6}{11}\left(\frac{11}{6}x\right)$ **32.** $\frac{3}{5}\left(\frac{5}{3}x\right)$ **33.** $-4\left(-\frac{1}{4}t\right)$ **34.** $-5\left(-\frac{1}{5}w\right)$

35. $-8 + (2 + y)$ **36.** $[x + (-5)] + 7$ **37.** $-5(2x)$ **38.** $-10(6t)$

Concept 3: Identity and Inverse Properties of Real Numbers

39. What is another name for multiplicative inverse? **40.** What is another name for additive inverse?

41. What is the additive identity? **42.** What is the multiplicative identity?

Concept 4: Distributive Property of Multiplication over Addition

For Exercises 43–62, use the distributive property to clear parentheses. **(See Examples 5–6.)**

43. $6(5x + 1)$ **44.** $2(x + 7)$ **45.** $-2(a + 8)$ **46.** $-3(2z + 9)$

47. $3(5c - d)$ **48.** $4(w - 13z)$ **49.** $-7(y - 2)$ **50.** $-2(4x - 1)$

51. $-\frac{2}{3}(x - 6)$ **52.** $-\frac{1}{4}(2b - 8)$ **53.** $\frac{1}{3}(m - 3)$ **54.** $\frac{2}{5}(n - 5)$

55. $-(2p + 10)$ **56.** $-(7q + 1)$ **57.** $-2(-3w - 5z + 8)$ **58.** $-4(-7a - b - 3)$

59. $4(x + 2y - z)$ **60.** $-6(2a - b + c)$ **61.** $-(-6w + x - 3y)$ **62.** $-(-p - 5q - 10r)$

Mixed Exercises

For Exercises 63–70, use the associative property or distributive property to clear parentheses.

63. $2(3 + x)$ **64.** $5(4 + y)$ **65.** $4(6z)$ **66.** $8(2p)$

67. $-2(7x)$ **68.** $3(-11t)$ **69.** $-4(1 + x)$ **70.** $-9(2 + y)$

For Exercises 71–79, match each statement with the property that describes it.

71. $6 \cdot \frac{1}{6} = 1$

72. $7(4 \cdot 9) = (7 \cdot 4)9$

73. $2(3 + k) = 6 + 2k$

74. $3 \cdot 7 = 7 \cdot 3$

75. $5 + (-5) = 0$

76. $18 \cdot 1 = 18$

77. $(3 + 7) + 19 = 3 + (7 + 19)$

78. $23 + 6 = 6 + 23$

79. $3 + 0 = 3$

a. Commutative property of addition

b. Inverse property of multiplication

c. Commutative property of multiplication

d. Associative property of addition

e. Identity property of multiplication

f. Associative property of multiplication

g. Inverse property of addition

h. Identity property of addition

i. Distributive property of multiplication over addition

Concept 5: Algebraic Expressions

For Exercises 80–83, for each expression list the terms and their coefficients. **(See Example 7.)**

80. $3xy - 6x^2 + y - 17$

Term	Coefficient

81. $2x - y + 18xy + 5$

Term	Coefficient

82. $x^4 - 10xy + 12 - y$

Term	Coefficient

83. $-x + 8y - 9x^2y - 3$

Term	Coefficient

84. Explain why $12x$ and $12x^2$ are not *like* terms.

85. Explain why $3x$ and $3xy$ are not *like* terms.

86. Explain why $7z$ and $\sqrt{13}z$ are *like* terms.

87. Explain why πx and $8x$ are *like* terms.

88. Write three different *like* terms.

89. Write three terms that are not *like*.

For Exercises 90–98, simplify by combining *like* terms. **(See Examples 8–9.)**

90. $5k - 10k$

91. $-4p - 2p$

92. $-7x^2 + 14x^2$

93. $2y^2 - 5y^2 - 3y^2$

94. $2ab + 5 + 3ab - 2$

95. $8x^3y + 3 - 7 - x^3y$

96. $\frac{1}{4}a + b - \frac{3}{4}a - 5b$

97. $\frac{2}{5} + 2t - \frac{3}{5} + t - \frac{6}{5}$

98. $2.8z - 8.1z + 6 - 15.2$

For Exercises 99–126, simplify by clearing parentheses and combining *like* terms. **(See Examples 10–12.)**

99. $-3(2x - 4) + 10$

100. $-2(4a + 3) - 14$

101. $4(w + 3) - 12$

102. $5(2r + 6) - 30$

103. $5 - 3(x - 4)$

104. $4 - 2(3x + 8)$

105. $-3(2t + 4w) + 8(2t - 4w)$

106. $-5(5y + 9z) + 3(3y + 6z)$

107. $2(q - 5u) - (2q + 8u)$

108. $6(x + 3y) - (6x - 5y)$

109. $-\frac{1}{3}(6t + 9) + 10$

110. $-\frac{3}{4}(8 + 4q) + 7$

111. $10(5.1a - 3.1) + 4$

112. $100(-3.14p - 1.05) + 212$

113. $-4m + 2(m - 3) + 2m$

114. $-3b + 4(b + 2) - 8b$

115. $\frac{1}{2}(10q - 2) + \frac{1}{3}(2 - 3q)$

116. $\frac{1}{5}(15 - 4p) - \frac{1}{10}(10p + 5)$

117. $7n - 2(n - 3) - 6 + n$

118. $8k - 4(k - 1) + 7 - k$

119. $6(x + 3) - 12 - 4(x - 3)$

120. $5(y - 4) + 3 - 6(y - 7)$

121. $0.2(6c - 1.6) + c$

122. $-1.1(5 + 8x) - 3.1$

123. $6 + 2[-8 - 3(2x + 4)] + 10x$

124. $-3 + 5[-3 - 4(y + 2)] - 8y$

125. $1 - 3[2(z + 1) - 5(z - 2)]$

126. $1 - 6[3(2t + 2) - 8(t + 2)]$

Expanding Your Skills

For Exercises 127–134, determine if the expressions are equivalent. If two expressions are not equivalent, state why.

127. $3a + b, b + 3a$

128. $4y + 1, 1 + 4y$

129. $2c + 7, 9c$

130. $5z + 4, 9z$

131. $5x - 3, 3 - 5x$

132. $6d - 7, 7 - 6d$

133. $5x - 3, -3 + 5x$

134. $8 - 2x, -2x + 8$

135. As a small child in school, the great mathematician Karl Friedrich Gauss (1777–1855) was said to have found the sum of the integers from 1 to 100 mentally:

$$1 + 2 + 3 + 4 + \cdots + 99 + 100$$

Rather than adding the numbers sequentially, he added the numbers in pairs:

$$(1 + 99) + (2 + 98) + (3 + 97) + \cdots + 100$$

a. Use this technique to add the integers from 1 to 10.

$$1 + 2 + 3 + 4 + 5 + 6 + 7 + 8 + 9 + 10$$

b. Use this technique to add the integers from 1 to 20.

Group Activity

Evaluating Formulas Using a Calculator

Materials: A calculator

Estimated Time: 20 minutes

Group Size: 2

In this chapter, we learned one of the most important concepts in mathematics—the order of operations. The proper order of operations is required whenever we evaluate any mathematical expression. The following formulas are taken from applications from science, math, statistics, and business. These are just some samples of what you may encounter as you work your way through college.

For Exercises 1–8, substitute the given values into the formula. Then use a calculator and the proper order of operations to simplify the result. Round to three decimal places if necessary.

1. $F = \frac{9}{5}C + 32$ (biology) $C = 35$

2. $V = \frac{nRT}{P}$ (chemistry) $n = 1.00, R = 0.0821, T = 273.15, P = 1.0$

3. $R = k\left(\frac{L}{r^2}\right)$ (electronics) $k = 0.05, L = 200, r = 0.5$

4. $m = \frac{y_2 - y_1}{x_2 - x_1}$ (mathematics) $x_1 = -8.3, x_2 = 3.3, y_1 = 4.6, y_2 = -9.2$

5. $z = \frac{\bar{x} - \mu}{\frac{\sigma}{\sqrt{n}}}$ (statistics) $\bar{x} = 69, \mu = 55, \sigma = 20, n = 25$

6. $S = R\left[\frac{(1 + i)^n - 1}{i}\right]$ (finance) $R = 200, i = 0.08, n = 30$

7. $x = \frac{-b + \sqrt{b^2 - 4ac}}{2a}$ (mathematics) $a = 2, b = -7, c = -15$

8. $h = \frac{1}{2}gt^2 + v_0t + h_0$ (physics) $g = -32, t = 2.4, v_0 = 192, h_0 = 288$

Chapter 1 Summary

Section 1.1 Fractions

Key Concepts

Simplifying Fractions

Divide the numerator and denominator by their greatest common factor.

Multiplication of Fractions

$$\frac{a}{b} \times \frac{c}{d} = \frac{a \times c}{b \times d}$$

Division of Fractions

$$\frac{a}{b} \div \frac{c}{d} = \frac{a}{b} \times \frac{d}{c}$$

Addition and Subtraction of Fractions

$$\frac{a}{b} + \frac{c}{b} = \frac{a + c}{b} \quad \text{and} \quad \frac{a}{b} - \frac{c}{b} = \frac{a - c}{b}$$

To perform operations on mixed numbers, convert to improper fractions.

Examples

Example 1

$$\frac{60}{84} = \frac{5 \times \overset{1}{\cancel{12}}}{7 \times \underset{1}{\cancel{12}}} = \frac{5}{7}$$

Example 2

$$\frac{25}{108} \times \frac{27}{40} = \frac{\overset{5}{\cancel{25}}}{\underset{4}{\cancel{108}}} \times \frac{\overset{1}{\cancel{27}}}{\underset{8}{\cancel{40}}}$$

$$= \frac{5 \times 1}{4 \times 8} = \frac{5}{32}$$

Example 3

$$\frac{95}{49} \div \frac{65}{42} = \frac{\overset{19}{\cancel{95}}}{\underset{7}{\cancel{49}}} \times \frac{\overset{6}{\cancel{42}}}{\underset{13}{\cancel{65}}}$$

$$= \frac{19 \times 6}{7 \times 13} = \frac{114}{91}$$

Example 4

$$\frac{8}{9} + \frac{2}{15} = \frac{8 \times 5}{9 \times 5} + \frac{2 \times 3}{15 \times 3}$$

$$= \frac{40}{45} + \frac{6}{45} = \frac{46}{45}$$

The least common denominator (LCD) of 9 and 15 is 45.

Example 5

$$2\frac{5}{6} - 1\frac{1}{3} = \frac{17}{6} - \frac{4}{3}$$

The LCD is 6.

$$= \frac{17}{6} - \frac{4 \times 2}{3 \times 2} = \frac{17}{6} - \frac{8}{6}$$

$$= \frac{9}{6}$$

$$= \frac{3}{2} \text{ or } 1\frac{1}{2}$$

Section 1.2 Introduction to Algebra and the Set of Real Numbers

Key Concepts

A **variable** is a symbol or letter used to represent an unknown number.

A **constant** is a value that is not variable.

An algebraic **expression** is a collection of variables and constants under algebraic operations.

Natural numbers: $\{1, 2, 3, \ldots\}$

Whole numbers: $\{0, 1, 2, 3, \ldots\}$

Integers: $\{\ldots -3, -2, -1, 0, 1, 2, 3, \ldots\}$

Rational numbers: The set of numbers that can be expressed in the form $\frac{p}{q}$, where p and q are integers and q does not equal 0. In decimal form, rational numbers are terminating or repeating decimals.

Irrational numbers: A subset of the real numbers whose elements cannot be written as a ratio of two integers. In decimal form, irrational numbers are nonterminating, nonrepeating decimals.

Real numbers: The set of both the rational numbers and the irrational numbers.

$a < b$ "a is less than b."

$a > b$ "a is greater than b."

$a \leq b$ "a is less than or equal to b."

$a \geq b$ "a is greater than or equal to b."

Two numbers that are the same distance from zero but on opposite sides of zero on the number line are called **opposites**. The opposite of a is denoted $-a$.

The **absolute value** of a real number, a, denoted $|a|$, is the distance between a and 0 on the number line.

If $a \geq 0$, $|a| = a$

If $a < 0$, $|a| = -a$

Examples

Example 1

Variables:	x, y, z, a, b
Constants:	$2, -3, \pi$
Expressions:	$2x + 5, 3a + b^2$

Example 2

-5, 0, and 4 are integers.

$-\frac{5}{2}$, -0.5, and $0.\overline{3}$ are rational numbers.

$\sqrt{7}$, $-\sqrt{2}$, and π are irrational numbers.

Example 3

All real numbers can be located on the real number line.

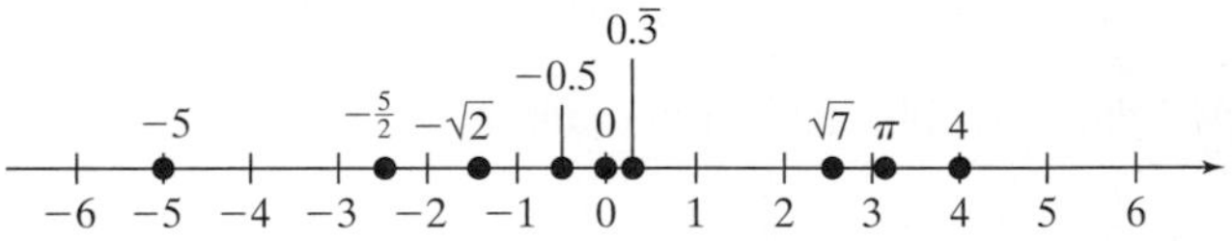

Example 4

$5 < 7$ "5 is less than 7."

$-2 > -10$ "-2 is greater than -10."

$y \leq 3.4$ "y is less than or equal to 3.4."

$x \geq \frac{1}{2}$ "x is greater than or equal to $\frac{1}{2}$."

Example 5

5 and -5 are opposites.

Example 6

$|7| = 7$

$|-7| = 7$

Section 1.3 Exponents, Square Roots, and the Order of Operations

Key Concepts

$b^n = \underbrace{b \cdot b \cdot b \cdot b \cdot \ldots b}_{n \text{ factors of } b}$ b is the **base**, n is the **exponent**

$\sqrt{x}$ is the positive **square root** of x.

The Order of Operations

1. Simplify expressions within parentheses and other grouping symbols first.
2. Evaluate expressions involving exponents, radicals, and absolute values.
3. Perform multiplication or division in the order that they occur from left to right.
4. Perform addition or subtraction in the order that they occur from left to right.

Examples

Example 1

$5^3 = 5 \cdot 5 \cdot 5 = 125$

Example 2

$\sqrt{49} = 7$

Example 3

$10 + 5(3 - 1)^2 - \sqrt{5 - 1}$

$= 10 + 5(2)^2 - \sqrt{4}$ Work within grouping symbols.

$= 10 + 5(4) - 2$ Simplify exponents and radicals.

$= 10 + 20 - 2$ Perform multiplication.

$= 30 - 2$ Add and subtract, left to right.

$= 28$

Section 1.4 Addition of Real Numbers

Key Concepts

Addition of Two Real Numbers

Same Signs. Add the absolute values of the numbers and apply the common sign to the sum.

Different Signs. Subtract the smaller absolute value from the larger absolute value. Then apply the sign of the number having the larger absolute value.

Examples

Example 1

$-3 + (-4) = -7$

$-1.3 + (-9.1) = -10.4$

Example 2

$-5 + 7 = 2$

$\frac{2}{3} + \left(-\frac{7}{3}\right) = -\frac{5}{3}$

Section 1.5 Subtraction of Real Numbers

Key Concepts

Subtraction of Two Real Numbers

Add the opposite of the second number to the first number. That is,

$a - b = a + (-b)$

Examples

Example 1

$7 - (-5) = 7 + (5) = 12$

$-3 - 5 = -3 + (-5) = -8$

$-11 - (-2) = -11 + (2) = -9$

Section 1.6 Multiplication and Division of Real Numbers

Key Concepts

Multiplication and Division of Two Real Numbers

Same Signs

Product is positive.

Quotient is positive.

Different Signs

Product is negative.

Quotient is negative.

The **reciprocal** of a nonzero number a is $\frac{1}{a}$.

Multiplication and Division Involving Zero

The product of any real number and 0 is 0.

The quotient of 0 and any nonzero real number is 0.

The quotient of any nonzero real number and 0 is undefined.

Examples

Example 1

$(-5)(-2) = 10 \qquad \frac{-20}{-4} = 5$

Example 2

$(-3)(7) = -21 \qquad \frac{-4}{8} = -\frac{1}{2}$

Example 3

$-3^4 = -1(3 \cdot 3 \cdot 3 \cdot 3) = -81$

$(-3)^4 = (-3)(-3)(-3)(-3) = 81$

Example 4

The reciprocal of -6 is $-\frac{1}{6}$.

Example 5

$4 \cdot 0 = 0$

$0 \div 4 = 0$

$4 \div 0$ is undefined.

Section 1.7 Properties of Real Numbers and Simplifying Expressions

Key Concepts

Properties of Real Numbers

Commutative Properties

$a + b = b + a$

$ab = ba$

Example 1

$(-5) + (-7) = (-7) + (-5)$

$3 \cdot 8 = 8 \cdot 3$

Associative Properties

$(a + b) + c = a + (b + c)$

$(ab)c = a(bc)$

Example 2

$(2 + 3) + 10 = 2 + (3 + 10)$

$(2 \cdot 4) \cdot 5 = 2 \cdot (4 \cdot 5)$

Identity Properties

$0 + a = a$

$1 \cdot a = a$

Example 3

$0 + (-5) = -5$

$1(-8) = -8$

Inverse Properties

$a + (-a) = 0$

$b \cdot \frac{1}{b} = 1$ for $b \neq 0$

Example 4

$1.5 + (-1.5) = 0$

$6 \cdot \frac{1}{6} = 1$

Distributive Property of Multiplication over Addition

$a(b + c) = ab + ac$

Example 5

$$\begin{aligned} -2(x - 3y) &= (-2)x + (-2)(-3y) \\ &= -2x + 6y \end{aligned}$$

A **term** is a constant or the product or quotient of constants and variables. The **coefficient** of a term is the numerical factor of the term.

***Like* terms** have the same variables, and the corresponding variables have the same powers.

Example 6

$-2x$ is a term with coefficient -2.
yz^2 is a term with coefficient 1.

$3x$ and $-5x$ are *like* terms.
$4a^2b$ and $4ab$ are not *like* terms.

Terms can be added or subtracted if they are *like* terms. Sometimes it is necessary to clear parentheses before adding or subtracting *like* terms.

Example 7

$-2w - 4(w - 2) + 3$

$= -2w - 4w + 8 + 3$ Clear parentheses.

$= -6w + 11$ Combine *like* terms.

Chapter 1 Review Exercises

Section 1.1

For Exercises 1–4, identify as a proper or improper fraction.

1. $\frac{14}{5}$ **2.** $\frac{1}{6}$ **3.** $\frac{3}{3}$ **4.** $\frac{7}{1}$

5. Write 112 as a product of primes.

6. Simplify. $\frac{84}{70}$

For Exercises 7–12, perform the indicated operations.

7. $\frac{2}{9} + \frac{3}{4}$ **8.** $\frac{7}{8} - \frac{1}{16}$ **9.** $\frac{21}{24} \times \frac{16}{49}$

10. $\frac{68}{34} \div \frac{20}{12}$ **11.** $5\frac{1}{3} \div 1\frac{7}{9}$ **12.** $3\frac{4}{5} - 2\frac{1}{10}$

13. The surface area of the Earth is approximately 510 million km^2. If water covers about $\frac{7}{10}$ of the surface, how many square kilometers of the Earth is covered by water?

Section 1.2

14. Given the set $\{7, \frac{1}{3}, -4, 0, -\sqrt{3}, -0.\overline{2}, \pi, 1\}$,

a. List the natural numbers.

b. List the integers.

c. List the whole numbers.

d. List the rational numbers.

e. List the irrational numbers.

f. List the real numbers.

For Exercises 15–18, determine the absolute value.

15. $\left|\frac{1}{2}\right|$ **16.** $|-6|$ **17.** $|-\sqrt{7}|$ **18.** $|0|$

For Exercises 19–27, identify whether the inequality is true or false.

19. $-6 > -1$ **20.** $0 < -5$ **21.** $-10 \le 0$

22. $5 \neq -5$ **23.** $7 \ge 7$ **24.** $7 \ge -7$

25. $0 \le -3$ **26.** $-\frac{2}{3} \le -\frac{2}{3}$ **27.** $|-3| > -|3|$

For Exercises 28–31, evaluate each expression for $x = 8$, $y = 4$, and $z = 1$.

28. $x - 2y$ **29.** $x^2 - y$

30. $\sqrt{x + z}$ **31.** $\sqrt{x + 2y}$

Section 1.3

For Exercises 32–37, write each English phrase as an algebraic expression.

32. The product of x and $\frac{2}{3}$

33. The quotient of 7 and y

34. The sum of 2 and $3b$

35. The difference of a and 5

36. Two more than $5k$

37. Seven less than $13z$

For Exercises 38–43, simplify the expressions.

38. 6^3 **39.** 15^2 **40.** $\sqrt{36}$

41. $\frac{1}{\sqrt{100}}$ **42.** $\left(\frac{1}{4}\right)^2$ **43.** $\left(\frac{3}{2}\right)^3$

For Exercises 44–47, perform the indicated operations.

44. $15 - 7 \cdot 2 + 12$ **45.** $|-11| + |5| - (7 - 2)$

46. $4^2 - (5 - 2)^2$ **47.** $22 - 3(8 \div 4)^2$

Section 1.4

For Exercises 48–60, add.

48. $-6 + 8$ **49.** $14 + (-10)$

50. $21 + (-6)$ **51.** $-12 + (-5)$

52. $\frac{2}{7} + \left(-\frac{1}{9}\right)$ **53.** $\left(-\frac{8}{11}\right) + \left(\frac{1}{2}\right)$

54. $\left(-\frac{1}{10}\right) + \left(-\frac{5}{6}\right)$ **55.** $\left(-\frac{5}{2}\right) + \left(-\frac{1}{5}\right)$

56. $-8.17 + 6.02$ **57.** $2.9 + (-7.18)$

58. $13 + (-2) + (-8)$

59. $-5 + (-7) + 20$

60. $2 + 5 + (-8) + (-7) + 0 + 13 + (-1)$

61. Under what conditions will the expression $a + b$ be negative?

62. Richard's checkbook was overdrawn by \$45 (that is, his balance was -45). He deposited \$117 but then wrote a check for \$80. Was the deposit enough to cover the check? Explain.

Section 1.5

For Exercises 63–75, subtract.

63. $13 - 25$

64. $31 - (-2)$

65. $-8 - (-7)$

66. $-2 - 15$

67. $\left(-\frac{7}{9}\right) - \frac{5}{6}$

68. $\frac{1}{3} - \frac{9}{8}$

69. $7 - 8.2$

70. $-1.05 - 3.2$

71. $-16.1 - (-5.9)$

72. $7.09 - (-5)$

73. $\frac{11}{2} - \left(-\frac{1}{6}\right) - \frac{7}{3}$

74. $-\frac{4}{5} - \frac{7}{10} - \left(-\frac{13}{20}\right)$

75. $6 - 14 - (-1) - 10 - (-21) - 5$

76. Under what conditions will the expression $a - b$ be negative?

For Exercises 77–81, write an algebraic expression and simplify.

77. -18 subtracted from -7

78. The difference of -6 and 41

79. Seven decreased by 13

80. Five subtracted from the difference of 20 and -7

81. The sum of 6 and -12, decreased by 21

82. In Nevada, the highest temperature ever recorded was 125°F and the lowest was -50°F. Find the difference between the highest and lowest temperatures. (*Source: Information Please Almanac*)

Section 1.6

For Exercises 83–100, multiply or divide as indicated.

83. $10(-17)$

84. $(-7)13$

85. $(-52) \div 26$

86. $(-48) \div (-16)$

87. $\frac{7}{4} \div \left(-\frac{21}{2}\right)$

88. $\frac{2}{3}\left(-\frac{12}{11}\right)$

89. $-\frac{21}{5} \cdot 0$

90. $\frac{3}{4} \div 0$

91. $0 \div (-14)$

92. $(-0.45)(-5)$

93. $\frac{-21}{14}$

94. $\frac{-13}{-52}$

95. $(5)(-2)(3)$

96. $(-6)(-5)(15)$

97. $\left(-\frac{1}{2}\right)\left(\frac{7}{8}\right)\left(-\frac{4}{7}\right)$

98. $\left(\frac{12}{13}\right)\left(-\frac{1}{6}\right)\left(\frac{13}{14}\right)$

99. $40 \div 4 \div (-5)$

100. $\frac{10}{11} \div \frac{7}{11} \div \frac{5}{9}$

For Exercises 101–106, perform the indicated operations.

101. $9 - 4[-2(4 - 8) - 5(3 - 1)]$

102. $\frac{8(-3) - 6}{-7 - (-2)}$

103. $\frac{2}{3} - \left(\frac{3}{8} + \frac{5}{6}\right) \div \frac{5}{3}$

104. $5.4 - (0.3)^2 \div 0.09$

105. $\frac{5 - [3 - (-4)^2]}{36 \div (-2)(3)}$

106. $|-8 + 5| - \sqrt{5^2 - 3^2}$

For Exercises 107–110, evaluate each expression given the values $x = 4$ and $y = -9$.

107. $3(x + 2) \div y$

108. $\sqrt{x} - y$

109. $-xy$

110. $3x + 2y$

111. In statistics, the formula $x = \mu + z\sigma$ is used to find cutoff values for data that follow a bell-shaped curve. Find x if $\mu = 100$, $z = -1.96$, and $\sigma = 15$.

For Exercises 112–118, answer true or false. If a statement is false, explain why.

112. If n is positive, then $-n$ is negative.

113. If m is negative, then m^4 is negative.

114. If m is negative, then m^3 is negative.

115. If $m > 0$ and $n > 0$, then $mn > 0$.

116. If $p < 0$ and $q < 0$, then $pq < 0$.

117. A number and its reciprocal have the same signs.

118. A nonzero number and its opposite have different signs.

Section 1.7

For Exercises 119–126, answers may vary.

119. Give an example of the commutative property of addition.

120. Give an example of the associative property of addition.

121. Give an example of the inverse property of addition.

122. Give an example of the identity property of addition.

123. Give an example of the commutative property of multiplication.

124. Give an example of the associative property of multiplication.

125. Give an example of the inverse property of multiplication.

126. Give an example of the identity property of multiplication.

127. Explain why $5x - 2y$ is the same as $-2y + 5x$.

128. Explain why $3a - 9y$ is the same as $-9y + 3a$.

129. List the terms of the expression: $3y + 10x - 12 + xy$

130. Identify the coefficients for the terms listed in Exercise 129.

For Exercises 131–132, simplify by combining *like* terms.

131. $3a + 3b - 4b + 5a - 10$

132. $-6p + 2q + 9 - 13q - p + 7$

For Exercises 133–134, use the distributive property to clear the parentheses.

133. $-2(4z + 9)$

134. $5(4w - 8y + 1)$

For Exercises 135–140, simplify each expression.

135. $2p - (p + 5w) + 3w$

136. $6(h + 3m) - 7h - 4m$

137. $\frac{1}{2}(-6q) + q - 4\left(3q + \frac{1}{4}\right)$

138. $0.3b + 12(0.2 - 0.5b)$

139. $-4[2(x + 1) - (3x + 8)]$

140. $5[(7y - 3) + 3(y + 8)]$

Chapter 1 Test

1. Simplify. $\frac{135}{36}$

2. Add and subtract. $\frac{5}{4} - \frac{5}{12} + \frac{2}{3}$

3. Divide. $4\frac{1}{12} \div 1\frac{1}{3}$

4. Subtract. $4\frac{1}{4} - 1\frac{7}{8}$

5. Is $0.\overline{315}$ a rational number or an irrational number? Explain your reasoning.

6. Use the definition of exponents to expand the expressions:

   a. $(4x)^3$ **b.** $4x^3$

7. Plot the points on a number line: $|3|, 0, -2, 0.5, |-\frac{3}{2}|, \sqrt{16}$.

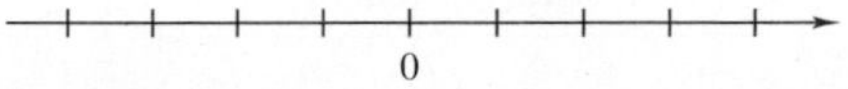

8. Use the number line in Exercise 7 to identify whether the statements are true or false.

   a. $|3| < -2$ **b.** $0 \le \left|-\frac{3}{2}\right|$

   c. $-2 < 0.5$ **d.** $|3| \ge \left|-\frac{3}{2}\right|$

9. Identify the property that justifies each statement.

   a. $6(-8) = (-8)6$ **b.** $5 + 0 = 5$

   c. $(2 + 3) + 4 = 2 + (3 + 4)$

   d. $\frac{1}{7} \cdot 7 = 1$ **e.** $8[7(-3)] = (8 \cdot 7)(-3)$

10. Write each expression as an English phrase.

    a. $2(a - b)$.

    b. $2a - b$. (Answers may vary.)

11. Write the phrase as an algebraic expression: "The quotient of the square root of c and the square of d."

For Exercises 12–14, write each English statement as an algebraic expression. Then simplify the expression.

12. Subtract -4 from 12

13. Find the difference of 6 and 8

14. The quotient of 10 and -12

For Exercises 15–29, perform the indicated operations.

15. $-\frac{1}{8} + \left(-\frac{3}{4}\right)$

16. $-84 \div 7$

17. $21 - (-7)$

18. $-15 - (-3)$

19. $-14 + (-2) - 16$

20. $(-16)(-2)(-1)(-3)$

21. $-22 \cdot 0$

22. $38 \div 0$

23. $18 + (-12)$

24. $-10.06 - (-14.72)$

25. $7(-4)$

26. $\frac{2}{5} \div \left(-\frac{7}{10}\right) \cdot \left(-\frac{7}{6}\right)$

27. $\frac{\sqrt{5^2 - 4^2}}{|-12 + 3|}$

28. $8 - [(2 - 4) - (8 - 9)]$

29. $(8 - 10) \cdot \frac{3}{2} + (-5)$

30. The average high temperature in January for Nova Scotia, Canada, is -1.2°C. The average low is -10.7°C. Find the difference between the average high and the average low.

31. In the third quarter of a football game, a quarterback made a 5-yd gain, a 2-yd gain, a 10-yd loss, and then a 4-yd gain.

    a. Write an expression using addition to describe the quarterback's movement.

    b. Evaluate the expression from part (a) to determine the quarterback's gain or loss in yards.

For Exercises 32–36, simplify each expression.

32. $3k - 20 + (-9k) + 12$

33. $-5x - 4y + 3 - 7x + 6y - 7$

34. $4(p - 5) - (8p + 3)$

35. $-3(4m + 8p - 7)$

36. $\frac{1}{2}(12p - 4) + \frac{1}{3}(2 - 6p)$

For Exercises 37–40, evaluate each expression given the values $x = 4$ and $y = -3$ and $z = -7$.

37. $y^2 - x$

38. $3x - 2y$

39. $y(x - 2)$

40. $-y^2 - 4x + z$

Linear Equations and Inequalities

2

CHAPTER OUTLINE

2.1 Addition, Subtraction, Multiplication, and Division Properties of Equality 100

2.2 Solving Linear Equations 112

2.3 Linear Equations: Clearing Fractions and Decimals 121

Problem Recognition Exercises: Equations vs. Expressions 128

2.4 Applications of Linear Equations: Introduction to Problem Solving 128

2.5 Applications Involving Percents 139

2.6 Formulas and Applications of Geometry 146

2.7 Mixture Applications and Uniform Motion 156

2.8 Linear Inequalities 165

Group Activity: Computing Body Mass Index (BMI) 180

Chapter 2

In Chapter 2, we learn how to solve linear equations and inequalities in one variable.

Are You Prepared?

One of the skills we need involves multiplying by fractions and decimals. The following set of problems will review that skill. For help with multiplying fractions, see Section 1.1.

Simplify each expression and fill in the blank with the correct answer written as a word. Then fill the word into the puzzle. The words will fit in the puzzle according to the number of letters each word has.

$8 \cdot \left(\frac{3}{8}\right) =$ ______ $6 \cdot \left(\frac{2}{3}\right) =$ ______ $100(0.17) =$ ______

$100(0.09) =$ ______ ______ $\cdot \left(\frac{2}{5}\right) = 2$ ______ $\cdot \left(\frac{6}{7}\right) = 6$

______ $\cdot \left(\frac{3}{4}\right) = 6$ ______ $\cdot \left(\frac{5}{6}\right) = 10$ ______ $\cdot (0.4) = 4$

Section 2.1 Addition, Subtraction, Multiplication, and Division Properties of Equality

Concepts

1. Definition of a Linear Equation in One Variable
2. Addition and Subtraction Properties of Equality
3. Multiplication and Division Properties of Equality
4. Translations

1. Definition of a Linear Equation in One Variable

An **equation** is a statement that indicates that two expressions are equal. The following are equations.

$$x = 5 \qquad y + 2 = 12 \qquad -4z = 28$$

All equations have an equal sign. Furthermore, notice that the equal sign separates the equation into two parts, the left-hand side and the right-hand side. A **solution to an equation** is a value of the variable that makes the equation a true statement. Substituting a solution into an equation for the variable makes the right-hand side equal to the left-hand side.

Equation	Solution	Check	
$x = 5$	5	$x = 5$ ↓ $5 = 5$ ✔	Substitute 5 for x. Right-hand side equals left-hand side.
$y + 2 = 12$	10	$y + 2 = 12$ ↓ $10 + 2 = 12$ ✔	Substitute 10 for y. Right-hand side equals left-hand side.
$-4z = 28$	-7	$-4z = 28$ ↓ $-4(-7) = 28$ ✔	Substitute -7 for z. Right-hand side equals left-hand side.

Avoiding Mistakes

Be sure to notice the difference between solving an equation versus simplifying an expression. For example, $2x + 1 = 7$ is an equation, whose solution is 3, while $2x + 1 + 7$ is an expression that simplifies to $2x + 8$.

Example 1 Determining Whether a Number Is a Solution to an Equation

Determine whether the given number is a solution to the equation.

a. $4x + 7 = 5;\quad -\frac{1}{2}$ **b.** $-4 = 6w - 14;\quad 3$

Solution:

a. $4x + 7 = 5$

$4(-\frac{1}{2}) + 7 \stackrel{?}{=} 5$ Substitute $-\frac{1}{2}$ for x.

$-2 + 7 \stackrel{?}{=} 5$ Simplify.

$5 \stackrel{?}{=} 5$ ✔ Right-hand side equals the left-hand side. Thus, $-\frac{1}{2}$ *is a solution* to the equation $4x + 7 = 5$.

b. $-4 = 6w - 14$

$-4 \stackrel{?}{=} 6(3) - 14$ Substitute 3 for w.

$-4 \stackrel{?}{=} 18 - 14$ Simplify.

$-4 \neq 4$ Right-hand side does not equal left-hand side. Thus, 3 *is not a solution* to the equation $-4 = 6w - 14$.

Skill Practice Determine whether the given number is a solution to the equation.

1. $4x - 1 = 7;\quad 3$ **2.** $9 = -2y + 5;\quad -2$

Answers

1. No **2.** Yes

The set of all solutions to an equation is called the **solution set** and is written with set braces. For example, the solution set for Example 1(a) is $\{-\frac{1}{2}\}$.

In the study of algebra, you will encounter a variety of equations. In this chapter, we will focus on a specific type of equation called a linear equation in one variable.

Definition of a Linear Equation in One Variable

Let a, b, and c be real numbers such that $a \neq 0$. A **linear equation in one variable** is an equation that can be written in the form

$$ax + b = c$$

Note: A linear equation in one variable is often called a first-degree equation because the variable x has an implied exponent of 1.

Examples	Notes
$2x + 4 = 20$	$a = 2, b = 4, c = 20$
$-3x - 5 = 16$ can be written as $-3x + (-5) = 16$	$a = -3, b = -5, c = 16$
$5x + 9 - 4x = 1$ can be written as $x + 9 = 1$	$a = 1, b = 9, c = 1$

2. Addition and Subtraction Properties of Equality

If two equations have the same solution set, then the equations are equivalent. For example, the following equations are equivalent because the solution set for each equation is {6}.

Equivalent Equations		Check the Solution 6
$2x - 5 = 7$	$\longrightarrow$	$2(6) - 5 \stackrel{?}{=} 7 \Rightarrow 12 - 5 \stackrel{?}{=} 7$ ✔
$2x = 12$	$\longrightarrow$	$2(6) \stackrel{?}{=} 12 \Rightarrow 12 \stackrel{?}{=} 12$ ✔
$x = 6$	$\longrightarrow$	$6 \stackrel{?}{=} 6 \Rightarrow 6 \stackrel{?}{=} 6$ ✔

To solve a linear equation, $ax + b = c$, the goal is to find *all* values of x that make the equation true. One general strategy for solving an equation is to rewrite it as an equivalent but simpler equation. This process is repeated until the equation can be written in the form $x =$ number. We call this "isolating the variable." The addition and subtraction properties of equality help us isolate the variable.

Addition and Subtraction Properties of Equality

Let a, b, and c represent algebraic expressions.

1. **Addition property of equality:** If $a = b$, then $a + c = b + c$
2. ***Subtraction property of equality:** If $a = b$, then $a - c = b - c$

*The subtraction property of equality follows directly from the addition property, because subtraction is defined in terms of addition.

If $a + (-c) = b + (-c)$

then, $a - c = b - c$

The addition and subtraction properties of equality indicate that adding or subtracting the same quantity on each side of an equation results in an equivalent equation. This means that if two equal quantities are increased or decreased by the same amount, then the resulting quantities will also be equal (Figure 2-1).

$$50 = 50$$
$$50 + 20 = 50 + 20$$
$$70 = 70$$

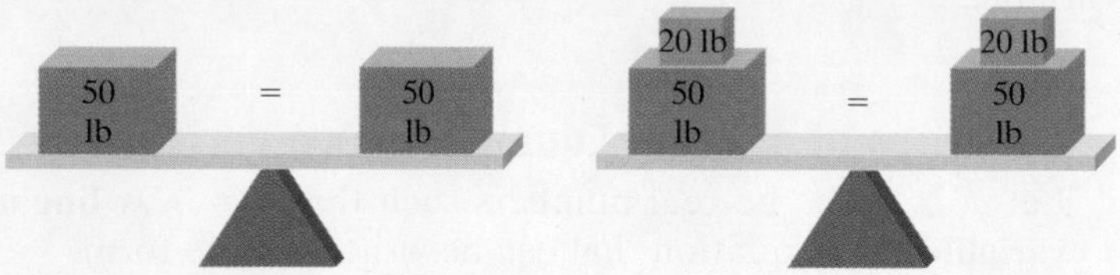

Figure 2-1

Example 2 Applying the Addition and Subtraction Properties of Equality

Solve the equations.

a. $p - 4 = 11$ **b.** $w + 5 = -2$

Solution:

In each equation, the goal is to isolate the variable on one side of the equation. To accomplish this, we use the fact that the sum of a number and its opposite is zero and the difference of a number and itself is zero.

a. $p - 4 = 11$

$p - 4 + 4 = 11 + 4$ To isolate p, add 4 to both sides $(-4 + 4 = 0)$.

$p + 0 = 15$ Simplify.

$p = 15$ Check by substituting $p = 15$ into the original equation.

Check: $p - 4 = 11$

$15 - 4 \stackrel{?}{=} 11$

$11 \stackrel{?}{=} 11$ ✔ True

The solution set is {15}.

b. $w + 5 = -2$

$w + 5 - 5 = -2 - 5$ To isolate w, subtract 5 from both sides. $(5 - 5 = 0)$.

$w + 0 = -7$ Simplify.

$w = -7$ Check by substituting $w = -7$ into the original equation.

Check: $w + 5 = -2$

$-7 + 5 \stackrel{?}{=} -2$

$-2 \stackrel{?}{=} -2$ ✔ True

The solution set is {−7}.

Skill Practice Solve the equations.

3. $v - 7 = 2$ **4.** $x + 4 = 4$

Answers

3. {9} **4.** {0}

Example 3 Applying the Addition and Subtraction Properties of Equality

Solve the equations.

a. $\frac{9}{4} = q - \frac{3}{4}$ **b.** $-1.2 + z = 4.6$

Solution:

a. $\frac{9}{4} = q - \frac{3}{4}$

$\frac{9}{4} + \frac{3}{4} = q - \frac{3}{4} + \frac{3}{4}$ To isolate q, add $\frac{3}{4}$ to both sides $(-\frac{3}{4} + \frac{3}{4} = 0)$.

$\frac{12}{4} = q + 0$ Simplify.

$3 = q$ or equivalently, $q = 3$

Check: $\frac{9}{4} = q - \frac{3}{4}$

$\frac{9}{4} \stackrel{?}{=} 3 - \frac{3}{4}$ Substitute $q = 3$.

$\frac{9}{4} \stackrel{?}{=} \frac{12}{4} - \frac{3}{4}$ Common denominator

The solution set is {3}. $\frac{9}{4} \stackrel{?}{=} \frac{9}{4}$ ✔ True

b. $-1.2 + z = 4.6$

$-1.2 + 1.2 + z = 4.6 + 1.2$ To isolate z, add 1.2 to both sides.

$0 + z = 5.8$

$z = 5.8$ Check: $-1.2 + z = 4.6$

$-1.2 + 5.8 \stackrel{?}{=} 4.6$ Substitute $z = 5.8$.

The solution set is {5.8}. $4.6 \stackrel{?}{=} 4.6$ ✔ True

Skill Practice Solve the equations.

5. $\frac{1}{4} = a - \frac{2}{3}$ **6.** $-8.1 + w = 11.5$

TIP: The variable may be isolated on either side of the equation.

3. Multiplication and Division Properties of Equality

Adding or subtracting the same quantity to both sides of an equation results in an equivalent equation. In a similar way, multiplying or dividing both sides of an equation by the same nonzero quantity also results in an equivalent equation. This is stated formally as the multiplication and division properties of equality.

Answers

5. $\left\{\frac{11}{12}\right\}$ **6.** {19.6}

Multiplication and Division Properties of Equality

Let a, b, and c represent algebraic expressions, $c \neq 0$.

1. Multiplication property of equality: If $a = b$, then $ac = bc$

2. *Division property of equality: If $a = b$ then $\dfrac{a}{c} = \dfrac{b}{c}$

*The division property of equality follows directly from the multiplication property because division is defined as multiplication by the reciprocal.

If $a \cdot \dfrac{1}{c} = b \cdot \dfrac{1}{c}$

then, $\dfrac{a}{c} = \dfrac{b}{c}$

To understand the multiplication property of equality, suppose we start with a true equation such as $10 = 10$. If both sides of the equation are multiplied by a constant such as 3, the result is also a true statement (Figure 2-2).

$$10 = 10$$
$$3 \cdot 10 = 3 \cdot 10$$
$$30 = 30$$

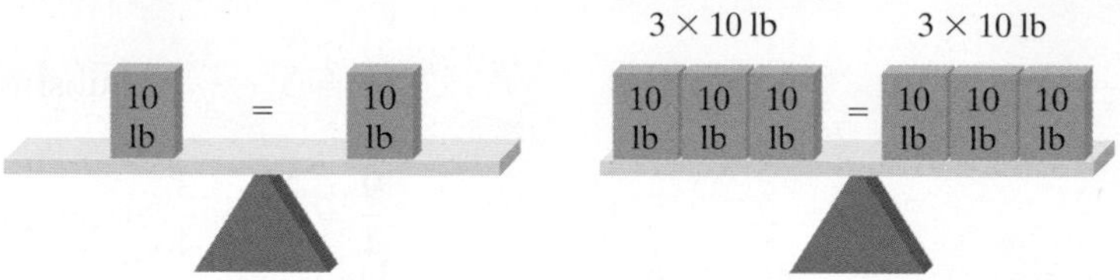

Figure 2-2

Similarly, if both sides of the equation are divided by a nonzero real number such as 2, the result is also a true statement (Figure 2-3).

$$10 = 10$$
$$\frac{10}{2} = \frac{10}{2}$$
$$5 = 5$$

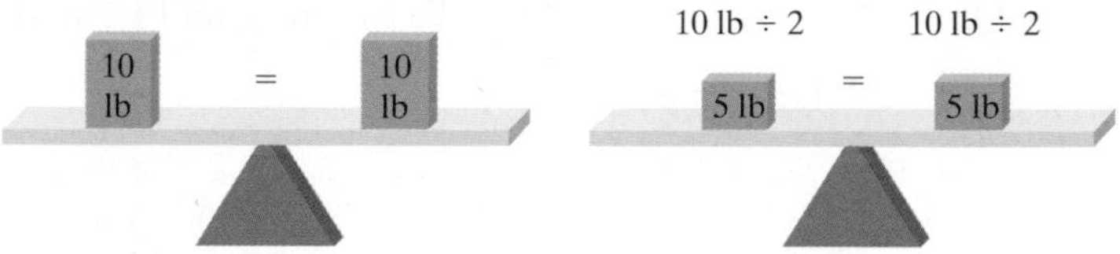

Figure 2-3

TIP: The product of a number and its reciprocal is always 1. For example:

$$\frac{1}{5}(5) = 1$$
$$-\frac{7}{2}\left(-\frac{2}{7}\right) = 1$$

To solve an equation in the variable x, the goal is to write the equation in the form $x =$ number. In particular, notice that we desire the coefficient of x to be 1. That is, we want to write the equation as $1x =$ number. Therefore, to solve an equation such as $5x = 15$, we can multiply both sides of the equation by the reciprocal of the x-term coefficient. In this case, multiply both sides by the reciprocal of 5, which is $\frac{1}{5}$.

$$5x = 15$$

$\dfrac{1}{5}(5x) = \dfrac{1}{5}(15)$ Multiply by $\dfrac{1}{5}$.

$1x = 3$ The coefficient of the x-term is now 1.

$$x = 3$$

The division property of equality can also be used to solve the equation $5x = 15$ by dividing both sides by the coefficient of the x-term. In this case, divide both sides by 5 to make the coefficient of x equal to 1.

$5x = 15$

$\frac{5x}{5} = \frac{15}{5}$ Divide by 5.

$1x = 3$ The coefficient of the x-term is now 1.

$x = 3$

TIP: The quotient of a nonzero real number and itself is always 1. For example:

$$\frac{5}{5} = 1$$

$$\frac{-3.5}{-3.5} = 1$$

Example 4 Applying the Division Property of Equality

Solve the equations using the division property of equality.

a. $12x = 60$ **b.** $48 = -8w$ **c.** $-x = 8$

Solution:

a. $12x = 60$

$\frac{12x}{12} = \frac{60}{12}$ To obtain a coefficient of 1 for the x-term, divide both sides by 12.

$1x = 5$ Simplify.

$x = 5$ Check: $12x = 60$

$12(5) \stackrel{?}{=} 60$

The solution set is {5}. $60 \stackrel{?}{=} 60$ ✔ True

b. $48 = -8w$

$\frac{48}{-8} = \frac{-8w}{-8}$ To obtain a coefficient of 1 for the w-term, divide both sides by -8.

$-6 = 1w$ Simplify.

$-6 = w$ Check: $48 = -8w$

$48 \stackrel{?}{=} -8(-6)$

The solution set is {−6}. $48 \stackrel{?}{=} 48$ ✔ True

c. $-x = 8$ Note that $-x$ is equivalent to $-1 \cdot x$.

$-1x = 8$

$\frac{-1x}{-1} = \frac{8}{-1}$ To obtain a coefficient of 1 for the x-term, divide by -1.

$x = -8$ Check: $-x = 8$

$-(-8) \stackrel{?}{=} 8$

The solution set is {−8}. $8 \stackrel{?}{=} 8$ ✔ True

TIP: In Example 4(c), we could also have *multiplied* both sides by −1 to create a coefficient of 1 on the x-term.

$$-x = 8$$

$$(-1)(-x) = (-1)8$$

$$x = -8$$

Skill Practice Solve the equations.

7. $4x = -20$ **8.** $100 = -4p$ **9.** $-y = -11$

Answers

7. {−5} **8.** {−25} **9.** {11}

4. Translations

We have already practiced writing an English sentence as a mathematical equation. Recall from Section 1.3 that several key words translate to the algebraic operations of addition, subtraction, multiplication, and division.

Example 8 Translating to a Linear Equation

Write an algebraic equation to represent each English sentence. Then solve the equation.

a. The quotient of a number and 4 is 6.

b. The product of a number and 4 is 6.

c. Negative twelve is equal to the sum of -5 and a number.

d. The value 1.4 subtracted from a number is 5.7.

Solution:

For each case we will let x represent the unknown number.

a. The quotient of a number and 4 is 6.

$$\frac{x}{4} = 6$$

$$4 \cdot \frac{x}{4} = 4 \cdot 6 \qquad \text{Multiply both sides by 4.}$$

$$\frac{4}{1} \cdot \frac{x}{4} = 4 \cdot 6$$

$$x = 24 \qquad \underline{\text{Check}}: \frac{24}{4} \stackrel{?}{=} 6 \checkmark \quad \text{True}$$

The number is 24.

b. The product of a number and 4 is 6.

$$4x = 6$$

$$\frac{4x}{4} = \frac{6}{4} \qquad \text{Divide both sides by 4.}$$

$$x = \frac{3}{2} \qquad \underline{\text{Check}}: 4\left(\frac{3}{2}\right) \stackrel{?}{=} 6 \checkmark \quad \text{True}$$

The number is $\frac{3}{2}$.

c. Negative twelve is equal to the sum of -5 and a number.

$$-12 = -5 + x$$

$$-12 + 5 = -5 + 5 + x \qquad \text{Add 5 to both sides.}$$

$$-7 = x \qquad \underline{\text{Check}}: -12 \stackrel{?}{=} -5 + (-7) \checkmark \quad \text{True}$$

The number is -7.

d. The value 1.4 subtracted from a number is 5.7.

$x - 1.4 = 5.7$

$x - 1.4 + 1.4 = 5.7 + 1.4$ Add 1.4 to both sides.

$x = 7.1$ Check: $7.1 - 1.4 \stackrel{?}{=} 5.7$ ✔ True

The number is 7.1.

Skill Practice Write an algebraic equation to represent each English sentence. Then solve the equation.

13. The quotient of a number and -2 is 8.

14. The product of a number and -3 is -24.

15. The sum of a number and 6 is -20.

16. 13 is equal to 5 subtracted from a number.

Answers

13. $\frac{x}{-2} = 8$; The number is -16.

14. $-3x = -24$; The number is 8.

15. $y + 6 = -20$; The number is -26.

16. $13 = x - 5$; The number is 18.

Section 2.1 Practice Exercises

Study Skills Exercise

After getting a test back, it is a good idea to correct the test so that you do not make the same errors again. One recommended approach is to use a clean sheet of paper, and divide the paper down the middle vertically as shown. For each problem that you missed on the test, rework the problem correctly on the left-hand side of the paper. Then give a written explanation on the right-hand side of the paper. To reinforce the correct procedure, do four more problems of that type.

Take the time this week to make corrections from your last test.

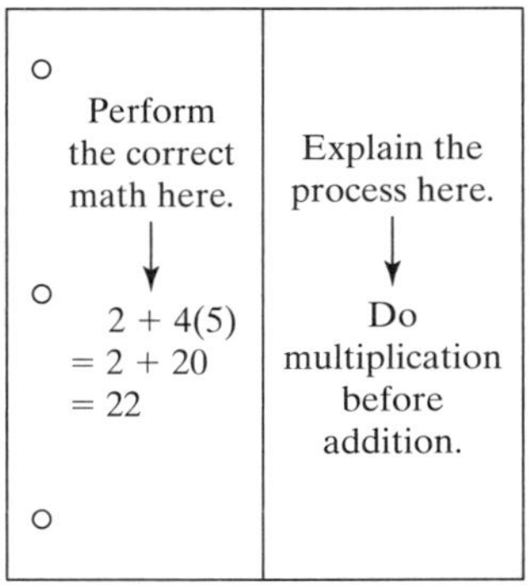

Vocabulary and Key Concepts

1. a. An ____________ is a statement that indicates that two expressions are equal.

b. A ____________ to an equation is a value of the variable that makes the equation a true statement.

c. An equation that can be written in the form $ax + b = c$ $(a \neq 0)$ is called a ____________ equation in one variable.

d. The set of all solutions to an equation is called the ____________.

Concept 1: Definition of a Linear Equation in One Variable

For Exercises 2–6, identify the following as either an expression or an equation.

2. $2 - 8x + 10$ **3.** $x - 4 + 5x$ **4.** $8x + 2 = 7$ **5.** $9 = 2x - 4$ **6.** $3x^2 + x = -3$

7. Explain how to determine if a number is a solution to an equation.

8. Explain why the equations $6x = 12$ and $x = 2$ are *equivalent equations*.

Section 2.2 Solving Linear Equations

Concepts

1. Linear Equations Involving Multiple Steps
2. Procedure for Solving a Linear Equation in One Variable
3. Conditional Equations, Identities, and Contradictions

1. Linear Equations Involving Multiple Steps

In Section 2.1, we studied a one-step process to solve linear equations by using the addition, subtraction, multiplication, and division properties of equality. In Example 1, we solve the equation $-2w - 7 = 11$. Solving this equation will require multiple steps. To understand the proper steps, always remember that the ultimate goal is to isolate the variable. Therefore, we will first isolate the *term* containing the variable before dividing both sides by -2.

Example 1 Solving a Linear Equation

Solve the equation. $-2w - 7 = 11$

Solution:

$$-2w - 7 = 11$$

$$-2w - 7 + 7 = 11 + 7$$ Add 7 to both sides of the equation. This isolates the w-term.

$$-2w = 18$$

$$\frac{-2w}{-2} = \frac{18}{-2}$$ Next, apply the division property of equality to obtain a coefficient of 1 for w. Divide by -2 on both sides.

$$w = -9$$

Check:

$$-2w - 7 = 11$$

$$-2(-9) - 7 \stackrel{?}{=} 11$$ Substitute $w = -9$ in the original equation.

$$18 - 7 \stackrel{?}{=} 11$$

$$11 \stackrel{?}{=} 11 \checkmark$$ True.

The solution set is $\{-9\}$.

Skill Practice Solve the equation.

1. $-5y - 5 = 10$

Example 2 Solving a Linear Equation

Solve the equation. $2 = \frac{1}{5}x + 3$

Solution:

$$2 = \frac{1}{5}x + 3$$

$$2 - 3 = \frac{1}{5}x + 3 - 3$$ Subtract 3 from both sides. This isolates the x-term.

$$-1 = \frac{1}{5}x$$ Simplify.

Answer

1. $\{-3\}$

$5(-1) = 5 \cdot \left(\frac{1}{5}x\right)$ Next, apply the multiplication property of equality to obtain a coefficient of 1 for x.

$-5 = 1x$

$-5 = x$ Simplify. The answer checks in the original equation.

The solution set is $\{-5\}$.

Skill Practice Solve the equation.

2. $2 = \frac{1}{2}a - 7$

In Example 3, the variable x appears on both sides of the equation. In this case, apply the addition or subtraction property of equality to collect the variable terms on one side of the equation and the constant terms on the other side. Then use the multiplication or division property of equality to get a coefficient equal to 1.

Example 3 Solving a Linear Equation

Solve the equation. $6x - 4 = 2x - 8$

Solution:

$6x - 4 = 2x - 8$

$6x - 2x - 4 = 2x - 2x - 8$ Subtract $2x$ from both sides leaving $0x$ on the right-hand side.

$4x - 4 = 0x - 8$ Simplify.

$4x - 4 = -8$ The x-terms have now been combined on one side of the equation.

$4x - 4 + 4 = -8 + 4$

$4x = -4$ Add 4 to both sides of the equation. This combines the constant terms on the *other* side of the equation.

$\frac{4x}{4} = \frac{-4}{4}$ To obtain a coefficient of 1 for x, divide both sides of the equation by 4.

$x = -1$ The answer checks in the original equation.

The solution set is $\{-1\}$.

Skill Practice Solve the equation.

3. $10x - 3 = 4x - 2$

Answers

2. $\{18\}$ **3.** $\left\{\frac{1}{6}\right\}$

Example 6 Solving a Linear Equation

Solve the equation. $2 + 7x - 5 = 6(x + 3) + 2x$

Solution:

$2 + 7x - 5 = 6(x + 3) + 2x$

$-3 + 7x = 6x + 18 + 2x$ **Step 1:** Add *like* terms on the left. Clear parentheses on the right.

$-3 + 7x = 8x + 18$ Combine *like* terms.

$-3 + 7x - 7x = 8x - 7x + 18$ **Step 2:** Subtract $7x$ from both sides.

$-3 = x + 18$ Simplify.

$-3 - 18 = x + 18 - 18$ **Step 3:** Subtract 18 from both sides.

$-21 = x$ **Step 4:** Because the coefficient of the x term is already 1, there is no need to apply the multiplication or division property of equality.

$x = -21$

The solution set is $\{-21\}$. **Step 5:** The check is left to the reader.

Skill Practice Solve the equation.

6. $4(2y - 1) + y = 6y + 3 - y$

Example 7 Solving a Linear Equation

Solve the equation. $9 - (z - 3) + 4z = 4z - 5(z + 2) - 6$

Solution:

$9 - (z - 3) + 4z = 4z - 5(z + 2) - 6$

$9 - z + 3 + 4z = 4z - 5z - 10 - 6$ **Step 1:** Clear parentheses.

$12 + 3z = -z - 16$ Combine *like* terms.

$12 + 3z + z = -z + z - 16$ **Step 2:** Add z to both sides.

$12 + 4z = -16$

$12 - 12 + 4z = -16 - 12$ **Step 3:** Subtract 12 from both sides.

$4z = -28$

$\frac{4z}{4} = \frac{-28}{4}$ **Step 4:** Divide both sides by 4.

$z = -7$ **Step 5:** The check is left for the reader.

The solution set is $\{-7\}$.

Avoiding Mistakes

When distributing a negative number through a set of parentheses, be sure to change the signs of every term within the parentheses.

Skill Practice Solve the equation.

7. $10 - (x + 5) + 3x = 6x - 5(x - 1) - 3$

Answers

6. $\left\{\frac{7}{4}\right\}$ 7. $\{-3\}$

3. Conditional Equations, Identities, and Contradictions

The solutions to a linear equation are the values of x that make the equation a true statement. A linear equation in one variable has one unique solution. Some types of equations, however, have no solution while others have infinitely many solutions.

I. Conditional Equations

An equation that is true for some values of the variable but false for other values is called a **conditional equation**. The equation $x + 4 = 6$, for example, is true on the condition that $x = 2$. For other values of x, the statement $x + 4 = 6$ is false.

$$x + 4 = 6$$
$$x + 4 - 4 = 6 - 4$$
$$x = 2 \quad \text{(Conditional equation)} \qquad \text{Solution set: } \{2\}$$

II. Contradictions

Some equations have no solution, such as $x + 1 = x + 2$. There is no value of x, that when increased by 1 will equal the same value increased by 2. If we tried to solve the equation by subtracting x from both sides, we get the contradiction $1 = 2$. This indicates that the equation has no solution. An equation that has no solution is called a **contradiction**. The solution set is the empty set. The **empty set** is the set with no elements and is denoted by { }.

TIP: The empty set is also called the null set and can be expressed by the symbol $\varnothing$.

$$x + 1 = x + 2$$
$$x - x + 1 = x - x + 2$$
$$1 = 2 \quad \text{(Contradiction)} \qquad \text{Solution set: } \{\ \}$$

Avoiding Mistakes

There are two ways to express the empty set: { } or $\varnothing$. Be sure that you do not use them together.

III. Identities

An equation that has all real numbers as its solution set is called an **identity**. For example, consider the equation, $x + 4 = x + 4$. Because the left- and right-hand sides are *identical*, any real number substituted for x will result in equal quantities on both sides. If we subtract x from both sides of the equation, we get the identity $4 = 4$. In such a case, the solution is the set of all real numbers.

$$x + 4 = x + 4$$
$$x - x + 4 = x - x + 4$$
$$4 = 4 \quad \text{(Identity)} \qquad \text{Solution set: The set of real numbers.}$$

Example 8 Identifying Conditional Equations, Contradictions, and Identities

Solve the equation. Identify each equation as a conditional equation, a contradiction, or an identity.

a. $4k - 5 = 2(2k - 3) + 1$ **b.** $2(b - 4) = 2b - 7$ **c.** $3x + 7 = 2x - 5$

Solution:

a.

$4k - 5 = 2(2k - 3) + 1$	
$4k - 5 = 4k - 6 + 1$	Clear parentheses.
$4k - 5 = 4k - 5$	Combine *like* terms.
$4k - 4k - 5 = 4k - 4k - 5$	Subtract $4k$ from both sides.
$-5 = -5$ (Identity)	

This is an identity. Solution set: The set of real numbers.

TIP: In Example 8(a), we could have stopped at the step $4k - 5 = 4k - 5$ because the expressions on the left and right are identical.

55. $-2[(4p + 1) - (3p - 1)] = 5(3 - p) - 9$

56. $5 - (6k + 1) = 2[(5k - 3) - (k - 2)]$

57. $3(-0.9n + 0.5) = -3.5n + 1.3$

58. $7(0.4m - 0.1) = 5.2m + 0.86$

Concept 3: Conditional Equations, Identities, and Contradictions

For Exercises 59–64, solve each equation. Identify as a conditional equation, an identity, or a contradiction. **(See Example 8.)**

59. $2(k - 7) = 2k - 13$

60. $5h + 4 = 5(h + 1) - 1$

61. $7x + 3 = 6(x - 2)$

62. $3y - 1 = 1 + 3y$

63. $3 - 5.2p = -5.2p + 3$

64. $2(q + 3) = 4q + q - 9$

65. A conditional linear equation has (choose one): one solution, no solution, or infinitely many solutions.

66. An equation that is a contradiction has (choose one): one solution, no solution, or infinitely many solutions.

67. An equation that is an identity has (choose one): one solution, no solution, or infinitely many solutions.

68. If the only solution to a linear equation is 5, then is the equation a conditional equation, an identity, or a contradiction?

Mixed Exercises

For Exercises 69–92, solve each equation.

69. $4p - 6 = 8 + 2p$

70. $\frac{1}{2}t - 2 = 3$

71. $2k - 9 = -8$

72. $3(y - 2) + 5 = 5$

73. $7(w - 2) = -14 - 3w$

74. $0.24 = 0.4m$

75. $2(x + 2) - 3 = 2x + 1$

76. $n + \frac{1}{4} = -\frac{1}{2}$

77. $0.5b = -23$

78. $3(2r + 1) = 6(r + 2) - 6$

79. $8 - 2q = 4$

80. $\frac{x}{7} - 3 = 1$

81. $2 - 4(y - 5) = -4$

82. $4 - 3(4p - 1) = -8$

83. $0.4(a + 20) = 6$

84. $2.2r - 12 = 3.4$

85. $10(2n + 1) - 6 = 20(n - 1) + 12$

86. $\frac{2}{5}y + 5 = -3$

87. $c + 0.123 = 2.328$

88. $4(2z + 3) = 8(z - 3) + 36$

89. $\frac{4}{5}t - 1 = \frac{1}{5}t + 5$

90. $6g - 8 = 4 - 3g$

91. $8 - (3q + 4) = 6 - q$

92. $6w - (8 + 2w) = 2(w - 4)$

Expanding Your Skills

93. Suppose the solution set for x in the equation $x + a = 10$ is $\{-5\}$. Find the value of a.

94. Suppose the solution set for x in the equation $x + a = -12$ is $\{6\}$. Find the value of a.

95. Suppose the solution set for x in the equation $ax = 12$ is $\{3\}$. Find the value of a.

96. Suppose the solution set for x in the equation $ax = 49.5$ is $\{11\}$. Find the value of a.

97. Write an equation that is an identity. Answers may vary.

98. Write an equation that is a contradiction. Answers may vary.

Linear Equations: Clearing Fractions and Decimals

Section 2.3

Concepts

1. **Linear Equations Containing Fractions**
2. **Linear Equations Containing Decimals**

1. Linear Equations Containing Fractions

Linear equations that contain fractions can be solved in different ways. The first procedure, illustrated here, uses the method outlined in Section 2.2.

$$\frac{5}{6}x - \frac{3}{4} = \frac{1}{3}$$

$$\frac{5}{6}x - \frac{3}{4} + \frac{3}{4} = \frac{1}{3} + \frac{3}{4}$$ To isolate the variable term, add $\frac{3}{4}$ to both sides.

$$\frac{5}{6}x = \frac{4}{12} + \frac{9}{12}$$ Find the common denominator on the right-hand side.

$$\frac{5}{6}x = \frac{13}{12}$$ Simplify.

$$\frac{6}{5}\left(\frac{5}{6}x\right) = \frac{\overset{1}{\cancel{6}}}{5}\left(\frac{13}{\underset{2}{\cancel{12}}}\right)$$ Multiply by the reciprocal of $\frac{5}{6}$, which is $\frac{6}{5}$.

$$x = \frac{13}{10}$$ The solution set is $\left\{\frac{13}{10}\right\}$.

Sometimes it is simpler to solve an equation with fractions by eliminating the fractions first by using a process called **clearing fractions**. To clear fractions in the equation $\frac{5}{6}x - \frac{3}{4} = \frac{1}{3}$, we can apply the multiplication property of equality to multiply both sides of the equation by the least common denominator (LCD). In this case, the LCD of $\frac{5}{6}x$, $-\frac{3}{4}$, and $\frac{1}{3}$ is 12. Because each denominator in the equation is a factor of 12, we can simplify common factors to leave integer coefficients for each term.

Example 1 Solving a Linear Equation by Clearing Fractions

Solve the equation by clearing fractions first. $\frac{5}{6}x - \frac{3}{4} = \frac{1}{3}$

Solution:

$$\frac{5}{6}x - \frac{3}{4} = \frac{1}{3}$$ The LCD of $\frac{5}{6}x, -\frac{3}{4}$, and $\frac{1}{3}$ is 12.

$$12\left(\frac{5}{6}x - \frac{3}{4}\right) = 12\left(\frac{1}{3}\right)$$ Multiply both sides of the equation by the LCD, 12.

$$\frac{\overset{2}{\cancel{12}}}{1}\left(\frac{5}{\cancel{6}}x\right) - \frac{\overset{3}{\cancel{12}}}{1}\left(\frac{3}{\cancel{4}}\right) = \frac{\overset{4}{\cancel{12}}}{1}\left(\frac{1}{\cancel{3}}\right)$$ Apply the distributive property (recall that $12 = \frac{12}{1}$).

$$2(5x) - 3(3) = 4(1)$$ Simplify common factors to clear the fractions.

$$10x - 9 = 4$$

$$10x - 9 + 9 = 4 + 9$$ Add 9 to both sides.

$$10x = 13$$

$$\frac{10x}{10} = \frac{13}{10}$$ Divide both sides by 10.

$$x = \frac{13}{10}$$ The solution set is $\left\{\frac{13}{10}\right\}$.

TIP: Recall that the multiplication property of equality indicates that multiplying both sides of an equation by a nonzero constant results in an equivalent equation.

TIP: The fractions in this equation can be eliminated by multiplying both sides of the equation by *any* common multiple of the denominators. These include 12, 24, 36, 48, and so on. We chose 12 because it is the *least* common multiple.

Skill Practice Solve the equation by clearing fractions.

1. $\frac{2}{5}y + \frac{1}{2} = -\frac{7}{10}$

In this section, we combine the process for clearing fractions and decimals with the general strategies for solving linear equations. To solve a linear equation, it is important to follow these steps.

Solving a Linear Equation in One Variable

Step 1 Simplify both sides of the equation.
- Clear parentheses
- Consider clearing fractions and decimals (if any are present) by multiplying both sides of the equation by a common denominator of all terms
- Combine *like* terms

Step 2 Use the addition or subtraction property of equality to collect the variable terms on one side of the equation.

Step 3 Use the addition or subtraction property of equality to collect the constant terms on the other side of the equation.

Step 4 Use the multiplication or division property of equality to make the coefficient of the variable term equal to 1.

Step 5 Check your answer.

Example 2 Solving a Linear Equation Containing Fractions

Solve the equation. $\frac{1}{6}x - \frac{2}{3} = \frac{1}{5}x - 1$

Solution:

$$\frac{1}{6}x - \frac{2}{3} = \frac{1}{5}x - 1$$ The LCD of $\frac{1}{6}x$, $-\frac{2}{3}$, $\frac{1}{5}x$, and $\frac{-1}{1}$ is 30.

$$30\left(\frac{1}{6}x - \frac{2}{3}\right) = 30\left(\frac{1}{5}x - 1\right)$$ Multiply by the LCD, 30.

$$\frac{\overset{5}{\cancel{30}}}{1} \cdot \frac{1}{\cancel{6}}x - \frac{\overset{10}{\cancel{30}}}{1} \cdot \frac{2}{\cancel{3}} = \frac{\overset{6}{\cancel{30}}}{1} \cdot \frac{1}{\cancel{5}}x - 30(1)$$ Apply the distributive property (recall $30 = \frac{30}{1}$).

$$5x - 20 = 6x - 30$$ Clear fractions.

$$5x - 6x - 20 = 6x - 6x - 30$$ Subtract $6x$ from both sides.

$$-x - 20 = -30$$

Answer

1. $\{-3\}$

$$-x - 20 + 20 = -30 + 20 \quad \text{Add 20 to both sides.}$$

$$-x = -10$$

$$\frac{-x}{-1} = \frac{-10}{-1} \quad \text{Divide both sides by } -1.$$

$$x = 10 \quad \text{The check is left to the reader.}$$

The solution set is {10}.

Skill Practice Solve the equation.

2. $\frac{2}{5}x - \frac{1}{2} = \frac{7}{4} + \frac{3}{10}x$

Example 3 Solving a Linear Equation Containing Fractions

Solve the equation. $\frac{1}{3}(x + 7) - \frac{1}{2}(x + 1) = 4$

Solution:

$$\frac{1}{3}(x + 7) - \frac{1}{2}(x + 1) = 4$$

$$\frac{1}{3}x + \frac{7}{3} - \frac{1}{2}x - \frac{1}{2} = 4 \quad \text{Clear parentheses.}$$

$$6\left(\frac{1}{3}x + \frac{7}{3} - \frac{1}{2}x - \frac{1}{2}\right) = 6(4) \quad \text{The LCD of } \tfrac{1}{3}x, \tfrac{7}{3}, -\tfrac{1}{2}x, \text{ and } -\tfrac{1}{2} \text{ is 6.}$$

$$\frac{\overset{2}{\cancel{6}}}{1} \cdot \frac{1}{\cancel{3}}x + \frac{\overset{2}{\cancel{6}}}{1} \cdot \frac{7}{\cancel{3}} + \frac{\overset{3}{\cancel{6}}}{1}\left(-\frac{1}{\cancel{2}}x\right) + \frac{\overset{3}{\cancel{6}}}{1}\left(-\frac{1}{\cancel{2}}\right) = 6(4) \quad \text{Apply the distributive property.}$$

$$2x + 14 - 3x - 3 = 24$$

$$-x + 11 = 24 \quad \text{Combine } \textit{like} \text{ terms.}$$

$$-x + 11 - 11 = 24 - 11 \quad \text{Subtract 11.}$$

$$-x = 13$$

$$\frac{-x}{-1} = \frac{13}{-1} \quad \text{Divide by } -1.$$

$$x = -13 \quad \text{The check is left to the reader.}$$

The solution set is {−13}.

Skill Practice Solve the equation.

3. $\frac{1}{5}(z + 1) + \frac{1}{4}(z + 3) = 2$

TIP: In Example 3 both parentheses and fractions are present within the equation. In such a case, we recommend that you clear parentheses first. Then clear the fractions.

Avoiding Mistakes

When multiplying an equation by the LCD, be sure to multiply all terms on both sides of the equation, including terms that are not fractions.

Answers

2. $\left\{\frac{45}{2}\right\}$ 3. $\left\{\frac{7}{3}\right\}$

Example 4 Solving a Linear Equation Containing Fractions

Solve the equation. $\frac{x-2}{5} - \frac{x-4}{2} = 2$

Solution:

$$\frac{x-2}{5} - \frac{x-4}{2} = \frac{2}{1}$$ The LCD of $\frac{x-2}{5}$, $\frac{x-4}{2}$, and $\frac{2}{1}$ is 10.

$$10\left(\frac{x-2}{5} - \frac{x-4}{2}\right) = 10\left(\frac{2}{1}\right)$$ Multiply both sides by 10.

$$\frac{\overset{2}{\cancel{10}}}{1} \cdot \left(\frac{x-2}{\cancel{5}}\right) - \frac{\overset{5}{\cancel{10}}}{1} \cdot \left(\frac{x-4}{\cancel{2}}\right) = \frac{10}{1} \cdot \left(\frac{2}{1}\right)$$ Apply the distributive property.

$$2(x-2) - 5(x-4) = 20$$ Clear fractions.

$$2x - 4 - 5x + 20 = 20$$ Apply the distributive property.

$$-3x + 16 = 20$$ Simplify both sides of the equation.

$$-3x + 16 - 16 = 20 - 16$$ Subtract 16 from both sides.

$$-3x = 4$$

$$\frac{-3x}{-3} = \frac{4}{-3}$$ Divide both sides by −3.

$$x = -\frac{4}{3}$$ The check is left to the reader.

The solution set is $\left\{-\frac{4}{3}\right\}$.

Avoiding Mistakes

In Example 4, several of the fractions in the equation have two terms in the numerator. It is important to enclose these fractions in parentheses when clearing fractions. In this way, we will remember to use the distributive property to multiply the factors shown in blue with both terms from the numerator of the fractions.

Skill Practice Solve the equation.

4. $\frac{x+1}{4} + \frac{x+2}{6} = 1$

2. Linear Equations Containing Decimals

The same procedure used to clear fractions in an equation can be used to **clear decimals**. For example, consider the equation

$$2.5x + 3 = 1.7x - 6.6$$

Recall that any terminating decimal can be written as a fraction. Therefore, the equation can be interpreted as

$$\frac{25}{10}x + 3 = \frac{17}{10}x - \frac{66}{10}$$

A convenient common denominator of all terms is 10. Therefore, we can multiply the original equation by 10 to clear decimals. The result is

$$25x + 30 = 17x - 66$$

Multiplying by the appropriate power of 10 moves the decimal points so that all coefficients become integers.

Answer

4. {1}

Example 5 Solving a Linear Equation Containing Decimals

Solve the equation by clearing decimals. $2.5x + 3 = 1.7x - 6.6$

Solution:

$$2.5x + 3 = 1.7x - 6.6$$

$$10(2.5x + 3) = 10(1.7x - 6.6)$$ Multiply both sides of the equation by 10.

$$25x + 30 = 17x - 66$$ Apply the distributive property.

$$25x - 17x + 30 = 17x - 17x - 66$$ Subtract $17x$ from both sides.

$$8x + 30 = -66$$

$$8x + 30 - 30 = -66 - 30$$ Subtract 30 from both sides.

$$8x = -96$$

$$\frac{8x}{8} = \frac{-96}{8}$$ Divide both sides by 8.

$$x = -12$$ The check is left to the reader.

The solution set is $\{-12\}$.

TIP: Notice that multiplying a decimal number by 10 has the effect of moving the decimal point one place to the right. Similarly, multiplying by 100 moves the decimal point two places to the right, and so on.

Skill Practice Solve the equation.

5. $1.2w + 3.5 = 2.1 + w$

Example 6 Solving a Linear Equation Containing Decimals

Solve the equation by clearing decimals. $0.2(x + 4) - 0.45(x + 9) = 12$

Solution:

$$0.2(x + 4) - 0.45(x + 9) = 12$$

$$0.2x + 0.8 - 0.45x - 4.05 = 12$$ Clear parentheses first.

$$100(0.2x + 0.8 - 0.45x - 4.05) = 100(12)$$ Multiply both sides by 100.

$$20x + 80 - 45x - 405 = 1200$$ Apply the distributive property.

$$-25x - 325 = 1200$$ Simplify both sides.

$$-25x - 325 + 325 = 1200 + 325$$ Add 325 to both sides.

$$-25x = 1525$$

$$\frac{-25x}{-25} = \frac{1525}{-25}$$ Divide both sides by -25.

$$x = -61$$ The check is left to the reader.

The solution set is $\{-61\}$.

TIP: The terms with the most digits following the decimal point are $-0.45x$ and -4.05. Each of these is written to the hundredths place. Therefore, we multiply both sides by 100.

Skill Practice Solve the equation.

6. $0.25(x + 2) - 0.15(x + 3) = 4$

Answers

5. $\{-7\}$ **6.** $\{39.5\}$

Section 2.3 Practice Exercises

Study Skills Exercise

Instructors vary in what they emphasize on tests. For example, test material may come from the textbook, notes, handouts, or homework. What does your instructor emphasize?

Vocabulary and Key Concepts

1. a. The process of eliminating fractions in an equation by multiplying both sides of the equation by the LCD is called ___________ ___________.

b. The process of eliminating decimals in an equation by multiplying both sides of the equation by a power of 10 is called ___________ ___________.

Review Exercises

For Exercises 2–8, solve each equation.

2. $-5t - 17 = -2t + 49$

3. $5(x + 2) - 3 = 4x + 5$

4. $-2(2x - 4x) = 6 + 18$

5. $3(2y + 3) - 4(-y + 1) = 7y - 10$

6. $-(3w + 4) + 5(w - 2) - 3(6w - 8) = 10$

7. $7x + 2 = 7(x - 12)$

8. $2(3x - 6) = 3(2x - 4)$

Concept 1: Linear Equations Containing Fractions

For Exercises 9–14, determine which of the values could be used to clear fractions or decimals in the given equation.

9. $\frac{2}{3}x - \frac{1}{6} = \frac{x}{9}$
Values: 6, 9, 12, 18, 24, 36

10. $\frac{1}{4}x - \frac{2}{7} = \frac{1}{2}x + 2$
Values: 4, 7, 14, 21, 28, 42

11. $0.02x + 0.5 = 0.35x + 1.2$
Values: 10; 100; 1000; 10,000

12. $0.003 - 0.002x = 0.1x$
Values: 10; 100; 1000; 10,000

13. $\frac{1}{6}x + \frac{7}{10} = x$
Values: 3, 6, 10, 30, 60

14. $2x - \frac{5}{2} = \frac{x}{3} - \frac{1}{4}$
Values: 2, 3, 4, 6, 12, 24

For Exercises 15–36, solve each equation. **(See Examples 1–4.)**

15. $\frac{1}{2}x + 3 = 5$

16. $\frac{1}{3}y - 4 = 9$

17. $\frac{2}{15}z + 3 = \frac{7}{5}$

18. $\frac{1}{6}y + 2 = \frac{5}{12}$

19. $\frac{1}{3}q + \frac{3}{5} = \frac{1}{15}q - \frac{2}{5}$

20. $\frac{3}{7}x - 5 = \frac{24}{7}x + 7$

21. $\frac{12}{5}w + 7 = 31 - \frac{3}{5}w$

22. $-\frac{1}{9}p - \frac{5}{18} = -\frac{1}{6}p + \frac{1}{3}$

23. $\frac{1}{4}(3m - 4) - \frac{1}{5} = \frac{1}{4}m + \frac{3}{10}$

24. $\frac{1}{25}(20 - t) = \frac{4}{25}t - \frac{3}{5}$

25. $\frac{1}{6}(5s + 3) = \frac{1}{2}(s + 11)$

26. $\frac{1}{12}(4n - 3) = \frac{1}{4}(2n + 1)$

27. $\frac{2}{3}x + 4 = \frac{2}{3}x - 6$

28. $-\frac{1}{9}a + \frac{2}{9} = \frac{1}{3} - \frac{1}{9}a$

29. $\frac{1}{6}(2c - 1) = \frac{1}{3}c - \frac{1}{6}$

30. $\frac{3}{2}b - 1 = \frac{1}{8}(12b - 8)$

31. $\frac{2x + 1}{3} + \frac{x - 1}{3} = 5$

32. $\frac{4y - 2}{5} - \frac{y + 4}{5} = -3$

33. $\frac{3w - 2}{6} = 1 - \frac{w - 1}{3}$

34. $\frac{z - 7}{4} = \frac{6z - 1}{8} - 2$

35. $\frac{x + 3}{3} - \frac{x - 1}{2} = 4$

36. $\frac{5y - 1}{2} - \frac{y + 4}{5} = 1$

Concept 2: Linear Equations Containing Decimals

For Exercises 37–54, solve each equation. **(See Examples 5–6.)**

37. $9.2y - 4.3 = 50.9$

38. $-6.3x + 1.5 = -4.8$

39. $0.05z + 0.2 = 0.15z - 10.5$

40. $21.1w + 4.6 = 10.9w + 35.2$

41. $0.2p - 1.4 = 0.2(p - 7)$

42. $0.5(3q + 87) = 1.5q + 43.5$

43. $0.20x + 53.60 = x$

44. $z + 0.06z = 3816$

45. $0.15(90) + 0.05p = 0.1(90 + p)$

46. $0.25(60) + 0.10x = 0.15(60 + x)$

47. $0.40(y + 10) - 0.60(y + 2) = 2$

48. $0.75(x - 2) + 0.25(x + 4) = 0.5$

49. $0.12x + 3 - 0.8x = 0.22x - 0.6$

50. $0.4x + 0.2 = -3.6 - 0.6x$

51. $0.06(x - 0.5) = 0.06x + 0.01$

52. $0.125x = 0.025(5x + 1)$

53. $-3.5x + 1.3 = -0.3(9x - 5)$

54. $x + 4 = 2(0.4x + 1.3)$

Mixed Exercises

For Exercises 55–64, solve each equation.

55. $0.2x - 1.8 = -3$

56. $9.8h + 2 = 3.8h + 20$

57. $\frac{1}{4}(x + 4) = \frac{1}{5}(2x + 3)$

58. $\frac{2}{3}(y - 1) = \frac{3}{4}(3y - 2)$

59. $0.05(2t - 1) - 0.03(4t - 1) = 0.2$

60. $0.3(x + 6) - 0.7(x + 2) = 4$

61. $\frac{2k + 5}{4} = 2 - \frac{k + 2}{3}$

62. $\frac{3d - 4}{6} + 1 = \frac{d + 1}{8}$

63. $\frac{1}{8}v + \frac{2}{3} = \frac{1}{6}v + \frac{3}{4}$

64. $\frac{2}{5}z - \frac{1}{4} = \frac{3}{10}z + \frac{1}{2}$

Expanding Your Skills

For Exercises 65–68, solve each equation.

65. $\frac{1}{2}a + 0.4 = -0.7 - \frac{3}{5}a$

66. $\frac{3}{4}c - 0.11 = 0.23(c - 5)$

67. $0.8 + \frac{7}{10}b = \frac{3}{2}b - 0.8$

68. $0.78 - \frac{1}{25}h = \frac{3}{5}h - 0.5$

Problem Recognition Exercises

Equations vs. Expressions

For Exercises 1–32, identify each exercise as an expression or an equation. Then simplify the expression or solve the equation.

1. $2b + 23 - 6b - 5$

2. $10p - 9 + 2p - 3 + 8p - 18$

3. $\frac{y}{4} = -2$

4. $-\frac{x}{2} = 7$

5. $3(4h - 2) - (5h - 8) = 8 - (2h + 3)$

6. $7y - 3(2y + 5) = 7 - (10 - 10y)$

7. $3(8z - 1) + 10 - 6(5 + 3z)$

8. $-5(1 - x) - 3(2x + 3) + 5$

9. $6c + 3(c + 1) = 10$

10. $-9 + 5(2y + 3) = -7$

11. $0.5(2a - 3) - 0.1 = 0.4(6 + 2a)$

12. $0.07(2v - 4) = 0.1(v - 4)$

13. $\frac{5}{9}w + \frac{11}{12} = \frac{23}{36}$

14. $\frac{3}{8}t - \frac{5}{8} = \frac{1}{2}t + \frac{1}{8}$

15. $\frac{3}{4}x + \frac{1}{2} - \frac{1}{8}x + \frac{5}{4}$

16. $\frac{7}{3}(6 - 12t) + \frac{1}{2}(4t + 8)$

17. $2z - 7 = 2(z - 13)$

18. $-6x + 2(x + 1) = -2(2x + 3)$

19. $\frac{2x - 1}{4} + \frac{3x + 2}{6} = 2$

20. $\frac{w - 4}{6} - \frac{3w - 1}{2} = -1$

21. $4b - 8 - b = -3b + 2(3b - 4)$

22. $-k - 41 - 2 - k = -2(20 + k) - 3$

23. $\frac{4}{3}(6y - 3) = 0$

24. $\frac{1}{2}(2c - 4) + 3 = \frac{1}{3}(6c + 3)$

25. $3(x + 6) - 7(x + 2) - 4(1 - x)$

26. $-10(2k + 1) - 4(4 - 5k) + 25$

27. $3 - 2[4a - 5(a + 1)]$

28. $-9 - 4[3 - 2(q + 3)]$

29. $4 + 2[8 - (6 + x)] = -2(x - 1) - 4 + x$

30. $-1 - 5[2 + 3(w - 2)] = 5(w + 4)$

31. $\frac{1}{6}y + y - \frac{1}{3}(4y - 1)$

32. $\frac{1}{2} - \frac{1}{5}\left(x + \frac{1}{2}\right) + \frac{9}{10}x$

Section 2.4 Applications of Linear Equations: Introduction to Problem Solving

Concepts

1. **Problem-Solving Strategies**
2. **Translations Involving Linear Equations**
3. **Consecutive Integer Problems**
4. **Applications of Linear Equations**

1. Problem-Solving Strategies

Linear equations can be used to solve many real-world applications. However, with "word problems," students often do not know where to start. To help organize the problem-solving process, we offer the following guidelines:

Problem-Solving Flowchart for Word Problems

Step 1	Read the problem carefully.	• Familiarize yourself with the problem. Identify the unknown, and if possible, estimate the answer.
Step 2	Assign labels to unknown quantities.	• Identify the unknown quantity or quantities. Let x or another variable represent one of the unknowns. Draw a picture and write down relevant formulas.
Step 3	Write a verbal model.	• Write an equation in *words*.
Step 4	Write a mathematical equation.	• Replace the verbal model with a mathematical equation using x or another variable.
Step 5	Solve the equation.	• Solve for the variable using the steps for solving linear equations.
Step 6	Interpret the results and write the final answer in words.	• Once you have obtained a numerical value for the variable, recall what it represents in the context of the problem. Can this value be used to determine other unknowns in the problem? Write an answer to the word problem in *words*.

Avoiding Mistakes

Once you have reached a solution to a word problem, verify that it is reasonable in the context of the problem.

2. Translations Involving Linear Equations

We have already practiced translating an English sentence to a mathematical equation. Recall from Section 1.3 that several key words translate to the algebraic operations of addition, subtraction, multiplication, and division.

Example 1 Translating to a Linear Equation

The sum of a number and negative eleven is negative fifteen. Find the number.

Solution:

Step 1: Read the problem.

Let x represent the unknown number. — **Step 2:** Label the unknown.

(the sum of → $+$; is → $=$)

$$(\text{a number}) + (-11) = (-15)$$ **Step 3:** Write a verbal model.

$$x + (-11) = -15$$ **Step 4:** Write an equation.

$$x + (-11) + 11 = -15 + 11$$ **Step 5:** Solve the equation.

$$x = -4$$

The number is -4. — **Step 6:** Write the final answer in words.

Skill Practice

1. The sum of a number and negative seven is 12. Find the number.

Answer

1. The number is 19.

Example 2 Translating to a Linear Equation

Forty less than five times a number is fifty-two less than the number. Find the number.

Solution:

Step 1: Read the problem.

Let x represent the unknown number. **Step 2:** Label the unknown.

Step 3: Write a verbal model.

$$\begin{pmatrix}\text{5 times}\\\text{a number}\end{pmatrix} \overset{\text{less}}{-} (40) \overset{\text{is}}{=} \begin{pmatrix}\text{the}\\\text{number}\end{pmatrix} \overset{\text{less}}{-} (52)$$

Step 4: Write an equation.

$$5x \quad - \; 40 \quad = \quad x \quad - \; 52$$

Step 5: Solve the equation.

$$5x - 40 = x - 52$$
$$5x - x - 40 = x - x - 52$$
$$4x - 40 = -52$$
$$4x - 40 + 40 = -52 + 40$$
$$4x = -12$$
$$\frac{4x}{4} = \frac{-12}{4}$$
$$x = -3$$

The number is -3. **Step 6:** Write the final answer in words.

Avoiding Mistakes

It is important to remember that subtraction is not a commutative operation. Therefore, the order in which two real numbers are subtracted affects the outcome. The expression "forty less than five times a number" must be translated as: $5x - 40$ (not $40 - 5x$). Similarly, "fifty-two less than the number" must be translated as: $x - 52$ (not $52 - x$).

Skill Practice

2. Thirteen more than twice a number is 5 more than the number. Find the number.

Example 3 Translating to a Linear Equation

Twice the sum of a number and six is two more than three times the number. Find the number.

Solution:

Step 1: Read the problem.

Let x represent the unknown number. **Step 2:** Label the unknown.

Step 3: Write a verbal model.

Step 4: Write an equation.

$$\underset{\text{twice}}{2}\;\underset{\text{the sum}}{(x + 6)} \overset{\text{is}}{=} \underbrace{3x}_{\text{three times a number}} \overset{\text{2 more than}}{+\, 2}$$

Answer

2. The number is -8.

$2(x + 6) = 3x + 2$ **Step 5:** Solve the equation.

$2x + 12 = 3x + 2$

$2x - 2x + 12 = 3x - 2x + 2$

$12 = x + 2$

$12 - 2 = x + 2 - 2$

$10 = x$

The number is 10. **Step 6:** Write the final answer in words.

Avoiding Mistakes

It is important to enclose "the sum of a number and six" within parentheses so that the entire quantity is multiplied by 2. Forgetting the parentheses would imply that only the x-term is multiplied by 2.

Correct: $2(x + 6)$

Skill Practice

3. Three times the sum of a number and eight is 4 more than the number. Find the number.

3. Consecutive Integer Problems

The word *consecutive* means "following one after the other in order without gaps." The numbers 6, 7, and 8 are examples of three **consecutive integers**. The numbers −4, −2, 0, and 2 are examples of **consecutive even integers**. The numbers 23, 25, and 27 are examples of **consecutive odd integers**.

Notice that any two consecutive integers differ by 1. Therefore, if x represents an integer, then $(x + 1)$ represents the next larger consecutive integer (Figure 2-4).

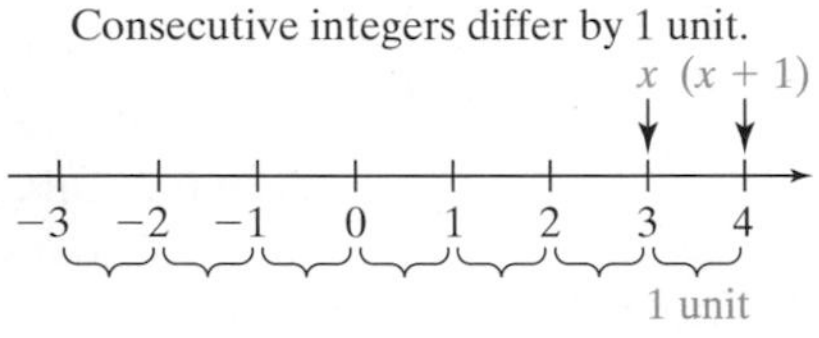

Figure 2-4

Any two consecutive even integers differ by 2. Therefore, if x represents an even integer, then $(x + 2)$ represents the next consecutive larger even integer (Figure 2-5).

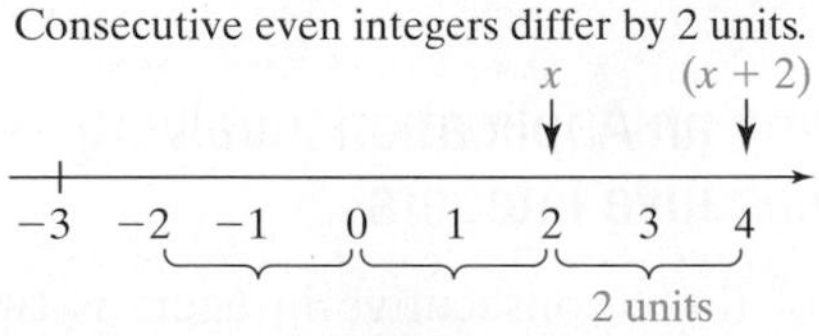

Figure 2-5

Likewise, any two consecutive odd integers differ by 2. If x represents an odd integer, then $(x + 2)$ is the next larger odd integer (Figure 2-6).

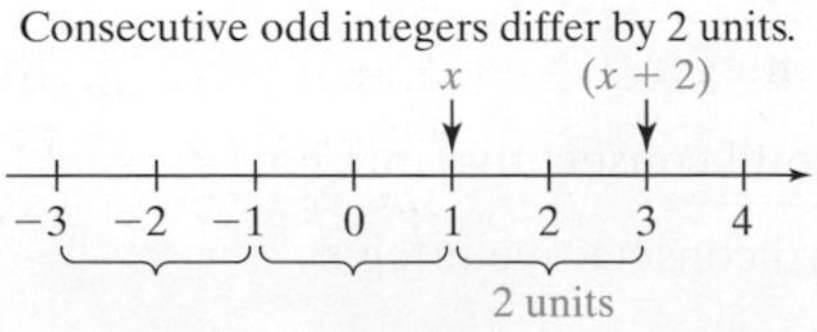

Figure 2-6

Answer

3. The number is −10.

Example 4 Solving an Application Involving Consecutive Integers

The sum of two consecutive odd integers is −188. Find the integers.

Solution:

In this example we have two unknown integers. We can let x represent either of the unknowns.

Step 1: Read the problem.

Suppose x represents the first odd integer. **Step 2:** Label the unknowns.

Then $(x + 2)$ represents the second odd integer.

$$\begin{pmatrix}\text{First}\\\text{integer}\end{pmatrix} + \begin{pmatrix}\text{second}\\\text{integer}\end{pmatrix} = (\text{total})$$

Step 3: Write a verbal model.

$$x + (x + 2) = -188$$

Step 4: Write a mathematical equation.

$$x + (x + 2) = -188$$
$$2x + 2 = -188$$
$$2x + 2 - 2 = -188 - 2$$
$$2x = -190$$
$$\frac{2x}{2} = \frac{-190}{2}$$
$$x = -95$$

Step 5: Solve for x.

The first integer is $x = -95$.

Step 6: Interpret the results and write the answer in words.

The second integer is $x + 2 = -95 + 2 = -93$.

The two integers are −95 and −93.

TIP: With word problems, it is advisable to check that the answer is reasonable.

The numbers −95 and −93 are consecutive odd integers. Furthermore, their sum is −188 as desired.

Skill Practice

4. The sum of two consecutive even integers is 66. Find the integers.

Example 5 Solving an Application Involving Consecutive Integers

Ten times the smallest of three consecutive integers is twenty-two more than three times the sum of the integers. Find the integers.

Solution:

Step 1: Read the problem.

Let x represent the first integer.

Step 2: Label the unknowns.

$x + 1$ represents the second consecutive integer.

$x + 2$ represents the third consecutive integer.

Answer

4. The integers are 32 and 34.

$$\begin{pmatrix}\text{10 times}\\ \text{the first}\\ \text{integer}\end{pmatrix} = \begin{pmatrix}\text{3 times}\\ \text{the sum of}\\ \text{the integers}\end{pmatrix} + 22$$

Step 3: Write a verbal model.

10 times the first integer ↓ | is ↓ | 3 times ↓ | 22 more than ↓

$$10x = 3\underbrace{[(x) + (x + 1) + (x + 2)]}_{\text{the sum of the integers}} + 22$$

Step 4: Write a mathematical equation.

$$10x = 3(x + x + 1 + x + 2) + 22$$

Step 5: Solve the equation.

$$10x = 3(3x + 3) + 22$$

Clear parentheses.

$$10x = 9x + 9 + 22$$

Combine *like* terms.

$$10x = 9x + 31$$

$$10x - 9x = 9x - 9x + 31$$

$$x = 31$$

Isolate the x-terms on one side.

The first integer is $x = 31$.

The second integer is $x + 1 = 31 + 1 = 32$.

The third integer is $x + 2 = 31 + 2 = 33$.

Step 6: Interpret the results and write the answer in words.

The three integers are 31, 32, and 33.

Skill Practice

5. Five times the smallest of three consecutive integers is 17 less than twice the sum of the integers. Find the integers.

4. Applications of Linear Equations

Example 6 Using a Linear Equation in an Application

A carpenter cuts a 6-ft board in two pieces. One piece must be three times as long as the other. Find the length of each piece.

Solution:

In this problem, one piece must be three times as long as the other. Thus, if x represents the length of one piece, then $3x$ can represent the length of the other.

Step 1: Read the problem completely.

x represents the length of the smaller piece.
$3x$ represents the length of the longer piece.

Step 2: Label the unknowns. Draw a figure.

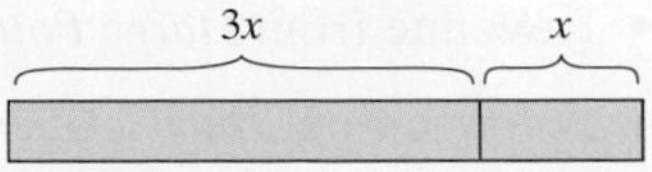

Answer

5. The integers are 11, 12, and 13.

$$\begin{pmatrix}\text{Length of}\\\text{one piece}\end{pmatrix} + \begin{pmatrix}\text{length of}\\\text{other piece}\end{pmatrix} = \begin{pmatrix}\text{total length}\\\text{of the board}\end{pmatrix}$$ **Step 3:** Write a verbal model.

$$x + 3x = 6$$ **Step 4:** Write an equation.

$$4x = 6$$ **Step 5:** Solve the equation.

$$\frac{4x}{4} = \frac{6}{4}$$

$$x = 1.5$$

The smaller piece is $x = 1.5$ ft. **Step 6:** Interpret the results.

The longer piece is $3x$ or $3(1.5 \text{ ft}) = 4.5$ ft.

TIP: The variable can represent either unknown. In Example 6, if we let x represent the length of the longer piece of board, then $\frac{1}{3}x$ would represent the length of the smaller piece. The equation would become $x + \frac{1}{3}x = 6$. Try solving this equation and interpreting the result.

Skill Practice

6. A plumber cuts a 96-in. piece of pipe into two pieces. One piece is five times longer than the other piece. How long is each piece?

Example 7 Using a Linear Equation in an Application

The hit movie *Harry Potter and the Deathly Hallows: Part 2* set a record for grossing the most money during its opening weekend. This amount surpassed the previous record set by the movie *The Dark Knight* by \$10.8 million. The revenue from these two movies was \$327.6 million. How much revenue did each movie bring in during its opening weekend?

Solution:

In this example, we have two unknowns. The variable x can represent *either* quantity. However, the revenue from *Harry Potter* is given in terms of the revenue for *The Dark Knight*. **Step 1:** Read the problem.

Let x represent the revenue for *The Dark Knight*. **Step 2:** Label the variables.

Then $x + 10.8$ represents the revenue for *Harry Potter*.

$$\begin{pmatrix}\text{Revenue from}\\\textit{The Dark Knight}\end{pmatrix} + \begin{pmatrix}\text{revenue from}\\\textit{Harry Potter}\end{pmatrix} = \begin{pmatrix}\text{total}\\\text{revenue}\end{pmatrix}$$ **Step 3:** Write a verbal model.

$$x + (x + 10.8) = 327.6$$ **Step 4:** Write an equation.

$$2x + 10.8 = 327.6$$ **Step 5:** Solve the equation.

$$2x = 316.8$$

$$x = 158.4$$

- Revenue from *The Dark Knight*: $x = 158.4$
- Revenue from *Harry Potter*: $x + 10.8 = 158.4 + 10.8 = 169.2$

The revenue from *Harry Potter and the Deathly Hallows: Part 2* was \$169.2 million for its opening weekend. The revenue for *The Dark Knight* was \$158.4 million.

Answer

6. One piece is 80 in. and the other is 16 in.

Skill Practice

7. There are 40 students in an algebra class. There are 4 more women than men. How many women and how many men are in the class?

Answer

7. There are 22 women and 18 men.

Section 2.4 Practice Exercises

Study Skills Exercise

After doing a section of homework, check the odd-numbered answers in the back of the text. Choose a method to identify the exercises that gave you trouble (i.e., circle the number or put a star by the number). List some reasons why it is important to label these problems.

Vocabulary and Key Concepts

1. **a.** Integers that follow one after the other without "gaps" are called ___________ integers.

   b. The integers $-2, 0, 2,$ and 4 are examples of consecutive ___________ integers.

   c. The integers $-3, -1, 1,$ and 3 are examples of consecutive ___________ integers.

   d. Two consecutive integers differ by ___________.

   e. Two consecutive odd integers differ by ___________.

   f. Two consecutive even integers differ by ___________.

Concept 2: Translations Involving Linear Equations

For Exercises 2–8, write an expression representing the unknown quantity.

2. In a math class, the number of students who received an "A" in the class was 5 more than the number of students who received a "B." If x represents the number of "B" students, write an expression for the number of "A" students.

3. There are 5,682,080 fewer men on Facebook than women. If x represents the number of women using Facebook, write an expression for the number of men using Facebook.

4. At a recent motorcycle rally, the number of men exceeded the number of women by 216. If x represents the number of women, write an expression for the number of men.

5. There are 10 times as many Facebook users as there are Twitter users. If x represents the number of Twitter users, write an expression for the number of Facebook users.

6. Rebecca downloaded twice as many songs as Nigel. If x represents the number of songs downloaded by Nigel, write an expression for the number downloaded by Rebecca.

7. Sidney made \$20 less than three times Casey's weekly salary. If x represents Casey's weekly salary, write an expression for Sidney's weekly salary.

8. David scored 26 points less than twice the number of points Rich scored in a video game. If x represents the number of points scored by Rich, write an expression representing the number of points scored by David.

For Exercises 9–18, use the problem-solving flowchart on page 129. **(See Examples 1–3.)**

9. Six less than a number is –10. Find the number.

10. Fifteen less than a number is 41. Find the number.

11. Twice the sum of a number and seven is eight. Find the number.

12. Twice the sum of a number and negative two is sixteen. Find the number.

13. A number added to five is the same as twice the number. Find the number.

14. Three times a number is the same as the difference of twice the number and seven. Find the number.

15. The sum of six times a number and ten is equal to the difference of the number and fifteen. Find the number.

16. The difference of fourteen and three times a number is the same as the sum of the number and negative ten. Find the number.

17. If the difference of a number and four is tripled, the result is six less than the number. Find the number.

18. Twice the sum of a number and eleven is twenty-two less than three times the number. Find the number.

Concept 3: Consecutive Integer Problems

19. **a.** If x represents the smallest of three consecutive integers, write an expression to represent each of the next two consecutive integers.

b. If x represents the largest of three consecutive integers, write an expression to represent each of the previous two consecutive integers.

20. **a.** If x represents the smallest of three consecutive odd integers, write an expression to represent each of the next two consecutive odd integers.

b. If x represents the largest of three consecutive odd integers, write an expression to represent each of the previous two consecutive odd integers.

For Exercises 21–30, use the problem-solving flowchart from page 129. **(See Examples 4–5.)**

21. The sum of two consecutive integers is -67. Find the integers.

22. The sum of two consecutive odd integers is 52. Find the integers.

23. The sum of two consecutive odd integers is 28. Find the integers.

24. The sum of three consecutive even integers is 66. Find the integers.

25. The perimeter of a pentagon (a five-sided polygon) is 80 in. The five sides are represented by consecutive integers. Find the measures of the sides.

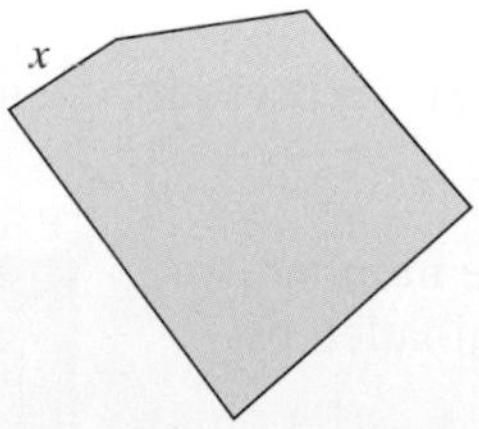

26. The perimeter of a triangle is 96 in. The lengths of the sides are represented by consecutive integers. Find the measures of the sides.

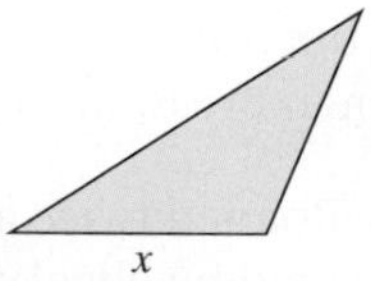

27. The sum of three consecutive even integers is 48 less than twice the smallest of the three integers. Find the integers.

28. The sum of three consecutive odd integers is 89 less than twice the largest integer. Find the integers.

29. Eight times the sum of three consecutive odd integers is 210 more than ten times the middle integer. Find the integers.

30. Five times the sum of three consecutive even integers is 140 more than ten times the smallest. Find the integers.

Concept 4: Applications of Linear Equations

For Exercises 31–42, use the problem-solving flowchart (page 129) to solve the problems.

31. A board is 86 cm in length and must be cut so that one piece is 20 cm longer than the other piece. Find the length of each piece. **(See Example 6.)**

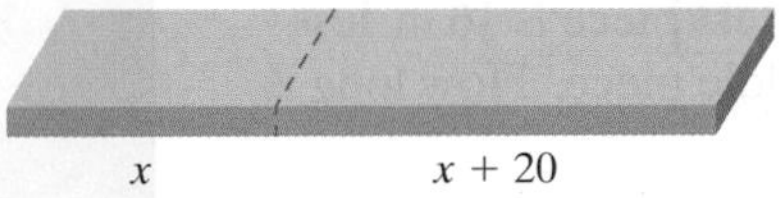

32. A rope is 54 in. in length and must be cut into two pieces. If one piece must be twice as long as the other, find the length of each piece.

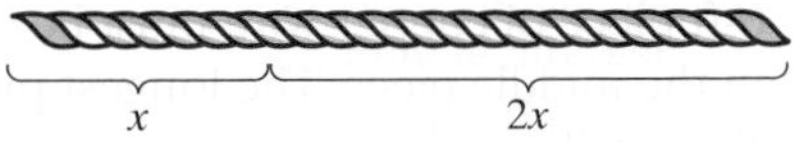

33. Karen's iPod contains 12 fewer playlists than Clarann's iPod. The total number of playlists on both iPods is 58. Find the number of playlists on each person's iPod.

34. Maria has 15 fewer apps on her phone than Orlando. If the total number of apps on both phones is 29, how many apps are on each phone?

35. For a recent year, 31 more Democrats than Republicans were in the U.S. House of Representatives. If the total number of representatives in the House from these two parties was 433, find the number of representatives from each party.

36. For a recent year, the number of men in the U.S. Senate totaled 4 more than five times the number of women. Find the number of men and the number of women in the Senate given that the Senate has 100 members.

37. During one week in a recent season, the show *CSI: Crime Scene Investigation* had 1.06 million fewer viewers than *Criminal Minds.* For both shows, the total number of viewers was 27.40 million. Find the number of viewers for each show during this week. **(See Example 7.)**

38. Two of the largest Internet retailers are eBay and Amazon.com. Recently, the estimated U.S. sales of eBay were \$0.1 billion less than twice the sales of Amazon.com. Given the total sales of \$5.6 billion, determine the sales of eBay and Amazon.com.

39. The longest river in Africa is the Nile. It is 2455 km longer than the Congo River, also in Africa. The sum of the lengths of these rivers is 11,195 km. What is the length of each river?

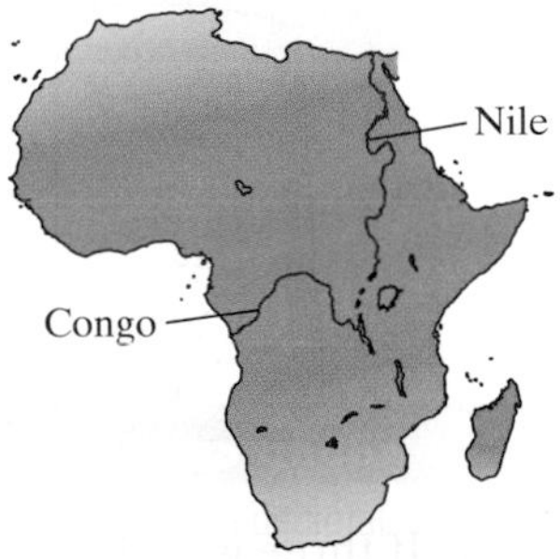

40. The average depth of the Gulf of Mexico is three times the depth of the Red Sea. The difference between the average depths is 1078 m. What is the average depth of the Gulf of Mexico and the average depth of the Red Sea?

41. Asia and Africa are the two largest continents in the world. The land area of Asia is approximately 14,514,000 km^2 larger than the land area of Africa. Together their total area is 74,644,000 km^2. Find the land area of Asia and the land area of Africa.

42. Mt. Everest, the highest mountain in the world, is 2654 m higher than Mt. McKinley, the highest mountain in the United States. If the sum of their heights is 15,042 m, find the height of each mountain.

Mixed Exercises

43. A group of hikers walked from Hawk Mt. Shelter to Blood Mt. Shelter along the Appalachian Trail, a total distance of 20.5 mi. It took 2 days for the walk. The second day the hikers walked 4.1 mi less than they did on the first day. How far did they walk each day?

Skill Practice

1. Find the amount of tax on a portable CD player that sells for \$89. Assume the tax rate is 6%.
2. Find the total cost including tax.

In Example 2, we solve a problem in which the percent is unknown.

Example 2 Finding an Unknown Percent

A group of 240 college men were asked what intramural sport they most enjoyed playing. The results are in the graph. What percent of the men surveyed preferred tennis?

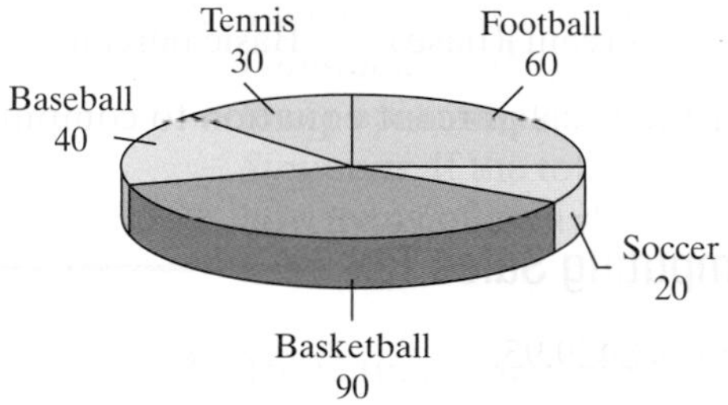

Solution:

	Step 1: Read the problem.
Let x represent the unknown percent (in decimal form).	**Step 2:** Label the variable.
The problem can be rephrased as:	
30 is what percent of 240?	**Step 3:** Write a verbal model.
$30 = x \cdot 240$	**Step 4:** Write a mathematical equation.
$30 = 240x$	**Step 5:** Solve the equation.
$\dfrac{30}{240} = \dfrac{240x}{240}$	Divide both sides by 240.
$0.125 = x$	
$0.125 \times 100\% = 12.5\%$	**Step 6:** Interpret the results. Change the value of x to a percent form by multiplying by 100%.
In this survey, 12.5% of men prefer tennis.	

Skill Practice Refer to the graph in Example 2.

3. What percent of the men surveyed prefer basketball as their favorite intramural sport?

Answers

1. The amount of tax is \$5.34.
2. The total cost is \$94.34.
3. 37.5% of the men surveyed prefer basketball.

Example 3 **Solving a Percent Equation with an Unknown Base**

Andrea spends 20% of her monthly paycheck on rent each month. If her rent payment is \$950, what is her monthly paycheck?

Solution:

	Step 1: Read the problem.
Let x represent the amount of Andrea's monthly paycheck.	**Step 2:** Label the variables.
The problem can be rephrased as:	
\$950 is 20% of what number? $\downarrow \; \downarrow \; \downarrow \; \downarrow \; \downarrow$	**Step 3:** Write a verbal model.
$950 = 0.20 \cdot x$	**Step 4:** Write a mathematical equation.
$950 = 0.20x$	**Step 5:** Solve the equation.
$\dfrac{950}{0.20} = \dfrac{0.20x}{0.20}$	Divide both sides by 0.20.
$4750 = x$	
Andrea's monthly paycheck is \$4750.	**Step 6:** Interpret the results.

Skill Practice

4. In order to pass an exam, a student must answer 70% of the questions correctly. If answering 42 questions correctly results in a 70% score, how many questions are on the test?

2. Applications Involving Simple Interest

One important application of percents is in computing simple interest on a loan or on an investment.

Simple interest is interest that is earned on principal (the original amount of money invested in an account). The following formula is used to compute simple interest:

$$\begin{pmatrix}\text{Simple}\\\text{interest}\end{pmatrix} = \begin{pmatrix}\text{principal}\\\text{invested}\end{pmatrix}\begin{pmatrix}\text{annual}\\\text{interest rate}\end{pmatrix}\begin{pmatrix}\text{time}\\\text{in years}\end{pmatrix}$$

This formula is often written symbolically as $I = Prt$.

For example, to find the simple interest earned on \$2000 invested at 7.5% interest for 3 years, we have

$$\begin{aligned} I &= Prt \\ \text{Interest} &= (\$2000)(0.075)(3) \\ &= \$450 \end{aligned}$$

Answer

4. There are 60 questions on the test.

Concept 1: Basic Percent Equations

For Exercises 5–16, find the missing values.

5. 45 is what percent of 360?

6. 338 is what percent of 520?

7. 544 is what percent of 640?

8. 576 is what percent of 800?

9. What is 0.5% of 150?

10. What is 9.5% of 616?

11. What is 142% of 740?

12. What is 156% of 280?

13. 177 is 20% of what number?

14. 126 is 15% of what number?

15. 275 is 12.5% of what number?

16. 594 is 45% of what number?

17. A Craftsman drill is on sale for $99.99. If the sales tax rate is 7%, how much will Molly have to pay for the drill? **(See Example 1.)**

18. Patrick purchased four new tires that were regularly priced at $94.99 each, but are on sale for $20 off per tire. If the sales tax rate is 6%, how much will be charged to Patrick's VISA card?

For Exercises 19–22, use the graph showing the distribution for leading forms of cancer in men. (*Source:* Centers for Disease Control)

Percent of Cancer Cases by Type (Men)

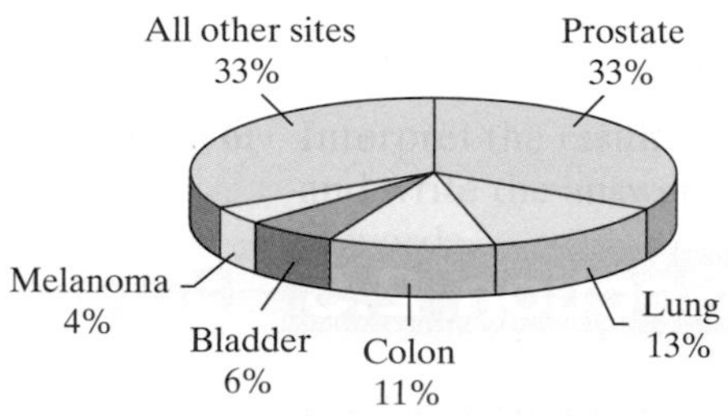

19. If there are 700,000 cases of cancer in men in the United States, approximately how many are prostate cancer?

20. Approximately how many cases of lung cancer would be expected in 700,000 cancer cases among men in the United States?

21. There were 14,000 cases of cancer of the pancreas diagnosed out of 700,000 cancer cases. What percent is this? **(See Example 2.)**

22. There were 21,000 cases of leukemia diagnosed out of 700,000 cancer cases. What percent is this?

23. Javon is in a 28% tax bracket for his federal income tax. If the amount of money that he paid for federal income tax was $23,520, what was his taxable income? **(See Example 3.)**

24. In a recent survey of college-educated adults, 155 indicated that they regularly work more than 50 hr a week. If this represents 31% of those surveyed, how many people were in the survey?

Concept 2: Applications Involving Simple Interest

25. Aidan is trying to save money and has $1800 to set aside in some type of savings account. He checked his bank one day, and found that the rate for a 12-month CD had an annual percentage yield (APY) of 4.25%. The interest rate on his savings account was 2.75% APY. How much more simple interest would Aidan earn if he invested in a CD for 12 months rather than leaving the $1800 in a regular savings account?

26. How much interest will Roxanne have to pay if she borrows $2000 for 2 years at a simple interest rate of 4%?

27. Bob borrowed money for 1 year at 5% simple interest. If he had to pay back a total of $1260, how much did he originally borrow? **(See Example 4.)**

28. Andrea borrowed some money for 2 years at 6% simple interest. If she had to pay back a total of $3640, how much did she originally borrow?

29. If $1500 grows to $1950 after 5 years, find the simple interest rate.

30. If $9000 grows to $10,440 in 2 years, find the simple interest rate.

31. Perry is planning a vacation to Europe in 2 years. How much should he invest in a certificate of deposit that pays 3% simple interest to get the $3500 that he needs for the trip? Round to the nearest dollar.

32. Sherica invested in a mutual fund and at the end of 20 years she has $14,300 in her account. If the mutual fund returned an average yield of 8%, how much did she originally invest?

Concept 3: Applications Involving Discount and Markup

33. A Pioneer car CD/MP3 player costs $170. Best Buy has it on sale for 12% off with free installation.

    a. What is the discount on the CD/MP3 player?

    b. What is the sale price?

34. An iPad, originally selling for $550 is on sale for 10% off.

    a. What is the discount on the iPad?

    b. What is the sale price?

35. A Sony digital camera is on sale for $400. This price is 15% off the original price. What was the original price? Round to the nearest cent. **(See Example 5.)**

36. The *Avatar* DVD is on sale for $18. If this represents an 18% discount rate, what was the original price of the DVD?

37. The original price of an Audio Jukebox was $250. It is on sale for $220. What percent discount does this represent?

38. During its first year, the Xbox 360 sold for $425 in stores. This product was in such demand that it sold for $800 online. What percent markup does this represent? (Round to the nearest whole percent.)

39. A doctor ordered a dosage of medicine for a patient. After 2 days, she increased the dosage by 20% and the new dosage came to 18 cc. What was the original dosage?

40. In one area, the cable company marked up the monthly cost by 6%. The new cost is $63.60 per month. What was the cost before the increase?

Mixed Exercises

41. Sun Lei bought a laptop computer for $1800. The total cost, including tax, came to $1890. What is the tax rate?

42. Jamie purchased a compact disk and paid $18.26. If the disk price is $16.99, what is the sales tax rate (round to the nearest tenth of a percent)?

43. To discourage tobacco use and to increase state revenue, several states tax tobacco products. One year, the state of New York increased taxes on tobacco, resulting in a 32% increase in the retail price of a pack of cigarettes. If the new price of a pack of cigarettes is $6.86, what was the cost before the increase in tax?

44. A hotel room rented for 5 nights costs $706.25 including 13% in taxes. Find the original price of the room (before tax) for the 5 nights. Then find the price per night.

Avoiding Mistakes

In the expression $\dfrac{-5x + 12}{2}$ do not try to divide the 2 into the 12. The divisor of 2 is dividing the entire quantity, $-5x + 12$ (not just the 12).

We may, however, apply the divisor to each term individually in the numerator. That is, $y = \dfrac{-5x + 12}{2}$ can be written in several different forms. Each is correct.

$$y = \frac{-5x + 12}{2} \quad \text{or} \quad y = \frac{-5x}{2} + \frac{12}{2} \Rightarrow y = -\frac{5}{2}x + 6$$

Skill Practice Solve for the indicated variable.

1. $A = lw$ for l
2. $-2a + 4b = 7$ for a

Example 2 Solving for an Indicated Variable

The formula $C = \frac{5}{9}(F - 32)$ is used to find the temperature, C, in degrees Celsius for a given temperature expressed in degrees Fahrenheit, F. Solve the formula $C = \frac{5}{9}(F - 32)$ for F.

Solution:

$$C = \frac{5}{9}(F - 32)$$

$$C = \frac{5}{9}F - \frac{5}{9} \cdot 32 \qquad \text{Clear parentheses.}$$

$$C = \frac{5}{9}F - \frac{160}{9} \qquad \text{Multiply: } \frac{5}{9} \cdot \frac{32}{1} = \frac{160}{9}.$$

$$9(C) = 9\left(\frac{5}{9}F - \frac{160}{9}\right) \qquad \text{Multiply by the LCD to clear fractions.}$$

$$9C = \frac{9}{1} \cdot \frac{5}{9}F - \frac{9}{1} \cdot \frac{160}{9} \qquad \text{Apply the distributive property.}$$

$$9C = 5F - 160 \qquad \text{Simplify.}$$

$$9C + 160 = 5F - 160 + 160 \qquad \text{Add 160 to both sides.}$$

$$9C + 160 = 5F$$

$$\frac{9C + 160}{5} = \frac{5F}{5} \qquad \text{Divide both sides by 5.}$$

$$\frac{9C + 160}{5} = F$$

The answer may be written in several forms:

$$F = \frac{9C + 160}{5} \quad \text{or} \quad F = \frac{9C}{5} + \frac{160}{5} \Rightarrow F = \frac{9}{5}C + 32$$

Skill Practice Solve for the indicated variable.

3. $y = \frac{1}{3}(x - 7)$ for x.

Answers

1. $l = \dfrac{A}{w}$
2. $a = \dfrac{7 - 4b}{-2}$ or $a = \dfrac{4b - 7}{2}$
3. $x = 3y + 7$

2. Geometry Applications

In Section A.2, we present numerous facts and formulas relating to geometry. There are also geometry formulas on the inside back cover of the text for quick reference.

Example 3 Solving a Geometry Application Involving Perimeter

The length of a rectangular lot is 1 m less than twice the width. If the perimeter is 190 m, find the length and width.

Solution:

	Step 1: Read the problem.
Let x represent the width of the rectangle.	**Step 2:** Label the variables.
Then $2x - 1$ represents the length.	

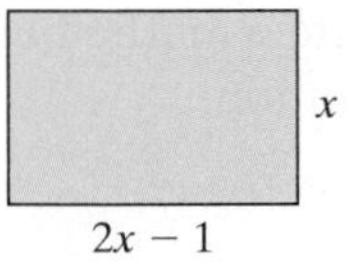

$P = 2l + 2w$	**Step 3:** Write the formula for perimeter.
$190 = 2(2x - 1) + 2(x)$	**Step 4:** Write an equation in terms of x.
$190 = 4x - 2 + 2x$	**Step 5:** Solve for x.
$190 = 6x - 2$	
$192 = 6x$	
$\frac{192}{6} = \frac{6x}{6}$	
$32 = x$	
The width is $x = 32$. The length is $2x - 1 = 2(32) - 1 = 63$.	**Step 6:** Interpret the results and write the answer in words.

The width of the rectangular lot is 32 m and the length is 63 m.

Skill Practice

4. The length of a rectangle is 10 ft less than twice the width. If the perimeter is 178 ft, find the length and width.

Recall some facts about angles.

- Two angles are complementary if the sum of their measures is 90°.
- Two angles are supplementary if the sum of their measures is 180°.
- The sum of the measures of the angles within a triangle is 180°.
- The measures of vertical angles are equal.

Answer

4. The length is 56 ft, and the width is 33 ft.

Example 4 Solving a Geometry Application Involving Complementary Angles

Two complementary angles are drawn such that one angle is 4° more than seven times the other angle. Find the measure of each angle.

Solution:

Step 1: Read the problem.

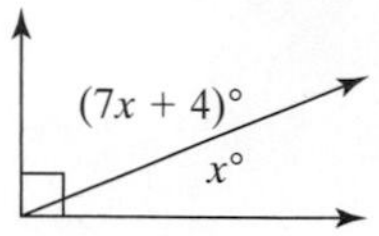

Let x represent the measure of one angle. **Step 2:** Label the variables.

Then $7x + 4$ represents the measure of the other angle.

The angles are complementary, so their sum must be 90°.

$$\begin{pmatrix}\text{Measure of}\\ \text{first angle}\end{pmatrix} + \begin{pmatrix}\text{measure of}\\ \text{second angle}\end{pmatrix} = 90°$$

Step 3: Write a verbal model.

$$x + 7x + 4 = 90$$

Step 4: Write a mathematical equation.

$$8x + 4 = 90$$

Step 5: Solve for x.

$$8x = 86$$

$$\frac{8x}{8} = \frac{86}{8}$$

$$x = 10.75$$

One angle is $x = 10.75$. **Step 6:** Interpret the results and write the answer in words.

The other angle is $7x + 4 = 7(10.75) + 4 = 79.25$.

The angles are 10.75° and 79.25°.

Skill Practice

5. Two complementary angles are constructed so that one measures 1° less than six times the other. Find the measures of the angles.

Example 5 Solving a Geometry Application Involving Angles in a Triangle

One angle in a triangle is twice as large as the smallest angle. The third angle is 10° more than seven times the smallest angle. Find the measure of each angle.

Solution:

Step 1: Read the problem.

Let x represent the measure of the smallest angle. **Step 2:** Label the variables.

Then $2x$ and $7x + 10$ represent the measures of the other two angles.

The sum of the angles must be 180°.

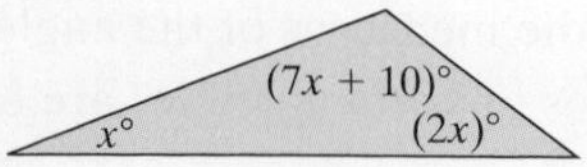

Answer

5. The angles are 13° and 77°.

$$\begin{pmatrix}\text{Measure of}\\\text{first angle}\end{pmatrix} + \begin{pmatrix}\text{measure of}\\\text{second angle}\end{pmatrix} + \begin{pmatrix}\text{measure of}\\\text{third angle}\end{pmatrix} = 180°$$

Step 3: Write a verbal model.

$$x \quad + \quad 2x \quad + \quad (7x + 10) = 180$$

Step 4: Write a mathematical equation.

$$x + 2x + 7x + 10 = 180$$

Step 5: Solve for x.

$$10x + 10 = 180$$

$$10x = 170$$

$$x = 17$$

Step 6: Interpret the results and write the answer in words.

The smallest angle is $x = 17$.

The other angles are $2x = 2(17) = 34$

$7x + 10 = 7(17) + 10 = 129$

The angles are 17°, 34°, and 129°.

Skill Practice

6. In a triangle, the measure of the first angle is 80° greater than the measure of the second angle. The measure of the third angle is twice that of the second. Find the measures of the angles.

Example 6 Solving a Geometry Application Involving Circumference

The distance around a circular garden is 188.4 ft. Find the radius to the nearest tenth of a foot. Use 3.14 for π.

Solution:

$C = 2\pi r$ Use the formula for the circumference of a circle.

$188.4 = 2\pi r$ Substitute 188.4 for C.

$\dfrac{188.4}{2\pi} = \dfrac{2\pi r}{2\pi}$ Divide both sides by 2π.

$\dfrac{188.4}{2\pi} = r$

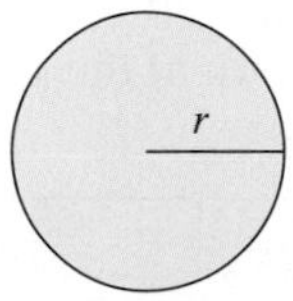

$C = 188.4$ ft

$r \approx \dfrac{188.4}{2(3.14)}$

$= 30.0$

The radius is approximately 30.0 ft.

Skill Practice

7. The circumference of a drain pipe is 12.5 cm. Find the radius. Round to the nearest tenth of a centimeter.

Answers

6. The angles are 25°, 50°, and 105°.

7. The radius is 2.0 cm.

Calculator Connections

Topic: Using the π Key on a Calculator

In Example 6 we could have obtained a more accurate result if we had used the π key on the calculator.

Note that parentheses are required to divide 188.4 by the quantity 2π. This guarantees that the calculator follows the implied order of operations. Without parentheses, the calculator would divide 188.4 by 2 and then multiply the result by π.

Scientific Calculator

Enter: 188.4 [÷] [(] 2 [×] [π] [)] [=] **Result:** 29.98479128 correct

Enter: 188.4 [÷] 2 [×] [π] [=] **Result:** 295.938028 incorrect

Graphing Calculator

```
188.4/(2π)
        29.98479128   ← Correct
188.4/2π
         295.938028   ← Incorrect
```

Calculator Exercises

Approximate the expressions with a calculator. Round to three decimal places if necessary.

1. $\dfrac{880}{2\pi}$

2. $\dfrac{1600}{\pi(4)^2}$

3. $\dfrac{20}{5\pi}$

4. $\dfrac{10}{7\pi}$

Section 2.6 Practice Exercises

Study Skills Exercise

A good technique for studying for a test is to choose four problems from each section of the chapter and write the problems along with the directions on 3×5 cards. On the back of each card, put the page number where you found that problem. Then shuffle the cards and test yourself on the procedure to solve each problem. If you find one that you do not know how to solve, look at the page number and do several of that type. Write four problems you would choose for this section.

Review Exercises

For Exercises 1–8, solve the equation.

1. $3(2y + 3) - 4(-y + 1) = 7y - 10$

2. $-(3w + 4) + 5(w - 2) - 3(6w - 8) = 10$

3. $\dfrac{1}{2}(x - 3) + \dfrac{3}{4} = 3x - \dfrac{3}{4}$

4. $\dfrac{5}{6}x + \dfrac{1}{2} = \dfrac{1}{4}(x - 4)$

5. $0.5(y + 2) - 0.3 = 0.4y + 0.5$

6. $0.25(500 - x) + 0.15x = 75$

7. $8b + 6(7 - 2b) = -4(b + 1)$

8. $2 - 5(t - 3) + t = 7t - (6t + 8)$

Concept 1: Literal Equations and Formulas

For Exercises 9–40, solve for the indicated variable. **(See Examples 1–2.)**

9. $P = a + b + c$ for a

10. $P = a + b + c$ for b

11. $x = y - z$ for y

12. $c + d = e$ for d

13. $p = 250 + q$ for q

14. $y = 35 + x$ for x

15. $A = bh$ for b

16. $d = rt$ for r

17. $PV = nrt$ for t

18. $P_1V_1 = P_2V_2$ for V_1

19. $x - y = 5$ for x

20. $x + y = -2$ for y

21. $3x + y = -19$ for y

22. $x - 6y = -10$ for x

23. $2x + 3y = 6$ for y

24. $7x + 3y = 1$ for y

25. $-2x - y = 9$ for x

26. $3x - y = -13$ for x

27. $4x - 3y = 12$ for y

28. $6x - 3y = 4$ for y

29. $ax + by = c$ for y

30. $ax + by = c$ for x

31. $A = P(1 + rt)$ for t

32. $P = 2(L + w)$ for L

33. $a = 2(b + c)$ for c

34. $3(x + y) = z$ for x

35. $Q = \frac{x + y}{2}$ for y

36. $Q = \frac{a - b}{2}$ for a

37. $M = \frac{a}{S}$ for a

38. $A = \frac{1}{3}(a + b + c)$ for c

39. $P = I^2R$ for R

40. $F = \frac{GMm}{d^2}$ for m

Concept 2: Geometry Applications

For Exercises 41–62, use the problem-solving flowchart (page 129) from Section 2.4.

41. The perimeter of a rectangular garden is 24 ft. The length is 2 ft more than the width. Find the length and the width of the garden. **(See Example 3.)**

42. In a small rectangular wallet photo, the width is 7 cm less than the length. If the border (perimeter) of the photo is 34 cm, find the length and width.

43. The length of a rectangular parking area is four times the width. The perimeter is 300 yd. Find the length and width of the parking area.

44. The width of Jason's workbench is $\frac{1}{2}$ the length. The perimeter is 240 in. Find the length and the width of the workbench.

45. A builder buys a rectangular lot of land such that the length is 5 m less than two times the width. If the perimeter is 590 m, find the length and the width.

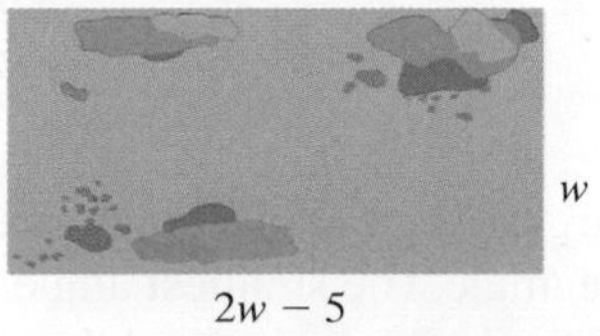

46. The perimeter of a rectangular pool is 140 yd. If the length is 20 yd less than twice the width, find the length and the width.

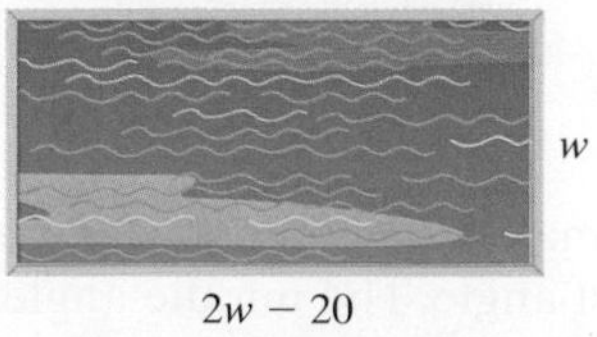

47. A triangular parking lot has two sides that are the same length and the third side is 5 m longer. If the perimeter is 71 m, find the lengths of the sides.

48. The perimeter of a triangle is 16 ft. One side is 3 ft longer than the shortest side. The third side is 1 ft longer than the shortest side. Find the lengths of all the sides.

49. Sometimes memory devices are helpful for remembering mathematical facts. Recall that the sum of two complementary angles is 90°. That is, two complementary angles when added together form a right angle or "corner." The words ***Complementary*** and ***Corner*** both start with the letter "***C***." Derive your own memory device for remembering that the sum of two supplementary angles is 180°.

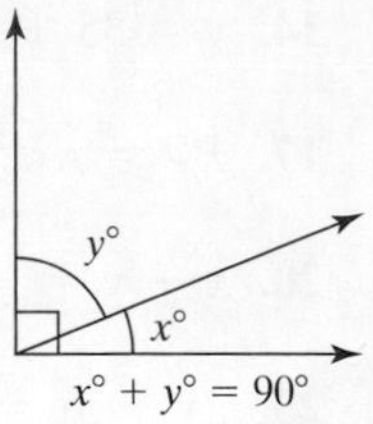

Complementary angles form a "Corner"

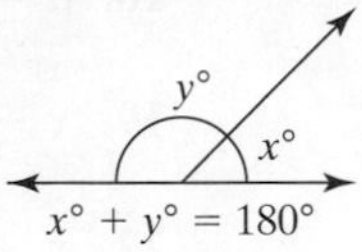

Supplementary angles . . .

50. Two angles are complementary. One angle is 20° less than the other angle. Find the measures of the angles.

51. Two angles are complementary. One angle is 4° less than three times the other angle. Find the measures of the angles. **(See Example 4.)**

52. Two angles are supplementary. One angle is three times as large as the other angle. Find the measures of the angles.

53. Two angles are supplementary. One angle is 6° more than four times the other. Find the measures of the two angles.

54. Refer to the figure. The angles, $\angle a$ and $\angle b$, are vertical angles.

a. If the measure of $\angle a$ is 32°, what is the measure of $\angle b$?

b. What is the measure of the supplement of $\angle a$?

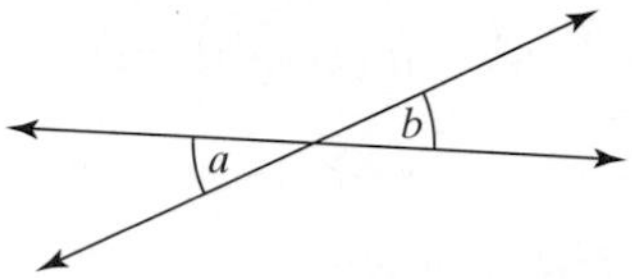

Figure for Exercise 54

55. Find the measures of the vertical angles labeled in the figure by first solving for x.

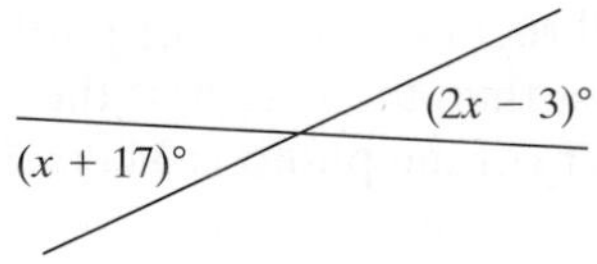

56. Find the measures of the vertical angles labeled in the figure by first solving for y.

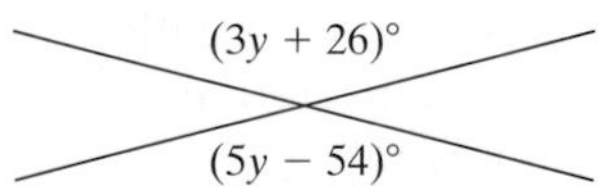

57. The largest angle in a triangle is three times the smallest angle. The middle angle is two times the smallest angle. Given that the sum of the angles in a triangle is 180°, find the measure of each angle. **(See Example 5.)**

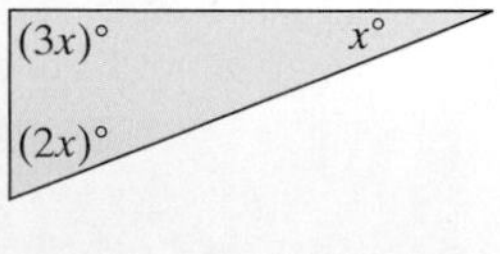

58. The smallest angle in a triangle measures 90° less than the largest angle. The middle angle measures 60° less than the largest angle. Find the measure of each angle.

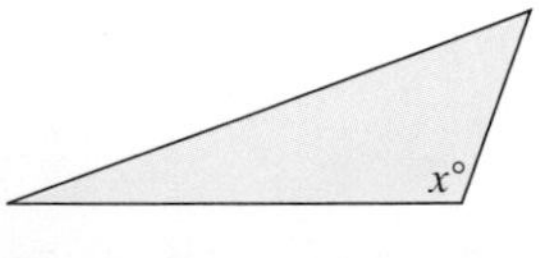

59. The smallest angle in a triangle is half the largest angle. The middle angle measures 30° less than the largest angle. Find the measure of each angle.

60. The largest angle of a triangle is three times the middle angle. The smallest angle measures 10° less than the middle angle. Find the measure of each angle.

61. Find the value of x and the measure of each angle labeled in the figure.

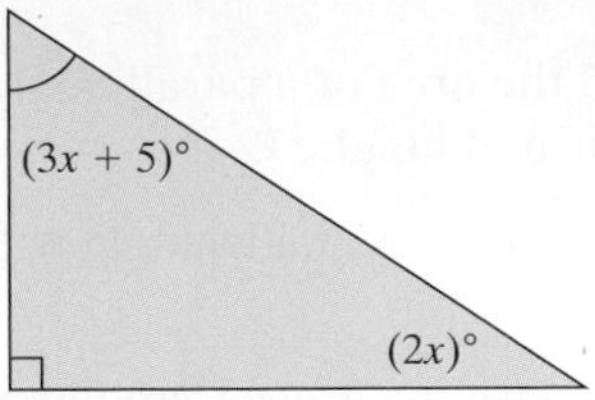

62. Find the value of y and the measure of each angle labeled in the figure.

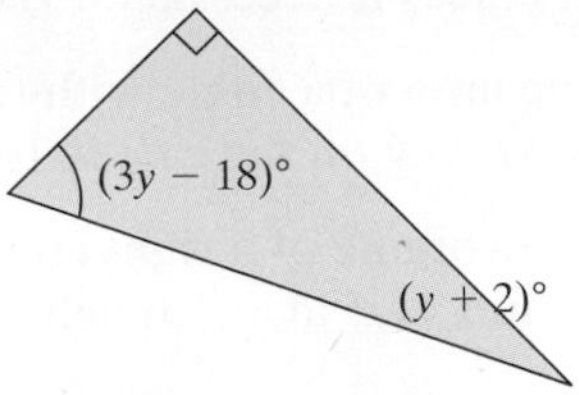

63. a. A rectangle has length l and width w. Write a formula for the area.

b. Solve the formula for the width, w.

c. The area of a rectangular volleyball court is 1740.5 ft^2 and the length is 59 ft. Find the width.

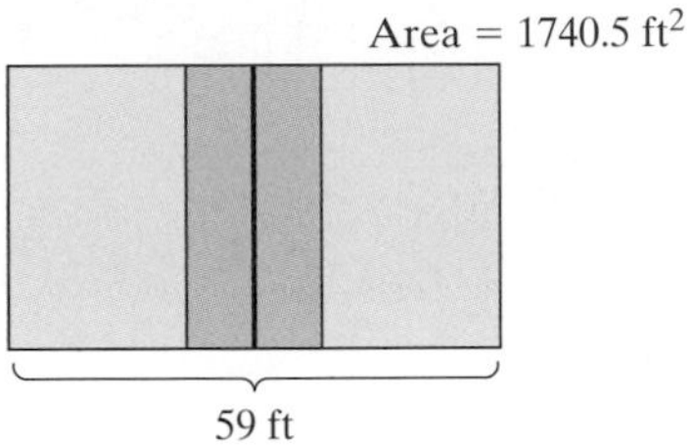

64. a. A parallelogram has height h and base b. Write a formula for the area.

b. Solve the formula for the base, b.

c. Find the base of the parallelogram pictured if the area is 40 m^2.

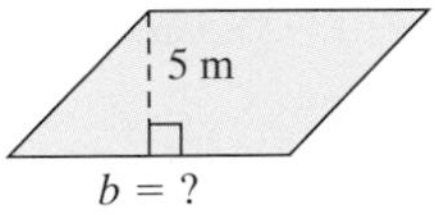

65. a. A rectangle has length l and width w. Write a formula for the perimeter.

b. Solve the formula for the length, l.

c. The perimeter of the soccer field at Giants Stadium is 338 m. If the width is 66 m, find the length.

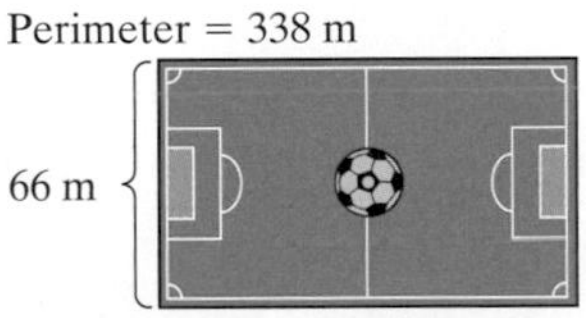

66. a. A triangle has height h and base b. Write a formula for the area.

b. Solve the formula for the height, h.

c. Find the height of the triangle pictured if the area is 12 km^2.

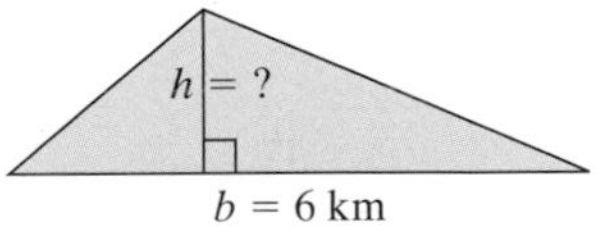

67. a. A circle has a radius of r. Write a formula for the circumference. **(See Example 6.)**

b. Solve the formula for the radius, r.

c. The circumference of the circular Buckingham Fountain in Chicago is approximately 880 ft. Find the radius. Round to the nearest foot.

68. a. The length of each side of a square is s. Write a formula for the perimeter of the square.

b. Solve the formula for the length of a side, s.

c. The Pyramid of Khufu (known as the Great Pyramid) at Giza has a square base. If the distance around the bottom is 921.6 m, find the length of the sides at the bottom of the pyramid.

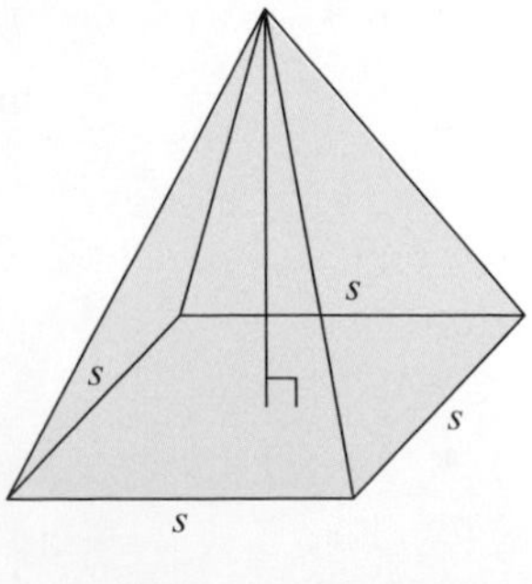

Expanding Your Skills

For Exercises 69–70, find the indicated area or volume. Be sure to include the proper units and round each answer to two decimal places if necessary.

69. a. Find the area of a circle with radius 11.5 m. Use the π key on the calculator.

b. Find the volume of a right circular cylinder with radius 11.5 m and height 25 m.

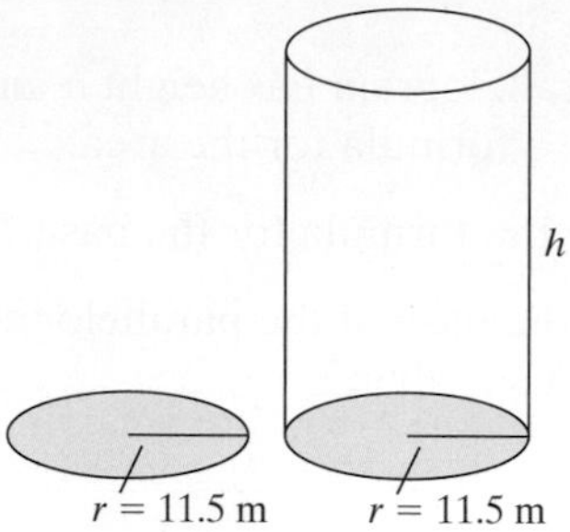

70. a. Find the area of a parallelogram with base 30 in. and height 12 in.

b. Find the area of a triangle with base 30 in. and height 12 in.

c. Compare the areas found in parts (a) and (b).

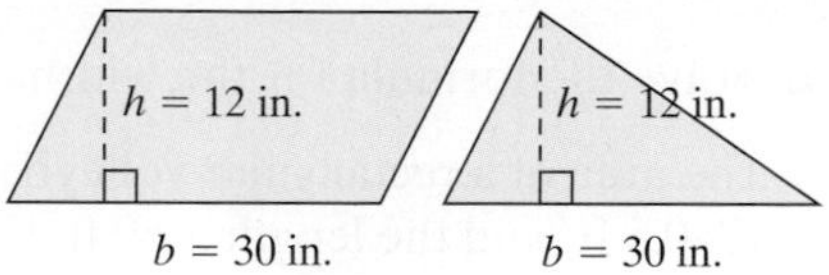

Section 2.7 Mixture Applications and Uniform Motion

Concepts

1. **Applications Involving Cost**
2. **Applications Involving Mixtures**
3. **Applications Involving Uniform Motion**

1. Applications Involving Cost

In Examples 1 and 2, we will look at different kinds of mixture problems. The first example "mixes" two types of movie tickets, adult tickets that sell for \$8 and children's tickets that sell for \$6. Furthermore, there were 300 tickets sold for a total revenue of \$2040. Before attempting the problem, we should try to gain some familiarity. Let's try a few combinations to see how many of each type of ticket might have been sold.

Suppose 100 adult tickets were sold and 200 children's tickets were sold (a total of 300 tickets).

- 100 adult tickets at \$8 each gives $100(\$8) = \$800$
- 200 children's tickets at \$6 each gives $200(\$6) = \$1200$

Total revenue: \$2000 (not enough)

Suppose 150 adult tickets were sold and 150 children's tickets were sold (a total of 300 tickets).

- 150 adult tickets at \$8 each gives $150(\$8) = \$1200$
- 150 children's tickets at \$6 each gives $150(\$6) = \$900$

Total revenue: \$2100 (too much)

As you can see, the trial-and-error process can be tedious and time-consuming. Therefore we will use algebra to determine the correct combination of each type of ticket.

Suppose we let x represent the number of adult tickets, then the number of children's tickets is the *total minus x*. That is,

$$\begin{pmatrix}\text{Number of}\\\text{children's tickets}\end{pmatrix} = \begin{pmatrix}\text{total number}\\\text{of tickets}\end{pmatrix} - \begin{pmatrix}\text{number of}\\\text{adult tickets, } x\end{pmatrix}$$

$$\text{Number of children's tickets} = 300 - x.$$

Notice that the number of tickets sold times the price per ticket gives the revenue.

- x adult tickets at \$8 each gives a revenue of: $x(\$8)$ or simply $8x$.
- $300 - x$ children's tickets at \$6 each gives: $(300 - x)(\$6)$ or $6(300 - x)$

This will help us set up an equation in Example 1.

Example 1 Solving a Mixture Problem Involving Ticket Sales

At an IMAX theater, 300 tickets were sold. Adult tickets cost \$8 and tickets for children cost \$6. If the total revenue from ticket sales was \$2040, determine the number of each type of ticket sold.

Solution:

Let x represent the number of adult tickets sold. **Step 1:** Read the problem.

$300 - x$ is the number of children's tickets. **Step 2:** Label the variables.

	\$8 Tickets	\$6 Tickets	Total
Number of tickets	x	$300 - x$	300
Revenue	$8x$	$6(300 - x)$	2040

$$\begin{pmatrix}\text{Revenue from}\\ \text{adult tickets}\end{pmatrix} + \begin{pmatrix}\text{revenue from}\\ \text{children's tickets}\end{pmatrix} = \begin{pmatrix}\text{total}\\ \text{revenue}\end{pmatrix}$$

Step 3: Write a verbal model.

$$8x \quad + \quad 6(300 - x) \quad = \quad 2040$$

Step 4: Write a mathematical equation.

$$8x + 6(300 - x) = 2040$$

Step 5: Solve the equation.

$$8x + 1800 - 6x = 2040$$
$$2x + 1800 = 2040$$
$$2x = 240$$
$$x = 120$$

Step 6: Interpret the results.

There were 120 adult tickets sold.
The number of children's tickets is $300 - x$ which is 180.

Avoiding Mistakes

Check that the answer is reasonable. 120 adult tickets and 180 children's tickets makes 300 total tickets.

Furthermore, 120 adult tickets at \$8 each amounts to \$960, and 180 children's tickets at \$6 amounts to \$1080. The total revenue is \$2040 as expected.

Skill Practice

1. At a Performing Arts Center, seats in the orchestra section cost \$18 and seats in the balcony cost \$12. If there were 120 seats sold for one performance, for a total revenue of \$1920, how many of each type of seat were sold?

Answer

1. There were 80 seats in the orchestra section, and there were 40 in the balcony.

2. Applications Involving Mixtures

Example 2 **Solving a Mixture Application**

How many liters (L) of a 60% antifreeze solution must be added to 8 L of a 10% antifreeze solution to produce a 20% antifreeze solution?

Solution:

The information can be organized in a table. Notice that an algebraic equation is derived from the second row of the table. This relates the number of liters of pure antifreeze in each container.

Step 1: Read the problem.

	60% Antifreeze	10% Antifreeze	Final Mixture: 20% Antifreeze
Number of liters of solution	x	8	$(8 + x)$
Number of liters of pure antifreeze	$0.60x$	0.10(8)	$0.20(8 + x)$

Step 2: Label the variables.

The amount of pure antifreeze in the final solution equals the sum of the amounts of antifreeze in the first two solutions.

$$\begin{pmatrix}\text{Pure antifreeze}\\ \text{from solution 1}\end{pmatrix} + \begin{pmatrix}\text{pure antifreeze}\\ \text{from solution 2}\end{pmatrix} = \begin{pmatrix}\text{pure antifreeze}\\ \text{in the final solution}\end{pmatrix}$$

Step 3: Write a verbal model.

$$0.60x \quad + \quad 0.10(8) \quad = \quad 0.20(8 + x)$$

$$0.60x + 0.10(8) = 0.20(8 + x)$$

Step 4: Write a mathematical equation.

$$0.6x + 0.8 = 1.6 + 0.2x$$

Step 5: Solve the equation.

$$0.6x - 0.2x + 0.8 = 1.6 + 0.2x - 0.2x$$ Subtract $0.2x$.

$$0.4x + 0.8 = 1.6$$

$$0.4x + 0.8 - 0.8 = 1.6 - 0.8$$ Subtract 0.8.

$$0.4x = 0.8$$

$$\frac{0.4x}{0.4} = \frac{0.8}{0.4}$$ Divide by 0.4.

$$x = 2$$

Step 6: Interpret the result.

Therefore, 2 L of 60% antifreeze solution is necessary to make a final solution that is 20% antifreeze.

Skill Practice

2. How many gallons of a 5% bleach solution must be added to 10 gallons (gal) of a 20% bleach solution to produce a solution that is 15% bleach?

Answer

2. 5 gal is needed.

3. Applications Involving Uniform Motion

The formula (distance) = (rate)(time) or simply, $d = rt$, relates the distance traveled to the rate of travel and the time of travel.

For example, if a car travels at 60 mph for 3 hours, then

$$d = (60 \text{ mph})(3 \text{ hours})$$
$$= 180 \text{ miles}$$

If a car travels at 60 mph for x hours, then

$$d = (60 \text{ mph})(x \text{ hours})$$
$$= 60x \text{ miles}$$

Example 3 **Solving an Application Involving Distance, Rate, and Time**

One bicyclist rides 4 mph faster than another bicyclist. The faster rider takes 3 hr to complete a race, while the slower rider takes 4 hr. Find the speed for each rider.

Solution:

Step 1: Read the problem.

The problem is asking us to find the speed of each rider.

Let x represent the speed of the slower rider. Then $(x + 4)$ is the speed of the faster rider.

Step 2: Label the variables and organize the information given in the problem. A distance-rate-time chart may be helpful.

	Distance	Rate	Time
Faster rider	$3(x + 4)$	$x + 4$	3
Slower rider	$4(x)$	x	4

To complete the first column, we can use the relationship, $d = rt$.

Because the riders are riding in the same race, their distances are equal.

$$\begin{pmatrix}\text{Distance}\\ \text{by faster rider}\end{pmatrix} = \begin{pmatrix}\text{distance}\\ \text{by slower rider}\end{pmatrix}$$

Step 3: Write a verbal model.

$$3(x + 4) = 4(x)$$

Step 4: Write a mathematical equation.

$$3x + 12 = 4x$$

Step 5: Solve the equation.

$$12 = x$$

Subtract $3x$ from both sides.

The variable x represents the slower rider's rate. The quantity $x + 4$ is the faster rider's rate. Thus, if $x = 12$, then $x + 4 = 16$.

The slower rider travels 12 mph and the faster rider travels 16 mph.

Avoiding Mistakes

Check that the answer is reasonable. If the slower rider rides at 12 mph for 4 hr, he travels 48 mi. If the faster rider rides at 16 mph for 3 hr, he also travels 48 mi as expected.

Skill Practice

3. An express train travels 25 mph faster than a cargo train. It takes the express train 6 hr to travel a route, and it takes 9 hr for the cargo train to travel the same route. Find the speed of each train.

Answer

3. The express train travels 75 mph, and the cargo train travels 50 mph.

Example 4 Solving an Application Involving Distance, Rate, and Time

Two families that live 270 mi apart plan to meet for an afternoon picnic at a park that is located between their two homes. Both families leave at 9.00 A.M., but one family averages 12 mph faster than the other family. If the families meet at the designated spot $2\frac{1}{2}$ hr later, determine

a. The average rate of speed for each family.

b. The distance each family traveled to the picnic.

Solution:

For simplicity, we will call the two families, Family A and Family B. Let Family A be the family that travels at the slower rate (Figure 2-9).

Step 1: Read the problem and draw a sketch.

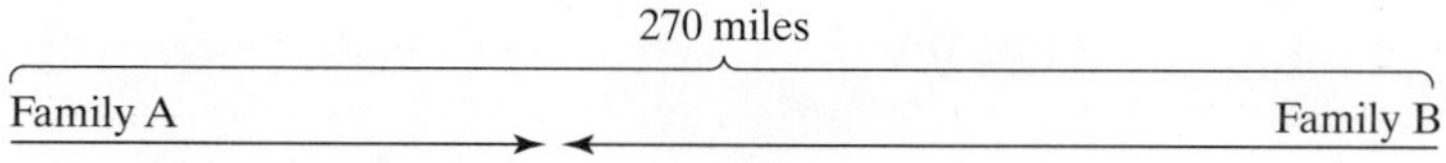

Figure 2-9

Let x represent the rate of Family A.

Then $(x + 12)$ is the rate of Family B.

Step 2: Label the variables.

	Distance	Rate	Time
Family A	$2.5x$	x	2.5
Family B	$2.5(x + 12)$	$x + 12$	2.5

To complete the first column, we can use the relationship $d = rt$.

To set up an equation, recall that the total distance between the two families is given as 270 mi.

$$\begin{pmatrix}\text{Distance}\\ \text{traveled by}\\ \text{Family A}\end{pmatrix} + \begin{pmatrix}\text{distance}\\ \text{traveled by}\\ \text{Family B}\end{pmatrix} = \begin{pmatrix}\text{total}\\ \text{distance}\end{pmatrix}$$

Step 3: Write a verbal model.

$$2.5x \quad + \quad 2.5(x + 12) \quad = \quad 270$$

Step 4: Write a mathematical equation.

$$2.5x + 2.5(x + 12) = 270$$
$$2.5x + 2.5x + 30 = 270$$
$$5.0x + 30 = 270$$
$$5x = 240$$
$$x = 48$$

Step 5: Solve for x.

a. Family A traveled 48 mph.

Family B traveled $x + 12 = 48 + 12 = 60$ mph.

Step 6: Interpret the results and write the answer in words.

b. To compute the distance each family traveled, use $d = rt$.

Family A traveled (48 mph)(2.5 hr) = 120 mi.

Family B traveled (60 mph)(2.5 hr) = 150 mi.

Skill Practice

4. A Piper airplane has an average air speed that is 10 mph faster than a Cessna 150 airplane. If the combined distance traveled by these two small planes is 690 mi after 3 hr, what is the average speed of each plane?

Answer

4. The Cessna's speed is 110 mph, and the Piper's speed is 120 mph.

Section 2.7 Practice Exercises

Study Skills Exercise

The following is a list of steps to help you solve word problems. Check those that you follow on a regular basis when solving a word problem. Place an asterisk next to the steps that you need to improve.

_____ Read through the entire problem before writing anything down.

_____ Write down exactly what you are being asked to find.

_____ Write down what is known and assign variables to what is unknown.

_____ Draw a figure or diagram if it will help you understand the problem.

_____ Highlight key words like total, sum, difference, etc.

_____ Translate the word problem to a mathematical problem.

_____ After solving, check that your answer makes sense.

Review Exercises

For Exercises 1–3, solve for the indicated variable.

1. $ax - by = c$ for x

2. $cd = r$ for c

3. $7x + xy = 18$ for y

For Exercises 4–6, solve each equation.

4. $-2d + 11 = 4 - d$

5. $3(2y + 5) - 8(y - 1) = 3y + 3$

6. $0.02x + 0.04(10 - x) = 1.26$

Concept 1: Applications Involving Cost

For Exercises 7–12, write an algebraic expression as indicated.

7. Two numbers total 200. Let t represent one of the numbers. Write an algebraic expression for the other number.

8. The total of two numbers is 43. Let s represent one of the numbers. Write an algebraic expression for the other number.

9. Olivia needs to bring 100 cookies to her friend's party. She has already baked x cookies. Write an algebraic expression for the number of cookies Olivia still needs to bake.

10. Rachel needs a mixture of 55 pounds (lb) of nuts consisting of peanuts and cashews. Let p represent the number of pounds of peanuts in the mixture. Write an algebraic expression for the number of pounds of cashews that she needs to add.

11. Max has a total of \$3000 in two bank accounts. Let y represent the amount in one account. Write an algebraic expression for the amount in the other account.

12. Roberto has a total of \$7500 in two savings accounts. Let z represent the amount in one account. Write an algebraic expression for the amount in the other account.

13. A church had an ice cream social and sold tickets for \$3 and \$2. When the social was over, 81 tickets had been sold totaling \$215. How many of each type of ticket did the church sell? **(See Example 1.)**

	\$3 Tickets	\$2 Tickets	Total
Number of tickets			
Cost of tickets			

14. Anna is a teacher at an elementary school. She purchased 72 tickets to take the first-grade children and some parents on a field trip to the zoo. She purchased children's tickets for \$10 each and adult tickets for \$18 each. She spent a total of \$856. How many of each ticket did she buy?

	Adults	Children	Total
Number of tickets			
Cost of tickets			

15. Josh downloaded 25 tunes from an online site for his MP3 player. Some songs cost \$0.90 each, while others were \$1.50 each. He spent a total of \$27.30. How many of each type of song did he download?

16. During the past year, Kris purchased 32 books at a wholesale club store. She purchased softcover books for \$4.50 each and hardcover books for \$13.50 each. The total cost of the books was \$243. How many of each type of book did she purchase?

17. Christopher has three times the number of Nintendo® DS games as Nintendo® Wii games. Each Nintendo® DS game costs \$30 while each Nintendo® Wii game costs \$50. How many games of each type does Christopher have if he spent a total of \$700 on all the games?

18. Steven wants to buy some candy with his birthday money. He can choose from Jelly Belly jelly beans that sell for \$6.99 per pound and Brach's variety that sells for \$3.99. He likes to have twice the amount of jelly beans as Brach's variety. If he spent a total of \$53.91, how many pounds of each type of candy did he buy?

Concept 2: Applications Involving Mixtures

For Exercises 19–22, write an algebraic expression as indicated.

19. A container holds 7 ounces (oz) of liquid. Let x represent the number of ounces of liquid in another container. Write an expression for the total amount of liquid.

20. A bucket contains 2.5 L of a bleach solution. Let n represent the number of liters of bleach solution in a second bucket. Write an expression for the total amount of bleach solution.

21. If Charlene invests $2000 in a certificate of deposit and d dollars in a stock, write an expression for the total amount she invested.

22. James has $5000 in one savings account. Let y represent the amount he has in another savings account. Write an expression for the total amount of money in both accounts.

23. How much of a 5% ethanol fuel mixture should be mixed with 2000 gal of 10% ethanol fuel mixture to get a mixture that is 9% ethanol. **(See Example 2.)**

Animation

	5% Ethanol	10% Ethanol	Final Mixture: 9% Ethanol
Number of gallons of fuel mixture			
Number of gallons of pure ethanol			

24. How many ounces of a 50% antifreeze solution must be mixed with 10 oz of an 80% antifreeze solution to produce a 60% antifreeze solution?

	50% Antifreeze	80% Antifreeze	Final Mixture: 60% Antifreeze
Number of ounces of solution			
Number of ounces of pure antifreeze			

25. A pharmacist needs to mix a 1% saline (salt) solution with 24 milliliters (mL) of a 16% saline solution to obtain a 9% saline solution. How many milliliters of the 1% solution must she use?

26. A landscaper needs to mix a 75% pesticide solution with 30 gal of a 25% pesticide solution to obtain a 60% pesticide solution. How many gallons of the 75% solution must he use?

27. To clean a concrete driveway, a contractor needs a solution that is 30% acid. How many ounces of a 50% acid solution must be mixed with 15 oz of a 21% solution to obtain a 30% acid solution?

28. A veterinarian needs a mixture that contains 12% of a certain medication to treat an injured bird. How many milliliters of a 16% solution should be mixed with 6 mL of a 7% solution to obtain a solution that is 12% medication?

Concept 3: Applications Involving Uniform Motion

29. **a.** If a car travels 60 mph for 5 hr, find the distance traveled.

b. If a car travels at x miles per hour for 5 hr, write an expression that represents the distance traveled.

c. If a car travels at $x + 12$ mph for 5 hr, write an expression that represents the distance traveled.

30. **a.** If a plane travels 550 mph for 2.5 hr, find the distance traveled.

b. If a plane travels at x miles per hour for 2.5 hr, write an expression that represents the distance traveled.

c. If a plane travels at $x - 100$ mph for 2.5 hr, write an expression that represents the distance traveled.

31. A woman can walk 2 mph faster down a trail to Cochita Lake than she can on the return trip uphill. It takes her 2 hr to get to the lake and 4 hr to return. What is her speed walking down to the lake? **(See Example 3.)**

	Distance	Rate	Time
Downhill to the lake			
Uphill from the lake			

32. A car travels 20 mph slower in a bad rain storm than in sunny weather. The car travels the same distance in 2 hr in sunny weather as it does in 3 hr in rainy weather. Find the speed of the car in sunny weather.

	Distance	Rate	Time
Rain storm			
Sunny weather			

33. Bryan hiked up to the top of City Creek in 3 hr and then returned down the canyon to the trailhead in another 2 hr. His speed downhill was 1 mph faster than his speed uphill. How far up the canyon did he hike?

34. Laura hiked up Lamb's Canyon in 2 hr and then ran back down in 1 hr. Her speed running downhill was 2.5 mph greater than her speed hiking uphill. How far up the canyon did she hike?

35. Hazel and Emilie fly from Atlanta to San Diego. The flight from Atlanta to San Diego is against the wind and takes 4 hr. The return flight with the wind takes 3.5 hr. If the wind speed is 40 mph, find the speed of the plane in still air.

36. A boat on the Potomac River travels the same distance downstream in $\frac{2}{3}$ hr as it does going upstream in 1 hr. If the speed of the current is 3 mph, find the speed of the boat in still water.

37. Two cars are 200 mi apart and traveling toward each other on the same road. They meet in 2 hr. One car is traveling 4 mph faster than the other. What is the speed of each car? **(See Example 4.)**

Animation

38. Two cars are 238 mi apart and traveling toward each other along the same road. They meet in 2 hr. One car is traveling 5 mph slower than the other. What is the speed of each car?

39. After Hurricane Katrina, a rescue vehicle leaves a station at noon and heads for New Orleans. An hour later a second vehicle traveling 10 mph faster leaves the same station. By 4:00 P.M., the first vehicle reaches its destination, and the second is still 10 mi away. How fast is each vehicle?

40. A truck leaves a truck stop at 9:00 A.M. and travels toward Sturgis, Wyoming. At 10:00 A.M., a motorcycle leaves the same truck stop and travels the same route. The motorcycle travels 15 mph faster than the truck. By noon, the truck has traveled 20 mi further than the motorcycle. How fast is each vehicle?

41. In the Disney Marathon, Jeanette's speed running was twice Sarah's speed walking. After 2 hr, Jeanette was 7 mi ahead of Sarah. Find Jeanette's speed and Sarah's speed.

42. Two canoes travel down a river, starting at 9:00 A.M. One canoe travels twice as fast as the other. After 3.5 hr, the canoes are 5.25 mi apart. Find the speed of each canoe.

Mixed Exercises

43. A certain granola mixture is 10% peanuts.

a. If a container has 20 lb of granola, how many pounds of peanuts are there?

b. If a container has x pounds of granola, write an expression that represents the number of pounds of peanuts in the granola.

c. If a container has $x + 3$ lb of granola, write an expression that represents the number of pounds of peanuts.

44. A certain blend of coffee sells for $9.00 per pound.

a. If a container has 20 lb of coffee, how much will it cost?

b. If a container has x pounds of coffee, write an expression that represents the cost.

c. If a container has $40 - x$ pounds of this coffee, write an expression that represents the cost.

45. The Coffee Company mixes coffee worth $12 per pound with coffee worth $8 per pound to produce 50 lb of coffee worth $8.80 per pound. How many pounds of the $12 coffee and how many pounds of the $8 coffee must be used?

	$12 Coffee	$8 Coffee	Total
Number of pounds			
Value of coffee			

46. The Nut House sells pecans worth $4 per pound and cashews worth $6 per pound. How many pounds of pecans and how many pounds of cashews must be mixed to form 16 lb of a nut mixture worth $4.50 per pound?

	$4 Pecans	$6 Cashews	Total
Number of pounds			
Value of nuts			

47. A boat in distress, 21 nautical miles from a marina, travels toward the marina at 3 knots (nautical miles per hour). A coast guard cruiser leaves the marina and travels toward the boat at 25 knots. How long will it take for the boats to reach each other?

48. An air traffic controller observes a plane heading from New York to San Francisco traveling at 450 mph. At the same time, another plane leaves San Francisco and travels 500 mph to New York. If the distance between the airports is 2850 mi, how long will it take for the planes to pass each other?

49. Surfer Sam purchased a total of 21 items at the surf shop. He bought wax for \$3.00 per package and sunscreen for \$8.00 per bottle. He spent a total amount of \$88.00. How many of each item did he purchase?

50. Tonya Toast loves jam. She purchased 30 jars of gourmet jam for \$178.50. She bought raspberry jam for \$6.25 per jar and strawberry jam for \$5.50 per jar. How many jars of each did she purchase?

51. How many quarts of 85% chlorine solution must be mixed with 5 quarts of 25% chlorine solution to obtain a 45% chlorine solution?

52. How many liters of a 58% sugar solution must be added to 14 L of a 40% sugar solution to obtain a 50% sugar solution?

Expanding Your Skills

53. How much pure water must be mixed with 12 L of a 40% alcohol solution to obtain a 15% alcohol solution? (*Hint:* Pure water is 0% alcohol.)

54. How much pure water must be mixed with 10 oz of a 60% alcohol solution to obtain a 25% alcohol solution?

55. Amtrak Acela Express is a high-speed train that runs in the United States between Washington, D.C. and Boston. In Japan, a bullet train along the Sanyo line operates at an average speed of 60 km/hr faster than the Amtrak Acela Express. It takes the Japanese bullet train 2.7 hr to travel the same distance as the Acela Express can travel in 3.375 hr. Find the speed of each train.

56. Amtrak Acela Express is a high-speed train along the northeast corridor between Washington, D.C. and Boston. Since its debut, it cuts the travel time from 4 hr 10 min to 3 hr 20 min. On average, if the Acela Express is 30 mph faster than the old train, find the speed of the Acela Express. (*Hint:* 4 hr 10 min $= 4\frac{1}{6}$ hr.)

Linear Inequalities

Section 2.8

Concepts

1. Graphing Linear Inequalities
2. Set-Builder Notation and Interval Notation
3. Addition and Subtraction Properties of Inequality
4. Multiplication and Division Properties of Inequality
5. Inequalities of the Form $a < x < b$
6. Applications of Linear Inequalities

1. Graphing Linear Inequalities

Consider the following two statements.

$$2x + 7 = 11 \quad \text{and} \quad 2x + 7 < 11$$

The first statement is an equation (it has an = sign). The second statement is an inequality (it has an inequality symbol, <). In this section, we will learn how to solve linear *inequalities*, such as $2x + 7 < 11$.

A Linear Inequality in One Variable

A **linear inequality in one variable**, x, is any inequality that can be written in the form:

$$ax + b < c, \; ax + b \le c, \; ax + b > c, \text{ or } ax + b \ge c, \text{ where } a \ne 0.$$

2. Set-Builder Notation and Interval Notation

Graphing the solution set to an inequality is one way to define the set. Two other methods are to use **set-builder notation** or **interval notation.**

Set-Builder Notation

The solution to the inequality $x \geq 2$ can be expressed in set-builder notation as follows:

$$\{x \mid x \geq 2\}$$

the set of all x such that x is greater than or equal to 2

Interval Notation

To understand interval notation, first think of a number line extending infinitely far to the right and infinitely far to the left. Sometimes we use the infinity symbol, ∞, or negative infinity symbol, $-\infty$, to label the far right and far left ends of the number line (Figure 2-10).

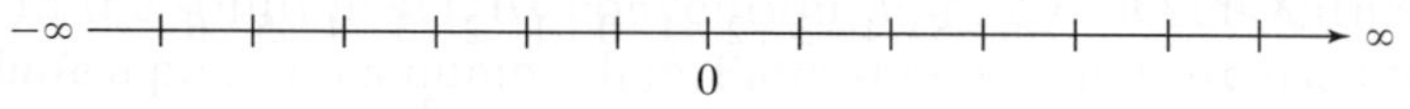

Figure 2-10

To express the solution set of an inequality in interval notation, sketch the graph first. Then use the endpoints to define the interval.

Inequality	Graph	Interval Notation
$x \geq 2$	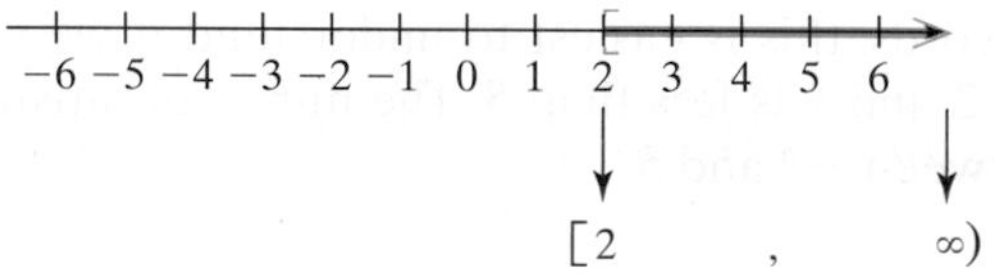	$[2, \infty)$

The graph of the solution set $x \geq 2$ begins at 2 and extends infinitely far to the right. The corresponding interval notation begins at 2 and extends to ∞. Notice that a square bracket [is used at 2 for both the graph and the interval notation. A parenthesis is always used at ∞ and for $-\infty$, because there is no endpoint.

Using Interval Notation

- The endpoints used in interval notation are always written from left to right. That is, the smaller number is written first, followed by a comma, followed by the larger number.
- A parenthesis, (or), indicates that an endpoint is excluded from the set.
- A square bracket, [or], indicates that an endpoint is included in the set.
- A parenthesis, (or), is always used with $-\infty$ or ∞, respectively.

In Table 2-1, we present examples of eight different scenarios for interval notation and the corresponding graph.

Table 2-1

Interval Notation	Graph	Interval Notation	Graph
(a, ∞)		$[a, \infty)$	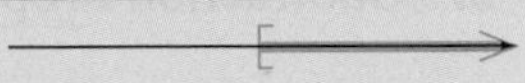
$(-\infty, a)$		$(-\infty, a]$	
(a, b)		$[a, b]$	
$(a, b]$		$[a, b)$	

Example 3 Using Set-Builder Notation and Interval Notation

Complete the chart.

Set-Builder Notation	Graph	Interval Notation
	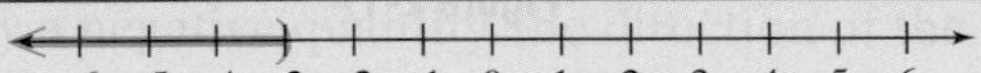	
		$[-\frac{1}{2}, \infty)$
$\{y \mid -2 \le y < 4\}$		

Solution:

Set-Builder Notation	Graph	Interval Notation
$\{x \mid x < -3\}$	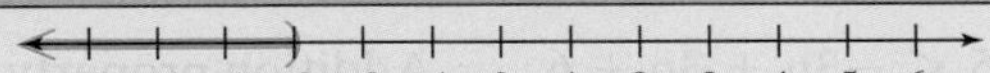	$(-\infty, -3)$
$\{x \mid x \ge -\frac{1}{2}\}$	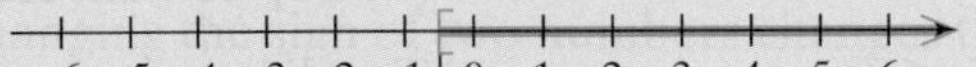	$[-\frac{1}{2}, \infty)$
$\{y \mid -2 \le y < 4\}$	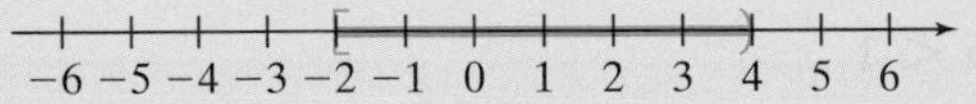	$[-2, 4)$

Skill Practice Express each of the following in set-builder notation and interval notation.

5. 

6. $x < \frac{3}{2}$

7. 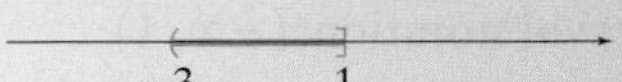

3. Addition and Subtraction Properties of Inequality

The process to solve a linear inequality is very similar to the method used to solve linear equations. Recall that adding or subtracting the same quantity to both sides of an equation results in an equivalent equation. The addition and subtraction properties of inequality state that the same is true for an inequality.

Answers

5. $\{x \mid x \ge -2\}$; $[-2, \infty)$

6. $\left\{x \mid x < \frac{3}{2}\right\}$; $\left(-\infty, \frac{3}{2}\right)$

7. $\{x \mid -3 < x \le 1\}$; $(-3, 1]$

Example 5 Solving a Linear Inequality

Solve the inequality and graph the solution set. Express the solution set in set-builder notation and in interval notation.

$$-5x - 3 \leq 12$$

Solution:

$-5x - 3 \leq 12$

$-5x - 3 + 3 \leq 12 + 3$ Add 3 to both sides.

$-5x \leq 15$

$\dfrac{-5x}{-5} \geq \dfrac{15}{-5}$ Divide by -5. Reverse the direction of the inequality sign.

$x \geq -3$

Set-builder notation: $\{x \mid x \geq -3\}$

Interval notation: $[-3, \infty)$

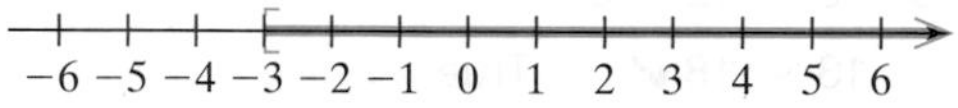

TIP: The inequality $-5x - 3 \leq 12$, could have been solved by isolating x on the right-hand side of the inequality. This would create a positive coefficient on the variable term and eliminate the need to divide by a negative number.

$-5x - 3 \leq 12$

$-3 \leq 5x + 12$

$-15 \leq 5x$ Notice that the coefficient of x is positive.

$\dfrac{-15}{5} \leq \dfrac{5x}{5}$ Do not reverse the inequality sign because we are dividing by a positive number.

$-3 \leq x$, or equivalently, $x \geq -3$

Skill Practice Solve the inequality and graph the solution set. Express the solution set in set-builder notation and in interval notation.

9. $-5p + 2 > 22$

Example 6 Solving a Linear Inequality

Solve the inequality and graph the solution set. Express the solution set in set-builder notation and in interval notation.

$$12 - 2(y + 3) < -3(2y - 1) + 2y$$

Solution:

$12 - 2(y + 3) < -3(2y - 1) + 2y$

$12 - 2y - 6 < -6y + 3 + 2y$ Clear parentheses.

$-2y + 6 < -4y + 3$ Combine *like* terms.

$-2y + 4y + 6 < -4y + 4y + 3$ Add $4y$ to both sides.

$2y + 6 < 3$ Simplify.

$2y + 6 + -6 < 3 + -6$ Add -6 to both sides.

$2y < -3$ Simplify.

$\dfrac{2y}{2} < \dfrac{-3}{2}$ Divide by 2. The direction of the inequality sign is *not* reversed because we divided by a positive number.

$y < -\dfrac{3}{2}$

Answer

9.

$\{p \mid p < -4\}$; $(-\infty, -4)$

Set-builder notation: $\left\{x \mid x < -\frac{3}{2}\right\}$

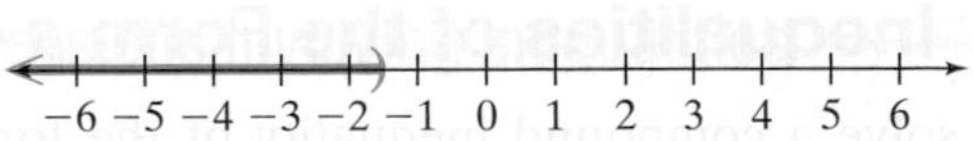

Interval notation: $\left(-\infty, -\frac{3}{2}\right)$

Skill Practice Solve the inequality and graph the solution set. Express the solution set in set-builder notation and in interval notation.

10. $-8 - 8(2x - 4) > -5(4x - 5) - 21$

Example 7 Solving a Linear Inequality

Solve the inequality and graph the solution set. Express the solution set in set-builder notation and in interval notation.

$$-\frac{1}{4}k + \frac{1}{6} \le 2 + \frac{2}{3}k$$

Solution:

$$-\frac{1}{4}k + \frac{1}{6} \le 2 + \frac{2}{3}k$$

$$12\left(-\frac{1}{4}k + \frac{1}{6}\right) \le 12\left(2 + \frac{2}{3}k\right)$$ Multiply both sides by 12 to clear fractions. (Because we multiplied by a positive number, the inequality sign is not reversed.)

$$\frac{12}{1}\left(-\frac{1}{4}k\right) + \frac{12}{1}\left(\frac{1}{6}\right) \le 12(2) + \frac{12}{1}\left(\frac{2}{3}k\right)$$ Apply the distributive property.

$$-3k + 2 \le 24 + 8k$$ Simplify.

$$-3k - 8k + 2 \le 24 + 8k - 8k$$ Subtract $8k$ from both sides.

$$-11k + 2 \le 24$$

$$-11k + 2 - 2 \le 24 - 2$$ Subtract 2 from both sides.

$$-11k \le 22$$

$$\frac{-11k}{-11} \ge \frac{22}{-11}$$ Divide both sides by -11. Reverse the inequality sign.

$$k \ge -2$$

Set-builder notation: $\{k \mid k \ge -2\}$

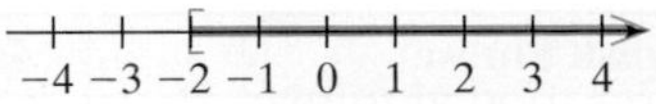

Interval notation: $[-2, \infty)$

Skill Practice Solve the inequality and graph the solution set. Express the solution set in set-builder notation and in interval notation.

11. $\frac{1}{5}t + 7 \le \frac{1}{2}t - 2$

Answers

10.

$\{x \mid x > -5\}$; $(-5, \infty)$

11.

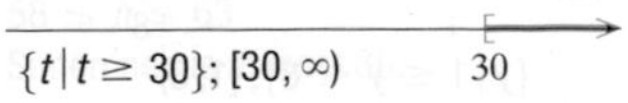

$\{t \mid t \ge 30\}$; $[30, \infty)$

Section 2.8 Practice Exercises

Study Skills Exercise

Find the page numbers for the Chapter Review Exercises, the Chapter Test, and the Cumulative Review Exercises for this chapter.

Chapter Review Exercises ______________ Chapter Test ______________

Cumulative Review Exercises ______________

Compare these features and state the advantages of each.

Vocabulary and Key Concepts

1. a. A relationship of the form $ax + b > c$ or $ax + b < c$ $(a \neq 0)$ is called a __________ in one variable.

b. A statement that involves more than one __________ is called a compound inequality.

c. The notation $\{x \mid x > -9\}$ is an example of __________ notation, whereas $(-9, \infty)$ is an example of __________ notation.

Review Problems

For Exercises 2–4, solve the equation.

2. $10y - 7(y + 8) + 13 = 13 - 6(2y + 1)$

3. $3(x + 2) - (2x - 7) = -(5x - 1) - 2(x + 6)$

4. $6 - 8(x + 3) + 5x = 5x - (2x - 5) + 13$

Concept 1: Graphing Linear Inequalities

For Exercises 5–16, graph the solution set of each inequality. **(See Examples 1–2.)**

5. $x > 5$

6. $x \geq -7.2$

7. $x \leq \dfrac{5}{2}$

8. $x < -1$

9. $13 > p$

10. $-12 \geq t$

11. $2 \leq y \leq 6.5$

12. $-3 \leq m \leq \dfrac{8}{9}$

13. $0 < x < 4$

14. $-4 < y < 1$

15. $1 < p \leq 8$

16. $-3 \leq t < 3$

Concept 2: Set-Builder Notation and Interval Notation

For Exercises 17–22, graph each inequality and write the solution set in interval notation. **(See Example 3.)**

Set-Builder Notation	Graph	Interval Notation
17. $\{x \mid x \geq 6\}$		
18. $\left\{x \mid \frac{1}{2} < x \leq 4\right\}$		
19. $\{x \mid x \leq 2.1\}$		
20. $\left\{x \mid x > \frac{7}{3}\right\}$		
21. $\{x \mid -2 < x \leq 7\}$		
22. $\{x \mid x < -5\}$		

For Exercises 23–28, write each set in set-builder notation and in interval notation. **(See Example 3.)**

Set-Builder Notation	Graph	Interval Notation
23.	$\frac{3}{4}$	
24.	-0.3	
25.	-1 8	
26.	0	
27.	-14	
28.	0 9	

For Exercises 29–34, graph each set and write the set in set-builder notation. **(See Example 3.)**

Set-Builder Notation	Graph	Interval Notation
29.		$[18, \infty)$
30.		$[-10, -2]$
31.		$(-\infty, -0.6)$
32.		$\left(-\infty, \frac{5}{3}\right)$
33.		$[-3.5, 7.1)$
34.		$[-10, \infty)$

Concepts 3–4: Properties of Inequality

For Exercises 35–42, solve the equation in part (a). For part (b), solve the inequality and graph the solution set. Write the answer in set-builder notation and interval notation. **(See Examples 4–7.)**

35. **a.** $x + 3 = 6$
b. $x + 3 > 6$

36. **a.** $y - 6 = 12$
b. $y - 6 \geq 12$

37. **a.** $p - 4 = 9$
b. $p - 4 \leq 9$

38. **a.** $k + 8 = 10$
b. $k + 8 < 10$

39. **a.** $4c = -12$
b. $4c < -12$

40. **a.** $5d = -35$
b. $5d > -35$

41. **a.** $-10z = 15$
b. $-10z \leq 15$

42. **a.** $-2w = 14$
b. $-2w < 14$

Concept 5: Inequalities of the Form $a < x < b$

For Exercises 43–48, graph the solution and write the set in interval notation. **(See Example 8.)**

43. $-1 < y \leq 4$

44. $2.5 \leq t < 5.7$

45. $0 < x + 3 < 8$

46. $-2 \leq x - 4 \leq 3$

47. $8 \leq 4x \leq 24$

48. $-9 < 3x < 12$

116. A wholesaler sells T-shirts to a surf shop at $8 per shirt. However, for large orders, the price per shirt is discounted by a percentage off the original price. Let x represent the number of shirts ordered. The corresponding discount is given in the table.

a. If the surf shop orders 50 shirts, compute the total cost.

b. Which costs more: 148 shirts or 150 shirts? Explain your answer.

Number of Shirts Ordered	Discount
$x \le 24$	0%
$25 \le x \le 49$	2%
$50 \le x \le 99$	4%
$100 \le x \le 149$	6%
$x \ge 150$	8%

117. A cell phone provider offers one plan that charges $4.95 for the text messaging feature plus $0.09 for each individual incoming or outgoing text. Alternatively, the provider offers a second plan with a flat rate of $18.00 for unlimited text messaging. How many text messages would result in the unlimited option being the better deal?

118. Melissa runs a landscaping business. She has equipment and fuel expenses of $313 per month. If she charges $45 for each lawn, how many lawns must she service to make a profit of at least $600 a month?

119. Madison is planning a 5-night trip to Cancun, Mexico, with her friends. The airfare is $475, her share of the hotel room is $54 per night, and her budget for food and entertainment is $350. She has $700 in savings and has a job earning $10 per hour babysitting. What is the minimum number of hours of babysitting that Madison needs so that she will earn enough money to take the trip?

120. Luke and Landon are both tutors. Luke charges $50 for an initial assessment and $25 per hour for each hour he tutors. Landon charges $100 for an initial assessment and $20 per hour for tutoring. After how many hours of tutoring will Luke surpass Landon in earnings?

Group Activity

Computing Body Mass Index (BMI)

Materials: Calculator

Estimated Time: 10 minutes

Group Size: 2

Body mass index is a statistical measure of an individual's weight in relation to the person's height. It is computed by

$$\text{BMI} = \frac{703W}{h^2}$$ where W is a person's weight in *pounds*. h is the person's height in *inches*.

The NIH categorizes body mass indices as follows:

Body Mass Index (BMI)	Weight Status
$18.5 \le \text{BMI} \le 24.9$	considered ideal
$25.0 \le \text{BMI} \le 29.9$	considered overweight
$\text{BMI} \ge 30.0$	considered obese

1. Compute the body mass index for a person 5′4″ tall weighing 160 lb. Is this person's weight considered ideal?

2. At the time that basketball legend Michael Jordan played for the Chicago Bulls, he was 210 lb and stood 6′6″ tall. What was Michael Jordan's body mass index?

3. For a fixed height, body mass index is a function of a person's weight only. For example, for a person 72 in. tall (6 ft), solve the following inequality to determine the person's ideal weight range.

$$18.5 \le \frac{703W}{(72)^2} \le 24.9$$

4. At the time that professional bodybuilder, Jay Cutler, won the Mr. Olympia contest he was 260 lb and stood 5′10″ tall.

a. What was Jay Cutler's body mass index?

b. As a bodybuilder, Jay Cutler has an extraordinarily small percentage of body fat. Yet, according to the chart, would he be considered overweight or obese? Why do you think that the formula is not an accurate measurement of Mr. Cutler's weight status?

Chapter 2 Summary

Section 2.1 Addition, Subtraction, Multiplication, and Division Properties of Equality

Key Concepts

An equation is an algebraic statement that indicates two expressions are equal. A **solution to an equation** is a value of the variable that makes the equation a true statement. The set of all solutions to an equation is the solution set of the equation.

A **linear equation in one variable** can be written in the form $ax + b = c$, where $a \neq 0$.

Addition Property of Equality:

If $a = b$, then $a + c = b + c$

Subtraction Property of Equality:

If $a = b$, then $a - c = b - c$

Multiplication Property of Equality:

If $a = b$, then $ac = bc \quad (c \neq 0)$

Division Property of Equality:

If $a = b$, then $\frac{a}{c} = \frac{b}{c} \quad (c \neq 0)$

Examples

Example 1

$2x + 1 = 9$ is an equation with solution set $\{4\}$.

Check: $2(4) + 1 \stackrel{?}{=} 9$

$8 + 1 \stackrel{?}{=} 9$

$9 \stackrel{?}{=} 9$ ✔ True

Example 2

$$x - 5 = 12$$
$$x - 5 + 5 = 12 + 5$$
$$x = 17$$

The solution set is $\{17\}$.

Example 3

$$z + 1.44 = 2.33$$
$$z + 1.44 - 1.44 = 2.33 - 1.44$$
$$z = 0.89$$

The solution set is $\{0.89\}$.

Example 4

$$\frac{3}{4}x = 12$$
$$\frac{4}{3} \cdot \frac{3}{4}x = 12 \cdot \frac{4}{3}$$
$$x = 16$$

The solution set is $\{16\}$.

Example 5

$$16 = 8y$$
$$\frac{16}{8} = \frac{8y}{8}$$
$$2 = y$$

The solution set is $\{2\}$.

Section 2.4 Applications of Linear Equations: Introduction to Problem Solving

Key Concepts

Problem-Solving Steps for Word Problems:

1. Read the problem carefully.
2. Assign labels to unknown quantities.
3. Write a verbal model.
4. Write a mathematical equation.
5. Solve the equation.
6. Interpret the results and write the answer in words.

Examples

Example 1

The perimeter of a triangle is 54 m. The lengths of the sides are represented by three consecutive even integers. Find the lengths of the three sides.

1. Read the problem.

2. Let x represent one side, $x + 2$ represent the second side, and $x + 4$ represent the third side.

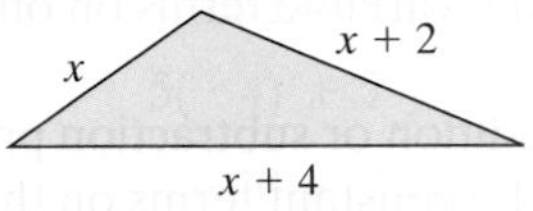

3. (First side) + (second side) + (third side) = perimeter

4. $x + (x + 2) + (x + 4) = 54$

5. $3x + 6 = 54$
   $3x = 48$
   $x = 16$

6. $x = 16$ represents the length of the shortest side. The lengths of the other sides are given by $x + 2 = 18$ and $x + 4 = 20$.

   The lengths of the three sides are 16 m, 18 m, and 20 m.

Section 2.5 Applications Involving Percents

Key Concepts

The following formula will help you solve basic percent problems.

$$\text{Amount} = (\text{percent})(\text{base})$$

One common use of percents is in computing **sales tax**.

Another use of percent is in computing **simple interest** using the formula:

$$\begin{pmatrix}\text{Simple}\\\text{interest}\end{pmatrix} = (\text{principal})\begin{pmatrix}\text{annual}\\\text{interest}\\\text{rate}\end{pmatrix}\begin{pmatrix}\text{time in}\\\text{years}\end{pmatrix}$$

or $I = Prt$.

Examples

Example 1

A flat screen television costs \$1260.00 after a 5% sales tax is included. What was the price before tax?

$$\begin{pmatrix}\text{Price}\\\text{before tax}\end{pmatrix} + (\text{tax}) = \begin{pmatrix}\text{total}\\\text{price}\end{pmatrix}$$

$$x + 0.05x = 1260$$

$$1.05x = 1260$$

$$x = 1200$$

The television cost \$1200 before tax.

Example 2

John Li invests \$5400 at 2.5% simple interest. How much interest does he earn after 5 years?

$I = Prt$

$I = (\$5400)(0.025)(5)$

$I = \$675$

Section 2.6 Formulas and Applications of Geometry

Key Concepts

A **literal equation** is an equation that has more than one variable. Often such an equation can be manipulated to solve for different variables.

Formulas from Section A.2 can be used in applications involving geometry.

Examples

Example 1

$P = 2a + b$, solve for a.

$P - b = 2a + b - b$

$P - b = 2a$

$\dfrac{P - b}{2} = \dfrac{2a}{2}$

$\dfrac{P - b}{2} = a$ or $a = \dfrac{P - b}{2}$

Example 2

Find the length of a side of a square whose perimeter is 28 ft.

Use the formula $P = 4s$. Substitute 28 for P and solve:

$P = 4s$

$28 = 4s$

$7 = s$

The length of a side of the square is 7 ft.

Section 2.7 Mixture Applications and Uniform Motion

Examples

Example 1 illustrates a mixture problem.

Example 1

How much 80% disinfectant solution should be mixed with 8 L of a 30% disinfectant solution to make a 40% solution?

	80% Solution	30% Solution	40% Solution
Amount of Solution	x	8	$x + 8$
Amount of Pure Disinfectant	$0.80x$	$0.30(8)$	$0.40(x + 8)$

$0.80x + 0.30(8) = 0.40(x + 8)$

$0.80x + 2.4 = 0.40x + 3.2$

$0.40x + 2.4 = 3.2$ Subtract $0.40x$.

$0.40x = 0.80$ Subtract 2.4.

$x = 2$ Divide by 0.40.

2 L of 80% solution is needed.

Examples

Example 2 illustrates a uniform motion problem.

Example 2

Jack and Diane participate in a bicycle race. Jack rides the first half of the race in 1.5 hr. Diane rides the second half at a rate 5 mph slower than Jack and completes her portion in 2 hr. How fast does each person ride?

	Distance	Rate	Time
Jack	$1.5x$	x	1.5
Diane	$2(x - 5)$	$x - 5$	2

$\begin{pmatrix}\text{Distance}\\ \text{Jack rides}\end{pmatrix} = \begin{pmatrix}\text{distance}\\ \text{Diane rides}\end{pmatrix}$

$1.5x = 2(x - 5)$

$1.5x = 2x - 10$

$-0.5x = -10$ Subtract $2x$.

$x = 20$ Divide by -0.5.

Jack's speed is x. Jack rides 20 mph. Diane's speed is $x - 5$, which is 15 mph.

Section 2.8 Linear Inequalities

Key Concepts

A **linear inequality in one variable**, x, is any relationship in the form: $ax + b < c$, $ax + b > c$, $ax + b \leq c$, or $ax + b \geq c$, where $a \neq 0$.

The solution set to an inequality can be expressed as a graph or in **set-builder notation** or in **interval notation**.

When graphing an inequality or when writing interval notation, a parenthesis, (or), is used to denote that an endpoint is *not included* in a solution set. A square bracket, [or], is used to show that an endpoint *is included* in a solution set. A parenthesis (or) is always used with $-\infty$ and ∞, respectively.

The inequality $a < x < b$ is used to show that x is greater than a and less than b. That is, x is *between* a and b.

Multiplying or dividing an inequality by a negative quantity requires the direction of the inequality sign to be reversed.

Example

Example 1

$-2x + 6 \geq 14$

$-2x + 6 - 6 \geq 14 - 6$ Subtract 6.

$-2x \geq 8$ Simplify.

$\dfrac{-2x}{-2} \leq \dfrac{8}{-2}$ Divide by -2. Reverse the inequality sign.

$x \leq -4$

Graph: 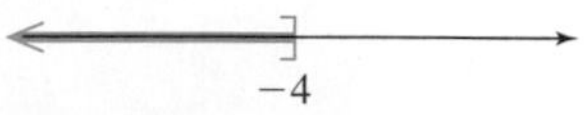

Set-builder notation: $\{x \mid x \leq -4\}$

Interval notation: $(-\infty, -4]$

Chapter 2 Review Exercises

Section 2.1

1. Label the following as either an expression or an equation:

   a. $3x + y = 10$ b. $9x + 10y - 2xy$

   c. $4(x + 3) = 12$ d. $-5x = 7$

2. Explain how to determine whether an equation is linear in one variable.

3. Determine if the given equation is a linear equation in one variable. Answer yes or no.

   a. $4x^2 + 8 = -10$ b. $x + 18 = 72$

   c. $-3 + 2y^2 = 0$ d. $-4p - 5 = 6p$

4. For the equation, $4y + 9 = -3$, determine if the given numbers are solutions.

   a. $y = 3$ b. $y = -3$

For Exercises 5–12, solve each equation using the addition property, subtraction property, multiplication property, or division property of equality.

5. $a + 6 = -2$

6. $6 = z - 9$

7. $-\frac{3}{4} + k = \frac{9}{2}$

8. $0.1r = 7$

9. $-5x = 21$

10. $\frac{t}{3} = -20$

11. $-\frac{2}{5}k = \frac{4}{7}$

12. $-m = -27$

13. The quotient of a number and negative six is equal to negative ten. Find the number.

14. The difference of a number and $-\frac{1}{8}$ is $\frac{5}{12}$. Find the number.

15. Four subtracted from a number is negative twelve. Find the number.

16. The product of a number and $\frac{1}{4}$ is $-\frac{1}{2}$. Find the number.

Section 2.2

For Exercises 17–28, solve each equation.

17. $4d + 2 = 6$

18. $5c - 6 = -9$

19. $-7c = -3c - 8$

20. $-28 = 5w + 2$

21. $\frac{b}{3} + 1 = 0$

22. $\frac{2}{3}h - 5 = 7$

23. $-3p + 7 = 5p + 1$

24. $4t - 6 = 12t + 18$

25. $4a - 9 = 3(a - 3)$

26. $3(2c + 5) = -2(c - 8)$

27. $7b + 3(b - 1) + 3 = 2(b + 8)$

28. $2 + (18 - x) + 2(x - 1) = 4(x + 2) - 8$

29. Explain the difference between an equation that is a contradiction and an equation that is an identity.

For Exercises 30–35, label each equation as a conditional equation, a contradiction, or an identity.

30. $x + 3 = 3 + x$

31. $3x - 19 = 2x + 1$

32. $5x + 6 = 5x - 28$

33. $2x - 8 = 2(x - 4)$

34. $-8x - 9 = -8(x - 9)$

35. $4x - 4 = 3x - 2$

Section 2.3

For Exercises 36–53, solve each equation.

36. $\frac{x}{8} - \frac{1}{4} = \frac{1}{2}$

37. $\frac{y}{15} - \frac{2}{3} = \frac{4}{5}$

38. $\frac{x + 5}{2} - \frac{2x + 10}{9} = 5$

39. $\frac{x - 6}{3} - \frac{2x + 8}{2} = 12$

40. $\frac{1}{10}p - 3 = \frac{2}{5}p$

41. $\frac{1}{4}y - \frac{3}{4} = \frac{1}{2}y + 1$

42. $-\frac{1}{4}(2 - 3t) = \frac{3}{4}$

43. $\frac{2}{7}(w + 4) = \frac{1}{2}$

44. $17.3 - 2.7q = 10.55$

45. $4.9z + 4.6 = 3.2z - 2.2$

46. $5.74a + 9.28 = 2.24a - 5.42$

47. $62.84t - 123.66 = 4(2.36 + 2.4t)$

48. $0.05x + 0.10(24 - x) = 0.75(24)$

49. $0.20(x + 4) + 0.65x = 0.20(854)$

50. $100 - (t - 6) = -(t - 1)$

51. $3 - (x + 4) + 5 = 3x + 10 - 4x$

52. $5t - (2t + 14) = 3t - 14$

53. $9 - 6(2z + 1) = -3(4z - 1)$

Section 2.4

54. Twelve added to the sum of a number and two is forty-four. Find the number.

55. Twenty added to the sum of a number and six is thirty-seven. Find the number.

56. Three times a number is the same as the difference of twice the number and seven. Find the number.

57. Eight less than five times a number is forty-eight less than the number. Find the number.

58. Three times the largest of three consecutive even integers is 76 more than the sum of the other two integers. Find the integers.

59. Ten times the smallest of three consecutive integers is 213 more than the sum of the other two integers. Find the integers.

60. The perimeter of a triangle is 78 in. The lengths of the sides are represented by three consecutive integers. Find the lengths of the sides of the triangle.

61. The perimeter of a pentagon (a five-sided polygon) is 190 cm. The five sides are represented by consecutive integers. Find the lengths of the sides.

62. Minimum salaries of major league baseball players soared after a new ruling in 1975. In 2010, the minimum salary for a major league player was $400,000. This is 25 times the minimum salary in 1975. Find the minimum salary in 1975.

63. The state of Indiana has approximately 2.1 million more people than Kentucky. Together their population totals 10.3 million. Approximately how many people are in each state?

Section 2.5

For Exercises 64–69, solve each problem involving percents.

64. What is 35% of 68?

65. What is 4% of 720?

66. 53.5 is what percent of 428?

67. 68.4 is what percent of 72?

68. 24 is 15% of what number?

69. 8.75 is 0.5% of what number?

70. A couple spent a total of $50.40 for dinner. This included a 20% tip and 6% sales tax on the price of the meal. What was the price of the dinner before tax and tip?

71. Anna Tsao invested $3000 in an account paying 8% simple interest.

a. How much interest will she earn in $3\frac{1}{2}$ years?

b. What will her balance be at that time?

72. Eduardo invested money in an account earning 4% simple interest. At the end of 5 years, he had a total of $14,400. How much money did he originally invest?

73. A novel is discounted 30%. The sale price is $20.65. What was the original price?

Section 2.6

For Exercises 74–81, solve for the indicated variable.

74. $C = K - 273$ for K

75. $K = C + 273$ for C

76. $P = 4s$ for s

77. $P = 3s$ for s

78. $y = mx + b$ for x

79. $a + bx = c$ for x

80. $2x + 5y = -2$ for y

81. $4(a + b) = Q$ for b

For Exercises 82–88, use the appropriate geometry formula to solve the problem.

82. Find the height of a parallelogram whose area is 42 m^2 and whose base is 6 m.

83. The volume of a cone is given by the formula $V = \frac{1}{3}\pi r^2 h$.

a. Solve the formula for h.

b. Find the height of a right circular cone whose volume is 47.8 $in.^3$ and whose radius is 3 in. Round to the nearest tenth of an inch.

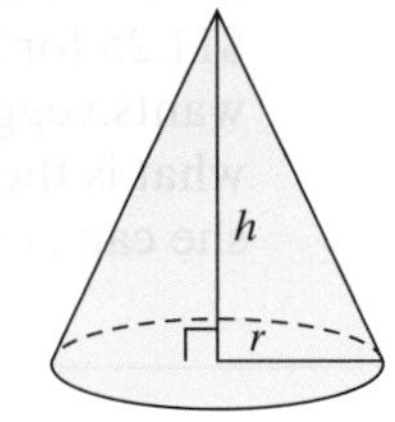

84. The smallest angle of a triangle is 2° more than $\frac{1}{4}$ of the largest angle. The middle angle is 2° less than the largest angle. Find the measure of each angle.

85. A carpenter uses a special saw to cut an angle on a piece of framing. If the angles are complementary and one angle is 10° more than the other, find the measure of each angle.

86. A rectangular window has width 1 ft less than its length. The perimeter is 18 ft. Find the length and the width of the window.

87. Find the measure of the vertical angles by first solving for x.

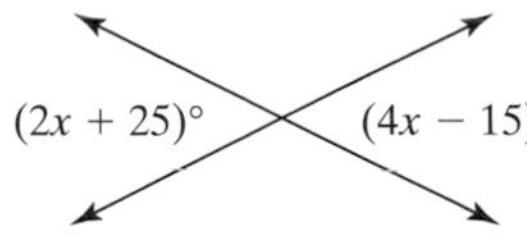

88. Find the measure of angle y.

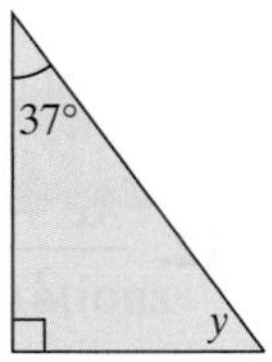

Section 2.7

89. In stormy conditions, a delivery truck can travel a route in 14 hr. In good weather, the same trip can be made in 10.5 hr because the truck travels 15 km/hr faster. Find the speed of the truck in stormy weather and the speed in good weather.

90. Winston and Gus ride their bicycles in a relay. Each person rides the same distance. Winston rides 3 mph faster than Gus and finishes the course in 2.5 hr. Gus finishes in 3 hr. How fast does each person ride?

91. Two cars leave a rest stop on Interstate I-10 at the same time. One heads east and the other heads west. One car travels 55 mph and the other 62 mph. How long will it take for them to be 327.6 mi apart?

92. Two hikers begin at the same time at opposite ends of a 9-mi trail and walk toward each other. One hiker walks 2.5 mph and the other walks 1.5 mph. How long will it be before they meet?

93. How much ground beef with 24% fat should be mixed with 8 lb of ground sirloin that is 6% fat to make a mixture that is 9.6% fat?

94. A soldering compound with 40% lead (the rest is tin) must be combined with 80 lb of solder that is 75% lead to make a compound that is 68% lead. How much solder with 40% lead should be used?

Section 2.8

For Exercises 95–97, graph each inequality and write the set in interval notation.

95. $\{x \mid x > -2\}$

96. $\left\{x \mid x \leq \frac{1}{2}\right\}$

97. $\{x \mid -1 < x \leq 4\}$

98. A landscaper buys potted geraniums from a nursery at a price of $5 per plant. However, for large orders, the price per plant is discounted by a percentage off the original price. Let x represent the number of potted plants ordered. The corresponding discount is given in the following table.

Number of Plants	Discount
$x \leq 99$	0%
$100 \leq x \leq 199$	2%
$200 \leq x \leq 299$	4%
$x \geq 300$	6%

a. Find the cost to purchase 130 plants.

b. Which costs more, 300 plants or 295 plants? Explain your answer.

12. $-5(p-3)+2p=3(5-p)$

13. $\dfrac{x+3}{5}-\dfrac{x+2}{2}=2$

14. $\dfrac{2}{9}x-\dfrac{1}{3}=x+\dfrac{1}{9}$

15. $-0.6w=48$

16. The sum of two consecutive odd integers is 156. Find the integers.

17. The cost of an iPod speaker dock (including sales tax) is $374.50. If the tax rate is 7%, find the cost of the speaker dock before tax.

18. The area of a triangle is 41 cm^2. Find the height of the triangle if the base is 12 cm.

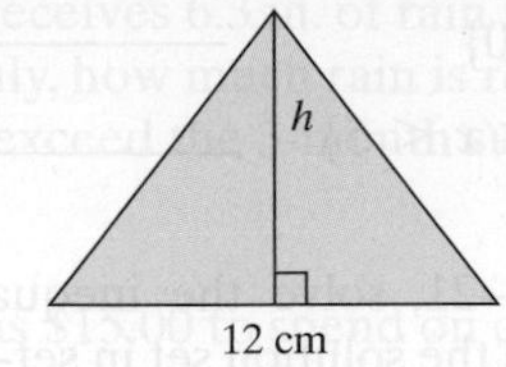

For Exercises 19–20, solve the inequality. Graph the solution set on a number line and express the solution in set-builder notation and interval notation.

19. $-3x-3(x+1)<9$

20. $-6\le 2x-4\le 14$

Graphing Linear Equations in Two Variables

3

CHAPTER OUTLINE

3.1 Rectangular Coordinate System 194

3.2 Linear Equations in Two Variables 203

3.3 Slope of a Line and Rate of Change 218

3.4 Slope-Intercept Form of a Linear Equation 232

Problem Recognition Exercises: Linear Equations in Two Variables 242

3.5 Point-Slope Formula 243

3.6 Applications of Linear Equations and Modeling 251

Group Activity: Modeling a Linear Equation 259

Chapter 3

In this chapter, we will need the skill of solving an equation for a particular variable.

Are You Prepared?

This puzzle will practice that skill. For each equation, solve for the variable *y*. Then match the equation with an answer below. Write the word associated with the answer in the blanks below to form a sentence.

1. $3x + 2y = 6$ **2.** $-4x - y = 7$ **3.** $x - 2y = -3$ **4.** $2x + y = 9$

5. $2x - 4y = 10$ **6.** $2x + 3y = 9$ **7.** $6x + 3y = -5$ **8.** $x - 3y = 1$

$y = \frac{1}{2}x + \frac{3}{2}$	IS	$y = -\frac{3}{2}x + 3$	THE
$y = -2x + 9$	WRITTEN	$y = 4x - 7$	POINT
$y = -2x - \frac{5}{3}$	INTERCEPT	$y = -\frac{2}{3}x + 3$	SLOPE
$y = -\frac{2}{3}x - 3$	TO	$y = -4x - 7$	EQUATION
$y = \frac{1}{2}x - \frac{5}{2}$	IN	$y = \frac{1}{3}x - \frac{1}{3}$	FORM

_____ (1) _____ (2) $y = mx + b$ _____ (3) _____ (4)

_____ (5) _____ (6) _____ (7) _____ (8)

Section 3.1 Rectangular Coordinate System

Concepts

1. Interpreting Graphs
2. Plotting Points in a Rectangular Coordinate System
3. Applications of Plotting and Identifying Points

1. Interpreting Graphs

Mathematics is a powerful tool used by scientists and has directly contributed to the highly technical world in which we live. Applications of mathematics have led to advances in the sciences, business, computer technology, and medicine.

One fundamental application of mathematics is the graphical representation of numerical information (or data). For example, Table 3-1 represents the number of clients admitted to a drug and alcohol rehabilitation program over a 12-month period.

Table 3-1

	Month	Number of Clients
Jan.	1	55
Feb.	2	62
March	3	64
April	4	60
May	5	70
June	6	73
July	7	77
Aug.	8	80
Sept.	9	80
Oct.	10	74
Nov.	11	85
Dec.	12	90

In table form, the information is difficult to picture and interpret. It appears that on a monthly basis, the number of clients fluctuates. However, when the data are represented in a graph, an upward trend is clear (Figure 3-1).

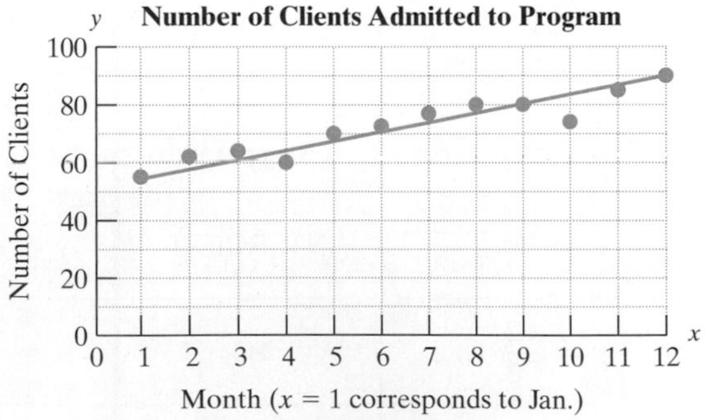

Figure 3-1

From the increase in clients shown in this graph, management for the rehabilitation center might make plans for the future. If the trend continues, management might consider expanding its facilities and increasing its staff to accommodate the expected increase in clients.

Example 1 Interpreting a Graph

Refer to Figure 3-1 and Table 3-1.

a. For which month was the number of clients the greatest?

b. How many clients were served in the first month (January)?

c. Which month corresponds to 60 clients served?

d. Between which two consecutive months did the number of clients decrease?

e. Between which two consecutive months did the number of clients remain the same?

Solution:

a. Month 12 (December) corresponds to the highest point on the graph. This represents the greatest number of clients, 90.

b. In month 1 (January), there were 55 clients served.

c. Month 4 (April).

d. The number of clients decreased between months 3 and 4 and between months 9 and 10.

e. The number of clients remained the same between months 8 and 9.

Skill Practice Refer to Figure 3-1 and Table 3-1.

1. How many clients were served in October?
2. Which month corresponds to 70 clients?
3. What is the difference between the number of clients in month 12 and month 1?
4. For which month was the number of clients the least?

2. Plotting Points in a Rectangular Coordinate System

The data in Table 3-1 represent a relationship between two variables—the month number and the number of clients. The graph in Figure 3-1 enables us to visualize this relationship. In picturing the relationship between two quantities, we often use a graph with two number lines drawn at right angles to each other (Figure 3-2). This forms a **rectangular coordinate system**. The horizontal line is called the ***x*-axis**, and the vertical line is called the ***y*-axis**. The point where the lines intersect is called the **origin**. On the x-axis, the numbers to the right of the origin are positive and the numbers to the left are negative. On the y-axis, the numbers above the origin are positive and the numbers below are negative. The x- and y-axes divide the graphing area into four regions called **quadrants**.

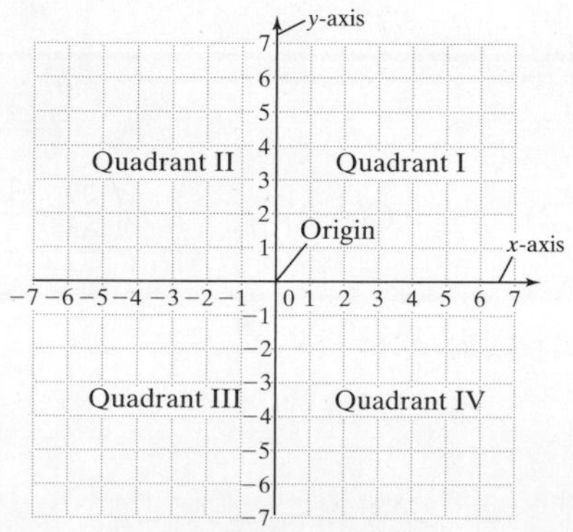

Figure 3-2

Animation

Answers

1. 74 clients
2. Month 5 (May)
3. 35 clients
4. Month 1 (January)

Points graphed in a rectangular coordinate system are defined by two numbers as an **ordered pair**, (x, y). The first number (called the ***x*-coordinate**, or the abscissa) is the horizontal position from the origin. The second number (called the ***y*-coordinate**, or the ordinate) is the vertical position from the origin. Example 2 shows how points are plotted in a rectangular coordinate system.

Example 2 Plotting Points in a Rectangular Coordinate System

Plot the points.

a. $(4, 5)$ **b.** $(-4, -5)$ **c.** $(-1, 3)$ **d.** $(3, -1)$

e. $\left(\frac{1}{2}, -\frac{7}{3}\right)$ **f.** $(-2, 0)$ **g.** $(0, 0)$ **h.** $(\pi, 1.1)$

Solution:

See Figure 3-3.

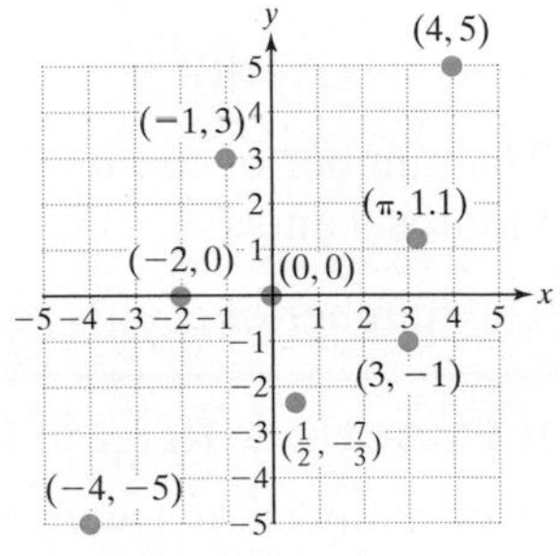

Figure 3-3

a. The ordered pair $(4, 5)$ indicates that $x = 4$ and $y = 5$. Beginning at the origin, move 4 units in the positive x-direction (4 units to the right), and from there move 5 units in the positive y-direction (5 units up). Then plot the point. The point is in Quadrant I.

b. The ordered pair $(-4, -5)$ indicates that $x = -4$ and $y = -5$. Move 4 units in the negative x-direction (4 units to the left), and from there move 5 units in the negative y-direction (5 units down). Then plot the point. The point is in Quadrant III.

c. The ordered pair $(-1, 3)$ indicates that $x = -1$ and $y = 3$. Move 1 unit to the left and 3 units up. The point is in Quadrant II.

d. The ordered pair $(3, -1)$ indicates that $x = 3$ and $y = -1$. Move 3 units to the right and 1 unit down. The point is in Quadrant IV.

e. The improper fraction $-\frac{7}{3}$ can be written as the mixed number $-2\frac{1}{3}$. Therefore, to plot the point $(\frac{1}{2}, -\frac{7}{3})$ move to the right $\frac{1}{2}$ unit, and down $2\frac{1}{3}$ units. The point is in Quadrant IV.

f. The point $(-2, 0)$ indicates $y = 0$. Therefore, the point is on the x-axis.

g. The point $(0, 0)$ is at the origin.

h. The irrational number, π, can be approximated as 3.14. Thus, the point $(\pi, 1.1)$ is located approximately 3.14 units to the right and 1.1 units up. The point is in Quadrant I.

TIP: Notice that changing the order of the x- and y-coordinates changes the location of the point. For example, the point $(-1, 3)$ is in Quadrant II, whereas $(3, -1)$ is in Quadrant IV (Figure 3-3). This is why points are represented by *ordered* pairs. The order of the coordinates is important.

Avoiding Mistakes

Points that lie on either of the axes do not lie in any quadrant.

Skill Practice

5. Plot the points.
$A(3, 4)$ $B(-2, 2)$ $C(4, 0)$ $D\left(\frac{5}{2}, -\frac{1}{2}\right)$ $E(-5, -2)$

Answer

5.

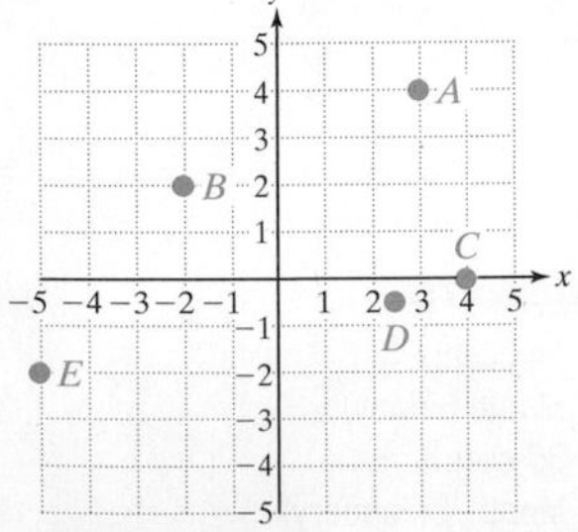

3. Applications of Plotting and Identifying Points

The effective use of graphs for mathematical models requires skill in identifying points and interpreting graphs.

Example 3 Determining Points from a Graph

A map of a national park is drawn so that the origin is placed at the ranger station (Figure 3-4). Four fire observation towers are located at points A, B, C, and D. Estimate the coordinates of the fire towers relative to the ranger station (all distances are in miles).

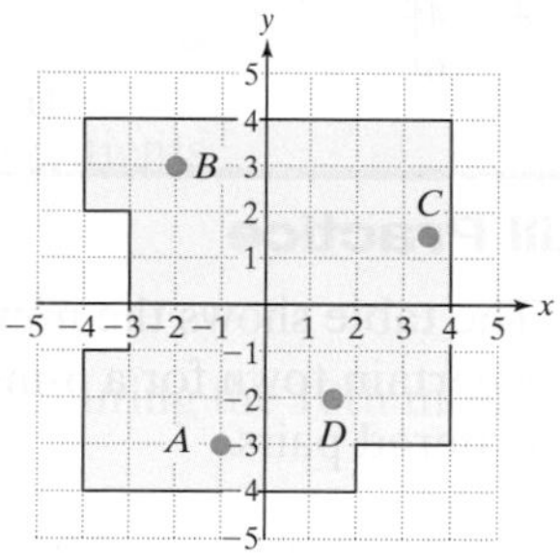

Figure 3-4

Solution:

Point A: $(-1, -3)$

Point B: $(-2, 3)$

Point C: $(3\frac{1}{2}, 1\frac{1}{2})$ or $(\frac{7}{2}, \frac{3}{2})$ or $(3.5, 1.5)$

Point D: $(1\frac{1}{2}, -2)$ or $(\frac{3}{2}, -2)$ or $(1.5, -2)$

Skill Practice

6. Towers are located at points A, B, C, and D. Estimate the coordinates of the towers.

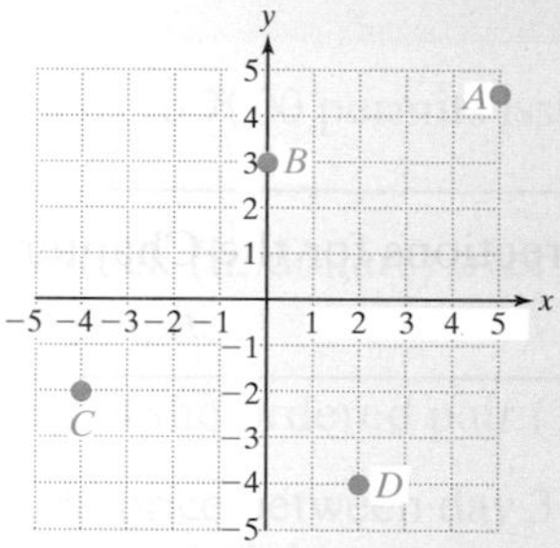

Example 4 Plotting Points in an Application

The daily low temperatures (in degrees Fahrenheit) for one week in January for Sudbury, Ontario, Canada, are given in Table 3-2.

a. Write an ordered pair for each row in the table using the day number as the x-coordinate and the temperature as the y-coordinate.

b. Plot the ordered pairs from part (a) on a rectangular coordinate system.

Table 3-2

Day Number, x	Temperature (°F), y
1	−3
2	−5
3	1
4	6
5	5
6	0
7	−4

Solution:

a. Each ordered pair represents the day number and the corresponding low temperature for that day.

$(1, -3)$ $(2, -5)$ $(3, 1)$ $(4, 6)$ $(5, 5)$ $(6, 0)$ $(7, -4)$

Answer

6. $A(5, 4\frac{1}{2})$
$B(0, 3)$
$C(-4, -2)$
$D(2, -4)$

Concept 2: Plotting Points in a Rectangular Coordinate System

7. Plot the points on a rectangular coordinate system. **(See Example 2.)**

a. $(2, 6)$ **b.** $(6, 2)$ **c.** $(-7, 3)$

d. $(-7, -3)$ **e.** $(0, -3)$ **f.** $(-3, 0)$

g. $(6, -4)$ **h.** $(0, 5)$

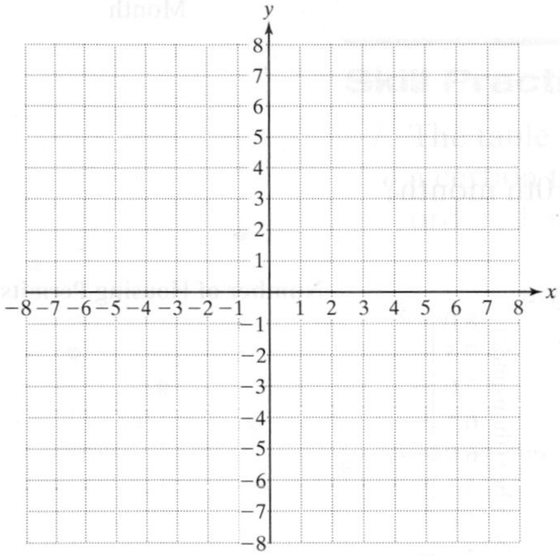

8. Plot the points on a rectangular coordinate system.

a. $(4, 5)$ **b.** $(-4, 5)$ **c.** $(-6, 0)$

d. $(6, 0)$ **e.** $(4, -5)$ **f.** $(-4, -5)$

g. $(0, -2)$ **h.** $(0, 0)$

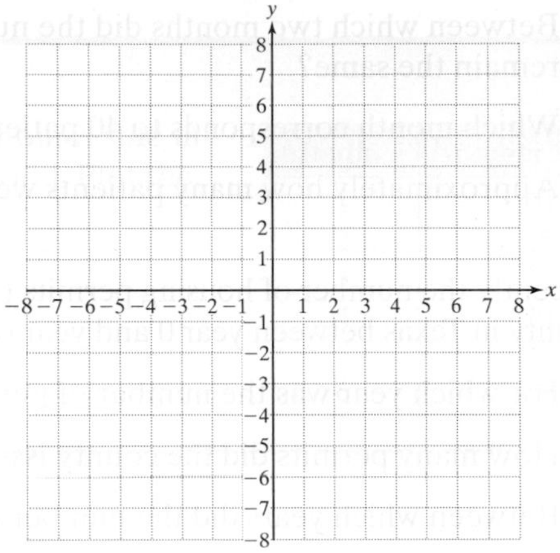

9. Plot the points on a rectangular coordinate system.

a. $(-1, 5)$ **b.** $(0, 4)$ **c.** $\left(-2, -\frac{3}{2}\right)$

d. $(2, -1.75)$ **e.** $(4, 2)$ **f.** $(-6, 0)$

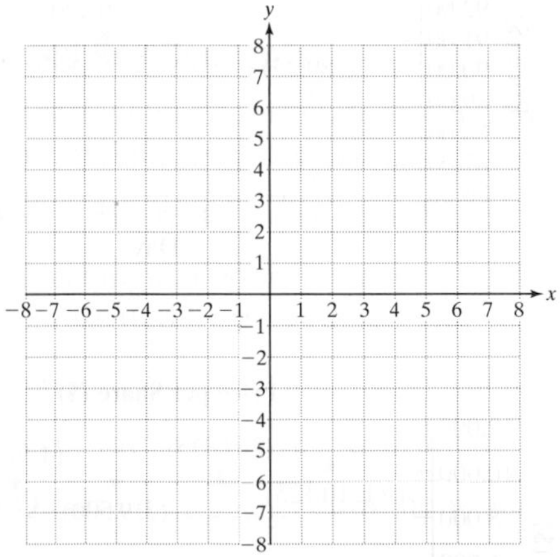

10. Plot the points on a rectangular coordinate system.

a. $(7, 0)$ **b.** $(-3, -2)$ **c.** $(6\frac{3}{5}, 1)$

d. $(0, 1.5)$ **e.** $\left(\frac{7}{2}, -4\right)$ **f.** $\left(-\frac{7}{2}, 4\right)$

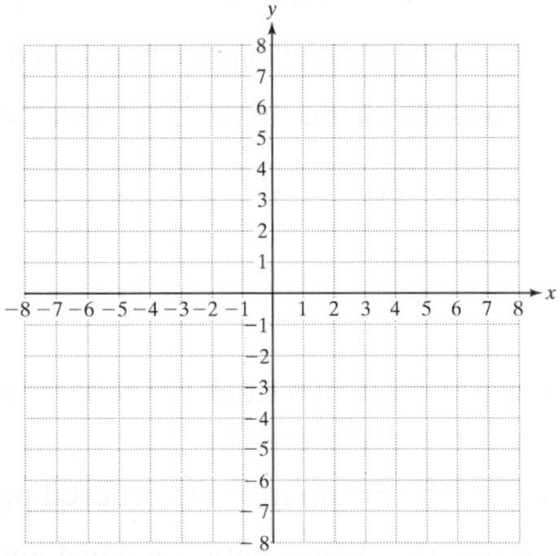

For Exercises 11–18, identify the quadrant in which the given point is located.

11. $(13, -2)$ **12.** $(25, 16)$ **13.** $(-8, 14)$ **14.** $(-82, -71)$

15. $(-5, -19)$ **16.** $(-31, 6)$ **17.** $\left(\frac{5}{2}, \frac{7}{4}\right)$ **18.** $(9, -40)$

19. Explain why the point $(0, -5)$ is *not* located in Quadrant IV.

20. Explain why the point $(-1, 0)$ is *not* located in Quadrant II.

21. Where is the point $(\frac{7}{8}, 0)$ located?

22. Where is the point $(0, \frac{6}{5})$ located?

Concept 3: Applications of Plotting and Identifying Points

For Exercises 23–24, refer to the graph. **(See Example 3.)**

23. Estimate the coordinates of the points A, B, C, D, E, and F.

24. Estimate the coordinates of the points G, H, I, J, K, and L.

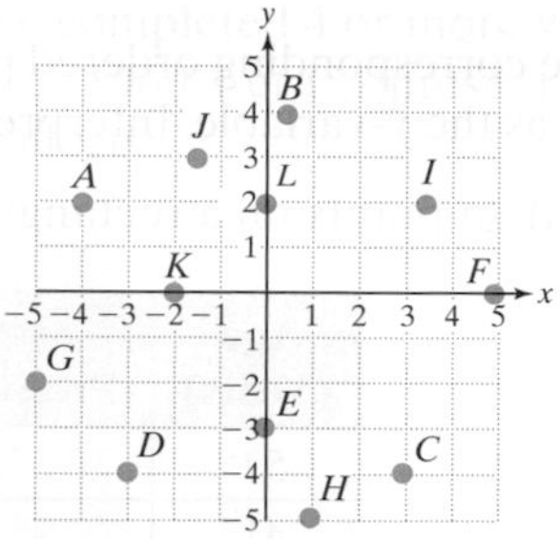

25. A map of a park is laid out with the visitor center located at the origin. Five visitors are in the park located at points A, B, C, D, and E. All distances are in meters.

a. Estimate the coordinates of each visitor. **(See Example 3.)**

b. How far apart are visitors C and D?

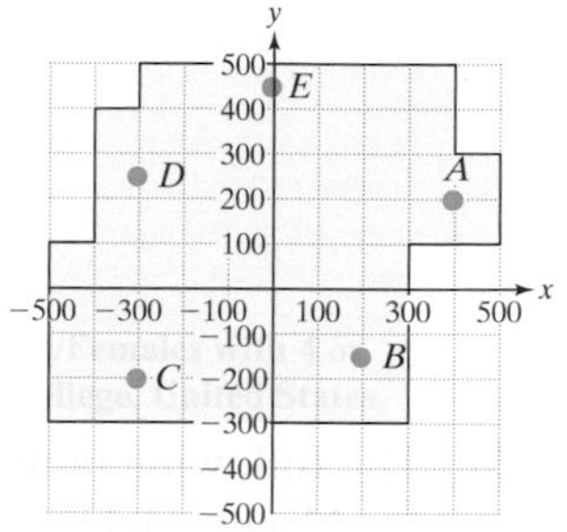

26. A townhouse has a sprinkler system in the backyard. With the water source at the origin, the sprinkler heads are located at points A, B, C, D, and E. All distances are in feet.

a. Estimate the coordinates of each sprinkler head.

b. How far is the distance from sprinkler head B to C?

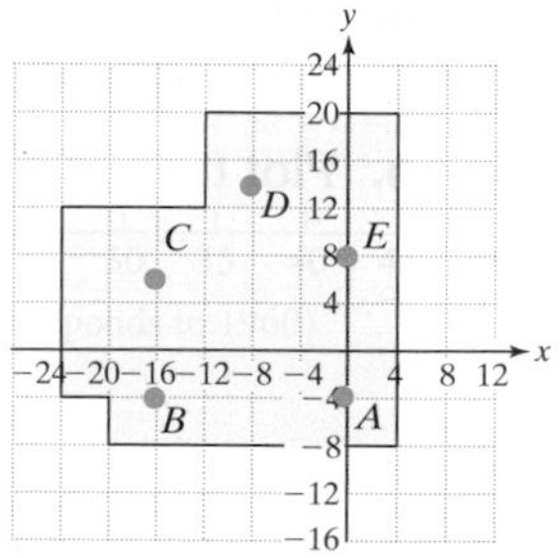

27. A movie theater has kept records of popcorn sales versus movie attendance.

a. Use the table to write the corresponding ordered pairs using the movie attendance as the x-variable and sales of popcorn as the y-variable. Interpret the meaning of the first ordered pair. **(See Example 4.)**

b. Plot the data points on a rectangular coordinate system.

Movie Attendance (Number of People)	Sales of Popcorn ($)
250	225
175	193
315	330
220	209
450	570
400	480
190	185

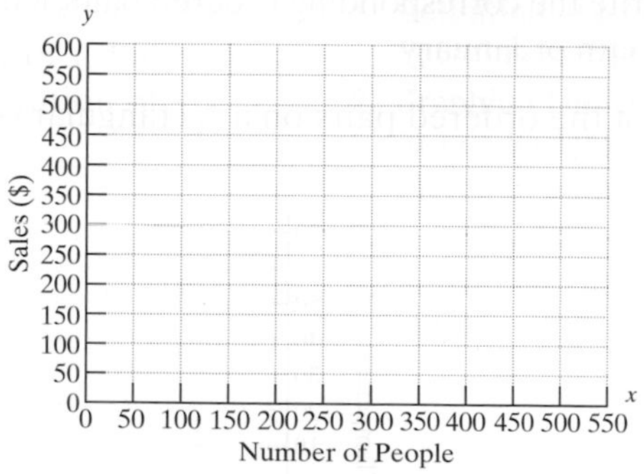

The equation $x + y = 4$ is a linear equation in two variables. A solution to such an equation is an ordered pair (x, y) that makes the equation a true statement. Several solutions to the equation $x + y = 4$ are listed here:

Solution:	**Check:**
(x, y)	$x + y = 4$
$(2, 2)$	$(2) + (2) = 4$ ✔
$(1, 3)$	$(1) + (3) = 4$ ✔
$(4, 0)$	$(4) + (0) = 4$ ✔
$(-1, 5)$	$(-1) + (5) = 4$ ✔

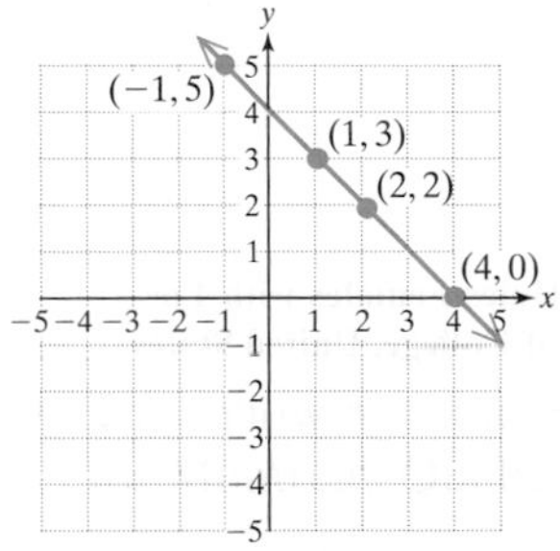

Figure 3-5

By graphing these ordered pairs, we see that the solution points line up (Figure 3-5).

Notice that there are infinitely many solutions to the equation $x + y = 4$ so they cannot all be listed. Therefore, to visualize all solutions to the equation $x + y = 4$, we draw the line through the points in the graph. Every point on the line represents an ordered pair solution to the equation $x + y = 4$, and the line represents thc set of *all* solutions to the equation.

Example 1 Determining Solutions to a Linear Equation

For the linear equation, $6x - 5y = 12$, determine whether the given ordered pair is a solution.

a. $(2, 0)$ **b.** $(3, 1)$ **c.** $\left(1, -\frac{6}{5}\right)$

Solution:

a. $6x - 5y = 12$

$6(2) - 5(0) \stackrel{?}{=} 12$ Substitute $x = 2$ and $y = 0$.

$12 - 0 \stackrel{?}{=} 12$ ✔ True The ordered pair $(2, 0)$ is a solution.

b. $6x - 5y = 12$

$6(3) - 5(1) \stackrel{?}{=} 12$ Substitute $x = 3$ and $y = 1$.

$18 - 5 \neq 12$ The ordered pair $(3, 1)$ is *not* a solution.

c. $6x - 5y = 12$

$6(1) - 5\left(-\frac{6}{5}\right) \stackrel{?}{=} 12$ Substitute $x = 1$ and $y = -\frac{6}{5}$.

$6 + 6 \stackrel{?}{=} 12$ ✔ True The ordered pair $\left(1, -\frac{6}{5}\right)$ is a solution.

Skill Practice Given the equation $3x - 2y = -12$, determine whether the given ordered pair is a solution.

1. $(4, 0)$ **2.** $(-2, 3)$ **3.** $\left(1, \frac{15}{2}\right)$

2. Graphing Linear Equations in Two Variables by Plotting Points

In this section, we will graph linear equations in two variables.

Answers

1. No **2.** Yes **3.** Yes

The Graph of an Equation in Two Variables

The graph of an equation in two variables is the graph of all ordered pair solutions to the equation.

The word *linear* means "relating to or resembling a line." It is not surprising then that the solution set for any linear equation in two variables forms a line in a rectangular coordinate system. Because two points determine a line, to graph a linear equation it is sufficient to find two solution points and draw the line between them. We will find three solution points and use the third point as a check point. This process is demonstrated in Example 2.

Example 2 Graphing a Linear Equation

Graph the equation $x - 2y = 8$.

Solution:

We will find three ordered pairs that are solutions to $x - 2y = 8$. To find the ordered pairs, choose an arbitrary value of x or of y. Three choices are recorded in the table. To complete the table, individually substitute each choice into the equation and solve for the missing variable. The substituted value and the solution to the equation form an ordered pair.

x	y	
2		→ (2,)
	−1	→ (, −1)
0		→ (0,)

TIP: Usually we try to choose arbitrary values that will be convenient to graph.

From the first row, substitute $x = 2$:

$$x - 2y = 8$$
$$(2) - 2y = 8$$
$$-2y = 6$$
$$y = -3$$

From the second row, substitute $y = -1$:

$$x - 2y = 8$$
$$x - 2(-1) = 8$$
$$x + 2 = 8$$
$$x = 6$$

From the third row, substitute $x = 0$:

$$x - 2y = 8$$
$$(0) - 2y = 8$$
$$-2y = 8$$
$$y = -4$$

The completed table is shown with the corresponding ordered pairs.

x	y	
2	−3	→ (2, −3)
6	−1	→ (6, −1)
0	−4	→ (0, −4)

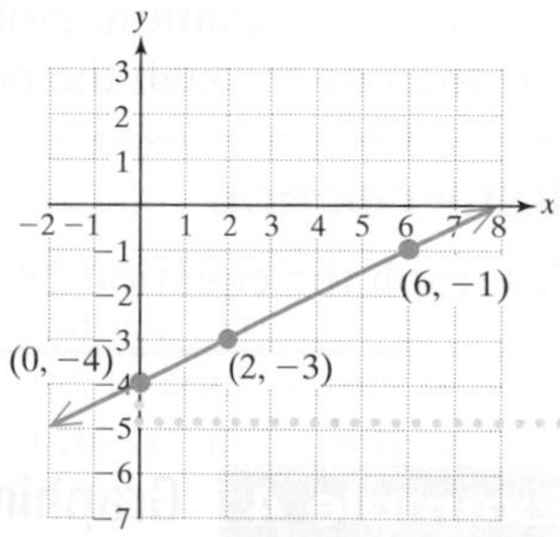

Figure 3-6

To graph the equation, plot the three solutions and draw the line through the points (Figure 3-6).

Avoiding Mistakes

Only two points are needed to graph a line. However, in Example 2, we found a third ordered pair, (0, −4). Notice that this point "lines up" with the other two points. If the three points do not line up, then we know that a mistake was made in solving for at least one of the ordered pairs.

Skill Practice

4. Graph the equation $2x + y = 6$.

Answer

4.

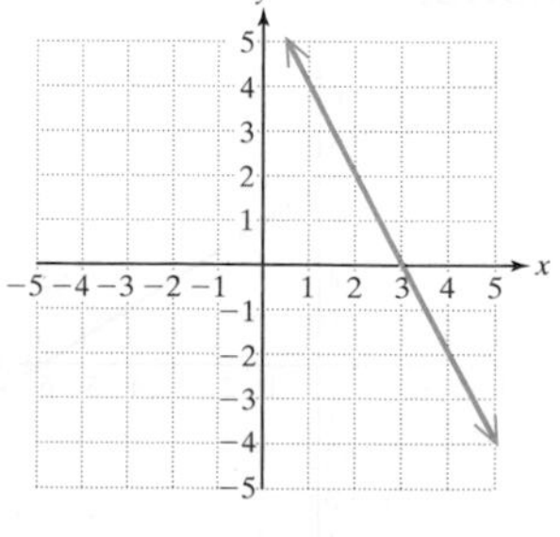

Example 5 Finding the *x*- and *y*-Intercepts of a Line

Given the equation $-3x + 2y = 8$,

a. Find the *x*-intercept.

b. Find the *y*-intercept.

c. Graph the equation.

Solution:

a. To find the *x*-intercept, substitute $y = 0$.

$$-3x + 2y = 8$$
$$-3x + 2(0) = 8$$
$$-3x = 8$$
$$\frac{-3x}{-3} = \frac{8}{-3}$$
$$x = -\frac{8}{3}$$

The *x*-intercept is $(-\frac{8}{3}, 0)$.

b. To find the *y*-intercept, substitute $x = 0$.

$$-3x + 2y = 8$$
$$-3(0) + 2y = 8$$
$$2y = 8$$
$$y = 4$$

The *y*-intercept is $(0, 4)$.

Avoiding Mistakes

Be sure to write the *x*- and *y*-intercepts as two separate ordered pairs: $(-\frac{8}{3}, 0)$ and $(0, 4)$.

c. The line through the ordered pairs $(-\frac{8}{3}, 0)$ and $(0, 4)$ is shown in Figure 3-9. Note that the point $(-\frac{8}{3}, 0)$ can be written as $(-2\frac{2}{3}, 0)$.

The line represents the set of all solutions to the equation $-3x + 2y = 8$.

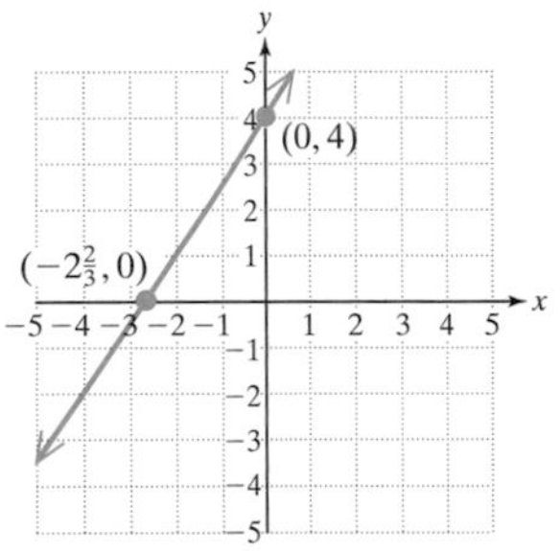

Figure 3-9

Skill Practice Given the equation $x - 3y = -4$,

7. Find the *x*-intercept. **8.** Find the *y*-intercept. **9.** Graph the equation.

Example 6 Finding the *x*- and *y*-Intercepts of a Line

Given the equation $4x + 5y = 0$,

a. Find the *x*-intercept.

b. Find the *y*-intercept.

c. Graph the equation.

Solution:

a. To find the *x*-intercept, substitute $y = 0$.

$$4x + 5y = 0$$
$$4x + 5(0) = 0$$
$$4x = 0$$
$$x = 0$$

The *x*-intercept is $(0, 0)$.

b. To find the *y*-intercept, substitute $x = 0$.

$$4x + 5y = 0$$
$$4(0) + 5y = 0$$
$$5y = 0$$
$$y = 0$$

The *y*-intercept is $(0, 0)$.

Answers

7. $(-4, 0)$ **8.** $\left(0, \frac{4}{3}\right)$

9.

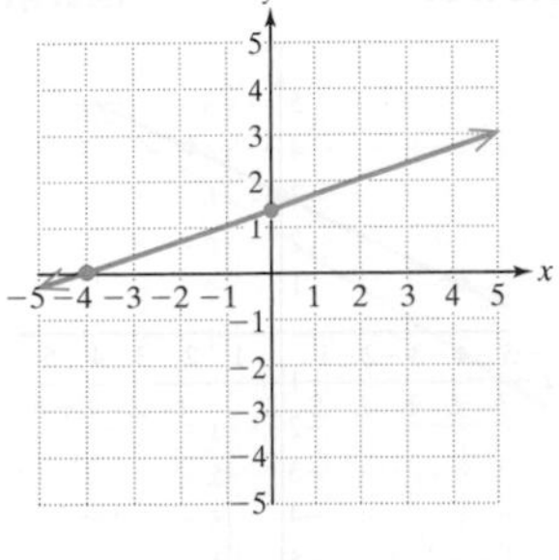

c. Because the x-intercept and the y-intercept are the same point (the origin), one or more additional points are needed to graph the line. In the table, we have arbitrarily selected additional values for x and y to find two more points on the line.

x	y
-5	
	2

Let $x = -5$:

$$4x + 5y = 0$$
$$4(-5) + 5y = 0$$
$$-20 + 5y = 0$$
$$5y = 20$$
$$y = 4$$

$(-5, 4)$ is a solution.

Let $y = 2$:

$$4x + 5y = 0$$
$$4x + 5(2) = 0$$
$$4x + 10 = 0$$
$$4x = -10$$
$$x = -\frac{10}{4}$$
$$x = -\frac{5}{2}$$

$(-\frac{5}{2}, 2)$ is a solution.

The line through the ordered pairs $(0, 0)$, $(-5, 4)$, and $(-\frac{5}{2}, 2)$ is shown in Figure 3-10. Note that the point $(-\frac{5}{2}, 2)$ can be written as $(-2\frac{1}{2}, 2)$.

The line represents the set of all solutions to the equation $4x + 5y = 0$.

x	y
-5	4
$-\frac{5}{2}$	2
0	0

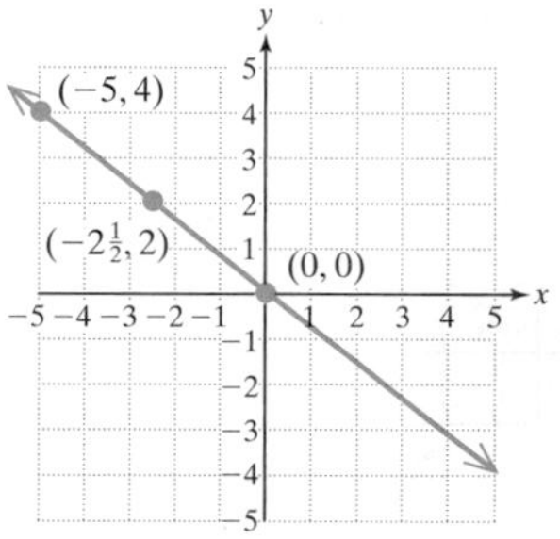

Figure 3-10

Skill Practice Given the equation $2x - 3y = 0$,

10. Find the x-intercept. **11.** Find the y-intercept.

12. Graph the equation. (*Hint:* You may need to find an additional point.)

4. Horizontal and Vertical Lines

Recall that a linear equation can be written in the form of $Ax + By = C$, where A and B are not both zero. However, if A or B is 0, then the line is either horizontal or vertical. A horizontal line either lies on the x-axis or is parallel to the x-axis. A vertical line either lies on the y-axis or is parallel to the y-axis.

Equations of Vertical and Horizontal Lines

1. A **vertical line** can be represented by an equation of the form $x = k$, where k is a constant.
2. A **horizontal line** can be represented by an equation of the form $y = k$, where k is a constant.

Avoiding Mistakes

Do not try to graph a line given only one point. There are infinitely many lines that pass through a single point.

Answers

10. (0, 0) **11.** (0, 0)

12.

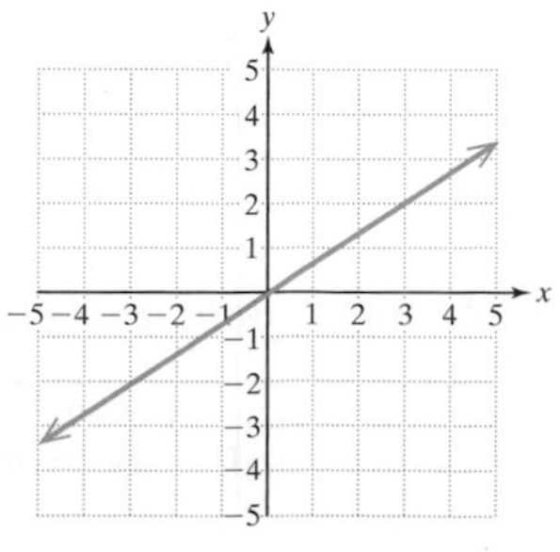

3. $y = \frac{1}{2}x - \frac{7}{2}$

4. $y = -\frac{3}{4}x + \frac{5}{3}$

5. $4x - 7y = 21$

6. $2x + 3y = 12$

7. $-3x - 4y = 6$

8. $-5x + 4y = 10$

For Exercises 9–12, graph the equations on the given viewing window.

9. $y = 3x + 15$ Window: $-10 \le x \le 10$, $-5 \le y \le 20$

10. $y = -2x - 25$ Window: $-30 \le x \le 30$, $-30 \le y \le 30$

Xscl = 3 (sets the x-axis tick marks to increments of 3)

Yscl = 3 (sets the y-axis tick marks to increments of 3)

11. $y = -0.2x + 0.04$ Window: $-0.1 \le x \le 0.3$, $-0.1 \le y \le 0.1$

Xscl = 0.01 (sets the x-axis tick marks to increments of 0.01)

Yscl = 0.01 (sets the y-axis tick marks to increments of 0.01)

12. $y = 0.3x - 0.5$ Window: $-1 \le x \le 3$, $-1 \le y \le 1$

Xscl = 0.1 (sets the x-axis tick marks to increments of 0.1)

Yscl = 0.1 (sets the y-axis tick marks to increments of 0.1)

Section 3.2 Practice Exercises

Study Skills Exercise

Check your progress by answering these questions.

Yes ______ No ______ Did you have sufficient time to study for the test on Chapter 2? If not, what could you have done to create more time for studying?

Yes ______ No ______ Did you work all of the assigned homework problems in Chapter 2?

Yes ______ No ______ If you encountered difficulty, did you see your instructor or tutor for help?

Yes ______ No ______ Have you taken advantage of the textbook supplements such as the *Student Solutions Manual*?

Vocabulary and Key Concepts

1. a. A linear equation in two variables is an equation that can be written in the form __________ where A and B are not both zero.

b. A point where a graph intersects the x-axis is called a(n) ________.

c. A point where a graph intersects the y-axis is called a(n) ________.

d. A ________ line can be represented by an equation of the form $x = k$, where k is a constant.

e. A ________ line can be represented by an equation of the form $y = k$, where k is a constant.

Review Exercises

For Exercises 2–8, refer to the figure to give the coordinates of the labeled points, and state the quadrant or axis where the point is located.

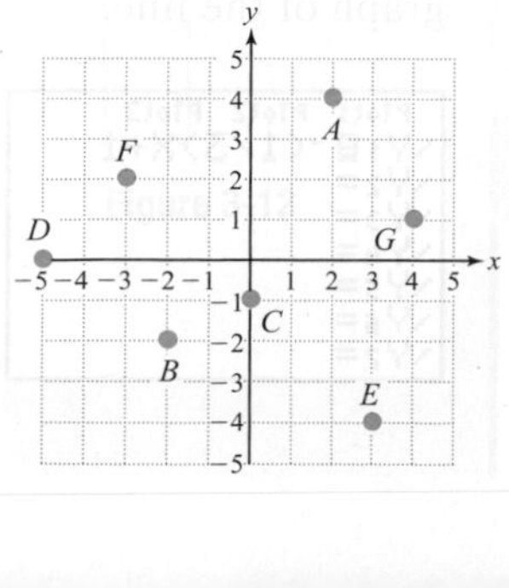

2. A

3. B

4. C

5. D

6. E

7. F

8. G

Concept 1: Definition of a Linear Equation in Two Variables

For Exercises 9–17, determine whether the given ordered pair is a solution to the equation. **(See Example 1.)**

9. $x - y = 6;\ (8, 2)$

10. $y = 3x - 2;\ (1, 1)$

11. $y = -\frac{1}{3}x + 3;\ (-3, 4)$

12. $y = -\frac{5}{2}x + 5;\ \left(\frac{4}{5}, -3\right)$

13. $4x + 5y = 1;\ \left(\frac{1}{4}, -\frac{2}{5}\right)$

14. $y = 7;\ (0, 7)$

15. $y = -2;\ (-2, 6)$

16. $x = 1;\ (0, 1)$

17. $x = -5;\ (-5, 6)$

Concept 2: Graphing Linear Equations in Two Variables by Plotting Points

For Exercises 18–31, complete each table, and graph the corresponding ordered pairs. Draw the line defined by the points to represent all solutions to the equation. **(See Examples 2–4.)**

18. $x + y = 3$

x	y
2	
	3
−1	
	0

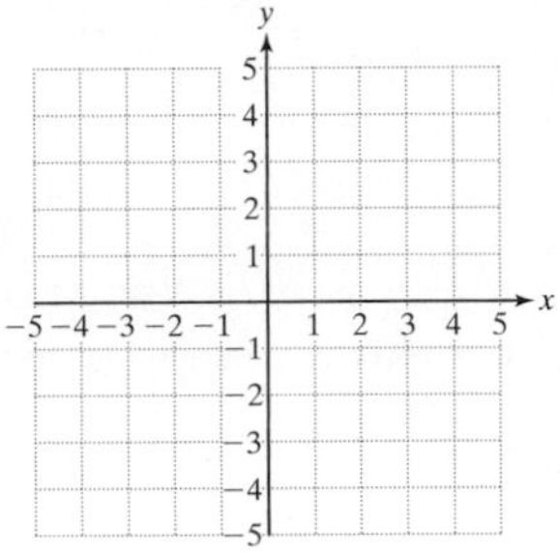

19. $x + y = -2$

x	y
1	
	0
−3	
	2

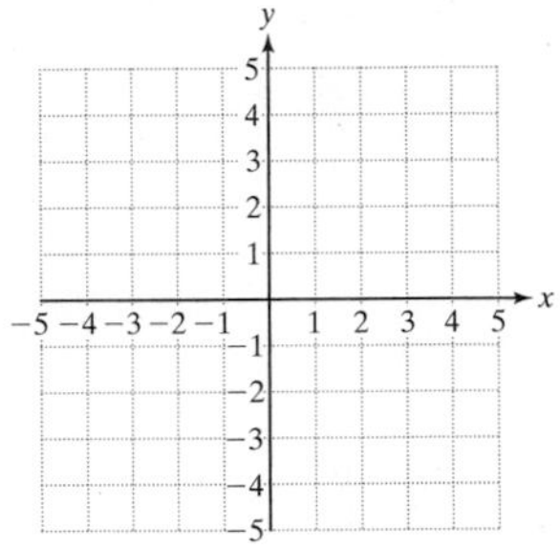

20. $y = 5x + 1$

x	y
1	
	1
−1	

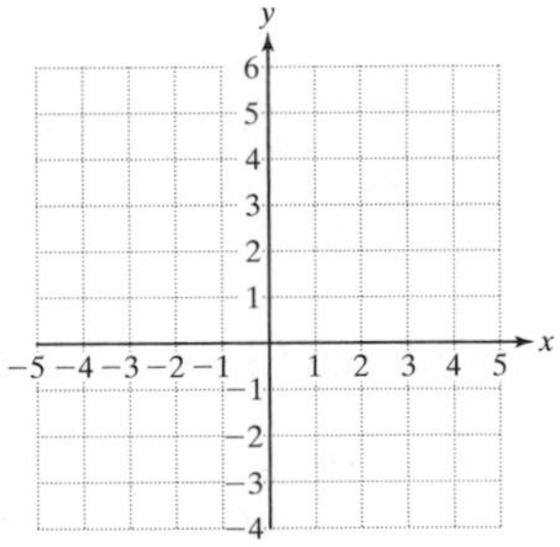

21. $y = -3x - 3$

x	y
−2	
	0
−4	

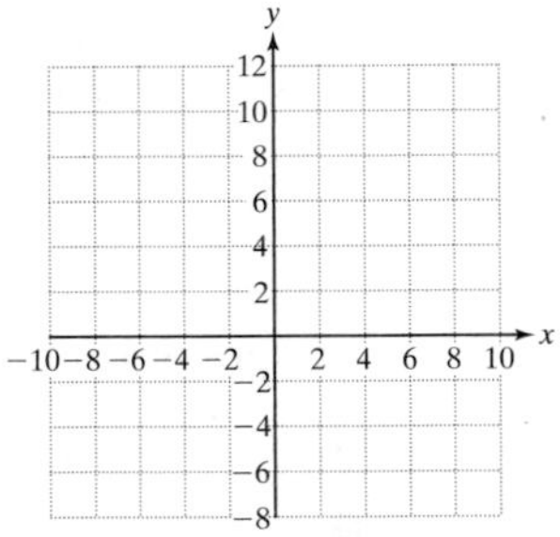

22. $2x - 3y = 6$

x	y
0	
	0
2	

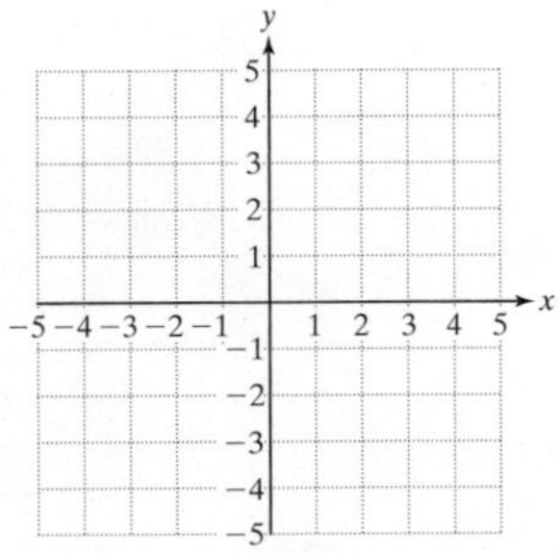

23. $4x + 2y = 8$

x	y
0	
	0
3	

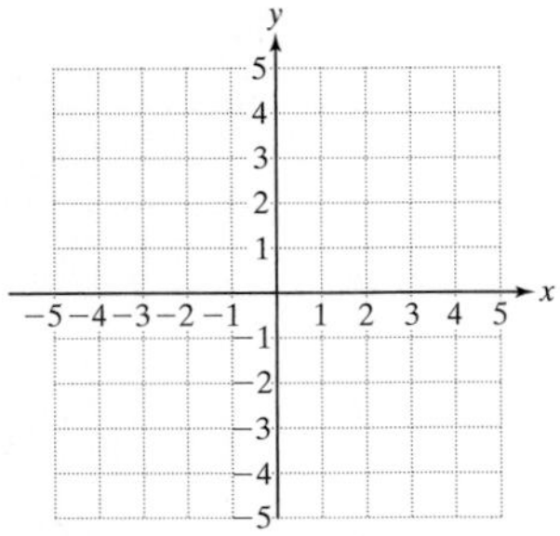

24. $y = \frac{2}{7}x - 5$

x	y
7	
−7	
0	

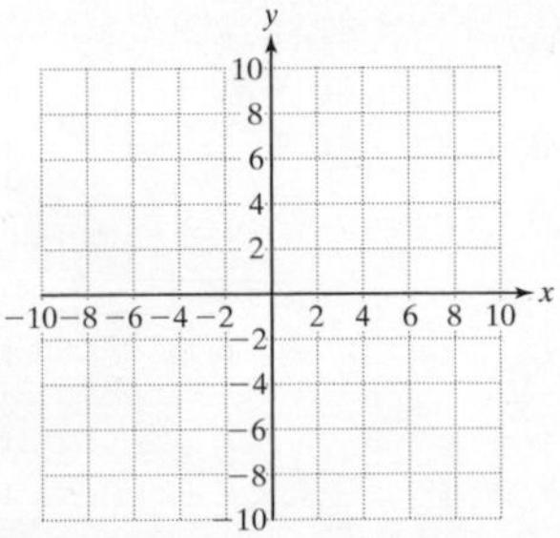

25. $y = -\frac{3}{5}x - 2$

x	y
0	
5	
10	

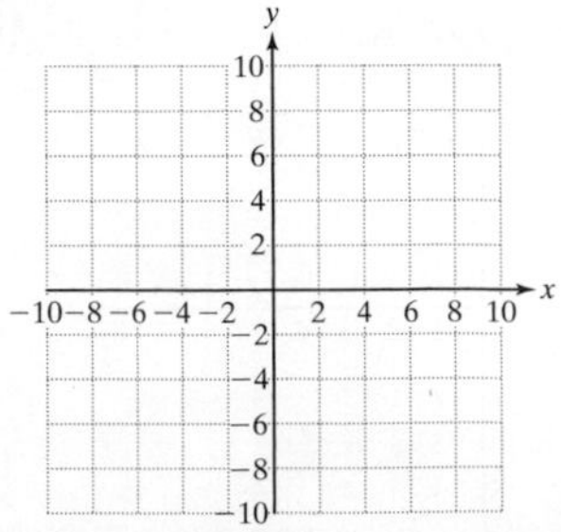

26. $y = 3$

x	y
2	
0	
−1	

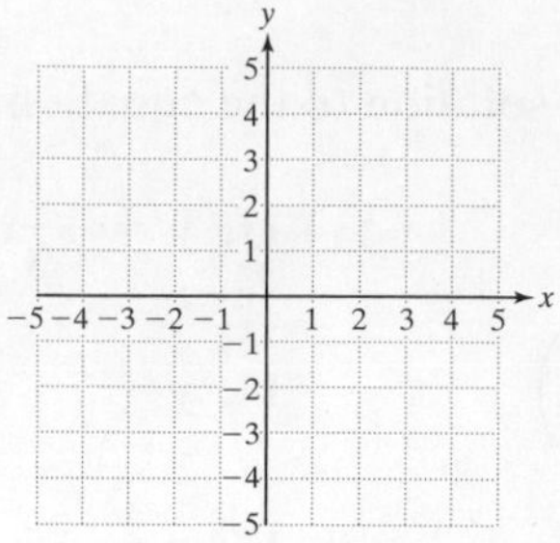

27. $y = -2$

x	y
0	
−3	
5	

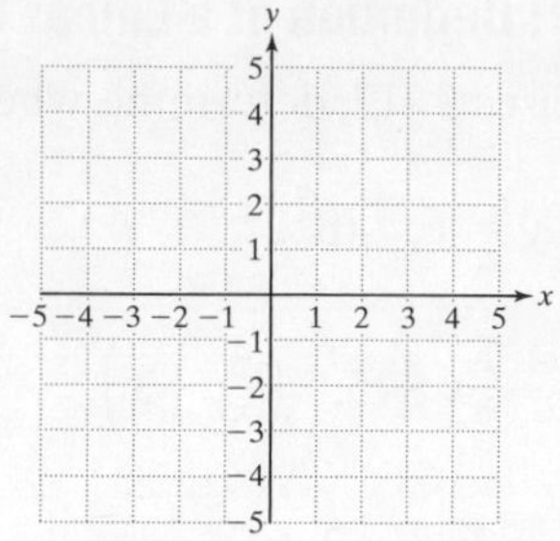

28. $x = -4$

x	y
	1
	−2
	4

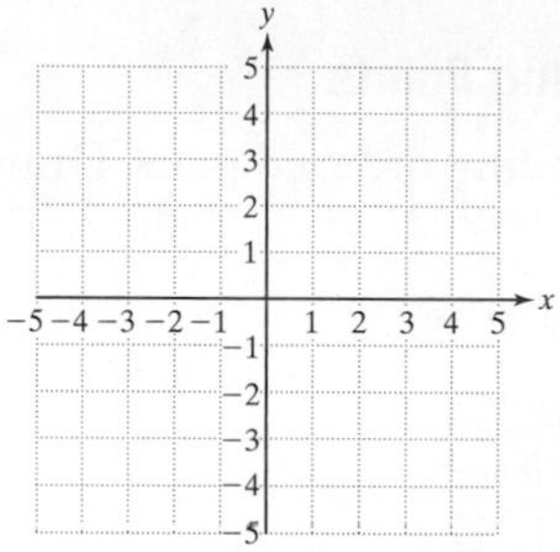

29. $x = \frac{3}{2}$

x	y
	−1
	2
	−3

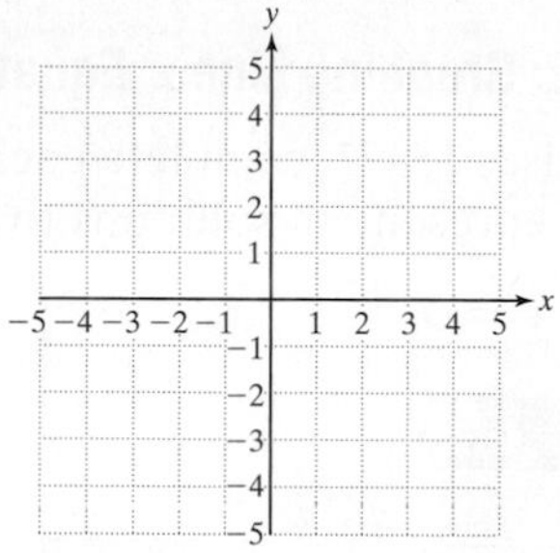

30. $y = -3.4x + 5.8$

x	y
0	
1	
2	

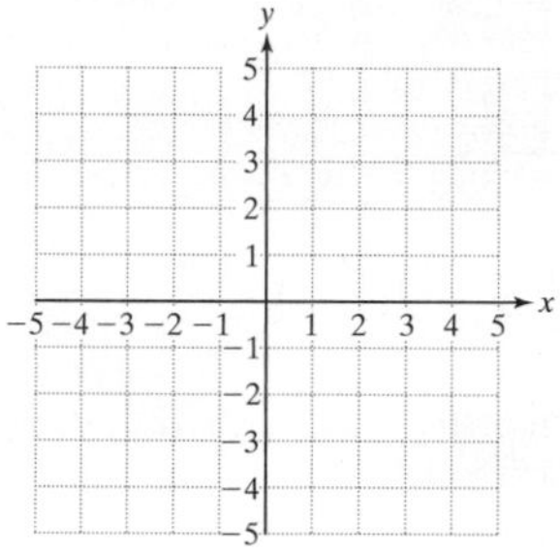

31. $y = -1.2x + 4.6$

x	y
0	
1	
2	

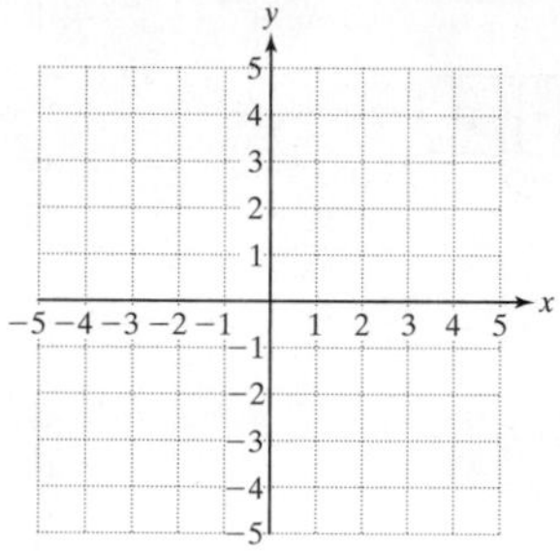

For Exercises 32–43, graph each line by making a table of at least three ordered pairs and plotting the points.

32. $x - y = 2$

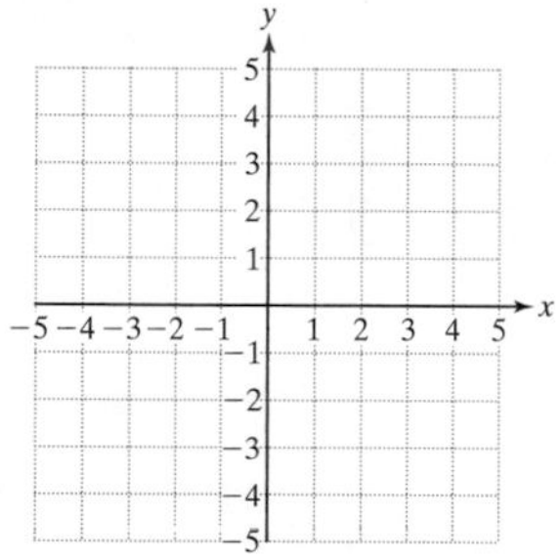

33. $x - y = 4$

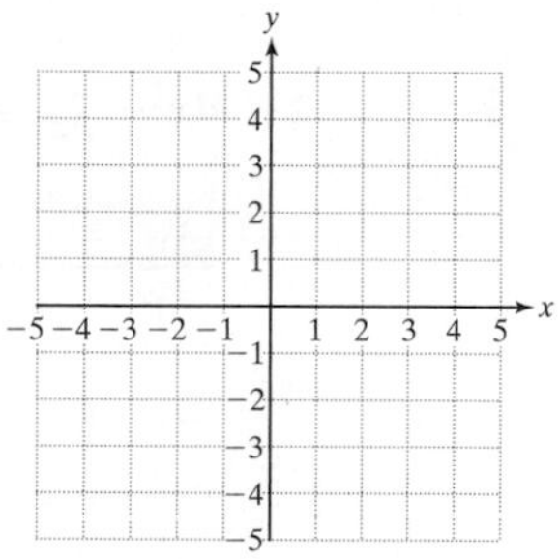

34. $-3x + y = -6$

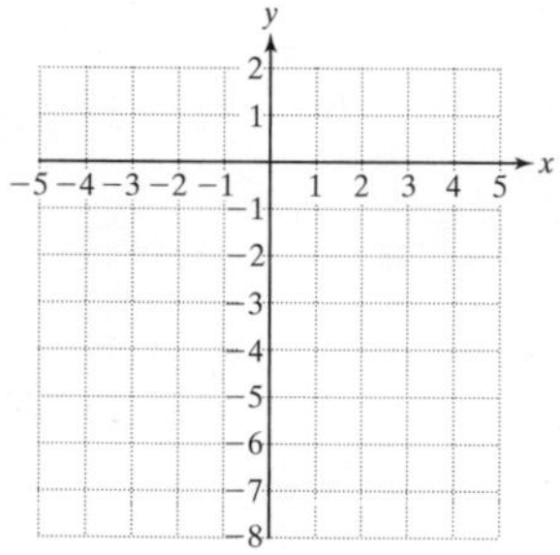

35. $2x - 5y = 10$

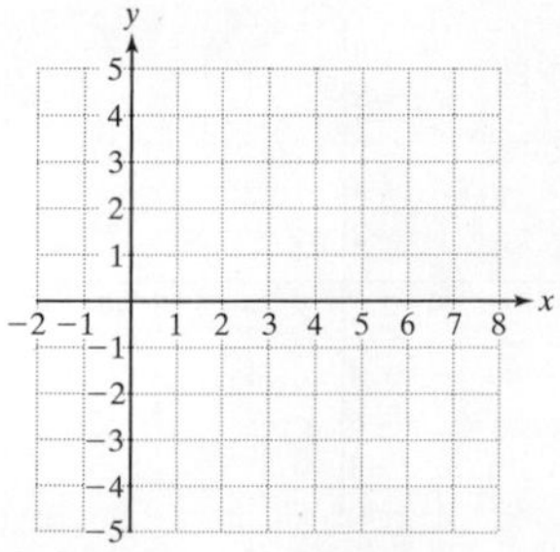

36. $y = 4x$

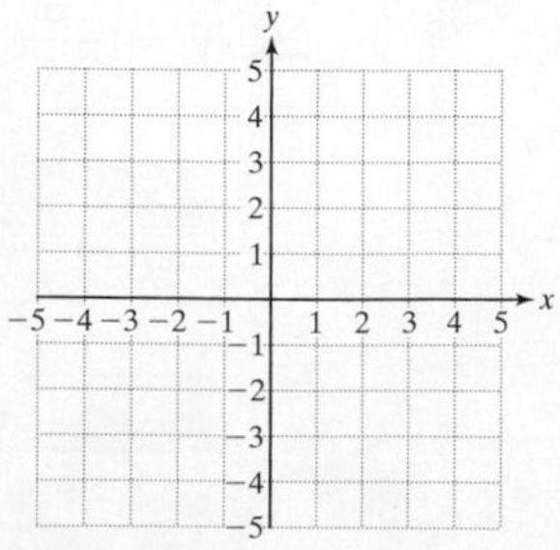

37. $y = -2x$

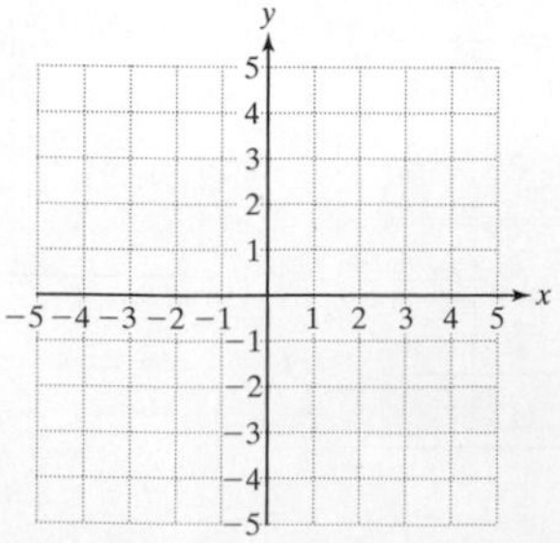

38. $y = -\frac{1}{2}x + 3$

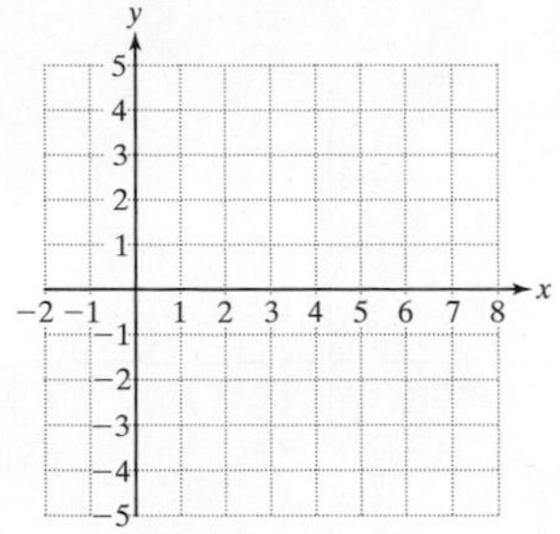

39. $y = \frac{1}{4}x - 2$

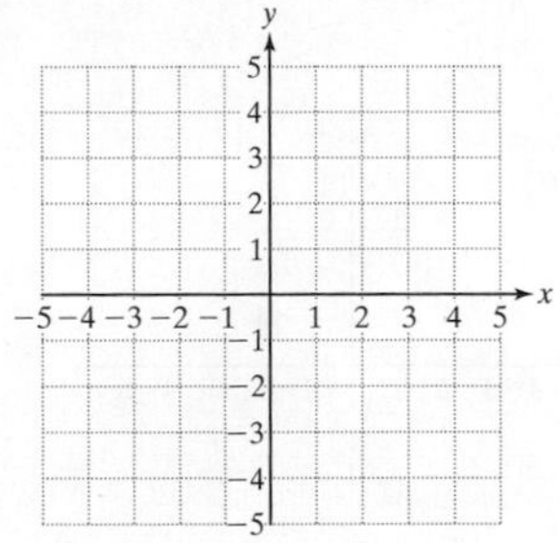

40. $x + y = 0$

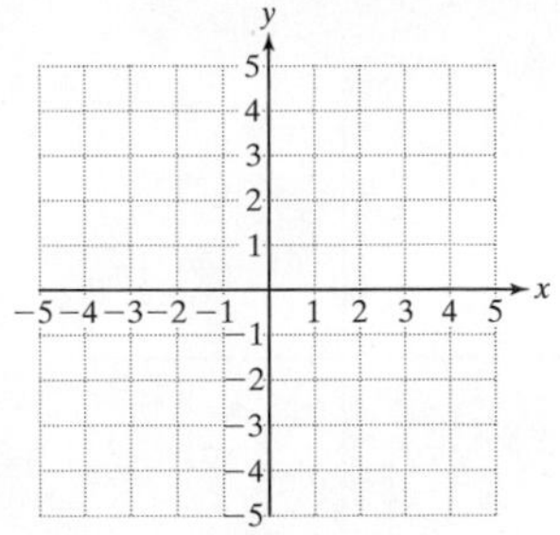

41. $-x + y = 0$

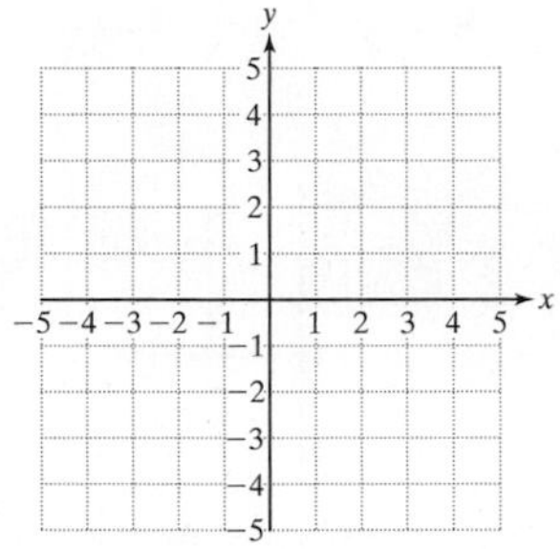

42. $50x - 40y = 200$

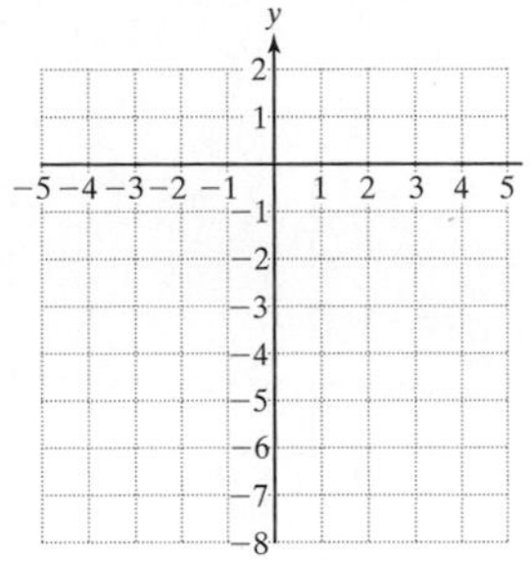

43. $-30x - 20y = 60$

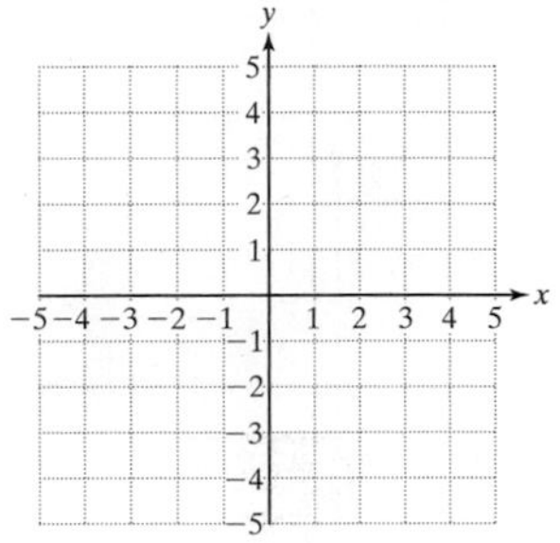

Concept 3: *x*- and *y*-Intercepts

44. The *x*-intercept is on which axis?

45. The *y*-intercept is on which axis?

For Exercises 46–49, estimate the coordinates of the *x*- and *y*-intercepts.

46.

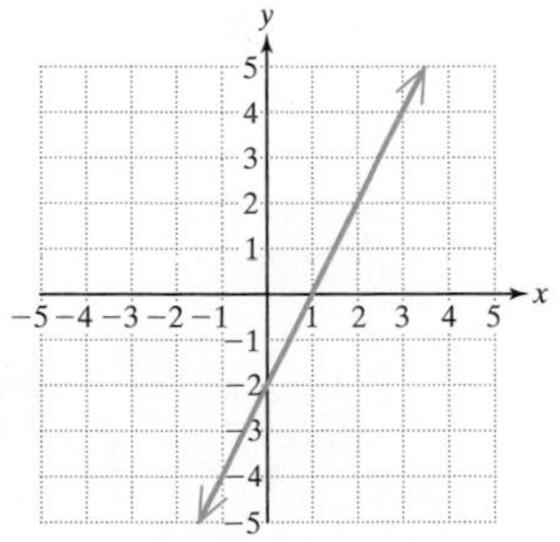

47.

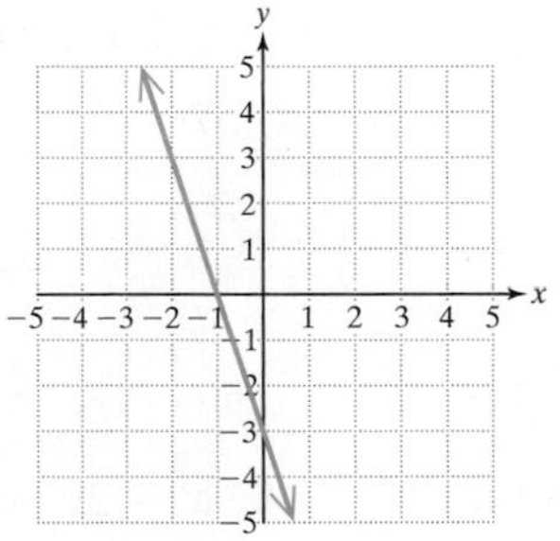

48.

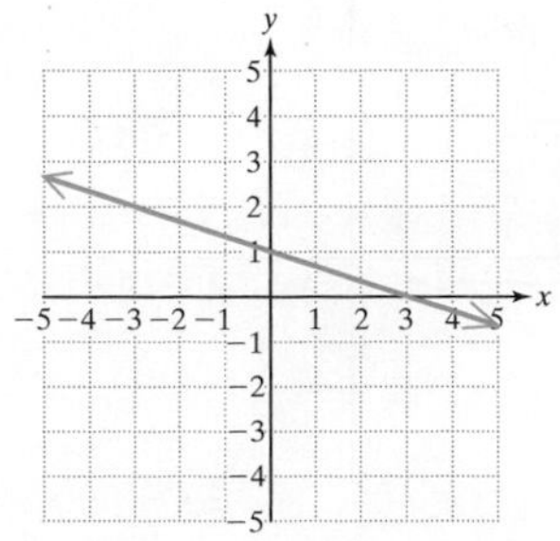

49.

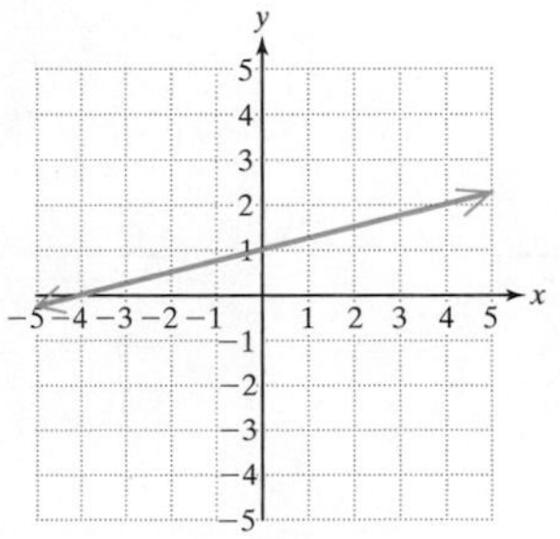

For Exercises 50–61, find the x- and y-intercepts (if they exist), and graph the line. **(See Examples 5–6.)**

50. $5x + 2y = 5$

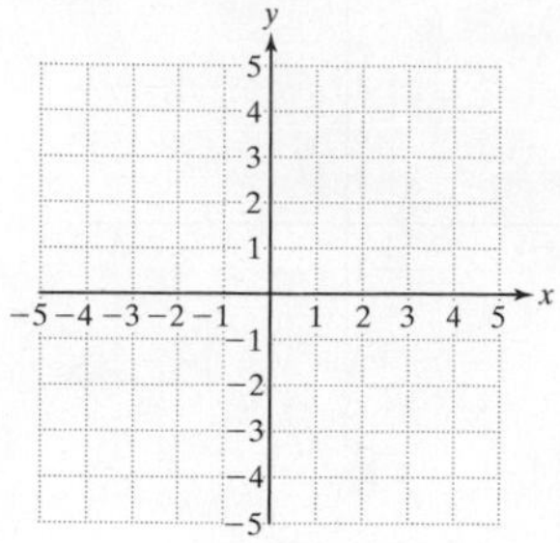

51. $4x - 3y = -9$

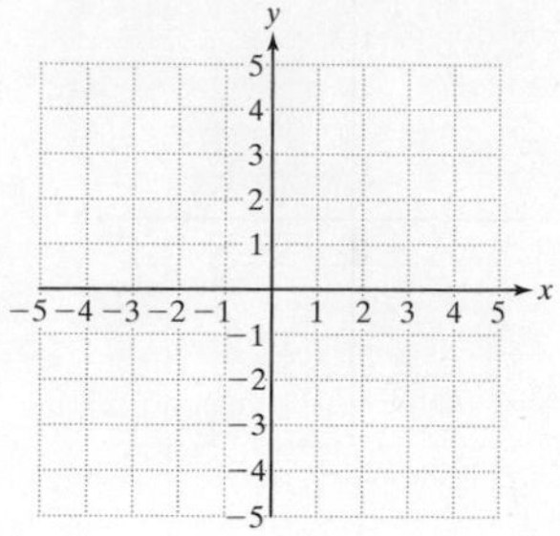

52. $y = \frac{2}{3}x - 1$

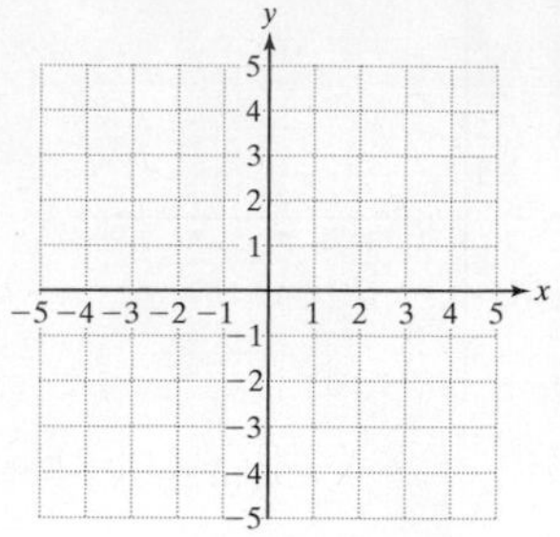

53. $y = -\frac{3}{4}x + 2$

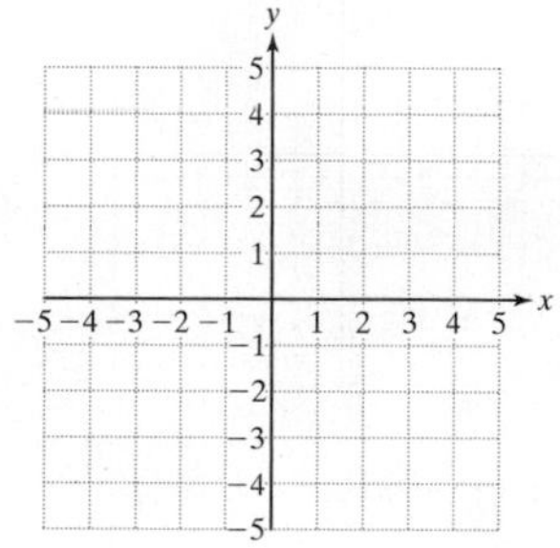

54. $x - 3 = y$

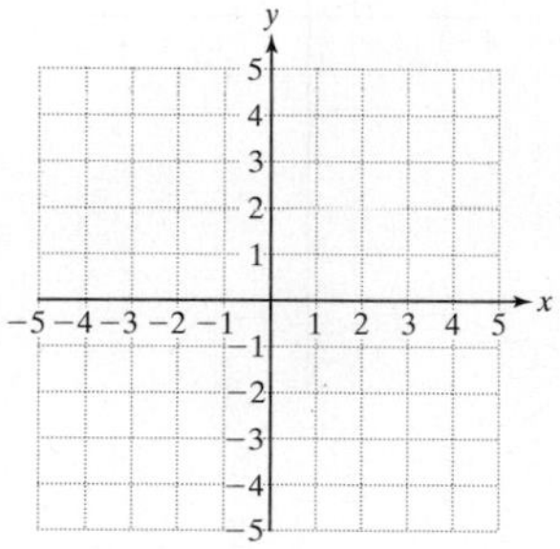

55. $2x + 8 = y$

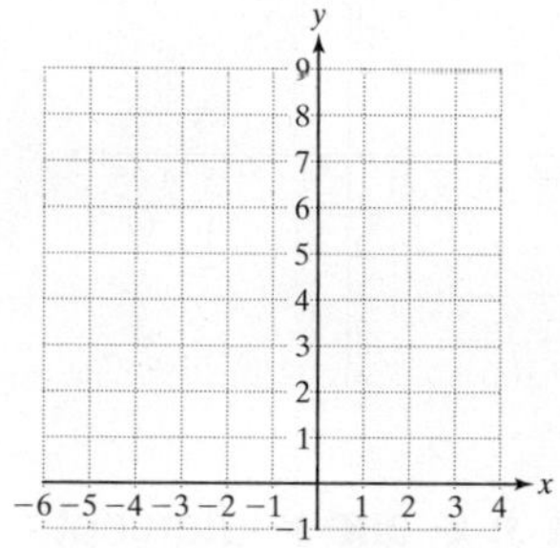

56. $-3x + y = 0$

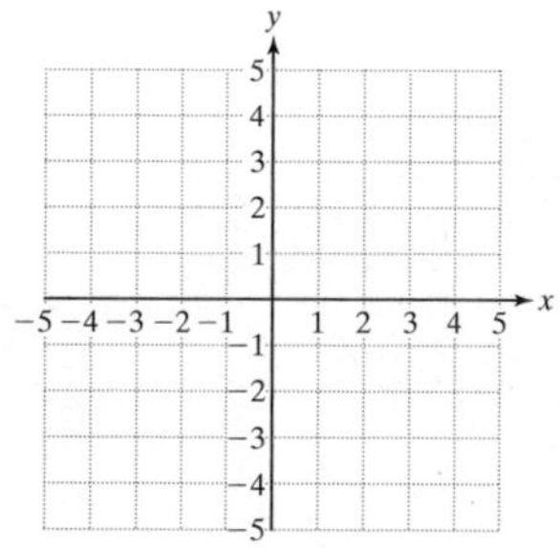

57. $2x - 2y = 0$

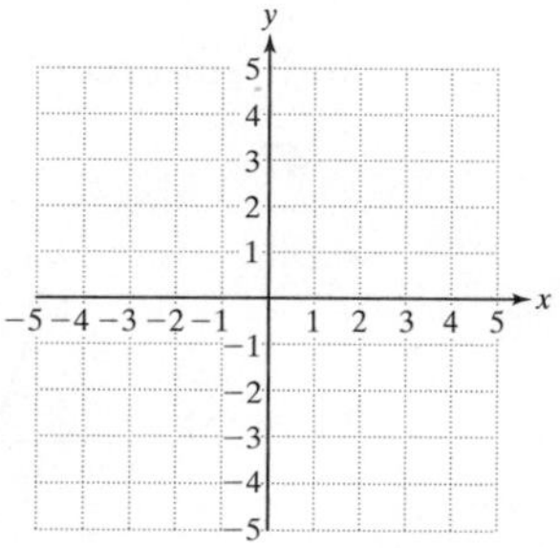

58. $25y = 10x + 100$

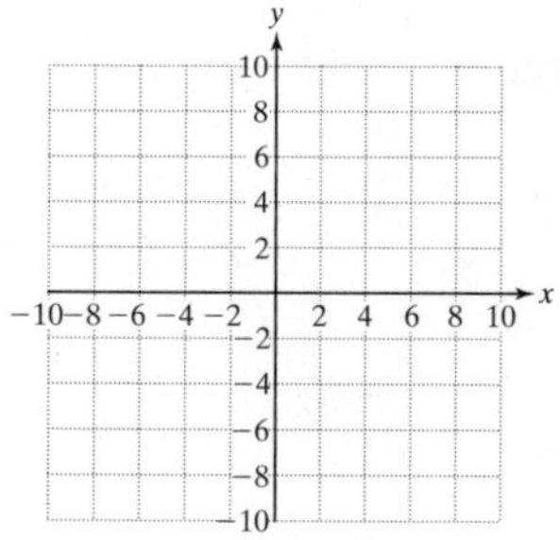

59. $20x = -40y + 200$

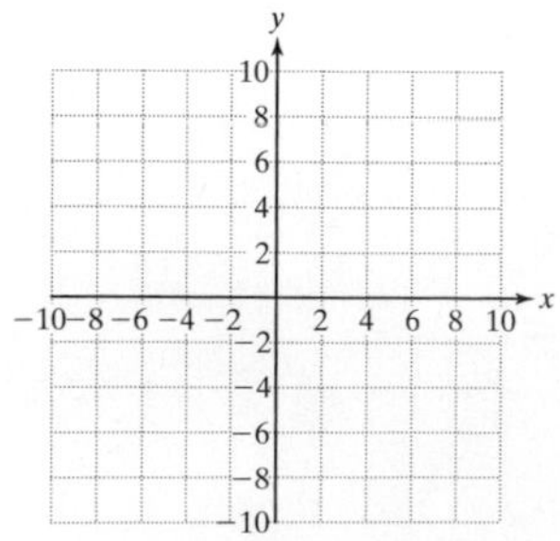

60. $x = 2y$

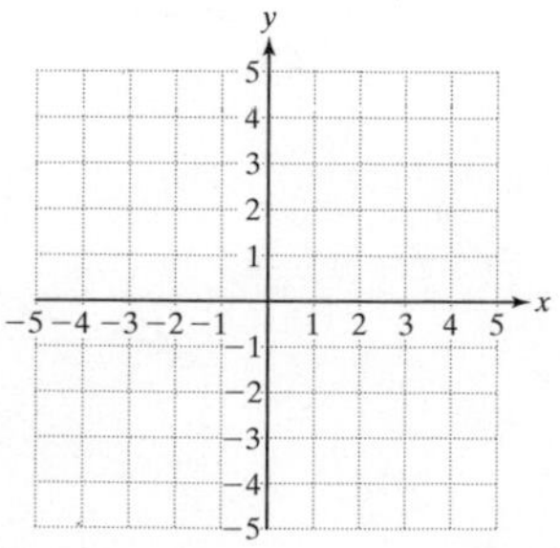

61. $x = -5y$

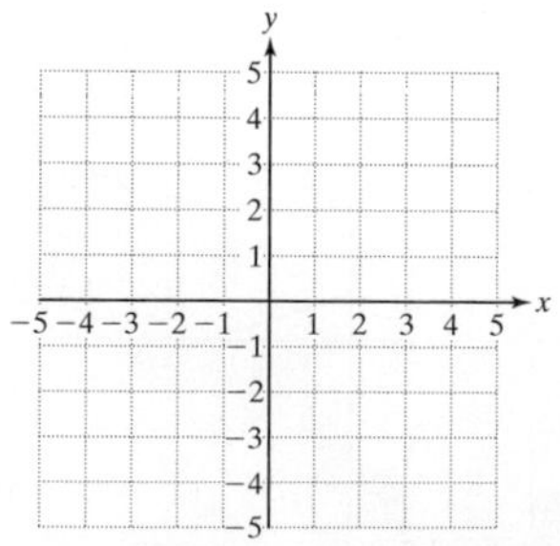

Concept 4: Horizontal and Vertical Lines

For Exercises 62–65, answer true or false. If the statement is false, rewrite it to be true.

62. The line defined by $x = 3$ is horizontal.

63. The line defined by $y = -4$ is horizontal.

64. A line parallel to the y-axis is vertical.

65. A line parallel to the x-axis is horizontal.

For Exercises 66–74,

a. Identify the equation as representing a horizontal or vertical line.

b. Graph the line.

c. Identify the x- and y-intercepts if they exist. **(See Examples 7–8.)**

66. $x = 3$

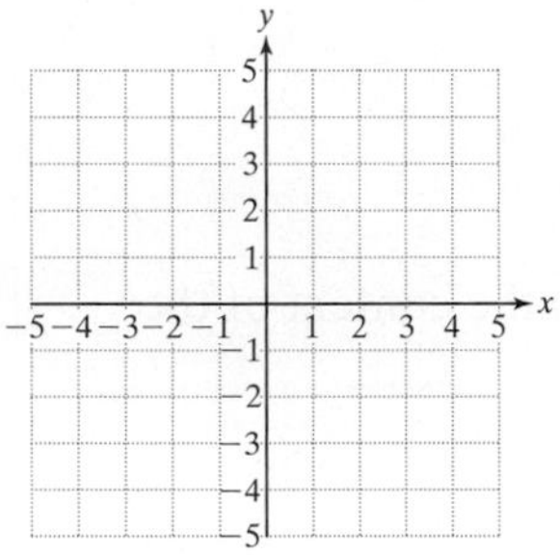

67. $y = -1$

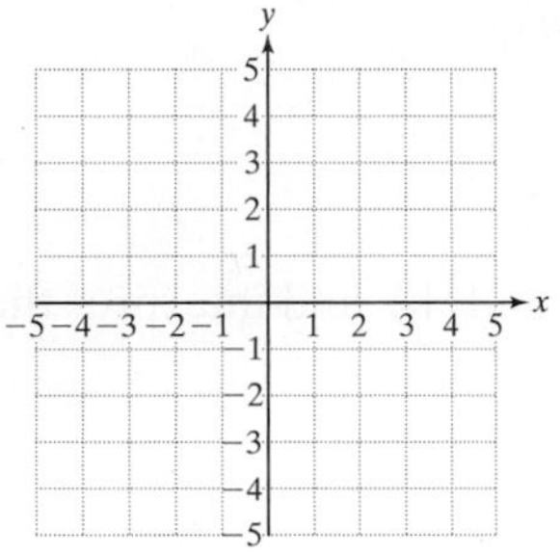

68. $-2y = 8$

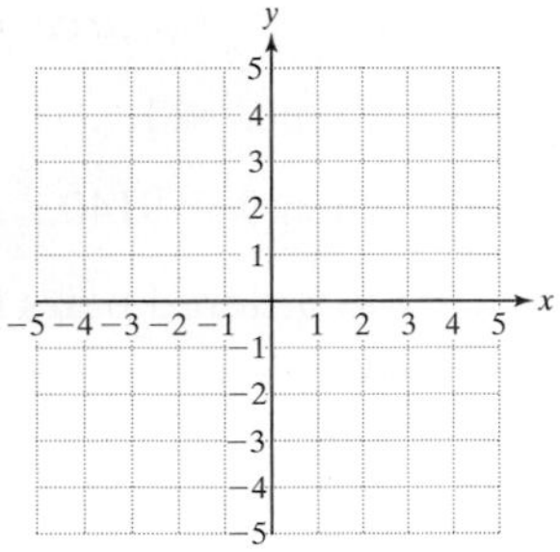

69. $5x = 20$

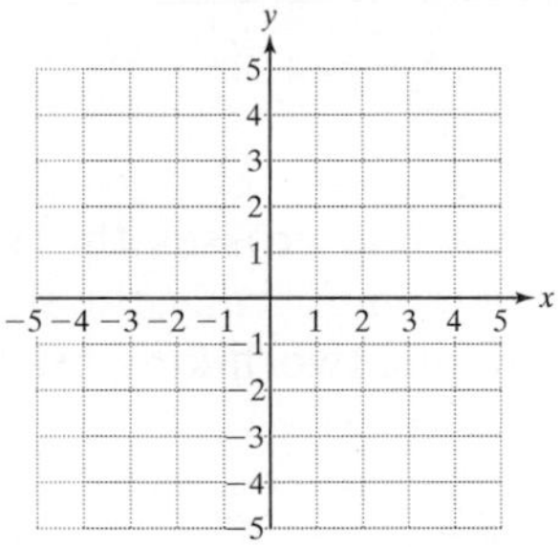

70. $x - 3 = -7$

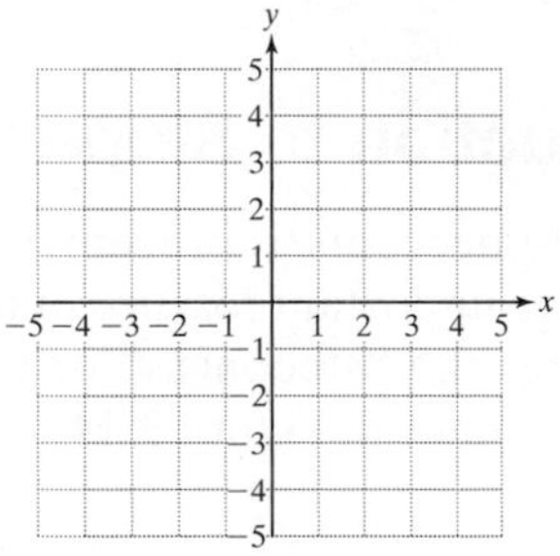

71. $y + 8 = 11$

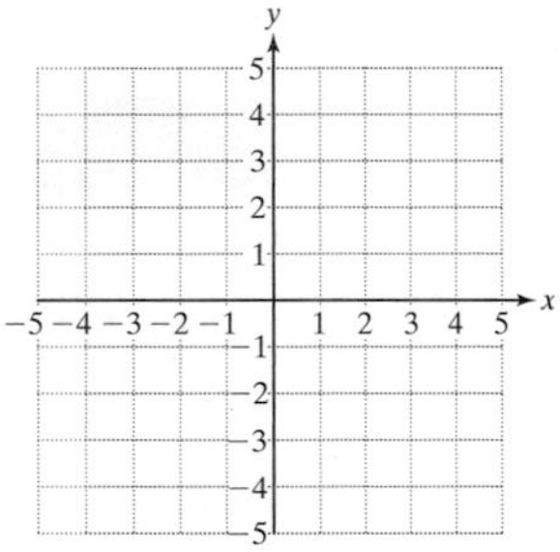

72. $3y = 0$

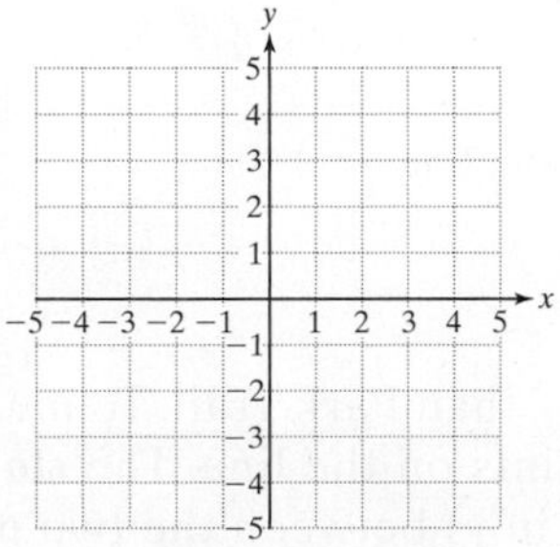

73. $5x = 0$

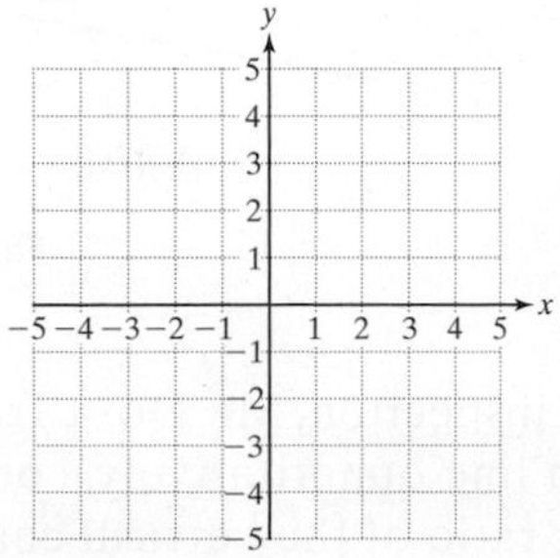

74. $2x + 7 = 10$

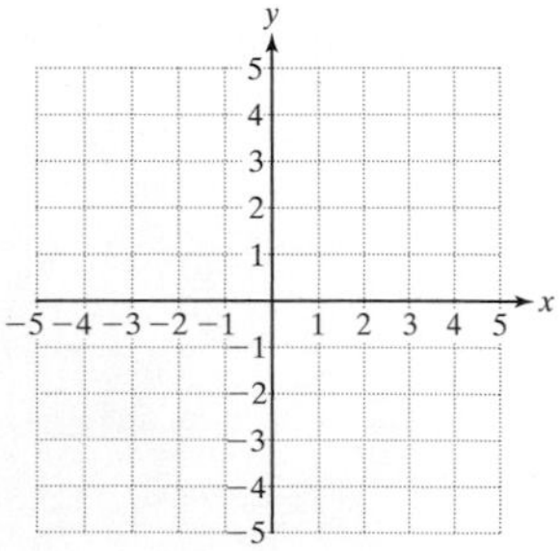

75. Explain why not every line has both an x- and a y-intercept.

76. Which of the lines has an x-intercept?

a. $2x - 3y = 6$ **b.** $x = 5$ **c.** $2y = 8$ **d.** $-x + y = 0$

77. Which of the lines has a y-intercept?

a. $y = 2$ **b.** $x + y = 0$ **c.** $2x - 10 = 2$ **d.** $x + 4y = 8$

Expanding Your Skills

78. The store "CDs R US" sells all compact discs for \$13.99. The following equation represents the revenue, y, (in dollars) generated by selling x CDs.

$$y = 13.99x \quad (x \geq 0)$$

a. Find y when $x = 13$.

b. Find x when $y = 279.80$.

c. Write the ordered pairs from parts (a) and (b), and interpret their meaning in the context of the problem.

d. Graph the ordered pairs and the line defined by the points.

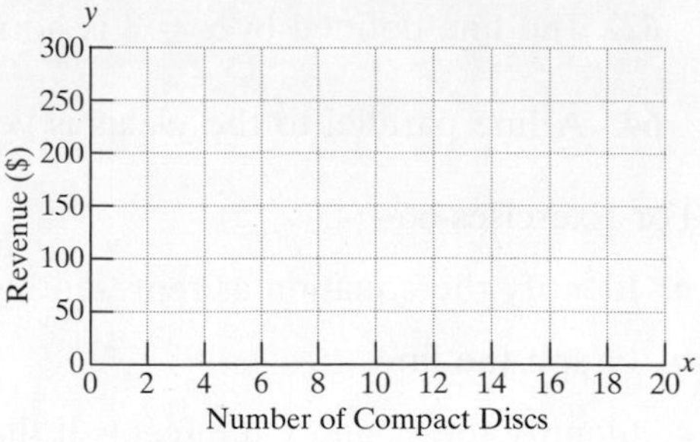

79. The value of a car depreciates once it is driven off of the dealer's lot. For a Hyundai Accent, the value of the car is given by the equation $y = -1025x + 12{,}215$ $(x \geq 0)$ where y is the value of the car in dollars x years after its purchase. (*Source: Kelly Blue Book*)

a. Find y when $x = 1$.

b. Find x when $y = 9140$.

c. Write the ordered pairs from parts (a) and (b), and interpret their meaning in the context of the problem.

Section 3.3 Slope of a Line and Rate of Change

Concepts

1. **Introduction to Slope**
2. **Slope Formula**
3. **Parallel and Perpendicular Lines**
4. **Applications of Slope: Rate of Change**

1. Introduction to Slope

The x- and y-intercepts represent the points where a line crosses the x- and y-axes. Another important feature of a line is its slope. Geometrically, the slope of a line measures the "steepness" of the line. For example, two hiking trails are depicted by the lines in Figure 3-14.

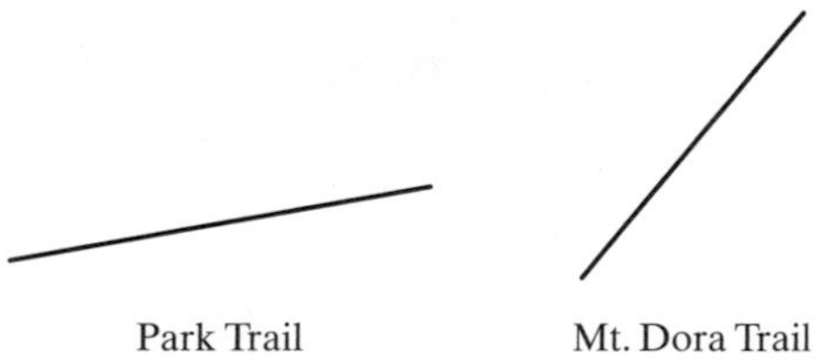

Figure 3-14

By visual inspection, Mt. Dora Trail is "steeper" than Park Trail. To measure the slope of a line quantitatively, consider two points on the line. The **slope** of the line is the ratio of the vertical change (change in y) between the two points and the horizontal change (change in x). As a memory device, we might think of the slope of a line as "rise over run." See Figure 3-15.

Animation

$$\text{Slope} = \frac{\text{change in } y}{\text{change in } x} = \frac{\text{rise}}{\text{run}}$$

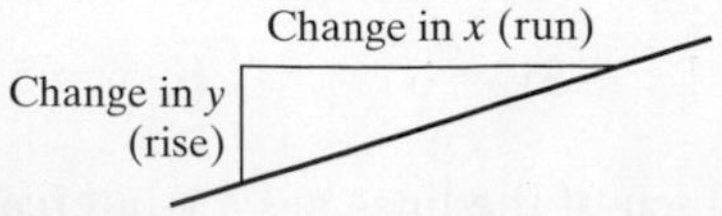

Figure 3-15

To move from point A to point B on Park Trail, rise 2 ft and move to the right 6 ft (Figure 3-16).

To move from point A to point B on Mt. Dora Trail, rise 5 ft and move to the right 4 ft (Figure 3-17).

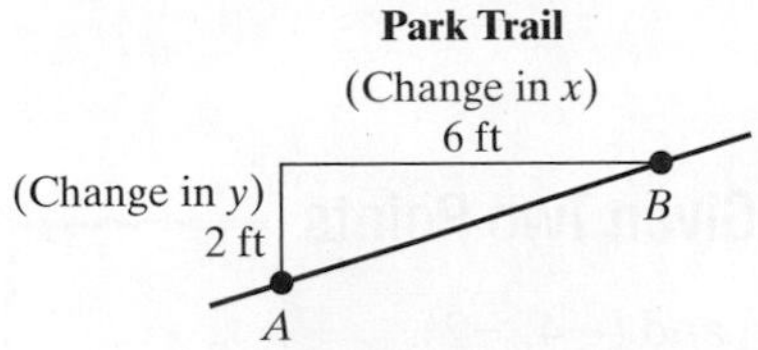

Figure 3-16

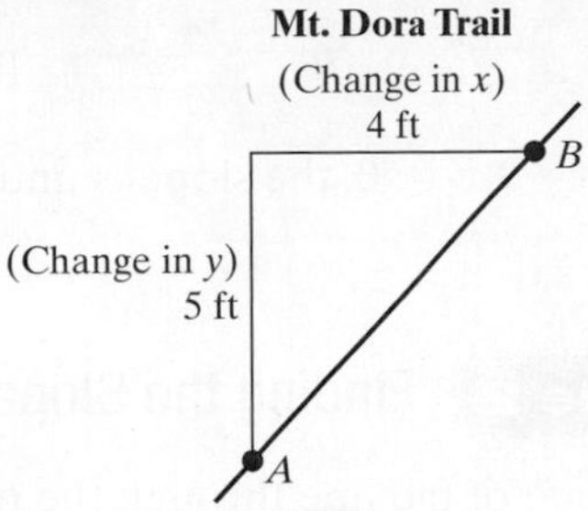

Figure 3-17

TIP: To find the slope, you can use any two points on the line. The ratio of rise to run will be the same.

$$\text{Slope} = \frac{\text{change in } y}{\text{change in } x} = \frac{2 \text{ ft}}{6 \text{ ft}} = \frac{1}{3}$$

$$\text{Slope} = \frac{\text{change in } y}{\text{change in } x} = \frac{5 \text{ ft}}{4 \text{ ft}} = \frac{5}{4}$$

The slope of Mt. Dora Trail is greater than the slope of Park Trail, confirming the observation that Mt. Dora Trail is steeper. On Mt. Dora Trail there is a 5-ft change in elevation for every 4 ft of horizontal distance (a 5:4 ratio). On Park Trail there is only a 2-ft change in elevation for every 6 ft of horizontal distance (a 1:3 ratio).

Example 1 Finding Slope in an Application

Determine the slope of the ramp up the stairs.

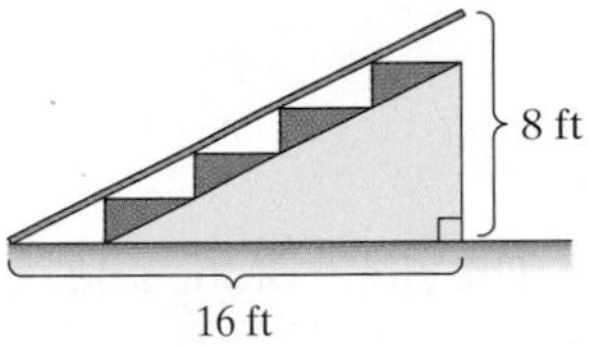

Solution:

$$\text{Slope} = \frac{\text{change in } y}{\text{change in } x} = \frac{8 \text{ ft}}{16 \text{ ft}}$$

$\frac{8}{16} = \frac{1}{2}$ Write the ratio for the slope and simplify.

The slope is $\frac{1}{2}$.

Skill Practice

1. Determine the slope of the aircraft's takeoff path.

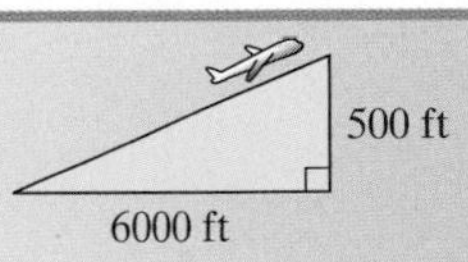

2. Slope Formula

The slope of a line may be found using any two points on the line—call these points (x_1, y_1) and (x_2, y_2). The numbers to the right and below the variables are called *subscripts*. In this instance, the subscript 1 indicates the coordinates of the first point, and the subscript 2 indicates the coordinates of the second point. The change in y between the points can be found by taking the difference of the y values: $y_2 - y_1$. The change in x can be found by taking the difference of the x values in the same order: $x_2 - x_1$ (Figure 3-18).

The slope of a line is often symbolized by the letter m and is given by the following formula.

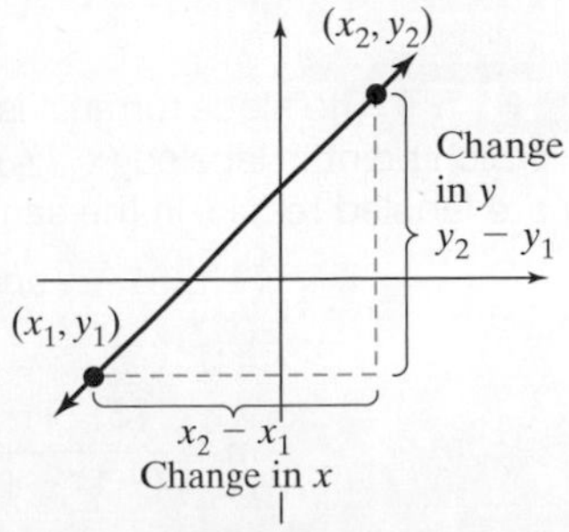

Figure 3-18

Answer

1. $\frac{500}{6000} = \frac{1}{12}$

Slope Formula

The slope of a line passing through the distinct points (x_1, y_1) and (x_2, y_2) is

$$m = \frac{y_2 - y_1}{x_2 - x_1} \quad \text{provided } x_2 - x_1 \neq 0.$$

Note: If $x_2 - x_1 = 0$, the slope is undefined.

Example 2 Finding the Slope of a Line Given Two Points

Find the slope of the line through the points $(-1, 3)$ and $(-4, -2)$.

Solution:

To use the slope formula, first label the coordinates of each point and then substitute the coordinates into the slope formula.

$\underset{(x_1, y_1)}{(-1, 3)}$ and $\underset{(x_2, y_2)}{(-4, -2)}$ Label the points.

$$m = \frac{y_2 - y_1}{x_2 - x_1} = \frac{(-2) - (3)}{(-4) - (-1)}$$ Apply the slope formula.

$$= \frac{-5}{-3}$$

$$= \frac{5}{3}$$ Simplify to lowest terms.

Avoiding Mistakes

When calculating slope, always write the change in y in the numerator.

The slope of the line can be verified from the graph (Figure 3-19).

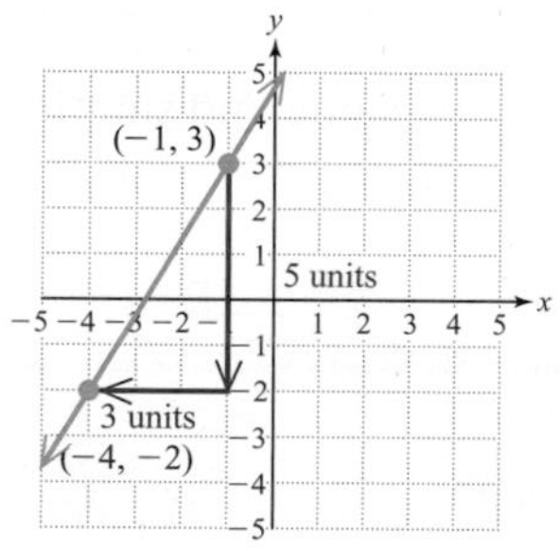

Figure 3-19

Skill Practice Find the slope of the line through the given points.

2. $(-5, 2)$ and $(1, 3)$

TIP: The slope formula is not dependent on which point is labeled (x_1, y_1) and which point is labeled (x_2, y_2). In Example 2, reversing the order in which the points are labeled results in the same slope.

$\underset{(x_2, y_2)}{(-1, 3)}$ and $\underset{(x_1, y_1)}{(-4, -2)}$ Label the points.

$$m = \frac{(3) - (-2)}{(-1) - (-4)} = \frac{5}{3}$$ Apply the slope formula.

Answer

2. $\frac{1}{6}$

When you apply the slope formula, you will see that the slope of a line may be positive, negative, zero, or undefined.

- Lines that increase, or rise, from left to right have a positive slope.
- Lines that decrease, or fall, from left to right have a negative slope.
- Horizontal lines have a slope of zero.
- Vertical lines have an undefined slope.

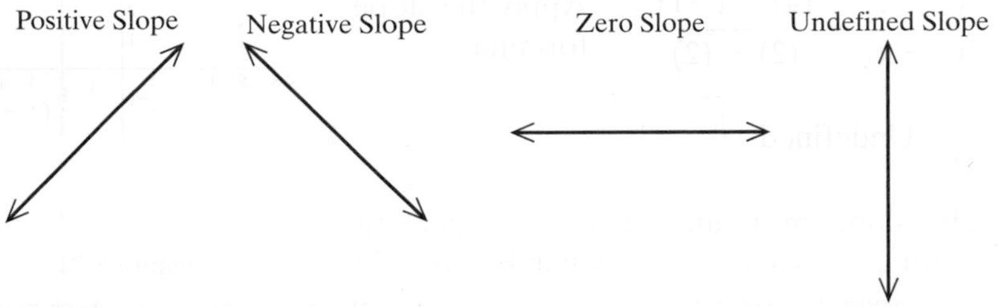

Example 3 Finding the Slope of a Line Given Two Points

Find the slope of the line passing through the points $(-5, \frac{1}{2})$ and $(2, -\frac{3}{2})$.

Solution:

$$\left(-5, \frac{1}{2}\right) \quad \text{and} \quad \left(2, -\frac{3}{2}\right)$$
$$(x_1, y_1) \qquad\qquad (x_2, y_2)$$

Label the points.

$$m = \frac{y_2 - y_1}{x_2 - x_1} = \frac{\left(-\frac{3}{2}\right) - \left(\frac{1}{2}\right)}{(2) - (-5)}$$

Apply the slope formula.

$$= \frac{-\frac{4}{2}}{2 + 5}$$

Simplify.

$$= \frac{-2}{7} \quad \text{or} \quad -\frac{2}{7}$$

By graphing the points $(-5, \frac{1}{2})$ and $(2, -\frac{3}{2})$, we can verify that the slope is $-\frac{2}{7}$ (Figure 3-20). Notice that the line slopes downward from left to right.

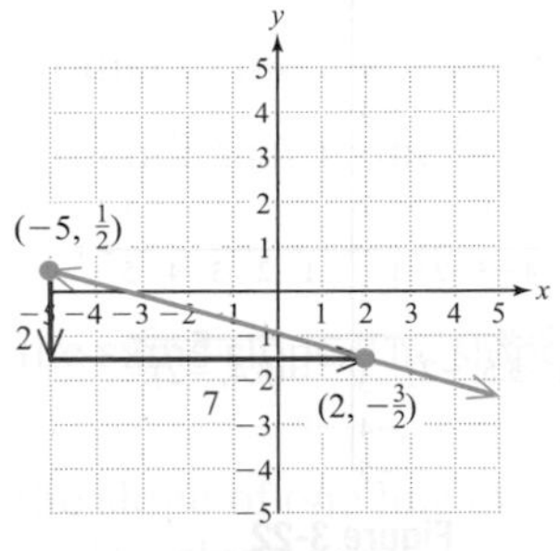

Figure 3-20

Skill Practice Find the slope of the line through the given points.

3. $\left(\frac{2}{3}, 0\right)$ and $\left(-\frac{1}{6}, 5\right)$

Avoiding Mistakes

When applying the slope formula, y_2 and x_2 are taken from the same ordered pair. Likewise y_1 and x_1 are taken from the same ordered pair.

Answer

3. −6

If the slopes of two lines are known, then we can compare the slopes to determine if the lines are parallel, perpendicular, or neither.

Example 7 Determining If Lines Are Parallel, Perpendicular, or Neither

Lines l_1 and l_2 pass through the given points. Determine if l_1 and l_2 are parallel, perpendicular, or neither.

l_1: $(2, -7)$ and $(4, 1)$ $\quad$ l_2: $(-3, 1)$ and $(1, 0)$

Solution:

Find the slope of each line.

l_1: $\underset{(x_1, y_1)}{(2, -7)}$ and $\underset{(x_2, y_2)}{(4, 1)}$ $\quad$ l_2: $\underset{(x_1, y_1)}{(-3, 1)}$ and $\underset{(x_2, y_2)}{(1, 0)}$

$$m_1 = \frac{1-(-7)}{4-2} \qquad m_2 = \frac{0-1}{1-(-3)}$$

$$m_1 = \frac{8}{2} \qquad m_2 = \frac{-1}{4}$$

$$m_1 = 4 \qquad m_2 = -\frac{1}{4}$$

TIP: You can check that two lines are perpendicular by checking that the product of their slopes is -1.

$$4\left(-\frac{1}{4}\right) = -1$$

One slope is the opposite of the reciprocal of the other slope. Therefore, the lines are perpendicular.

Skill Practice Determine if lines l_1 and l_2 are parallel, perpendicular, or neither.

8. l_1: $(-2, -3)$ and $(4, -1)$
l_2: $(0, 2)$ and $(-3, 1)$

4. Applications of Slope: Rate of Change

In many applications, the interpretation of slope refers to the *rate of change* of the y-variable to the x-variable.

Example 8 Interpreting Slope in an Application

The annual median income for males in the United States for selected years is shown in Figure 3-25. The trend is approximately linear. Find the slope of the line and interpret the meaning of the slope in the context of the problem.

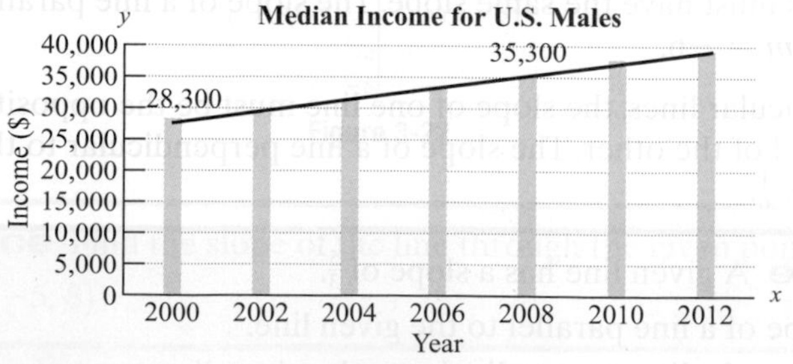

Figure 3-25

Source: U.S. Department of the Census

Answer

8. Parallel

Solution:

To determine the slope we need to know two points on the line. From the graph, the median income for males in the year 2000 was approximately $28,300. This gives us the ordered pair (2000, 28,300). In the year 2008, the income was $35,300. This gives the ordered pair (2008, 35,300).

$$\underset{(x_1, y_1)}{(2000, 28{,}300)} \quad \text{and} \quad \underset{(x_2, y_2)}{(2008, 35{,}300)}$$ Label the points.

$$m = \frac{y_2 - y_1}{x_2 - x_1} = \frac{35{,}300 - 28{,}300}{2008 - 2000}$$ Apply the slope formula.

$$= \frac{7000}{8}$$

$$= 875$$ Simplify.

The slope is 875. This tells us the rate of change of the y-variable (income) to the x-variable (years). This means that men's median income in the United States increased at a rate of $875 per year during this time period.

Skill Practice

9. In the year 2000, the population of Alaska was approximately 630,000. By 2010, it had grown to 700,000. Use the ordered pairs (2000, 630,000) and (2010, 700,000) to determine the slope of the line through the points. Then interpret the meaning in the context of this problem.

Answer

9. $m = 7000$; The population of Alaska increased at a rate of 7000 people per year.

Section 3.3 Practice Exercises

Study Skills Exercise

Each day after finishing your homework, choose two or three odd-numbered problems or examples from that section. Write the problem with the directions on one side of a 3×5 card. On the back write the section, page, and problem number along with the answer. Each week, shuffle your cards and pull out a few at random, to give yourself a review of $\frac{1}{2}$-hr or more.

Vocabulary and Key Concepts

1. **a.** The ratio of the vertical change and the horizontal change between two distinct points (x_1, y_1) and (x_2, y_2) on a line is called the _____ of the line. The slope can be computed from the formula $m =$ _____.

   b. Lines in the same plane that do not intersect are called ________ lines.

   c. Two lines are perpendicular if they intersect at a ________ angle.

   d. If m_1 and m_2 represent the slopes of two nonvertical perpendicular lines then $m_1 \cdot m_2 =$ ________.

   e. The slope of a vertical line is ________. The slope of a ________ line is 0.

Review Exercises

For Exercises 2–6, find the x- and y-intercepts (if they exist). Then graph the line.

2. $x - 5 = 2$

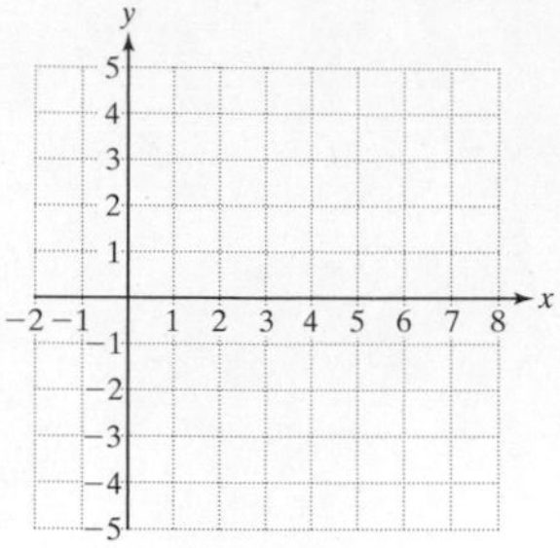

3. $x - 3y = 6$

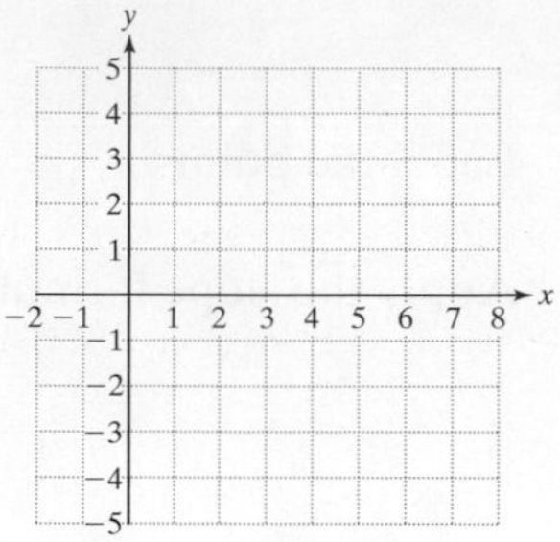

4. $y = \frac{2}{3}x$

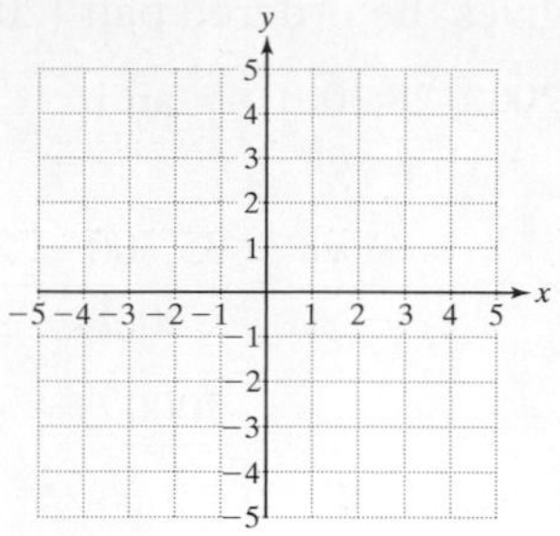

5. $2y - 3 = 0$

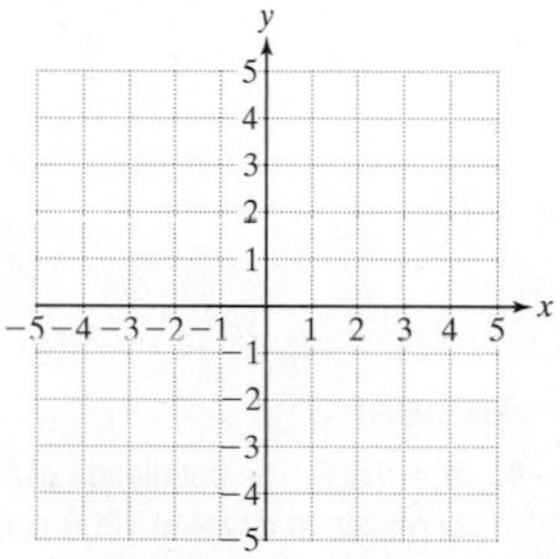

6. $2x = 4y$

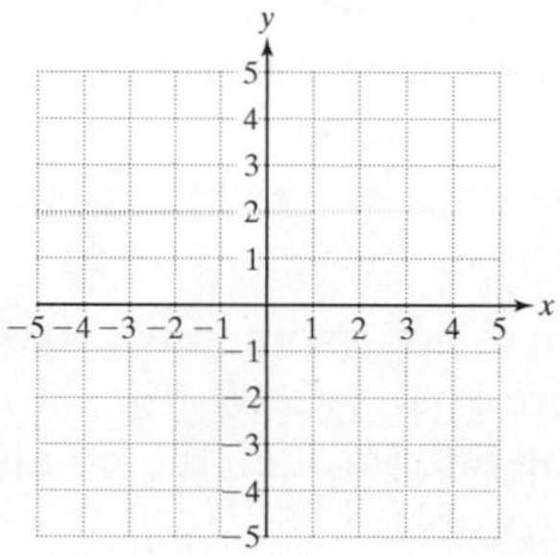

Concept 1: Introduction to Slope

7. Determine the slope of the roof.
(See Example 1.)

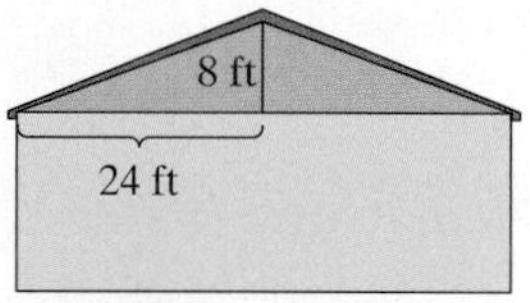

8. Determine the slope of the stairs.

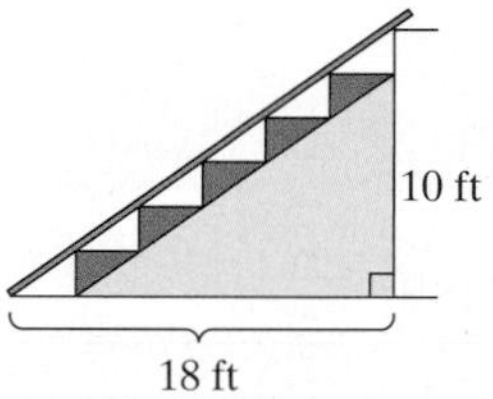

9. Calculate the slope of the handrail.

10. Determine the slope of the treadmill

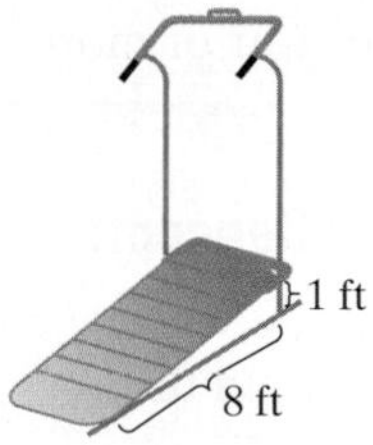

Concept 2: Slope Formula

For Exercises 11–14, fill in the blank with the appropriate term: *zero*, *negative*, *positive*, or *undefined*.

11. The slope of a line parallel to the y-axis is ________.

12. The slope of a horizontal line is ____.

13. The slope of a line that rises from left to right is ______.

14. The slope of a line that falls from left to right is ________.

For Exercises 15–23, determine if the slope is positive, negative, zero, or undefined.

15.

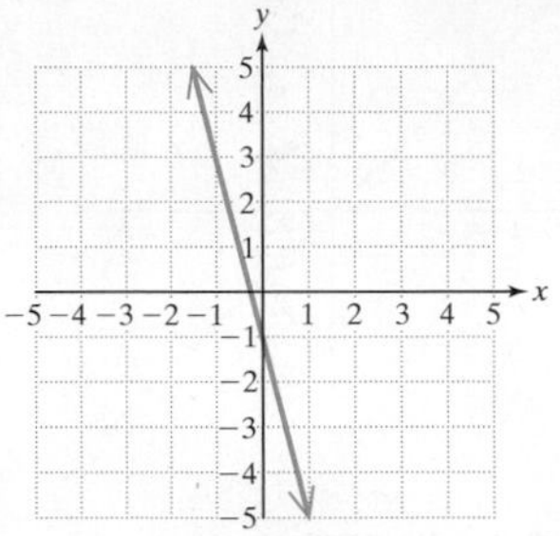

16.

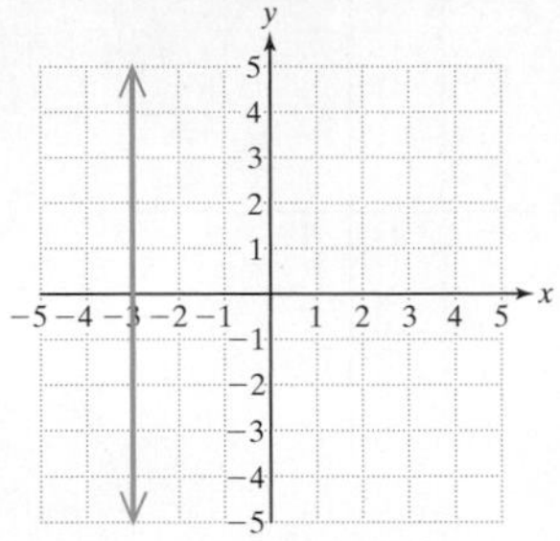

17.

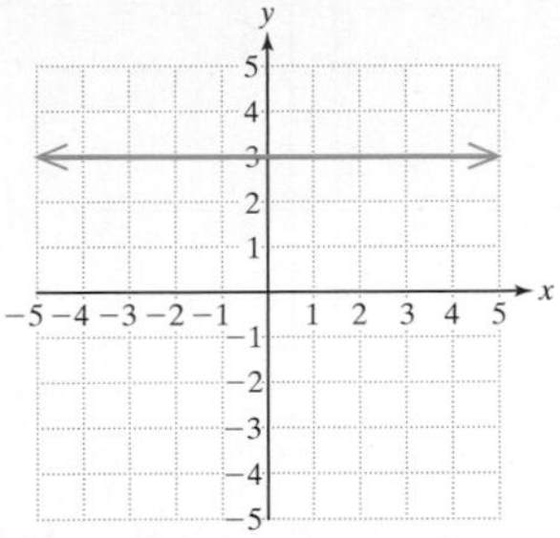

18.

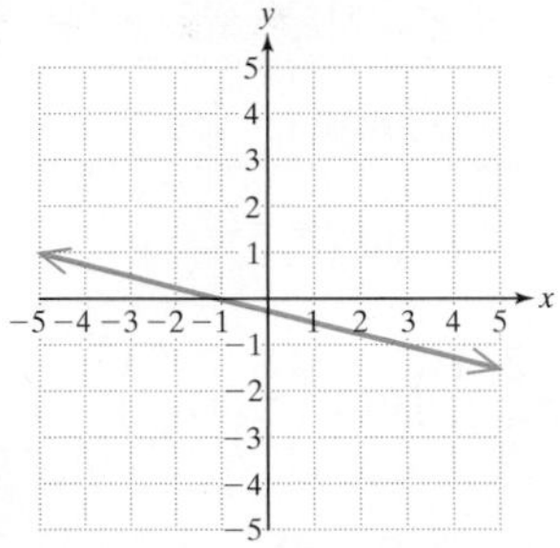

19.

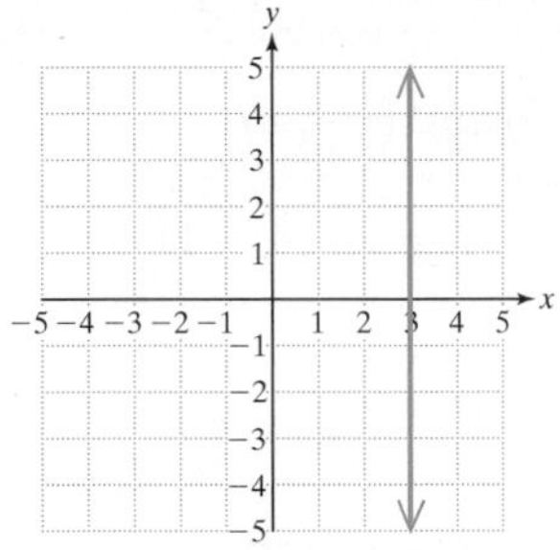

20.

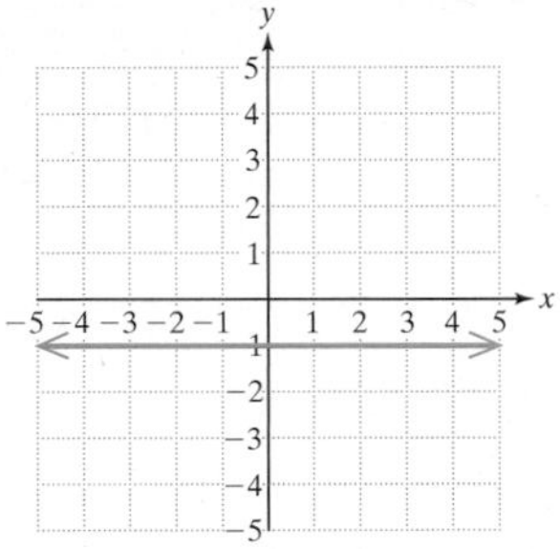

21.

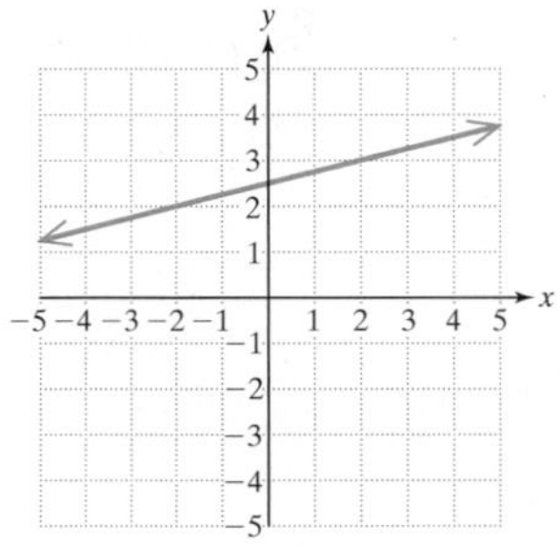

22.

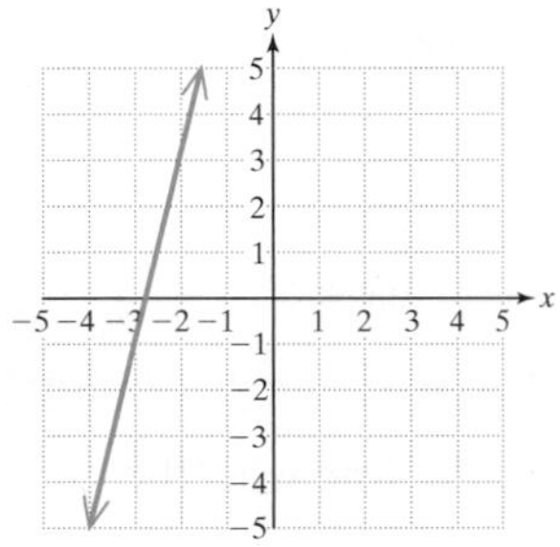

23.

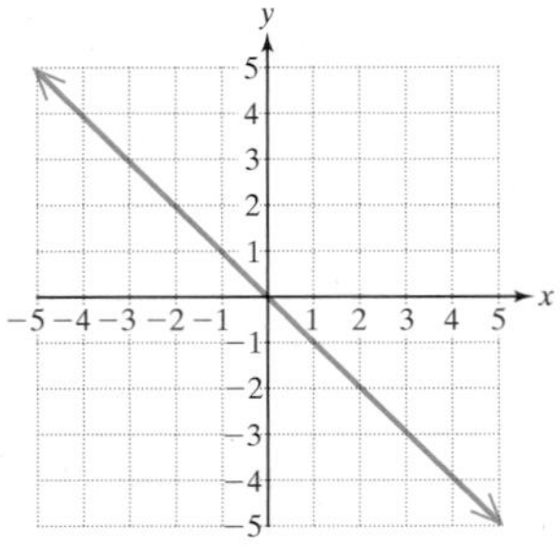

For Exercises 24–32, determine the slope by using the slope formula and any two points on the line. Check your answer by drawing a right triangle, where appropriate, and labeling the “rise” and “run.”

24.

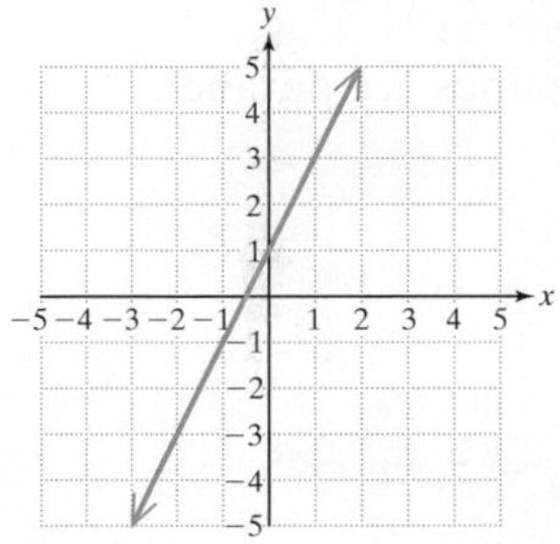

25.

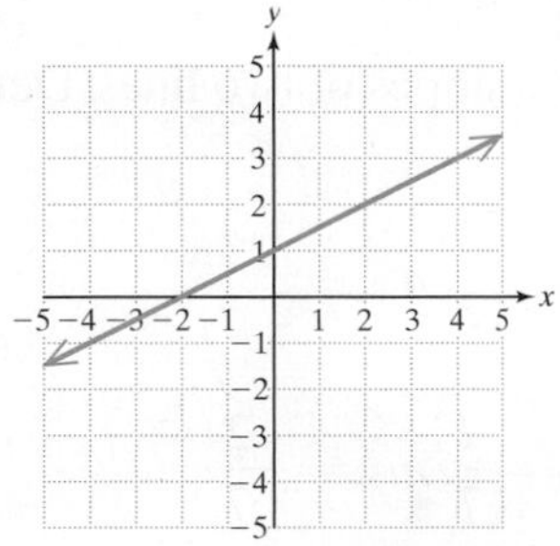

26.

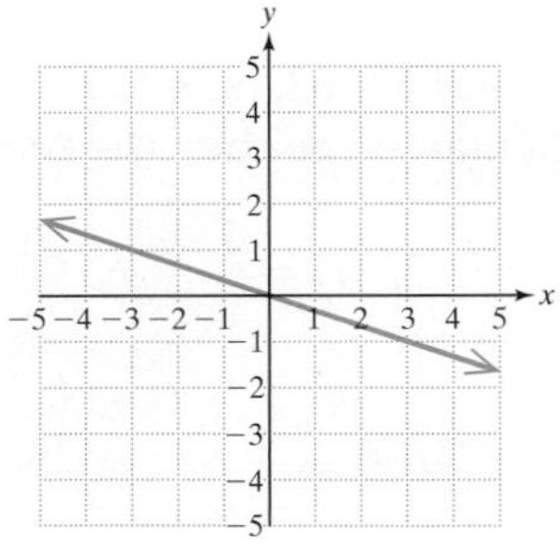

27.

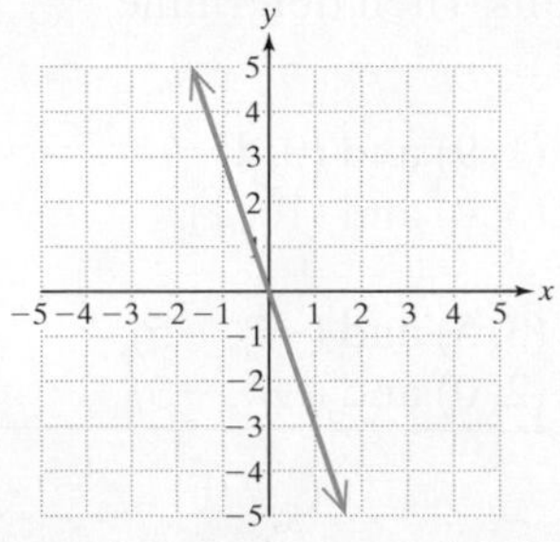

28.

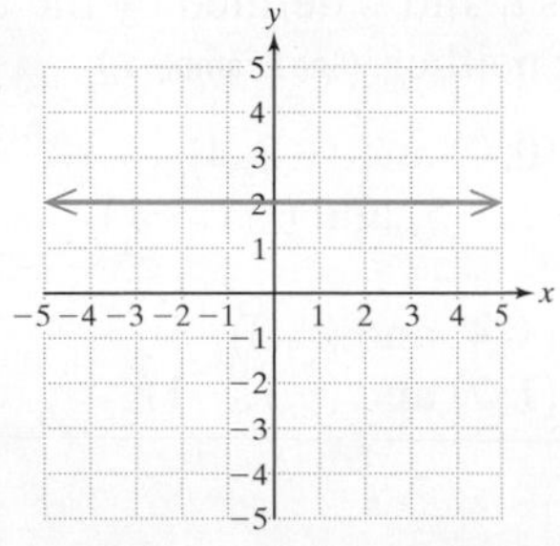

29.

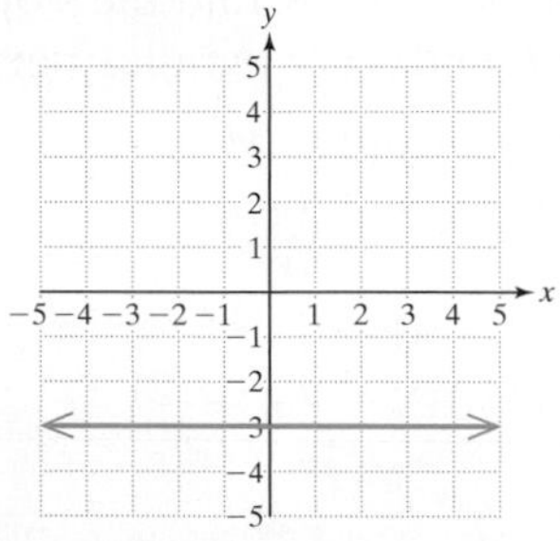

30.

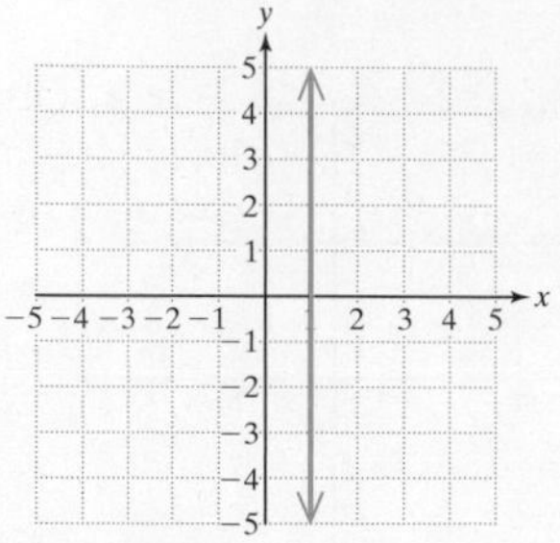

31.

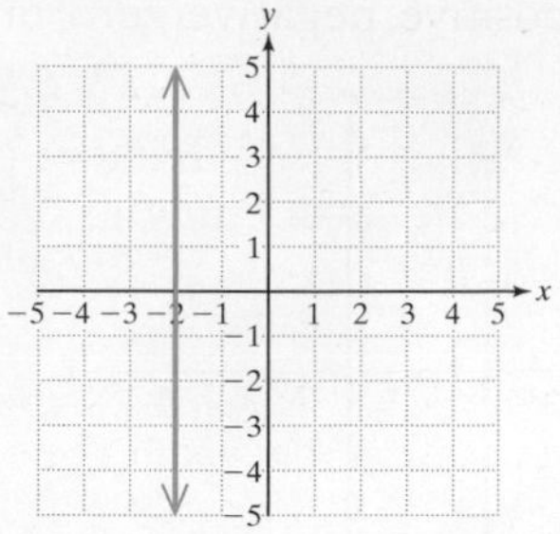

32.

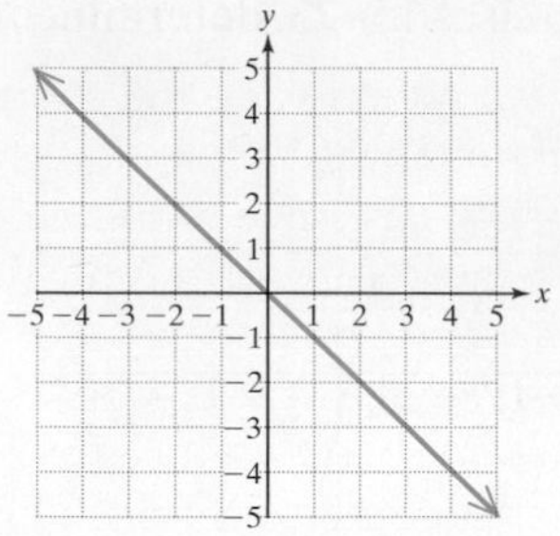

For Exercises 33–50, find the slope of the line that passes through the two points. **(See Examples 2–5.)**

33. (2, 4) and (−4, 2)

34. (−5, 4) and (−11, 12)

35. (−2, 3) and (1, −6)

36. (−3, −4) and (1, −5)

37. (1, 5) and (−4, 2)

38. (−6, −1) and (−2, −3)

39. (5, 3) and (−2, 3)

40. (0, −1) and (−4, −1)

41. (2, −7) and (2, 5)

42. (−4, 3) and (−4, −4)

43. $\left(\frac{1}{2}, \frac{3}{5}\right)$ and $\left(\frac{1}{4}, -\frac{4}{5}\right)$

44. $\left(-\frac{2}{7}, \frac{1}{3}\right)$ and $\left(\frac{8}{7}, -\frac{5}{6}\right)$

45. (3, −1) and (−5, 6)

46. (−6, 5) and (−10, 4)

47. (6.8, −3.4) and (−3.2, 1.1)

48. (−3.15, 8.25) and (6.85, −4.25)

49. (1994, 3.5) and (2000, 2.6)

50. (1988, 4.65) and (1998, 9.25)

Concept 3: Parallel and Perpendicular Lines

For Exercises 51–56, the slope of a line is given. **(See Example 6.)**

a. Determine the slope of a line parallel to the line with the given slope.

b. Determine the slope of a line perpendicular to the line with the given slope.

51. $m = -2$

52. $m = \frac{2}{3}$

53. $m = 0$

54. The slope is undefined.

55. $m = \frac{4}{5}$

56. $m = -4$

For Exercises 57–62, let m_1 and m_2 represent the slopes of two lines. Determine if the lines are parallel, perpendicular, or neither. **(See Example 6.)**

57. $m_1 = -2, m_2 = \frac{1}{2}$

58. $m_1 = \frac{2}{3}, m_2 = \frac{3}{2}$

59. $m_1 = 1, m_2 = \frac{4}{4}$

60. $m_1 = \frac{3}{4}, m_2 = -\frac{8}{6}$

61. $m_1 = \frac{2}{7}, m_2 = -\frac{2}{7}$

62. $m_1 = 5, m_2 = 5$

For Exercises 63–68, find the slopes of the lines l_1 and l_2 defined by the two given points. Then determine whether l_1 and l_2 are parallel, perpendicular, or neither. **(See Example 7.)**

63. l_1: (2, 4) and (−1, −2)
l_2: (1, 7) and (0, 5)

64. l_1: (0, 0) and (−2, 4)
l_2: (1, −5) and (−1, −1)

65. l_1: (1, 9) and (0, 4)
l_2: (5, 2) and (10, 1)

66. l_1: (3, −4) and (−1, −8)
l_2: (5, −5) and (−2, 2)

67. l_1: (4, 4) and (0, 3)
l_2: (1, 7) and (−1, −1)

68. l_1: (3, 5) and (−2, −5)
l_2: (2, 0) and (−4, −3)

Concept 4: Applications of Slope: Rate of Change

69. For a recent year, the average earnings for male workers between the ages of 25 and 34 with a high school diploma was \$32,000. Comparing this value in constant dollars to the average earnings 15 yr later showed that the average earnings have decreased to \$29,600. Find the average rate of change in dollars per year. [*Hint:* Use the ordered pairs (0, 32,000) and (15, 29,600).]

70. In 1985, the U.S. Postal Service charged \$0.22 for first class letters and cards up to 1 oz. By 2009, the price had increased to \$0.44. Let x represent the year, and y represent the cost for 1 oz of first class postage. Find the average rate of change of the cost per year.

71. In 1985, there were 539 thousand male inmates in federal and state prisons. By 2010, the number increased to 1714 thousand. Let x represent the year, and let y represent the number of prisoners (in thousands). **(See Example 8.)**

a. Using the ordered pairs (1985, 539) and (2010, 1714), find the slope of the line.

b. Interpret the slope in the context of this problem.

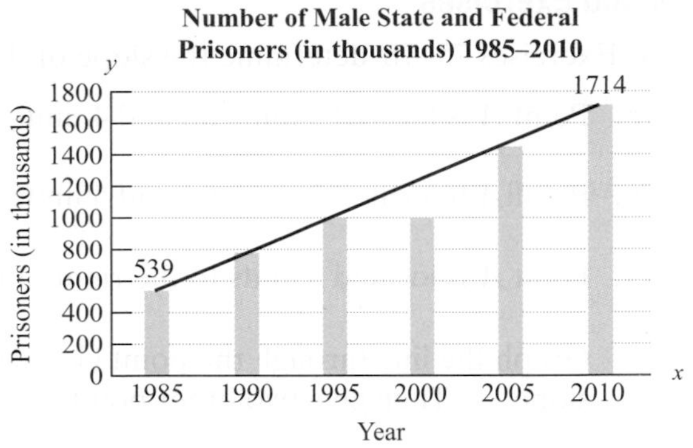

(*Source:* U.S. Bureau of Justice Statistics)

72. In the year 1985, there were 30 thousand female inmates in federal and state prisons. By 2010, the number increased to 120 thousand. Let x represent the year, and let y represent the number of prisoners (in thousands).

a. Using the ordered pairs (1985, 30) and (2010, 120), find the slope of the line.

b. Interpret the slope in the context of this problem.

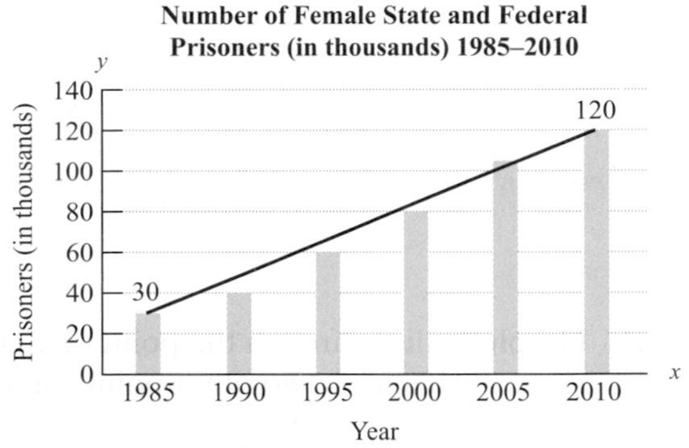

(*Source:* U.S. Bureau of Justice Statistics)

73. The distance, d (in miles), between a lightning strike and an observer is given by the equation $d = 0.2t$, where t is the time (in seconds) between seeing lightning and hearing thunder.

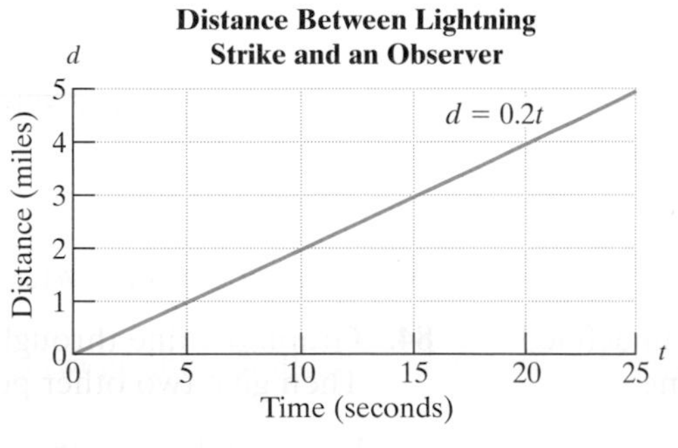

a. If an observer counts 5 sec between seeing lightning and hearing thunder, how far away was the lightning strike?

b. If an observer counts 10 sec between seeing lightning and hearing thunder, how far away was the lightning strike?

c. If an observer counts 15 sec between seeing lightning and hearing thunder, how far away was the lightning strike?

d. What is the slope of the line? Interpret the meaning of the slope in the context of this problem.

Section 3.4 Slope-Intercept Form of a Linear Equation

Concepts

1. **Slope-Intercept Form of a Linear Equation**
2. **Graphing a Line from Its Slope and *y*-Intercept**
3. **Determining Whether Two Lines Are Parallel, Perpendicular, or Neither**
4. **Writing an Equation of a Line Using Slope-Intercept Form**

1. Slope-Intercept Form of a Linear Equation

In Section 3.2, we learned that the solutions to an equation of the form $Ax + By = C$ (where A and B are not both zero) represent a line in a rectangular coordinate system. An equation of a line written in this way is said to be in **standard form**. In this section, we will learn a new form, called **slope-intercept form**, that can be used to determine the slope and y-intercept of a line.

Let $(0, b)$ represent the y-intercept of a line. Let (x, y) represent any other point on the line. See Figure 3-26. Then the slope, m, of the line can be found as follows:

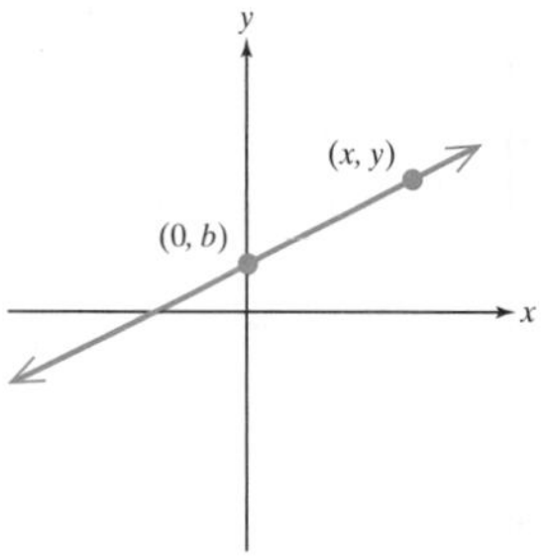

Figure 3-26

Let $(0, b)$ represent (x_1, y_1), and let (x, y) represent (x_2, y_2). Apply the slope formula.

$$m = \frac{(y_2 - y_1)}{(x_2 - x_1)} \rightarrow m = \frac{y - b}{x - 0}$$ Apply the slope formula.

$$m = \frac{y - b}{x}$$ Simplify.

$$mx = \left(\frac{y - b}{x}\right)x$$ Multiply by x to clear fractions.

$$mx = y - b$$

$$mx + b = y - b + b$$ To isolate y, add b to both sides.

$$mx + b = y \quad \text{or} \quad y = mx + b$$ The equation is in slope-intercept form.

> **Slope-Intercept Form of a Linear Equation**
>
> $y = mx + b$ is the slope-intercept form of a linear equation.
> m is the slope and the point $(0, b)$ is the y-intercept.

Example 1 Identifying the Slope and *y*-Intercept From a Linear Equation

For each equation, identify the slope and y-intercept.

a. $y = 3x - 1$ **b.** $y = -2.7x + 5$ **c.** $y = 4x$

Solution:

Each equation is written in slope-intercept form, $y = mx + b$. The slope is the coefficient of x, and the y-intercept is determined by the constant term.

a. $y = 3x - 1$ The slope is 3. The y-intercept is $(0, -1)$.

b. $y = -2.7x + 5$ The slope is -2.7. The y-intercept is $(0, 5)$.

c. $y = 4x$ can be written as $y = 4x + 0$. The slope is 4. The y-intercept is $(0, 0)$.

Skill Practice Identify the slope and the y-intercept.

1. $y = 4x + 6$ **2.** $y = 3.5x - 4.2$ **3.** $y = -7$

Answers

1. slope: 4; y-intercept: $(0, 6)$
2. slope: 3.5; y-intercept: $(0, -4.2)$
3. slope: 0; y-intercept: $(0, -7)$

Given the equation of a line, we can write the equation in slope-intercept form by solving the equation for the y-variable. This is demonstrated in Example 2.

Example 2 **Identifying the Slope and y-Intercept From a Linear Equation**

Given the equation of the line $-5x - 2y = 6$,

a. Write the equation in slope-intercept form.

b. Identify the slope and y-intercept.

Solution:

a. Write the equation in slope-intercept form, $y = mx + b$, by solving for y.

$$-5x - 2y = 6$$

$$-2y = 5x + 6 \qquad \text{Add } 5x \text{ to both sides.}$$

$$\frac{-2y}{-2} = \frac{5x + 6}{-2} \qquad \text{Divide both sides by } -2.$$

$$y = \frac{5x}{-2} + \frac{6}{-2} \qquad \text{Divide each term by } -2 \text{ and simplify.}$$

$$y = -\frac{5}{2}x - 3 \qquad \text{Slope-intercept form}$$

b. The slope is $-\frac{5}{2}$, and the y-intercept is $(0, -3)$.

Skill Practice Given the equation of the line $2x - 6y = -3$.

4. Write the equation in slope-intercept form.

5. Identify the slope and the y-intercept.

2. Graphing a Line from Its Slope and y-Intercept

Slope-intercept form is a useful tool to graph a line. The y-intercept is a known point on the line. The slope indicates the direction of the line and can be used to find a second point. Using slope-intercept form to graph a line is demonstrated in the next example.

Animation

Example 3 **Graphing a Line Using the Slope and y-Intercept**

Graph the equation of the line $y = -\frac{5}{2}x - 3$ by using the slope and y-intercept.

Solution:

First plot the y-intercept, $(0, -3)$.

The slope $m = -\frac{5}{2}$ can be written as

$$m = \frac{-5}{2} \begin{array}{l} \leftarrow \text{The change in } y \text{ is } -5. \\ \leftarrow \text{The change in } x \text{ is } 2. \end{array}$$

To find a second point on the line, start at the y-intercept and move down 5 units and to the right 2 units. Then draw the line through the two points (Figure 3-27).

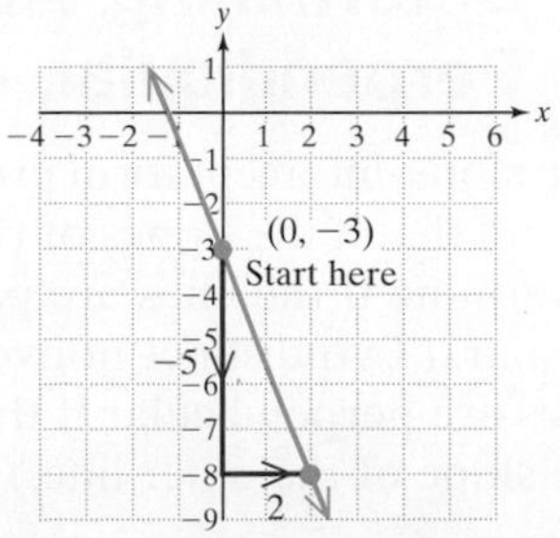

Figure 3-27

Answers

4. $y = \frac{1}{3}x + \frac{1}{2}$

5. slope is $\frac{1}{3}$; y-intercept is $\left(0, \frac{1}{2}\right)$

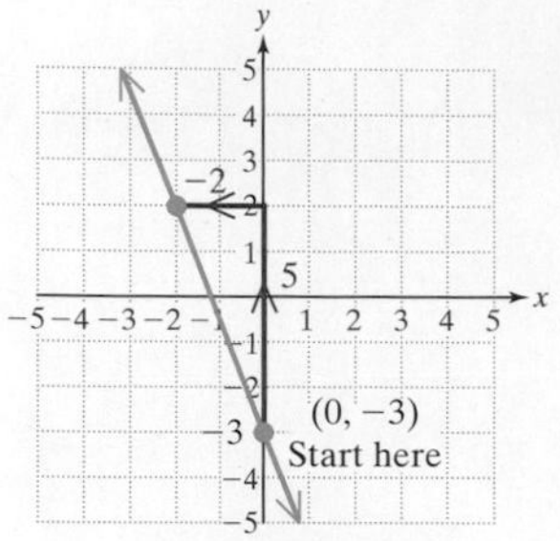

Figure 3-28

Similarly, the slope can be written as

$$m = \frac{5}{-2} \quad \begin{array}{l}\leftarrow \text{The change in } y \text{ is } 5.\\ \leftarrow \text{The change in } x \text{ is } -2.\end{array}$$

To find a second point, start at the y-intercept and move up 5 units and to the left 2 units. Then draw the line through the two points (Figure 3-28).

Skill Practice

6. Graph the equation by using the slope and the y-intercept. $y = 2x - 3$

Example 4 Graphing a Line Using the Slope and y-Intercept

Graph the equation of the line $y = 4x$ by using the slope and y-intercept.

Solution:

The line can be written as $y = 4x + 0$. Therefore, we can plot the y-intercept at $(0, 0)$. The slope $m = 4$ can be written as

$$m = \frac{4}{1} \quad \begin{array}{l}\leftarrow \text{The change in } y \text{ is } 4.\\ \leftarrow \text{The change in } x \text{ is } 1.\end{array}$$

To find a second point on the line, start at the y-intercept and move up 4 units and to the right 1 unit. Then draw the line through the two points (Figure 3-29).

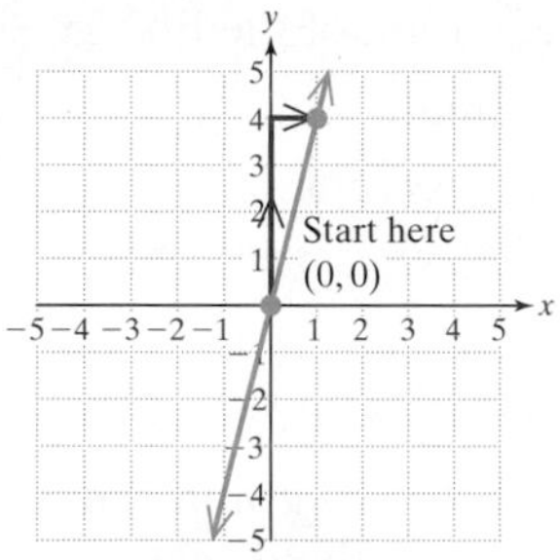

Figure 3-29

Skill Practice

7. Graph the equation by using the slope and the y-intercept. $y = -\frac{1}{4}x$

3. Determining Whether Two Lines Are Parallel, Perpendicular, or Neither

The slope-intercept form provides a means to find the slope of a line by inspection. Recall that if the slopes of two lines are known, then we can compare the slopes to determine if the lines are parallel, perpendicular, or neither parallel nor perpendicular. (Two distinct nonvertical lines are parallel if their slopes are equal. Two lines are perpendicular if the slope of one line is the opposite of the reciprocal of the slope of the other line.)

Answers

6–7.

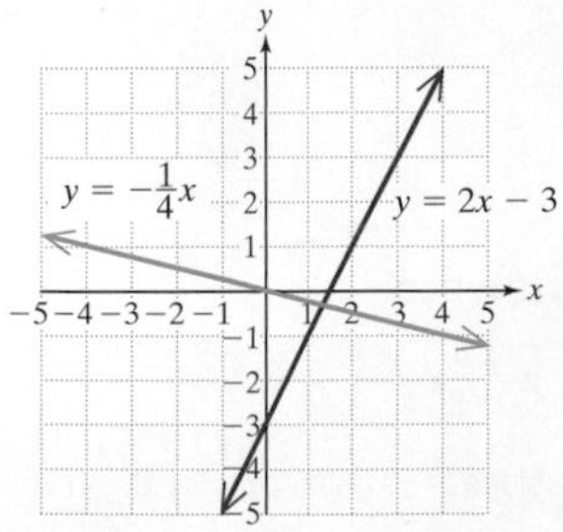

Example 5 Determining If Two Lines Are Parallel, Perpendicular, or Neither

For each pair of lines, determine if they are parallel, perpendicular, or neither.

a. l_1: $y = 3x - 5$
l_2: $y = 3x + 1$

b. l_1: $y = \frac{3}{2}x + 2$
l_2: $y = \frac{2}{3}x + 1$

Solution:

a. l_1: $y = 3x - 5$ The slope of l_1 is 3.
l_2: $y = 3x + 1$ The slope of l_2 is 3.

Because the slopes are the same, the lines are parallel.

b. l_1: $y = \frac{3}{2}x + 2$ The slope of l_1 is $\frac{3}{2}$.
l_2: $y = \frac{2}{3}x + 1$ The slope of l_2 is $\frac{2}{3}$.

The slopes are not the same. Therefore, the lines are not parallel. The values of the slopes are reciprocals, but they are not opposite in sign. Therefore, the lines are not perpendicular. The lines are neither parallel nor perpendicular.

Skill Practice For each pair of lines determine if they are parallel, perpendicular, or neither.

8. $y = 3x - 5$
$y = -3x - 15$

9. $y = \dfrac{5}{6}x - \dfrac{1}{2}$
$y = \dfrac{5}{6}x + \dfrac{1}{2}$

Example 6 Determining If Two Lines Are Parallel, Perpendicular, or Neither

For each pair of lines, determine if they are parallel, perpendicular, or neither.

a. l_1: $x - 3y = -9$
l_2: $3x = -y + 4$

b. l_1: $x = 2$
l_2: $2y = 8$

Solution:

a. First write the equation of each line in slope-intercept form.

l_1:
$$x - 3y = -9$$
$$-3y = -x - 9$$
$$\frac{-3y}{-3} = \frac{-x}{-3} - \frac{9}{-3}$$
$$y = \frac{1}{3}x + 3$$

l_2:
$$3x = -y + 4$$
$$3x + y = 4$$
$$y = -3x + 4$$

l_1: $y = \frac{1}{3}x + 3$ The slope of l_1 is $\frac{1}{3}$.
l_2: $y = -3x + 4$ The slope of l_2 is -3.

The slope of $\frac{1}{3}$ is the opposite of the reciprocal of -3. Therefore, the lines are perpendicular.

Answers
8. Neither **9.** Parallel

b. The equation $x = 2$ represents a vertical line because the equation is in the form $x = k$.

The equation $2y = 8$ can be simplified to $y = 4$, which represents a horizontal line.

In this example, we do not need to analyze the slopes because vertical lines and horizontal lines are perpendicular.

Skill Practice For each pair of lines, determine if they are parallel, perpendicular, or neither.

10. $x - 5y = 10$
$5x - 1 = -y$

11. $y = -5$
$x = 6$

4. Writing an Equation of a Line Using Slope-Intercept Form

The slope-intercept form of a linear equation can be used to write an equation of a line when the slope is known and the y-intercept is known.

Example 7 Writing an Equation of a Line Using Slope-Intercept Form

Write an equation of the line whose slope is $\frac{2}{3}$ and whose y-intercept is $(0, 8)$.

Solution:

The slope is given as $m = \frac{2}{3}$, and the y-intercept $(0, b)$ is given as $(0, 8)$. Substitute the values $m = \frac{2}{3}$ and $b = 8$ into the slope-intercept form of a line.

$$y = mx + b$$

$$y = \frac{2}{3}x + 8$$

Skill Practice

12. Write an equation of the line whose slope is -4 and y-intercept is $(0, -10)$.

Example 8 Writing an Equation of a Line Using Slope-Intercept Form

Write an equation of the line having a slope of 2 and passing through the point $(-3, 1)$.

Solution:

To find an equation of a line using slope-intercept form, it is necessary to find the value of m and b. The slope is given in the problem as $m = 2$. Therefore, the slope-intercept form becomes

$$y = mx + b$$

$$y = 2x + b$$

Answers

10. Perpendicular **11.** Perpendicular
12. $y = -4x - 10$

Because the point $(-3, 1)$ is on the line, it is a solution to the equation. Therefore, to find b, substitute the values of x and y from the ordered pair $(-3, 1)$ and solve the resulting equation.

$$y = 2x + b$$

$$1 = 2(-3) + b \qquad \text{Substitute } y = 1 \text{ and } x = -3.$$

$$1 = -6 + b \qquad \text{Simplify and solve for } b.$$

$$7 = b$$

Now with m and b known, the slope-intercept form is $y = 2x + 7$.

TIP: The equation from Example 8 can be checked by graphing the line $y = 2x + 7$. The slope $m = 2$ can be written as $m = \frac{2}{1}$. Therefore, to graph the line, start at the y-intercept (0, 7) and move up 2 units and to the right 1 unit.

The graph verifies that the line passes through the point $(-3, 1)$ as it should.

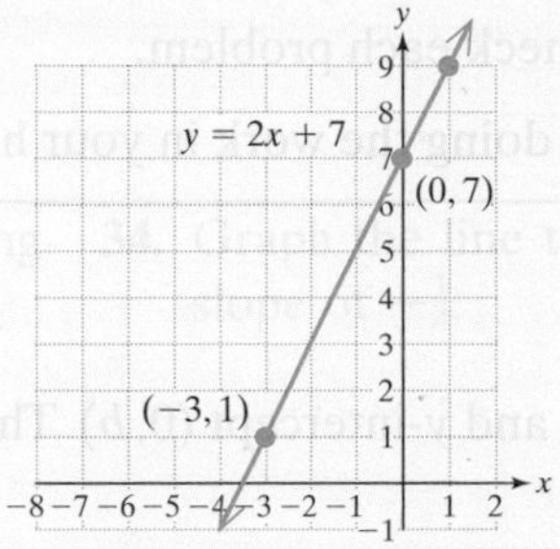

Skill Practice

13. Write an equation of the line having a slope of -3 and passing through the point $(-2, -5)$.

Answer

13. $y = -3x - 11$

Calculator Connections

Topic: Using the *ZSquare* Option in Zoom

In Example 6(a) we found that the equations $y = \frac{1}{3}x + 3$ and $y = -3x + 4$ represent perpendicular lines. We can verify our results by graphing the lines on a graphing calculator.

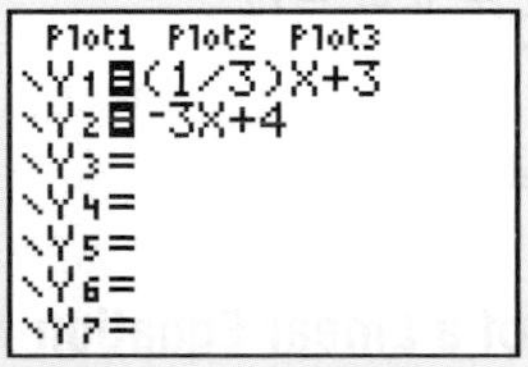

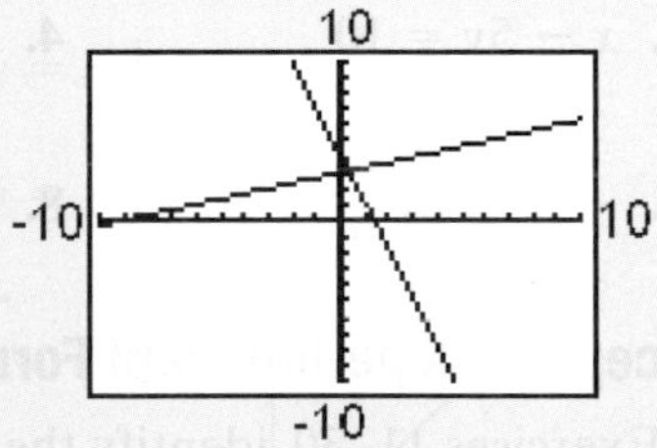

Notice that the lines do not appear perpendicular in the calculator display. That is, they do not appear to form a right angle at the point of intersection. Because many calculators have a rectangular screen, the standard viewing window is elongated in the horizontal direction. To eliminate this distortion, try using a *ZSquare* option, which is located under the Zoom menu. This feature will set the viewing window so that equal distances on the display denote an equal number of units on the graph.

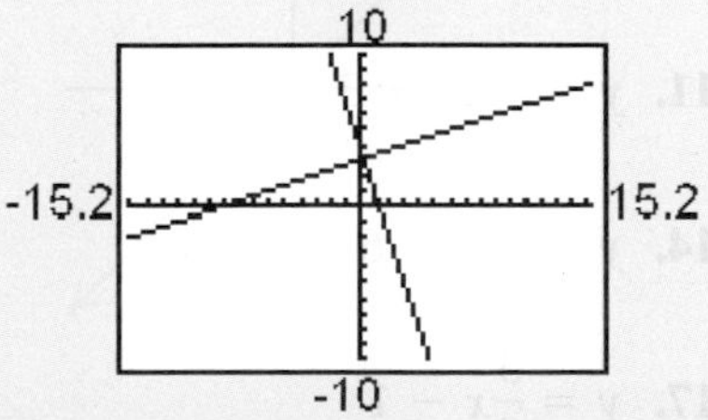

Calculator Exercises

For each pair of lines, determine if the lines are parallel, perpendicular, or neither. Then use a square viewing window to graph the lines on a graphing calculator to verify your results.

1. $x + y = 1$
$x - y = -3$

2. $3x + y = -2$
$6x + 2y = 6$

3. $2x - y = 4$
$3x + 2y = 4$

4. Graph the lines defined by $y = x + 1$ and $y = 0.99x + 3$. Are these lines parallel? Explain.

5. Graph the lines defined by $y = -2x - 1$ and $y = -2x - 0.99$. Are these lines the same? Explain.

6. Graph the line defined by $y = 0.001x + 3$. Is this line horizontal? Explain.

For Exercises 41–52, write each equation in slope-intercept form (if possible) and graph the line. **(See Examples 3–4.)**

41. $2x + y = 9$

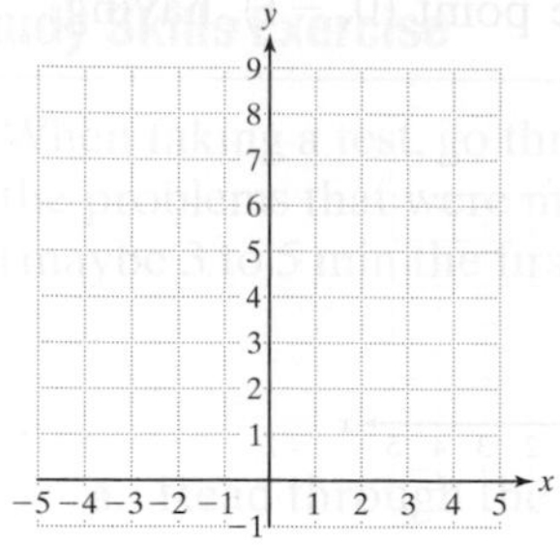

42. $-6x + y = 8$

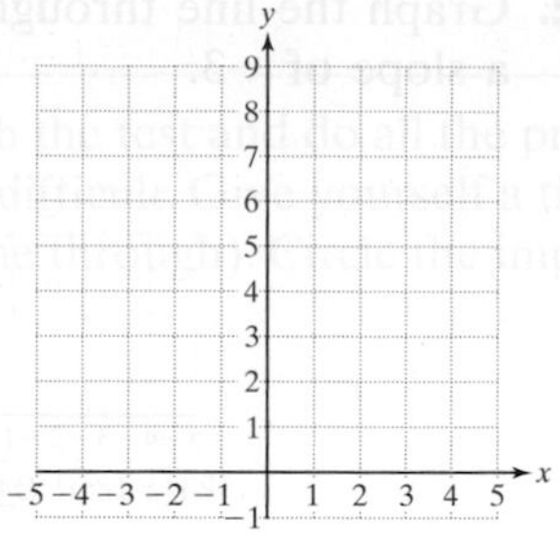

43. $x - 2y = 6$

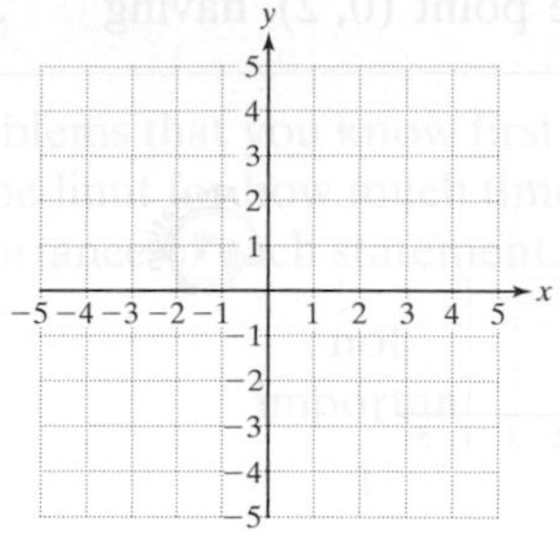

44. $5x - 2y = 2$

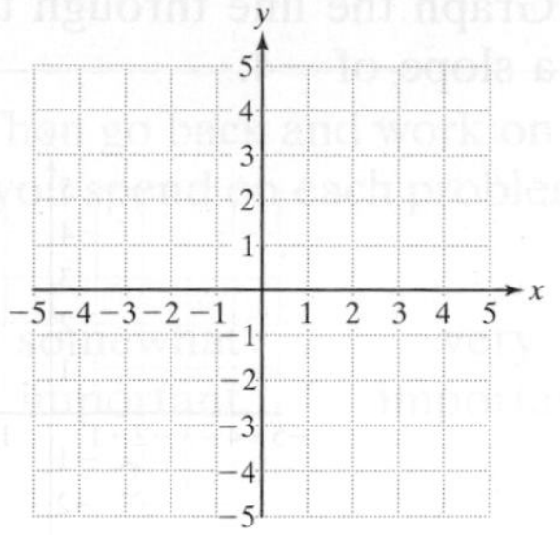

45. $2x = -4y + 6$

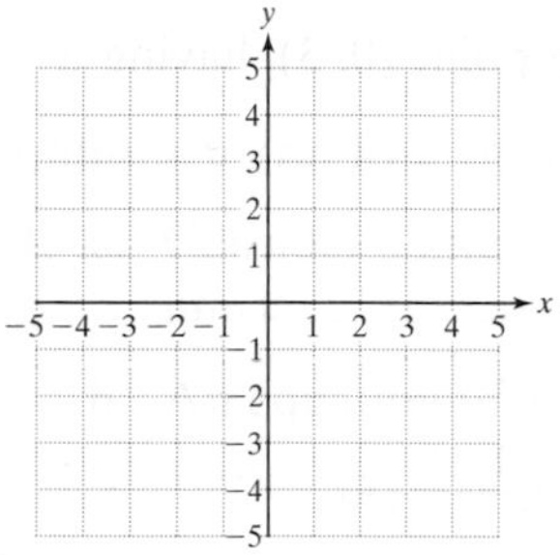

46. $6x = 2y - 14$

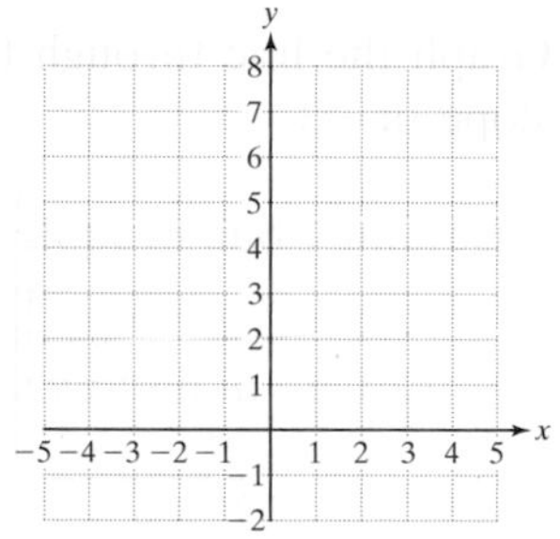

47. $x + y = 0$

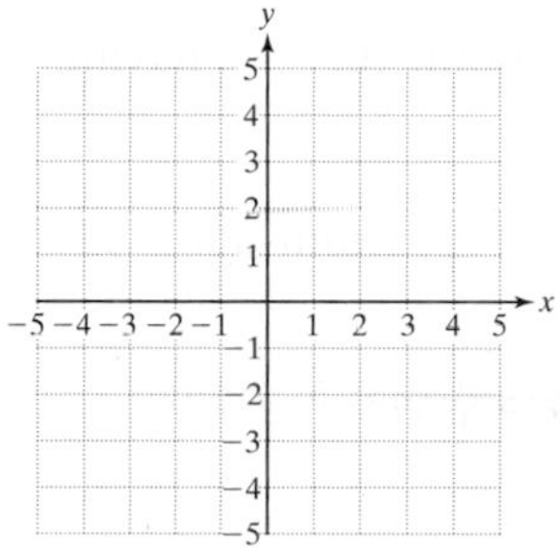

48. $x - y = 0$

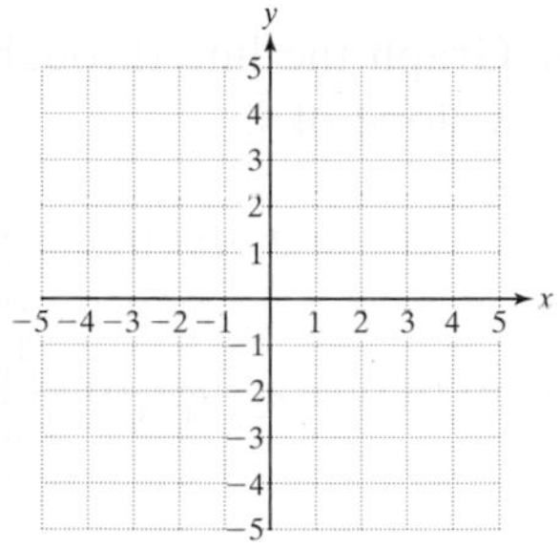

49. $5y = 4x$

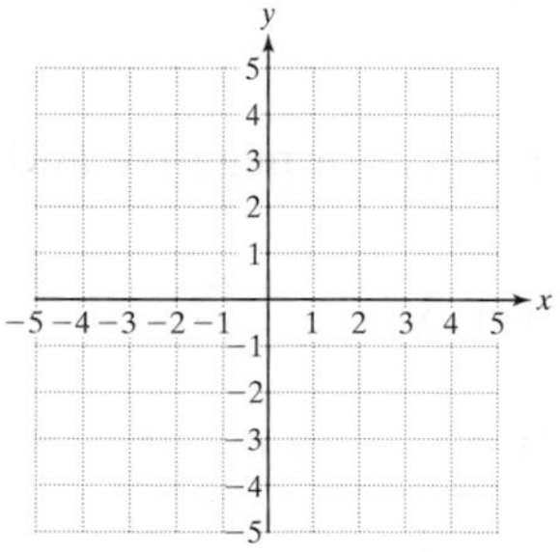

50. $-2x = 5y$

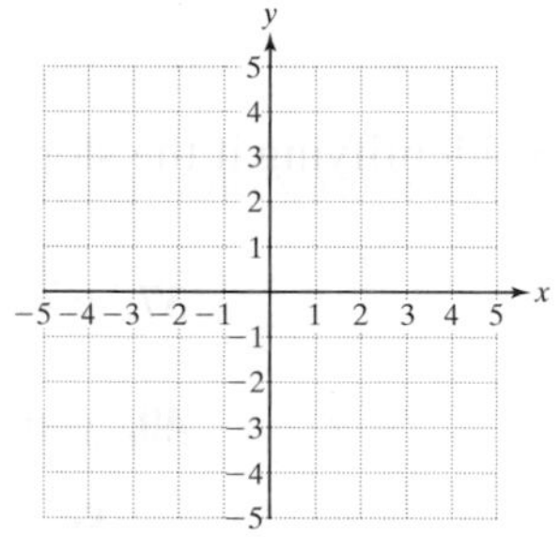

51. $3y + 2 = 0$

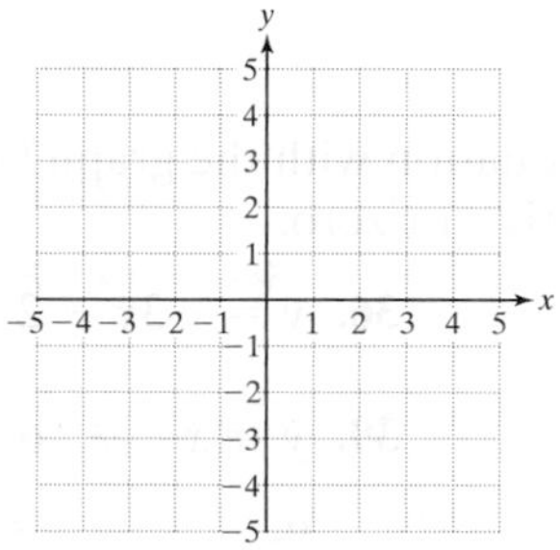

52. $1 + 5y = 6$

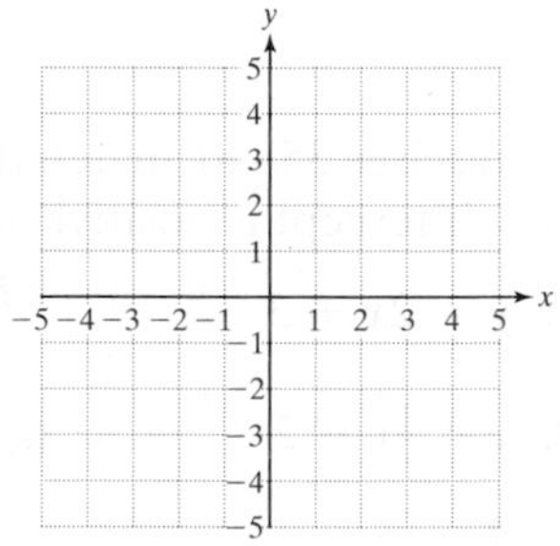

Concept 3: Determining Whether Two Lines Are Parallel, Perpendicular, or Neither

For Exercises 53–68, determine if the equations represent parallel lines, perpendicular lines, or neither. **(See Examples 5–6.)**

53. l_1: $y = -2x - 3$
l_2: $y = \frac{1}{2}x + 4$

54. l_1: $y = \frac{4}{3}x - 2$
l_2: $y = -\frac{3}{4}x + 6$

55. l_1: $y = \frac{4}{5}x - \frac{1}{2}$
l_2: $y = \frac{5}{4}x - \frac{2}{3}$

56. l_1: $y = \frac{1}{5}x + 1$
l_2: $y = 5x - 3$

57. l_1: $y = -9x + 6$
l_2: $y = -9x - 1$

58. l_1: $y = 4x - 1$
l_2: $y = 4x + \frac{1}{2}$

59. l_1: $x = 3$
l_2: $y = \frac{7}{4}$

60. l_1: $y = \frac{2}{3}$
l_2: $x = 6$

61. l_1: $2x = 4$
l_2: $6 = x$

62. l_1: $2y = 7$
l_2: $y = 4$

63. l_1: $2x + 3y = 6$
l_2: $3x - 2y = 12$

64. l_1: $4x + 5y = 20$
l_2: $5x - 4y = 60$

65. l_1: $4x + 2y = 6$
l_2: $4x + 8y = 16$

66. l_1: $3x + y = 5$
l_2: $x + 3y = 18$

67. l_1: $y = \frac{1}{5}x - 3$
l_2: $2x - 10y = 20$

68. l_1: $y = \frac{1}{3}x + 2$
l_2: $-x + 3y = 12$

Concept 4: Writing an Equation of a Line Using Slope-Intercept Form

For Exercises 69–80, write an equation of the line given the following information. Write the answer in slope-intercept form if possible. **(See Examples 7–8.)**

69. The slope is $-\frac{1}{3}$, and the y-intercept is $(0, 2)$.

70. The slope is $\frac{2}{3}$, and the y-intercept is $(0, -1)$.

71. The slope is 10, and the y-intercept is $(0, -19)$.

72. The slope is -14, and the y-intercept is $(0, 2)$.

73. The slope is 6, and the line passes through the point $(1, -2)$.

74. The slope is -4, and the line passes through the point $(4, -3)$.

75. The slope is $\frac{1}{2}$, and the line passes through the point $(-4, -5)$.

76. The slope is $-\frac{2}{3}$, and the line passes through the point $(3, -1)$.

77. The slope is 0, and the y-intercept is -11.

78. The slope is 0, and the y-intercept is $\dfrac{6}{7}$.

79. The slope is 5, and the line passes through the origin.

80. The slope is -3, and the line passes through the origin.

Expanding Your Skills

For Exercises 81–86, write an equation of the line that passes through two points by following these steps:

Step 1: Find the slope of the line using the slope formula, $m = \dfrac{y_2 - y_1}{x_2 - x_1}$.

Step 2: Using the slope from Step 1 and either given point, follow the procedure given in Example 8 to find an equation of the line in slope-intercept form.

81. $(2, -1)$ and $(0, 3)$

82. $(4, -8)$ and $(0, -4)$

83. $(3, 1)$ and $(-3, 3)$

84. $(2, -3)$ and $(4, -2)$

85. $(1, 3)$ and $(-2, -9)$

86. $(1, 7)$ and $(-2, 4)$

87. The number of reported cases of Lyme disease in the United States can be modeled by the equation $y = 1203x + 10{,}006$. In this equation, x represents the number of years since 1993, and y represents the number of cases of Lyme disease.

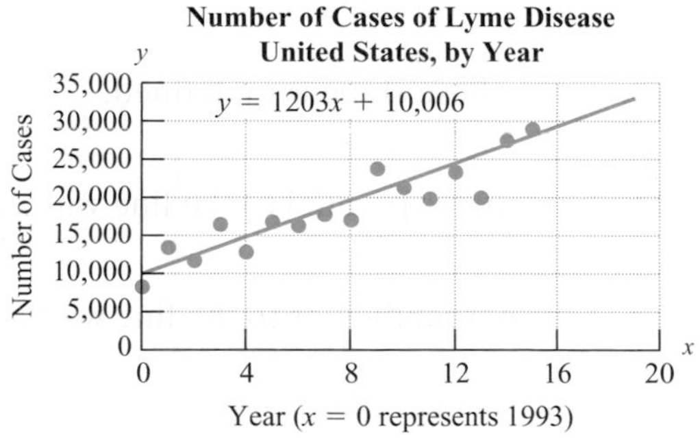

a. What is the slope of this line and what does it mean in the context of this problem?

b. What is the y-intercept, and what does it mean in the context of this problem?

c. Use the model to estimate the number of cases of Lyme disease in the year 2010.

d. During what year would the predicted number of cases be 36,472?

88. A phone bill is determined each month by a \$16.95 flat fee plus \$0.10/min of long distance. The equation, $C = 0.10x + 16.95$ represents the total monthly cost, C, for x minutes of long distance.

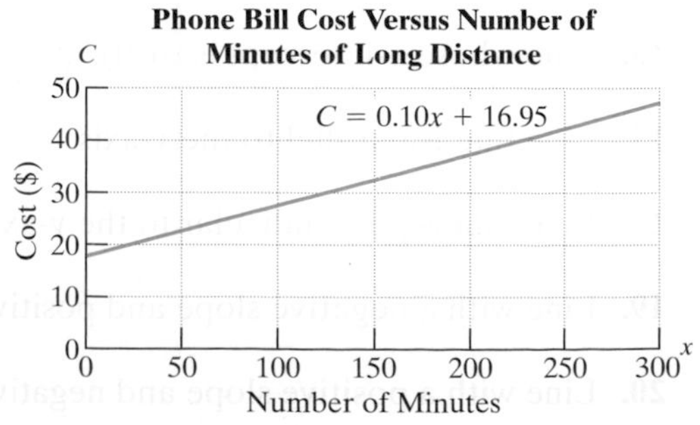

a. Identify the slope. Interpret the meaning of the slope in the context of this problem.

b. Identify the C-intercept. Interpret the meaning of the C-intercept in the context of this problem.

c. Use the equation to determine the total cost of 234 min of long distance.

Skill Practice

1. Use the point-slope formula to write an equation of the line having a slope of -4 and passing through $(-1, 5)$. Write the answer in slope-intercept form.

The equation $y = 3x + 2$ from Example 1 is graphed in Figure 3-30. Notice that the line does indeed pass through the point $(-2, -4)$.

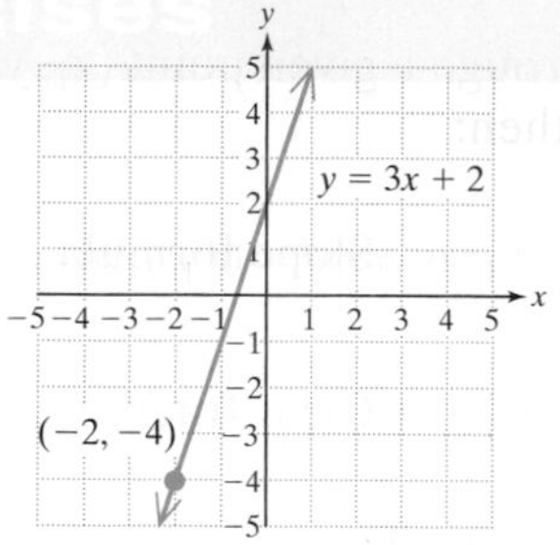

Figure 3-30

2. Writing an Equation of a Line Given Two Points

Example 2 is similar to Example 1; however, the slope must first be found from two given points.

Example 2 Writing an Equation of a Line Given Two Points

Use the point-slope formula to find an equation of the line passing through the points $(-2, 5)$ and $(4, -1)$. Write the final answer in slope-intercept form.

Solution:

Given two points on a line, the slope can be found with the slope formula.

$(-2, 5)$ and $(4, -1)$

(x_1, y_1) (x_2, y_2) Label the points.

$$m = \frac{y_2 - y_1}{x_2 - x_1} = \frac{(-1) - (5)}{(4) - (-2)} = \frac{-6}{6} = -1$$

To apply the point-slope formula, use the slope, $m = -1$ and either given point. We will choose the point $(-2, 5)$ as (x_1, y_1).

$y - y_1 = m(x - x_1)$

$y - 5 = -1[x - (-2)]$ Substitute $m = -1$, $x_1 = -2$, and $y_1 = 5$.

$y - 5 = -1(x + 2)$ Simplify.

$y - 5 = -x - 2$

$y = -x + 3$

TIP: The point-slope formula can be applied using either given point for (x_1, y_1). In Example 2, using the point $(4, -1)$ for (x_1, y_1) produces the same result.

$y - y_1 = m(x - x_1)$

$y - (-1) = -1(x - 4)$

$y + 1 = -x + 4$

$y = -x + 3$

Skill Practice

2. Use the point-slope formula to write an equation of the line passing through the points $(1, -1)$ and $(-1, -5)$.

Answers

1. $y = -4x + 1$ 2. $y = 2x - 3$

The solution to Example 2 can be checked by graphing the line $y = -x + 3$ using the slope and y-intercept. Notice that the line passes through the points $(-2, 5)$ and $(4, -1)$ as expected. See Figure 3-31.

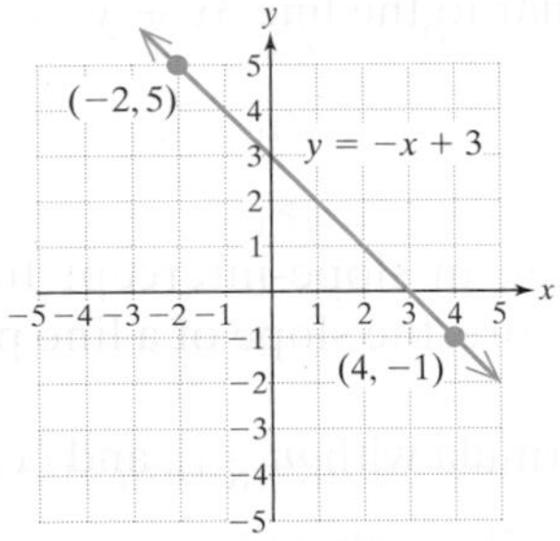

Figure 3-31

3. Writing an Equation of a Line Parallel or Perpendicular to Another Line

To write an equation of a line using the point-slope formula, the slope must be known. If the slope is not explicitly given, then other information must be used to determine the slope. In Example 2, the slope was found using the slope formula. Examples 3 and 4 show other situations in which we might find the slope.

Example 3 Writing an Equation of a Line Parallel to Another Line

Use the point-slope formula to find an equation of the line passing through the point $(-1, 0)$ and parallel to the line $y = -4x + 3$. Write the final answer in slope-intercept form.

Solution:

Figure 3-32 shows the line $y = -4x + 3$ (pictured in black) and a line parallel to it (pictured in blue) that passes through the point $(-1, 0)$. The equation of the given line, $y = -4x + 3$, is written in slope-intercept form, and its slope is easily identified as -4. The line parallel to the given line must also have a slope of -4.

Apply the point-slope formula using $m = -4$ and the point $(x_1, y_1) = (-1, 0)$.

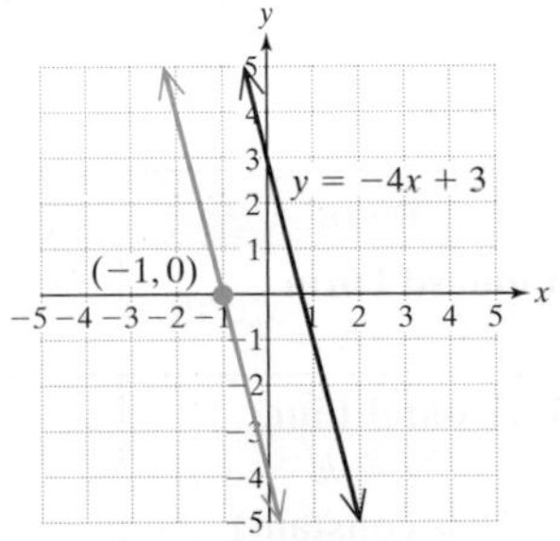

Figure 3-32

$$y - y_1 = m(x - x_1)$$
$$y - 0 = -4[x - (-1)]$$
$$y = -4(x + 1)$$
$$y = -4x - 4$$

Skill Practice

3. Use the point-slope formula to write an equation of the line passing through $(8, 2)$ and parallel to the line $y = \frac{3}{4}x - \frac{1}{2}$.

TIP: When writing an equation of a line, slope-intercept form or standard form is usually preferred. For instance, the solution to Example 3 can be written as follows.

Slope-intercept form:
$y = -4x - 4$

Standard form:
$4x + y = -4$

Answer

3. $y = \frac{3}{4}x - 4$

Vocabulary and Key Concepts

1. **a.** The standard form of an equation of a line is ______________, where A and B are not both zero and C is a constant.

b. A line defined by an equation $y = k$, where k is a constant is a (horizontal/vertical) line.

c. A line defined by an equation $x = k$, where k is a constant is a (horizontal/vertical) line.

d. Given the slope-intercept form of an equation of a line, $y = mx + b$, the value of m is the ______________ and b is the ______________.

e. Given a point (x_1, y_1) on a line with slope m, the point-slope formula is given by ______________.

Review Exercises

For Exercises 2–6, graph each equation.

2. $-5x - 15 = 0$

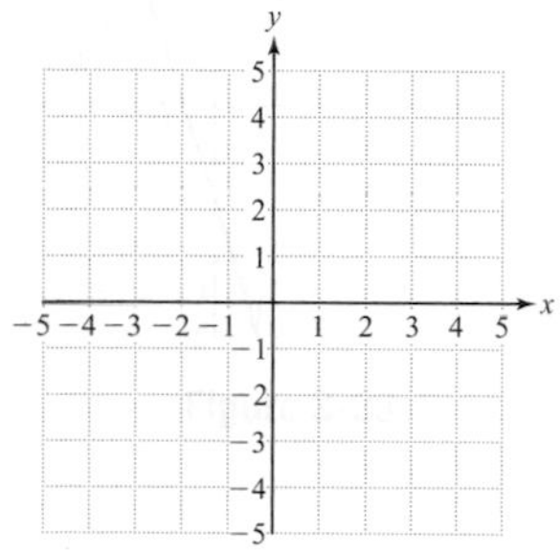

3. $2x - 3y = -3$

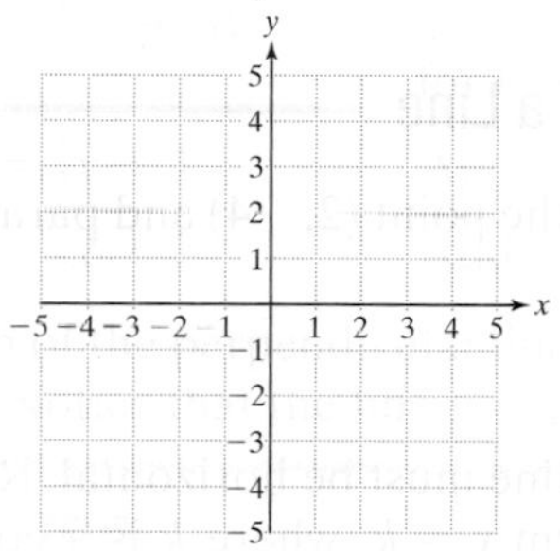

4. $y = -2x$

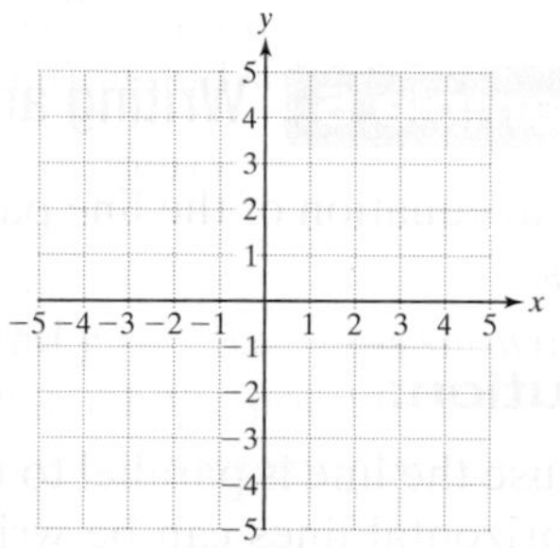

5. $3 - y = 9$

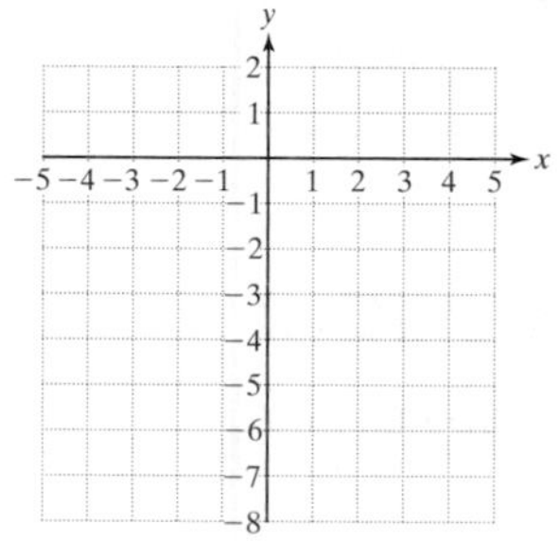

6. $y = \frac{4}{5}x$

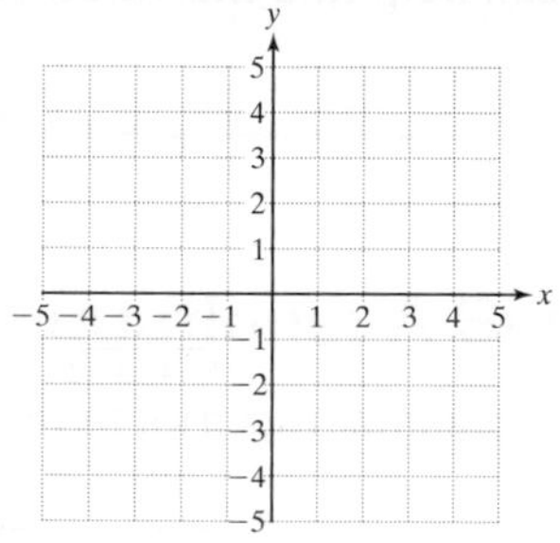

For Exercises 7–10, find the slope of the line that passes through the given points.

7. $(1, -3)$ and $(2, 6)$

8. $(2, -4)$ and $(-2, 4)$

9. $(-2, 5)$ and $(5, 5)$

10. $(6.1, 2.5)$ and $(6.1, -1.5)$

Concept 1: Writing an Equation of a Line Using the Point-Slope Formula

For Exercises 11–16, use the point-slope formula (if possible) to write an equation of the line given the following information. **(See Example 1.)**

11. The slope is 3, and the line passes through the point $(-2, 1)$.

12. The slope is -2, and the line passes through the point $(1, -5)$.

13. The slope is -4, and the line passes through the point $(-3, -2)$.

14. The slope is 5, and the line passes through the point $(-1, -3)$.

15. The slope is $-\frac{1}{2}$, and the line passes through $(-1, 0)$.

16. The slope is $-\frac{3}{4}$, and the line passes through $(2, 0)$.

Concept 2: Writing an Equation of a Line Given Two Points

For Exercises 17–22, use the point-slope formula to write an equation of the line given the following information. **(See Example 2.)**

17. The line passes through the points $(-2, -6)$ and $(1, 0)$.

18. The line passes through the points $(-2, 5)$ and $(0, 1)$.

19. The line passes through the points $(0, -4)$ and $(-1, -3)$.

20. The line passes through the points $(1, -3)$ and $(-7, 2)$.

21. The line passes through the points $(2.2, -3.3)$ and $(12.2, -5.3)$.

22. The line passes through the points $(4.7, -2.2)$ and $(-0.3, 6.8)$.

For Exercises 23–28, find an equation of the line through the given points. Write the final answer in slope-intercept form.

23.

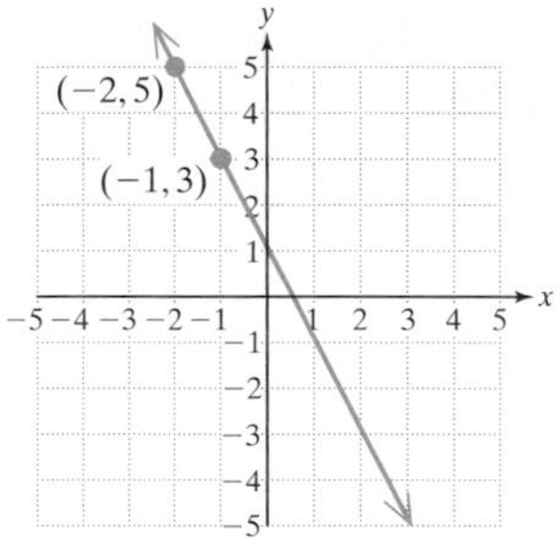

24.

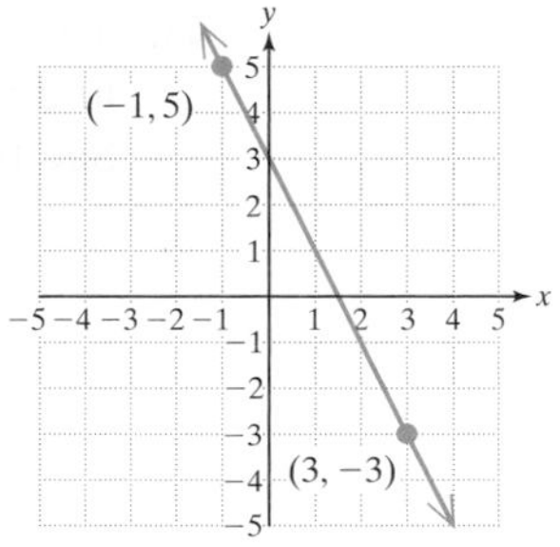

25.

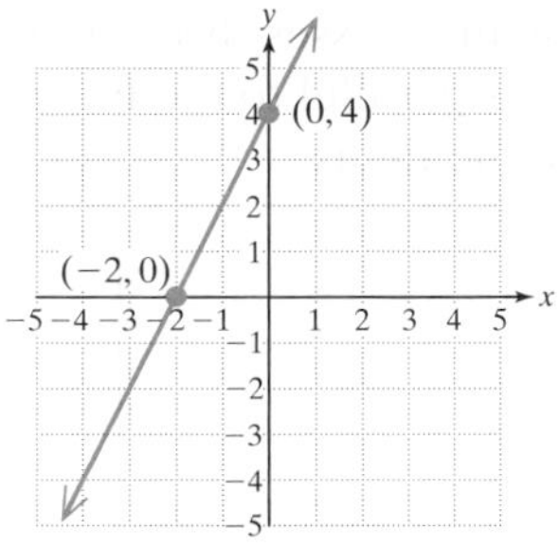

26.

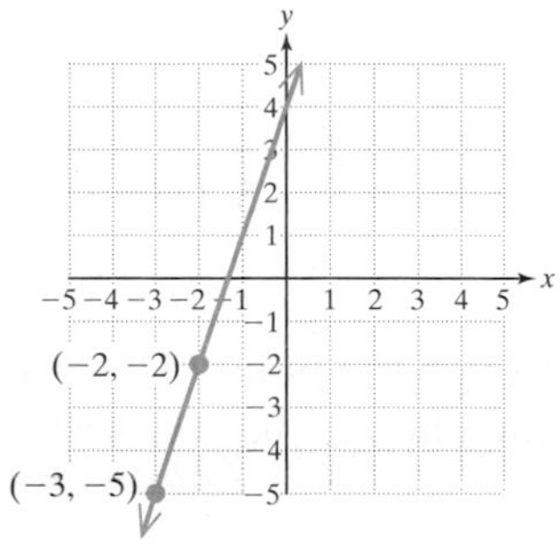

27.

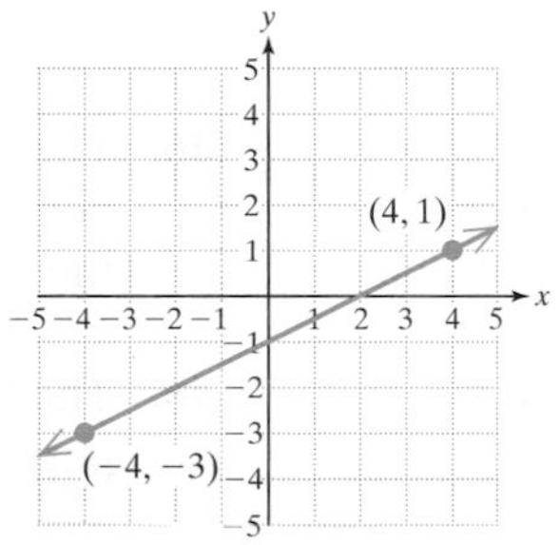

28.

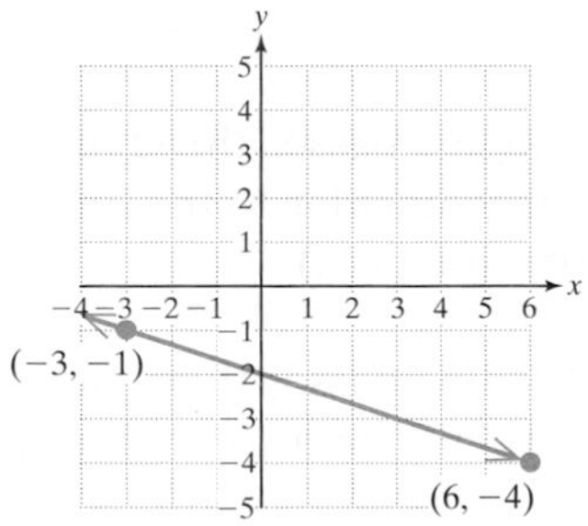

Concept 3: Writing an Equation of a Line Parallel or Perpendicular to Another Line

For Exercises 29–36, use the point-slope formula to write an equation of the line given the following information. **(See Examples 3–4.)**

29. The line passes through the point $(-3, 1)$ and is parallel to the line $y = 4x + 3$.

30. The line passes through the point $(4, -1)$ and is parallel to the line $y = 3x + 1$.

31. The line passes through the point $(4, 0)$ and is parallel to the line $3x + 2y = 8$.

32. The line passes through the point $(2, 0)$ and is parallel to the line $5x + 3y = 6$.

33. The line passes through the point $(-5, 2)$ and is perpendicular to the line $y = \frac{1}{2}x + 3$.

34. The line passes through the point $(-2, -2)$ and is perpendicular to the line $y = \frac{1}{3}x - 5$.

35. The line passes through the point $(0, -6)$ and is perpendicular to the line $-5x + y = 4$.

36. The line passes through the point $(0, -8)$ and is perpendicular to the line $2x - y = 5$.

a. Use the equation to predict the number of tigers in 1960.

b. Use the equation to predict the number of tigers in 2015.

c. Determine the slope of the line. Interpret the meaning of the slope in terms of the number of tigers and the year.

d. Determine the x-intercept. Interpret the meaning of the x-intercept in terms of the number of tigers.

Solution:

a. The year 1960 is 60 yr since 1900. Substitute $x = 60$ into the equation.

$$y = -350x + 42{,}000$$
$$y = -350(60) + 42{,}000$$
$$= 21{,}000$$

There were approximately 21,000 tigers in India in 1960.

b. The year 2015 is 115 yr since 1900. Substitute $x = 115$.

$$y = -350(115) + 42{,}000$$
$$= 1750$$

There will be approximately 1750 tigers in India in 2015.

c. The slope is -350. The slope means that the tiger population is decreasing by 350 tigers per year.

d. To find the x-intercept, substitute $y = 0$.

$$y = -350x + 42{,}000$$
$$0 = -350x + 42{,}000 \qquad \text{Substitute 0 for } y.$$
$$-42{,}000 = -350x$$
$$120 = x$$

The x-intercept is (120, 0). This means that 120 yr after the year 1900, the tiger population would be expected to reach zero. That is, in the year 2020, there will be no tigers left in India if this linear trend continues.

Skill Practice

1. The cost y (in dollars) for a local move by a small moving company is given by $y = 60x + 100$, where x is the number of hours required for the move.

a. How much would be charged for a move that required 3 hr?

b. How much would be charged for a move that required 8 hr?

c. What is the slope of the line and what does it mean in the context of this problem?

d. Determine the y-intercept and interpret its meaning in the context of this problem.

Answers

1. a. \$280 **b.** \$580

c. 60; This means that for each additional hour of service, the cost of the move goes up by \$60.

d. (0, 100); The \$100 charge is a fixed fee in addition to the hourly rate.

2. Writing a Linear Model Using Observed Data Points

Example 2 **Writing a Linear Model from Observed Data Points**

The monthly sales of hybrid cars sold in the United States are given for a recent year. The sales for the first 8 months of the year are shown in Figure 3-35. The value $x = 0$ represents January, $x = 1$ represents February, and so on.

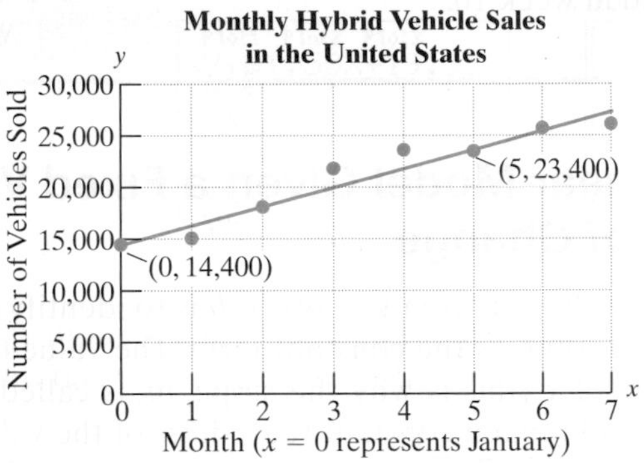

Figure 3-35

a. Use the data points from Figure 3-35 to find a linear equation that represents the monthly sales of hybrid cars in the United States. Let x represent the month number and let y represent the number of vehicles sold.

b. Use the linear equation in part (a) to estimate the number of hybrid vehicles sold in month 7 (August).

Solution:

a. The ordered pairs (0, 14,400) and (5, 23,400) are given in the graph. Use these points to find the slope.

$(0, 14{,}400)$ and $(5, 23{,}400)$ — Label the points.

(x_1, y_1) $\quad$ (x_2, y_2)

$$m = \frac{y_2 - y_1}{x_2 - x_1} = \frac{23{,}400 - 14{,}400}{5 - 0}$$

$$= \frac{9000}{5}$$

$$= 1800$$

The slope is 1800. This indicates that sales increased by approximately 1800 per month during this time period.

With $m = 1800$, and the y-intercept given as (0, 14,400), we have the following linear equation in slope-intercept form.

$$y = 1800x + 14{,}400$$

b. To approximate the sales in month number 7, substitute $x = 7$ into the equation from part (a).

$$y = 1800(7) + 14{,}400$$ Substitute $x = 7$.

$$= 27{,}000$$

The monthly sales for August (month 7) would be 27,000 vehicles.

Concept 1: Interpreting a Linear Equation in Two Variables

9. The minimum hourly wage, y (in dollars per hour), in the United States can be approximated by the equation $y = 0.14x + 1.60$. In this equation, x represents the number of years since 1970 ($x = 0$ represents 1970, $x = 5$ represents 1975, and so on). **(See Example 1.)**

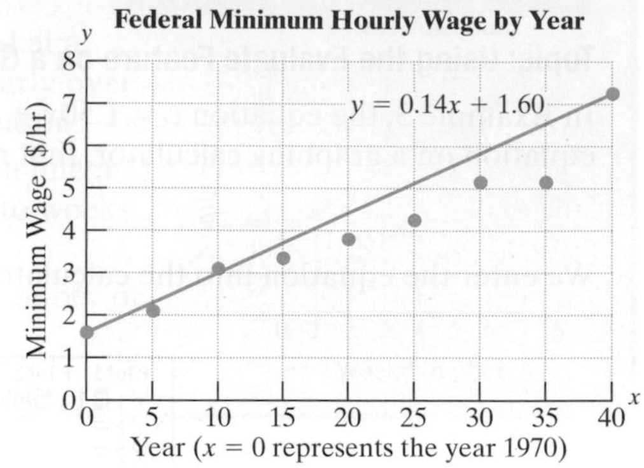

a. Use the equation to approximate the minimum wage in the year 1980.

b. Use the equation to predict the minimum wage in 2015.

c. Determine the y-intercept. Interpret the meaning of the y-intercept in the context of this problem.

d. Determine the slope. Interpret the meaning of the slope in the context of this problem.

10. The average daily temperature in January for cities along the eastern seaboard of the United States and Canada generally decreases for cities farther north. A city's latitude in the northern hemisphere is a measure of how far north it is on the globe.

The average temperature, y (measured in degrees Fahrenheit), can be described by the equation

$y = -2.333x + 124.0$ where x is the latitude of the city.

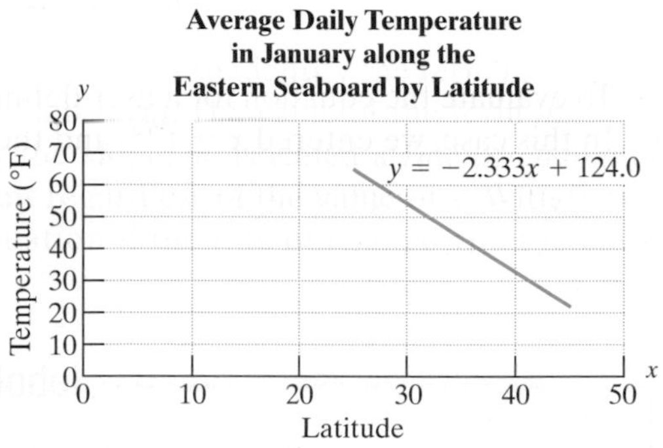

(*Source:* U.S. National Oceanic and Atmospheric Administration)

a. Use the equation to predict the average daily temperature in January for Philadelphia, Pennsylvania, whose latitude is 40.0°N. Round to one decimal place.

b. Use the equation to predict the average daily temperature in January for Edmundston, New Brunswick, Canada, whose latitude is 47.4°N. Round to one decimal place.

c. What is the slope of the line? Interpret the meaning of the slope in terms of latitude and temperature.

d. From the equation, determine the value of the x-intercept. Round to one decimal place. Interpret the meaning of the x-intercept in terms of latitude and temperature.

11. Veterinarians keep records of the weights of animals that are brought in for examination. Grindel, the cat, weighed 42 oz when she was 70 days old. She weighed 46 oz when she was 84 days old. Her sister, Frisco, weighed 40 oz when she was 70 days old and 48 oz at 84 days old.

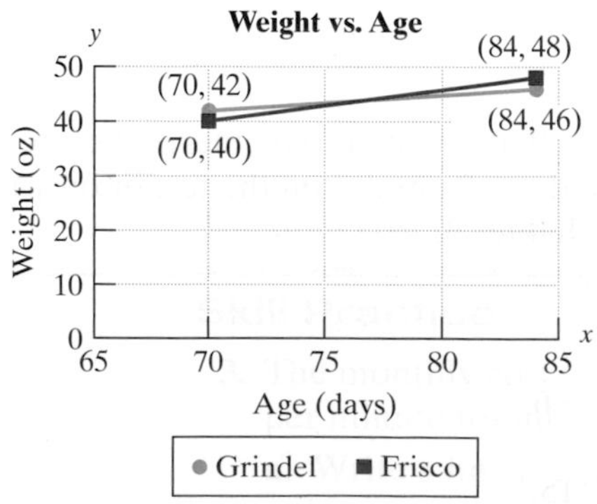

a. Compute the slope of the line representing Grindel's weight.

b. Compute the slope of the line representing Frisco's weight.

c. Interpret the meaning of each slope in the context of this problem.

d. Which cat gained weight more rapidly during this time period?

12. The graph depicts the rise in the number of jail inmates in the United States since 2000. Two linear equations are given: one to describe the number of female inmates and one to describe the number of male inmates by year.

Let y represent the number of inmates (in thousands). Let x represent the number of years since 2000.

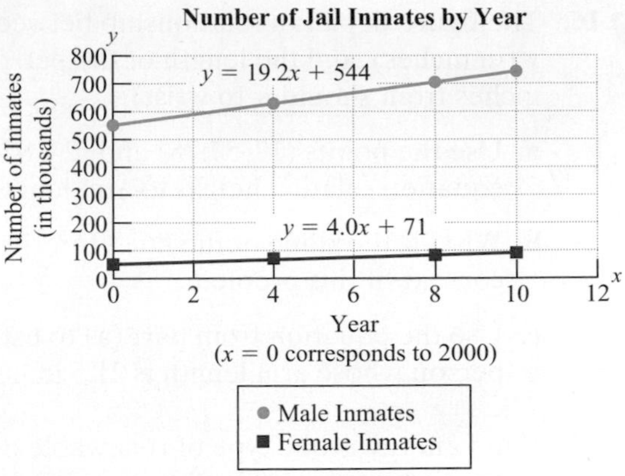

(*Source:* U.S. Bureau of Justice Statistics)

a. What is the slope of the line representing the number of female inmates? Interpret the meaning of the slope in the context of this problem.

b. What is the slope of the line representing the number of male inmates? Interpret the meaning of the slope in the context of this problem.

c. Which group, males or females, has the larger slope? What does this imply about the rise in the number of male and female prisoners?

d. Assuming this trend continues, use the equation to predict the number of female inmates in 2015.

13. The electric bill charge for a certain utility company is \$0.095 per kilowatt-hour plus a fixed monthly tax of \$11.95. The total cost, y, depends on the number of kilowatt-hours, x, according to the equation $y = 0.095x + 11.95,\ x \geq 0$.

a. Determine the cost of using 1000 kilowatt-hours.

b. Determine the cost of using 2000 kilowatt-hours.

c. Determine the y-intercept. Interpret the meaning of the y-intercept in the context of this problem.

d. Determine the slope. Interpret the meaning of the slope in the context of this problem.

14. For a recent year, children's admission to the Minnesota State Fair was \$8. Ride tickets were \$0.75 each. The equation $y = 0.75x + 8$ represented the cost, y, in dollars to be admitted to the fair and to purchase x ride tickets.

a. Determine the slope of the line represented by $y = 0.75x + 8$. Interpret the meaning of the slope in the context of this problem.

b. Determine the y-intercept. Interpret its meaning in the context of this problem.

c. Use the equation to determine how much money a child needed for admission and to ride 10 rides.

Concept 2: Writing a Linear Model Using Observed Data Points

15. Meteorologists often measure the intensity of a tropical storm or hurricane by the maximum sustained wind speed and the minimum pressure. The relationship between these two quantities is approximately linear. Hurricane Katrina had a maximum sustained wind speed of 150 knots and a minimum pressure of 902 mb (millibars). Hurricane Ophelia had maximum sustained winds of 75 knots and a pressure of 976 mb. **(See Example 2.)**

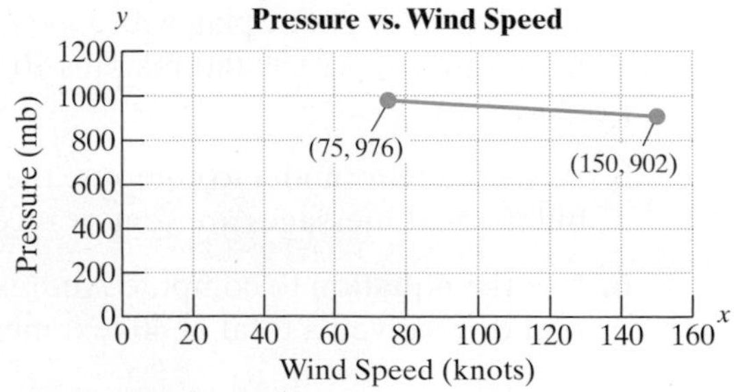

a. Find the slope of the line between these two points. Round to one decimal place.

b. Using the slope found in part (a) and the point (75, 976), find a linear model that represents the minimum pressure of a hurricane, y, versus its maximum sustained wind speed, x.

c. Hurricane Dennis had a maximum wind speed of 130 knots. Using the equation you found in part (b), predict the minimum pressure.

16. The figure depicts a relationship between a person's height, y (in inches), and the length of the person's arm, x (measured in inches from shoulder to wrist).

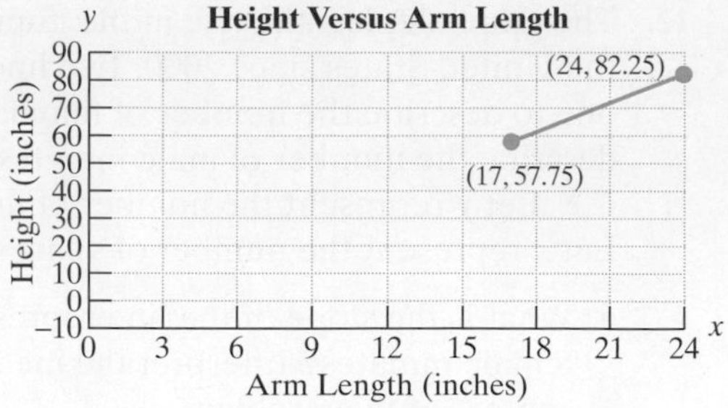

a. Use the points (17, 57.75) and (24, 82.25) to find a linear equation relating height to arm length.

b. What is the slope of the line? Interpret the slope in the context of this problem.

c. Use the equation from part (a) to estimate the height of a person whose arm length is 21.5 in.

17. Wind energy is one type of renewable energy that does not produce dangerous greenhouse gases as a by-product. The graph shows the consumption of wind energy in the United States for selected years. The variable y represents the amount of wind energy in trillions of Btu, and the variable x represents the number of years since 2000.

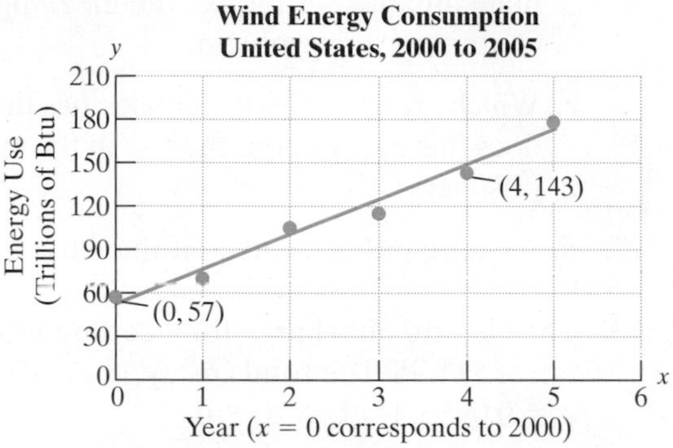

(*Source:* United States Department of Energy)

a. Use the points (0, 57) and (4, 143) to determine the slope of the line.

b. Interpret the slope in the context of this problem?

c. Use the points (0, 57) and (4, 143) to find a linear equation relating the consumption of wind energy, y, to the number of years, x, since 2000.

d. If this linear trend continues beyond the observed data values, use the equation in part (c) to predict the consumption of wind energy in the year 2010.

18. The graph shows the average height for boys based on age. Let x represent a boy's age, and let y represent his height (in inches).

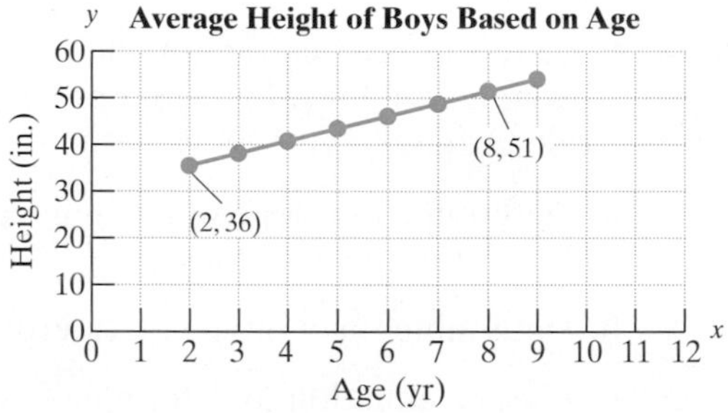

(*Source:* National Parenting Council)

a. Find a linear equation that represents the height of a boy versus his age.

b. Use the linear equation found in part (a) to predict the average height of a 5-year-old boy.

Concept 3: Writing a Linear Model Given a Fixed Value and a Rate of Change

19. Andrés has a cell phone plan with a local telephone company. His bill is determined each month by a \$39.99 flat fee plus \$0.20 for each text message sent or received. **(See Example 3.)**

a. Write a linear model to compute the monthly cost, y, of Andrés' cell phone bill if x text messages are sent or received.

b. Use the equation to compute Andrés' cell phone bill for a month in which he sent or received a total of 40 text messages.

20. Anabel lives in New York and likes to keep in touch with her family in Texas. She uses 10-10-987 to call them. The cost of a long distance call is \$0.53 plus \$0.06 per minute.

a. Write an equation that represents the cost, C, of a long distance call that is x minutes long.

b. Use the equation to compute the cost of a long distance phone call that lasted 32 minutes.

21. The cost to rent a 10 ft by 10 ft storage space is \$90 per month plus a nonrefundable deposit of \$105.

a. Write a linear equation to compute the cost, y, of renting a 10 ft by 10 ft space for x months.

b. What is the cost of renting such a storage space for 1 year (12 months)?

22. An air-conditioning and heating company has a fixed monthly cost of \$5000. Furthermore, each service call costs the company \$25.

a. Write a linear equation to compute the total cost, y, for 1 month if x service calls are made.

b. Use the equation to compute the cost for 1 month if 150 service calls are made.

23. A bakery that specializes in bread rents a booth at a flea market. The daily cost to rent the booth is \$100. Each loaf of bread costs the bakery \$0.80 to produce.

a. Write a linear equation to compute the total cost, y, for 1 day if x loaves of bread are produced.

b. Use the equation to compute the cost for 1 day if 200 loaves of bread are produced.

24. A beverage company rents a booth at an art show to sell lemonade. The daily cost to rent a booth is \$35. Each lemonade costs \$0.50 to produce.

a. Write a linear equation to compute the total cost, y, for 1 day if x lemonades are produced.

b. Use the equation to compute the cost for 1 day if 350 lemonades are produced.

Group Activity

Modeling a Linear Equation

Materials: Yardstick or other device for making linear measurements

Estimated Time: 15–20 minutes

Group Size: 3

1. The members of each group should measure the length of their arms (in inches) from elbow to wrist. Record this measurement as x and the person's height (in inches) as y. Write these values as ordered pairs for each member of the group. Then write the ordered pairs on the board.

2. Next, copy the ordered pairs collected from all groups in the class and plot the ordered pairs. (This is called a "scatter diagram.")

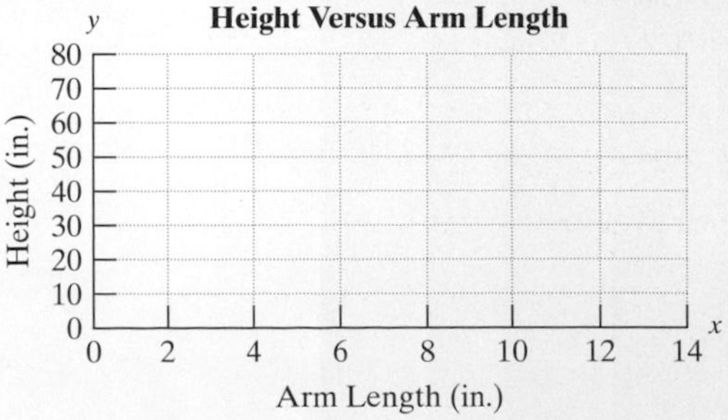

3. Select two ordered pairs that seem to follow the upward trend of the data. Using these data points, determine the slope of the line.

Slope: ______________________

4. Using the data points and slope from question 3, find an equation of the line through the two points. Write the equation in slope-intercept form, $y = mx + b$.

Equation: ______________________

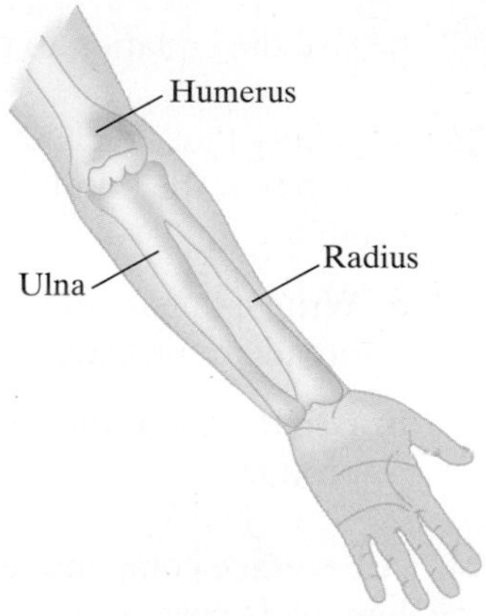

5. Using the equation from question 4, estimate the height of a person whose arm length from elbow to wrist is 8.5 in.

6. Suppose a crime scene investigator uncovers a partial skeleton and identifies a bone as a human ulna (the ulna is one of two bones in the forearm and extends from elbow to wrist). If the length of the bone is 12 in., estimate the height of the person before death. Would you expect this person to be male or female?

Chapter 3 Summary

Section 3.1 Rectangular Coordinate System

Key Concepts

Graphical representation of numerical data is often helpful to study problems in real-world applications.

A **rectangular coordinate system** is made up of a horizontal line called the ***x*-axis** and a vertical line called the ***y*-axis**. The point where the lines meet is the **origin**. The four regions of the plane are called **quadrants**.

The point (x, y) is an **ordered pair**. The first element in the ordered pair is the point's horizontal position from the origin. The second element in the ordered pair is the point's vertical position from the origin.

Example

Example 1

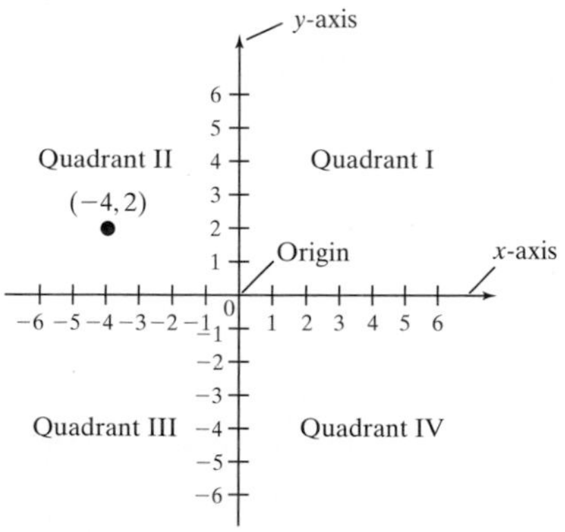

Section 3.2 Linear Equations in Two Variables

Key Concepts

An equation written in the form $Ax + By = C$ (where A and B are not both zero) is a **linear equation in two variables**.

A solution to a linear equation in x and y is an ordered pair (x, y) that makes the equation a true statement. The graph of the set of all solutions of a linear equation in two variables is a line in a rectangular coordinate system.

A linear equation can be graphed by finding at least two solutions and graphing the line through the points.

Examples

Example 1

Graph the equation $2x + y = 2$.

Select arbitrary values of x or y such as those shown in the table. Then complete the table to find the corresponding ordered pairs.

x	y	
0	2	⟶ $(0, 2)$
−1	4	⟶ $(-1, 4)$
1	0	⟶ $(1, 0)$

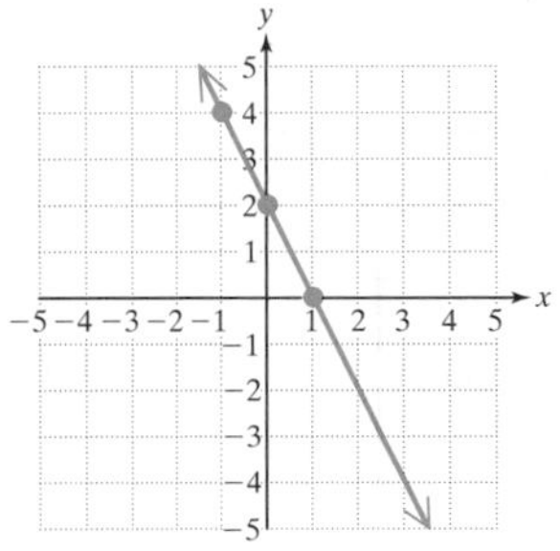

An ***x*-intercept** of a graph is a point $(a, 0)$ where the graph intersects the x-axis.
To find the x-intercept, let $y = 0$ and solve for x.
A ***y*-intercept** of a graph is a point $(0, b)$ where the graph intersects the y-axis.
To find the y-intercept, let $x = 0$ and solve for y.

Example 2

For the line $2x + y = 2$, find the x- and y-intercepts.

x-intercept	y-intercept
$2x + (0) = 2$	$2(0) + y = 2$
$2x = 2$	$0 + y = 2$
$x = 1$	$y = 2$
$(1, 0)$	$(0, 2)$

A **vertical line** can be represented by an equation of the form $x = k$.
A **horizontal line** can be represented by an equation of the form $y = k$.

Example 3

$x = 3$ represents a vertical line

$y = 3$ represents a horizontal line

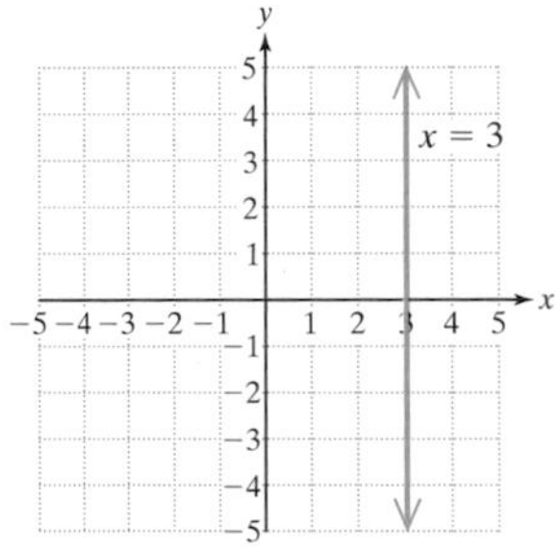

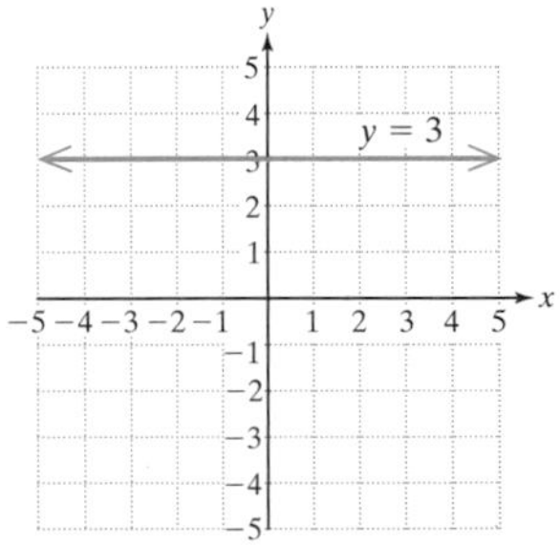

Section 3.6 Applications of Linear Equations and Modeling

Key Concepts

Linear equations can often be used to describe or model the relationship between variables in a real-world event. In such applications, the slope may be interpreted as a rate of change.

Example

Example 1

The number of drug-related arrests for a small city has been growing approximately linearly since 1985.

Let y represent the number of drug arrests, and let x represent the number of years after 1985.

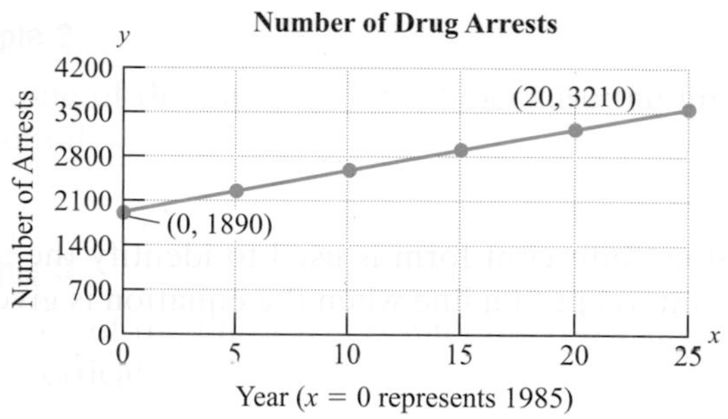

a. Use the ordered pairs (0, 1890) and (20, 3210) to find an equation of the line shown in the graph.

$$m = \frac{y_2 - y_1}{x_2 - x_1} = \frac{3210 - 1890}{20 - 0}$$

$$= \frac{1320}{20} = 66$$

The slope is 66, indicating that the number of drug arrests is increasing at a rate of 66 per year. $m = 66$, and the y-intercept is (0, 1890). Hence:

$$y = mx + b \Rightarrow y = 66x + 1890$$

b. Use the equation in part (a) to predict the number of drug-related arrests in the year 2015. (The year 2015 is 30 years after 1985. Hence, $x = 30$.)

$$y = 66(30) + 1890$$

$$y = 3870$$

The number of drug arrests is predicted to be 3870 by the year 2015.

Chapter 3 Review Exercises

Section 3.1

1. Graph the points on a rectangular coordinate system.

a. $\left(\frac{1}{2}, 5\right)$ **b.** $(-1, 4)$ **c.** $(2, -1)$

d. $(0, 3)$ **e.** $(0, 0)$ **f.** $\left(-\frac{8}{5}, 0\right)$

g. $(-2, -5)$ **h.** $(3, 1)$

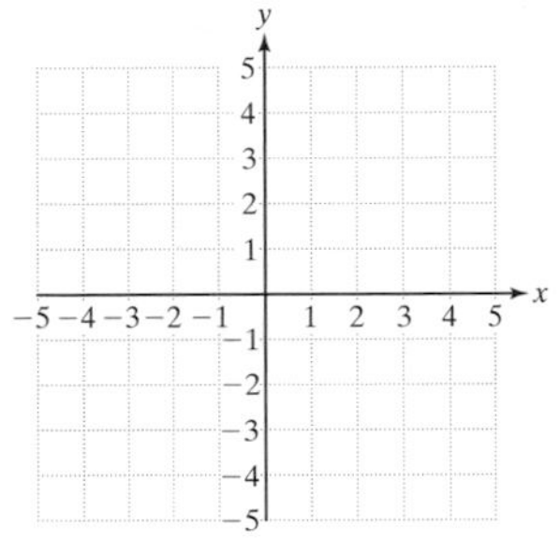

2. Estimate the coordinates of the points A, B, C, D, E, and F.

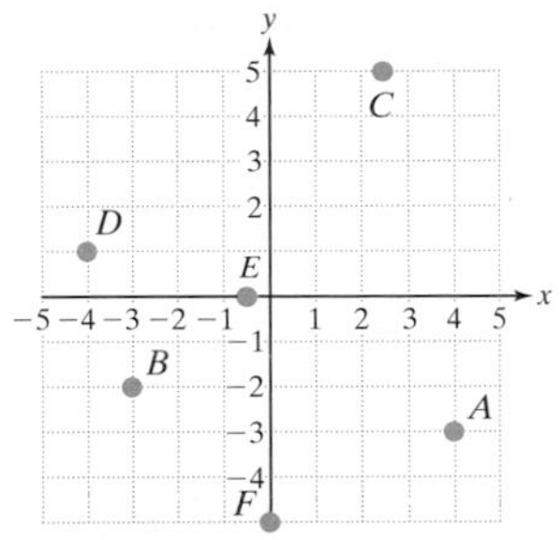

For Exercises 3–8, determine the quadrant in which the given point is located.

3. $(-2, -10)$ **4.** $(-4, 6)$

5. $(3, -5)$ **6.** $\left(\frac{1}{2}, \frac{7}{5}\right)$

7. $(\pi, -2.7)$ **8.** $(-1.2, -6.8)$

9. On which axis is the point $(2, 0)$ located?

10. On which axis is the point $(0, -3)$ located?

11. The price per share of a stock (in dollars) over a period of 5 days is shown in the graph.

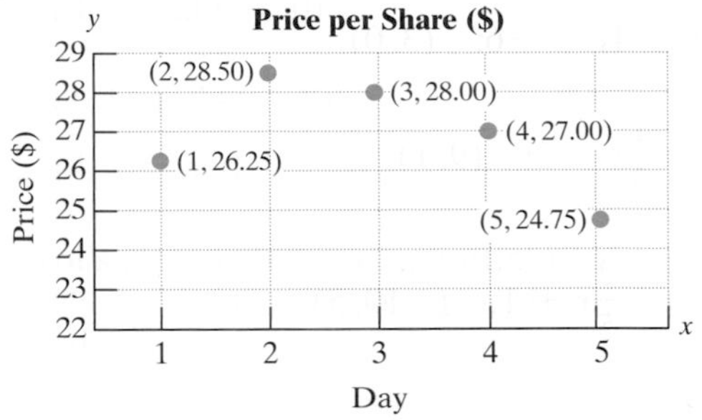

a. Interpret the meaning of the ordered pair $(1, 26.25)$.

b. On which day was the price the highest?

c. What was the increase in price between day 1 and day 2?

12. The number of space shuttle launches for selected years is given by the ordered pairs. Let x represent the number of years since 1995. Let y represent the number of launches.

$(1, 7)$ $(2, 8)$ $(3, 5)$ $(4, 3)$

$(5, 5)$ $(6, 6)$ $(7, 5)$ $(8, 1)$

a. Interpret the meaning of the ordered pair $(8, 1)$.

b. Plot the points on a rectangular coordinate system.

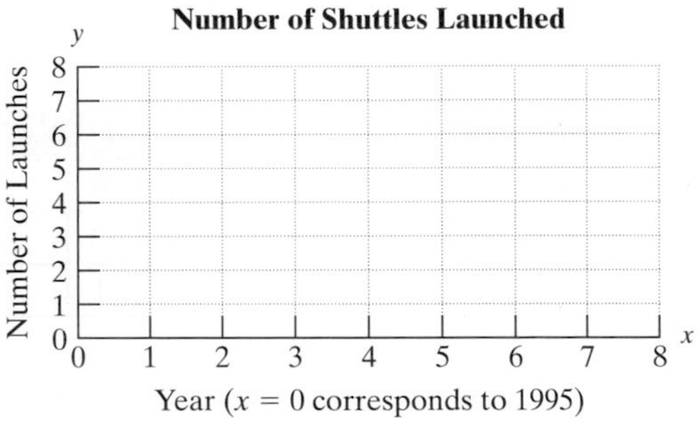

Section 3.4

For Exercises 51–56, write each equation in slope-intercept form. Identify the slope and the y-intercept.

51. $5x - 2y = 10$

52. $3x + 4y = 12$

53. $x - 3y = 0$

54. $5y - 8 = 4$

55. $2y = -5$

56. $y - x = 0$

For Exercises 57–62, determine whether the equations represent parallel lines, perpendicular lines, or neither.

57. l_1: $y = \frac{3}{5}x + 3$
l_2: $y = \frac{5}{3}x + 1$

58. l_1: $2x - 5y = 10$
l_2: $5x + 2y = 20$

59. l_1: $3x + 2y = 6$
l_2: $-6x - 4y = 4$

60. l_1: $y = \frac{1}{4}x - 3$
l_2: $-x + 4y = 8$

61. l_1: $2x = 4$
l_2: $y = 6$

62. l_1: $y = \frac{2}{9}x + 4$
l_2: $y = \frac{9}{2}x - 3$

63. Write an equation of the line whose slope is $-\frac{4}{3}$ and whose y-intercept is $(0, -1)$.

64. Write an equation of the line that passes through the origin and has a slope of 5.

65. Write an equation of the line with slope $-\frac{4}{3}$ that passes through the point $(-6, 2)$.

66. Write an equation of the line with slope 5 that passes through the point $(-1, -8)$.

Section 3.5

67. Write a linear equation in two variables in slope-intercept form. (Answers may vary.)

68. Write a linear equation in two variables in standard form. (Answers may vary.)

69. Write the slope formula to find the slope of the line between the points (x_1, y_1) and (x_2, y_2).

70. Write the point-slope formula.

71. Write an equation of a vertical line (answers may vary).

72. Write an equation of a horizontal line (answers may vary).

For Exercises 73–78, write an equation of a line given the following information.

73. The slope is -6, and the line passes through the point $(-1, 8)$.

74. The slope is $\frac{2}{3}$, and the line passes through the point $(5, 5)$.

75. The line passes through the points $(0, -4)$ and $(8, -2)$.

76. The line passes through the points $(2, -5)$ and $(8, -5)$.

77. The line passes through the point $(5, 12)$ and is perpendicular to the line $y = -\frac{5}{6}x - 3$.

78. The line passes through the point $(-6, 7)$ and is parallel to the line $4x - y = 0$.

Section 3.6

79. The graph shows the average height for girls based on age. (*Source:* National Parenting Council) Let x represent a girl's age, and let y represent her height (in inches).

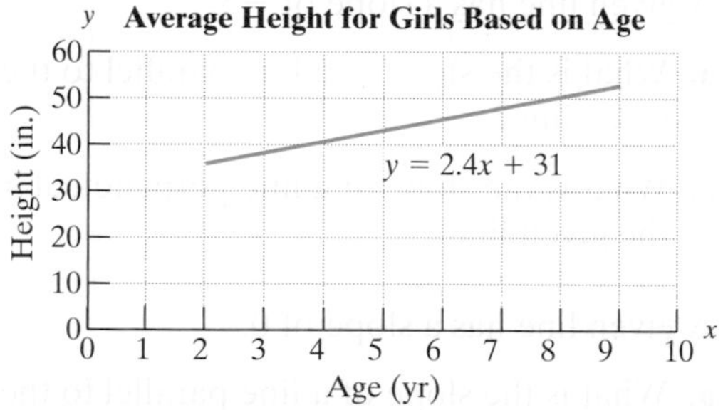

a. Use the equation to estimate the average height of a 7-year-old girl.

b. What is the slope of the line? Interpret the meaning of the slope in the context of the problem.

80. The number of drug prescriptions increased between 2000 and 2010 (see graph). Let x represent the number of years since 2000. Let y represent the number of prescriptions (in millions).

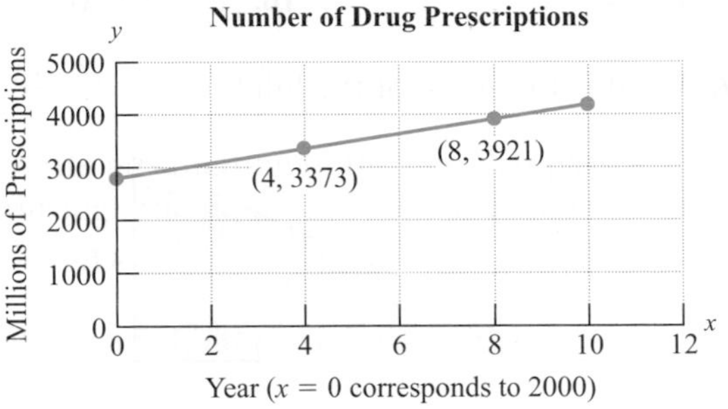

a. Using the ordered pairs (4, 3373) and (8, 3921) find the slope of the line.

b. Interpret the meaning of the slope in the context of this problem.

c. Find a linear equation that represents the number of prescriptions, y, versus the year, x.

d. Predict the number of prescriptions for the year 2015.

81. A water purification company charges \$20 per month and a \$55 installation fee.

a. Write a linear equation to compute the total cost, y, of renting this system for x months.

b. Use the equation from part (a) to determine the total cost to rent the system for 9 months.

82. A small cleaning company has a fixed monthly cost of \$700 and a variable cost of \$8 per service call.

a. Write a linear equation to compute the total cost, y, of making x service calls in one month.

b. Use the equation from part (a) to determine the total cost of making 80 service calls.

Chapter 3 Test

1. In which quadrant is the given point located?

a. $\left(-\frac{7}{2}, 4\right)$ **b.** $(4.6, -2)$ **c.** $(-37, -45)$

2. What is the y-coordinate for a point on the x-axis?

3. What is the x-coordinate for a point on the y-axis?

4. Bamboo is the fastest growing woody plant on earth. At a bamboo farm, the height of a black bamboo plant (phyllostachys nigra) is measured for selected days. Let x represent the day number and y represent the height of the plant.

Day, x	Height (inches), y
4	14
8	28
12	42
16	56
20	70

a. Write the data as ordered pairs and interpret the meaning of the first ordered pair.

b. Graph the ordered pairs on a rectangular coordinate system.

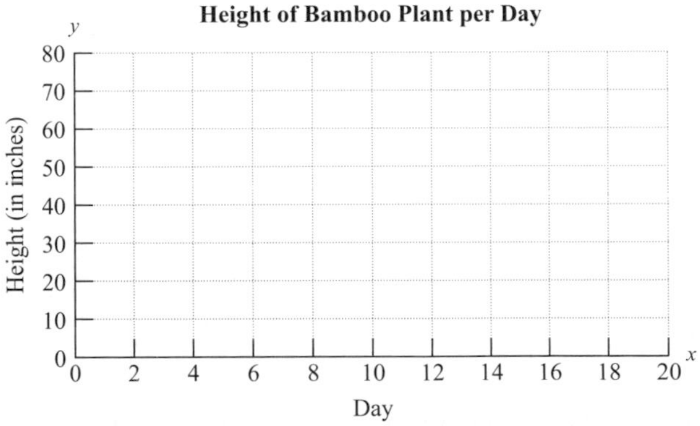

c. From the graph, estimate the height of the bamboo plant after 10 days.

5. Determine whether the ordered pair is a solution to the equation $2x - y = 6$.

a. $(0, 6)$ **b.** $(4, 2)$

c. $(3, 0)$ **d.** $\left(\frac{9}{2}, 3\right)$

For Exercises 9–12, solve each equation.

9. $6x - 10 = 14$

10. $3(m + 2) - 3 = 2m + 8$

11. $\frac{2}{3}y - \frac{1}{6} = y + \frac{4}{3}$

12. $1.7z + 2 = -2(0.3z + 1.3)$

13. The area of Texas is 267,277 mi^2. If this is 712 mi^2 less than 29 times the area of Maine, find the area of Maine.

14. For the formula $3a + b = c$, solve for a.

15. Graph the equation $-6x + 2y = 0$.

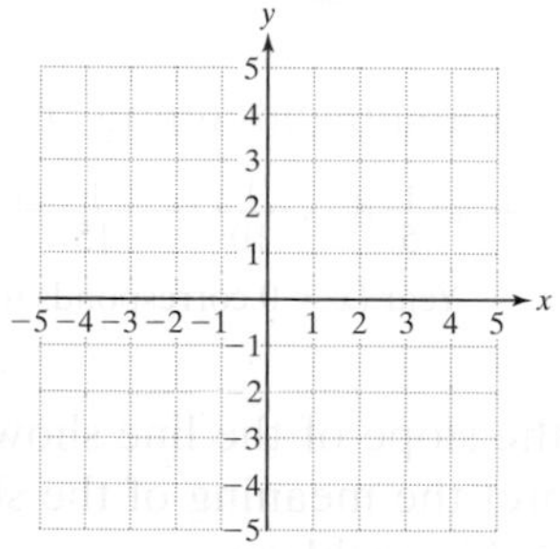

16. Find the x- and y-intercepts of $-2x + 4y = 4$.

17. Write the equation in slope-intercept form. Then identify the slope and the y-intercept.
$3x + 2y = -12$

18. Explain why the line $2x + 3 = 5$ has only one intercept.

19. Find an equation of a line passing through $(2, -5)$ with slope -3.

20. Find an equation of the line passing through $(0, 6)$ and $(-3, 4)$.

Systems of Linear Equations

4

CHAPTER OUTLINE

4.1 Solving Systems of Equations by the Graphing Method 274

4.2 Solving Systems of Equations by the Substitution Method 284

4.3 Solving Systems of Equations by the Addition Method 294

Problem Recognition Exercises: Systems of Equations 304

4.4 Applications of Linear Equations in Two Variables 305

4.5 Systems of Linear Equations in Three Variables 314

4.6 Applications of Systems of Linear Equations in Three Variables 323

Group Activity: Creating Linear Models from Data 327

Chapter 4

This chapter is devoted to solving systems of linear equations. Applications of systems of equations involve two or more variables subject to two or more constraints.

Are You Prepared?

To prepare yourself, consider this example. At a movie theater, one group of students bought three drinks and two popcorns for a total of \$20.50 (excluding tax). Another group bought five drinks and three popcorns for \$32.50. There are two unknown quantities in this scenario: the cost per drink and the cost per popcorn.

Fill in the blanks below using trial and error to determine the cost per drink and the cost per popcorn. You have the correct answer if both equations are true.

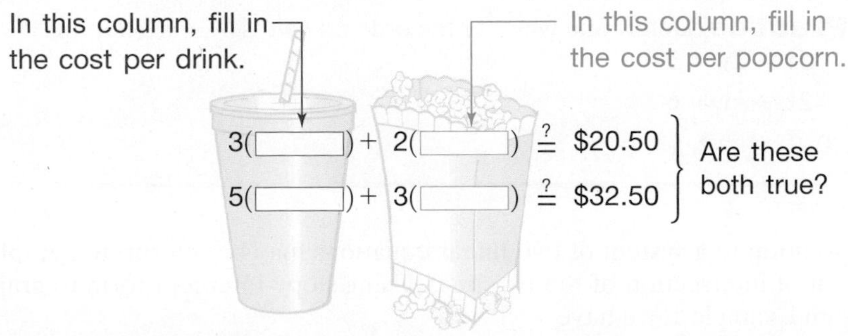

If you have trouble with this puzzle, don't fret. Later in the chapter, we'll use the power of algebra to set up and solve a system of equations that will take the guesswork away!

Section 4.1 Solving Systems of Equations by the Graphing Method

Concepts

1. Solutions to a System of Linear Equations
2. Solving Systems of Linear Equations by Graphing

1. Solutions to a System of Linear Equations

Recall from Section 3.2 that a linear equation in two variables has an infinite number of solutions. The set of all solutions to a linear equation forms a line in a rectangular coordinate system. Two or more linear equations form a **system of linear equations**. For example, here are three systems of equations:

$$x - 3y = -5 \qquad y = \tfrac{1}{4}x - \tfrac{3}{4} \qquad 5a + b = 4$$
$$2x + 4y = 10 \qquad -2x + 8y = -6 \qquad -10a - 2b = 8$$

A **solution to a system of linear equations** is an ordered pair that is a solution to *both* individual linear equations.

Example 1 Determining Solutions to a System of Linear Equations

Determine whether the ordered pairs are solutions to the system.

$$x + y = 4$$
$$-2x + y = -5$$

a. $(3, 1)$ **b.** $(0, 4)$

Solution:

a. Substitute the ordered pair $(3, 1)$ into both equations:

$$x + y = 4 \longrightarrow (3) + (1) \stackrel{?}{=} 4 \checkmark \quad \text{True}$$
$$-2x + y = -5 \longrightarrow -2(3) + (1) \stackrel{?}{=} -5 \checkmark \quad \text{True}$$

Because the ordered pair $(3, 1)$ is a solution to both equations, it is a solution to the *system* of equations.

b. Substitute the ordered pair $(0, 4)$ into both equations.

$$x + y = 4 \longrightarrow (0) + (4) \stackrel{?}{=} 4 \checkmark \quad \text{True}$$
$$-2x + y = -5 \longrightarrow -2(0) + (4) \stackrel{?}{=} -5 \quad \text{False}$$

Because the ordered pair $(0, 4)$ is not a solution to the second equation, it is *not* a solution to the system of equations.

Avoiding Mistakes

It is important to test an ordered pair in *both* equations to determine if the ordered pair is a solution.

Skill Practice Determine whether the ordered pair is a solution to the system. $5x - 2y = 24$
$2x + y = 6$

1. $(6, 3)$ **2.** $(4, -2)$

A solution to a system of two linear equations may be interpreted graphically as a point of intersection of the two lines. Using slope-intercept form to graph the lines from Example 1, we have

$$l_1: \quad x + y = 4 \longrightarrow y = -x + 4$$
$$l_2: \quad -2x + y = -5 \longrightarrow y = 2x - 5$$

Answers

1. No
2. Yes

All points on l_1 are solutions to the equation $y = -x + 4$.
All points on l_2 are solutions to the equation $y = 2x - 5$.
The point of intersection (3, 1) is the only point that is a solution to both equations. (See Figure 4-1).

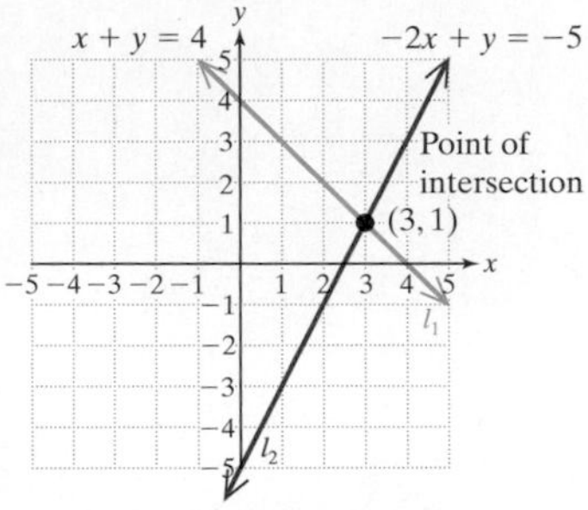

Figure 4-1

When two lines are drawn in a rectangular coordinate system, three geometric relationships are possible:

1. Two lines may intersect at *exactly one point*.

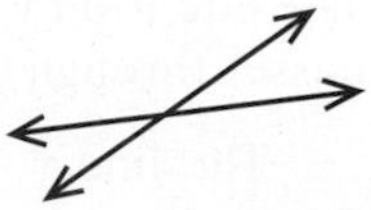

2. Two lines may intersect at *no point*. This occurs if the lines are parallel.

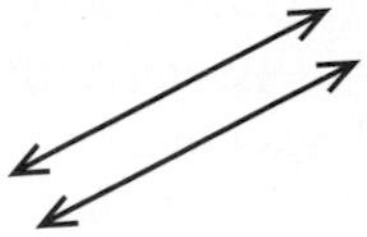

3. Two lines may intersect at *infinitely many points* along the line. This occurs if the equations represent the same line (the lines coincide).

If a system of linear equations has one or more solutions, the system is said to be **consistent**. If a system of linear equations has no solution, it is said to be **inconsistent**.

If two equations represent the same line, the equations are said to be **dependent equations**. In this case, all points on the line are solutions to the system. If two equations represent two different lines, the equations are said to be **independent equations**. In this case, the lines either intersect at one point or are parallel.

Solutions to Systems of Linear Equations in Two Variables

One Unique Solution

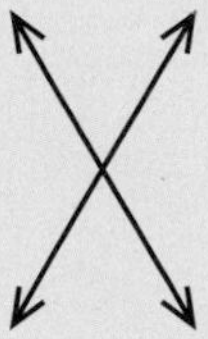

One point of intersection
- System is consistent.
- Equations are independent.

No Solution

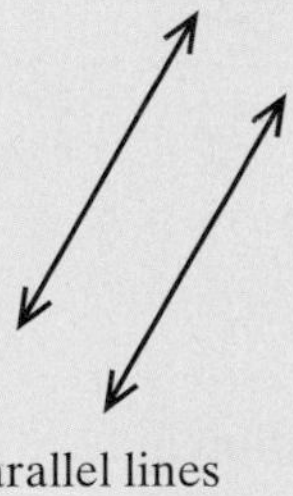

Parallel lines
- System is inconsistent.
- Equations are independent.

Infinitely Many Solutions

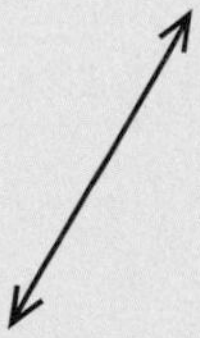

Coinciding lines
- System is consistent.
- Equations are dependent.

2. Solving Systems of Linear Equations by Graphing

One way to find a solution to a system of equations is to graph the equations and find the point (or points) of intersection. This is called the *graphing method* to solve a system of equations.

Example 2 Solving a System of Linear Equations by Graphing

Solve the system by the graphing method.

$$y = 2x$$
$$y = 2$$

Solution:

The equation $y = 2x$ is written in slope-intercept form as $y = 2x + 0$. The line passes through the origin, with a slope of 2.

The line $y = 2$ is a horizontal line and has a slope of 0.

Because the lines have different slopes, the lines must be different and nonparallel. From this, we know that the lines must intersect at exactly one point. Graph the lines to find the point of intersection (Figure 4-2).

The point (1, 2) appears to be the point of intersection. This can be confirmed by substituting $x = 1$ and $y = 2$ into both original equations.

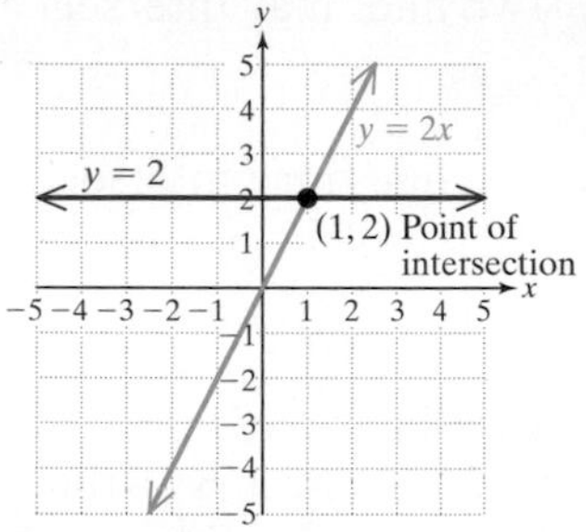

Figure 4-2

$y = 2x \qquad (2) \stackrel{?}{=} 2(1)$ ✔ True

$y = 2 \qquad (2) \stackrel{?}{=} 2$ ✔ True

The solution set is $\{(1, 2)\}$.

Skill Practice Solve the system by the graphing method.

3. $y = -3x$
$x = -1$

Example 3 Solving a System of Linear Equations by Graphing

Solve the system by the graphing method.

$$x - 2y = -2$$
$$-3x + 2y = 6$$

Solution:

To graph each equation, write the equation in slope-intercept form, $y = mx + b$.

Equation 1	**Equation 2**
$x - 2y = -2$	$-3x + 2y = 6$
$-2y = -x - 2$	$2y = 3x + 6$
$\dfrac{-2y}{-2} = \dfrac{-x}{-2} - \dfrac{2}{-2}$	$\dfrac{2y}{2} = \dfrac{3x}{2} + \dfrac{6}{2}$
$y = \dfrac{1}{2}x + 1$	$y = \dfrac{3}{2}x + 3$

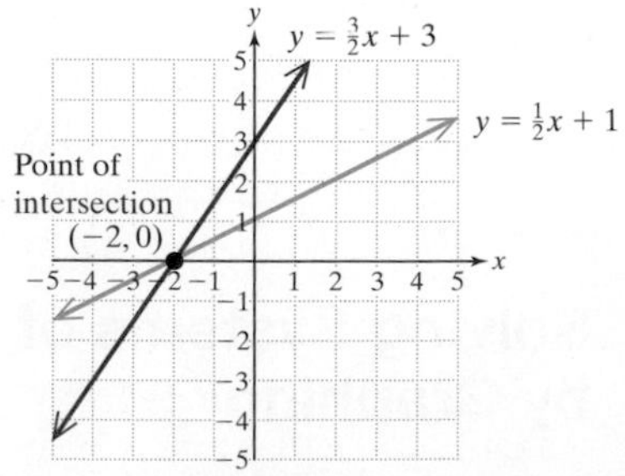

Figure 4-3

From their slope-intercept forms, we see that the lines have different slopes, indicating that the lines are different and nonparallel. Therefore, the lines must intersect at exactly one point. Graph the lines to find that point (Figure 4-3).

Answer

3. $\{(-1, 3)\}$

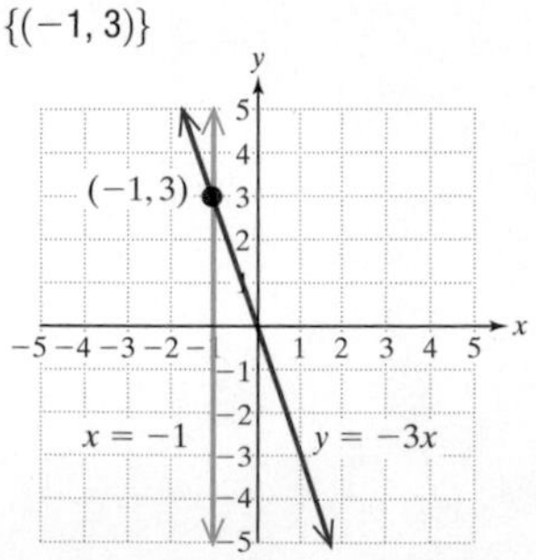

The point $(-2, 0)$ appears to be the point of intersection. This can be confirmed by substituting $x = -2$ and $y = 0$ into both equations.

$$x - 2y = -2 \longrightarrow (-2) - 2(0) \stackrel{?}{=} -2 \checkmark \quad \text{True}$$

$$-3x + 2y = 6 \longrightarrow -3(-2) + 2(0) \stackrel{?}{=} 6 \checkmark \quad \text{True}$$

The solution set is $\{(-2, 0)\}$.

Skill Practice Solve the system by the graphing method.

4. $y = 2x - 3$
$6x + 2y = 4$

TIP: In Examples 2 and 3, the lines could also have been graphed by using the *x*- and *y*-intercepts or by using a table of points. However, the advantage of writing the equations in slope-intercept form is that we can compare the slopes and *y*-intercepts of the two lines.

1. If the slopes differ, the lines are different and nonparallel and must intersect at exactly one point.
2. If the slopes are the same and the *y*-intercepts are different, the lines are parallel and will not intersect.
3. If the slopes are the same and the *y*-intercepts are the same, the two equations represent the same line.

Example 4 Graphing an Inconsistent System

Solve the system by graphing.

$$-x + 3y = -6$$
$$6y = 2x + 6$$

Solution:

To graph the lines, write each equation in slope-intercept form.

Equation 1

$-x + 3y = -6$

$3y = x - 6$

$\dfrac{3y}{3} = \dfrac{x}{3} - \dfrac{6}{3}$

$y = \dfrac{1}{3}x - 2$

Equation 2

$6y = 2x + 6$

$\dfrac{6y}{6} = \dfrac{2x}{6} + \dfrac{6}{6}$

$y = \dfrac{1}{3}x + 1$

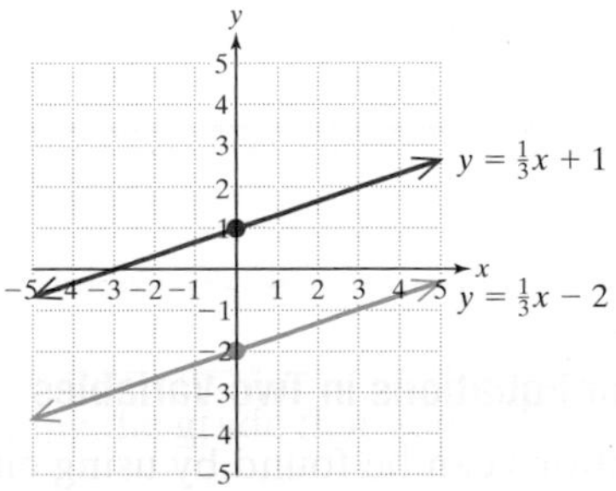

Figure 4-4

Because the lines have the same slope but different *y*-intercepts, they are parallel (Figure 4-4). Two parallel lines do not intersect, which implies that the system has no solution, { }. The system is inconsistent.

Skill Practice Solve the system by graphing.

5. $4x + y = 8$
$y = -4x + 3$

Answers

4. $\{(1, -1)\}$

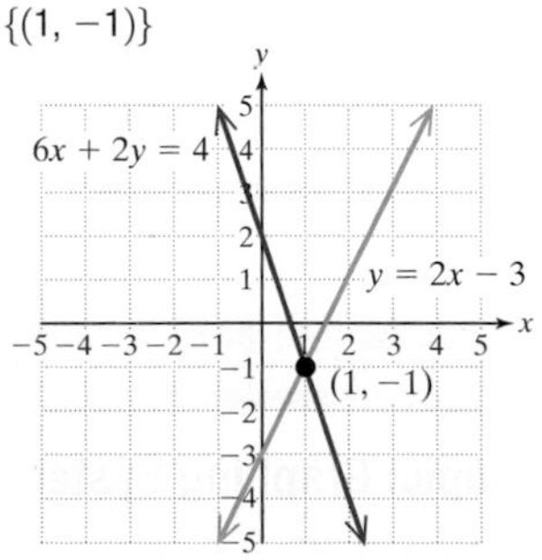

5.

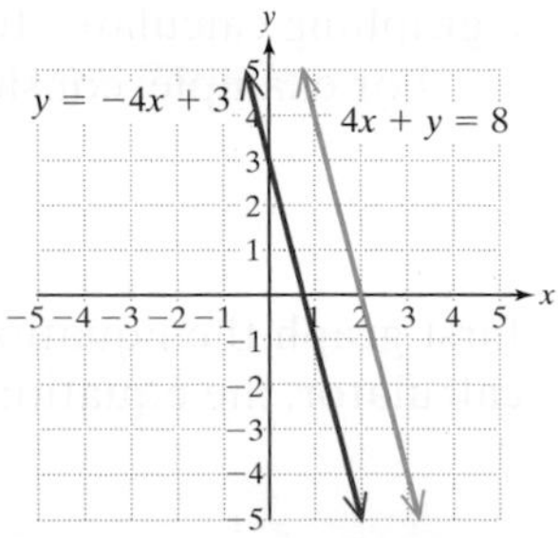

{ } The lines are parallel. The system is inconsistent.

Vocabulary and Key Concepts

1. **a.** A ______ of linear equations consists of two or more linear equations.

   b. A ______ to a system of linear equations must be a solution to both individual equations in the system.

   c. Graphically, a solution to a system of linear equations in two variables is a point where the lines ________.

   d. A system of equations that has one or more solutions is said to be _______.

   e. The solution set to an inconsistent system of equations is ______.

   f. Two equations in a system of linear equations in two variables are said to be ____ if they represent the same line.

   g. Two equations in a system of linear equations in two variables are said to be ________ if they represent different lines.

Concept 1: Solutions to a System of Linear Equations

For Exercises 2–10, determine if the given point is a solution to the system. **(See Example 1.)**

2. $6x - y = -9$, $x + 2y = 5$ $\quad(-1, 3)$

3. $3x - y = 7$, $x - 2y = 4$ $\quad(2, -1)$

4. $x - y = 3$, $x + y = 5$ $\quad(4, 1)$

5. $4y = -3x + 12$, $y = \frac{2}{3}x - 4$ $\quad(0, 4)$

6. $y = -\frac{1}{3}x + 2$, $x = 2y + 6$ $\quad(9, -1)$

7. $3x - 6y = 9$, $x - 2y = 3$ $\quad\left(4, \frac{1}{2}\right)$

8. $x - y = 4$, $3x - 3y = 12$ $\quad(6, 2)$

9. $\frac{1}{3}x = \frac{2}{5}y - \frac{4}{5}$, $\frac{3}{4}x + \frac{1}{2}y = 2$ $\quad(0, 2)$

10. $\frac{1}{4}x + \frac{1}{2}y = \frac{3}{2}$, $y = \frac{3}{2}x - 6$ $\quad(4, 1)$

For Exercises 11–14, match the graph of the system of equations with the appropriate description of the solution.

11.

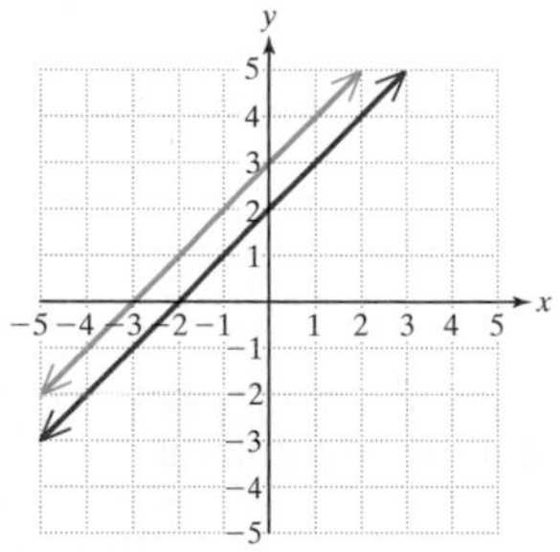

a. The solution set is {(1, 3)}.

b. { }

c. There are infinitely many solutions.

d. The solution set is {(0, 0)}.

12.

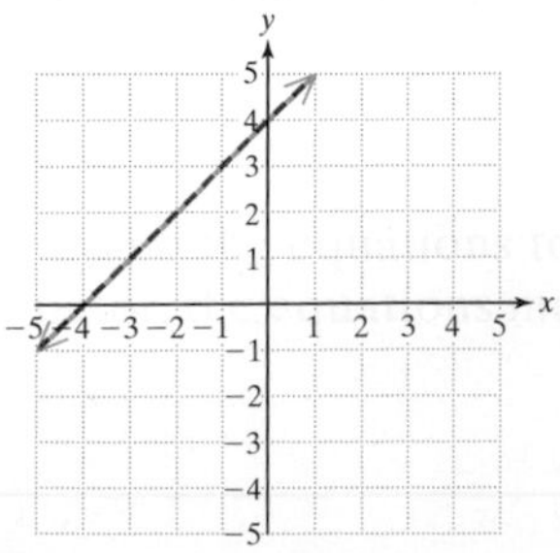

13.

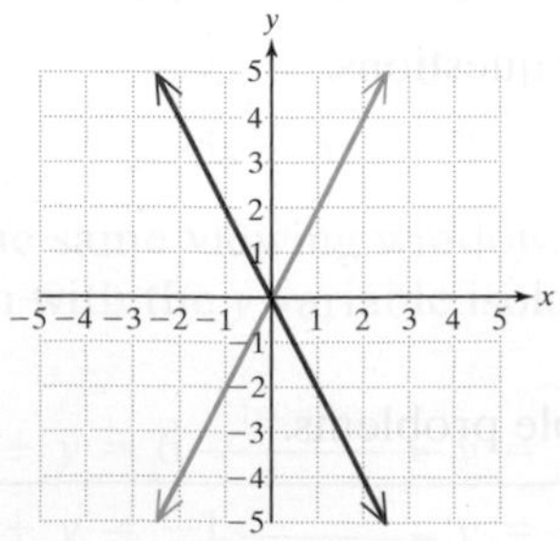

14.

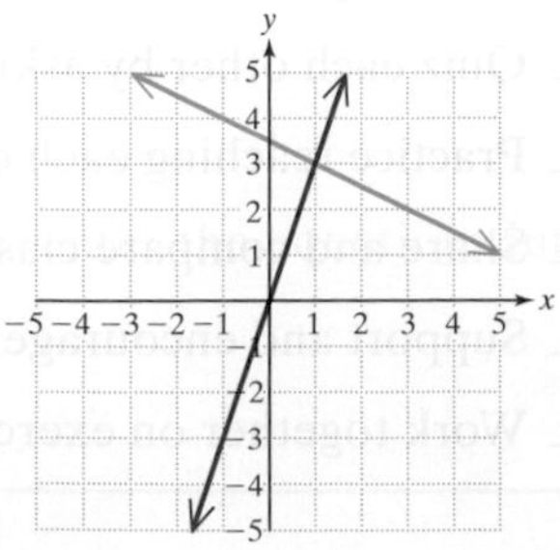

15. Graph each system of equations.

a. $y = 2x - 3$
$y = 2x + 5$

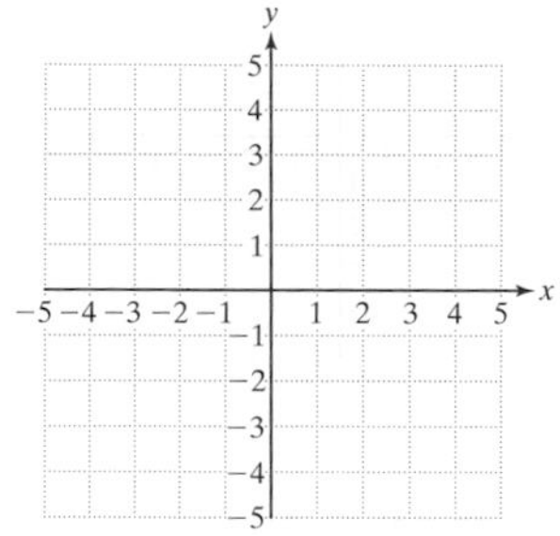

b. $y = 2x + 1$
$y = 4x - 1$

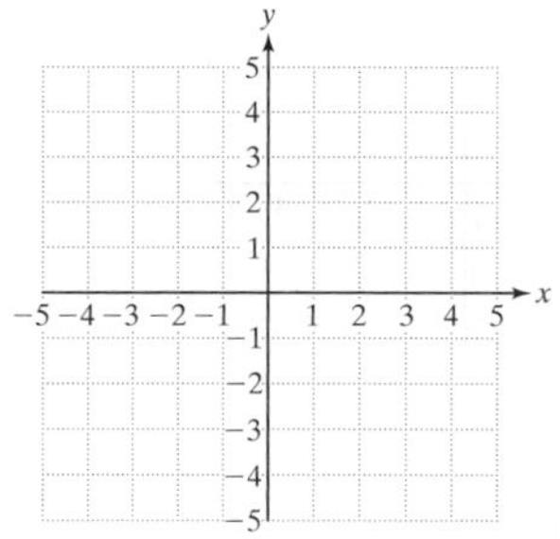

c. $y = 3x - 5$
$y = 3x - 5$

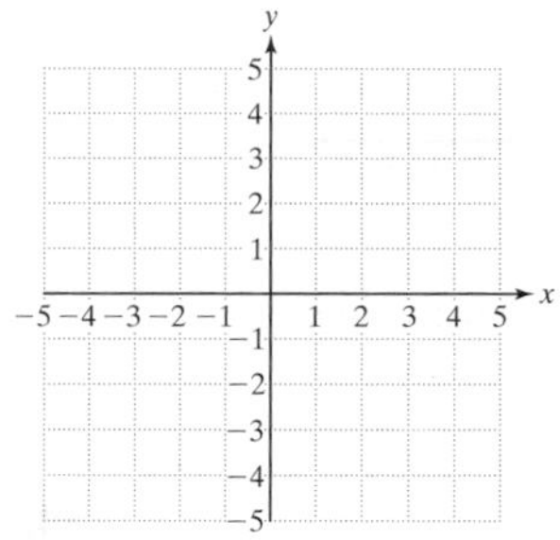

For Exercises 16–26, determine which system of equations (a, b, or c) makes the statement true. (*Hint:* Refer to the graphs from Exercise 15.)

a. $y = 2x - 3$
$y = 2x + 5$

b. $y = 2x + 1$
$y = 4x - 1$

c. $y = 3x - 5$
$y = 3x - 5$

16. The lines are parallel.

17. The lines coincide.

18. The lines intersect at exactly one point.

19. The system is inconsistent.

20. The equations are dependent.

21. The lines have the same slope but different y-intercepts.

22. The lines have the same slope and same y-intercept.

23. The lines have different slopes.

24. The system has exactly one solution.

25. The system has infinitely many solutions.

26. The system has no solution.

Concept 2: Solving Systems of Linear Equations by Graphing

For Exercises 27–50, solve the system by graphing. For systems that do not have one unique solution, also state the number of solutions and whether the system is inconsistent or the equations are dependent. **(See Examples 2–5.)**

27. $y = -x + 4$
$y = x - 2$

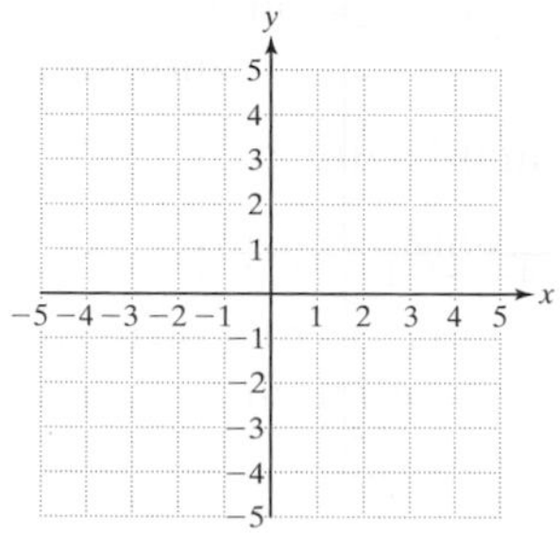

28. $y = 3x + 2$
$y = 2x$

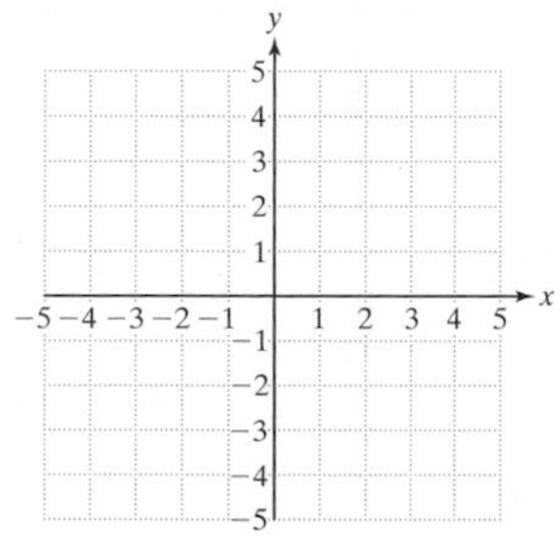

29. $2x + y = 0$
$3x + y = 1$

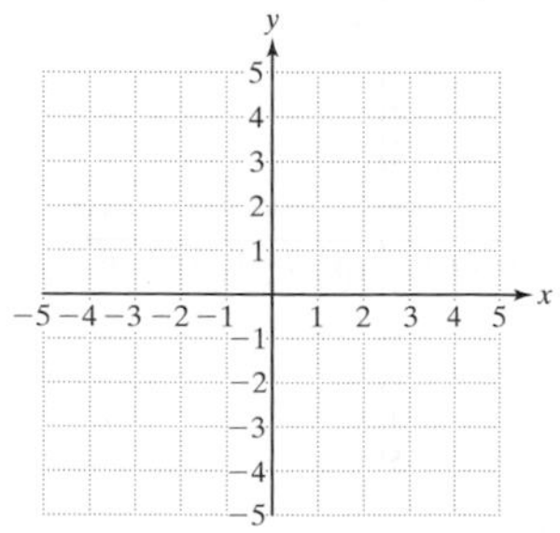

52. The cost to rent a 10 ft by 10 ft storage space is different for two different storage companies. The Storage Bin charges \$90 per month plus a nonrefundable deposit of \$120. AAA Storage charges \$110 per month with no deposit. The total cost, y, to rent a 10 ft by 10 ft space depends on the number of months, x, according to the equations

The Storage Bin: $y = 90x + 120$

AAA Storage: $y = 110x$

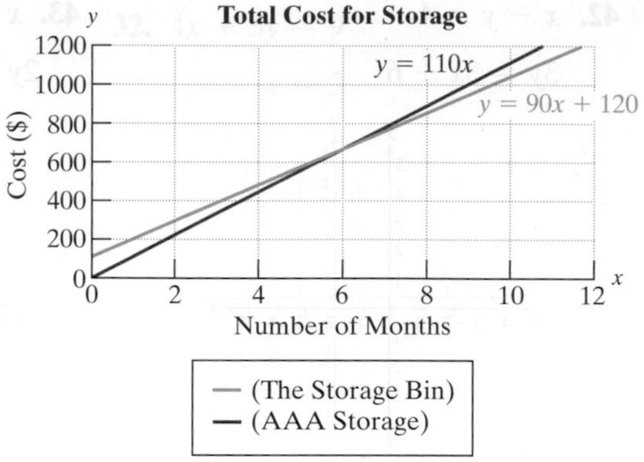

From the graph, determine the number of months required for which the cost to rent space is equal for both companies.

For the systems graphed in Exercises 53–54, explain why the ordered pair cannot be a solution to the system of equations.

53. $(-3, 1)$

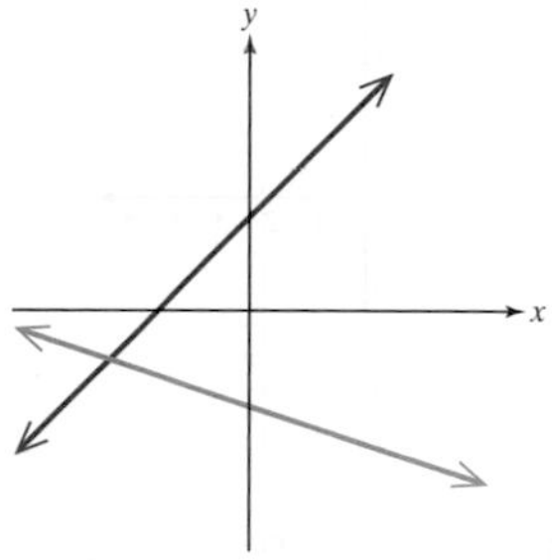

54. $(-1, -4)$

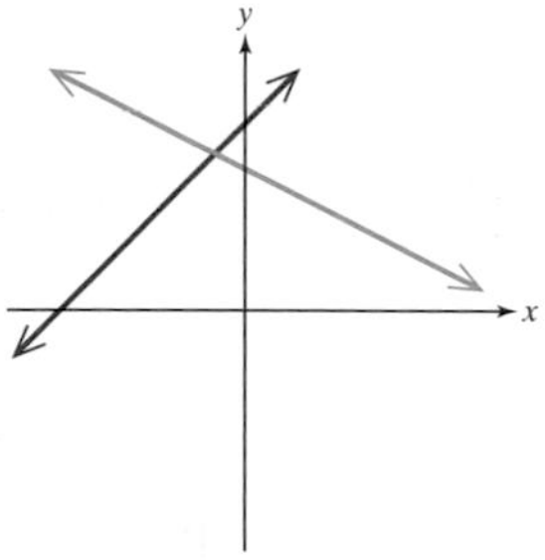

Expanding Your Skills

55. Write a system of linear equations whose solution set is $\{(2, 1)\}$.

56. Write a system of linear equations whose solution set is $\{(1, 4)\}$.

57. One equation in a system of linear equations is $x + y = 4$. Write a second equation such that the system will have no solution. (Answers may vary.)

58. One equation in a system of linear equations is $x - y = 3$. Write a second equation such that the system will have infinitely many solutions. (Answers may vary.)

Section 4.2 Solving Systems of Equations by the Substitution Method

Concepts

1. **Solving Systems of Linear Equations by Using the Substitution Method**
2. **Applications of the Substitution Method**

1. Solving Systems of Linear Equations by Using the Substitution Method

In Section 4.1, we used the graphing method to find the solution set to a system of equations. However, sometimes it is difficult to determine the solution using this method because of limitations in the accuracy of the graph. This is particularly true when the coordinates of a solution are not integer values or when the solution is a point not sufficiently close to the origin. Identifying the coordinates of the point $(\frac{3}{17}, -\frac{23}{9})$ or $(-251, 8349)$, for example, might be difficult from a graph.

In this section and the next, we will cover two algebraic methods to solve a system of equations that do not require graphing. The first method, called the *substitution method*, is demonstrated in Examples 1–5.

Example 1 **Solving a System of Linear Equations by Using the Substitution Method**

Solve the system by using the substitution method.

$$x = 2y - 3$$
$$-4x + 3y = 2$$

Solution:

The variable x has been isolated in the first equation. The quantity $2y - 3$ is equal to x and therefore can be substituted for x in the second equation. This leaves the second equation in terms of y only.

First equation: $x = \underbrace{2y - 3}$

Second equation: $-4x + 3y = 2$

$-4(2y - 3) + 3y = 2$ This equation now contains only one variable.

$-8y + 12 + 3y = 2$ Solve the resulting equation.

$$-5y + 12 = 2$$
$$-5y = -10$$
$$y = 2$$

To find x, substitute $y = 2$ back into the first equation.

$$x = 2y - 3$$
$$x = 2(2) - 3$$
$$x = 1$$

Avoiding Mistakes

Remember to solve for *both* variables in the system.

Check the ordered pair $(1, 2)$ in both original equations.

$x = 2y - 3 \longrightarrow 1 \stackrel{?}{=} 2(2) - 3$ ✔ True

$-4x + 3y = 2 \longrightarrow -4(1) + 3(2) \stackrel{?}{=} 2$ ✔ True

The solution set is $\{(1, 2)\}$.

Skill Practice Solve the system by using the substitution method.

1. $2x + 3y = -2$
$y = x + 1$

In Example 1, we eliminated the x variable from the second equation by substituting an equivalent expression for x. The resulting equation was relatively simple to solve because it had only one variable. This is the premise of the substitution method.

Answer

1. $\{(-1, 0)\}$

The substitution method can be summarized as follows.

Solving a System of Equations by Using the Substitution Method

Step 1 Isolate one of the variables from one equation.
Step 2 Substitute the expression found in step 1 into the other equation.
Step 3 Solve the resulting equation.
Step 4 Substitute the value found in step 3 back into the equation in step 1 to find the value of the remaining variable.
Step 5 Check the ordered pair in both original equations.

Example 2 **Solving a System of Linear Equations by Using the Substitution Method**

Solve the system by using the substitution method.

$$x + y = 4$$
$$-5x + 3y = -12$$

Solution:

The x or y variable in the first equation is easy to isolate because the coefficients are both 1. While either variable can be isolated, we arbitrarily choose to solve for the x variable.

$x + y = 4 \longrightarrow x = 4 - y$ **Step 1:** Isolate x in the first equation.

$-5(4 - y) + 3y = -12$ **Step 2:** Substitute $4 - y$ for x in the other equation.

$-20 + 5y + 3y = -12$ **Step 3:** Solve for y.

$-20 + 8y = -12$

$8y = 8$

$y = 1$

$x = 4 - y$ **Step 4:** Substitute $y = 1$ into the equation $x = 4 - y$.

$x = 4 - 1$

$x = 3$

Step 5: Check the ordered pair (3, 1) in both original equations.

$x + y = 4$	$(3) + (1) \stackrel{?}{=} 4$ ✔	True
$-5x + 3y = -12$	$-5(3) + 3(1) \stackrel{?}{=} -12$ ✔	True

The solution set is $\{(3, 1)\}$.

Skill Practice Solve the system by using the substitution method.

2. $x + y = 3$
$-2x + 3y = 9$

Avoiding Mistakes

Although we solved for y first, be sure to write the x-coordinate first in the ordered pair. Remember that (1, 3) is not the same as (3, 1).

TIP: The solution to a system of linear equations can be confirmed by graphing. The system from Example 2 is graphed here.

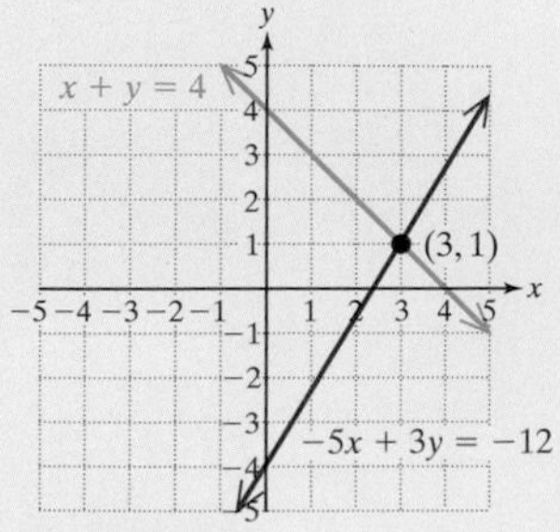

Answer

2. $\{(0, 3)\}$

Example 3 Solving a System of Linear Equations by Using the Substitution Method

Solve the system by using the substitution method.

$$3x + 5y = 17$$
$$2x - y = -6$$

Solution:

The y variable in the second equation is the easiest variable to isolate because its coefficient is -1.

$3x + 5y = 17$

$2x - y = -6 \longrightarrow -y = -2x - 6$

$y = \underbrace{2x + 6}$ **Step 1:** Isolate y in the second equation.

$3x + 5(2x + 6) = 17$ **Step 2:** Substitute the quantity $2x + 6$ for y in the other equation.

Avoiding Mistakes

Do not substitute $y = 2x + 6$ into the same equation from which it came. This mistake will result in an identity:

$$2x - y = -6$$
$$2x - (2x + 6) = -6$$
$$2x - 2x - 6 = -6$$
$$-6 = -6$$

$3x + 10x + 30 = 17$ **Step 3:** Solve for x.

$13x + 30 = 17$

$13x = 17 - 30$

$13x = -13$

$x = -1$

$y = 2x + 6$ **Step 4:** Substitute $x = -1$ into the equation $y = 2x + 6$.

$y = 2(-1) + 6$

$y = -2 + 6$

$y = 4$

Step 5: The ordered pair $(-1, 4)$ can be checked in the original equations to verify the answer.

$3x + 5y = 17 \longrightarrow 3(-1) + 5(4) \stackrel{?}{=} 17 \longrightarrow -3 + 20 \stackrel{?}{=} 17$ ✔ True

$2x - y = -6 \longrightarrow 2(-1) - (4) \stackrel{?}{=} -6 \longrightarrow -2 - 4 \stackrel{?}{=} -6$ ✔ True

The solution set is $\{(-1, 4)\}$.

Skill Practice Solve the system by using the substitution method.

3. $x + 4y = 11$
$2x - 5y = -4$

Answer
3. $\{(3, 2)\}$

Recall from Section 4.1, that a system of linear equations may represent two parallel lines. In such a case, there is no solution to the system.

Example 4 Solving an Inconsistent System Using Substitution

Solve the system by using the substitution method.

$$2x + 3y = 6$$
$$y = -\tfrac{2}{3}x + 4$$

Solution:

$$2x + 3y = 6$$

$y = \underbrace{-\tfrac{2}{3}x + 4}$ **Step 1:** The variable y is already isolated in the second equation.

$2x + 3(-\tfrac{2}{3}x + 4) = 6$ **Step 2:** Substitute $y = -\tfrac{2}{3}x + 4$ from the second equation into the first equation.

$2x - 2x + 12 = 6$ **Step 3:** Solve the resulting equation.

$12 = 6$ (contradiction)

The equation results in a contradiction. There are no values of x and y that will make 12 equal to 6. Therefore, the solution set is { }, and the system is inconsistent.

Skill Practice Solve the system by using the substitution method.

4. $y = -\dfrac{1}{2}x + 3$

   $2x + 4y = 5$

TIP: The answer to Example 4 can be verified by writing each equation in slope-intercept form and graphing the lines.

Equation 1

$$2x + 3y = 6$$
$$3y = -2x + 6$$
$$\frac{3y}{3} = \frac{-2x}{3} + \frac{6}{3}$$
$$y = -\frac{2}{3}x + 2$$

Equation 2

$$y = -\frac{2}{3}x + 4$$

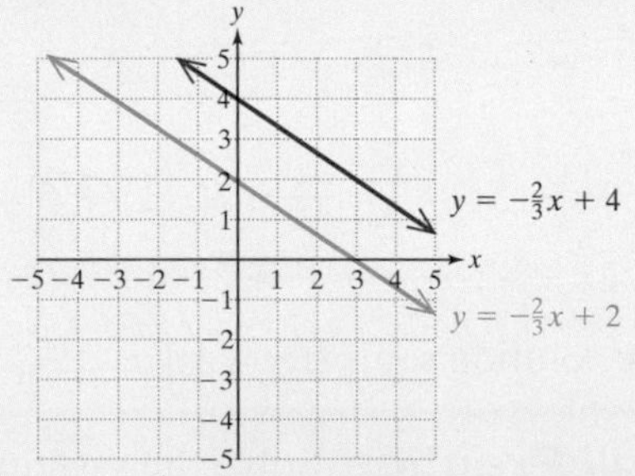

The equations indicate that the lines have the same slope but different y-intercepts. Therefore, the lines must be parallel. There is no point of intersection, indicating that the system has no solution, { }.

Answer

4. { }

Recall that a system of two linear equations may represent the same line. In such a case, the solution is the set of all points on the line.

Example 5 Solving a System of Dependent Equations Using Substitution

Solve the system by using the substitution method.

$$\frac{1}{2}x - \frac{1}{4}y = 1$$
$$6x - 3y = 12$$

Solution:

$\frac{1}{2}x - \frac{1}{4}y = 1$

$6x - 3y = 12$

To make the first equation easier to work with, we have the option of clearing fractions.

$$\frac{1}{2}x - \frac{1}{4}y = 1 \xrightarrow{\text{Multiply by 4.}} 4\left(\frac{1}{2}x\right) - 4\left(\frac{1}{4}y\right) = 4(1) \rightarrow 2x - y = 4$$

Now the system becomes:

$2x - y = 4$

$6x - 3y = 12$

The y variable in the first equation is the easiest to isolate because its coefficient is -1.

$2x - y = 4 \xrightarrow{\text{Solve for } y.} -y = -2x + 4 \rightarrow y = 2x - 4$ **Step 1:** Isolate one of the variables.

$6x - 3y = 12$

$6x - 3(2x - 4) = 12$ **Step 2:** Substitute $y = 2x - 4$ from the first equation into the second equation.

$6x - 6x + 12 = 12$ **Step 3:** Solve the resulting equation.

$12 = 12$ (identity)

Because the equation produces an identity, all values of x make this equation true. Thus, x can be any real number. Substituting any real number, x, into the equation $y = 2x - 4$ produces an ordered pair on the line $y = 2x - 4$. Hence, the solution set to the system of equations is the set of all ordered pairs on the line $y = 2x - 4$. This can be written as $\{(x, y) \mid y = 2x - 4\}$. The equations are dependent.

Skill Practice Solve the system by using the substitution method.

5. $2x + \frac{1}{3}y = -\frac{1}{3}$

$12x + 2y = -2$

Answer

5. Infinitely many solutions; $\{(x, y) \mid 12x + 2y = -2\}$; dependent equations

TIP: The solution to Example 5 can be verified by writing each equation in slope-intercept form and graphing the lines.

Equation 1	**Equation 2**
$\frac{1}{2}x - \frac{1}{4}y = 1$	$6x - 3y = 12$
Clear fractions $2x - y = 4$	$-3y = -6x + 12$
$-y = -2x + 4$	$\frac{-3y}{-3} = \frac{-6x}{-3} + \frac{12}{-3}$
$y = 2x - 4$	$y = 2x - 4$

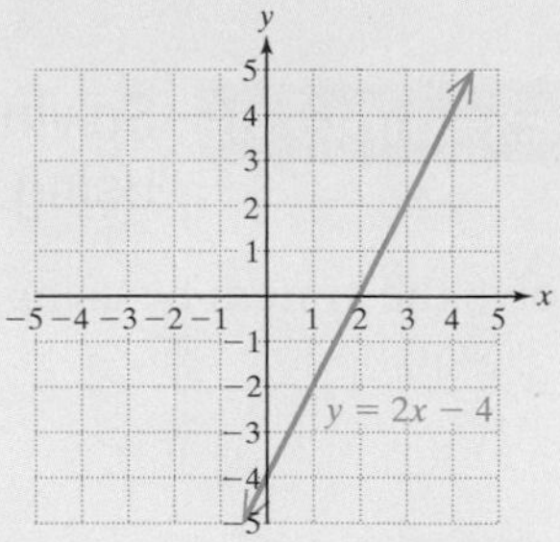

Notice that the slope-intercept forms for both equations are identical. The equations represent the same line, indicating that they are dependent. Each point on the line is a solution to the system of equations.

The following summary reviews the three different geometric relationships between two lines and the solutions to the corresponding systems of equations.

Interpreting Solutions to a System of Two Linear Equations

- The lines may intersect at one point (yielding one unique solution).
- The lines may be parallel and have no point of intersection (yielding no solution). This is detected algebraically when a contradiction (false statement) is obtained (for example, $0 = -3$ or $12 = 6$).
- The lines may be the same and intersect at all points on the line (yielding an infinite number of solutions). This is detected algebraically when an identity is obtained (for example, $0 = 0$ or $12 = 12$).

2. Applications of the Substitution Method

In Chapter 2, we solved word problems using one linear equation and one variable. In this chapter, we investigate application problems with two unknowns. In such a case, we can use two variables to represent the unknown quantities. However, if two variables are used, we must write a system of *two* distinct equations.

Example 6 Applying the Substitution Method

One number is 3 more than 4 times another. Their sum is 133. Find the numbers.

Solution:

We can use two variables to represent the two unknown numbers.

Let x represent one number.
Let y represent the other number. Label the variables.

We must now write two equations. Each of the first two sentences gives a relationship between x and y:

One number is 3 more than 4 times another. ⟶ $x = 4y + 3$ (first equation)

Their sum is 133. ⟶ $x + y = 133$ (second equation)

$(4y + 3) + y = 133$	Substitute $x = 4y + 3$ into the second equation, $x + y = 133$.
$5y + 3 = 133$	Solve the resulting equation.
$5y = 130$	
$y = 26$	
$x = 4y + 3$	
$x = 4(26) + 3$	To solve for x, substitute $y = 26$ into the equation $x = 4y + 3$.
$x = 104 + 3$	
$x = 107$	

One number is 26, and the other is 107.

Avoiding Mistakes

Notice that the answer for an application is not represented by an ordered pair.

TIP: Check that the numbers 26 and 107 meet the conditions of Example 6.

- 4 times 26 is 104. Three more than 104 is 107. ✔
- The sum of the numbers should be 133: $26 + 107 = 133$ ✔

Skill Practice

6. One number is 16 more than another. Their sum is 92. Use a system of equations to find the numbers.

Example 7 Using the Substitution Method in a Geometry Application

Two angles are supplementary. The measure of one angle is 15° more than twice the measure of the other angle. Find the measures of the two angles.

Solution:

Let x represent the measure of one angle.
Let y represent the measure of the other angle.

The sum of the measures of supplementary angles is 180°. ⟶ $x + y = 180$

The measure of one angle is 15° more than twice the other angle. ⟶ $x = 2y + 15$

$x + y = 180$	
$x = 2y + 15$	The x variable in the second equation is already isolated.
$(2y + 15) + y = 180$	Substitute $2y + 15$ into the first equation for x.
$2y + 15 + y = 180$	Solve the resulting equation.
$3y + 15 = 180$	
$3y = 165$	
$y = 55$	
$x = 2y + 15$	Substitute $y = 55$ into the equation $x = 2y + 15$.
$x = 2(55) + 15$	
$x = 110 + 15$	
$x = 125$	

One angle is 55°, and the other is 125°.

TIP: Check that the angles 55° and 125° meet the conditions of Example 7.

- Because $55° + 125° = 180°$, the angles are supplementary. ✔
- The angle 125° is 15° more than twice 55°: $125° = 2(55°) + 15°$ ✔

Answer

6. One number is 38, and the other number is 54.

Skill Practice

7. The measure of one angle is 2° less than 3 times the measure of another angle. The angles are complementary. Use a system of equations to find the measures of the two angles.

Answer

7. The measures of the angles are 23° and 67°.

Section 4.2 Practice Exercises

Review Exercises

For Exercises 1–6, write each pair of lines in slope-intercept form. Then identify whether the lines intersect in exactly one point or if the lines are parallel or coinciding.

1. $2x - y = 4$
$-2y = -4x + 8$

2. $x - 2y = 5$
$3x = 6y + 15$

3. $2x + 3y = 6$
$x - y = 5$

4. $x - y = -1$
$x + 2y = 4$

5. $2x = \frac{1}{2}y + 2$
$4x - y = 13$

6. $4y = 3x$
$3x - 4y = 15$

Concept 1: Solving Systems of Linear Equations by Using the Substitution Method

For Exercises 7–10, solve each system using the substitution method. **(See Example 1.)**

7. $3x + 2y = -3$
$y = 2x - 12$

8. $4x - 3y = -19$
$y = -2x + 13$

9. $x = -4y + 16$
$3x + 5y = 20$

10. $x = -y + 3$
$-2x + y = 6$

11. Given the system: $4x - 2y = -6$
$3x + y = 8$

a. Which variable from which equation is easiest to isolate and why?

b. Solve the system using the substitution method.

12. Given the system: $x - 5y = 2$
$11x + 13y = 22$

a. Which variable from which equation is easiest to isolate and why?

b. Solve the system using the substitution method.

For Exercises 13–48, solve the system by using the substitution method. For systems that do not have one unique solution, also state the number of solutions and whether the system is inconsistent or the equations are dependent. **(See Examples 1–5.)**

13. $x = 3y - 1$
$2x - 4y = 2$

14. $2y = x + 9$
$y = -3x + 1$

15. $-2x + 5y = 5$
$x = 4y - 10$

16. $y = -2x + 27$
$3x - 7y = -2$

17. $4x - y = -1$
$2x + 4y = 13$

18. $5x - 3y = -2$
$10x - y = 1$

19. $4x - 3y = 11$
$x = 5$

20. $y = -3x - 9$
$y = 12$

21. $4x = 8y + 4$
$5x - 3y = 5$

22. $3y = 6x - 6$
$-3x + y = -4$

23. $x - 3y = -11$
$6x - y = 2$

24. $-2x - y = 9$
$x + 7y = 15$

25. $3x + 2y = -1$
$\frac{3}{2}x + y = 4$

26. $5x - 2y = 6$
$-\frac{5}{2}x + y = 5$

27. $10x - 30y = -10$
$2x - 6y = -2$

28. $3x + 6y = 6$
$-6x - 12y = -12$

29. $2x + y = 3$
$y = -7$

30. $-3x = 2y + 23$
$x = -1$

31. $x + 2y = -2$
$4x = -2y - 17$

32. $x + y = 1$
$2x - y = -2$

33. $y = -\frac{1}{2}x - 4$
$y = 4x - 13$

34. $y = \frac{2}{3}x - 3$
$y = 6x - 19$

35. $y = 6$
$y - 4 = -2x - 6$

36. $x = 9$
$x - 3 = 6y + 12$

37. $3x + 2y = 4$
$2x - 3y = -6$

38. $4x + 3y = 4$
$-2x + 5y = -2$

39. $y = 0.25x + 1$
$-x + 4y = 4$

40. $y = 0.75x - 3$
$-3x + 4y = -12$

41. $11x + 6y = 17$
$5x - 4y = 1$

42. $3x - 8y = 7$
$10x - 5y = 45$

43. $x + 2y = 4$
$4y = -2x - 8$

44. $-y = x - 6$
$2x + 2y = 4$

45. $2x = 3 - y$
$x + y = 4$

46. $2x = 4 + 2y$
$3x + y = 10$

47. $\frac{x}{3} + \frac{y}{2} = -4$
$x - 3y = 6$

48. $x - 2y = -5$
$\frac{2x}{3} + \frac{y}{3} = 0$

Concept 2: Applications of the Substitution Method

For Exercises 49–58, set up a system of linear equations and solve for the indicated quantities. **(See Examples 6–7.)**

49. Two numbers have a sum of 106. One number is 10 less than the other. Find the numbers.

50. Two positive numbers have a difference of 8. The larger number is 2 less than 3 times the smaller number. Find the numbers.

51. The difference between two positive numbers is 26. The larger number is 3 times the smaller. Find the numbers.

52. The sum of two numbers is 956. One number is 94 less than 6 times the other. Find the numbers.

53. Two angles are supplementary. One angle is 15° more than 10 times the other angle. Find the measure of each angle.

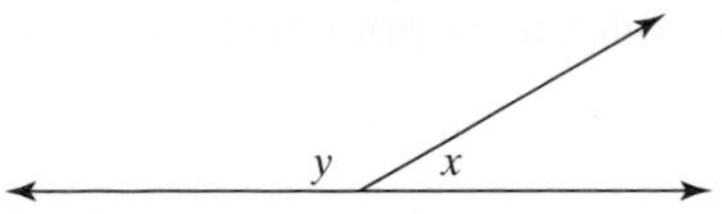

54. Two angles are complementary. One angle is 1° less than 6 times the other angle. Find the measure of each angle.

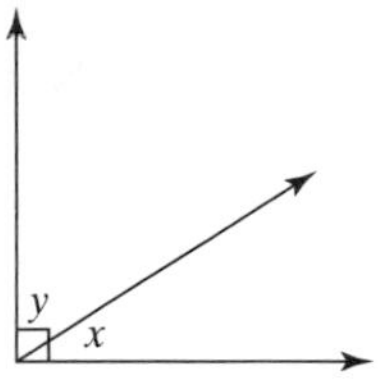

55. Two angles are complementary. One angle is 10° more than 3 times the other angle. Find the measure of each angle.

56. Two angles are supplementary. One angle is 5° less than twice the other angle. Find the measure of each angle.

57. In a right triangle, one of the acute angles is 6° less than the other acute angle. Find the measure of each acute angle.

58. In a right triangle, one of the acute angles is 9° less than twice the other acute angle. Find the measure of each acute angle.

Example 2 Solving a System of Linear Equations by Using the Addition Method

Solve the system by using the addition method.

$$3x + 5y = 17$$
$$2x - y = -6$$

Solution:

$3x + 5y = 17$ **Step 1:** Both equations are already written in standard form.

$2x - y = -6$ **Step 2:** There are no fractions or decimals.

Notice that neither the coefficients of x nor the coefficients of y are opposites. However, multiplying the second equation by 5 creates the term $-5y$ in the second equation. This is the opposite of the term $+5y$ in the first equation.

$$\begin{array}{lcl} 3x + 5y = 17 & & 3x + 5y = 17 \\ 2x - y = -6 & \xrightarrow[\text{Multiply by 5.}]{} & 10x - 5y = -30 \\ & & 13x = -13 \end{array}$$

Step 3: Multiply the second equation by 5.

Step 4: Add the equations.

$$13x = -13$$
$$x = -1$$

Step 5: Solve the equation.

Avoiding Mistakes

Remember to multiply the chosen constant on *both* sides of the equation.

$3x + 5y = 17$ First equation

$3(-1) + 5y = 17$

$-3 + 5y = 17$

$5y = 20$

$y = 4$

Step 6: Substitute $x = -1$ into one of the original equations.

Step 7: Check $(-1, 4)$ in both original equations.

TIP: In Example 2, we could have eliminated the x variable by multiplying the first equation by 2 and the second equation by -3.

Check:

$3x + 5y = 17 \longrightarrow 3(-1) + 5(4) \stackrel{?}{=} 17 \longrightarrow -3 + 20 \stackrel{?}{=} 17$ ✔ True

$2x - y = -6 \longrightarrow 2(-1) - (4) \stackrel{?}{=} -6 \longrightarrow -2 - 4 \stackrel{?}{=} -6$ ✔ True

The solution set is $\{(-1, 4)\}$.

Skill Practice Solve the system by using the addition method.

2. $4x + 3y = 3$

$x - 2y = 9$

In Example 3, the system of equations uses the variables a and b instead of x and y. In such a case, we will write the solution as an ordered pair with the variables written in alphabetical order, such as (a, b).

Answer

2. $\{(3, -3)\}$

Example 3 Solving a System of Linear Equations by Using the Addition Method

Solve the system by using the addition method.

$$5b = 7a + 8$$
$$-4a - 2b = -10$$

Solution:

Step 1: Write the equations in standard form.

The first equation becomes: $5b = 7a + 8 \longrightarrow -7a + 5b = 8$

The system becomes:
$$-7a + 5b = 8$$
$$-4a - 2b = -10$$

Step 2: There are no fractions or decimals.

Step 3: We need to obtain opposite coefficients on either the a or b term.

Notice that neither the coefficients of a nor the coefficients of b are opposites. However, it is possible to change the coefficients of b to 10 and -10 (this is because the LCM of 5 and 2 is 10). This is accomplished by multiplying the first equation by 2 and the second equation by 5.

$$-7a + 5b = 8 \xrightarrow{\text{Multiply by 2.}} -14a + 10b = 16$$
$$-4a - 2b = -10 \xrightarrow[\text{Multiply by 5.}]{} \underline{-20a - 10b = -50}$$
$$-34a = -34$$

Step 4: Add the equations.

$$-34a = -34$$
$$\frac{-34a}{-34} = \frac{-34}{-34}$$
$$a = 1$$

Step 5: Solve the resulting equation.

$5b = 7a + 8$ First equation

Step 6: Substitute $a = 1$ into one of the original equations.

$$5b = 7(1) + 8$$
$$5b = 15$$
$$b = 3$$

Step 7: Check $(1, 3)$ in the original equations.

Check:

$5b = 7a + 8 \longrightarrow 5(3) \stackrel{?}{=} 7(1) + 8 \longrightarrow 15 \stackrel{?}{=} 7 + 8$ ✔ True

$-4a - 2b = -10 \longrightarrow -4(1) - 2(3) \stackrel{?}{=} -10 \longrightarrow -4 - 6 \stackrel{?}{=} -10$ ✔ True

The solution set is $\{(1, 3)\}$.

Skill Practice Solve the system by using the addition method.

3. $8n = 4 - 5m$
   $7m + 6n = -10$

Answer

3. $\{(-4, 3)\}$

Example 6 **Solving a System of Dependent Equations by the Addition Method**

Solve the system by using the addition method. $3x - y = 4$

$2y = 6x - 8$

Solution:

$3x - y = 4 \longrightarrow 3x - y = 4$ **Step 1:** Write the equations in standard form.

$2y = 6x - 8 \longrightarrow -6x + 2y = -8$ **Step 2:** There are no fractions or decimals.

Notice that the equations differ exactly by a factor of −2, which indicates that these two equations represent the same line. Multiply the first equation by 2 to create opposite coefficients for the variables.

$$\begin{array}{lcr} 3x - y = 4 & \xrightarrow{\text{Multiply by 2.}} & 6x - 2y = 8 \\ -6x + 2y = -8 & & -6x + 2y = -8 \\ \hline & & 0 = 0 \end{array}$$

Step 3: Create opposite coefficients.

Step 4: Add the equations.

Because the resulting equation is an identity, the original equations represent the same line. This can be confirmed by writing each equation in slope-intercept form.

$$3x - y = 4 \longrightarrow -y = -3x + 4 \longrightarrow y = 3x - 4$$
$$-6x + 2y = -8 \longrightarrow 2y = 6x - 8 \longrightarrow y = 3x - 4$$

The solution is the set of all points on the line, or equivalently, $\{(x, y) | y = 3x - 4\}$.

Skill Practice Solve the system by using the addition method.

6. $3x = 3y + 15$
$2x - 2y = 10$

2. Summary of Methods for Solving Systems of Linear Equations in Two Variables

If no method of solving a system of linear equations is specified, you may use the method of your choice. However, we recommend the following guidelines:

1. If one of the equations is written with a variable isolated, the substitution method is a good choice. For example:

$$2x + 5y = 2 \qquad \text{or} \qquad y = \frac{1}{3}x - 2$$
$$x = y - 6 \qquad\qquad x - 6y = 9$$

2. If both equations are written in standard form, $Ax + By = C$, where none of the variables has coefficients of 1 or −1, then the addition method is a good choice.

$$4x + 5y = 12$$
$$5x + 3y = 15$$

3. If both equations are written in standard form, $Ax + By = C$, and at least one variable has a coefficient of 1 or −1, then either the substitution method or the addition method is a good choice.

Answer

6. $\{(x, y) | 2x - 2y = 10\}$

Section 4.3 Practice Exercises

Study Skills Exercise

Now that you have learned three methods of solving a system of linear equations with two variables, choose a system and solve it all three ways. There are two advantages to this. One is to check your answer (you should get the same answer using all three methods). The second advantage is to show you which method is the easiest for you to use.

Solve the system by using the graphing method, the substitution method, and the addition method.

$$2x + y = -7$$
$$x - 10 = 4y$$

Review Exercises

For Exercises 1–5, check whether the given ordered pair is a solution to the system.

1. $-\frac{3}{4}x + 2y = -10$ $(8, -2)$
$x - \frac{1}{2}y = 7$

2. $x + y = 8$ $(5, 3)$
$y = x - 2$

3. $x = y + 1$ $(3, 2)$
$-x + 2y = 0$

4. $3x + 2y = 14$ $(5, -2)$
$5x - 2y = 29$

5. $x = 2y - 11$ $(-3, 4)$
$-x + 5y = 23$

Concept 1: Solving Systems of Linear Equations by Using the Addition Method

For Exercises 6–7, answer as true or false.

6. Given the system $5x - 4y = 1$
$7x - 2y = 5$

a. To eliminate the y variable using the addition method, multiply the second equation by 2.

b. To eliminate the x variable using the addition method, multiply the first equation by 7 and the second equation by -5.

7. Given the system $3x + 5y = -1$
$9x - 8y = -26$

a. To eliminate the x variable using the addition method, multiply the first equation by -3.

b. To eliminate the y variable using the addition method, multiply the first equation by 8 and the second equation by -5.

8. Given the system $3x - 4y = 2$
$17x + y = 35$

a. Which variable, x or y, is easier to eliminate using the addition method?

b. Solve the system using the addition method.

9. Given the system $-2x + 5y = -15$
$6x - 7y = 21$

a. Which variable, x or y, is easier to eliminate using the addition method?

b. Solve the system using the addition method.

For Exercises 10–24, solve each system using the addition method. **(See Examples 1–4.)**

10. $x + 2y = 8$
$5x - 2y = 4$

11. $2x - 3y = 11$
$-4x + 3y = -19$

12. $a + b = 3$
$3a + b = 13$

13. $-2u + 6v = 10$
$-2u + v = -5$

14. $-3x + y = 1$
$-6x - 2y = -2$

15. $5m - 2n = 4$
$3m + n = 9$

Problem Recognition Exercises

Systems of Equations

For Exercises 1–6 determine the number of solutions to the system without solving the system. Explain your answers.

1. $y = -4x + 2$
$y = -4x + 2$

2. $y = -4x + 6$
$y = -4x + 1$

3. $y = 4x - 3$
$y = -4x + 5$

4. $y = 7$
$2x + 3y = 1$

5. $2x + 3y = 1$
$2x + 3y = 8$

6. $8x - 2y = 6$
$12x - 3y = 9$

For Exercises 7–10, a method of solving has been suggested for each system of equations. Explain why that method was suggested for the system and then solve the system using the method given.

7. $2x - 5y = -11$ Addition Method
$7x + 5y = -16$

8. $4x + 11y = 56$ Addition Method
$-2x - 5y = -26$

9. $x = -3y + 4$ Substitution Method
$5x + 4y = -2$

10. $2x + 3y = 16$ Substitution Method
$y = x - 8$

For Exercises 11–30, solve each system using the method of your choice. For systems that do not have one unique solution, also state the number of solutions and whether the system is inconsistent or the equations are dependent.

11. $x = -2y + 5$
$2x - 4y = 10$

12. $y = -3x - 4$
$2x - y = 9$

13. $3x - 2y = 22$
$5x + 2y = 10$

14. $-4x + 2y = -2$
$4x - 5y = -7$

15. $\frac{1}{3}x + \frac{1}{2}y = \frac{2}{3}$
$-\frac{2}{3}x + y = -\frac{4}{3}$

16. $\frac{1}{4}x + \frac{2}{5}y = 6$
$\frac{1}{2}x - \frac{1}{10}y = 3$

17. $2c + 7d = -1$
$c = 2$

18. $-3w + 5z = -6$
$z = -4$

19. $y = 0.4x - 0.3$
$-4x + 10y = 20$

20. $x = -0.5y + 0.1$
$-10x - 5y = 2$

21. $3a + 7b = -3$
$-11a + 3b = 11$

22. $2v - 5w = 10$
$9v + 7w = 45$

23. $y = 2x - 14$
$4x - 2y = 28$

24. $x = 5y - 9$
$-2x + 10y = 18$

25. $x + y = 3200$
$0.06x + 0.04y = 172$

26. $x + y = 4500$
$0.07x + 0.05y = 291$

27. $3x + y - 7 = x - 4$
$3x - 4y + 4 = -6y + 5$

28. $7y - 8y - 3 = -3x + 4$
$10x - 5y - 12 = 13$

29. $3x - 6y = -1$
$9x + 4y = 8$

30. $8x - 2y = 5$
$12x + 4y = -3$

Applications of Linear Equations in Two Variables

Section 4.4

Concepts

1. **Applications Involving Cost**
2. **Applications Involving Principal and Interest**
3. **Applications Involving Mixtures**
4. **Applications Involving Distance, Rate, and Time**

1. Applications Involving Cost

In Sections 2.4–2.7, we solved several applied problems by setting up a linear equation in one variable. When solving an application that involves two unknowns, sometimes it is convenient to use a system of linear equations in two variables.

Example 1 Using a System of Linear Equations Involving Cost

At a movie theater a couple buys one large popcorn and two small drinks for \$12.50. A group of teenagers buys two large popcorns and five small drinks for \$28.50. Find the cost of one large popcorn and the cost of one small drink.

Solution:

In this application we have two unknowns, which we can represent by x and y.

Let x represent the cost of one large popcorn.
Let y represent the cost of one small drink.

We must now write two equations. Each of the first two sentences in the problem gives a relationship between x and y:

$$\begin{pmatrix}\text{Cost of 1}\\\text{popcorn}\end{pmatrix} + \begin{pmatrix}\text{cost of 2}\\\text{drinks}\end{pmatrix} = \begin{pmatrix}\text{total}\\\text{cost}\end{pmatrix} \longrightarrow x + 2y = 12.50$$

$$\begin{pmatrix}\text{Cost of 2}\\\text{popcorns}\end{pmatrix} + \begin{pmatrix}\text{cost of 5}\\\text{drinks}\end{pmatrix} = \begin{pmatrix}\text{total}\\\text{cost}\end{pmatrix} \longrightarrow 2x + 5y = 28.50$$

To solve this system, we may either use the substitution method or the addition method. We will use the substitution method by solving for x in the first equation.

$$x + 2y = 12.50 \longrightarrow x = -2y + 12.50 \quad \text{Isolate } x \text{ in the first equation.}$$

$$2x + 5y = 28.50$$

$$2(-2y + 12.50) + 5y = 28.50 \quad \text{Substitute } x = -2y + 12.50 \text{ into the other equation.}$$

$$-4y + 25.00 + 5y = 28.50 \quad \text{Solve for } y.$$

$$y + 25.00 = 28.50$$

$$y = 3.50$$

$$x = -2y + 12.50$$

$$x = -2(3.50) + 12.50 \quad \text{Substitute } y = 3.50 \text{ into the equation } x = -2y + 12.50.$$

$$x = -7.00 + 12.50$$

$$x = 5.50$$

The cost of one large popcorn is \$5.50 and the cost of one small drink is \$3.50.

Check by verifying that the solutions meet the specified conditions.

1 popcorn + 2 drinks = 1(\$5.50) + 2(\$3.50) = \$12.50 ✔ True

2 popcorns + 5 drinks = 2(\$5.50) + 5(\$3.50) = \$28.50 ✔ True

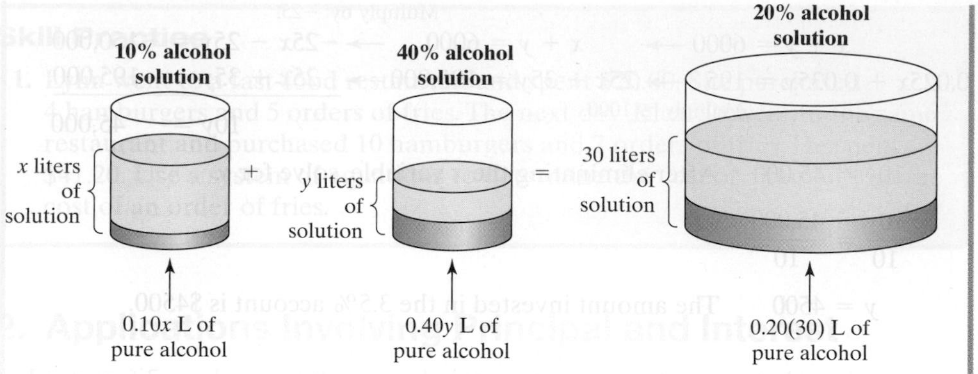

Figure 4-9

The information given in the statement of the problem can be organized in a chart.

	10% Alcohol	40% Alcohol	20% Alcohol
Number of liters of solution	x	y	30
Number of liters of pure alcohol	$0.10x$	$0.40y$	$0.20(30) = 6$

From the first row, we have

$$\begin{pmatrix}\text{Amount of}\\ \text{10\% solution}\end{pmatrix} + \begin{pmatrix}\text{amount of}\\ \text{40\% solution}\end{pmatrix} = \begin{pmatrix}\text{total amount}\\ \text{of 20\% solution}\end{pmatrix} \rightarrow x + y = 30$$

From the second row, we have

$$\begin{pmatrix}\text{Amount of}\\ \text{alcohol in}\\ \text{10\% solution}\end{pmatrix} + \begin{pmatrix}\text{amount of}\\ \text{alcohol in}\\ \text{40\% solution}\end{pmatrix} = \begin{pmatrix}\text{total amount of}\\ \text{alcohol in}\\ \text{20\% solution}\end{pmatrix} \rightarrow 0.10x + 0.40y = 6$$

We will solve the system with the addition method by first clearing decimals.

$$\begin{array}{rcrcr} x + y = 30 & \longrightarrow & x + y = 30 & \xrightarrow{\text{Multiply by } -1.} & -x - y = -30 \\ 0.10x + 0.40y = 6 & \xrightarrow[\text{Multiply by 10.}]{} & x + 4y = 60 & \longrightarrow & x + 4y = 60 \\ & & & & \overline{3y = 30} \end{array}$$

$3y = 30$ After eliminating the x variable, solve for y.

$y = 10$ 10 L of 40% solution is needed.

$x + y = 30$ Substitute $y = 10$ into either of the original equations.

$x + (10) = 30$

$x = 20$ 20 L of 10% solution is needed.

10 L of 40% solution must be mixed with 20 L of 10% solution.

Skill Practice

3. How many ounces of 20% and 35% acid solution should be mixed together to obtain 15 oz of 30% acid solution?

Answer

3. 10 oz of the 35% solution, and 5 oz of the 20% solution.

4. Applications Involving Distance, Rate, and Time

The following formula relates the distance traveled to the rate and time of travel.

$$d = rt \qquad \text{distance} = \text{rate} \cdot \text{time}$$

For example, if a car travels at 60 mph for 3 hr, then

$$d = (60 \text{ mph})(3 \text{ hr})$$
$$= 180 \text{ mi}$$

If a car travels at 60 mph for x hr, then

$$d = (60 \text{ mph})(x \text{ hr})$$
$$= 60x \text{ mi}$$

The relationship $d = rt$ is used in Example 4.

Example 4 Using a System of Linear Equations in a Distance, Rate, and Time Application

A plane travels with the wind from Kansas City, Missouri, to Denver, Colorado, a distance of 600 mi in 2 hr. The return trip against the same wind takes 3 hr. Find the speed of the plane in still air, and find the speed of the wind.

Solution:

Let p represent the speed of the plane in still air.
Let w represent the speed of the wind.

Notice that when the plane travels with the wind, the net speed is $p + w$. When the plane travels against the wind, the net speed is $p - w$.

The information given in the problem can be organized in a chart.

	Distance	Rate	Time
With the wind	600	$p + w$	2
Against the wind	600	$p - w$	3

To set up two equations in p and w, recall that $d = rt$.

From the first row, we have

$$\begin{pmatrix}\text{Distance}\\ \text{with the wind}\end{pmatrix} = \begin{pmatrix}\text{rate with}\\ \text{the wind}\end{pmatrix}\begin{pmatrix}\text{time traveled}\\ \text{with the wind}\end{pmatrix} \longrightarrow 600 = (p + w) \cdot 2$$

From the second row, we have

$$\begin{pmatrix}\text{Distance}\\ \text{against the wind}\end{pmatrix} = \begin{pmatrix}\text{rate against}\\ \text{the wind}\end{pmatrix}\begin{pmatrix}\text{time traveled}\\ \text{against the wind}\end{pmatrix} \longrightarrow 600 = (p - w) \cdot 3$$

Using the distributive property to clear parentheses produces the following system:

$$2p + 2w = 600$$
$$3p - 3w = 600$$

19. Suppose a rich uncle dies and leaves you an inheritance of \$30,000. You decide to invest part of the money in a relatively safe bond fund that returns 8%. You invest the rest of the money in a riskier stock fund that you hope will return 12% at the end of 1 year. If you need \$3120 at the end of 1 year to make a down payment on a car, how much should you invest at each rate?

20. As part of his retirement strategy, John plans to invest \$200,000 in two different funds. He projects that the moderately high risk investments should return, over time, about 9% per year, while the low risk investments should return about 4% per year. If he wants a supplemental income of \$12,000 a year, how should he divide his investments?

Concept 3: Applications Involving Mixtures

21. How much 50% disinfectant solution must be mixed with a 40% disinfectant solution to produce 25 gal of a 46% disinfectant solution? **(See Example 3.)**

	50% Mixture	40% Mixture	46% Mixture
Amount of solution			
Amount of disinfectant			

22. How many gallons of 20% antifreeze solution and a 10% antifreeze solution must be mixed to obtain 40 gal of a 16% antifreeze solution?

	20% Mixture	10% Mixture	16% Mixture
Amount of solution			
Amount of antifreeze			

23. How much 45% disinfectant solution must be mixed with a 30% disinfectant solution to produce 20 gal of a 39% disinfectant solution?

24. How many gallons of a 25% antifreeze solution and a 15% antifreeze solution must be mixed to obtain 15 gal of a 23% antifreeze solution?

25. A nurse needs 50 mL of a 16% salt solution for a patient. She can only find a 13% salt solution and an 18% salt solution in the supply room. How many milliliters of the 13% solution should be mixed with the 18% solution to produce the desired amount of the 16% solution?

26. Meadowsilver Dairy keeps two kinds of milk on hand, skim milk that has 0.3% butterfat and whole milk that contains 3.3% butterfat. How many gallons of each type of milk does the company need to produce 300 gal of 1% milk for the P&A grocery store?

27. The cooling system in most cars requires a mixture that is 50% antifreeze. How many liters of pure antifreeze and how many liters of 40% antifreeze solution should Chad mix to obtain 6 L of 50% antifreeze solution? (*Hint:* Pure antifreeze is 100% antifreeze.)

28. Silvia wants to mix a 40% apple juice drink with pure apple juice to make 2 L of a juice drink that is 80% apple juice. How much pure apple juice should she use?

Concept 4: Applications Involving Distance, Rate, and Time

29. It takes a boat 2 hr to go 16 mi downstream with the current and 4 hr to return against the current. Find the speed of the boat in still water and the speed of the current. **(See Example 4.)**

	Distance	Rate	Time
Downstream			
Upstream			

30. A boat takes 1.5 hr to go 12 mi upstream against the current. It can go 24 mi downstream with the current in the same amount of time. Find the speed of the current and the speed of the boat in still water.

	Distance	Rate	Time
Upstream			
Downstream			

31. A plane can fly 960 mi with the wind in 3 hr. It takes the same amount of time to fly 840 mi against the wind. What is the speed of the plane in still air and the speed of the wind?

32. A plane flies 720 mi with the wind in 3 hr. The return trip takes 4 hr. What is the speed of the wind and the speed of the plane in still air?

33. Tony Markins flew from JFK Airport to London. It took him 6 hr to fly with the wind, and 8 hr on the return flight against the wind. If the distance is approximately 3600 mi, determine the speed of the plane in still air and the speed of the wind.

34. A riverboat cruise travels upstream on the Mississippi River from New Orleans, Louisiana, to Natchez, Mississippi, takes 10 hr and covers 140 mi. The return trip downstream with the current takes only 7 hr. Find the speed of the riverboat in still water and the speed of the current.

Mixed Exercises

35. Debi has \$2.80 in a collection of dimes and nickels. The number of nickels is five more than the number of dimes. Find the number of each type of coin.

36. A child is collecting state quarters and new \$1 coins. If she has a total of 25 coins, and the number of quarters is nine more than the number of dollar coins, how many of each type of coin does she have?

37. How many quarts of water should be mixed with a 30% vinegar solution to obtain 12 qt of a 25% vinegar solution? (*Hint:* Water is 0% vinegar.)

38. How much water should be mixed with an 8% plant fertilizer solution to make a half gallon of a 6% plant fertilizer solution?

39. In the 1961–1962 NBA basketball season, Wilt Chamberlain of the Philadelphia Warriors made 2432 baskets. Some of the baskets were free throws (worth 1 point each) and some were field goals (worth 2 points each). The number of field goals was 762 more than the number of free throws.

a. How many field goals did he make and how many free throws did he make?

b. What was the total number of points scored?

c. If Wilt Chamberlain played 80 games during this season, what was the average number of points per game?

40. In the 1971–1972 NBA basketball season, Kareem Abdul-Jabbar of the Milwaukee Bucks made 1663 baskets. Some of the baskets were free throws (worth 1 point each) and some were field goals (worth 2 points each). The number of field goals he scored was 151 more than twice the number of free throws.

a. How many field goals did he make and how many free throws did he make?

b. What was the total number of points scored?

c. If Kareem Abdul-Jabbar played 81 games during this season, what was the average number of points per game?

41. A small plane can fly 350 mi with a tailwind in $1\frac{3}{4}$ hr. In the same amount of time, the same plane can travel only 210 mi with a headwind. What is the speed of the plane in still air and the speed of the wind?

42. A plane takes 2 hr to travel 1000 mi with the wind. It can travel only 880 mi against the wind in the same amount of time. Find the speed of the wind and the speed of the plane in still air.

43. A total of \$60,000 is invested in two accounts, one that earns 5.5% simple interest, and one that earns 6.5% simple interest. If the total interest at the end of 1 year is \$3750, find the amount invested in each account.

44. Jacques borrows a total of \$15,000. Part of the money is borrowed from a bank that charges 12% simple interest per year. Jacques borrows the remaining part of the money from his sister and promises to pay her 7% simple interest per year. If Jacques' total interest for the year is \$1475, find the amount he borrowed from each source.

45. At the holidays, Erica likes to sell a candy/nut mixture to her neighbors. She wants to combine candy that costs \$1.80 per pound with nuts that cost \$1.20 per pound. If Erica needs 20 lb of mixture that will sell for \$1.56 per pound, how many pounds of candy and how many pounds of nuts should she use?

46. Mary Lee's natural food store sells a combination of teas. The most popular is a mixture of a tea that sells for \$3.00 per pound with one that sells for \$4.00 per pound. If she needs 40 lb of tea that will sell for \$3.65 per pound, how many pounds of each tea should she use?

47. In the 1994 Super Bowl, the Dallas Cowboys scored four more points than twice the number of points scored by the Buffalo Bills. If the total number of points scored by both teams was 43, find the number of points scored by each team.

48. In the 1973 Super Bowl, the Miami Dolphins scored twice as many points as the Washington Redskins. If the total number of points scored by both teams was 21, find the number of points scored by each team.

Expanding Your Skills

49. In a survey conducted among 500 college students, 340 said that the campus lacked adequate lighting. If $\frac{4}{5}$ of the women and $\frac{1}{2}$ of the men said that they thought the campus lacked adequate lighting, how many men and how many women were in the survey?

50. During a 1-hr television program, there were 22 commercials. Some commercials were 15 sec and some were 30 sec long. Find the number of 15-sec commercials and the number of 30-sec commercials if the total playing time for commercials was 9.5 min.

Section 4.5 Systems of Linear Equations in Three Variables

Concepts

1. **Solutions to Systems of Linear Equations in Three Variables**
2. **Solving Systems of Linear Equations in Three Variables**

1. Solutions to Systems of Linear Equations in Three Variables

In Sections 4.1–4.3, we solved systems of linear equations in two variables. In this section, we will expand the discussion to solving systems involving three variables.

A **linear equation in three variables** can be written in the form $Ax + By + Cz = D$, where A, B, and C are not all zero. For example, the equation $2x + 3y + z = 6$ is a linear equation in three variables. Solutions to this equation are **ordered triples** of the form (x, y, z) that satisfy the equation. Some solutions to the equation $2x + 3y + z = 6$ are

Solution:	Check:
$(1, 1, 1) \longrightarrow$	$2(1) + 3(1) + (1) = 6$ ✔ True
$(2, 0, 2) \longrightarrow$	$2(2) + 3(0) + (2) = 6$ ✔ True
$(0, 1, 3) \longrightarrow$	$2(0) + 3(1) + (3) = 6$ ✔ True

Infinitely many ordered triples serve as solutions to the equation $2x + 3y + z = 6$.

The set of all ordered triples that are solutions to a linear equation in three variables may be represented graphically by a plane in space. Figure 4-10 shows a portion of the plane $2x + 3y + z = 6$ in a 3-dimensional coordinate system.

A solution to a system of linear equations in three variables is an ordered triple that satisfies *each* equation. Geometrically, a solution is a point of intersection of the planes represented by the equations in the system.

A system of linear equations in three variables may have *one unique solution, infinitely many solutions,* or *no solution.*

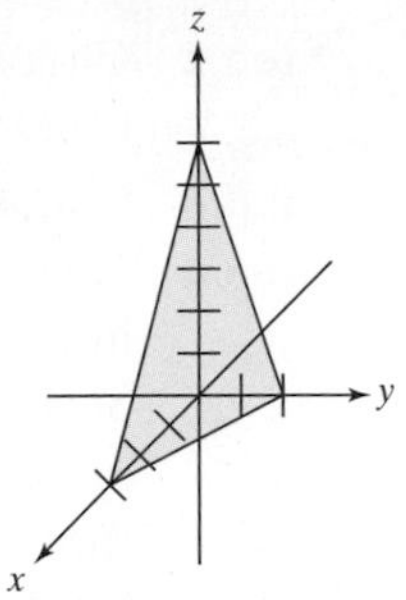

Figure 4-10

One unique solution (planes intersect at one point)
- The system is consistent.
- The equations are independent.

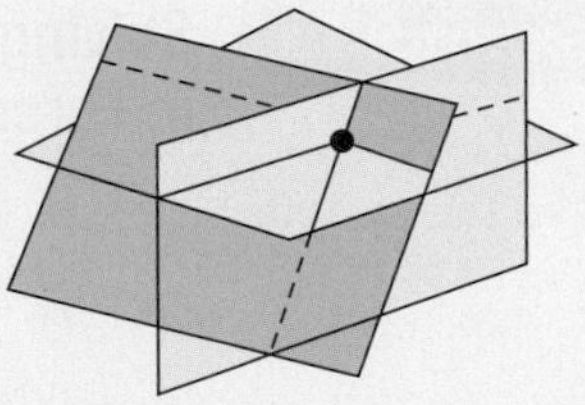

No solution (the three planes do not all intersect)
- The system is inconsistent.
- The equations are independent.

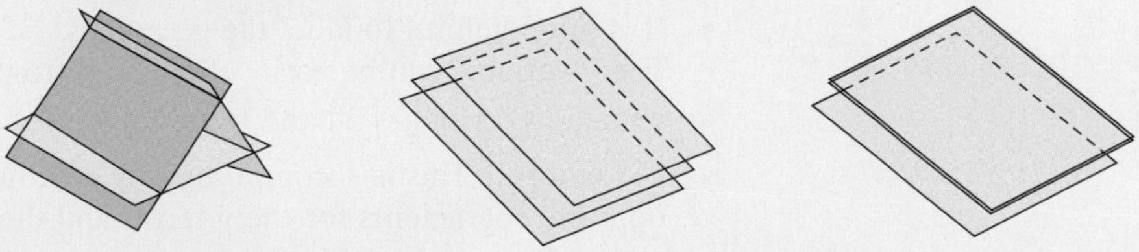

Infinitely many solutions (planes intersect at infinitely many points)
- The system is consistent.
- The equations are dependent.

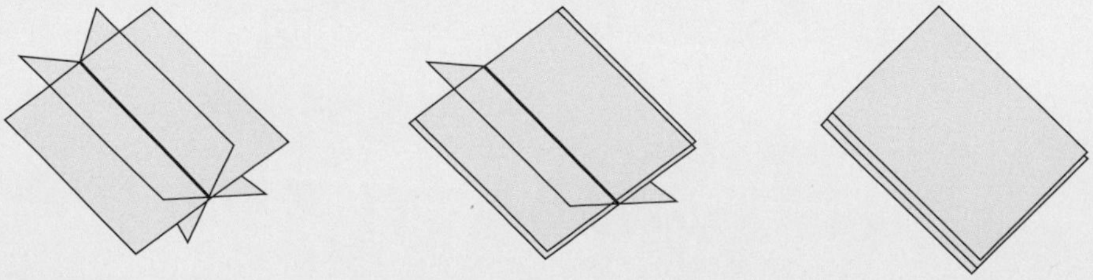

2. Solving Systems of Linear Equations in Three Variables

To solve a system involving three variables, the goal is to eliminate one variable. This reduces the system to two equations in two variables. One strategy for eliminating a variable is to pair up the original equations two at a time.

Solving a System of Three Linear Equations in Three Variables

Step 1 Write each equation in standard form $Ax + By + Cz = D$.

Step 2 Choose a pair of equations, and eliminate one of the variables by using the addition method.

Step 3 Choose a different pair of equations and eliminate the *same* variable.

Step 4 Once steps 2 and 3 are complete, you should have two equations in two variables. Solve this system by using the methods from Sections 4.2 and 4.3.

Step 5 Substitute the values of the variables found in step 4 into any of the three original equations that contain the third variable. Solve for the third variable.

Step 6 Check the ordered triple in each of the original equations.

Example 1 Solving a System of Linear Equations in Three Variables

Solve the system.

$$\begin{aligned} 2x + y - 3z &= -7 \\ 3x - 2y + z &= 11 \\ -2x - 3y - 2z &= 3 \end{aligned}$$

Solution:

$$\begin{aligned} \boxed{A}\quad 2x + y - 3z &= -7 \\ \boxed{B}\quad 3x - 2y + z &= 11 \\ \boxed{C}\quad -2x - 3y - 2z &= 3 \end{aligned}$$

Step 1: The equations are already in standard form.

- It is often helpful to label the equations.
- The y-variable can be easily eliminated from equations $\boxed{A}$ and $\boxed{B}$ and from equations $\boxed{A}$ and $\boxed{C}$. This is accomplished by creating opposite coefficients for the y-terms and then adding the equations.

Step 2: Eliminate the y-variable from equations $\boxed{A}$ and $\boxed{B}$.

$$\begin{aligned} \boxed{A}\quad 2x + y - 3z = -7 \quad &\xrightarrow{\text{Multiply by 2.}} \quad 4x + 2y - 6z = -14 \\ \boxed{B}\quad 3x - 2y + z = 11 \quad &\longrightarrow \quad \underline{3x - 2y + z = 11} \\ & \qquad\quad 7x \qquad - 5z = -3 \quad \boxed{D} \end{aligned}$$

Step 3: Eliminate the y-variable again, this time from equations $\boxed{A}$ and $\boxed{C}$.

$$\boxed{A}\quad 2x + y - 3z = -7 \xrightarrow{\text{Multiply by 3.}} 6x + 3y - 9z = -21$$
$$\boxed{C}\quad -2x - 3y - 2z = 3 \longrightarrow -2x - 3y - 2z = 3$$
$$4x - 11z = -18 \quad \boxed{E}$$

Step 4: Now equations $\boxed{D}$ and $\boxed{E}$ can be paired up to form a linear system in two variables. Solve this system.

$$\boxed{D}\quad 7x - 5z = -3 \xrightarrow{\text{Multiply by } -4.} -28x + 20z = 12$$
$$\boxed{E}\quad 4x - 11z = -18 \xrightarrow[\text{Multiply by 7.}]{} 28x - 77z = -126$$
$$-57z = -114$$
$$z = 2$$

Once one variable has been found, substitute this value into either equation in the two-variable system, that is, either equation $\boxed{D}$ or $\boxed{E}$.

$$\boxed{D}\quad 7x - 5z = -3$$
$$7x - 5(2) = -3 \qquad \text{Substitute } z = 2 \text{ into equation } \boxed{D}.$$
$$7x - 10 = -3$$
$$7x = 7$$
$$x = 1$$

$$\boxed{A}\quad 2x + y - 3z = -7$$
$$2(1) + y - 3(2) = -7$$
$$2 + y - 6 = -7$$
$$y - 4 = -7$$
$$y = -3$$

Step 5: Now that two variables are known, substitute these values for x and z into any of the original three equations to find the remaining variable y. Substitute $x = 1$ and $z = 2$ into equation $\boxed{A}$.

Step 6: Check the ordered triple, $(1, -3, 2)$, in the three original equations.

<u>Check</u>:
$$2x + y - 3z = -7 \rightarrow 2(1) + (-3) - 3(2) = -7 \ ✔ \text{ True}$$
$$3x - 2y + z = 11 \rightarrow 3(1) - 2(-3) + (2) = 11 \ ✔ \text{ True}$$
$$-2x - 3y - 2z = 3 \rightarrow -2(1) - 3(-3) - 2(2) = 3 \ ✔ \text{ True}$$

The solution set is $\{(1, -3, 2)\}$.

Skill Practice Solve the system.

1.
$$x + 2y + z = 1$$
$$3x - y + 2z = 13$$
$$2x + 3y - z = -8$$

TIP: It is important to note that in steps 2 and 3, the *same* variable is eliminated.

Answer

1. $\{(1, -2, 4)\}$

Example 2 **Solving a System of Linear Equations in Three Variables**

Solve the system:

$$\begin{aligned} 3x + y - 5 &= 0 \\ z &= 7 + 2y \\ x + 3z &= 17 \end{aligned}$$

Solution:

$\boxed{A}$ $3x + y = 5$

$\boxed{B}$ $-2y + z = 7$

$\boxed{C}$ $x + 3z = 17$

Step 1: Write equations in standard form, $Ax + By + Cz = D$.

Steps 2 and 3: Note equation $\boxed{C}$ is missing a y-variable. Therefore, we can eliminate the y-variable by pairing up equations $\boxed{A}$ and $\boxed{B}$.

$\boxed{A}$ $3x + y = 5$ $\xrightarrow{\text{Multiply by 2.}}$ $6x + 2y = 10$

$\boxed{B}$ $-2y + z = 7$ $\longrightarrow$ $-2y + z = 7$

$6x + z = 17$ $\boxed{D}$

Step 4: Now we pair up equations $\boxed{C}$ and $\boxed{D}$ to eliminate the z-variable.

$\boxed{C}$ $x + 3z = 17$ $\longrightarrow$ $x + 3z = 17$

$\boxed{D}$ $6x + z = 17$ $\xrightarrow[\text{Multiply by } -3.]{}$ $-18x - 3z = -51$

$$\begin{aligned} -17x &= -34 \\ x &= 2 \end{aligned}$$

Step 5: Now substitute $x = 2$ into equations $\boxed{A}$ and $\boxed{C}$ to find the remaining variables.

$\boxed{A}$

$$\begin{aligned} 3x + y &= 5 \\ 3(2) + y &= 5 \\ 6 + y &= 5 \\ y &= -1 \end{aligned}$$

$\boxed{C}$

$$\begin{aligned} x + 3z &= 17 \\ (2) + 3z &= 17 \\ 3z &= 15 \\ z &= 5 \end{aligned}$$

Step 6: Check $(2, -1, 5)$ in the three original equations.

Check: $3x + y - 5 = 0 \longrightarrow 3(2) + (-1) - 5 = 0$ ✔ True

$z = 7 + 2y \longrightarrow 5 = 7 + 2(-1)$ ✔ True

$x + 3z = 17 \longrightarrow (2) + 3(5) = 17$ ✔ True

The solution set is $\{(2, -1, 5)\}$.

Skill Practice Solve the system.

2. $$\begin{aligned} 4y &= x + 4 \\ 2x + z &= 5 \\ y - 14 &= 4z \end{aligned}$$

Answer

2. $\{(4, 2, -3)\}$

Example 3 Solving a System of Dependent Equations

Solve the system. If there is not a unique solution, state the number of solutions and whether the system is inconsistent or the equations are dependent.

$$\boxed{A}\ 3x + y - z = 8$$
$$\boxed{B}\ 2x - y + 2z = 3$$
$$\boxed{C}\ x + 2y - 3z = 5$$

Solution:

First, make a decision regarding the variable to eliminate. The y-variable is particularly easy to eliminate because the coefficients of y in equations $\boxed{A}$ and $\boxed{B}$ are already opposites. The y-variable can be eliminated from equations $\boxed{B}$ and $\boxed{C}$ by multiplying equation $\boxed{B}$ by 2.

$$\begin{array}{ll} \boxed{A} & 3x + y - z = 8 \\ \boxed{B} & 2x - y + 2z = 3 \\ \hline & 5x \qquad + z = 11 \quad \boxed{D} \end{array}$$

Pair up equations $\boxed{A}$ and $\boxed{B}$ to eliminate y.

$$\begin{array}{lll} \boxed{B}\ 2x - y + 2z = 3 & \xrightarrow{\text{Multiply by 2.}} & 4x - 2y + 4z = 6 \\ \boxed{C}\ x + 2y - 3z = 5 & \longrightarrow & x + 2y - 3z = 5 \\ \hline & & 5x \qquad + z = 11 \quad \boxed{E} \end{array}$$

Pair up equations $\boxed{B}$ and $\boxed{C}$ to eliminate y.

Because equations $\boxed{D}$ and $\boxed{E}$ are equivalent equations, it appears that this is a dependent system. By eliminating variables we obtain the identity $0 = 0$.

$$\begin{array}{lll} \boxed{D}\ 5x + z = 11 & \xrightarrow{\text{Multiply by } -1.} & -5x - z = -11 \\ \boxed{E}\ 5x + z = 11 & \longrightarrow & 5x + z = 11 \\ \hline & & 0 = 0 \end{array}$$

The result $0 = 0$ indicates that there are infinitely many solutions and that the equations are dependent.

Skill Practice Solve the system. If the system does not have a unique solution, state the number of solutions and whether the system is inconsistent or the equations are dependent.

3.
$$x + y + z = 8$$
$$2x - y + z = 6$$
$$-5x - 2y - 4z = -30$$

Answer

3. Infinitely many solutions; dependent equations

Example 4 **Solving an Inconsistent System of Linear Equations**

Solve the system. If there is not a unique solution, state the number of solutions and whether the system is inconsistent or the equations are dependent.

$$\begin{aligned} 2x + 3y - 7z &= 4 \\ -4x - 6y + 14z &= 1 \\ 5x + y - 3z &= 6 \end{aligned}$$

Solution:

We will eliminate the x-variable.

$$\begin{array}{llcr} \boxed{A} & 2x + 3y - 7z = 4 & \xrightarrow{\text{Multiply by 2.}} & 4x + 6y - 14z = 8 \\ \boxed{B} & -4x - 6y + 14z = 1 & \longrightarrow & \underline{-4x - 6y + 14z = 1} \\ \boxed{C} & 5x + y - 3z = 6 & & 0 = 9 \quad \text{(contradiction)} \end{array}$$

The result $0 = 9$ is a contradiction, indicating that the system has no solution. The system is inconsistent.

Skill Practice Solve the system. If the system does not have a unique solution, state the number of solutions and whether the system is inconsistent or the equations are dependent.

4. $$\begin{aligned} x - 2y + z &= 5 \\ x - 3y + 2z &= -7 \\ -2x + 4y - 2z &= 6 \end{aligned}$$

Answer

4. No solution; inconsistent system

Section 4.5 Practice Exercises

Vocabulary and Key Concepts

1. **a.** An equation written in the form $Ax + By + Cz = D$, where A, B, and C are not all zero, is called a ____________ equation in three variables.

   b. Solutions to a linear equation in three variables are of the form (x, y, z) and are called ____________ ____________.

Review Exercises

For Exercises 2–4, solve the systems by using two methods: (**a**) the substitution method and (**b**) the addition method.

2. $$\begin{aligned} 3x + y &= 4 \\ 4x + y &= 5 \end{aligned}$$

3. $$\begin{aligned} 2x - 5y &= 3 \\ -4x + 10y &= 3 \end{aligned}$$

4. $$\begin{aligned} 4x - 6y &= 5 \\ x &= \frac{3}{2}y + \frac{5}{4} \end{aligned}$$

5. Two cars leave Kansas City at the same time. One travels east and one travels west. After 3 hr the cars are 369 mi apart. If one car travels 7 mph slower than the other, find the speed of each car.

Concept 1: Solutions to Systems of Linear Equations in Three Variables

6. How many solutions are possible when solving a system of three equations with three variables?

7. Which of the following points are solutions to the system?

$(2, 1, 7), (3, -10, -6), (4, 0, 2)$

$$\begin{aligned} 2x - y + z &= 10 \\ 4x + 2y - 3z &= 10 \\ x - 3y + 2z &= 8 \end{aligned}$$

8. Which of the following points are solutions to the system?

$(1, 1, 3), (0, 0, 4), (4, 2, 1)$

$$\begin{aligned} -3x - 3y - 6z &= -24 \\ -9x - 6y + 3z &= -45 \\ 9x + 3y - 9z &= 33 \end{aligned}$$

9. Which of the following points are solutions to the system?

$(12, 2, -2), (4, 2, 1), (1, 1, 1)$

$$\begin{aligned} -x - y - 4z &= -6 \\ x - 3y + z &= -1 \\ 4x + y - z &= 4 \end{aligned}$$

10. Which of the following points are solutions to the system?

$(0, 4, 3), (3, 6, 10), (3, 3, 1)$

$$\begin{aligned} x + 2y - z &= 5 \\ x - 3y + z &= -5 \\ -2x + y - z &= -4 \end{aligned}$$

Concept 2: Solving Systems of Linear Equations in Three Variables

For Exercises 11–34, solve the system of equations. **(See Examples 1–2.)**

11. $$\begin{aligned} 2x + y - 3z &= -12 \\ 3x - 2y - z &= 3 \\ -x + 5y + 2z &= -3 \end{aligned}$$

12. $$\begin{aligned} -3x - 2y + 4z &= -15 \\ 2x + 5y - 3z &= 3 \\ 4x - y + 7z &= 15 \end{aligned}$$

13. $$\begin{aligned} x - 3y - 4z &= -7 \\ 5x + 2y + 2z &= -1 \\ 4x - y - 5z &= -6 \end{aligned}$$

14. $$\begin{aligned} 6x - 5y + z &= 7 \\ 5x + 3y + 2z &= 0 \\ -2x + y - 3z &= 11 \end{aligned}$$

15. $$\begin{aligned} -3x + y - z &= 8 \\ -4x + 2y + 3z &= -3 \\ 2x + 3y - 2z &= -1 \end{aligned}$$

16. $$\begin{aligned} 2x + 3y + 3z &= 15 \\ 3x - 6y - 6z &= -23 \\ -9x - 3y + 6z &= 8 \end{aligned}$$

17. $$\begin{aligned} 4x + 2z &= 12 + 3y \\ 2y &= 3x + 3z - 5 \\ y &= 2x + 7z + 8 \end{aligned}$$

18. $$\begin{aligned} y &= 2x + z + 1 \\ -3x - 1 &= -2y + 2z \\ 5x + 3z &= 16 - 3y \end{aligned}$$

19. $$\begin{aligned} x + y + z &= 6 \\ -x + y - z &= -2 \\ 2x + 3y + z &= 11 \end{aligned}$$

20. $$\begin{aligned} x - y - z &= -11 \\ x + y - z &= 15 \\ 2x - y + z &= -9 \end{aligned}$$

21. $$\begin{aligned} 2x - 3y + 2z &= -1 \\ x + 2y &= -4 \\ x + z &= 1 \end{aligned}$$

22. $$\begin{aligned} x + y + z &= 2 \\ 2x - z &= 5 \\ 3y + z &= 2 \end{aligned}$$

23. $$\begin{aligned} 4x + 9y &= 8 \\ 8x + 6z &= -1 \\ 6y + 6z &= -1 \end{aligned}$$

24. $$\begin{aligned} 3x + 2z &= 11 \\ y - 7z &= 4 \\ x - 6y &= 1 \end{aligned}$$

25. $$\begin{aligned} 2x + 3y - 2z &= 8 \\ x - 4y + z &= -8 \\ -4x + 3y + 2z &= 3 \end{aligned}$$

26. $$\begin{aligned} 5x - 3y + z &= 4 \\ -x + 6y + 4z &= 1 \\ 2x + 3y - z &= 3 \end{aligned}$$

27. $$\begin{aligned} 5y &= -7 + 4z \\ x + 3y + 3 &= 0 \\ 2x &= 14 + z \end{aligned}$$

28. $$\begin{aligned} 4(x - z) &= -1 \\ 3y + z &= 1 \\ 4x &= 3 + y \end{aligned}$$

29. $$\begin{aligned} x + z &= -16 + 3y \\ 2(x + z) &= 12 - 5y \\ 3x + 8 &= y - z \end{aligned}$$

30. $$\begin{aligned} 4(x - 2y) &= 8 - 3z \\ 4y + 13 &= 3x + z \\ x - 3y &= -2(z + 2) \end{aligned}$$

31. $$\begin{aligned} \tfrac{1}{3}x + \tfrac{1}{2}y + \tfrac{1}{6}z &= \tfrac{1}{6} \\ \tfrac{1}{5}x + y - \tfrac{3}{5}z &= \tfrac{4}{5} \\ x - \tfrac{4}{9}y + \tfrac{2}{3}z &= \tfrac{1}{3} \end{aligned}$$

32. $$\begin{aligned} \tfrac{1}{2}x \phantom{{}- \tfrac{1}{6}y} + \tfrac{5}{2}z &= -1 \\ \tfrac{1}{4}x - \tfrac{1}{6}y - \tfrac{2}{3}z &= 3 \\ -\tfrac{1}{2}x + \tfrac{5}{8}y + \tfrac{1}{8}z &= -3 \end{aligned}$$

33. $$\begin{aligned} 0.1x - 0.6y + z &= -6.8 \\ 0.7x - 0.3z &= -14 \\ y + 0.5z &= 8 \end{aligned}$$

34. $$\begin{aligned} 0.5x + y &= 10 \\ -0.2y + 0.5z &= 0.5 \\ -0.3x - z &= -6 \end{aligned}$$

Mixed Exercises

For Exercises 35–46, solve the system. If there is not a unique solution, state whether the system is inconsistent or the equations are dependent. **(See Examples 1–4.)**

35. $$\begin{aligned} 2x + y + 3z &= 2 \\ x - y + 2z &= -4 \\ -2x + 2y - 4z &= 8 \end{aligned}$$

36. $$\begin{aligned} x + y &= z \\ 2x + 4y - 2z &= 6 \\ 3x + 6y - 3z &= 9 \end{aligned}$$

37. $$\begin{aligned} 6x - 2y + 2z &= 2 \\ 4x + 8y - 2z &= 5 \\ -2x - 4y + z &= -2 \end{aligned}$$

38. $$\begin{aligned} 3x + 2y + z &= 3 \\ x - 3y + z &= 4 \\ -6x - 4y - 2z &= 1 \end{aligned}$$

39. $$\begin{aligned} \tfrac{1}{2}x + \tfrac{2}{3}y &= \tfrac{5}{2} \\ \tfrac{1}{5}x - \tfrac{1}{2}z &= -\tfrac{3}{10} \\ \tfrac{1}{3}y - \tfrac{1}{4}z &= \tfrac{3}{4} \end{aligned}$$

40. $$\begin{aligned} \tfrac{1}{2}x + \tfrac{1}{4}y + z &= 3 \\ \tfrac{1}{8}x + \tfrac{1}{4}y + \tfrac{1}{4}z &= \tfrac{9}{8} \\ x - y - \tfrac{2}{3}z &= \tfrac{1}{3} \end{aligned}$$

41. $$\begin{aligned} 3(2x + y) &= 4(3z - 1) \\ y + 4z &= 2(3 + 5x) \\ 2(x + z) &= y - 1 \end{aligned}$$

42. $$\begin{aligned} 5(y - 2z) &= 9x - 11 \\ 2(3x + z) &= 5 + y \\ 3x &= z + 2(y + 1) \end{aligned}$$

43. $$\begin{aligned} 2x + y &= 3(z - 1) \\ 3x - 2(y - 2z) &= 1 \\ 2(2x - 3z) &= -6 - 2y \end{aligned}$$

44. $$\begin{aligned} 2x + y &= -3 \\ 2y + 16z &= -10 \\ -7x - 3y + 4z &= 8 \end{aligned}$$

45. $$\begin{aligned} -0.1y + 0.2z &= 0.2 \\ 0.1x + 0.1y + 0.1z &= 0.2 \\ -0.1x + 0.3z &= 0.2 \end{aligned}$$

46. $$\begin{aligned} 0.1x - 0.2y &= 0 \\ 0.3y + 0.1z &= -0.1 \\ 0.4x - 0.1z &= 1.2 \end{aligned}$$

Expanding Your Skills

The systems in Exercises 47–50 are called homogeneous systems because each system has (0, 0, 0) as a solution. However, if the equations are dependent, there will be infinitely many more solutions. For each system determine whether (0, 0, 0) is the only solution or if the equations are dependent.

47. $$\begin{aligned} 2x - 4y + 8z &= 0 \\ -x - 3y + z &= 0 \\ x - 2y + 5z &= 0 \end{aligned}$$

48. $$\begin{aligned} 2x - 4y + z &= 0 \\ x - 3y - z &= 0 \\ 3x - y + 2z &= 0 \end{aligned}$$

49. $$\begin{aligned} 4x - 2y - 3z &= 0 \\ -8x - y + z &= 0 \\ 2x - y - \frac{3}{2}z &= 0 \end{aligned}$$

50. $$\begin{aligned} 5x + y &= 0 \\ 4y - z &= 0 \\ 5x + 5y - z &= 0 \end{aligned}$$

Applications of Systems of Linear Equations in Three Variables

Section 4.6

Objectives

1. Applications Involving Geometry
2. Applications Involving Mixtures

1. Applications Involving Geometry

In this section we solve several applications of linear equations in three variables.

Example 1 Applying Systems of Linear Equations in Three Variables

In a triangle, the smallest angle measures 10° more than one-half of the largest angle. The middle angle measures 12° more than the smallest angle. Find the measure of each angle.

Solution:

Let x represent the measure of the smallest angle.

Let y represent the measure of the middle angle.

Let z represent the measure of the largest angle.

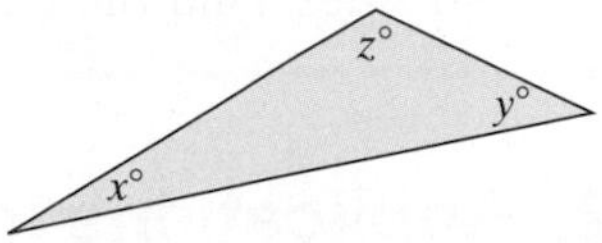

To solve for three variables, we need to establish three independent relationships among x, y, and z.

A $x = \frac{1}{2}z + 10$	The smallest angle measures 10° more than one-half the measure of the largest angle.
B $y = x + 12$	The middle angle measures 12° more than the measure of the smallest angle.
C $x + y + z = 180$	The sum of the interior angles of a triangle measures 180°.
	Clear fractions and write each equation in standard form.

Standard Form

A $x = \frac{1}{2}z + 10 \xrightarrow{\text{Multiply by 2.}} 2x = z + 20 \longrightarrow 2x - z = 20$

B $y = x + 12 \longrightarrow -x + y = 12$

C $x + y + z = 180 \longrightarrow x + y + z = 180$

Notice equation B is missing the z-variable. Therefore, we can eliminate z again by pairing up equations A and C.

A $2x - z = 20$

C $x + y + z = 180$

$3x + y = 200$ D

$$\begin{array}{lll} \boxed{B}\ -x + y = 12 & \xrightarrow{\text{Multiply by } -1.} & x - y = -12 \\ \boxed{D}\ 3x + y = 200 & \longrightarrow & \underline{3x + y = 200} \\ & & 4x \quad = 188 \end{array}$$

Pair up equations $\boxed{B}$ and $\boxed{D}$ to form a system of two variables.

$$x = 47$$

Solve for x.

From equation $\boxed{B}$ we have $-x + y = 12 \longrightarrow -47 + y = 12 \rightarrow y = 59$

From equation $\boxed{C}$ we have $x + y + z = 180 \rightarrow 47 + 59 + z = 180 \rightarrow z = 74$

The smallest angle measures 47°, the middle angle measures 59°, and the largest angle measures 74°.

Skill Practice

1. The perimeter of a triangle is 30 in. The shortest side is 4 in. shorter than the longest side. The longest side is 6 in. less than the sum of the other two sides. Find the length of each side.

2. Applications Involving Mixtures

Example 2 **Applying Systems of Linear Equations to Nutrition**

Doctors have become increasingly concerned about the sodium intake in the U.S. diet. Recommendations by the American Medical Association indicate that most individuals should not exceed 2400 mg of sodium per day.

Liz ate 1 slice of pizza, 1 serving of ice cream, and 1 glass of soda for a total of 1030 mg of sodium. David ate 3 slices of pizza, no ice cream, and 2 glasses of soda for a total of 2420 mg of sodium. Melinda ate 2 slices of pizza, 1 serving of ice cream, and 2 glasses of soda for a total of 1910 mg of sodium. How much sodium is in one serving of each item?

Solution:

Let x represent the sodium content of 1 slice of pizza.

Let y represent the sodium content of 1 serving of ice cream.

Let z represent the sodium content of 1 glass of soda.

From Liz's meal we have: $\boxed{A}\ x + y + z = 1030$

From David's meal we have: $\boxed{B}\ 3x + 2z = 2420$

From Melinda's meal we have: $\boxed{C}\ 2x + y + 2z = 1910$

Equation $\boxed{B}$ is missing the y-variable. Eliminating y from equations $\boxed{A}$ and $\boxed{C}$, we have

$$\begin{array}{lll} \boxed{A}\ x + y + z = 1030 & \xrightarrow{\text{Multiply by } -1.} & -x - y - z = -1030 \\ \boxed{C}\ 2x + y + 2z = 1910 & \longrightarrow & \underline{2x + y + 2z = 1910} \\ & & \boxed{D}\ x \quad + z = 880 \end{array}$$

Solve the system formed by equations $\boxed{B}$ and $\boxed{D}$.

$$\begin{array}{lll} \boxed{B}\ 3x + 2z = 2420 & \longrightarrow & 3x + 2z = 2420 \\ \boxed{D}\ x + z = 880 & \xrightarrow[\text{Multiply by } -2.]{} & \underline{-2x - 2z = -1760} \\ & & x \quad = 660 \end{array}$$

Answer

1. The sides are 8 in., 10 in., and 12 in.

From equation D we have $x + z = 880 \longrightarrow 660 + z = 880 \longrightarrow z = 220$

From equation A we have $x + y + z = 1030 \rightarrow 660 + y + 220 = 1030 \rightarrow y = 150$

Therefore, 1 slice of pizza has 660 mg of sodium, 1 serving of ice cream has 150 mg of sodium, and 1 glass of soda has 220 mg of sodium.

Skill Practice

2. Annette, Barb, and Carlita work in a clothing shop. One day the three had combined sales of \$1480. Annette sold \$120 more than Barb. Barb and Carlita combined sold \$280 more than Annette. How much did each person sell?

Answer

2. Annette sold \$600, Barb sold \$480, and Carlita sold \$400.

Section 4.6 Practice Exercises

Review Exercises

For Exercises 1–4, solve the system. If there is not a unique solution, state whether the system is inconsistent or the equations are dependent.

1. $$\begin{aligned} -5y - z &= -8 \\ x + 10y + 2z &= 9 \\ -3x + y &= 21 \end{aligned}$$

2. $$\begin{aligned} 8x - y + 2z &= 18 \\ x + y - 5z &= -21 \\ 4x - 0.5y + z &= 9 \end{aligned}$$

3. $$\begin{aligned} \frac{1}{2}x - y + \frac{5}{6}z &= 4 \\ \frac{3}{2}x - 3y + \frac{5}{2}z &= 6 \\ -\frac{1}{4}x + y - \frac{1}{3}z &= -2 \end{aligned}$$

4. $$\begin{aligned} 12x - y + z &= -6 \\ -6x + 2y - 3z &= 5 \\ 6x + y - z &= 3 \end{aligned}$$

Concept 1: Applications Involving Geometry

5. A triangle has one angle that measures 5° more than twice the smallest angle, and the largest angle measures 11° less than 3 times the measure of the smallest angle. Find the measures of the three angles. **(See Example 1.)**

6. The largest angle of a triangle measures 4° less than 5 times the measure of the smallest angle. The middle angle measures twice that of the smallest angle. Find the measures of the three angles.

7. One angle of a triangle measures 6° more than twice the measure of the smallest angle. The third angle measures 1° less than four times the smallest. Find the measures of the three angles.

8. In a triangle the smallest angle measures 12° less than the middle angle. The measure of the largest angle is equal to the sum of the other two. Find the measures of the three angles.

9. The perimeter of a triangle is 55 cm. The measure of the shortest side is 8 cm less than the middle side. The measure of the longest side is 1 cm less than the sum of the other two sides. Find the lengths of the sides.

10. The perimeter of a triangle is 5 ft. The longest side of the triangle measures 20 in. more than the shortest side. The middle side is 3 times the measure of the shortest side. Find the lengths of the three sides in *inches*.

11. The perimeter of a triangle is 4.5 ft. The shortest side measures 2 in. less than half the longest side. The longest side measures 2 in. less than the sum of the other two sides. Find the lengths of the sides in *inches.*

12. The perimeter of a triagle is 7 m. The length of the longest side is twice the length of the shortest side. The sum of the lengths of the shortest side and the middle side is 1 m more than the length of the longest side. Find the lengths of the sides.

Concept 2: Applications Involving Mixtures

13. Sean kept track of his fiber intake from three sources for 3 weeks. The first week he had 3 servings of a fiber supplement, 1 serving of oatmeal, and 4 servings of cereal, which totaled 19 g of fiber. The second week he had 2 servings of the fiber supplement, 4 servings of oatmeal, and 2 servings of cereal totaling 25 g. The third week he had 5 servings of the fiber supplement, 3 servings of oatmeal, and 2 servings of cereal for a total of 30 g. Find the amount of fiber in one serving of each of the following: the fiber supplement, the oatmeal, and the cereal. **(See Example 2.)**

14. Natalie kept track of her calcium intake from three sources for 3 days. The first day she had 1 glass of milk, 1 serving of ice cream, and 1 calcium supplement in pill form which totaled 1180 mg of calcium. The second day she had 2 glasses of milk, 1 serving of ice cream, and 1 calcium supplement totaling 1680 mg. The third day she had 1 glass of milk, 2 servings of ice cream, and 1 calcium supplement for a total of 1260 mg. Find the amount of calcium in one glass of milk, in one serving of ice cream, and in one calcium supplement.

15. Kyoki invested a total of $10,000 into bonds, mutual funds, and a money market account. He put the same amount of money in the money market account as he did in bonds. For 1 year, the bonds paid 5% interest, the mutual funds paid 8%, and the money market paid 4%. At the end of the year, Kyoki earned $660 in interest. How much did he invest in each account?

16. Walter had $25,000 to invest. He split the money into three types of investment: small caps earning 6%, global market investments earning 10%, and a balanced fund earning 9%. He put twice as much money in the global account as he did in the balanced fund. If his earnings for the first year totaled $2160, how much did he invest in each account?

17. Winston deposited $4500 into three certificates of deposit: a 24-month CD paying 5% interest, a 30-month CD paying 5.5% interest, and an 18-month CD paying 4% interest. He put $1000 more in the CD with the 5.5% rate than he put in the 4% rate. After the first year, he earned a total of $225 interest. How much did he deposit into each CD?

18. Raeann deposited $8000 into three accounts at her credit union: a checking account that pays 1.2% interest, a savings account that pays 2.5% interest, and a money market account that pays 3% interest. If she put three times more money in the 3% account than she did in the 1.2% account, and her total interest for 1 year was $202, how much did she deposit into each account?

19. A basketball player scored 29 points in one game. In basketball, some baskets are worth 3 points, some are worth 2 points, and free throws are worth 1 point. He scored four more 2-point baskets than he did 3-point baskets. The number of free throws is one less than the number of 2-point baskets. How many free throws, 2-point shots, and 3-point shots did he make?

20. Goofie Golf has 18 holes that are par 3, par 4, or par 5. Most of the holes are par 4. In fact, there are 3 times as many par 4s as par 3s. There are 3 more par 5s than par 3s. How many of each type are there?

21. Combining peanuts, pecans, and cashews makes a party mixture of nuts. If the amount of peanuts equals the amount of pecans and cashews combined, and if there are twice as many cashews as pecans, how many ounces of each nut is used to make 48 oz of party mixture?

22. Souvenir hats, T-shirts, and jackets are sold at a rock concert. Three hats, two T-shirts, and one jacket cost \$140. Two hats, two T-shirts, and two jackets cost \$170. One hat, three T-shirts, and two jackets cost \$180. Find the prices of the individual items.

23. A theater charges \$70 per seat for seats in section A, \$65 per seat for seats in section B, and \$44 per seat for seats in section C. 2400 tickets are sold for a total of \$153,000 in revenue. If there are 600 more seats sold in section A than the other two sections combined, how many seats in each section were sold?

24. Annie and Maria traveled overseas for seven days and stayed in three different hotels in three different cities: Stockholm, Sweden; Oslo, Norway; and Paris, France.

The total bill for all seven nights (not including tax) was \$1040. The total tax was \$106. The nightly cost (excluding tax) to stay at the hotel in Paris was \$80 more than the nightly cost (excluding tax) to stay in Oslo. Find the cost per night for each hotel excluding tax.

City	Number of Nights	Cost/Night (\$)	Tax Rate
Paris, France	1	x	8%
Stockholm, Sweden	4	y	11%
Oslo, Norway	2	z	10%

Group Activity

Creating Linear Models from Data

Materials: Two pieces of rope for each group. The ropes should be of different thicknesses. The piece of thicker rope should be between 4 and 5 ft long. The thinner piece of rope should be 8 to 12 in. shorter than the thicker rope. You will also need a yardstick or other device for making linear measurements.

Estimated Time: 30–35 minutes

Group Size: 4 (2 pairs)

1. Each group of 4 should divide into two pairs, and each pair will be given a piece of rope. Each pair will measure the initial length of rope. Then students will tie a series of knots in the rope and measure the new length after each knot is tied. (*Hint:* Try to tie the knots with an equal amount of force each time. Also, as the ropes are straightened for measurement, try to use the same amount of tension in the rope.) The results should be recorded in the table.

Thick Rope	
Number of Knots, x	**Length (in.), y**
0	
1	
2	
3	
4	

Thin Rope	
Number of Knots, x	**Length (in.), y**
0	
1	
2	
3	
4	

2. Graph each set of data points. Use a different color pen or pencil for each set of points. Does it appear that each set of data follows a linear trend? Draw a line through each set of points.

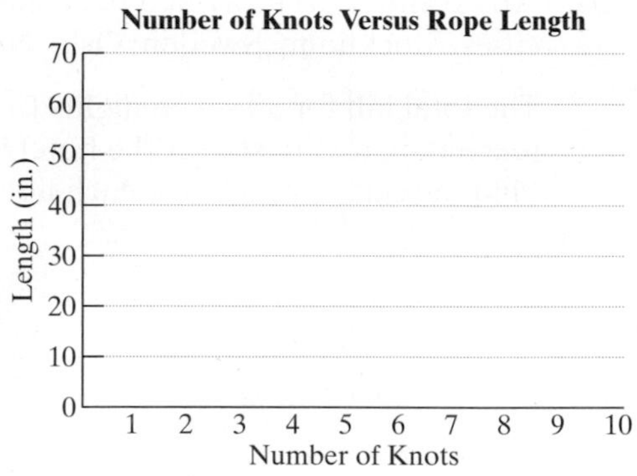

3. Each time a knot is tied, the rope decreases in length. Using the results from question 1, compute the average amount of length lost per knot tied.

For the thick rope, the length decreases by ___________ inches per knot tied.

For the thin rope, the length decreases by ___________ inches per knot tied.

4. For each set of data points, find an equation of the line through the points. Write the equation in slope-intercept form, $y = mx + b$.

[*Hint:* The slope of the line will be negative and will be represented by the amount of length lost per knot (see question 3). The value of b will be the original length of the rope.]

Equation for the thick rope: ______________________________

Equation for the thin rope: ______________________________

5. Next, you will try to predict the number of knots that you need to tie in each rope so that the ropes will be equal in length. To do this, solve the system of equations in question 4.

Solution to the system of equations: (____, ____)

number of knots, x ↑ length, y ↑

Interpret the meaning of the ordered pair in terms of the number of knots tied and the length of the ropes.

6. Check your answer from question 5 by actually tying the required number of knots in each rope. After doing this, are the ropes the same length? What is the length of each rope? Does this match the length predicted from question 5?

Chapter 4 Summary

Section 4.1 Solving Systems of Equations by the Graphing Method

Key Concepts

A **system of two linear equations** can be solved by graphing.

A **solution to a system of linear equations** is an ordered pair that satisfies both equations in the system. Graphically, this represents a point of intersection of the lines.

There may be one solution, infinitely many solutions, or no solution.

One solution	Infinitely many solutions	No solution
Consistent	Consistent	Inconsistent
Independent	Dependent	Independent

A system of equations is **consistent** if there is at least one solution. A system is **inconsistent** if there is no solution.

If two equations represent the same line, the equations are said to be **dependent equations**. In this case, all points on the line are solutions to the system. If two equations represent two different lines, the equations are said to be **independent equations**. In this case, the lines either intersect at one point or are parallel.

Examples

Example 1

Solve by using the graphing method.

$x + y = 3$

$2x - y = 0$

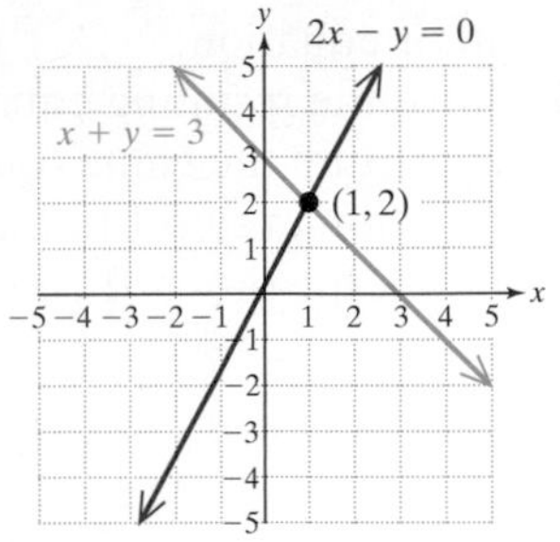

The solution set is $\{(1, 2)\}$.

Example 2

Solve by using the graphing method.

$3x - 2y = 2$

$-6x + 4y = 4$

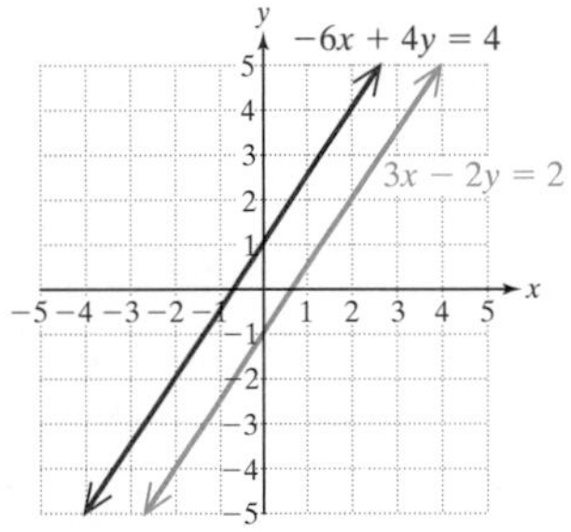

There is no solution, { }. The system is inconsistent.

Example 3

Solve by using the graphing method.

$x + 2y = 2$

$-3x - 6y = -6$

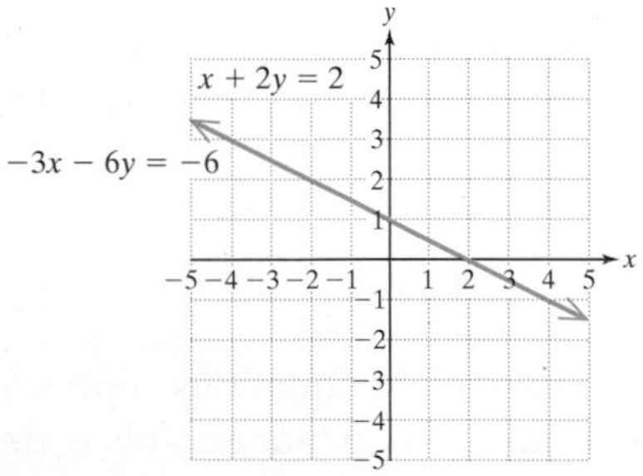

The equations are dependent, and the solution set consists of all points on the line, given by $\{(x, y) | x + 2y = 2\}$.

Section 4.2 Solving Systems of Equations by the Substitution Method

Key Concepts

Solving a System of Equations by Using the Substitution Method:

1. Isolate one of the variables from one equation.
2. Substitute the expression found in step 1 into the other equation.
3. Solve the resulting equation.
4. Substitute the value found in step 3 back into the equation in step 1 to find the remaining variable.
5. Check the ordered pair in both original equations.

An inconsistent system has no solution and is detected algebraically by a contradiction (such as $0 = 3$).

If two linear equations represent the same line, the equations are dependent. This is detected algebraically by an identity (such as $0 = 0$).

Examples

Example 1

Solve by using the substitution method.

$x + 4y = -11$

$3x - 2y = -5$

Isolate x in the first equation: $x = -4y - 11$
Substitute into the second equation.

$$3(-4y - 11) - 2y = -5$$
Solve the equation.
$$-12y - 33 - 2y = -5$$
$$-14y = 28$$
$$y = -2$$

$$x = -4y - 11$$
Substitute $y = -2$.
$$x = -4(-2) - 11$$
Solve for x.
$$x = -3$$

The ordered pair $(-3, -2)$ checks in the original equation. The solution set is $\{(-3, -2)\}$.

Example 2

Solve by using the substitution method.

$3x + y = 4$

$-6x - 2y = 2$

Isolate y in the first equation: $y = -3x + 4$.
Substitute into the second equation.

$$-6x - 2(-3x + 4) = 2$$
$$-6x + 6x - 8 = 2$$
$$-8 = 2$$
Contradiction

The system is inconsistent and has no solution, $\{ \}$.

Example 3

Solve by using the substitution method.

$y = x + 2$ y is already isolated.

$x - y = -2$

$$x - (x + 2) = -2$$
Substitute $y = x + 2$ into the second equation.
$$x - x - 2 = -2$$
$$-2 = -2$$
Identity

The equations are dependent. The solution set is all points on the line $y = x + 2$ or $\{(x, y) \mid y = x + 2\}$.

Section 4.3 Solving Systems of Equations by the Addition Method

Key Concepts

Solving a System of Linear Equations by Using the Addition Method:

1. Write both equations in standard form: $Ax + By = C$.
2. Clear fractions or decimals (optional).
3. Multiply one or both equations by a nonzero constant to create opposite coefficients for one of the variables.
4. Add the equations to eliminate one variable.
5. Solve for the remaining variable.
6. Substitute the known value into one of the original equations to solve for the other variable.
7. Check the ordered pair in both equations.

Examples

Example 1

Solve by using the addition method.

$$5x = -4y - 7$$
$$6x - 3y = 15$$

Write the first equation in standard form.

$$5x + 4y = -7 \xrightarrow{\text{Multiply by 3.}} 15x + 12y = -21$$
$$6x - 3y = 15 \xrightarrow{\text{Multiply by 4.}} 24x - 12y = 60$$
$$39x = 39$$
$$x = 1$$

$$5x = -4y - 7$$
$$5(1) = -4y - 7$$
$$5 = -4y - 7$$
$$12 = -4y$$
$$-3 = y$$

The ordered pair $(1, -3)$ checks in both original equations. The solution set is $\{(1, -3)\}$.

Section 4.4 Applications of Linear Equations in Two Variables

Examples

Example 1

A riverboat travels 36 mi with the current in 2 hr. The return trip takes 3 hr against the current. Find the speed of the current and the speed of the boat in still water.

Let x represent the speed of the boat in still water.
Let y represent the speed of the current.

	Distance	Rate	Time
Against current	36	$x - y$	3
With current	36	$x + y$	2

Distance = (rate)(time)

$$36 = (x - y) \cdot 3 \longrightarrow 36 = 3x - 3y$$

$$36 = (x + y) \cdot 2 \longrightarrow 36 = 2x + 2y$$

$$36 = 3x - 3y \xrightarrow{\text{Multiply by 2.}} 72 = 6x - 6y$$

$$36 = 2x + 2y \xrightarrow[\text{Multiply by 3.}]{} 108 = 6x + 6y$$

$$180 = 12x$$

$$15 = x$$

$$36 = 2(15) + 2y$$

$$36 = 30 + 2y$$

$$6 = 2y$$

$$3 = y$$

The speed of the boat in still water is 15 mph, and the speed of the current is 3 mph.

Example 2

Diane borrows a total of \$15,000. Part of the money is borrowed from a lender that charges 8% simple interest. She borrows the rest of the money from her mother and will pay back the money at 5% interest. If the total interest after 1 year is \$900, how much did she borrow from each source?

	8%	5%	Total
Principal	x	y	15,000
Interest	$0.08x$	$0.05y$	900

$$x + y = 15{,}000$$

$$0.08x + 0.05y = 900$$

Substitute $x = 15{,}000 - y$ into the second equation.

$$0.08(15{,}000 - y) + 0.05y = 900$$

$$1200 - 0.08y + 0.05y = 900$$

$$1200 - 0.03y = 900$$

$$-0.03y = -300$$

$$y = 10{,}000$$

$$x = 15{,}000 - 10{,}000$$

$$= 5{,}000$$

The amount borrowed at 8% is \$5,000.
The amount borrowed from her mother is \$10,000.

Section 4.5 Systems of Linear Equations in Three Variables

Key Concepts

A **linear equation in three variables** can be written in the form $Ax + By + Cz = D$, where A, B, and C are not all zero. The graph of a linear equation in three variables is a plane in space.

A solution to a system of linear equations in three variables is an **ordered triple** that satisfies each equation. Graphically, a solution is a point of intersection among three planes.

A system of linear equations in three variables may have one unique solution, infinitely many solutions (dependent equations), or no solution (inconsistent system).

Example

Example 1

$\boxed{A}\quad x + 2y - z = 4$

$\boxed{B}\quad 3x - y + z = 5$

$\boxed{C}\quad 2x + 3y + 2z = 7$

$\boxed{A}$ and $\boxed{B}$

$$\begin{aligned} x + 2y - z &= 4 \\ 3x - y + z &= 5 \\ \hline 4x + y &= 9 \quad \boxed{D} \end{aligned}$$

$2 \cdot \boxed{A}$ and $\boxed{C}$

$$\begin{aligned} 2x + 4y - 2z &= 8 \\ 2x + 3y + 2z &= 7 \\ \hline 4x + 7y &= 15 \quad \boxed{E} \end{aligned}$$

$\boxed{D}\quad 4x + y = 9 \rightarrow -4x - y = -9$

$\boxed{E}\quad 4x + 7y = 15 \rightarrow 4x + 7y = 15$

$$6y = 6$$

$$y = 1$$

Substitute $y = 1$ into either equation $\boxed{D}$ or $\boxed{E}$.

$\boxed{D}\quad 4x + (1) = 9$

$$4x = 8$$

$$x = 2$$

Substitute $x = 2$ and $y = 1$ into equation $\boxed{A}$, $\boxed{B}$, or $\boxed{C}$.

$\boxed{A}\quad (2) + 2(1) - z = 4$

$$z = 0$$

The solution set is $\{(2, 1, 0)\}$.

For Exercises 20–23, solve each system using the substitution method.

20. $6x + y = 2$
$y = 3x - 4$

21. $2x + 3y = -5$
$x = y - 5$

22. $2x + 6y = 10$
$x = -3y + 6$

23. $4x + 2y = 4$
$y = -2x + 2$

24. Given the system: $x + 2y = 11$
$5x + 4y = 40$

a. Which variable from which equation is easiest to isolate and why?

b. Solve the system using the substitution method.

25. Given the system: $4x - 3y = 9$
$2x + y = 12$

a. Which variable from which equation is easiest to isolate and why?

b. Solve the system using the substitution method.

For Exercises 26–29, solve each system using the substitution method.

26. $3x - 2y = 23$
$x + 5y = -15$

27. $x + 5y = 20$
$3x + 2y = 8$

28. $x - 3y = 9$
$5x - 15y = 45$

29. $-3x + y = 15$
$6x - 2y = 12$

30. The difference of two positive numbers is 42. The larger number is 2 more than 6 times the smaller number. Find the numbers.

31. In a right triangle, one of the acute angles is 6° less than the other acute angle. Find the measure of each acute angle.

32. Two angles are supplementary. One angle measures 14° less than two times the other angle. Find the measure of each angle.

Section 4.3

33. Explain the process for solving a system of two equations using the addition method.

34. Given the system: $3x - 5y = 1$
$2x - y = -4$

a. Which variable, x or y, is easier to eliminate using the addition method? (Answers may vary.)

b. Solve the system using the addition method.

35. Given the system: $9x - 2y = 14$
$4x + 3y = 14$

a. Which variable, x or y, is easier to eliminate using the addition method? (Answers may vary.)

b. Solve the system using the addition method.

For Exercises 36–43, solve each system using the addition method.

36. $2x + 3y = 1$
$x - 2y = 4$

37. $x + 3y = 0$
$-3x - 10y = -2$

38. $8x + 8 = -6y + 6$
$10x = 9y - 8$

39. $12x = 5y + 5$
$5y = -1 - 4x$

40. $-4x - 6y = -2$
$6x + 9y = 3$

41. $-8x - 4y = 16$
$10x + 5y = 5$

42. $\frac{1}{2}x - \frac{3}{4}y = -\frac{1}{2}$
$\frac{1}{3}x + y = -\frac{10}{3}$

43. $0.5x - 0.2y = 0.5$
$0.4x + 0.7y = 0.4$

44. Given the system: $4x + 9y = -7$
$y = 2x - 13$

a. Which method would you choose to solve the system, the substitution method or the addition method? Explain your choice. (Answers may vary.)

b. Solve the system.

45. Given the system: $5x - 8y = -2$
$3x - 7y = 1$

a. Which method would you choose to solve the system, the substitution method or the addition method? Explain your choice. (Answers may vary.)

b. Solve the system.

Section 4.4

46. Miami Metrozoo charges $11.50 for adult admission and $6.75 for children under 12. The total bill before tax for a school group of 60 people is $443. How many adults and how many children were admitted?

47. As part of his retirement strategy Winston plans to invest $600,000 in two different funds. He projects that the high-risk investments should return, over time, about 12% per year, while the low-risk investments should return about 4% per year. If he wants a supplemental income of $30,000 a year, how should he divide his investments?

48. Suppose that whole milk with 4% fat is mixed with 1% low fat milk to make a 2% reduced fat milk. How much of the whole milk should be mixed with the low fat milk to make 60 gal of 2% reduced fat milk?

49. A boat travels 80 mi downstream with the current in 4 hr and 80 mi upstream against the current in 5 hr. Find the speed of the current and the speed of the boat in still water.

50. A plane travels 870 mi against a headwind in 3 hr. Traveling with a tailwind, the plane travels 700 mi in 2 hr. Find the speed of the plane in still air and the speed of the wind.

51. At Conseco Fieldhouse, home of the Indiana Pacers, the total cost of a soft drink and a hot dog is $8.00. The price of the hot dog is $1.00 more than the cost of the soft drink. Find the cost of a soft drink and the cost of a hot dog.

52. Ray played two rounds of golf at Pebble Beach for a total score of 154. If his score in the second round is 10 more than his score in the first round, find the scores for each round.

Section 4.5

For Exercises 53–58, solve the systems of equations. If a system does not have a unique solution, state whether the system is inconsistent or the equations are dependent.

53. $$\begin{aligned} 5x + 5y + 5z &= 30 \\ -x + y + z &= 2 \\ 10x + 6y - 2z &= 4 \end{aligned}$$

54. $$\begin{aligned} 5x + 3y - z &= 5 \\ x + 2y + z &= 6 \\ -x - 2y - z &= 8 \end{aligned}$$

55. $$\begin{aligned} x + y + z &= 4 \\ -x - 2y - 3z &= -6 \\ 2x + 4y + 6z &= 12 \end{aligned}$$

56. $$\begin{aligned} 3x \phantom{{}-5y} + 4z &= 5 \\ 2y + 3z &= 2 \\ 2x - 5y \phantom{{}+3z} &= 8 \end{aligned}$$

57. $$\begin{aligned} 3(x - y) &= -1 - 5z - y \\ 3y + 6 &= 2z + x \\ 5x + 1 &= 3(z - y) - y \end{aligned}$$

58. $$\begin{aligned} 2a &= -3c - 2 \\ 2b - 8 &= 5c \\ 7a + 3b &= 5 \end{aligned}$$

Section 4.6

59. The perimeter of a right triangle is 30 ft. One leg is 2 ft longer than twice the shortest leg. The hypotenuse is 2 ft less than 3 times the shortest leg. Find the lengths of the sides of this triangle.

60. Three pumps are working to drain a construction site. Working together, the pumps can drain 950 gal/hr of water. The slowest pump drains 150 gal/hr less than the fastest pump. The fastest pump drains 150 gal/hr less than the sum of the other two pumps. How many gallons can each pump drain per hour?

61. Theresa had $12,000 to invest among three mutual funds. Fund A had a 5% yield for the year. Fund B had a 3.5% yield, and Fund C lost 2% for the year. She invested three times as much in Fund A as in Fund C. If she gained $400, in 1 year, how much was invested in each fund?

62. In a triangle, the largest angle measures 76° more than the sum of the other two angles. The middle angle measures 3 times the smallest angle. Find the measure of each angle.

8. Two hikers start at opposite ends of an 18-mi trail and walk toward each other. One hiker walks predominately down hill and averages 2 mph faster than the other hiker. Find the average rate of each hiker if they meet in 3 hr.

9. Jesse Ventura became the 38th governor of Minnesota by receiving 37% of the votes. If approximately 2,060,000 votes were cast, how many did Mr. Ventura get?

10. The YMCA wants to raise $2500 for its summer program for disadvantaged children. If the YMCA has already raised $900, what percent of its goal has been achieved?

11. Two angles are complementary. One angle measures 17° more than the other angle. Find the measure of each angle.

12. Find the slope and y-intercept of the line $5x + 3y = -6$.

13. The slope of a given line is $-\frac{2}{3}$.

a. What is the slope of a line parallel to the given line?

b. What is the slope of a line perpendicular to the given line?

14. Find an equation of the line passing through the point $(2, -3)$ and having a slope of -3. Write the final answer in slope-intercept form.

15. Sketch the following equations on the same graph.

a. $2x + 5y = 10$

b. $2y = 4$

c. Find the point of intersection and check the solution in each equation.

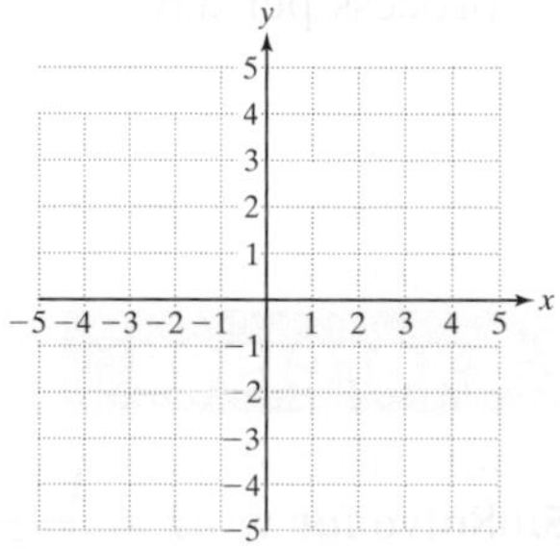

16. Solve the system of equations by using the substitution method.

$$2x + 5y = 10$$
$$2y = 4$$

17. How many gallons of a 15% antifreeze solution should be mixed with a 60% antifreeze solution to produce 60 gal of a 45% antifreeze solution?

18. Use a system of linear equations to solve for x and y.

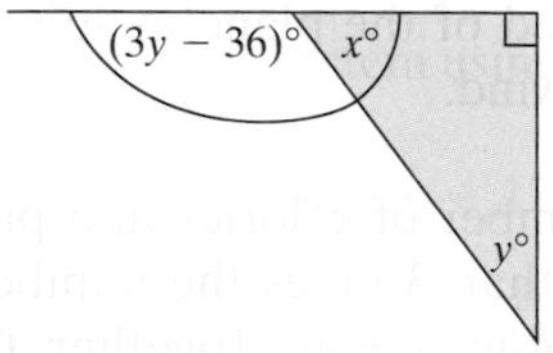

19. In 1920, the average speed for the winner of the Indianapolis 500 car race was 88.6 mph. In 1990, a track record was reached with the speed of 186.0 mph.

a. Find the slope of the line shown in the figure. Round to one decimal place.

b. Interpret the meaning of the slope in the context of this problem.

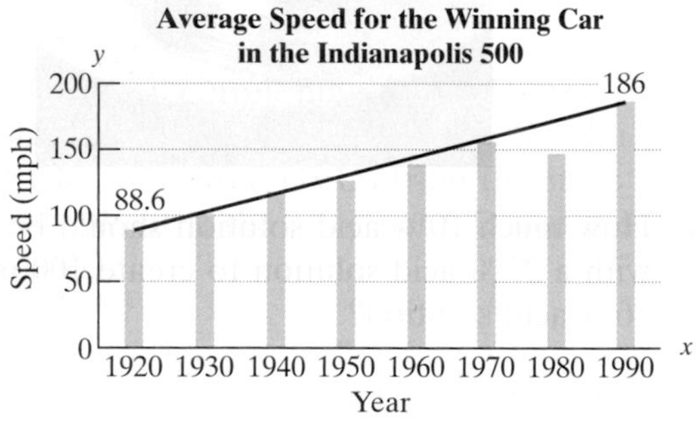

20. Solve the system.

$$x + 3y + z = 5$$
$$2x + 4y - z = -2$$
$$6x + 2y + 5z = 26$$

Polynomials and Properties of Exponents

5

CHAPTER OUTLINE

5.1 Multiplying and Dividing Expressions with Common Bases 342

5.2 More Properties of Exponents 352

5.3 Definitions of b^0 and b^{-n} 357

Problem Recognition Exercises: Properties of Exponents 366

5.4 Scientific Notation 367

5.5 Addition and Subtraction of Polynomials 373

5.6 Multiplication of Polynomials and Special Products 382

5.7 Division of Polynomials 392

Problem Recognition Exercises: Operations on Polynomials 403

Group Activity: The Pythagorean Theorem and a Geometric "Proof" 404

Chapter 5

In this chapter we will learn how to add, subtract, multiply, and divide polynomials. In addition, we will simplify expressions with exponents and expressions involving scientific notation.

Are You Prepared?

The skills we need to practice include clearing parentheses and combining like terms.

Simplify each expression. Find the answer in the table and cross out the letter above it. When you have finished, the answer to the statement will remain.

1. $6x - (4x + 2) - 7$

2. $2x + 3(x - 5) + x$

3. $5 + 2(4x - 1) + 2x$

4. $5(x - 6) - 3(2x + 1)$

5. $3(8 - x) + 5x$

6. $7(2 + 3x) - 8$

A polynomial that has two terms is called a ________.

P	B	E	I	N	D	O	K	M	Y	T	I	A	L
$-x - 33$	$8x + 24$	$2x + 24$	$5x - 14$	$2x - 5$	$6x - 15$	$-x - 27$	$10x + 3$	$8x + 5$	$2x - 9$	$21x + 6$	$35x - 8$	$-8x - 30$	$x - 21$

Section 5.1 Multiplying and Dividing Expressions with Common Bases

Concepts

1. Review of Exponential Notation
2. Evaluating Expressions with Exponents
3. Multiplying and Dividing Expressions with Common Bases
4. Simplifying Expressions with Exponents
5. Applications of Exponents

1. Review of Exponential Notation

Recall that an **exponent** is used to show repeated multiplication of the **base**.

Definition of b^n

Let b represent any real number and n represent a positive integer. Then,

$$b^n = \underbrace{b \cdot b \cdot b \cdot b \cdot \ldots b}_{n \text{ factors of } b}$$

Example 1 Evaluating Expressions with Exponents

For each expression, identify the exponent and base. Then evaluate the expression.

a. 6^2 **b.** $\left(-\frac{1}{2}\right)^3$ **c.** 0.8^4

Solution:

Expression	Base	Exponent	Result
a. 6^2	6	2	$(6)(6) = 36$
b. $\left(-\frac{1}{2}\right)^3$	$-\frac{1}{2}$	3	$\left(-\frac{1}{2}\right)\left(-\frac{1}{2}\right)\left(-\frac{1}{2}\right) = -\frac{1}{8}$
c. 0.8^4	0.8	4	$(0.8)(0.8)(0.8)(0.8) = 0.4096$

Skill Practice For each expression, identify the base and exponent.

1. 8^3 **2.** $\left(-\frac{1}{4}\right)^2$ **3.** 0.2^4

Note that if no exponent is explicitly written for an expression, then the expression has an implied exponent of 1. For example, $x = x^1$.

Consider an expression such as $3y^6$. The factor 3 has an exponent of 1, and the factor y has an exponent of 6. That is, the expression $3y^6$ is interpreted as 3^1y^6.

2. Evaluating Expressions with Exponents

Recall from Section 1.3 that particular care must be taken when evaluating exponential expressions involving negative numbers. An exponential expression with a negative base is written with parentheses around the base, such as $(-3)^2$.

To evaluate $(-3)^2$, we have: $\quad (-3)^2 = (-3)(-3) = 9$

If no parentheses are present, the expression -3^2 is the *opposite* of 3^2, or equivalently, $-1 \cdot 3^2$.

$$-3^2 = -1(3^2) = -1(3)(3) = -9$$

Answers

1. Base 8; exponent 3
2. Base $-\frac{1}{4}$; exponent 2
3. Base 0.2; exponent 4

Example 2 Evaluating Expressions with Exponents

Evaluate each expression.

a. -5^4 **b.** $(-5)^4$ **c.** $(-0.2)^3$ **d.** -0.2^3

Solution:

a. -5^4

$= -1 \cdot 5^4$	5 is the base with exponent 4.
$= -1 \cdot 5 \cdot 5 \cdot 5 \cdot 5$	Multiply -1 by four factors of 5.
$= -625$	

b. $(-5)^4$

$= (-5)(-5)(-5)(-5)$	Parentheses indicate that -5 is the base with exponent 4.
$= 625$	Multiply four factors of -5.

c. $(-0.2)^3$ Parentheses indicate that -0.2 is the base with exponent 3.

$= (-0.2)(-0.2)(-0.2)$	Multiply three factors of -0.2.
$= -0.008$	

d. -0.2^3

$= -1 \cdot 0.2^3$	0.2 is the base with exponent 3.
$= -1 \cdot 0.2 \cdot 0.2 \cdot 0.2$	Multiply -1 by three factors of 0.2.
$= -0.008$	

Skill Practice Evaluate each expression.

4. -2^4 **5.** $(-2)^4$ **6.** $(-0.1)^3$ **7.** -0.1^3

Example 3 Evaluating Expressions with Exponents

Evaluate each expression for $a = 2$ and $b = -3$.

a. $5a^2$ **b.** $(5a)^2$ **c.** $5ab^2$ **d.** $(b + a)^2$

Solution:

a. $5a^2$

$= 5(\ )^2$	Use parentheses to substitute a number for a variable.
$= 5(2)^2$	Substitute $a = 2$.
$= 5(4)$	Simplify exponents before multiplying.
$= 20$	

b. $(5a)^2$

$= [5(\ )]^2$	Use parentheses to substitute a number for a variable. The original parentheses are replaced with brackets.
$= [5(2)]^2$	Substitute $a = 2$.
$= (10)^2$	Simplify inside the parentheses first.
$= 100$	

Answers

4. -16 **5.** 16

6. -0.001 **7.** -0.001

Avoiding Mistakes

In the expression $5ab^2$, the exponent, 2, applies only to the variable b. The constant 5 and the variable a both have an implied exponent of 1.

c. $5ab^2$

$= 5(2)(-3)^2$ Substitute $a = 2$, $b = -3$.

$= 5(2)(9)$ Simplify exponents before multiplying.

$= 90$ Multiply.

Avoiding Mistakes

Be sure to follow the order of operations. In Example 3(d), it would be incorrect to square the terms within the parentheses before adding.

d. $(b + a)^2$

$= [(-3) + (2)]^2$ Substitute $b = -3$ and $a = 2$.

$= (-1)^2$ Simplify within the parentheses first.

$= 1$

Skill Practice Evaluate each expression for $x = 2$ and $y = -5$.

8. $6x^2$ **9.** $(6x)^2$ **10.** $2xy^2$ **11.** $(y - x)^2$

3. Multiplying and Dividing Expressions with Common Bases

In this section, we investigate the effect of multiplying or dividing two quantities with the same base. For example, consider the expressions: x^5x^2 and $\frac{x^5}{x^2}$. Simplifying each expression, we have:

$$x^5x^2 = (x \cdot x \cdot x \cdot x \cdot x)(x \cdot x) = \overbrace{x \cdot x \cdot x \cdot x \cdot x \cdot x \cdot x}^{\text{7 factors of } x} = x^7$$

$$\frac{x^5}{x^2} = \frac{x \cdot x \cdot x \cdot \overset{1}{\cancel{x}} \cdot \overset{1}{\cancel{x}}}{\cancel{x} \cdot \cancel{x}} = \frac{x \cdot x \cdot x}{1} = x^3$$

These examples suggest that to multiply two quantities with the same base, we add the exponents. To divide two quantities with the same base, we subtract the exponent in the denominator from the exponent in the numerator. These rules are stated formally in the following two properties.

Multiplication of Expressions with Like Bases

Assume that b is a real number and that m and n represent positive integers. Then,

$$b^mb^n = b^{m+n}$$

Division of Expressions with Like Bases

Assume that $b \neq 0$ is a real number and that m and n represent positive integers. Then,

$$\frac{b^m}{b^n} = b^{m-n}$$

Answers

8. 24 **9.** 144 **10.** 100
11. 49

Example 4 Simplifying Expressions with Exponents

Simplify the expressions. **a.** w^3w^4 **b.** $2^3 \cdot 2^4$

Solution:

a. w^3w^4 $\quad (w \cdot w \cdot w)(w \cdot w \cdot w \cdot w)$

$= w^{3+4}$ To multiply expressions with like bases, add the exponents.

$= w^7$

b. $2^3 \cdot 2^4$ $\quad (2 \cdot 2 \cdot 2)(2 \cdot 2 \cdot 2 \cdot 2)$

$= 2^{3+4}$ To multiply expressions with like bases, add the exponents (the base is unchanged).

$= 2^7$ or 128

Skill Practice Simplify the expressions.

12. q^4q^8 **13.** $8^4 \cdot 8^8$

Avoiding Mistakes

When we multiply expressions with like bases, we add the exponents. The base does not change. In Example 4(b), we have $2^3 \cdot 2^4 = 2^7$.

Example 5 Simplifying Expressions with Exponents

Simplify the expressions. **a.** $\dfrac{t^6}{t^4}$ **b.** $\dfrac{5^6}{5^4}$

Solution:

a. $\dfrac{t^6}{t^4}$ $\quad \dfrac{t \cdot t \cdot t \cdot t \cdot t \cdot t}{t \cdot t \cdot t \cdot t}$

$= t^{6-4}$ To divide expressions with like bases, subtract the exponents.

$= t^2$

b. $\dfrac{5^6}{5^4}$ $\quad \dfrac{5 \cdot 5 \cdot 5 \cdot 5 \cdot 5 \cdot 5}{5 \cdot 5 \cdot 5 \cdot 5}$

$= 5^{6-4}$ To divide expressions with like bases, subtract the exponents (the base is unchanged).

$= 5^2$ or 25

Skill Practice Simplify the expressions.

14. $\dfrac{y^{15}}{y^8}$ **15.** $\dfrac{3^{15}}{3^8}$

Answers

12. q^{12} **13.** 8^{12}
14. y^7 **15.** 3^7

Example 6 Simplifying Expressions with Exponents

Simplify the expressions. **a.** $\dfrac{z^4z^5}{z^3}$ **b.** $\dfrac{10^7}{10^2 \cdot 10}$

Solution:

a. $\dfrac{z^4z^5}{z^3}$

$= \dfrac{z^{4+5}}{z^3}$ Add the exponents in the numerator (the base is unchanged).

$= \dfrac{z^9}{z^3}$

$= z^{9-3}$ Subtract the exponents.

$= z^6$

b. $\dfrac{10^7}{10^2 \cdot 10}$

$= \dfrac{10^7}{10^2 \cdot 10^1}$ Note that 10 is equivalent to 10^1.

$= \dfrac{10^7}{10^{2+1}}$ Add the exponents in the denominator (the base is unchanged).

$= \dfrac{10^7}{10^3}$

$= 10^{7-3}$ Subtract the exponents.

$= 10^4$ or 10,000 Simplify.

Skill Practice Simplify the expressions.

16. $\dfrac{a^3a^8}{a^7}$ **17.** $\dfrac{5^9}{5^2 \cdot 5^5}$

4. Simplifying Expressions with Exponents

Example 7 Simplifying Expressions with Exponents

Use the commutative and associative properties of real numbers and the properties of exponents to simplify the expressions.

a. $(-3p^2q^4)(2pq^5)$ **b.** $\dfrac{16w^9z^3}{4w^8z}$

Solution:

a. $(-3p^2q^4)(2pq^5)$

$= (-3 \cdot 2)(p^2p)(q^4q^5)$ Apply the associative and commutative properties of multiplication to group coefficients and like bases.

$= (-3 \cdot 2)p^{2+1}q^{4+5}$ Add the exponents when multiplying expressions with like bases.

$= -6p^3q^9$ Simplify.

Avoiding Mistakes

To simplify the expression in Example 7(a) we multiply the coefficients. However, to multiply expressions with like bases, we add the exponents.

Answers

16. a^4 **17.** 5^2 or 25

b. $\dfrac{16w^9z^3}{4w^8z}$

$= \left(\dfrac{16}{4}\right)\left(\dfrac{w^9}{w^8}\right)\left(\dfrac{z^3}{z}\right)$ Group coefficients and like bases.

$= 4w^{9-8}z^{3-1}$ Subtract the exponents when dividing expressions with like bases.

$= 4wz^2$ Simplify.

Avoiding Mistakes

In Example 7(b) we divide the coefficients. However, to divide expressions with like bases, we subtract the exponents.

Skill Practice Simplify the expressions.

18. $(-4x^2y^3)(3x^5y^7)$ **19.** $\dfrac{81x^4y^7}{9xy^3}$

5. Applications of Exponents

Simple interest on an investment or loan is computed by the formula $I = Prt$, where P is the amount of principal, r is the annual interest rate, and t is the time in years. Simple interest is based only on the original principal. However, in most day-to-day applications, the interest computed on money invested or borrowed is compound interest. **Compound interest** is computed on the original principal and on the interest already accrued.

Suppose \$1000 is invested at 8% interest for 3 years. Compare the total amount in the account if the money earns simple interest versus if the interest is compounded annually.

Simple Interest

The simple interest earned is given by $I = Prt$

$$= (1000)(0.08)(3)$$
$$= \$240$$

The total amount, A, at the end of 3 years is $A = P + I$

$$= \$1000 + \$240$$
$$= \$1240$$

Compound Annual Interest

The total amount, A, in an account earning compound annual interest may be computed using the following formula:

$A = P(1 + r)^t$ where P is the amount of principal, r is the annual interest rate (expressed in decimal form), and t is the number of years.

For example, for \$1000 invested at 8% interest compounded annually for 3 years, we have $P = 1000$, $r = 0.08$, and $t = 3$.

$$A = P(1 + r)^t$$
$$A = 1000(1 + 0.08)^3$$
$$= 1000(1.08)^3$$
$$= 1000(1.259712)$$
$$= 1259.712$$

Rounding to the nearest cent, we have $A = \$1259.71$.

Answers

18. $-12x^7y^{10}$ **19.** $9x^3y^4$

Example 8 Using Exponents in an Application

Find the amount in an account after 8 years if the initial investment is \$7000, invested at 2.25% interest compounded annually.

Solution:

Identify the values for each variable.

$P = 7000$

$r = 0.0225$ — Note that the decimal form of a percent is used for calculations.

$t = 8$

$A = P(1 + r)^t$	
$= 7000(1 + 0.0225)^8$	Substitute.
$= 7000(1.0225)^8$	Simplify inside the parentheses.
$\approx 7000(1.194831142)$	Approximate $(1.0225)^8$.
≈ 8363.82	Multiply (round to the nearest cent).

The amount in the account after 8 years is \$8363.82.

Skill Practice

20. Find the amount in an account after 3 years if the initial investment is \$4000 invested at 5% interest compounded annually.

Answer

20. \$4630.50

Calculator Connections

Topic: Review of Evaluating Exponential Expressions on a Calculator

In Example 8, it was necessary to evaluate the expression $(1.0225)^8$. Recall that the [^] or [y^x] key may be used to enter expressions with exponents.

Scientific Calculator

Enter: 1.0225 [y^x] 8 [=] **Result:** 1.194831142

Graphing Calculator

```
1.0225^8
         1.194831142
```

Calculator Exercises

Use a calculator to evaluate the expressions.

1. $(1.06)^5$ **2.** $(1.02)^{40}$ **3.** $5000(1.06)^5$

4. $2000(1.02)^{40}$ **5.** $3000(1 + 0.06)^2$ **6.** $1000(1 + 0.05)^3$

Section 5.1 Practice Exercises

For this exercise set, assume all variables represent nonzero real numbers.

Vocabulary and Key Concepts

1. **a.** A(n) ________ is used to show repeated multiplication of the base.
   b. Given the expression b^n, the value b is the ________ and n is the ________.
   c. Given the expression x, the value of the exponent on x is understood to be ________.
   d. The formula to compute simple interest is ________.
   e. Interest that is computed on the original principal and on the accrued interest is called ________ ________.

Concept 1: Review of Exponential Notation

For Exercises 2–13, identify the base and the exponent. **(See Example 1.)**

2. c^3 **3.** x^4 **4.** 5^2 **5.** 3^5

6. $(-4)^8$ **7.** $(-1)^4$ **8.** x **9.** 13

10. -4^2 **11.** -10^3 **12.** $-y^5$ **13.** $-t^6$

14. What base corresponds to the exponent 5 in the expression $x^3y^5z^2$?

15. What base corresponds to the exponent 2 in the expression w^3v^2?

16. What is the exponent for the factor of 2 in the expression $2x^3$?

17. What is the exponent for the factor of p in the expression pq^7?

For Exercises 18–26, write the expression using exponents.

18. $(4n)(4n)(4n)$ **19.** $(-6b)(-6b)$ **20.** $4 \cdot n \cdot n \cdot n$

21. $-6 \cdot b \cdot b$ **22.** $(x - 5)(x - 5)(x - 5)$ **23.** $(y + 2)(y + 2)(y + 2)(y + 2)$

24. $\dfrac{4}{x \cdot x \cdot x \cdot x \cdot x}$ **25.** $\dfrac{-2}{t \cdot t \cdot t}$ **26.** $\dfrac{5 \cdot x \cdot x \cdot x}{(y - 7)(y - 7)}$

Concept 2: Evaluating Expressions with Exponents

For Exercises 27–34, evaluate the two expressions and compare the answers. Do the expressions have the same value? **(See Example 2.)**

27. -5^2 and $(-5)^2$ **28.** -3^4 and $(-3)^4$ **29.** -2^5 and $(-2)^5$ **30.** -5^3 and $(-5)^3$

31. $\left(\frac{1}{2}\right)^3$ and $\frac{1}{2^3}$ **32.** $\left(\frac{1}{5}\right)^2$ and $\frac{1}{5^2}$ **33.** $-(-2)^4$ and $-(2)^4$ **34.** $-(-3)^3$ and $-(3)^3$

For Exercises 35–42, evaluate each expression. **(See Example 2.)**

35. 16^1 **36.** 20^1 **37.** $(-1)^{21}$ **38.** $(-1)^{30}$

39. $\left(-\frac{1}{3}\right)^2$ **40.** $\left(-\frac{1}{4}\right)^3$ **41.** $-\left(\frac{2}{5}\right)^2$ **42.** $-\left(\frac{3}{5}\right)^2$

Section 5.2 More Properties of Exponents

Concepts

1. Power Rule for Exponents
2. The Properties $(ab)^m = a^m b^m$ and $\left(\frac{a}{b}\right)^m = \frac{a^m}{b^m}$

1. Power Rule for Exponents

The expression $(x^2)^3$ indicates that the quantity x^2 is cubed.

$$(x^2)^3 = (x^2)(x^2)(x^2) = (x \cdot x)(x \cdot x)(x \cdot x) = x^6$$

From this example, it appears that to raise a base to successive powers, we multiply the exponents and leave the base unchanged. This is stated formally as the power rule for exponents.

Power Rule for Exponents

Assume that b is a real number and that m and n represent positive integers. Then,

$$(b^m)^n = b^{m \cdot n}$$

Example 1 Simplifying Expressions with Exponents

Simplify the expressions.

a. $(s^4)^2$ **b.** $(3^4)^2$ **c.** $(x^2x^5)^4$

Solution:

a. $(s^4)^2$

$= s^{4 \cdot 2}$ Multiply exponents (the base is unchanged).

$= s^8$

b. $(3^4)^2$

$= 3^{4 \cdot 2}$ Multiply exponents (the base is unchanged).

$= 3^8$ or 6561

c. $(x^2x^5)^4$

$= (x^7)^4$ Simplify inside the parentheses by adding exponents.

$= x^{7 \cdot 4}$ Multiply exponents (the base is unchanged).

$= x^{28}$

Skill Practice Simplify the expressions.

1. $(y^3)^5$ **2.** $(2^8)^{10}$ **3.** $(q^5q^4)^3$

2. The Properties $(ab)^m = a^m b^m$ and $\left(\frac{a}{b}\right)^m = \frac{a^m}{b^m}$

Consider the following expressions and their simplified forms:

$$(xy)^3 = (xy)(xy)(xy) = (x \cdot x \cdot x)(y \cdot y \cdot y) = x^3y^3$$

$$\left(\frac{x}{y}\right)^3 = \left(\frac{x}{y}\right)\left(\frac{x}{y}\right)\left(\frac{x}{y}\right) = \left(\frac{x \cdot x \cdot x}{y \cdot y \cdot y}\right) = \frac{x^3}{y^3}$$

The expressions were simplified using the commutative and associative properties of multiplication. The simplified forms for each expression could have been reached in one step by applying the exponent to each factor inside the parentheses.

Answers

1. y^{15} 2. 2^{80} 3. q^{27}

Power of a Product and Power of a Quotient

Assume that a and b are real numbers. Let m represent a positive integer. Then,

$$(ab)^m = a^m b^m$$

$$\left(\frac{a}{b}\right)^m = \frac{a^m}{b^m}, \quad b \neq 0$$

Avoiding Mistakes

The power rule of exponents can be applied to a product of bases but in general cannot be applied to a sum or difference of bases.

$$(ab)^n = a^n b^n$$

but $(a + b)^n \neq a^n + b^n$

Applying these properties of exponents, we have

$$(xy)^3 = x^3y^3 \quad \text{and} \quad \left(\frac{x}{y}\right)^3 = \frac{x^3}{y^3}$$

Example 2 Simplifying Expressions with Exponents

Simplify the expressions.

a. $(-2xyz)^4$ **b.** $(5x^2y^7)^3$ **c.** $\left(\frac{2}{5}\right)^3$ **d.** $\left(\frac{1}{3xy^4}\right)^2$

Solution:

a. $(-2xyz)^4$

$= (-2)^4x^4y^4z^4$ Raise each factor within parentheses to the fourth power.

$= 16x^4y^4z^4$

b. $(5x^2y^7)^3$

$= 5^3(x^2)^3(y^7)^3$ Raise each factor within parentheses to the third power.

$= 125x^6y^{21}$ Multiply exponents and simplify.

c. $\left(\frac{2}{5}\right)^3$

$= \frac{(2)^3}{(5)^3}$ Raise each factor within parentheses to the third power.

$= \frac{8}{125}$ Simplify.

d. $\left(\frac{1}{3xy^4}\right)^2$

$= \frac{1^2}{3^2x^2(y^4)^2}$ Square each factor within parentheses.

$= \frac{1}{9x^2y^8}$ Multiply exponents and simplify.

Skill Practice Simplify the expressions.

4. $(3abc)^5$ **5.** $(-2t^2w^4)^3$ **6.** $\left(\frac{3}{4}\right)^3$ **7.** $\left(\frac{2x^3}{y^5}\right)^2$

Answers

4. $3^5a^5b^5c^5$ or $243a^5b^5c^5$

5. $-8t^6w^{12}$ **6.** $\frac{27}{64}$ **7.** $\frac{4x^6}{y^{10}}$

The properties of exponents can be used along with the properties of real numbers to simplify complicated expressions.

Example 3 **Simplifying Expressions with Exponents**

Simplify the expression. $\dfrac{(x^2)^6(x^3)}{(x^7)^2}$

Solution:

$\dfrac{(x^2)^6(x^3)}{(x^7)^2}$ Clear parentheses by applying the power rule.

$= \dfrac{x^{2\cdot 6}x^3}{x^{7\cdot 2}}$ Multiply exponents.

$= \dfrac{x^{12}x^3}{x^{14}}$

$= \dfrac{x^{12+3}}{x^{14}}$ Add exponents in the numerator.

$= \dfrac{x^{15}}{x^{14}}$

$= x^{15-14}$ Subtract exponents.

$= x$ Simplify.

Skill Practice Simplify the expression.

8. $\dfrac{(k^5)^2k^8}{(k^2)^4}$

Example 4 **Simplifying Expressions with Exponents**

Simplify the expression. $(3cd^2)(2cd^3)^3$

Solution:

$(3cd^2)(2cd^3)^3$ Clear parentheses by applying the power rule.

$= 3cd^2 \cdot 2^3c^3d^9$ Raise each factor in the second parentheses to the third power.

$= 3 \cdot 2^3cc^3d^2d^9$ Group like factors.

$= 3 \cdot 8c^{1+3}d^{2+9}$ Add exponents on like bases.

$= 24c^4d^{11}$ Simplify.

Skill Practice Simplify the expression.

9. $(4x^4y)(2x^3y^4)^4$

Answers

8. k^{10} **9.** $64x^{16}y^{17}$

Example 5 **Simplifying Expressions with Exponents**

Simplify the expression. $\left(\dfrac{x^7yz^4}{8xz^3}\right)^2$

Solution:

$$\left(\frac{x^7yz^4}{8xz^3}\right)^2$$

$$= \left(\frac{x^{7-1}yz^{4-3}}{8}\right)^2$$ First simplify inside the parentheses by subtracting exponents on like bases.

$$= \left(\frac{x^6yz}{8}\right)^2$$

$$= \frac{(x^6)^2y^2z^2}{8^2}$$ Apply the power rule of exponents.

$$= \frac{x^{12}y^2z^2}{64}$$

Skill Practice Simplify the expression.

10. $\left(\dfrac{w^2xy^4}{6xy^3}\right)^2$

Answer

10. $\dfrac{w^4y^2}{36}$

Section 5.2 Practice Exercises

For this exercise set assume all variables represent nonzero real numbers.

Review Exercises

For Exercises 1–8, simplify.

1. $4^2 \cdot 4^7$ **2.** $5^8 \cdot 5^3 \cdot 5$ **3.** $a^{13} \cdot a \cdot a^6$ **4.** $y^{14}y^3$

5. $\dfrac{d^{13}d}{d^5}$ **6.** $\dfrac{3^8 \cdot 3}{3^2}$ **7.** $\dfrac{7^{11}}{7^5}$ **8.** $\dfrac{z^4}{z^3}$

9. Explain when to add exponents versus when to multiply exponents.

10. Explain when to add exponents versus when to subtract exponents.

Concept 1: Power Rule for Exponents

For Exercises 11–22, simplify and write answers in exponent form. **(See Example 1.)**

11. $(5^3)^4$ **12.** $(2^8)^7$ **13.** $(12^3)^2$ **14.** $(6^4)^4$

15. $(y^7)^2$ **16.** $(z^6)^4$ **17.** $(w^5)^5$ **18.** $(t^3)^6$

19. $(a^2a^4)^6$ **20.** $(z \cdot z^3)^2$ **21.** $(y^3y^4)^2$ **22.** $(w^5w)^4$

23. Evaluate the two expressions and compare the answers: $(2^2)^3$ and $(2^3)^2$.

24. Evaluate the two expressions and compare the answers: $(4^4)^2$ and $(4^2)^4$.

25. Evaluate the two expressions and compare the answers. Which expression is greater? Why?

4^{3^2} and $(4^3)^2$

26. Evaluate the two expressions and compare the answers. Which expression is greater? Why?

3^{5^2} and $(3^5)^2$

Concept 2: The Properties $(ab)^m = a^m b^m$ and $\left(\frac{a}{b}\right)^m = \frac{a^m}{b^m}$

For Exercises 27–42, use the appropriate property to clear the parentheses. **(See Example 2.)**

27. $(5w)^2$ **28.** $(4y)^3$ **29.** $(srt)^4$ **30.** $(wxy)^6$

31. $\left(\frac{2}{r}\right)^4$ **32.** $\left(\frac{1}{t}\right)^8$ **33.** $\left(\frac{x}{y}\right)^5$ **34.** $\left(\frac{w}{z}\right)^7$

35. $(-3a)^4$ **36.** $(2x)^5$ **37.** $(-3abc)^3$ **38.** $(-5xyz)^2$

39. $\left(-\frac{4}{x}\right)^3$ **40.** $\left(-\frac{1}{w}\right)^4$ **41.** $\left(-\frac{a}{b}\right)^2$ **42.** $\left(-\frac{r}{s}\right)^3$

Mixed Exercises

For Exercises 43–74, simplify. **(See Examples 3–5.)**

43. $(6u^2v^4)^3$ **44.** $(3a^5b^2)^6$ **45.** $5(x^2y)^4$ **46.** $18(u^3v^4)^2$

47. $(-h^4)^7$ **48.** $(-k^6)^3$ **49.** $(-m^2)^6$ **50.** $(-n^3)^8$

51. $\left(\frac{4}{rs^4}\right)^5$ **52.** $\left(\frac{2}{h^7k}\right)^3$ **53.** $\left(\frac{3p}{q^3}\right)^5$ **54.** $\left(\frac{5x^2}{y^3}\right)^4$

55. $\frac{y^8(y^3)^4}{(y^2)^3}$ **56.** $\frac{(w^3)^2(w^4)^5}{(w^4)^2}$ **57.** $(x^2)^5(x^3)^7$ **58.** $(y^3)^4(y^2)^5$

59. $(2a^2b)^3(5a^4b^3)^2$ **60.** $(4c^3d^5)^2(3cd^3)^2$ **61.** $(-2p^2q^4)^4$ **62.** $(-7x^4y^5)^2$

63. $(-m^7n^3)^5$ **64.** $(-a^3b^6)^7$ **65.** $\frac{(5a^3b)^4(a^2b)^4}{(5ab)^2}$ **66.** $\frac{(6s^3)^2(s^4t^5)^2}{(3s^4t^2)^2}$

67. $\left(\frac{2c^3d^4}{3c^2d}\right)^2$ **68.** $\left(\frac{x^3y^5z}{5xy^2}\right)^2$ **69.** $(2c^3d^2)^5\left(\frac{c^6d^8}{4c^2d}\right)^3$ **70.** $\left(\frac{s^5t^6}{2s^2t}\right)^2(10s^3t^3)^2$

71. $\left(\frac{-3a^3b}{c^2}\right)^3$ **72.** $\left(\frac{-4x^2}{y^4z}\right)^3$ **73.** $\frac{(-8b^6)^2(b^3)^5}{4b}$ **74.** $\frac{(-6a^2)^2(a^3)^4}{9a}$

Expanding Your Skills

For Exercises 75–82, simplify each expression using the addition or subtraction properties of exponents. Assume that a, b, m, n, and x represent positive integers.

75. $(x^m)^2$ **76.** $(y^3)^n$ **77.** $(5a^{2n})^3$ **78.** $(3b^4)^m$

79. $\left(\frac{m^2}{n^3}\right)^b$ **80.** $\left(\frac{x^5}{y^3}\right)^m$ **81.** $\left(\frac{3a^3}{5b^4}\right)^n$ **82.** $\left(\frac{4m^6}{3n^2}\right)^x$

Definitions of b^0 and b^{-n}

Section 5.3

Concepts

1. Definition of b^0
2. Definition of b^{-n}
3. Properties of Integer Exponents: A Summary

In Sections 5.1 and 5.2, we learned several rules that enable us to manipulate expressions containing *positive* integer exponents. In this section, we present definitions that can be used to simplify expressions with negative exponents or with an exponent of zero.

1. Definition of b^0

To begin, consider the following pattern.

$3^3 = 27$ — Divide by 3.

$3^2 = 9$ — Divide by 3.

$3^1 = 3$ — Divide by 3.

$3^0 = 1$

As the exponents decrease by 1, the resulting expressions are divided by 3.

For the pattern to continue, we define $3^0 = 1$.

This pattern suggests that we should define an expression with a zero exponent as follows.

Definition of b^0

Let b be a nonzero real number. Then, $b^0 = 1$.

Note: The value of 0^0 is not defined by this definition because the base b must not equal zero.

Example 1 Simplifying Expressions with a Zero Exponent

Simplify. Assume that $z \neq 0$.

a. 4^0 **b.** $(-4)^0$ **c.** -4^0

d. z^0 **e.** $-4z^0$ **f.** $(4z)^0$

Solution:

a. $4^0 = 1$ By definition

b. $(-4)^0 = 1$ By definition

c. $-4^0 = -1 \cdot 4^0 = -1 \cdot 1 = -1$ The exponent 0 applies only to 4.

d. $z^0 = 1$ By definition

e. $-4z^0 = -4 \cdot z^0 = -4 \cdot 1 = -4$ The exponent 0 applies only to z.

f. $(4z)^0 = 1$ The parentheses indicate that the exponent, 0, applies to both factors 4 and z.

Skill Practice Evaluate the expressions. Assume that $x \neq 0$ and $y \neq 0$.

1. 7^0 **2.** $(-7)^0$ **3.** -5^0

4. y^0 **5.** $-2x^0$ **6.** $(2x)^0$

Answers

1. 1 **2.** 1 **3.** −1

4. 1 **5.** −2 **6.** 1

Example 4 **Simplifying Expressions with Negative Exponents**

Simplify. Assume that $x \neq 0$.

a. $(5x)^{-3}$ **b.** $5x^{-3}$ **c.** $-5x^{-3}$

Solution:

a. $(5x)^{-3} = \left(\dfrac{1}{5x}\right)^3$ Take the reciprocal of the base, and change the sign of the exponent.

$= \dfrac{(1)^3}{(5x)^3}$ Apply the exponent of 3 to each factor within parentheses.

$= \dfrac{1}{125x^3}$ Simplify.

b. $5x^{-3} = 5 \cdot x^{-3}$ Note that the exponent, -3, applies only to x.

$= 5 \cdot \dfrac{1}{x^3}$ Rewrite x^{-3} as $\dfrac{1}{x^3}$.

$= \dfrac{5}{x^3}$ Multiply.

c. $-5x^{-3} = -5 \cdot x^{-3}$ Note that the exponent, -3, applies only to x, and that -5 is a coefficient.

$= -5 \cdot \dfrac{1}{x^3}$ Rewrite x^{-3} as $\dfrac{1}{x^3}$.

$= -\dfrac{5}{x^3}$ Multiply.

Skill Practice Simplify. Assume that $w \neq 0$.

13. $(2w)^{-4}$ **14.** $2w^{-4}$ **15.** $-2w^{-4}$

It is important to note that the definition of b^{-n} is consistent with the other properties of exponents learned thus far. For example, consider the expression

$$\frac{x^4}{x^7} = \frac{\cancel{x} \cdot \cancel{x} \cdot \cancel{x} \cdot \cancel{x}}{\cancel{x} \cdot \cancel{x} \cdot \cancel{x} \cdot \cancel{x} \cdot x \cdot x \cdot x} = \frac{1}{x^3}$$

Subtract exponents.

By subtracting exponents, we have $\dfrac{x^4}{x^7} = x^{4-7} = x^{-3}$

Hence, $x^{-3} = \dfrac{1}{x^3}$

3. Properties of Integer Exponents: A Summary

The definitions of b^0 and b^{-n} allow us to extend the properties of exponents learned in Sections 5.1 and 5.2 to include integer exponents. These are summarized in Table 5-1.

Answers

13. $\dfrac{1}{16w^4}$ **14.** $\dfrac{2}{w^4}$

15. $-\dfrac{2}{w^4}$

Table 5-1

Properties of Integer Exponents Assume that a and b are real numbers ($b \neq 0$) and that m and n represent integers.		
Property	**Example**	**Details/Notes**
Multiplication of Expressions with Like Bases $b^m b^n = b^{m+n}$	$b^2 b^4 = b^{2+4} = b^6$	$b^2 b^4 = (b \cdot b)(b \cdot b \cdot b \cdot b) = b^6$
Division of Expressions with Like Bases $\frac{b^m}{b^n} = b^{m-n}$	$\frac{b^5}{b^2} = b^{5-2} = b^3$	$\frac{b^5}{b^2} = \frac{\cancel{b} \cdot \cancel{b} \cdot b \cdot b \cdot b}{\cancel{b} \cdot \cancel{b}} = b^3$
The Power Rule $(b^m)^n = b^{m \cdot n}$	$(b^4)^2 = b^{4 \cdot 2} = b^8$	$(b^4)^2 = (b \cdot b \cdot b \cdot b)(b \cdot b \cdot b \cdot b) = b^8$
Power of a Product $(ab)^m = a^m b^m$	$(ab)^3 = a^3 b^3$	$(ab)^3 = (ab)(ab)(ab)$ $= (a \cdot a \cdot a)(b \cdot b \cdot b) = a^3 b^3$
Power of a Quotient $\left(\frac{a}{b}\right)^m = \frac{a^m}{b^m}$	$\left(\frac{a}{b}\right)^3 = \frac{a^3}{b^3}$	$\left(\frac{a}{b}\right)^3 = \left(\frac{a}{b}\right)\left(\frac{a}{b}\right)\left(\frac{a}{b}\right) = \frac{a \cdot a \cdot a}{b \cdot b \cdot b} = \frac{a^3}{b^3}$

Definitions Assume that b is a real number ($b \neq 0$) and that n represents an integer.		
Definition	**Example**	**Details/Notes**
$b^0 = 1$	$(4)^0 = 1$	Any nonzero quantity raised to the zero power equals 1.
$b^{-n} = \left(\frac{1}{b}\right)^n = \frac{1}{b^n}$	$b^{-5} = \left(\frac{1}{b}\right)^5 = \frac{1}{b^5}$	To simplify a negative exponent, take the reciprocal of the base and make the exponent positive.

Example 5 Simplifying Expressions with Exponents

Simplify the expressions. Write the answers with positive exponents only. Assume all variables are nonzero.

a. $\frac{a^3 b^{-2}}{c^{-5}}$ **b.** $\frac{x^2 x^{-7}}{x^3}$ **c.** $\frac{z^2}{w^{-4} w^4 z^{-8}}$

Solution:

a. $\frac{a^3 b^{-2}}{c^{-5}}$

$= \frac{a^3}{1} \cdot \frac{b^{-2}}{1} \cdot \frac{1}{c^{-5}}$

$= \frac{a^3}{1} \cdot \frac{1}{b^2} \cdot \frac{c^5}{1}$ Simplify negative exponents.

$= \frac{a^3 c^5}{b^2}$ Multiply.

b. $\dfrac{x^2x^{-7}}{x^3}$

$= \dfrac{x^{2+(-7)}}{x^3}$ Add the exponents in the numerator.

$= \dfrac{x^{-5}}{x^3}$ Simplify.

$= x^{-5-3}$ Subtract the exponents.

$= x^{-8}$

$= \dfrac{1}{x^8}$ Simplify the negative exponent.

c. $\dfrac{z^2}{w^{-4}w^4z^{-8}}$

$= \dfrac{z^2}{w^{-4+4}z^{-8}}$ Add the exponents in the denominator.

$= \dfrac{z^2}{w^0z^{-8}}$

$= \dfrac{z^2}{(1)z^{-8}}$ Recall that $w^0 = 1$.

$= z^{2-(-8)}$ Subtract the exponents.

$= z^{10}$ Simplify.

Skill Practice Simplify the expressions. Assume all variables are nonzero.

16. $\dfrac{x^{-6}}{y^4z^{-8}}$ **17.** $\dfrac{x^3x^{-8}}{x^4}$ **18.** $\dfrac{p^3}{w^7w^{-7}z^{-2}}$

Example 6 Simplifying Expressions with Exponents

Simplify the expressions. Write the answers with positive exponents only. Assume that all variables are nonzero.

a. $(-4ab^{-2})^{-3}$ **b.** $\left(\dfrac{2p^{-4}q^3}{5p^2q}\right)^{-2}$

Solution:

a. $(-4ab^{-2})^{-3}$

$= (-4)^{-3}a^{-3}(b^{-2})^{-3}$ Apply the power rule of exponents.

$= (-4)^{-3}a^{-3}b^6$

$= \dfrac{1}{(-4)^3} \cdot \dfrac{1}{a^3} \cdot b^6$ Simplify the negative exponents.

$= \dfrac{1}{-64} \cdot \dfrac{1}{a^3} \cdot b^6$ Simplify.

$= -\dfrac{b^6}{64a^3}$ Multiply fractions.

Answers

16. $\dfrac{z^8}{y^4x^6}$ **17.** $\dfrac{1}{x^9}$ **18.** p^3z^2

b. $\left(\dfrac{2p^{-4}q^3}{5p^2q}\right)^{-2}$ First simplify within the parentheses.

$= \left(\dfrac{2p^{-4-2}q^{3-1}}{5}\right)^{-2}$ Divide expressions with like bases by subtracting exponents.

$= \left(\dfrac{2p^{-6}q^2}{5}\right)^{-2}$ Simplify.

$= \dfrac{(2p^{-6}q^2)^{-2}}{(5)^{-2}}$ Apply the power rule of a quotient.

$= \dfrac{2^{-2}(p^{-6})^{-2}(q^2)^{-2}}{5^{-2}}$ Apply the power rule of a product.

$= \dfrac{2^{-2}p^{12}q^{-4}}{5^{-2}}$ Simplify.

$= \dfrac{5^2p^{12}}{2^2q^4}$ Simplify the negative exponents.

$= \dfrac{25p^{12}}{4q^4}$ Simplify.

TIP: For Example 6(b), the power rule of exponents can be performed first. In that case, the second step would be

$$\frac{2^{-2}p^8q^{-6}}{5^{-2}p^{-4}q^{-2}}$$

Skill Practice Simplify the expressions. Assume all variables are nonzero.

19. $(-5x^{-2}y^3)^{-2}$ **20.** $\left(\dfrac{3x^{-3}y^{-2}}{4xy^{-3}}\right)^{-2}$

Example 7 Simplifying an Expression with Exponents

Simplify the expression $2^{-1} + 3^{-1} + 5^0$. Write the answer with positive exponents only.

Solution:

$2^{-1} + 3^{-1} + 5^0$

$= \dfrac{1}{2} + \dfrac{1}{3} + 1$ Simplify negative exponents. Simplify $5^0 = 1$.

$= \dfrac{3}{6} + \dfrac{2}{6} + \dfrac{6}{6}$ The least common denominator is 6.

$= \dfrac{11}{6}$ Simplify.

Skill Practice Simplify the expressions.

21. $2^{-1} + 4^{-2} + 3^0$

Answers

19. $\dfrac{x^4}{25y^6}$ **20.** $\dfrac{16x^8}{9y^2}$ **21.** $\dfrac{25}{16}$

Section 5.3 Practice Exercises

For this exercise set, assume all variables represent nonzero real numbers.

Study Skills Exercise

To help you remember the properties of exponents, write them on 3 × 5 cards. On each card, write a property on one side and an example using that property on the other side. Keep these cards with you, and when you have a spare moment (such as waiting at the doctor's office), pull out these cards and go over the properties.

Vocabulary and Key Concepts

1. **a.** The expression b^0 is defined to be __________ provided that $b \neq 0$.

b. The expression b^{-n} is defined as __________ provided that $b \neq 0$.

Review Exercises

For Exercises 2–9, simplify.

2. b^3b^8 **3.** c^7c^2 **4.** $\dfrac{x^6}{x^2}$ **5.** $\dfrac{y^9}{y^8}$

6. $\dfrac{9^4 \cdot 9^8}{9}$ **7.** $\dfrac{3^{14}}{3^3 \cdot 3^5}$ **8.** $(6ab^3c^2)^5$ **9.** $(7w^7z^2)^4$

Concept 1: Definition of b^0

10. Simplify.

a. 8^0 **b.** $\dfrac{8^4}{8^4}$

11. Simplify.

a. d^0 **b.** $\dfrac{d^3}{d^3}$

12. Simplify.

a. m^0 **b.** $\dfrac{m^5}{m^5}$

For Exercises 13–24, simplify. **(See Example 1.)**

13. p^0 **14.** k^0 **15.** 5^0 **16.** 2^0

17. -4^0 **18.** -1^0 **19.** $(-6)^0$ **20.** $(-2)^0$

21. $(8x)^0$ **22.** $(-3y^3)^0$ **23.** $-7x^0$ **24.** $6y^0$

Concept 2: Definition of b^{-n}

25. Simplify and write the answers with positive exponents.

a. t^{-5} **b.** $\dfrac{t^3}{t^8}$

26. Simplify and write the answers with positive exponents.

a. 4^{-3} **b.** $\dfrac{4^2}{4^5}$

For Exercises 27–46, simplify. **(See Examples 2–4.)**

27. $\left(\dfrac{2}{7}\right)^{-3}$ **28.** $\left(\dfrac{5}{4}\right)^{-1}$ **29.** $\left(-\dfrac{1}{5}\right)^{-2}$ **30.** $\left(-\dfrac{1}{3}\right)^{-3}$

31. a^{-3} **32.** c^{-5} **33.** 12^{-1} **34.** 4^{-2}

35. $(4b)^{-2}$ **36.** $(3z)^{-1}$ **37.** $6x^{-2}$ **38.** $7y^{-1}$

39. $(-8)^{-2}$ **40.** -8^{-2} **41.** $-3y^{-4}$ **42.** $-6a^{-2}$

43. $(-t)^{-3}$ **44.** $(-r)^{-5}$ **45.** $\dfrac{1}{a^{-5}}$ **46.** $\dfrac{1}{b^{-6}}$

Concept 3: Properties of Integer Exponents: A Summary

For Exercises 47–50, correct the statement.

47. $\dfrac{x^4}{x^{-6}} = x^{4-6} = x^{-2}$ **48.** $\dfrac{y^5}{y^{-3}} = y^{5-3} = y^2$

49. $2a^{-3} = \dfrac{1}{2a^3}$ **50.** $5b^{-2} = \dfrac{1}{5b^2}$

Mixed Exercises

For Exercises 51–94, simplify each expression. Write the answer with positive exponents only. **(See Examples 5–6.)**

51. $x^{-8}x^4$ **52.** s^5s^{-6} **53.** $a^{-8}a^8$ **54.** q^3q^{-3}

55. $y^{17}y^{-13}$ **56.** $b^{20}b^{-14}$ **57.** $(m^{-6}n^9)^3$ **58.** $(c^4d^{-5})^{-2}$

59. $(-3j^{-5}k^6)^4$ **60.** $(6xy^{-11})^{-3}$ **61.** $\dfrac{p^3}{p^9}$ **62.** $\dfrac{q^2}{q^{10}}$

63. $\dfrac{r^{-5}}{r^{-2}}$ **64.** $\dfrac{u^{-2}}{u^{-6}}$ **65.** $\dfrac{a^2}{a^{-6}}$ **66.** $\dfrac{p^3}{p^{-5}}$

67. $\dfrac{y^{-2}}{y^6}$ **68.** $\dfrac{s^{-4}}{s^3}$ **69.** $\dfrac{7^3}{7^2 \cdot 7^8}$ **70.** $\dfrac{3^4 \cdot 3}{3^7}$

71. $\dfrac{a^2a}{a^3}$ **72.** $\dfrac{t^5}{t^2t^3}$ **73.** $\dfrac{a^{-1}b^2}{a^3b^8}$ **74.** $\dfrac{k^{-4}h^{-1}}{k^6h}$

75. $\dfrac{w^{-8}(w^2)^{-5}}{w^3}$ **76.** $\dfrac{p^2p^{-7}}{(p^2)^3}$ **77.** $\dfrac{3^{-2}}{3}$ **78.** $\dfrac{5^{-1}}{5}$

79. $\left(\dfrac{p^{-1}q^5}{p^{-6}}\right)^0$ **80.** $\left(\dfrac{ab^{-4}}{a^{-5}}\right)^0$ **81.** $(8x^3y^0)^{-2}$ **82.** $(3u^2v^0)^{-3}$

83. $(-8y^{-12})(2y^{16}z^{-2})$ **84.** $(5p^{-2}q^5)(-2p^{-4}q^{-1})$ **85.** $\dfrac{-18a^{10}b^6}{108a^{-2}b^6}$ **86.** $\dfrac{-35x^{-4}y^{-3}}{-21x^2y^{-3}}$

87. $\dfrac{(-4c^{12}d^7)^2}{(5c^{-3}d^{10})^{-1}}$ **88.** $\dfrac{(s^3t^{-2})^4}{(3s^{-4}t^6)^{-2}}$ **89.** $\dfrac{(2x^3y^2)^{-3}}{(3x^2y^4)^{-2}}$ **90.** $\dfrac{(5p^4q)^{-3}}{(p^3q^5)^{-4}}$

91. $\left(\dfrac{5cd^{-3}}{10d^5}\right)^{-2}$ **92.** $\left(\dfrac{4m^{10}n^4}{2m^{12}n^{-2}}\right)^{-1}$ **93.** $(2xy^3)\left(\dfrac{9xy}{4x^3y^2}\right)$ **94.** $(-3a^3)\left(\dfrac{ab}{27a^4b^2}\right)$

For Exercises 95–102, simplify. **(See Example 7.)**

95. $5^{-1} + 2^{-2}$ **96.** $4^{-2} + 8^{-1}$ **97.** $10^0 - 10^{-1}$ **98.** $3^0 - 3^{-2}$

99. $2^{-2} + 1^{-2}$ **100.** $4^{-1} + 8^{-1}$ **101.** $4 \cdot 5^0 - 2 \cdot 3^{-1}$ **102.** $2 \cdot 4^0 - 3 \cdot 4^{-1}$

Example 1 **Writing Numbers in Scientific Notation**

Write the numbers in scientific notation.

a. 53,000 **b.** 0.00053

Solution:

a. $53{,}000. = 5.3 \times 10^4$ To write 53,000 in scientific notation, the decimal point must be moved four places to the left. Because 53,000 is larger than 10, a *positive* power of 10 is used.

b. $0.00053 = 5.3 \times 10^{-4}$ To write 0.00053 in scientific notation, the decimal point must be moved four places to the right. Because 0.00053 is less than 1, a *negative* power of 10 is used.

Skill Practice Write the numbers in scientific notation.

1. 175,000,000 **2.** 0.000005

Example 2 **Writing Numbers in Scientific Notation**

Write the numbers in scientific notation.

a. The number of movie tickets sold in the United States for a recent year is estimated to be 1,500,000,000.

b. The weight of a flea is approximately 0.00066 lb.

c. The temperature on a January day in Fargo dropped to $-43°F$.

d. A bench is 8.2 ft long.

Solution:

a. $1{,}500{,}000{,}000 = 1.5 \times 10^9$ **b.** $0.00066 \text{ lb} = 6.6 \times 10^{-4} \text{ lb}$

c. $-43°F = -4.3 \times 10^1 \, °F$ **d.** $8.2 \text{ ft} = 8.2 \times 10^0 \text{ ft}$

Skill Practice Write the numbers in scientific notation.

3. In the year 2011, the population of the Earth was approximately 7,000,000,000.

4. The weight of a grain of salt is approximately 0.000002 ounce.

2. Writing Numbers in Standard Form

Example 3 **Writing Numbers in Standard Form**

Write the numbers in standard form.

a. The mass of a proton is approximately 1.67×10^{-24} g.

b. The "nearby" star Vega is approximately 1.552×10^{14} miles from Earth.

Solution:

a. $1.67 \times 10^{-24} \text{ g} = 0.000\,000\,000\,000\,000\,000\,000\,001\,67 \text{ g}$

Because the power of 10 is negative, the value of 1.67×10^{-24} is a decimal number between 0 and 1. Move the decimal point 24 places to the *left*.

b. $1.552 \times 10^{14} \text{ miles} = 155{,}200{,}000{,}000{,}000 \text{ miles}$

Because the power of 10 is a positive integer, the value of 1.552×10^{14} is a large number greater than 10. Move the decimal point 14 places to the *right*.

Answers

1. 1.75×10^8 **2.** 5×10^{-6}
3. 7×10^9 **4.** 2×10^{-6} oz

Skill Practice Write the numbers in standard form.

5. The probability of winning the California Super Lotto Jackpot is 5.5×10^{-8}.
6. The Sun's mass is 2×10^{30} kilograms.

3. Multiplying and Dividing Numbers in Scientific Notation

To multiply or divide two numbers in scientific notation, use the commutative and associative properties of multiplication to group the powers of 10. For example:

$$400 \times 2000 = (4 \times 10^2)(2 \times 10^3) = (4 \cdot 2) \times (10^2 \cdot 10^3) = 8 \times 10^5$$

$$\frac{0.00054}{150} = \frac{5.4 \times 10^{-4}}{1.5 \times 10^2} = \left(\frac{5.4}{1.5}\right) \times \left(\frac{10^{-4}}{10^2}\right) = 3.6 \times 10^{-6}$$

Example 4 **Multiplying and Dividing Numbers in Scientific Notation**

Multiply or divide as indicated.

a. $(8.7 \times 10^4)(2.5 \times 10^{-12})$ **b.** $\dfrac{4.25 \times 10^{13}}{8.5 \times 10^{-2}}$

Solution:

a. $(8.7 \times 10^4)(2.5 \times 10^{-12})$

$= (8.7 \cdot 2.5) \times (10^4 \cdot 10^{-12})$ Regroup factors using the commutative and associative properties of multiplication.

$= 21.75 \times 10^{-8}$ The number 21.75 is not in proper scientific notation because 21.75 is not between 1 and 10.

$= (2.175 \times 10^1) \times 10^{-8}$ Rewrite 21.75 as 2.175×10^1.

$= 2.175 \times (10^1 \times 10^{-8})$ Associative property of multiplication

$= 2.175 \times 10^{-7}$ Simplify.

b. $\dfrac{4.25 \times 10^{13}}{8.5 \times 10^{-2}}$

$= \left(\dfrac{4.25}{8.5}\right) \times \left(\dfrac{10^{13}}{10^{-2}}\right)$ Regroup factors using the commutative and associative properties.

$= 0.5 \times 10^{15}$ The number 0.5×10^{15} is not in proper scientific notation because 0.5 is not between 1 and 10.

$= (5.0 \times 10^{-1}) \times 10^{15}$ Rewrite 0.5 as 5.0×10^{-1}.

$= 5.0 \times (10^{-1} \times 10^{15})$ Associative property of multiplication

$= 5.0 \times 10^{14}$ Simplify.

Skill Practice Multiply or divide as indicated.

7. $(7 \times 10^5)(5 \times 10^3)$
8. $\dfrac{1 \times 10^{-2}}{4 \times 10^{-7}}$

Answers

5. 0.000 000 055
6. 2,000,000,000,000,000,000,000,000,000,000
7. 3.5×10^9
8. 2.5×10^4

Concept 2: Writing Numbers in Standard Form

35. Explain how you would write the number 3.1×10^{-9} in standard form.

36. Explain how you would write the number 3.1×10^{9} in standard form.

For Exercises 37–52, write each number in standard form. **(See Example 3.)**

37. 5×10^{-5}

38. 2×10^{-7}

39. 2.8×10^{3}

40. 9.1×10^{6}

41. 6.03×10^{-4}

42. 7.01×10^{-3}

43. 2.4×10^{6}

44. 3.1×10^{4}

45. 1.9×10^{-2}

46. 2.8×10^{-6}

47. 7.032×10^{3}

48. 8.205×10^{2}

49. One picogram (pg) is equal to 1×10^{-12} g.

50. A nanometer (nm) is approximately 3.94×10^{-8} in.

51. A normal diet contains between 1.6×10^{3} Cal and 2.8×10^{3} Cal per day.

52. The total land area of Texas is approximately 2.62×10^{5} square miles.

Concept 3: Multiplying and Dividing Numbers in Scientific Notation

For Exercises 53–72, multiply or divide as indicated. Write the answers in scientific notation. **(See Example 4.)**

53. $(2.5 \times 10^{6})(2 \times 10^{-2})$

54. $(2 \times 10^{-7})(3 \times 10^{13})$

55. $(1.2 \times 10^{4})(3 \times 10^{7})$

56. $(3.2 \times 10^{-3})(2.5 \times 10^{8})$

57. $\dfrac{7.7 \times 10^{6}}{3.5 \times 10^{2}}$

58. $\dfrac{9.5 \times 10^{11}}{1.9 \times 10^{3}}$

59. $\dfrac{9 \times 10^{-6}}{4 \times 10^{7}}$

60. $\dfrac{7 \times 10^{-2}}{5 \times 10^{9}}$

61. $80{,}000{,}000{,}000 \times 4000$

62. 0.0006×0.03

63. $(3.2 \times 10^{-4})(7.6 \times 10^{-7})$

64. $(5.9 \times 10^{12})(3.6 \times 10^{9})$

65. $\dfrac{210{,}000{,}000{,}000}{0.007}$

66. $\dfrac{160{,}000{,}000{,}000{,}000}{0.00008}$

67. $\dfrac{5.7 \times 10^{-2}}{9.5 \times 10^{-8}}$

68. $\dfrac{2.72 \times 10^{-6}}{6.8 \times 10^{-4}}$

69. $6{,}000{,}000{,}000 \times 0.0000000023$

70. $0.000055 \times 40{,}000$

71. $\dfrac{0.0000000003}{6000}$

72. $\dfrac{420{,}000}{0.0000021}$

Mixed Exercises

73. If a piece of paper is 3×10^{-3} in. thick, how thick is a stack of 1.25×10^{3} pieces of paper?

74. A box of staples contains 5×10^{3} staples and weighs 15 oz. How much does one staple weigh? Write your answer in scientific notation.

75. Bill Gates owned approximately 1,100,000,000 shares of Microsoft stock. If the stock price was \$27 per share, how much was Bill Gates' stock worth?

76. A state lottery had a jackpot of $\$5.2 \times 10^7$. This week the winner was a group of office employees that included 13 people. How much would each person receive?

77. Dinosaurs became extinct about 65 million years ago.

a. Write the number 65 million in scientific notation.

b. How many days is 65 million years?

c. How many hours is 65 million years?

d. How many seconds is 65 million years?

78. The Earth is 150,000,000 km from the Sun.

a. Write the number 150,000,000 in scientific notation.

b. There are 1000 m in a kilometer. How many meters is the Earth from the Sun?

c. There are 100 cm in a meter. How many centimeters is the Earth from the Sun?

Addition and Subtraction of Polynomials

Section 5.5

Concepts

1. Introduction to Polynomials
2. Addition of Polynomials
3. Subtraction of Polynomials
4. Polynomials and Applications to Geometry

1. Introduction to Polynomials

One commonly used algebraic expression is called a polynomial. A **polynomial** in one variable, x, is defined as a single term or a sum of terms of the form ax^n, where a is a real number and the exponent, n, is a nonnegative integer. For each term, a is called the **coefficient**, and n is called the **degree of the term.** For example:

Term (Expressed in the Form ax^n)	Coefficient	Degree
$-12z^7$	-12	7
$x^3 \rightarrow$ rewrite as $1x^3$	1	3
$10w \rightarrow$ rewrite as $10w^1$	10	1
$7 \rightarrow$ rewrite as $7x^0$	7	0

If a polynomial has exactly one term, it is categorized as a **monomial**. A two-term polynomial is called a **binomial**, and a three-term polynomial is called a **trinomial**. Usually the terms of a polynomial are written in descending order according to degree. The term with highest degree is called the **leading term**, and its coefficient is called the **leading coefficient**. The **degree of a polynomial** is the greatest degree of all of its terms. A polynomial in one variable is written in **descending order** if the term with highest degree is written first, followed by the term of next highest degree and so on. Thus, for a polynomial written in descending order, the leading term determines the degree of the polynomial.

	Expression	Descending Order	Leading Coefficient	Degree of Polynomial
Monomials	$-3x^4$	$-3x^4$	-3	4
	17	17	17	0
Binomials	$4y^3 - 6y^5$	$-6y^5 + 4y^3$	-6	5
	$\frac{1}{2} - \frac{1}{4}c$	$-\frac{1}{4}c + \frac{1}{2}$	$-\frac{1}{4}$	1
Trinomials	$4p - 3p^3 + 8p^6$	$8p^6 - 3p^3 + 4p$	8	6
	$7a^4 - 1.2a^8 + 3a^3$	$-1.2a^8 + 7a^4 + 3a^3$	-1.2	8

Example 1 Identifying the Parts of a Polynomial

Given the polynomial: $3a - 2a^4 + 6 - a^3$

a. List the terms of the polynomial, and state the coefficient and degree of each term.

b. Write the polynomial in descending order.

c. State the degree of the polynomial and the leading coefficient.

d. Evaluate the polynomial for $a = -2$.

Solution:

a.

term: $3a$	coefficient: 3	degree: 1
term: $-2a^4$	coefficient: -2	degree: 4
term: 6	coefficient: 6	degree: 0
term: $-a^3$	coefficient: -1	degree: 3

b. $-2a^4 - a^3 + 3a + 6$

c. The degree of the polynomial is 4 and the leading coefficient is -2.

d. $-2a^4 - a^3 + 3a + 6$

$= -2(-2)^4 - (-2)^3 + 3(-2) + 6$	Substitute -2 for the variable, a. Remember to use parentheses when replacing a variable.
$= -2(16) - (-8) + 3(-2) + 6$	Simplify exponents first.
$= -32 - (-8) + (-6) + 6$	Perform multiplication before addition and subtraction.
$= -24$	Simplify.

Skill Practice

1. Given the polynomial: $5x^3 - x + 8x^4 + 3x^2$

a. Write the polynomial in descending order.

b. State the degree of the polynomial.

c. State the coefficient of the leading term.

d. Evaluate the polynomial for $x = -1$.

Polynomials may have more than one variable. In such a case, the degree of a term is the sum of the exponents of the variables contained in the term. For example, the term, $32x^2y^5z$, has degree 8 because the exponents applied to x, y, and z are 2, 5, and 1, respectively. The following polynomial has a degree of 11 because the highest degree of its terms is 11.

$$\underbrace{32x^2y^5z}_{\text{degree } 8} - \underbrace{2x^3y}_{\text{degree } 4} + \underbrace{2x^2yz^8}_{\text{degree } 11} + \underbrace{7}_{\text{degree } 0}$$

Answers

1. **a.** $8x^4 + 5x^3 + 3x^2 - x$ **b.** 4 **c.** 8 **d.** 7

2. Addition of Polynomials

Recall that two terms are *like* terms if they each have the same variables, and the corresponding variables are raised to the same powers.

Like Terms: $3x^2, -7x^2$ (Same exponents; Same variables) $\quad -5yz^3, yz^3$ (Same exponents; Same variables)

Unlike Terms: $9z^2, 12z^6$ (Different exponents) $\quad \frac{1}{3}w^6, \frac{2}{5}p^6$ (Different variables) $\quad 4y, 7$ (Different variables)

Recall that the distributive property is used to add or subtract *like* terms. For example,

$$3x^2 + 9x^2 - 2x^2$$

$= (3 + 9 - 2)x^2$ Apply the distributive property.

$= (10)x^2$ Simplify.

$= 10x^2$

Avoiding Mistakes

Note that when adding terms, the exponents do *not* change.

$$2x^3 + 3x^3 \neq 5x^6$$

Example 2 **Adding Polynomials**

Add the polynomials. $3x^2y + 5x^2y$

Solution:

$$3x^2y + 5x^2y$$

$= (3 + 5)x^2y$ Apply the distributive property.

$= (8)x^2y$

$= 8x^2y$ Simplify.

Skill Practice Add the polynomials.

2. $13a^2b^3 + 2a^2b^3$

It is the distributive property that enables us to add *like* terms. We shorten the process by adding the coefficients of *like* terms.

Example 3 **Adding Polynomials**

Add the polynomials. $(-3c^3 + 5c^2 - 7c) + (11c^3 + 6c^2 + 3)$

Solution:

$$(-3c^3 + 5c^2 - 7c) + (11c^3 + 6c^2 + 3)$$

$= -3c^3 + 11c^3 + 5c^2 + 6c^2 - 7c$ Clear parentheses, and group *like* terms.

$= 8c^3 + 11c^2 - 7c + 3$ Combine *like* terms.

Avoiding Mistakes

When *adding* like terms, the exponents do not change.

Answer

2. $15a^2b^3$

TIP: Polynomials can also be added by combining *like* terms in columns. The sum of the polynomials from Example 3 is shown here.

$$\begin{array}{r} -3c^3 + 5c^2 - 7c + 0 \\ + \; 11c^3 + 6c^2 + 0c + 3 \\ \hline 8c^3 + 11c^2 - 7c + 3 \end{array}$$

Place holders such as 0 and 0*c* may be used to help line up *like* terms.

Skill Practice Add the polynomials.

3. $(7q^2 - 2q + 4) + (5q^2 + 6q - 9)$

Example 4 **Adding Polynomials**

Add the polynomials. $(4w^2 - 2x) + (3w^2 - 4x^2 + 6x)$

Solution:

$(4w^2 - 2x) + (3w^2 - 4x^2 + 6x)$

$= 4w^2 + 3w^2 - 4x^2 - 2x + 6x$ Clear parentheses and group *like* terms.

$= 7w^2 - 4x^2 + 4x$

Skill Practice Add the polynomials.

4. $(5x^2 - 4xy + y^2) + (-3x^2 - 5y^2)$

3. Subtraction of Polynomials

Subtraction of two polynomials requires us to find the opposite of the polynomial being subtracted. To find the opposite of a polynomial, take the opposite of each term. This is equivalent to multiplying the polynomial by -1.

Example 5 **Finding the Opposite of a Polynomial**

Find the opposite of the polynomials.

a. $5x$ **b.** $3a - 4b - c$ **c.** $5.5y^4 - 2.4y^3 + 1.1y$

Solution:

Expression	Opposite	Simplified Form
a. $5x$	$-(5x)$	$-5x$
b. $3a - 4b - c$	$-(3a - 4b - c)$	$-3a + 4b + c$
c. $5.5y^4 - 2.4y^3 + 1.1y$	$-(5.5y^4 - 2.4y^3 + 1.1y)$	$-5.5y^4 + 2.4y^3 - 1.1y$

TIP: Notice that the sign of each term is changed when finding the opposite of a polynomial.

Skill Practice Find the opposite of the polynomials.

5. $x - 3$ **6.** $3y^2 - 2xy + 6x + 2$ **7.** $-2.1w^3 + 4.9w^2 - 1.9w$

Subtraction of two polynomials is similar to subtracting real numbers. Add the opposite of the second polynomial to the first polynomial.

Answers

3. $12q^2 + 4q - 5$
4. $2x^2 - 4xy - 4y^2$
5. $-x + 3$
6. $-3y^2 + 2xy - 6x - 2$
7. $2.1w^3 - 4.9w^2 + 1.9w$

Subtraction of Polynomials

If A and B are polynomials, then $A - B = A + (-B)$.

Example 6 Subtracting Polynomials

Subtract the polynomials. $(-4p^4 + 5p^2 - 3) - (11p^2 + 4p - 6)$

Solution:

$(-4p^4 + 5p^2 - 3) - (11p^2 + 4p - 6)$

$= (-4p^4 + 5p^2 - 3) + (-11p^2 - 4p + 6)$ Add the opposite of the second polynomial.

$= -4p^4 + 5p^2 - 11p^2 - 4p - 3 + 6$ Group *like* terms.

$= -4p^4 - 6p^2 - 4p + 3$ Combine *like* terms.

TIP: Two polynomials can also be subtracted in columns by adding the opposite of the second polynomial to the first polynomial. Place holders (shown in red) may be used to help line up *like* terms.

$$\begin{array}{r} -4p^4 + 0p^3 + 5p^2 + 0p - 3 \\ -(0p^4 + 0p^3 + 11p^2 + 4p - 6) \end{array} \xrightarrow{\text{Add the opposite}} \begin{array}{r} -4p^4 + 0p^3 + 5p^2 + 0p - 3 \\ + \underline{-0p^4 - 0p^3 - 11p^2 - 4p + 6} \\ -4p^4 \qquad - 6p^2 - 4p + 3 \end{array}$$

The difference of the polynomials is $-4p^4 - 6p^2 - 4p + 3$.

Skill Practice Subtract the polynomials.

8. $(x^2 + 3x - 2) - (4x^2 + 6x + 1)$

Example 7 Subtracting Polynomials

Subtract the polynomials. $(a^2 - 2ab + 7b^2) - (-8a^2 - 6ab + 2b^2)$

Solution:

$(a^2 - 2ab + 7b^2) - (-8a^2 - 6ab + 2b^2)$

$= (a^2 - 2ab + 7b^2) + (8a^2 + 6ab - 2b^2)$ Add the opposite of the second polynomial.

$= a^2 + 8a^2 - 2ab + 6ab + 7b^2 - 2b^2$ Group *like* terms.

$= 9a^2 + 4ab + 5b^2$ Combine *like* terms.

Skill Practice Subtract the polynomials.

9. $(-3y^2 + xy + 2x^2) - (-2y^2 - 3xy - 8x^2)$

Answers

8. $-3x^2 - 3x - 3$

9. $-y^2 + 4xy + 10x^2$

Example 8 **Subtracting Polynomials**

Subtract $\frac{1}{3}t^4 + \frac{1}{2}t^2$ from $t^2 - 4$, and simplify the result.

Solution:

To subtract a from b, we write $b - a$. Thus, to subtract $\overbrace{\frac{1}{3}t^4 + \frac{1}{2}t^2}^{a}$ from $\overbrace{t^2 - 4}^{b}$, we have

Avoiding Mistakes

Example 8 involves subtracting two *expressions*. This is not an equation. Therefore, we cannot clear fractions.

$$\overbrace{(t^2 - 4)}^{b} \overbrace{-}^{-} \overbrace{\left(\frac{1}{3}t^4 + \frac{1}{2}t^2\right)}^{a}$$

$= t^2 - 4 - \frac{1}{3}t^4 - \frac{1}{2}t^2$ Apply the distributive property.

$= -\frac{1}{3}t^4 + t^2 - \frac{1}{2}t^2 - 4$ Group *like* terms in descending order.

$= -\frac{1}{3}t^4 + \frac{2}{2}t^2 - \frac{1}{2}t^2 - 4$ The t^2-terms are the only *like* terms. Get a common denominator for the t^2-terms.

$= -\frac{1}{3}t^4 + \frac{1}{2}t^2 - 4$ Add *like* terms.

Skill Practice

10. Subtract $\frac{3}{4}x^2 + \frac{2}{5}$ from $x^2 + 3x$.

4. Polynomials and Applications to Geometry

Example 9 **Subtracting Polynomials in Geometry**

If the perimeter of the triangle in Figure 5-1 can be represented by the polynomial $2x^2 + 5x + 6$, find a polynomial that represents the length of the missing side.

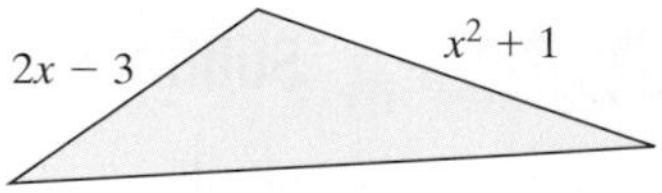

Figure 5-1

Solution:

The missing side of the triangle can be found by subtracting the sum of the two known sides from the perimeter.

$$\begin{pmatrix}\text{Length}\\ \text{of missing}\\ \text{side}\end{pmatrix} = (\text{perimeter}) - \left[\begin{matrix}\text{sum of the}\\ \text{two known sides}\end{matrix}\right]$$

$$\begin{pmatrix}\text{Length}\\ \text{of missing}\\ \text{side}\end{pmatrix} = (2x^2 + 5x + 6) - [(2x - 3) + (x^2 + 1)]$$

Answer

10. $\frac{1}{4}x^2 + 3x - \frac{2}{5}$

$= 2x^2 + 5x + 6 - [2x - 3 + x^2 + 1]$	Clear inner parentheses.
$= 2x^2 + 5x + 6 - (x^2 + 2x - 2)$	Combine *like* terms within [ ].
$= 2x^2 + 5x + 6 - x^2 - 2x + 2$	Apply the distributive property.
$= 2x^2 - x^2 + 5x - 2x + 6 + 2$	Group *like* terms.
$= x^2 + 3x + 8$	Combine *like* terms.

The polynomial $x^2 + 3x + 8$ represents the length of the missing side.

Skill Practice

11. If the perimeter of the triangle is represented by the polynomial $6x - 9$, find the polynomial that represents the missing side.

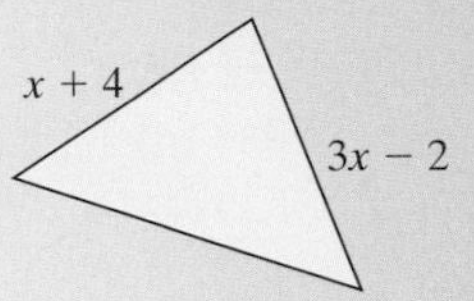

Answer

11. $2x - 11$

Section 5.5 Practice Exercises

Vocabulary and Key Concepts

1. a. A ___________ is a single term or a sum of terms.

b. For the term ax^n, a is called the ___________ and n is called the ___________ of the term.

c. Given the term x, the coefficient of the term is ______.

d. A monomial is a polynomial with exactly ___________ term(s).

e. A ___________ is a polynomial with exactly two terms.

f. A ___________ is a polynomial with exactly three terms.

g. The term with the highest degree is called the ___________ term and its coefficient is called the ___________ ___________.

h. The degree of a polynomial is the ___________ degree of all of its terms.

i. The degree of a nonzero constant such as 5 is ___________.

Review Exercises

For Exercises 2–7, simplify each expression.

2. $\dfrac{p^3 \cdot 4p}{p^2}$

3. $(3x)^2(5x^{-4})$

4. $(6y^{-3})(2y^9)$

5. $\dfrac{8t^{-6}}{4t^{-2}}$

6. $\dfrac{8^3 \cdot 8^{-4}}{8^{-2} \cdot 8^6}$

7. $\dfrac{3^4 \cdot 3^{-8}}{3^{12} \cdot 3^{-4}}$

8. Explain the difference between 3×10^7 and 3^7.

9. Explain the difference between 4×10^{-2} and 4^{-2}.

Concept 1: Introduction to Polynomials

For Exercises 10–12,

a. write the polynomial in descending order.

b. identify the leading coefficient.

c. identify the degree of the polynomial. **(See Example 1.)**

10. $10 - 8a - a^3 + 2a^2 + a^5$

11. $6 + 7x^2 - 7x^5 + 9x$

12. $\frac{1}{2}y + y^2 - 12y^4 + y^3 - 6$

For Exercises 13–22, categorize each expression as a monomial, a binomial, or a trinomial. Then evaluate the polynomial given $x = -3, y = 2$, and $z = -1$. **(See Example 1.)**

13. $10x^2 + 5x$

14. $7z + 13z^2 - 15$

15. $6x^2$

16. 9

17. $2y - y^4$

18. $7x + 2$

19. $2y^4 - 3y + 1$

20. 23

21. $-32xyz$

22. $y^4 - x^2$

Concept 2: Addition of Polynomials

23. Explain why the terms $3x$ and $3x^2$ are not *like* terms.

24. Explain why the terms $4w^3$ and $4z^3$ are not *like* terms.

For Exercises 25–42, add the polynomials. **(See Examples 2–4.)**

25. $23x^2y + 12x^2y$

26. $-5ab^3 + 17ab^3$

27. $3b^5d^2 + (5b^5d^2 - 9d)$

28. $4c^2d^3 + (3cd - 10c^2d^3)$

29. $(7y^2 + 2y - 9) + (-3y^2 - y)$

30. $(-3w^2 + 4w - 6) + (5w^2 + 2)$

31. $(5x + 3x^2 - x^3) + (2x^2 + 4x - 10)$

32. $(t^2 - 4t + t^4) + (3t^4 + 2t + 6)$

33. $(6.1y + 3.2x) + (4.8y - 3.2x)$

34. $(2.7m - 0.5h) + (-3.2m + 0.2h)$

35.
$$\begin{array}{r} 6a + 2b - 5c \\ + \underline{-2a - 2b - 3c} \end{array}$$

36.
$$\begin{array}{r} -13x + 5y + 10z \\ + \underline{-3x - 3y + 2z} \end{array}$$

37. $\left(\frac{2}{5}a + \frac{1}{4}b - \frac{5}{6}\right) + \left(\frac{3}{5}a - \frac{3}{4}b - \frac{7}{6}\right)$

38. $\left(\frac{5}{9}x + \frac{1}{10}y\right) + \left(-\frac{4}{9}x + \frac{3}{10}y\right)$

39. $\left(z - \frac{8}{3}\right) + \left(\frac{4}{3}z^2 - z + 1\right)$

40. $\left(-\frac{7}{5}r + 1\right) + \left(-\frac{3}{5}r^2 + \frac{7}{5}r + 1\right)$

41.
$$\begin{array}{rrrr} & 7.9t^3 & & + 2.6t - 1.1 \\ + & \underline{} & \underline{-3.4t^2} & \underline{+ 3.4t - 3.1} \end{array}$$

42.
$$\begin{array}{rrr} & 0.34y^2 & + 1.23 \\ + & \underline{ 3.42y} & \underline{- 7.56} \end{array}$$

Concept 3: Subtraction of Polynomials

For Exercises 43–48, find the opposite of each polynomial. **(See Example 5.)**

43. $4h - 5$

44. $5k - 12$

45. $-2.3m^2 + 3.1m - 1.5$

46. $-11.8n^2 - 6.7n + 9.3$

47. $3v^3 + 5v^2 + 10v + 22$

48. $7u^4 + 3v^2 + 17$

For Exercises 49–68, subtract the polynomials. **(See Examples 6–7.)**

49. $4a^3b^2 - 12a^3b^2$

50. $5yz^4 - 14yz^4$

51. $-32x^3 - 21x^3$

52. $-23c^5 - 12c^5$

53. $(7a - 7) - (12a - 4)$

54. $(4x + 3v) - (-3x + v)$

55.
$$\begin{array}{r} 4k + 3 \\ -\ \underline{(-12k - 6)} \end{array}$$

56.
$$\begin{array}{r} 3h - 15 \\ -\ \underline{(8h + 13)} \end{array}$$

57. $25m^4 - (23m^4 + 14m)$

58. $3x^2 - (-x^2 - 12)$

59. $(5s^2 - 3st - 2t^2) - (2s^2 + st + t^2)$

60. $(6k^2 + 2kp + p^2) - (3k^2 - 6kp + 2p^2)$

61.
$$\begin{array}{r} 10r - 6s + 2t \\ -\ \underline{(12r - 3s - t)} \end{array}$$

62.
$$\begin{array}{r} a - 14b + 7c \\ -\ \underline{(-3a - 8b + 2c)} \end{array}$$

63. $\left(\frac{7}{8}x + \frac{2}{3}y - \frac{3}{10}\right) - \left(\frac{1}{8}x + \frac{1}{3}y\right)$

64. $\left(r - \frac{1}{12}s\right) - \left(\frac{1}{2}r - \frac{5}{12}s - \frac{4}{11}\right)$

65. $\left(\frac{2}{3}h^2 - \frac{1}{5}h - \frac{3}{4}\right) - \left(\frac{4}{3}h^2 - \frac{4}{5}h + \frac{7}{4}\right)$

66. $\left(\frac{3}{8}p^3 - \frac{5}{7}p^2 - \frac{2}{5}\right) - \left(\frac{5}{8}p^3 - \frac{2}{7}p^2 + \frac{7}{5}\right)$

67.
$$\begin{array}{r} 4.5x^4 - 3.1x^2 \qquad\quad - 6.7 \\ -\ \underline{(2.1x^4 \qquad\qquad + 4.4x + 1.2)} \end{array}$$

68.
$$\begin{array}{r} 1.3c^2 \qquad\quad + 4.8 \\ -\ \underline{(4.3c^2 - 2c - 2.2)} \end{array}$$

69. Find the difference of $(4b^3 + 6b - 7)$ and $(-12b^2 + 11b + 5)$.

70. Find the difference of $(-5y^2 + 3y - 21)$ and $(-4y^2 - 5y + 23)$.

71. Subtract $\left(\frac{3}{2}x^2 - 5x\right)$ from $(-2x^2 - 11)$. **(See Example 8.)**

72. Subtract $\left(a^5 - \frac{1}{3}a^3 + 5a\right)$ from $\left(\frac{3}{4}a^5 + \frac{1}{2}a^4 + 6a\right)$.

Concept 4: Polynomials and Applications to Geometry

73. Find a polynomial that represents the perimeter of the figure.

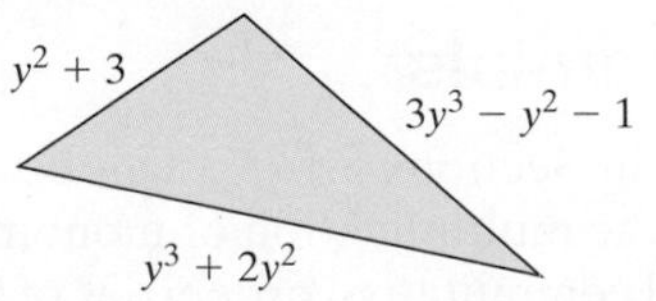

74. Find a polynomial that represents the perimeter of the figure.

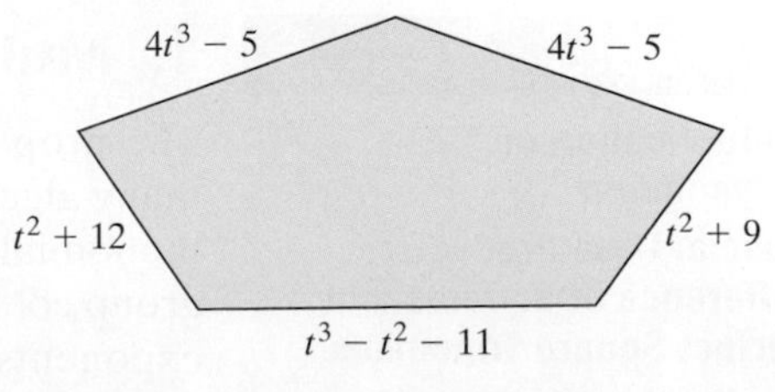

75. If the perimeter of the figure can be represented by the polynomial $5a^2 - 2a + 1$, find a polynomial that represents the length of the missing side. **(See Example 9.)**

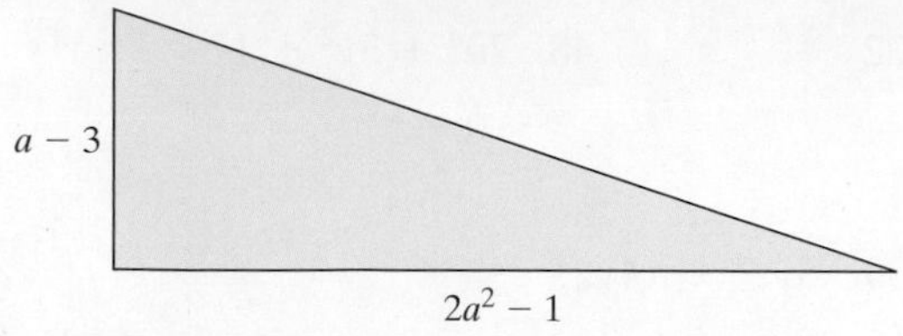

76. If the perimeter of the figure can be represented by the polynomial $6w^3 - 2w - 3$, find a polynomial that represents the length of the missing side.

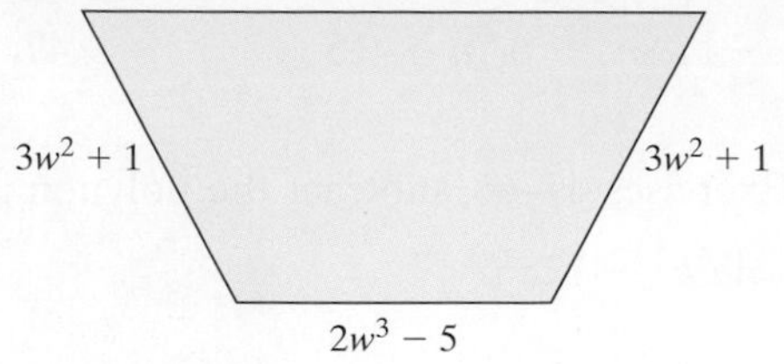

Mixed Exercises

For Exercises 77–92, perform the indicated operation.

77. $(2ab^2 + 9a^2b) + (7ab^2 - 3ab + 7a^2b)$

78. $(8x^2y - 3xy - 6xy^2) + (3x^2y - 12xy)$

79.
$$\begin{array}{r} 4z^5 \qquad + z^3 - 3z + 13 \\ -(\quad - z^4 - 8z^3 \qquad + 15) \\ \hline \end{array}$$

80.
$$\begin{array}{r} -15t^4 \qquad - 23t^2 + 16t \\ -(\qquad 21t^3 + 18t^2 + \quad t) \\ \hline \end{array}$$

81. $(9x^4 + 2x^3 - x + 5) + (9x^3 - 3x^2 + 8x + 3) - (7x^4 - x + 12)$

82. $(-6y^3 - 9y^2 + 23) - (7y^2 + 2y - 11) + (3y^3 - 25)$

83. $(0.2w^2 + 3w + 1.3) - (w^3 - 0.7w + 2)$

84. $(8.1u^3 - 5.2u^2 + 4) + (2.8u^3 + 6.3u - 7)$

85. $(7p^2q - 3pq^2) - (8p^2q + pq) + (4pq - pq^2)$

86. $(12c^2d - 2cd + 8cd^2) - (-c^2d + 4cd) - (5cd - 2cd^2)$

87. $(5x - 2x^3) + (2x^3 - 5x)$

88. $(p^2 - 4p + 2) - (2 + p^2 - 4p)$

89.
$$\begin{array}{r} 2a^2b - 4ab + \ ab^2 \\ -(2a^2b + \ ab - 5ab^2) \\ \hline \end{array}$$

90.
$$\begin{array}{r} -3xy + \ 7xy^2 + 5x^2y \\ +(-8xy - 11xy^2 + 3x^2y) \\ \hline \end{array}$$

91. $[(3y^2 - 5y) - (2y^2 + y - 1)] + (10y^2 - 4y - 5)$

92. $(12c^3 - 5c^2 - 2c) + [(7c^3 - 2c^2 + c) - (4c^3 + 4c)]$

Expanding Your Skills

93. Write a binomial of degree 3. (Answers may vary.)

94. Write a trinomial of degree 6. (Answers may vary.)

95. Write a monomial of degree 5. (Answers may vary.)

96. Write a monomial of degree 1. (Answers may vary.)

97. Write a trinomial with the leading coefficient -6. (Answers may vary.)

98. Write a binomial with the leading coefficient 13. (Answers may vary.)

Section 5.6 Multiplication of Polynomials and Special Products

Concepts

1. **Multiplication of Polynomials**
2. **Special Case Products: Difference of Squares and Perfect Square Trinomials**
3. **Applications to Geometry**

1. Multiplication of Polynomials

The properties of exponents covered in Sections 5.1–5.3 can be used to simplify many algebraic expressions including the multiplication of monomials. To multiply monomials, first use the associative and commutative properties of multiplication to group coefficients and like bases. Then simplify the result by using the properties of exponents.

Example 1 Multiplying Monomials

Multiply the monomials.

a. $(3x^4)(4x^2)$ **b.** $(-4c^5d)(2c^2d^3e)$ **c.** $\left(\frac{1}{3}a^4b^3\right)\left(\frac{3}{4}b^7\right)$

Solution:

a. $(3x^4)(4x^2)$

$= (3 \cdot 4)(x^4x^2)$ Group coefficients and like bases.

$= 12x^6$ Multiply the coefficients and add the exponents on x.

b. $(-4c^5d)(2c^2d^3e)$

$= (-4 \cdot 2)(c^5c^2)(dd^3)(e)$ Group coefficients and like bases.

$= -8c^7d^4e$ Simplify.

c. $\left(\frac{1}{3}a^4b^3\right)\left(\frac{3}{4}b^7\right)$

$= \left(\frac{1}{3} \cdot \frac{3}{4}\right)(a^4)(b^3b^7)$ Group coefficients and like bases.

$= \frac{1}{4}a^4b^{10}$ Simplify.

Skill Practice Multiply the monomials.

1. $(-5y)(6y^3)$ **2.** $(7x^2y)(-2x^3y^4)$ **3.** $\left(\frac{2}{5}w^5z^3\right)\left(\frac{15}{4}w^4\right)$

The distributive property is used to multiply polynomials: $a(b + c) = ab + ac$.

Example 2 Multiplying a Polynomial by a Monomial

Multiply the polynomials.

a. $2t(4t - 3)$ **b.** $-3a^2\left(-4a^2 + 2a - \frac{1}{3}\right)$

Solution:

a. $2t(4t - 3)$

$= (2t)(4t) + (2t)(-3)$ Apply the distributive property by multiplying each term by $2t$.

$= 8t^2 - 6t$ Simplify each term.

b. $-3a^2\left(-4a^2 + 2a - \frac{1}{3}\right)$

$= (-3a^2)(-4a^2) + (-3a^2)(2a) + (-3a^2)\left(-\frac{1}{3}\right)$ Apply the distributive property by multiplying each term by $-3a^2$.

$= 12a^4 - 6a^3 + a^2$ Simplify each term.

Answers

1. $-30y^4$
2. $-14x^5y^5$
3. $\frac{3}{2}w^9z^3$

Skill Practice Multiply the polynomials.

4. $-4a(5a - 3)$ **5.** $-4p\left(2p^2 - 6p + \frac{1}{4}\right)$

Thus far, we have illustrated polynomial multiplication involving monomials. Next, the distributive property will be used to multiply polynomials with more than one term.

$$(x + 3)(x + 5) = x(x + 5) + 3(x + 5)$$ Apply the distributive property.

$$= x(x + 5) + 3(x + 5)$$ Apply the distributive property again.

$$= (x)(x) + (x)(5) + (3)(x) + (3)(5)$$

$$= x^2 + 5x + 3x + 15$$

$$= x^2 + 8x + 15$$ Combine *like* terms.

Note: Using the distributive property results in multiplying each term of the first polynomial by each term of the second polynomial.

$$(x + 3)(x + 5) = (x)(x) + (x)(5) + (3)(x) + (3)(5)$$

$$= x^2 + 5x + 3x + 15$$

$$= x^2 + 8x + 15$$

Example 3 Multiplying a Polynomial by a Polynomial

Multiply the polynomials. $(c - 7)(c + 2)$

Solution:

$(c - 7)(c + 2)$ Multiply each term in the first polynomial by each term in the second. That is, apply the distributive property.

$$= (c)(c) + (c)(2) + (-7)(c) + (-7)(2)$$

$$= c^2 + 2c - 7c - 14$$ Simplify.

$$= c^2 - 5c - 14$$ Combine *like* terms.

TIP: Notice that the product of two *binomials* equals the sum of the products of the **F**irst terms, the **O**uter terms, the **I**nner terms, and the **L**ast terms. The acronym **FOIL** (First Outer Inner Last) can be used as a memory device to multiply two binomials.

Outer terms, First terms, Inner terms, Last terms

First, Outer, Inner, Last

$$(c - 7)(c + 2) = (c)(c) + (c)(2) + (-7)(c) + (-7)(2)$$

$$= c^2 + 2c - 7c - 14$$

$$= c^2 - 5c - 14$$

Skill Practice Multiply the polynomials.

6. $(x + 2)(x + 8)$

Answers

4. $-20a^2 + 12a$

5. $-8p^3 + 24p^2 - p$

6. $x^2 + 10x + 16$

Example 4 Multiplying a Polynomial by a Polynomial

Multiply the polynomials. $(y - 2)(3y^2 + y - 5)$

Solution:

$(y - 2)(3y^2 + y - 5)$ Multiply each term in the first polynomial by each term in the second.

$= (y)(3y^2) + (y)(y) + (y)(-5) + (-2)(3y^2) + (-2)(y) + (-2)(-5)$

$= 3y^3 + y^2 - 5y - 6y^2 - 2y + 10$ Simplify each term.

$= 3y^3 - 5y^2 - 7y + 10$ Combine *like* terms.

TIP: Multiplication of polynomials can be performed vertically by a process similar to column multiplication of real numbers. For example,

$$\begin{array}{r} 235 \\ \times\ 21 \\ \hline 235 \\ 4700 \\ \hline 4935 \end{array} \qquad \begin{array}{rrrr} 3y^2 & + & y - & 5 \\ \times & & y - & 2 \\ \hline & -6y^2 & - 2y + & 10 \\ 3y^3 + & y^2 & - 5y + & 0 \\ \hline 3y^3 - & 5y^2 & - 7y + & 10 \end{array}$$

Note: When multiplying by the column method, it is important to *align like* terms vertically before adding terms.

Avoiding Mistakes

It is important to note that the acronym FOIL does not apply to Example 4 because the product does not involve two binomials.

Skill Practice Multiply the polynomials.

7. $(2y + 4)(3y^2 - 5y + 2)$

Example 5 Multiplying Polynomials

Multiply the polynomials. $2(10x + 3y)(2x - 4y)$

Solution:

$2(10x + 3y)(2x - 4y)$ In this case we are multiplying three polynomials—a monomial times two binomials. The associative property of multiplication allows us to choose which two polynomials to multiply first.

$= 2[(10x + 3y)(2x - 4y)]$ First we will multiply the binomials. Multiply each term in the first binomial by each term in the second binomial. That is, apply the distributive property.

$= 2[(10x)(2x) + (10x)(-4y) + (3y)(2x) + (3y)(-4y)]$

$= 2[20x^2 - 40xy + 6xy - 12y^2]$ Simplify each term.

$= 2(20x^2 - 34xy - 12y^2)$ Combine *like* terms.

$= 40x^2 - 68xy - 24y^2$ Multiply by 2 using the distributive property.

TIP: When multiplying three polynomials, first multiply two of the polynomials. Then multiply the result by the third polynomial.

Skill Practice Multiply.

8. $3(4a - 3c)(5a - 2c)$

Answers

7. $6y^3 + 2y^2 - 16y + 8$
8. $60a^2 - 69ac + 18c^2$

2. Special Case Products: Difference of Squares and Perfect Square Trinomials

In some cases the product of two binomials takes on a special pattern.

I. The first special case occurs when multiplying the sum and difference of the same two terms. For example:

$(2x + 3)(2x - 3)$

$= 4x^2 - 6x + 6x - 9$

$= 4x^2 - 9$

Notice that the middle terms are opposites. This leaves only the difference between the square of the first term and the square of the second term. For this reason, the product is called a *difference of squares*.

Note: The binomials $2x + 3$ and $2x - 3$ are called **conjugates**. In one expression, $2x$ and 3 are added, and in the other, $2x$ and 3 are subtracted.

II. The second special case involves the square of a binomial. For example:

$(3x + 7)^2$

$= (3x + 7)(3x + 7)$

$= 9x^2 + 21x + 21x + 49$

$= 9x^2 + 42x + 49$

$= (3x)^2 + 2(3x)(7) + (7)^2$

When squaring a binomial, the product will be a trinomial called a *perfect square trinomial.* The first and third terms are formed by squaring each term of the binomial. The middle term equals twice the product of the terms in the binomial.

Note: The expression $(3x - 7)^2$ also expands to a perfect square trinomial, but the middle term will be negative:

$$(3x - 7)(3x - 7) = 9x^2 - 21x - 21x + 49 = 9x^2 - 42x + 49$$

Special Case Product Formulas

1. $(a + b)(a - b) = a^2 - b^2$ The product is called a **difference of squares**.
2. $\left.\begin{array}{l}(a + b)^2 = a^2 + 2ab + b^2 \\ (a - b)^2 = a^2 - 2ab + b^2\end{array}\right\}$ The product is called a **perfect square trinomial**.

You should become familiar with these special case products because they will be used again in the next chapter to factor polynomials.

Example 6 Multiplying Conjugates

Multiply the conjugates.

a. $(x - 9)(x + 9)$ **b.** $\left(\frac{1}{2}p + 6\right)\left(\frac{1}{2}p - 6\right)$

Solution:

a. $(x - 9)(x + 9)$ Apply the formula: $(a + b)(a - b) = a^2 - b^2$.

$a^2 - b^2$

$= (x)^2 - (9)^2$ Substitute $a = x$ and $b = 9$.

$= x^2 - 81$

TIP: The product of two conjugates can be checked by applying the distributive property:

$(x - 9)(x + 9)$

$= x^2 + 9x - 9x - 81$

$= x^2 - 81$

b. $\left(\frac{1}{2}p + 6\right)\left(\frac{1}{2}p - 6\right)$ Apply the formula: $(a + b)(a - b) = a^2 - b^2$.

$a^2 - b^2$

$= \left(\frac{1}{2}p\right)^2 - (6)^2$ Substitute $a = \frac{1}{2}p$ and $b = 6$.

$= \frac{1}{4}p^2 - 36$ Simplify each term.

Skill Practice Multiply the conjugates.

9. $(a + 7)(a - 7)$ **10.** $\left(\frac{4}{5}x - 10\right)\left(\frac{4}{5}x + 10\right)$

Example 7 Squaring Binomials

Square the binomials.

a. $(3w - 4)^2$ **b.** $(5x^2 + 2)^2$

Solution:

a. $(3w - 4)^2$ Apply the formula: $(a - b)^2 = a^2 - 2ab + b^2$.

$a^2 - 2ab + b^2$

$= (3w)^2 - 2(3w)(4) + (4)^2$ Substitute $a = 3w$, $b = 4$.

$= 9w^2 - 24w + 16$ Simplify each term.

TIP: The square of a binomial can be checked by explicitly writing the product of the two binomials and applying the distributive property:

$$(3w - 4)^2 = (3w - 4)(3w - 4) = 9w^2 - 12w - 12w + 16$$
$$= 9w^2 - 24w + 16$$

b. $(5x^2 + 2)^2$ Apply the formula: $(a + b)^2 = a^2 + 2ab + b^2$.

$a^2 + 2ab + b^2$

$= (5x^2)^2 + 2(5x^2)(2) + (2)^2$ Substitute $a = 5x^2$, $b = 2$.

$= 25x^4 + 20x^2 + 4$ Simplify each term.

Avoiding Mistakes

The property for squaring two factors is different than the property for squaring two terms:
$(ab)^2 = a^2b^2$ but
$(a + b)^2 = a^2 + 2ab + b^2$

Skill Practice Square the binomials.

11. $(2x + 3)^2$ **12.** $(5c^2 - 6)^2$

Answers

9. $a^2 - 49$
10. $\frac{16}{25}x^2 - 100$
11. $4x^2 + 12x + 9$
12. $25c^4 - 60c^2 + 36$

3. Applications to Geometry

Example 8 Using Special Case Products in an Application of Geometry

Find a polynomial that represents the volume of the cube (Figure 5-2).

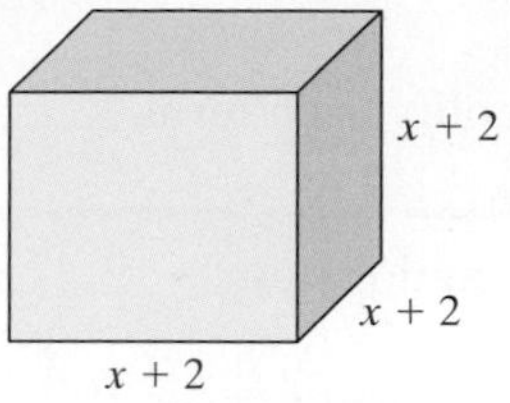

Figure 5-2

Solution:

Volume = (length)(width)(height)

$$V = (x + 2)(x + 2)(x + 2) \quad \text{or} \quad V = (x + 2)^3$$

To expand $(x + 2)(x + 2)(x + 2)$, multiply the first two factors. Then multiply the result by the last factor.

$$V = \underbrace{(x + 2)(x + 2)}(x + 2)$$
$$= (x^2 + 4x + 4)(x + 2)$$

TIP: $(x + 2)(x + 2) = (x + 2)^2$ and results in a perfect square trinomial.

$$(x + 2)^2 = (x)^2 + 2(x)(2) + (2)^2$$
$$= x^2 + 4x + 4$$

$$= (x^2)(x) + (x^2)(2) + (4x)(x) + (4x)(2) + (4)(x) + (4)(2)$$ Apply the distributive property.

$$= x^3 + 2x^2 + 4x^2 + 8x + 4x + 8$$ Group *like* terms.

$$= x^3 + 6x^2 + 12x + 8$$ Combine *like* terms.

The volume of the cube can be represented by

$$V = (x + 2)^3 = x^3 + 6x^2 + 12x + 8.$$

Skill Practice

13. Find the polynomial that represents the volume of the cube.

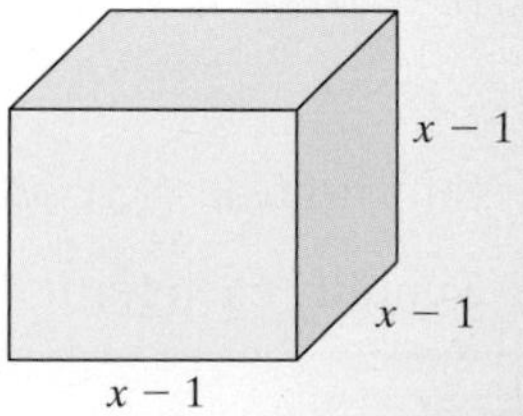

Answer

13. The volume of the cube can be represented by $x^3 - 3x^2 + 3x - 1$.

Section 5.6 Practice Exercises

Vocabulary and Key Concepts

1. **a.** The conjugate of $5 + 2x$ is ___________.

   b. When two conjugates are multiplied the resulting binomial is a difference of ___________. This is given by the formula $(a + b)(a - b) =$ ___________.

   c. When a binomial is squared, the resulting trinomial is a ___________ square trinomial. This is given by the formula $(a + b)^2 =$ ___________.

Review Exercises

For Exercises 2–9, simplify each expression (if possible).

2. $4x + 5x$ **3.** $2y^2 - 4y^2$ **4.** $(4x)(5x)$ **5.** $(2y^2)(-4y^2)$

6. $-5a^3b - 2a^3b$ **7.** $7uvw^2 + uvw^2$ **8.** $(-5a^3b)(-2a^3b)$ **9.** $(7uvw^2)(uvw^2)$

Concept 1: Multiplication of Polynomials

For Exercises 10–18, multiply the expressions. **(See Example 1.)**

10. $8(4x)$ **11.** $-2(6y)$ **12.** $-10(5z)$

13. $7(3p)$ **14.** $(x^{10})(4x^3)$ **15.** $(a^{13}b^4)(12ab^4)$

16. $(4m^3n^7)(-3m^6n)$ **17.** $(2c^7d)(-c^3d^{11})$ **18.** $(-5u^2v)(-8u^3v^2)$

For Exercises 19–54, multiply the polynomials. **(See Examples 2–5.)**

19. $8pq(2pq - 3p + 5q)$ **20.** $5ab(2ab + 6a - 3b)$ **21.** $(k^2 - 13k - 6)(-4k)$

22. $(h^2 + 5h - 12)(-2h)$ **23.** $-15pq(3p^2 + p^3q^2 - 2q)$ **24.** $-4u^2v(2u - 5uv^3 + v)$

25. $(y + 10)(y + 9)$ **26.** $(x + 5)(x + 6)$ **27.** $(m - 12)(m - 2)$

28. $(n - 7)(n - 2)$ **29.** $(3p - 2)(4p + 1)$ **30.** $(7q + 11)(q - 5)$

31. $(8 - 4w)(-3w + 2)$ **32.** $(-6z + 10)(4 - 2z)$ **33.** $(p - 3w)(p - 11w)$

34. $(y - 7x)(y - 10x)$ **35.** $(6x - 1)(2x + 5)$ **36.** $(3x + 7)(x - 8)$

37. $(4a - 9)(1.5a - 2)$ **38.** $(2.1y - 0.5)(y + 3)$ **39.** $(3t - 7)(1 + 3t^2)$

40. $(2 - 5w)(2w^2 - 5)$ **41.** $3(3m + 4n)(m + 2n)$ **42.** $2(7y + z)(3y + 5z)$

43. $(5s + 3)(s^2 + s - 2)$ **44.** $(t - 4)(2t^2 - t + 6)$ **45.** $(3w - 2)(9w^2 + 6w + 4)$

46. $(z + 5)(z^2 - 5z + 25)$ **47.** $(p^2 + p - 5)(p^2 + 4p - 1)$ **48.** $(-x^2 - 2x + 4)(x^2 + 2x - 6)$

49.
$$\begin{array}{r} 3a^2 - 4a + 9 \\ \times \quad 2a - 5 \\ \hline \end{array}$$

50.
$$\begin{array}{r} 7x^2 - 3x - 4 \\ \times \quad 5x + 1 \\ \hline \end{array}$$

51.
$$\begin{array}{r} 4x^2 - 12xy + 9y^2 \\ \times \quad 2x - 3y \\ \hline \end{array}$$

52.
$$\begin{array}{r} 25a^2 + 10ab + b^2 \\ \times \quad 5a + b \\ \hline \end{array}$$

53.
$$\begin{array}{r} 6x + 2y \\ \times\ 0.2x + 1.2y \\ \hline \end{array}$$

54.
$$\begin{array}{r} 4.5a + 2b \\ \times \quad 2a - 1.8b \\ \hline \end{array}$$

Expanding Your Skills

For Exercises 119–122, multiply the expressions containing more than two factors.

119. $2a(3a - 4)(a + 5)$

120. $5x(x + 2)(6x - 1)$

121. $(x - 3)(2x + 1)(x - 4)$

122. $(y - 2)(2y - 3)(y + 3)$

123. What binomial when multiplied by $(3x + 5)$ will produce a product of $6x^2 - 11x - 35$? [*Hint:* Let the quantity $(a + b)$ represent the unknown binomial. Then find a and b such that $(3x + 5)(a + b) = 6x^2 - 11x - 35$.]

124. What binomial when multiplied by $(2x - 4)$ will produce a product of $2x^2 + 8x - 24$?

For Exercises 125–127, determine what values of k would create a perfect square trinomial.

125. $x^2 + kx + 25$

126. $w^2 + kw + 9$

127. $a^2 + ka + 16$

Section 5.7 Division of Polynomials

Concepts

1. **Division by a Monomial**
2. **Long Division**
3. **Synthetic Division**

Division of polynomials will be presented in this section as two separate cases: The first case illustrates division by a monomial divisor. The second case illustrates long division by a polynomial with two or more terms.

1. Division by a Monomial

To divide a polynomial by a monomial, divide each individual term in the polynomial by the divisor and simplify the result.

Dividing a Polynomial by a Monomial

If a, b, and c are polynomials such that $c \neq 0$, then

$$\frac{a+b}{c} = \frac{a}{c} + \frac{b}{c} \qquad \text{Similarly,} \qquad \frac{a-b}{c} = \frac{a}{c} - \frac{b}{c}$$

Example 1 Dividing a Polynomial by a Monomial

Divide the polynomials.

a. $\dfrac{5a^3 - 10a^2 + 20}{5a}$

b. $(12y^2z^3 - 15yz^2 + 6y^2z) \div (-6y^2z)$

Solution:

a. $\dfrac{5a^3 - 10a^2 + 20}{5a}$

$= \dfrac{5a^3}{5a} - \dfrac{10a^2}{5a} + \dfrac{20}{5a}$ Divide each term in the numerator by $5a$.

$= a^2 - 2a + \dfrac{4}{a}$ Simplify each term using the properties of exponents.

b. $(12y^2z^3 - 15yz^2 + 6y^2z) \div (-6y^2z)$

$$= \frac{12y^2z^3 - 15yz^2 + 6y^2z}{-6y^2z}$$

$$= \frac{12y^2z^3}{-6y^2z} - \frac{15yz^2}{-6y^2z} + \frac{6y^2z}{-6y^2z}$$ Divide each term by $-6y^2z$.

$$= -2z^2 + \frac{5z}{2y} - 1$$ Simplify each term.

Skill Practice Divide the polynomials.

1. $(36a^4 - 48a^3 + 12a^2) \div (6a^3)$ **2.** $\dfrac{-15x^3y^4 + 25x^2y^3 - 5xy^2}{-5xy^2}$

2. Long Division

If the divisor has two or more terms, a *long division* process similar to the division of real numbers is used. Take a minute to review the long division process for real numbers by dividing 2273 by 5.

```
  454  ←— Quotient
5)2273
 -20↓
   27
  -25↓
    23
   -20
     3 ←— Remainder
```

Therefore, $2273 \div 5 = 454\frac{3}{5}$

A similar procedure is used for long division of polynomials as shown in Example 2.

Example 2 Using Long Division to Divide Polynomials

Divide the polynomials using long division: $(2x^2 - x + 3) \div (x - 3)$

Solution:

$x - 3\overline{)2x^2 - x + 3}$ Divide the leading term in the dividend by the leading term in the divisor.

$$\frac{2x^2}{x} = 2x$$

This is the first term in the quotient.

$$\begin{array}{r} 2x \qquad\qquad \\ x - 3\overline{)2x^2 - x + 3} \\ -(2x^2 - 6x) \qquad \end{array}$$

Multiply $2x$ by the divisor: $2x(x - 3) = 2x^2 - 6x$ and subtract the result.

TIP: Recall that taking the opposite of a polynomial changes the sign of each term of the polynomial.

Answers

1. $6a - 8 + \dfrac{2}{a}$

2. $3x^2y^2 - 5xy + 1$

In Example 3, the remainder is zero. Therefore, we say that $3w - 1$ divides evenly into $3w^3 + 26w^2 - 3$. For this reason, the divisor and quotient are factors of $3w^3 + 26w^2 - 3$. To check, we have

$$\text{Dividend} = (\text{divisor})(\text{quotient}) + \text{remainder}$$

$$\begin{aligned} 3w^3 + 26w^2 - 3 &\stackrel{?}{=} (3w - 1)(w^2 + 9w + 3) + 0 \\ &\stackrel{?}{=} 3w^3 + 27w^2 + 9w - w^2 - 9w - 3 \\ &= 3w^3 + 26w^2 - 3 \checkmark \end{aligned}$$

Example 4 Using Long Division to Divide Polynomials

Divide the polynomials using long division.

$$\frac{2y + y^4 - 5}{1 + y^2}$$

Solution:

First note that both the dividend and divisor should be written in descending order:

$$\frac{y^4 + 2y - 5}{y^2 + 1}$$

Also note that the dividend and the divisor have missing powers of y. Leave place holders.

$$y^2 + 0y + 1\overline{)y^4 + 0y^3 + 0y^2 + 2y - 5}$$

$$\begin{array}{r} y^2 \\ y^2 + 0y + 1\overline{)y^4 + 0y^3 + 0y^2 + 2y - 5} \\ -(y^4 + 0y^3 + y^2) \end{array}$$

Divide $y^4 \div y^2 = y^2$. This is the first term of the quotient.

Multiply $y^2(y^2 + 0y + 1) = y^4 + 0y^3 + y^2$.

$$\begin{array}{r} y^2 \\ y^2 + 0y + 1\overline{)y^4 + 0y^3 + 0y^2 + 2y - 5} \\ \underline{-y^4 - 0y^3 - y^2} \\ -y^2 + 2y - 5 \end{array}$$

Subtract by adding the opposite.

Bring down the next columns.

$$\begin{array}{r} y^2 -1 \\ y^2 + 0y + 1\overline{)y^4 + 0y^3 + 0y^2 + 2y - 5} \\ \underline{-y^4 - 0y^3 - y^2} \\ -y^2 + 2y - 5 \\ -(\underline{-y^2 - 0y - 1}) \end{array}$$

Divide $-y^2 \div y^2 = -1$.

Multiply $-1(y^2 + 0y + 1) = -y^2 - 0y - 1$.

$$\begin{array}{r} y^2 -1 \\ y^2 + 0y + 1\overline{)y^4 + 0y^3 + 0y^2 + 2y - 5} \\ \underline{-y^4 - 0y^3 - y^2} \\ -y^2 + 2y - 5 \\ \underline{y^2 + 0y + 1} \\ 2y - 4 \end{array}$$

Subtract by adding the opposite.

Remainder

Therefore, $\dfrac{y^4 + 2y - 5}{y^2 + 1} = y^2 - 1 + \dfrac{2y - 4}{y^2 + 1}$

Skill Practice Divide the polynomials using long division.

5. $(4 - x^2 + x^3) \div (2 + x^2)$

Answer

5. $x - 1 + \dfrac{-2x + 6}{x^2 + 2}$

Example 5 **Determining Whether Long Division Is Necessary**

Determine whether long division is necessary for each division of polynomials.

a. $\dfrac{2p^5 - 8p^4 + 4p - 16}{p^2 - 2p + 1}$ **b.** $\dfrac{2p^5 - 8p^4 + 4p - 16}{2p^2}$

c. $(3z^3 - 5z^2 + 10) \div (15z^3)$ **d.** $(3z^3 - 5z^2 + 10) \div (3z + 1)$

Solution:

a. $\dfrac{2p^5 - 8p^4 + 4p - 16}{p^2 - 2p + 1}$ The divisor has three terms. Use long division.

b. $\dfrac{2p^5 - 8p^4 + 4p - 16}{2p^2}$ The divisor has one term. No long division.

c. $(3z^3 - 5z^2 + 10) \div (15z^3)$ The divisor has one term. No long division.

d. $(3z^3 - 5z^2 + 10) \div (3z + 1)$ The divisor has two terms. Use long division.

TIP:

- Long division is used when the divisor has *two or more terms*.
- If the divisor has *one term*, then divide each term in the dividend by the monomial divisor.

Skill Practice Divide the polynomials using the appropriate method of division.

6. $\dfrac{6x^3 - x^2 + 3x - 5}{2x + 3}$ **7.** $\dfrac{9w^3 - 18w^2 + 6w + 12}{3w}$

3. Synthetic Division

In this section, we introduced the process of long division to divide two polynomials. Next, we will learn another technique, called **synthetic division**, to divide two polynomials. Synthetic division can be used when dividing a polynomial by a first-degree divisor of the form $x - r$, where r is a constant. Synthetic division is considered a "shortcut" because it uses the coefficients of the divisor and dividend without writing the variables.

Consider dividing the polynomials $(3x^2 - 14x - 10) \div (x - 2)$.

$$\begin{array}{r} 3x - 8 \\ x - 2\overline{)3x^2 - 14x - 10} \\ -(3x^2 - 6x) \\ \hline -8x - 10 \\ -(-8x + 16) \\ \hline -26 \end{array}$$

Avoiding Mistakes

It is important to check that the divisor is in the form $(x - r)$ before applying synthetic division. The variable x in the divisor must be of first degree, and its coefficient must be 1.

Answers

6. $3x^2 - 5x + 9 + \dfrac{-32}{2x + 3}$

7. $3w^2 - 6w + 2 + \dfrac{4}{w}$

First note that the divisor $x - 2$ is in the form $x - r$, where $r = 2$. Therefore, synthetic division can be used to find the quotient and remainder.

Step 1: Write the value of r in a box.

Step 2: Write the coefficients of the dividend to the right of the box.

$$\begin{array}{r|rrr} 2 & 3 & -14 & -10 \\ & & & \\ \hline & 3 & & \end{array}$$

Step 3: Skip a line and draw a horizontal line below the list of coefficients.

Step 4: Bring down the leading coefficient from the dividend and write it below the line.

$$\begin{array}{r|rrr} 2 & 3 & -14 & -10 \\ & & 6 & \\ \hline & 3 & -8 & \end{array}$$

Step 5: Multiply the value of r by the number below the line $(2 \times 3 = 6)$. Write the result in the next column above the line.

Step 6: Add the numbers in the column above the line $(-14 + 6)$, and write the result below the line.

Repeat steps 5 and 6 until all columns have been completed.

Step 7: To get the final result, we use the numbers below the line. The number in the last column is the remainder. The other numbers are the coefficients of the quotient.

$$\begin{array}{r|rrr} 2 & 3 & -14 & -10 \\ & & 6 & -16 \\ \hline & 3 & -8 & \boxed{-26} \end{array}$$

A box is usually drawn around the remainder.

Quotient: $3x - 8$, remainder: -26

The degree of the quotient will always be 1 less than that of the dividend. Because the dividend is a second-degree polynomial, the quotient will be a first-degree polynomial. In this case, the quotient is $3x - 8$ and the remainder is -26.

Example 6 Using Synthetic Division to Divide Polynomials

Divide the polynomials $(5x + 4x^3 - 6 + x^4) \div (x + 3)$ by using synthetic division.

Solution:

As with long division, the terms of the dividend and divisor should be written in descending order. Furthermore, missing powers must be accounted for by using placeholders (shown here in red).

$$5x + 4x^3 - 6 + x^4$$
$$= x^4 + 4x^3 + 0x^2 + 5x - 6$$

To use synthetic division, the divisor must be in the form $(x - r)$. The divisor $x + 3$ can be written as $x - (-3)$. Hence, $r = -3$.

Step 1: Write the value of r in a box.

Step 2: Write the coefficients of the dividend to the right of the box.

Step 3: Skip a line and draw a horizontal line below the list of coefficients.

Step 4: Bring down the leading coefficient from the dividend and write it below the line.

$$\begin{array}{r|rrrrr} -3 & 1 & 4 & 0 & 5 & -6 \\ & & & & & \\ \hline & 1 & & & & \end{array}$$

Step 5: Multiply the value of r by the number below the line $(-3 \times 1 = -3)$. Write the result in the next column above the line.

Step 6: Add the numbers in the column above the line: $4 + (-3) = 1$.

$$\begin{array}{r|rrrrr} -3 & 1 & 4 & 0 & 5 & -6 \\ & & -3 & & & \\ \hline & 1 & 1 & & & \end{array}$$

Repeat steps 5 and 6:

$$\begin{array}{r|rrrrr} -3 & 1 & 4 & 0 & 5 & -6 \\ & & -3 & -3 & 9 & -42 \\ \hline & 1 & 1 & -3 & 14 & \boxed{-48} \end{array}$$

(-48: remainder; 14: constant; -3: x-term coefficient; 1: x^2-term coefficient; 1: x^3-term coefficient)

The quotient is

$x^3 + x^2 - 3x + 14$.

The remainder is -48.

The answer is $x^3 + x^2 - 3x + 14 + \dfrac{-48}{x + 3}$.

Skill Practice Divide the polynomials by using synthetic division.

8. $(5y^2 - 4y + 2y^3 - 5) \div (y + 3)$

TIP: It is interesting to compare the long division process to the synthetic division process. For Example 6, long division is shown on the left, and synthetic division is shown on the right. Notice that the same pattern of coefficients used in long division appears in the synthetic division process.

$$\begin{array}{r} x^3 + x^2 - 3x + 14 \\ x + 3\,\overline{)\,x^4 + 4x^3 + 0x^2 + 5x - 6} \\ -(x^4 + 3x^3) \\ \hline x^3 + 0x^2 \\ -(x^3 + 3x^2) \\ \hline -3x^2 + 5x \\ -(-3x^2 - 9x) \\ \hline 14x - 6 \\ -(14x + 42) \\ \hline -48 \end{array}$$

$$\begin{array}{r|rrrrr} -3 & 1 & 4 & 0 & 5 & -6 \\ & & -3 & -3 & 9 & -42 \\ \hline & 1 & 1 & -3 & 14 & \boxed{-48} \\ & x^3 & x^2 & x & \text{constant} & \text{remainder} \end{array}$$

Quotient: $x^3 + x^2 - 3x + 14$

Remainder: -48

Answer

8. $2y^2 - y - 1 + \dfrac{-2}{y + 3}$

Example 7 Using Synthetic Division to Divide Polynomials

Divide the polynomials by using synthetic division. $(p^4 - 81) \div (p - 3)$

Solution:

$(p^4 - 81) \div (p - 3)$

$(p^4 + 0p^3 + 0p^2 + 0p - 81) \div (p - 3)$ Insert placeholders (red) for missing powers of p.

$$\begin{array}{r|rrrrr} 3 & 1 & 0 & 0 & 0 & -81 \\ & & 3 & 9 & 27 & 81 \\ \hline & 1 & 3 & 9 & 27 & \boxed{0} \end{array}$$

Quotient: $p^3 + 3p^2 + 9p + 27$

Remainder: 0

The answer is $p^3 + 3p^2 + 9p + 27$.

Skill Practice Divide the polynomials by using synthetic division.

9. $(x^3 + 1) \div (x + 1)$

Answer

9. $x^2 - x + 1$

Section 5.7 Practice Exercises

Vocabulary and Key Concepts

1. a. The __________ algorithm states that:
Dividend = (divisor)(__________) + (__________)

b. __________ division or long division can be used when dividing a polynomial by a divisor of the form $x - r$, where r is a constant.

Review Exercises

2. a. Add $(3x + 1) + (2x - 5)$.

b. Multiply $(3x + 1)(2x - 5)$.

3. a. Subtract $(a - 10b) - (5a + b)$.

b. Multiply $(a - 10b)(5a + b)$.

4. a. Subtract $(2y^2 + 1) - (y^2 - 5y + 1)$.

b. Multiply $(2y^2 + 1)(y^2 - 5y + 1)$.

5. a. Add $(x^2 - x) + (6x^2 + x + 2)$.

b. Multiply $(x^2 - x)(6x^2 + x + 2)$.

For Exercises 6–8, answers may vary.

6. Write an example of a product of two binomials and simplify.

7. Write an example of the square of a binomial and simplify.

8. Write an example of the product of conjugates and simplify.

Concept 1: Division by a Monomial

For Exercises 9–24, divide the polynomials. Check your answer by multiplication. **(See Example 1.)**

9. $\dfrac{16t^4 - 4t^2 + 20t}{-4t}$

10. $\dfrac{2x^3 + 8x^2 - 2x}{-2x}$

11. $(36y + 24y^2 + 6y^3) \div (3y)$

12. $(6p^2 - 18p^4 + 30p^5) \div (6p)$

13. $(4x^3y + 12x^2y^2 - 4xy^3) \div (4xy)$

14. $(25m^5n - 10m^4n + m^3n) \div (5m^3n)$

15. $(-8y^4 - 12y^3 + 32y^2) \div (-4y^2)$

16. $(12y^5 - 8y^6 + 16y^4 - 10y^3) \div (2y^3)$

17. $(3p^4 - 6p^3 + 2p^2 - p) \div (-6p)$

18. $(-4q^3 + 8q^2 - q) \div (-12q)$

19. $(a^3 + 5a^2 + a - 5) \div (a)$

20. $(2m^5 - 3m^4 + m^3 - m^2 + 9m) \div (m^2)$

21. $\dfrac{6s^3t^5 - 8s^2t^4 + 10st^2}{-2st^4}$

22. $\dfrac{-8r^4w^2 - 4r^3w + 2w^3}{-4r^3w}$

23. $(8p^4q^7 - 9p^5q^6 - 11p^3q - 4) \div (p^2q)$

24. $(20a^5b^5 - 20a^3b^2 + 5a^2b + 6) \div (a^2b)$

Concept 2: Long Division

25. **a.** Divide $(2x^3 - 7x^2 + 5x - 1) \div (x - 2)$, and identify the divisor, quotient, and remainder.

    b. Explain how to check by using multiplication.

26. **a.** Divide $(x^3 + 4x^2 + 7x - 3) \div (x + 3)$, and identify the divisor, quotient, and remainder.

    b. Explain how to check by using multiplication.

For Exercises 27–48, divide the polynomials by using long division. Check your answer by multiplication. **(See Examples 2–4.)**

27. $(x^2 + 11x + 19) \div (x + 4)$

28. $(x^3 - 7x^2 - 13x + 3) \div (x + 2)$

29. $(3y^3 - 7y^2 - 4y + 3) \div (y - 3)$

30. $(z^3 - 2z^2 + 2z - 5) \div (z - 4)$

31. $(-12a^2 + 77a - 121) \div (3a - 11)$

32. $(28x^2 - 29x + 6) \div (4x - 3)$

33. $(9y + 18y^2 - 20) \div (3y + 4)$

34. $(-2y + 3y^2 - 1) \div (y - 1)$

35. $(18x^3 + 7x + 12) \div (3x - 2)$

36. $(8x^3 - 6x + 22) \div (2x - 1)$

37. $(8a^3 + 1) \div (2a + 1)$

38. $(81x^4 - 1) \div (3x + 1)$

39. $(x^4 - x^3 - x^2 + 4x - 2) \div (x^2 + x - 1)$

40. $(2a^5 - 7a^4 + 11a^3 - 22a^2 + 29a - 10) \div (2a^2 - 5a + 2)$

41. $(2x^3 - 10x + x^4 - 25) \div (x^2 - 5)$

42. $(-5x^3 + x^4 - 4 - 10x) \div (x^2 + 2)$

43. $(x^4 - 3x^2 + 10) \div (x^2 - 2)$

44. $(3y^4 - 25y^2 - 18) \div (y^2 - 3)$

45. $(n^4 - 16) \div (n - 2)$

46. $(m^3 + 27) \div (m + 3)$

47. $\dfrac{3y^4 + 2y + 3}{y^2 + 1}$

48. $\dfrac{2x^4 + 6x + 4}{2 + x^2}$

Group Activity

The Pythagorean Theorem and a Geometric "Proof"

Estimated Time: 25–30 minutes

Group Size: 2

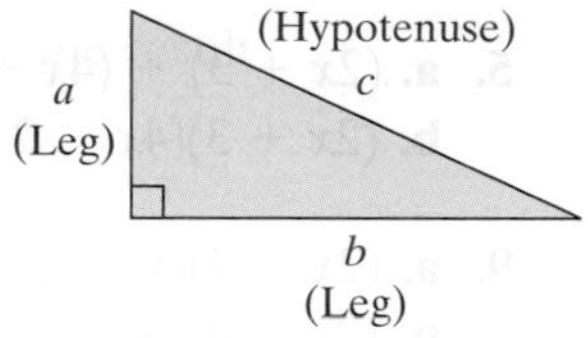

Right triangles occur in many applications of mathematics. By definition, a right triangle is a triangle that contains a 90° angle. The two shorter sides in a right triangle are referred to as the "legs," and the longest side is called the "hypotenuse." In the triangle, the legs are labeled as a and b, and the hypotenuse is labeled as c.

Right triangles have an important property that the sum of the squares of the two legs of a right triangle equals the square of the hypotenuse. This fact is referred to as the Pythagorean theorem. In symbols, the Pythagorean theorem is stated as:

$$a^2 + b^2 = c^2$$

1. The following triangles are right triangles. Verify that $a^2 + b^2 = c^2$. (The units may be left off when performing these calculations.)

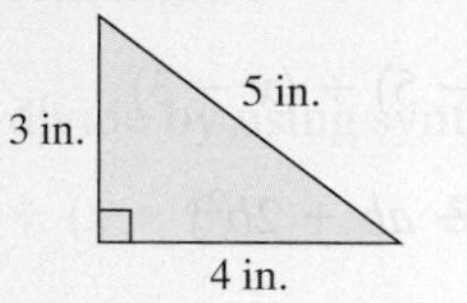

$a = 3$
$b = 4$
$c = 5$

$$a^2 + b^2 = c^2$$
$$(3)^2 + (4)^2 \stackrel{?}{=} (5)^2$$
$$9 + 16 = 25 \checkmark$$

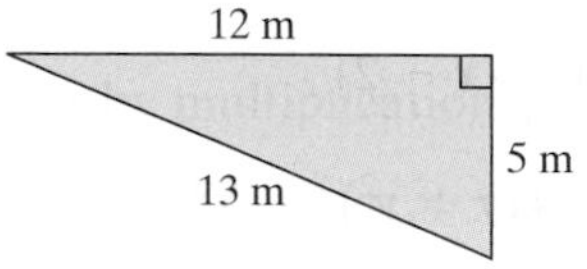

$a =$ ______
$b =$ ______
$c =$ ______

$$a^2 + b^2 = c^2$$
$$(\_\_\_)^2 + (\_\_\_)^2 \stackrel{?}{=} (\_\_\_)^2$$
$$\_\_\_ + \_\_\_ = \_\_\_ \checkmark$$

2. The following geometric "proof" of the Pythagorean theorem uses addition, subtraction, and multiplication of polynomials. Consider the square figure. The length of each side of the large outer square is $(a + b)$. Therefore, the area of the large outer square is $(a + b)^2$.

The area of the large outer square can also be found by adding the area of the inner square (pictured in light gray) plus the area of the four right triangles (pictured in dark gray).

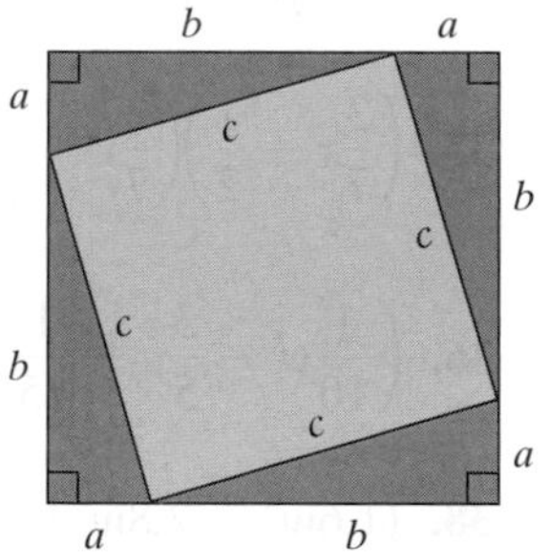

Area of inner square: c^2 Area of the four right triangles: $4 \cdot \left(\frac{1}{2}\ a\ b\right)$

½ Base · Height

3. Now equate the two expressions representing the area of the large outer square:

$$\begin{pmatrix}\text{Area of outer}\\ \text{square}\end{pmatrix} = \begin{pmatrix}\text{area of inner}\\ \text{square}\end{pmatrix} + \begin{pmatrix}\text{4 times the area}\\ \text{of the right triangles}\end{pmatrix}$$

______ = ______ + ______

______ = ______ + ______ ← Clear parentheses on both sides of the equation.

______ = ______ ← Subtract $2ab$ from both sides.

Chapter 5 Summary

Section 5.1 Multiplying and Dividing Expressions with Common Bases

Key Concepts

Definition

$b^n = \underbrace{b \cdot b \cdot b \cdot b \cdot \ldots b}_{n \text{ factors of } b}$ b is the base, n is the exponent

Multiplying Like Bases

$b^m b^n = b^{m+n}$ (m, n positive integers)

Dividing Like Bases

$\dfrac{b^m}{b^n} = b^{m-n}$ ($b \neq 0, m, n,$ positive integers)

Examples

Example 1

$3^4 = 3 \cdot 3 \cdot 3 \cdot 3 = 81$ 3 is the base, 4 is the exponent

Example 2

Compare: $(-5)^2$ versus -5^2

$(-5)^2 = (-5)(-5) = 25$

versus

$-5^2 = -1(5^2) = -1(5)(5) = -25$

Example 3

Simplify: $x^3 \cdot x^4 \cdot x^2 \cdot x = x^{10}$

Example 4

Simplify: $\dfrac{c^4d^{10}}{cd^5} = c^{4-1}d^{10-5} = c^3d^5$

Section 5.2 More Properties of Exponents

Key Concepts

Power Rule for Exponents

$(b^m)^n = b^{mn}$ ($b \neq 0, m, n$ positive integers)

Power of a Product and Power of a Quotient

Assume m and n are positive integers and a and b are real numbers where $b \neq 0$.
Then,

$(ab)^m = a^m b^m$ and $\left(\dfrac{a}{b}\right)^m = \dfrac{a^m}{b^m}$

Examples

Example 1

Simplify: $(x^4)^5 = x^{20}$

Example 2

Simplify: $(4uv^2)^3 = 4^3u^3(v^2)^3 = 64u^3v^6$

Example 3

Simplify: $\left(\dfrac{p^5q^3}{5pq^2}\right)^2 = \left(\dfrac{p^{5-1}q^{3-2}}{5}\right)^2 = \left(\dfrac{p^4q}{5}\right)^2$

$= \dfrac{p^8q^2}{25}$

Section 5.3 Definitions of b^0 and b^{-n}

Key Concepts

Definitions

If b is a nonzero real number and n is an integer, then:

1. $b^0 = 1$

2. $b^{-n} = \left(\frac{1}{b}\right)^n = \frac{1}{b^n}$

Examples

Example 1

Simplify: $4^0 = 1$

Example 2

Simplify: $y^{-7} = \frac{1}{y^7}$

Example 3

Simplify: $\frac{8a^0b^{-2}}{c^{-5}d}$

$= \frac{8(1)c^5}{b^2d} = \frac{8c^5}{b^2d}$

Section 5.4 Scientific Notation

Key Concepts

A positive number written in **scientific notation** is expressed in the form:

$a \times 10^n$ where $1 \le a < 10$ and n is an integer.

$35{,}000 = 3.5 \times 10^4$

$0.000\,000\,548 = 5.48 \times 10^{-7}$

Examples

Example 1

Multiply: $(3.5 \times 10^4)(2 \times 10^{-6})$

$= 7 \times 10^{-2}$

Example 2

Divide: $\frac{2.1 \times 10^{-9}}{8.4 \times 10^3} = 0.25 \times 10^{-9-3}$

$= 0.25 \times 10^{-12}$

$= (2.5 \times 10^{-1}) \times 10^{-12}$

$= 2.5 \times 10^{-13}$

Section 5.5 Addition and Subtraction of Polynomials

Key Concepts

A **polynomial** in one variable is a sum of terms of the form ax^n, where a is a real number and the exponent, n, is a nonnegative integer. For each term, a is called the **coefficient** of the term and n is the **degree of the term**. The term with highest degree is the **leading term**, and its coefficient is called the **leading coefficient**. The **degree of the polynomial** is the largest degree of all its terms.

To add or subtract polynomials, add or subtract *like* terms.

Examples

Example 1

Given: $4x^5 - 8x^3 + 9x - 5$

Coefficients of each term: $4, -8, 9, -5$

Degree of each term: $5, 3, 1, 0$

Leading term: $4x^5$

Leading coefficient: 4

Degree of polynomial: 5

Example 2

Perform the indicated operations:

$$(2x^4 - 5x^3 + 1) - (x^4 + 3) + (x^3 - 4x - 7)$$
$$= 2x^4 - 5x^3 + 1 - x^4 - 3 + x^3 - 4x - 7$$
$$= 2x^4 - x^4 - 5x^3 + x^3 - 4x + 1 - 3 - 7$$
$$= x^4 - 4x^3 - 4x - 9$$

Section 5.6 Multiplication of Polynomials and Special Products

Key Concepts

Multiplying Monomials

Use the commutative and associative properties of multiplication to group coefficients and like bases.

Multiplying Polynomials

Multiply each term in the first polynomial by each term in the second polynomial.

Product of Conjugates

Results in a **difference of squares**

$(a + b)(a - b) = a^2 - b^2$

Square of a Binomial

Results in a **perfect square trinomial**

$(a + b)^2 = a^2 + 2ab + b^2$

$(a - b)^2 = a^2 - 2ab + b^2$

Examples

Example 1

Multiply: $(5a^2b)(-2ab^3)$

$$= (5 \cdot -2)(a^2a)(bb^3)$$
$$= -10a^3b^4$$

Example 2

Multiply: $(x - 2)(3x^2 - 4x + 11)$

$$= 3x^3 - 4x^2 + 11x - 6x^2 + 8x - 22$$
$$= 3x^3 - 10x^2 + 19x - 22$$

Example 3

Multiply: $(3w - 4v)(3w + 4v)$

$$= (3w)^2 - (4v)^2$$
$$= 9w^2 - 16v^2$$

Example 4

Multiply: $(5c - 8d)^2$

$$= (5c)^2 - 2(5c)(8d) + (8d)^2$$
$$= 25c^2 - 80cd + 64d^2$$

Section 5.7 Division of Polynomials

Key Concepts

Division of Polynomials

1. Division by a monomial, use the properties:

$$\frac{a+b}{c} = \frac{a}{c} + \frac{b}{c} \quad \text{and} \quad \frac{a-b}{c} = \frac{a}{c} - \frac{b}{c}$$

2. If the divisor has more than one term, use long division.

3. If the divisor is of the form $x - r$, then synthetic division may be used.

Examples

Example 1

Divide: $\dfrac{-3x^2 - 6x + 9}{-3x}$

$$= \frac{-3x^2}{-3x} - \frac{6x}{-3x} + \frac{9}{-3x}$$

$$= x + 2 - \frac{3}{x}$$

Example 2

Divide: $(3x^2 - 5x + 1) \div (x + 2)$

$$\begin{array}{r} 3x - 11 \\ x+2\overline{)3x^2 - 5x + 1} \\ -(3x^2 + 6x) \\ \hline -11x + 1 \\ -(-11x - 22) \\ \hline 23 \end{array}$$

$$3x - 11 + \frac{23}{x+2}$$

Example 3

Divide: $(4x^3 - 2x - 5) \div (x - 1)$

$$\begin{array}{r|rrrr} 1 & 4 & 0 & -2 & -5 \\ & & 4 & 4 & 2 \\ \hline & 4 & 4 & 2 & \boxed{-3} \end{array}$$

$$4x^2 + 4x + 2 + \frac{-3}{x-1}$$

Chapter 5 Review Exercises

Section 5.1

For Exercises 1–4, identify the base and the exponent.

1. 5^3 **2.** x^4 **3.** $(-2)^0$ **4.** y

5. Evaluate the expressions.

a. 6^2 **b.** $(-6)^2$ **c.** -6^2

6. Evaluate the expressions.

a. 4^3 **b.** $(-4)^3$ **c.** -4^3

For Exercises 7–18, simplify and write the answers in exponent form. Assume that all variables represent nonzero real numbers.

7. $5^3 \cdot 5^{10}$ **8.** a^7a^4

9. $x \cdot x^6 \cdot x^2$ **10.** $6^3 \cdot 6 \cdot 6^5$

11. $\dfrac{10^7}{10^4}$ **12.** $\dfrac{y^{14}}{y^8}$

13. $\dfrac{b^9}{b}$ **14.** $\dfrac{7^8}{7}$

15. $\dfrac{k^2k^3}{k^4}$

16. $\dfrac{8^4 \cdot 8^7}{8^{11}}$

17. $\dfrac{2^8 \cdot 2^{10}}{2^3 \cdot 2^7}$

18. $\dfrac{q^3q^{12}}{qq^8}$

19. Explain why $2^2 \cdot 4^4$ does *not* equal 8^6.

20. Explain why $\frac{10^5}{5^2}$ does *not* equal 2^3.

For Exercises 21–22, use the formula

$$A = P(1 + r)^t$$

21. Find the amount in an account after 3 years if the initial investment is \$6000, invested at 6% interest compounded annually.

22. Find the amount in an account after 2 years if the initial investment is \$20,000, invested at 5% interest compounded annually.

Section 5.2

For Exercises 23–40, simplify each expression. Write the answer in exponent form. Assume all variables represent nonzero real numbers.

23. $(7^3)^4$

24. $(c^2)^6$

25. $(p^4p^2)^3$

26. $(9^5 \cdot 9^2)^4$

27. $\left(\dfrac{a}{b}\right)^2$

28. $\left(\dfrac{1}{3}\right)^4$

29. $\left(\dfrac{5}{c^2d^5}\right)^2$

30. $\left(-\dfrac{m^2}{4n^6}\right)^5$

31. $(2ab^2)^4$

32. $(-x^7y)^2$

33. $\left(\dfrac{-3x^3}{5y^2z}\right)^3$

34. $\left(\dfrac{r^3}{s^2t^6}\right)^5$

35. $\dfrac{a^4(a^2)^8}{(a^3)^3}$

36. $\dfrac{(8^3)^4 \cdot 8^{10}}{(8^4)^5}$

37. $\dfrac{(4h^2k)^2(h^3k)^4}{(2hk^3)^2}$

38. $\dfrac{(p^3q)^3(2p^2q^4)^4}{(8p)(pq^3)^2}$

39. $\left(\dfrac{2x^4y^3}{4xy^2}\right)^2$

40. $\left(\dfrac{a^4b^6}{ab^4}\right)^3$

Section 5.3

For Exercises 41–62, simplify each expression. Write the answers with positive exponents. Assume all variables represent nonzero real numbers.

41. 8^0

42. $(-b)^0$

43. $-x^0$

44. 1^0

45. $2y^0$

46. $(2y)^0$

47. z^{-5}

48. 10^{-4}

49. $(6a)^{-2}$

50. $6a^{-2}$

51. $4^0 + 4^{-2}$

52. $9^{-1} + 9^0$

53. $t^{-6}t^{-2}$

54. r^8r^{-9}

55. $\dfrac{12x^{-2}y^3}{6x^4y^{-4}}$

56. $\dfrac{8ab^{-3}c^0}{10a^{-5}b^{-4}c^{-1}}$

57. $(-2m^2n^{-4})^{-4}$

58. $(3u^{-5}v^2)^{-3}$

59. $\dfrac{(k^{-6})^{-2}(k^3)}{5k^{-6}k^0}$

60. $\dfrac{(3h)^{-2}(h^{-5})^{-3}}{h^{-4}h^8}$

61. $2 \cdot 3^{-1} - 6^{-1}$

62. $2^{-1} - 2^{-2} + 2^0$

Section 5.4

63. Write the numbers in scientific notation.

a. In a recent year there were 97,400,000 packages of M&Ms sold in the United States.

b. The thickness of a piece of paper is 0.0042 in.

64. Write the numbers in standard form.

a. A pH of 10 means the hydrogen ion concentration is 1×10^{-10} units.

b. A fundraising event for neurospinal research raised \$$2.56 \times 10^5$.

For Exercises 65–68, perform the indicated operations. Write the answers in scientific notation.

65. $(4.1 \times 10^{-6})(2.3 \times 10^{11})$

66. $\dfrac{9.3 \times 10^3}{6 \times 10^{-7}}$

67. $\dfrac{2000}{0.000008}$

68. (0.000078)(21,000,000)

69. Use your calculator to evaluate 5^{20}. Why is scientific notation necessary on your calculator to express the answer?

70. Use your calculator to evaluate $(0.4)^{30}$. Why is scientific notation necessary on your calculator to express the answer?

71. The average distance between the Earth and Sun is 9.3×10^7 mi.

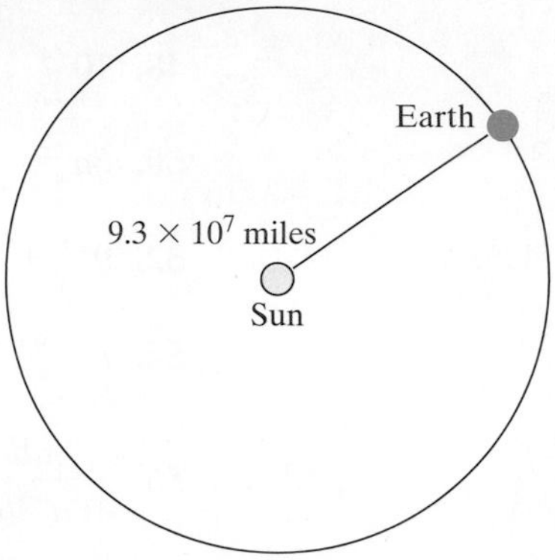

a. If the Earth's orbit is approximated by a circle, find the total distance the Earth travels around the Sun in one orbit. (*Hint:* The circumference of a circle is given by $C = 2\pi r$.) Express the answer in scientific notation.

b. If the Earth makes one complete trip around the Sun in 1 year (365 days $= 8.76 \times 10^3$ hr), find the average speed that the Earth travels around the Sun in miles per hour. Express the answer in scientific notation.

72. The average distance between the planet Mercury and the Sun is 3.6×10^7 mi.

a. If Mercury's orbit is approximated by a circle, find the total distance Mercury travels around the Sun in one orbit. (*Hint:* The circumference of a circle is given by $C = 2\pi r$.) Express the answer in scientific notation.

b. If Mercury makes one complete trip around the Sun in 88 days (2.112×10^3 hr), find the average speed that Mercury travels around the Sun in miles per hour. Express the answer in scientific notation.

Section 5.5

73. For the polynomial $7x^4 - x + 6$

a. Classify as a monomial, a binomial, or a trinomial.

b. Identify the degree of the polynomial.

c. Identify the leading coefficient.

74. For the polynomial $2y^3 - 5y^7$

a. Classify as a monomial, a binomial, or a trinomial.

b. Identify the degree of the polynomial.

c. Identify the leading coefficient.

For Exercises 75 – 80, add or subtract as indicated.

75. $(4x + 2) + (3x - 5)$

76. $(7y^2 - 11y - 6) - (8y^2 + 3y - 4)$

77. $(9a^2 - 6) - (-5a^2 + 2a)$

78. $\left(5x^3 - \frac{1}{4}x^2 + \frac{5}{8}x + 2\right) + \left(\frac{5}{2}x^3 + \frac{1}{2}x^2 - \frac{1}{8}x\right)$

79.
$$\begin{array}{r} 8w^4 \qquad\qquad - 6w + 3 \\ +\ \underline{2w^4 + 2w^3 - \quad w + 1} \end{array}$$

80.
$$\begin{array}{r} -0.02b^5 + b^4 \qquad\qquad - 0.7b + 0.3 \\ +\ \underline{0.03b^5 \qquad - 0.1b^3 + \qquad b + 0.03} \end{array}$$

81. Subtract $(9x^2 + 4x + 6)$ from $(7x^2 - 5x)$.

82. Find the difference of $(x^2 - 5x - 3)$ and $(6x^2 + 4x + 9)$.

83. Write a trinomial of degree 2 with a leading coefficient of -5. (Answers may vary.)

84. Write a binomial of degree 5 with leading coefficient 6. (Answers may vary.)

85. Find a polynomial that represents the perimeter of the given rectangle.

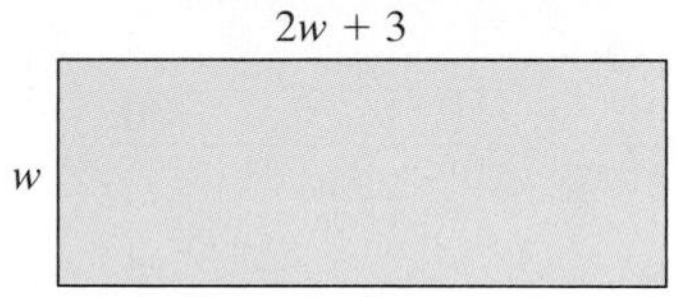

Section 5.6

For Exercises 86–103, multiply the expressions.

86. $(25x^4y^3)(-3x^2y)$

87. $(9a^6)(2a^2b^4)$

88. $5c(3c^3 - 7c + 5)$

89. $(x^2 + 5x - 3)(-2x)$

90. $(5k - 4)(k + 1)$

91. $(4t - 1)(5t + 2)$

92. $(q + 8)(6q - 1)$

93. $(2a - 6)(a + 5)$

94. $\left(7a + \frac{1}{2}\right)^2$

95. $(b - 4)^2$

96. $(4p^2 + 6p + 9)(2p - 3)$

97. $(2w - 1)(-w^2 - 3w - 4)$

98. $\begin{array}{r} 2x^2 - 3x + 4 \\ \times \quad\quad 2x - 1 \\ \hline \end{array}$

99. $\begin{array}{r} 4a^2 + a - 5 \\ \times \quad\quad 3a + 2 \\ \hline \end{array}$

100. $(b - 4)(b + 4)$

101. $\left(\frac{1}{3}r^4 - s^2\right)\left(\frac{1}{3}r^4 + s^2\right)$

102. $(-7z^2 + 6)^2$

103. $(2h + 3)(h^4 - h^3 + h^2 - h + 1)$

104. Find a polynomial that represents the area of the given rectangle.

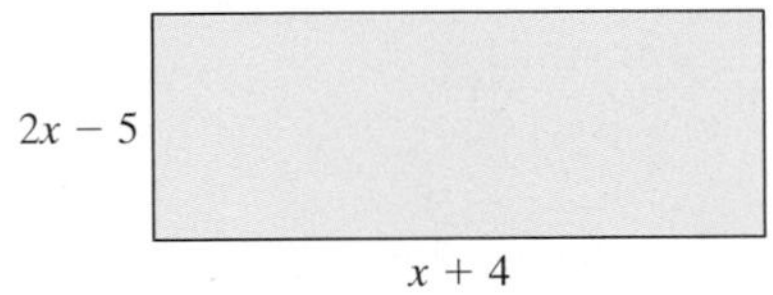

Section 5.7

For Exercises 105–117, divide the polynomials.

105. $\dfrac{20y^3 - 10y^2}{5y}$

106. $(18a^3b^2 - 9a^2b - 27ab^2) \div 9ab$

107. $(12x^4 - 8x^3 + 4x^2) \div (-4x^2)$

108. $\dfrac{10z^7w^4 - 15z^3w^2 - 20zw}{-20z^2w}$

109. $\dfrac{x^2 + 7x + 10}{x + 5}$

110. $(2t^2 + t - 10) \div (t - 2)$

111. $(2p^2 + p - 16) \div (2p + 7)$

112. $\dfrac{5a^2 + 27a - 22}{5a - 3}$

113. $\dfrac{b^3 - 125}{b - 5}$

114. $(z^3 + 4z^2 + 5z + 20) \div (5 + z^2)$

115. $(y^4 - 4y^3 + 5y^2 - 3y + 2) \div (y^2 + 3)$

116. $(3t^4 - 8t^3 + t^2 - 4t - 5) \div (3t^2 + t + 1)$

117. $\dfrac{2w^4 + w^3 + 4w - 3}{2w^2 - w + 3}$

Chapter 5 Test

Assume all variables represent nonzero real numbers.

1. Expand the expression using the definition of exponents, then simplify: $\dfrac{3^4 \cdot 3^3}{3^6}$

For Exercises 2–13, simplify each expression. Write the answer with positive exponents only.

2. $9^5 \cdot 9$

3. $\dfrac{q^{10}}{q^2}$

4. $(-7)^0$

5. c^{-3}

6. $3^0 + 2^{-1} - 4^{-1}$

7. $4 \cdot 8^{-1} + 16^0$

8. $(3a^2b)^3$

9. $\left(\dfrac{2x}{y^3}\right)^4$

10. $\dfrac{14^3 \cdot 14^9}{14^{10} \cdot 14}$

11. $\dfrac{(s^2t)^3(7s^4t)^4}{(7s^2t^3)^2}$

12. $(2a^0b^{-6})^2$

13. $\left(\dfrac{6a^{-5}b}{8ab^{-2}}\right)^{-2}$

14. **a.** Write the number in scientific notation: 43,000,000,000

b. Write the number in standard form: 5.6×10^{-6}

15. Multiply: $(1.2 \times 10^6)(7 \times 10^{-15})$

16. Divide: $\dfrac{60{,}000}{0.008}$

17. The average amount of water flowing over Niagara Falls is 1.68×10^5 m^3/min.

a. How many cubic meters of water flow over the falls in one day?

b. How many cubic meters of water flow over the falls in one year?

18. Write the polynomial in descending order: $4x + 5x^3 - 7x^2 + 11$

a. Identify the degree of the polynomial.

b. Identify the leading coefficient of the polynomial.

For Exercises 19–28, perform the indicated operations.

19. $(5t^4 - 2t^2 - 17) + (12t^3 + 2t^2 + 7t - 2)$

20. $(7w^2 - 11w - 6) + (8w^2 + 3w + 4) - (-9w^2 - 5w + 2)$

21. $-2x^3(5x^2 + x - 15)$

22. $(4a - 3)(2a - 1)$

23. $(4y - 5)(y^2 - 5y + 3)$

24. $(2 + 3b)(2 - 3b)$

25. $(5z - 6)^2$

26. $(5x + 3)(3x - 2)$

27. $(2x^2 + 5x) - (6x^2 - 7)$

28. $(y^2 - 5y + 2)(y - 6)$

29. Subtract $(3x^2 - 5x^3 + 2x)$ from $(10x^3 - 4x^2 + 1)$.

30. Find the perimeter and the area of the rectangle shown in the figure.

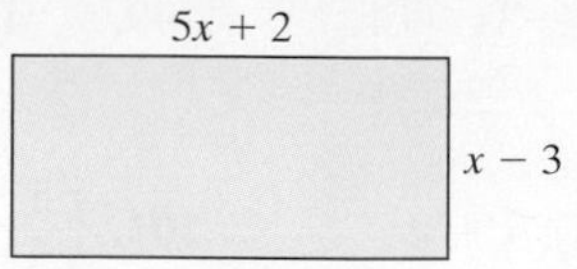

For Exercises 31–35, divide:

31. $(-12x^8 + x^6 - 8x^3) \div (4x^2)$

32. $\dfrac{16a^3b - 2a^2b^2 + 8ab}{-4ab}$

33. $\dfrac{2y^2 - 13y + 21}{y - 3}$

34. $(-5w^2 + 2w^3 - 2w + 5) \div (2w + 3)$

35. $\dfrac{3x^4 + x^3 + 4x - 33}{x^2 + 4}$

Chapters 1–5 Cumulative Review Exercises

For Exercises 1–2, simplify completely.

1. $-5 - \frac{1}{2}[4 - 3(-7)]$

2. $|-3^2 + 5|$

3. Translate the phrase into a mathematical expression and simplify:

The difference of the square of five and the square root of four.

4. Solve for x: $\frac{1}{2}(x - 6) + \frac{2}{3} = \frac{1}{4}x$

5. Solve for y: $-2y - 3 = -5(y - 1) + 3y$

6. For a point in a rectangular coordinate system, in which quadrant are both the x- and y-coordinates negative?

7. For a point in a rectangular coordinate system, on which axis is the x-coordinate zero and the y-coordinate nonzero?

8. In a triangle, one angle measures 23° more than the smallest angle. The third angle measures 10° more than the sum of the other two angles. Find the measure of each angle.

9. A snow storm lasts for 9 hr and dumps snow at a rate of $1\frac{1}{2}$ in./hr. If there was already 6 in. of snow on the ground before the storm, the snow depth is given by the equation:

$y = \frac{3}{2}x + 6$ where y is the snow depth in inches and $x \geq 0$ is the time in hours.

a. Find the snow depth after 4 hr.

b. Find the snow depth at the end of the storm.

c. How long had it snowed when the total depth of snow was $14\frac{1}{4}$ in.?

10. Solve the system of equations.

$$5x + 3y = -3$$
$$3x + 2y = -1$$

11. Solve the inequality. Graph the solution set on the real number line and express the solution in interval notation. $2 - 3(2x + 4) \le -2x - (x - 5)$

For Exercises 12–15, perform the indicated operations.

12. $(2x^2 + 3x - 7) - (-3x^2 + 12x + 8)$

13. $(2y + 3z)(-y - 5z)$

14. $(4t - 3)^2$

15. $\left(\frac{2}{5}a + \frac{1}{3}\right)\left(\frac{2}{5}a - \frac{1}{3}\right)$

For Exercises 16–17, divide the polynomials.

16. $(12a^4b^3 - 6a^2b^2 + 3ab) \div (-3ab)$

17. $\dfrac{4m^3 - 5m + 2}{m - 2}$

For Exercises 18–19, use the properties of exponents to simplify the expressions. Write the answers with positive exponents only. Assume all variables represent nonzero real numbers.

18. $\left(\dfrac{2c^2d^4}{8cd^6}\right)^2$

19. $\dfrac{10a^{-2}b^{-3}}{5a^0b^{-6}}$

20. Perform the indicated operations, and write the final answer in scientific notation.

$$\frac{8.2 \times 10^{-2}}{2 \times 10^{-5}}$$

Factoring Polynomials

6

CHAPTER OUTLINE

6.1 Greatest Common Factor and Factoring by Grouping 416

6.2 Factoring Trinomials of the Form $x^2 + bx + c$ 426

6.3 Factoring Trinomials: Trial-and-Error Method 432

6.4 Factoring Trinomials: AC-Method 441

6.5 Difference of Squares and Perfect Square Trinomials 448

6.6 Sum and Difference of Cubes 454

Problem Recognition Exercises: Factoring Strategy 461

6.7 Solving Equations Using the Zero Product Rule 462

Problem Recognition Exercises: Polynomial Expressions Versus Polynomial Equations 469

6.8 Applications of Quadratic Equations 470

Group Activity: Building a Factoring Test 477

Chapter 6

This chapter is devoted to factoring polynomials for the purpose of solving equations.

Are You Prepared?

Along the way, we will need the skill of recognizing perfect squares and perfect cubes. A perfect square is a number that is a square of a rational number. For example, 49 is a perfect square because $49 = 7^2$. We also will need to recognize perfect cubes. A perfect cube is a number that is a cube of a rational number. For example, 125 is a perfect cube because $125 = 5^3$.

To complete the puzzle, first answer the questions and fill in the appropriate box. Then fill the grid so that every row, every column, and every 2×3 box contains the digits 1 through 6.

A. What number squared is 1?
B. What number squared is 16?
C. What number cubed is 1?
D. What number squared is 36?
E. What number squared is 25?
F. What number cubed is 64?
G. What number cubed is 8?
H. What number cubed is 27?
I. What number squared is 4?
J. What number squared is 9?

			A		B
	C			D	E
F		1		G	H
I		5			
1	4				2
	5		J		

Section 6.1 Greatest Common Factor and Factoring by Grouping

Concepts

1. Identifying the Greatest Common Factor
2. Factoring out the Greatest Common Factor
3. Factoring out a Negative Factor
4. Factoring out a Binomial Factor
5. Factoring by Grouping

1. Identifying the Greatest Common Factor

Chapter 6 is devoted to a mathematical operation called **factoring**. To factor an integer means to write the integer as a product of two or more integers. To factor a polynomial means to express the polynomial as a product of two or more polynomials.

In the product $2 \cdot 5 = 10$, for example, 2 and 5 are factors of 10.

In the product $(3x + 4)(2x - 1) = 6x^2 + 5x - 4$, the quantities $(3x + 4)$ and $(2x - 1)$ are factors of $6x^2 + 5x - 4$.

We begin our study of factoring by factoring integers. The number 20, for example, can be factored as $1 \cdot 20$ or $2 \cdot 10$ or $4 \cdot 5$ or $2 \cdot 2 \cdot 5$. The product $2 \cdot 2 \cdot 5$ (or equivalently $2^2 \cdot 5$) consists only of prime numbers and is called the **prime factorization**.

The **greatest common factor** (denoted **GCF**) of two or more integers is the largest factor common to each integer. To find the greatest common factor of two or more integers, it is often helpful to express the numbers as a product of prime factors as shown in the next example.

Example 1 Identifying the Greatest Common Factor

Find the greatest common factor.

a. 24 and 36 **b.** 105, 40, and 60

Solution:

First find the prime factorization of each number. Then find the product of common factors.

a.

2⌊24	2⌊36
2⌊12	2⌊18
2⌊6	3⌊9
3	3

Factors of $24 = 2 \cdot 2 \cdot 2 \cdot 3$

Factors of $36 = 2 \cdot 2 \cdot 3 \cdot 3$

Common factors are circled.

The numbers 24 and 36 share two factors of 2 and one factor of 3. Therefore, the greatest common factor is $2 \cdot 2 \cdot 3 = 12$.

b.

5⌊105	5⌊40	5⌊60
3⌊21	2⌊8	3⌊12
7	2⌊4	2⌊4
	2	2

Factors of $105 = 3 \cdot 7 \cdot 5$

Factors of $40 = 2 \cdot 2 \cdot 2 \cdot 5$

Factors of $60 = 2 \cdot 2 \cdot 3 \cdot 5$

The greatest common factor is 5.

Skill Practice Find the GCF.

1. 12 and 20 **2.** 45, 75, and 30

Answers

1. 4 **2.** 15

In Example 2, we find the greatest common factor of two or more variable terms.

Example 2 Identifying the Greatest Common Factor

Find the GCF among each group of terms.

a. $7x^3, 14x^2, 21x^4$ **b.** $15a^4b, 25a^3b^2$

Solution:

List the factors of each term.

a. $7x^3 = 7 \cdot x \cdot x \cdot x$

$14x^2 = 2 \cdot 7 \cdot x \cdot x$

$21x^4 = 3 \cdot 7 \cdot x \cdot x \cdot x \cdot x$

The GCF is $7x^2$.

b. $15a^4b = 3 \cdot 5 \cdot a \cdot a \cdot a \cdot a \cdot b$

$25a^3b^2 = 5 \cdot 5 \cdot a \cdot a \cdot a \cdot b \cdot b$

The GCF is $5a^3b$.

TIP: Notice in Example 2(b) the expressions $15a^4b$ and $25a^3b^2$ share factors of 5, *a*, and *b*. The GCF is the product of the common factors, where each factor is raised to the lowest power to which it occurs in all the original expressions.

$$\left.\begin{aligned} 15a^4b &= 3 \cdot 5a^4b \\ 25a^3b^2 &= 5^2a^3b^2 \end{aligned}\right\} \quad \left.\begin{aligned} &\text{Lowest power of 5 is 1:} \quad 5^1 \\ &\text{Lowest power of } a \text{ is 3:} \quad a^3 \\ &\text{Lowest power of } b \text{ is 1:} \quad b^1 \end{aligned}\right\} \quad \text{The GCF is } 5a^3b.$$

Skill Practice Find the GCF.

3. $10z^3, 15z^5, 40z$ **4.** $6w^3y^5, 21w^4y^2$

Example 3 Identifying the Greatest Common Factor

Find the GCF of the terms $8c^2d^7e$ and $6c^3d^4$.

Solution:

$$\left.\begin{aligned} 8c^2d^7e &= 2^3c^2d^7e \\ 6c^3d^4 &= 2 \cdot 3c^3d^4 \end{aligned}\right\} \quad \text{The common factors are 2, } c\text{, and } d.$$

$$\left.\begin{aligned} &\text{The lowest power of 2 is 1:} \quad 2^1 \\ &\text{The lowest power of } c \text{ is 2:} \quad c^2 \\ &\text{The lowest power of } d \text{ is 4:} \quad d^4 \end{aligned}\right\} \quad \text{The GCF is } 2c^2d^4.$$

Skill Practice Find the GCF.

5. $9m^2np^8, 15n^4p^5$

Sometimes polynomials share a common binomial factor, as shown in Example 4.

Answers

3. $5z$ **4.** $3w^3y^2$

5. $3np^5$

Example 4 **Identifying the Greatest Common Binomial Factor**

Find the greatest common factor of the terms $3x(a + b)$ and $2y(a + b)$.

Solution:

$\left.\begin{array}{l}3x(a+b)\\2y(a+b)\end{array}\right\}$ The only common factor is the binomial $(a + b)$. The GCF is $(a + b)$.

Skill Practice Find the GCF.

6. $a(x + 2)$ and $b(x + 2)$

2. Factoring out the Greatest Common Factor

The process of factoring a polynomial is the reverse process of multiplying polynomials. Both operations use the distributive property: $ab + ac = a(b + c)$.

Multiply

$$5y(y^2 + 3y + 1) = 5y(y^2) + 5y(3y) + 5y(1)$$
$$= 5y^3 + 15y^2 + 5y$$

Factor

$$5y^3 + 15y^2 + 5y = 5y(y^2) + 5y(3y) + 5y(1)$$
$$= 5y(y^2 + 3y + 1)$$

Factoring out the Greatest Common Factor

Step 1 Identify the GCF of all terms of the polynomial.

Step 2 Write each term as the product of the GCF and another factor.

Step 3 Use the distributive property to remove the GCF.

Note: To check the factorization, multiply the polynomials to remove parentheses.

Example 5 **Factoring out the Greatest Common Factor**

Factor out the GCF.

a. $4x - 20$ **b.** $6w^2 + 3w$

Solution:

a. $4x - 20$ The GCF is 4.

$= 4(x) - 4(5)$ Write each term as the product of the GCF and another factor.

$= 4(x - 5)$ Use the distributive property to factor out the GCF.

TIP: Any factoring problem can be checked by multiplying the factors:

Check: $4(x - 5) = 4x - 20$ ✔

Answer

6. $(x + 2)$

b. $6w^2 + 3w$ — The GCF is $3w$.

$= 3w(2w) + 3w(1)$ — Write each term as the product of $3w$ and another factor.

$= 3w(2w + 1)$ — Use the distributive property to factor out the GCF.

Check: $3w(2w + 1) = 6w^2 + 3w$ ✔

Avoiding Mistakes

In Example 5(b), the GCF, $3w$, is equal to one of the terms of the polynomial. In such a case, you must leave a 1 in place of that term after the GCF is factored out.

Skill Practice Factor out the GCF.

7. $6w + 18$ **8.** $21m^3 - 7m$

Example 6 Factoring out the Greatest Common Factor

Factor out the GCF.

a. $15y^3 + 12y^4$ **b.** $9a^4b - 18a^5b + 27a^6b$

Solution:

a. $15y^3 + 12y^4$ — The GCF is $3y^3$.

$= 3y^3(5) + 3y^3(4y)$ — Write each term as the product of $3y^3$ and another factor.

$= 3y^3(5 + 4y)$ — Use the distributive property to factor out the GCF.

Check: $3y^3(5 + 4y) = 15y^3 + 12y^4$ ✔

TIP: When factoring out the GCF from a polynomial, the terms within parentheses are found by dividing the original terms by the GCF. For example:

$15y^3 + 12y^4$ The GCF is $3y^3$.

$$\frac{15y^3}{3y^3} = 5 \quad \text{and} \quad \frac{12y^4}{3y^3} = 4y$$

Thus, $15y^3 + 12y^4 = 3y^3(5 + 4y)$

b. $9a^4b - 18a^5b + 27a^6b$ — The GCF is $9a^4b$.

$= 9a^4b(1) - 9a^4b(2a) + 9a^4b(3a^2)$ — Write each term as the product of $9a^4b$ and another factor.

$= 9a^4b(1 - 2a + 3a^2)$ — Use the distributive property to factor out the GCF.

Check: $9a^4b(1 - 2a + 3a^2)$
$= 9a^4b - 18a^5b + 27a^6b$ ✔

Avoiding Mistakes

The GCF is $9a^4b$, not $3a^4b$. The expression $3a^4b(3 - 6a + 9a^2)$ is not factored completely.

Skill Practice Factor out the GCF.

9. $9y^2 - 6y^5$ **10.** $50s^3t - 40st^2 + 10st$

The greatest common factor of the polynomial $2x + 5y$ is 1. If we factor out the GCF, we have $1(2x + 5y)$. A polynomial whose only factors are itself and 1 is called a **prime polynomial**.

Answers

7. $6(w + 3)$
8. $7m(3m^2 - 1)$
9. $3y^2(3 - 2y^3)$
10. $10st(5s^2 - 4t + 1)$

3. Factoring out a Negative Factor

Usually it is advantageous to factor out the *opposite* of the GCF when the leading coefficient of the polynomial is negative. This is demonstrated in Example 7. Notice that this *changes the signs* of the remaining terms inside the parentheses.

Example 7 Factoring out a Negative Factor

Factor out −3 from the polynomial $-3x^2 + 6x - 33$.

Solution:

$-3x^2 + 6x - 33$ The GCF is 3. However, in this case, we will factor out the *opposite* of the GCF, −3.

$= -3(x^2) + (-3)(-2x) + (-3)(11)$ Write each term as the product of −3 and another factor.

$= -3[x^2 + (-2x) + 11]$ Factor out −3.

$= -3(x^2 - 2x + 11)$ Simplify. Notice that each sign within the trinomial has changed.

Check: $-3(x^2 - 2x + 11) = -3x^2 + 6x - 33$ ✔

Skill Practice Factor out −2 from the polynomial.

11. $-2x^2 - 10x + 16$

Example 8 Factoring out a Negative Factor

Factor out the quantity $-4pq$ from the polynomial $-12p^3q - 8p^2q^2 + 4pq^3$.

Solution:

$-12p^3q - 8p^2q^2 + 4pq^3$ The GCF is $4pq$. However, in this case, we will factor out the *opposite* of the GCF, $-4pq$.

$= -4pq(3p^2) + (-4pq)(2pq) + (-4pq)(-q^2)$ Write each term as the product of $-4pq$ and another factor.

$= -4pq[3p^2 + 2pq + (-q^2)]$ Factor out $-4pq$. Notice that each sign within the trinomial has changed.

$= -4pq(3p^2 + 2pq - q^2)$ To verify that this is the correct factorization and that the signs are correct, multiply the factors.

Check: $-4pq(3p^2 + 2pq - q^2) = -12p^3q - 8p^2q^2 + 4pq^3$ ✔

Skill Practice Factor out $-5xy$ from the polynomial.

12. $-10x^2y + 5xy - 15xy^2$

4. Factoring out a Binomial Factor

The distributive property can also be used to factor out a common factor that consists of more than one term, as shown in Example 9.

Answers

11. $-2(x^2 + 5x - 8)$
12. $-5xy(2x - 1 + 3y)$

Example 9 **Factoring out a Binomial Factor**

Factor out the GCF. $2w(x + 3) - 5(x + 3)$

Solution:

$2w(x + 3) - 5(x + 3)$	The greatest common factor is the quantity $(x + 3)$.
$= (x + 3)(2w - 5)$	Use the distributive property to factor out the GCF.

Skill Practice Factor out the GCF.

13. $8y(a + b) + 9(a + b)$

5. Factoring by Grouping

When two binomials are multiplied, the product before simplifying contains four terms. For example:

$$(x + 4)(3a + 2b) = (x + 4)(3a) + (x + 4)(2b)$$
$$= (x + 4)(3a) + (x + 4)(2b)$$
$$= 3ax + 12a + 2bx + 8b$$

In Example 10, we learn how to reverse this process. That is, given a four-term polynomial, we will factor it as a product of two binomials. The process is called *factoring by grouping*.

Factoring by Grouping

To factor a four-term polynomial by grouping:

Step 1 Identify and factor out the GCF from all four terms.

Step 2 Factor out the GCF from the first pair of terms. Factor out the GCF from the second pair of terms. (Sometimes it is necessary to factor out the opposite of the GCF.)

Step 3 If the two terms share a common binomial factor, factor out the binomial factor.

Example 10 **Factoring by Grouping**

Factor by grouping. $3ax + 12a + 2bx + 8b$

Solution:

$3ax + 12a + 2bx + 8b$	**Step 1:** Identify and factor out the GCF from all four terms. In this case, the GCF is 1.
$= 3ax + 12a \;\vdots\; + 2bx + 8b$	Group the first pair of terms and the second pair of terms.

Answer

13. $(a + b)(8y + 9)$

$= 3a(x + 4) + 2b(x + 4)$ **Step 2:** Factor out the GCF from each pair of terms. *Note:* The two terms now share a common binomial factor of $(x + 4)$.

$= (x + 4)(3a + 2b)$ **Step 3:** Factor out the common binomial factor.

Check: $(x + 4)(3a + 2b) = 3ax + 2bx + 12a + 8b$ ✔

Note: Step 2 results in two terms with a common binomial factor. If the two binomials are different, step 3 cannot be performed. In such a case, the original polynomial may not be factorable by grouping, or different pairs of terms may need to be grouped and inspected.

Skill Practice Factor by grouping.

14. $5x + 10y + ax + 2ay$

TIP: One frequently asked question when factoring is whether the order can be switched between the factors. The answer is yes. Because multiplication is commutative, the order in which the factors are written does not matter.

$$(x + 4)(3a + 2b) = (3a + 2b)(x + 4)$$

Example 11 Factoring by Grouping

Factor by grouping. $ax + ay - x - y$

Solution:

$ax + ay - x - y$ **Step 1:** Identify and factor out the GCF from all four terms. In this case, the GCF is 1.

$= ax + ay \mid - x - y$ Group the first pair of terms and the second pair of terms.

$= a(x + y) - 1(x + y)$ **Step 2:** Factor out a from the first pair of terms.

Factor out -1 from the second pair of terms. (This causes sign changes within the second parentheses.) The terms in parentheses now match.

$= (x + y)(a - 1)$ **Step 3:** Factor out the common binomial factor.

Check: $(x + y)(a - 1) = x(a) + x(-1) + y(a) + y(-1)$

$= ax - x + ay - y$ ✔

Avoiding Mistakes

In step 2, the expression $a(x + y) - (x + y)$ is not yet factored completely because it is a *difference*, not a product. To factor the expression, you must carry it one step further.

$$a(x + y) - 1(x + y)$$
$$= (x + y)(a - 1)$$

The factored form must be represented as a product.

Skill Practice Factor by grouping.

15. $tu - tv - u + v$

Answers

14. $(x + 2y)(5 + a)$
15. $(u - v)(t - 1)$

Example 12 Factoring by Grouping

Factor by grouping. $16w^4 - 40w^3 - 12w^2 + 30w$

Solution:

$16w^4 - 40w^3 - 12w^2 + 30w$

$= 2w[8w^3 - 20w^2 - 6w + 15]$

Step 1: Identify and factor out the GCF from all four terms. In this case, the GCF is $2w$.

$= 2w[8w^3 - 20w^2 \,\vdots\, - 6w + 15]$

Group the first pair of terms and the second pair of terms.

$= 2w[4w^2(2w - 5) - 3(2w - 5)]$

Step 2: Factor out $4w^2$ from the first pair of terms.

Factor out -3 from the second pair of terms. (This causes sign changes within the second parentheses.) The terms in parentheses now match.

$= 2w[(2w - 5)(4w^2 - 3)]$

Step 3: Factor out the common binomial factor.

$= 2w(2w - 5)(4w^2 - 3)$

Skill Practice Factor by grouping.

16. $3ab^2 + 6b^2 - 12ab - 24b$

Answer

16. $3b(a + 2)(b - 4)$

Section 6.1 Practice Exercises

Study Skills Exercise

The final exam is just around the corner. Your old tests and quizzes provide good material to study for the final exam. Use your old tests to make a list of the chapters on which you need to concentrate. Ask your professor for help if there are still concepts that you do not understand.

Vocabulary and Key Concepts

1. a. Factoring a polynomial means to write it as a _______ of two or more polynomials.

b. The prime factorization of a number consists of only _______ factors.

c. The _______ _______ _______ (GCF) of two or more integers is the largest whole number that is a factor of each integer.

d. A polynomial whose only factors are 1 and itself is called a _______ polynomial.

e. The first step toward factoring a polynomial is to factor out the _______ _______ _______.

f. To factor a four-term polynomial, we try the process of factoring by _______.

Concept 1: Identifying the Greatest Common Factor

2. List all the factors of 24.

For Exercises 3–14, identify the greatest common factor. **(See Examples 1–4.)**

3. 28, 63
4. 24, 40
5. 42, 30, 60
6. 20, 52, 32
7. $3xy, 7y$
8. $10mn, 11n$
9. $12w^3z, 16w^2z$
10. $20cd, 15c^3d$
11. $8x^3y^4z^2, 12xy^5z^4, 6x^2y^8z^3$
12. $15r^2s^2t^5, 5r^3s^4t^3, 30r^4s^3t^2$
13. $7(x - y), 9(x - y)$
14. $(2a - b), 3(2a - b)$

Concept 2: Factoring out the Greatest Common Factor

15. a. Use the distributive property to multiply $3(x - 2y)$.

b. Use the distributive property to factor $3x - 6y$.

16. a. Use the distributive property to multiply $a^2(5a + b)$.

b. Use the distributive property to factor $5a^3 + a^2b$.

For Exercises 17–36, factor out the GCF. **(See Examples 5–6.)**

17. $4p + 12$
18. $3q - 15$
19. $5c^2 - 10c + 15$
20. $16d^3 + 24d^2 + 32d$
21. $x^5 + x^3$
22. $y^2 - y^3$
23. $t^4 - 4t + 8t^2$
24. $7r^3 - r^5 + r^4$
25. $2ab + 4a^3b$
26. $5u^3v^2 - 5uv$
27. $38x^2y - 19x^2y^4$
28. $100a^5b^3 + 16a^2b$
29. $6x^3y^5 - 18xy^9z$
30. $15mp^7q^4 + 12m^4q^3$
31. $5 + 7y^3$
32. $w^3 - 5u^3v^2$
33. $42p^3q^2 + 14pq^2 - 7p^4q^4$
34. $8m^2n^3 - 24m^2n^2 + 4m^3n$
35. $t^5 + 2rt^3 - 3t^4 + 4r^2t^2$
36. $u^2v + 5u^3v^2 - 2u^2 + 8uv$

Concept 3: Factoring out a Negative Factor

37. For the polynomial $-2x^3 - 4x^2 + 8x$

a. Factor out $-2x$. **b.** Factor out $2x$.

38. For the polynomial $-9y^5 + 3y^3 - 12y$

a. Factor out $-3y$. **b.** Factor out $3y$.

39. Factor out -1 from the polynomial $-8t^2 - 9t - 2$.

40. Factor out -1 from the polynomial $-6x^3 - 2x - 5$.

For Exercises 41–46, factor out the opposite of the greatest common factor. **(See Examples 7–8.)**

41. $-15p^3 - 30p^2$
42. $-24m^3 - 12m^4$
43. $-3m^4n^2 + 6m^2n - 9mn^2$
44. $-12p^3t + 2p^2t^3 + 6pt^2$
45. $-7x - 6y - 2z$
46. $-4a + 5b - c$

Concept 4: Factoring out a Binomial Factor

For Exercises 47–52, factor out the GCF. **(See Example 9.)**

47. $13(a + 6) - 4b(a + 6)$
48. $7(x^2 + 1) - y(x^2 + 1)$
49. $8v(w^2 - 2) + (w^2 - 2)$
50. $t(r + 2) + (r + 2)$
51. $21x(x + 3) + 7x^2(x + 3)$
52. $5y^3(y - 2) - 15y(y - 2)$

Concept 5: Factoring by Grouping

For Exercises 53–72, factor by grouping. **(See Examples 10–11.)**

53. $8a^2 - 4ab + 6ac - 3bc$

54. $4x^3 + 3x^2y + 4xy^2 + 3y^3$

55. $3q + 3p + qr + pr$

56. $xy - xz + 7y - 7z$

57. $6x^2 + 3x + 4x + 2$

58. $4y^2 + 8y + 7y + 14$

59. $2t^2 + 6t - t - 3$

60. $2p^2 - p - 2p + 1$

61. $6y^2 - 2y - 9y + 3$

62. $5a^2 + 30a - 2a - 12$

63. $b^4 + b^3 - 4b - 4$

64. $8w^5 + 12w^2 - 10w^3 - 15$

65. $3j^2k + 15k + j^2 + 5$

66. $2ab^2 - 6ac + b^2 - 3c$

67. $14w^6x^6 + 7w^6 - 2x^6 - 1$

68. $18p^4x - 4x - 9p^5 + 2p$

69. $ay + bx + by + ax$
(*Hint:* Rearrange the terms.)

70. $2c + 3ay + ac + 6y$

71. $vw^2 - 3 + w - 3wv$

72. $2x^2 + 6m + 12 + x^2m$

Mixed Exercises

For Exercises 73–78, factor out the GCF first. Then factor by grouping. **(See Example 12.)**

73. $15x^4 + 15x^2y^2 + 10x^3y + 10xy^3$

74. $2a^3b - 4a^2b + 32ab - 64b$

75. $4abx - 4b^2x - 4ab + 4b^2$

76. $p^2q - pq^2 - rp^2q + rpq^2$

77. $6st^2 - 18st - 6t^4 + 18t^3$

78. $15j^3 - 10j^2k - 15j^2k^2 + 10jk^3$

79. The formula $P = 2l + 2w$ represents the perimeter, P, of a rectangle given the length, l, and the width, w. Factor out the GCF and write an equivalent formula in factored form.

80. The formula $P = 2a + 2b$ represents the perimeter, P, of a parallelogram given the base, b, and an adjacent side, a. Factor out the GCF and write an equivalent formula in factored form.

81. The formula $S = 2\pi r^2 + 2\pi rh$ represents the surface area, S, of a cylinder with radius, r, and height, h. Factor out the GCF and write an equivalent formula in factored form.

82. The formula $A = P + Prt$ represents the total amount of money, A, in an account that earns simple interest at a rate, r, for t years. Factor out the GCF and write an equivalent formula in factored form.

Expanding Your Skills

83. Factor out $\frac{1}{7}$ from $\frac{1}{7}x^2 + \frac{3}{7}x - \frac{5}{7}$.

84. Factor out $\frac{1}{5}$ from $\frac{6}{5}y^2 - \frac{4}{5}y + \frac{1}{5}$.

85. Factor out $\frac{1}{4}$ from $\frac{5}{4}w^2 + \frac{3}{4}w + \frac{9}{4}$.

86. Factor out $\frac{1}{6}$ from $\frac{1}{6}p^2 - \frac{3}{6}p + \frac{5}{6}$.

87. Write a polynomial that has a GCF of $3x$. (Answers may vary.)

88. Write a polynomial that has a GCF of $7y$. (Answers may vary.)

89. Write a polynomial that has a GCF of $4p^2q$. (Answers may vary.)

90. Write a polynomial that has a GCF of $2ab^2$. (Answers may vary.)

Section 6.2 Factoring Trinomials of the Form $x^2 + bx + c$

Concept

1. Factoring Trinomials with a Leading Coefficient of 1

1. Factoring Trinomials with a Leading Coefficient of 1

In Section 5.6, we learned how to multiply two binomials. We also saw that such a product often results in a trinomial. For example:

$$(x + 3)(x + 7) = \underbrace{x^2}_{\text{Product of first terms}} + \underbrace{7x + 3x}_{\text{Sum of products of inner terms and outer terms}} + \underbrace{21}_{\text{Product of last terms}} = x^2 + 10x + 21$$

In this section, we want to reverse the process. That is, given a trinomial, we want to *factor* it as a product of two binomials. In particular, we begin our study with the case in which a trinomial has a leading coefficient of 1.

Consider the quadratic trinomial $x^2 + bx + c$. To produce a leading term of x^2, we can construct binomials of the form $(x + \quad)(x + \quad)$. The remaining terms can be obtained from two integers, p and q, whose product is c and whose sum is b.

$$x^2 + bx + c = (x + \overbrace{p)(x + q}^{\text{Factors of } c}) = x^2 + qx + px + pq$$

$$= x^2 + \underbrace{(q + p)}_{\text{Sum} = b}x + \underbrace{pq}_{\text{Product} = c}$$

This process is demonstrated in Example 1.

Example 1 Factoring a Trinomial of the Form $x^2 + bx + c$

Factor. $x^2 + 4x - 45$

Solution:

$x^2 + 4x - 45 = (x + \square)(x + \square)$ The product of the first terms in the binomials must equal the leading term of the trinomial $x \cdot x = x^2$.

We must fill in the blanks with two integers whose product is -45 and whose sum is 4. The factors must have opposite signs to produce a negative product. The possible factorizations of -45 are

Product = −45	Sum
$-1 \cdot 45$	44
$-3 \cdot 15$	12
$-5 \cdot 9$	4
$-9 \cdot 5$	-4
$-15 \cdot 3$	-12
$-45 \cdot 1$	-44

$x^2 + 4x - 45 = (x + \square)(x + \square)$

$= [x + (-5)](x + 9)$ Fill in the blanks with -5 and 9.

$= (x - 5)(x + 9)$ Factored form

Check:
$(x - 5)(x + 9) = x^2 + 9x - 5x - 45$
$= x^2 + 4x - 45$ ✔

Skill Practice Factor.

1. $x^2 - 5x - 14$

Multiplication of polynomials is a commutative operation. Therefore, in Example 1, we can express the factorization as $(x - 5)(x + 9)$ or as $(x + 9)(x - 5)$.

Example 2 Factoring a Trinomial of the Form $x^2 + bx + c$

Factor. $w^2 - 15w + 50$

Solution:

$w^2 - 15w + 50 = (w + \square)(w + \square)$ The product $w \cdot w = w^2$.

Find two integers whose product is 50 and whose sum is -15. To form a positive product, the factors must be either both positive or both negative. The sum must be negative, so we will choose negative factors of 50.

Product = 50	Sum
$(-1)(-50)$	-51
$(-2)(-25)$	-27
$(-5)(-10)$	-15

$w^2 - 15w + 50 = (w + \square)(w + \square)$

$= [w + (-5)][w + (-10)]$

$= (w - 5)(w - 10)$ Factored form

Check:

$(w - 5)(w - 10) = w^2 - 10w - 5w + 50$
$= w^2 - 15w + 50$ ✔

Skill Practice Factor.

2. $z^2 - 16z + 48$

TIP: Practice will help you become proficient in factoring polynomials. As you do your homework, keep these important guidelines in mind:

- To factor a trinomial, write the trinomial in descending order such as $x^2 + bx + c$.
- For all factoring problems, always factor out the GCF from all terms first.

Answers

1. $(x - 7)(x + 2)$
2. $(z - 4)(z - 12)$

Furthermore, we offer the following rules for determining the signs within the binomial factors.

Sign Rules for Factoring Trinomials

Given the trinomial $x^2 + bx + c$, the signs within the binomial factors are determined as follows:

Case 1 If c is *positive*, then the signs in the binomials must be the same (either both positive or both negative). The correct choice is determined by the middle term. If the middle term is positive, then both signs must be positive. If the middle term is negative, then both signs must be negative.

c is positive.	c is positive.
$x^2 + 6x + 8$	$x^2 - 6x + 8$
$(x + 2)(x + 4)$	$(x - 2)(x - 4)$
Same signs	Same signs

Case 2 If c is *negative*, then the signs in the binomials must be different.

c is negative.	c is negative.
$x^2 + 2x - 35$	$x^2 - 2x - 35$
$(x + 7)(x - 5)$	$(x - 7)(x + 5)$
Different signs	Different signs

Example 3 Factoring Trinomials

Factor. **a.** $-8p - 48 + p^2$ **b.** $-40t - 30t^2 + 10t^3$

Solution:

a. $-8p - 48 + p^2$

$= p^2 - 8p - 48$ Write in descending order.

$= (p \quad \square)(p \quad \square)$ Find two integers whose product is -48 and whose sum is -8. The numbers are -12 and 4.

$= (p - 12)(p + 4)$ Factored form

b. $-40t - 30t^2 + 10t^3$

$= 10t^3 - 30t^2 - 40t$ Write in descending order.

$= 10t(t^2 - 3t - 4)$ Factor out the GCF.

$= 10t(t \quad \square)(t \quad \square)$ Find two integers whose product is -4 and whose sum is -3. The numbers are -4 and 1.

$= 10t(t - 4)(t + 1)$ Factored form

Skill Practice Factor.

3. $-5w + w^2 - 6$ **4.** $30y^3 + 2y^4 + 112y^2$

Answers

3. $(w - 6)(w + 1)$

4. $2y^2(y + 8)(y + 7)$

Example 4 Factoring Trinomials

Factor. **a.** $-a^2 + 6a - 8$ **b.** $-2c^2 - 22cd - 60d^2$

Solution:

a. $-a^2 + 6a - 8$

$= -1(a^2 - 6a + 8)$ It is generally easier to factor a trinomial with a *positive* leading coefficient. Therefore, we will factor out -1 from all terms.

$= -1(a \quad \square)(a \quad \square)$ Find two integers whose product is 8 and whose sum is -6. The numbers are -4 and -2.

$= -1(a - 4)(a - 2)$

$= -(a - 4)(a - 2)$

Avoiding Mistakes

Recall that factoring out -1 from a polynomial changes the signs of all terms within parentheses.

b. $-2c^2 - 22cd - 60d^2$

$= -2(c^2 + 11cd + 30d^2)$ Factor out -2.

$= -2(c \quad \square d)(c \quad \square d)$ Notice that the second pair of terms has a factor of d. This will produce a product of d^2.

$= -2(c + 5d)(c + 6d)$ Find two integers whose product is 30 and whose sum is 11. The numbers are 5 and 6.

Skill Practice Factor.

5. $-x^2 + x + 12$ **6.** $-3a^2 + 15ab - 12b^2$

To factor a trinomial of the form $x^2 + bx + c$, we must find two integers whose product is c and whose sum is b. If no such integers exist, then the trinomial is prime.

Example 5 Factoring Trinomials

Factor. $x^2 - 13x + 14$

Solution:

$x^2 - 13x + 14$ The trinomial is in descending order. The GCF is 1.

$= (x \quad \square)(x \quad \square)$ Find two integers whose product is 14 and whose sum is -13. No such integers exist.

The trinomial $x^2 - 13x + 14$ is prime.

Skill Practice Factor.

7. $x^2 - 7x + 28$

Answers

5. $-(x - 4)(x + 3)$
6. $-3(a - b)(a - 4b)$
7. Prime

Section 6.2 Practice Exercises

Vocabulary and Key Concepts

1. **a.** Given a trinomial $x^2 + bx + c$, if c is positive, then the signs in the binomial factors are either both ________ or both negative.

   b. Given a trinomial $x^2 + bx + c$, if c is negative, then the signs in the binomial factors are (choose one: both positive, both negative, different).

   c. Which is the correct factored form of $x^2 - 7x - 44$? The product $(x + 4)(x - 11)$ or $(x - 11)(x + 4)$?

   d. Which is the complete factorization of $3x^2 + 24x + 36$? The product $(3x + 6)(x + 6)$ or $3(x + 6)(x + 2)$?

Review Exercises

For Exercises 2–6, factor completely.

2. $9a^6b^3 - 27a^3b^6 - 3a^2b^2$

3. $3t(t - 5) - 6(t - 5)$

4. $4(3x - 2) + 8x(3x - 2)$

5. $ax + 2bx - 5a - 10b$

6. $m^2 - mx - 3pm + 3px$

Concept 1: Factoring Trinomials with a Leading Coefficient of 1

Animation

For Exercises 7–20, factor completely. **(See Examples 1, 2, and 5.)**

7. $x^2 + 10x + 16$

8. $y^2 + 18y + 80$

9. $z^2 - 11z + 18$

10. $w^2 - 7w + 12$

11. $z^2 - 3z - 18$

12. $w^2 + 4w - 12$

13. $p^2 - 3p - 40$

14. $a^2 - 10a + 9$

15. $t^2 + 6t - 40$

16. $m^2 - 12m + 11$

17. $x^2 - 3x + 20$

18. $y^2 + 6y + 18$

19. $n^2 + 8n + 16$

20. $v^2 + 10v + 25$

For Exercises 21–24, assume that b and c represent positive integers.

21. When factoring a polynomial of the form $x^2 + bx + c$, pick an appropriate combination of signs.

a. (+)(+) **b.** (−)(−) **c.** (+)(−)

22. When factoring a polynomial of the form $x^2 + bx - c$, pick an appropriate combination of signs.

a. (+)(+) **b.** (−)(−) **c.** (+)(−)

23. When factoring a polynomial of the form $x^2 - bx - c$, pick an appropriate combination of signs.

a. (+)(+) **b.** (−)(−) **c.** (+)(−)

24. When factoring a polynomial of the form $x^2 - bx + c$, pick an appropriate combination of signs.

a. (+)(+) **b.** (−)(−) **c.** (+)(−)

25. Which is the correct factorization of $y^2 - y - 12$? Explain. $(y - 4)(y + 3)$ or $(y + 3)(y - 4)$

26. Which is the correct factorization of $x^2 + 14x + 13$? Explain. $(x + 13)(x + 1)$ or $(x + 1)(x + 13)$

27. Which is the correct factorization of $w^2 + 2w + 1$? Explain. $(w + 1)(w + 1)$ or $(w + 1)^2$

28. Which is the correct factorization of $z^2 - 4z + 4$? Explain. $(z - 2)(z - 2)$ or $(z - 2)^2$

29. In what order should a trinomial be written before attempting to factor it?

30. Referring to page 427, write two important guidelines to follow when factoring trinomials.

For Exercises 31–66, factor completely. Be sure to factor out the GCF when necessary. **(See Examples 3–4.)**

31. $-13x + x^2 - 30$

32. $12y - 160 + y^2$

33. $-18w + 65 + w^2$

34. $17t + t^2 + 72$

35. $22t + t^2 + 72$

36. $10q - 1200 + q^2$

37. $3x^2 - 30x - 72$

38. $2z^2 + 4z - 198$

39. $8p^3 - 40p^2 + 32p$

40. $5w^4 - 35w^3 + 50w^2$

41. $y^4z^2 - 12y^3z^2 + 36y^2z^2$

42. $t^4u^2 + 6t^3u^2 + 9t^2u^2$

43. $-x^2 + 10x - 24$

44. $-y^2 - 12y - 35$

45. $-5a^2 + 5ax + 30x^2$

46. $-2m^2 + 10mn + 12n^2$

47. $-4 - 2c^2 - 6c$

48. $-40d - 30 - 10d^2$

49. $x^3y^3 - 19x^2y^3 + 60xy^3$

50. $y^2z^5 + 17yz^5 + 60z^5$

51. $12p^2 - 96p + 84$

52. $5w^2 - 40w - 45$

53. $-2m^2 + 22m - 20$

54. $-3x^2 - 36x - 81$

55. $c^2 + 6cd + 5d^2$

56. $x^2 + 8xy + 12y^2$

57. $a^2 - 9ab + 14b^2$

58. $m^2 - 15mn + 44n^2$

59. $a^2 + 4a + 18$

60. $b^2 - 6a + 15$

61. $2q + q^2 - 63$

62. $-32 - 4t + t^2$

63. $x^2 + 20x + 100$

64. $z^2 - 24z + 144$

65. $t^2 + 18t - 40$

66. $d^2 + 2d - 99$

67. A student factored a trinomial as $(2x - 4)(x - 3)$. The instructor did not give full credit. Why?

68. A student factored a trinomial as $(y + 2)(5y - 15)$. The instructor did not give full credit. Why?

69. What polynomial factors as $(x - 4)(x + 13)$?

70. What polynomial factors as $(q - 7)(q + 10)$?

71. Raul purchased a parcel of land in the country. The given expressions represent the lengths of the boundary lines of his property.

a. Write the perimeter of the land as a polynomial in simplified form.

b. Write the polynomial from part (a) in factored form.

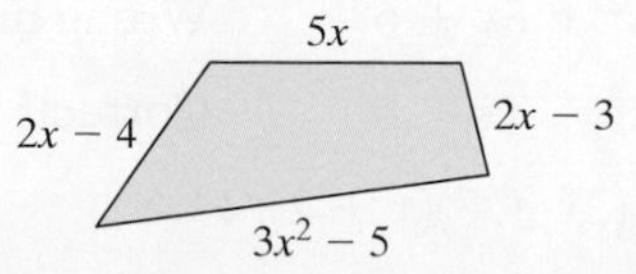

72. Jamison painted a mural in the shape of a triangle on the wall of a building. The given expressions represent the lengths of the sides of the triangle.

a. Write the perimeter of the triangle as a polynomial in simplified form.

b. Write the polynomial in factored form.

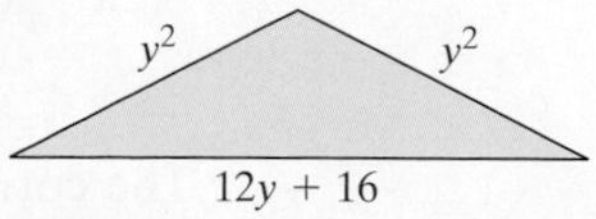

Expanding Your Skills

For Exercises 73–76, factor completely.

73. $x^4 + 10x^2 + 9$ **74.** $y^4 + 4y^2 - 21$ **75.** $w^4 + 2w^2 - 15$ **76.** $p^4 - 13p^2 + 40$

77. Find all integers, b, that make the trinomial $x^2 + bx + 6$ factorable.

78. Find all integers, b, that make the trinomial $x^2 + bx + 10$ factorable.

79. Find a value of c that makes the trinomial $x^2 + 6x + c$ factorable.

80. Find a value of c that makes the trinomial $x^2 + 8x + c$ factorable.

Section 6.3 Factoring Trinomials: Trial-and-Error Method

Concept

1. Factoring Trinomials by the Trial-and-Error Method

In Section 6.2, we learned how to factor trinomials of the form $x^2 + bx + c$. These trinomials have a leading coefficient of 1. In this section and Section 6.4, we will consider the more general case in which the leading coefficient may be *any* nonzero integer. That is, we will factor quadratic trinomials of the form $ax^2 + bx + c$ (where $a \neq 0$). The method presented in this section is called the trial-and-error method.

1. Factoring Trinomials by the Trial-and-Error Method

To understand the basis of factoring trinomials of the form $ax^2 + bx + c$, first consider the multiplication of two binomials:

Product of 2 · 1 Product of 3 · 2

$$(2x + 3)(1x + 2) = 2x^2 + \underbrace{\mathbf{4x + 3x}}_{\text{Sum of products of inner terms and outer terms}} + 6 = 2x^2 + 7x + 6$$

To factor the trinomial, $2x^2 + 7x + 6$, this operation is reversed.

Factors of 2

$$2x^2 + 7x + 6 = (\square x \quad \square)(\square x \quad \square)$$

Factors of 6

We need to fill in the blanks so that the product of the first terms in the binomials is $2x^2$ and the product of the last terms in the binomials is 6. Furthermore, the factors of $2x^2$ and 6 must be chosen so that the sum of the products of the inner terms and outer terms equals $7x$.

To produce the product $2x^2$, we might try the factors $2x$ and x within the binomials:

$$(2x \quad \square)(x \quad \square)$$

To produce a product of 6, the remaining terms in the binomials must either both be positive or both be negative. To produce a positive middle term, we will try positive factors of 6 in the remaining blanks until the correct product is found. The possibilities are $1 \cdot 6$, $2 \cdot 3$, $3 \cdot 2$, and $6 \cdot 1$.

$(2x + 1)(x + 6) = 2x^2 + 12x + 1x + 6 = 2x^2 + 13x + 6$	Wrong middle term
$(2x + 2)(x + 3) = 2x^2 + 6x + 2x + 6 = 2x^2 + 8x + 6$	Wrong middle term
$(2x + 6)(x + 1) = 2x^2 + 2x + 6x + 6 = 2x^2 + 8x + 6$	Wrong middle term
$(2x + 3)(x + 2) = 2x^2 + 4x + 3x + 6 = 2x^2 + 7x + 6$	Correct!

The correct factorization of $2x^2 + 7x + 6$ is $(2x + 3)(x + 2)$. ✔

As this example shows, we factor a trinomial of the form $ax^2 + bx + c$ by shuffling the factors of a and c within the binomials until the correct product is obtained. However, sometimes it is not necessary to test all the possible combinations of factors. In the previous example, the GCF of the original trinomial is 1. Therefore, any binomial factor whose terms share a common factor *greater than 1* does not need to be considered. In this case, the possibilities $(2x + 2)(x + 3)$ and $(2x + 6)(x + 1)$ cannot work.

$$\underbrace{(2x + 2)}_{\text{Common factor of 2}}(x + 3) \qquad \underbrace{(2x + 6)}_{\text{Common factor of 2}}(x + 1)$$

Trial-and-Error Method to Factor $ax^2 + bx + c$

Step 1 Factor out the GCF.

Step 2 List all pairs of positive factors of a and pairs of positive factors of c. Consider the reverse order for one of the lists of factors.

Step 3 Construct two binomials of the form:

Factors of a

$$(\square x \quad \square)(\square x \quad \square)$$

Factors of c

Step 4 Test each combination of factors and signs until the correct product is found.

Step 5 If no combination of factors produces the correct product, the trinomial cannot be factored further and is a *prime polynomial.*

Before we begin Example 1, keep these two important guidelines in mind:

- For any factoring problem you encounter, always factor out the GCF from all terms first.
- To factor a trinomial, write the trinomial in the form $ax^2 + bx + c$.

Example 1 Factoring a Trinomial by the Trial-and-Error Method

Factor the trinomial by the trial-and-error method. $10x^2 + 11x + 1$

Solution:

$10x^2 + 11x + 1$ **Step 1:** Factor out the GCF from all terms. In this case, the GCF is 1.

The trinomial is written in the form $ax^2 + bx + c$.

To factor $10x^2 + 11x + 1$, two binomials must be constructed in the form:

Factors of 10

$$(\square x \quad \square)(\square x \quad \square)$$

Factors of 1

Step 2: To produce the product $10x^2$, we might try $5x$ and $2x$, or $10x$ and $1x$. To produce a product of 1, we will try the factors $(1)(1)$ and $(-1)(-1)$.

Step 3: Construct all possible binomial factors using different combinations of the factors of $10x^2$ and 1.

$(5x + 1)(2x + 1) = 10x^2 + 5x + 2x + 1 = 10x^2 + 7x + 1$ Wrong middle term

$(5x - 1)(2x - 1) = 10x^2 - 5x - 2x + 1 = 10x^2 - 7x + 1$ Wrong middle term

Because the numbers 1 and -1 did not produce the correct trinomial when coupled with $5x$ and $2x$, try using $10x$ and $1x$.

$(10x - 1)(1x - 1) = 10x^2 - 10x - 1x + 1 = 10x^2 - 11x + 1$ Wrong sign on the middle term

$(10x + 1)(1x + 1) = 10x^2 + 10x + 1x + 1 = 10x^2 + 11x + 1$ Correct!

Therefore, $10x^2 + 11x + 1 = (10x + 1)(x + 1)$.

Skill Practice Factor using the trial-and-error method.

1. $3b^2 + 8b + 4$

In Example 1, the factors of 1 must have the same signs to produce a positive product. Therefore, the binomial factors must both be sums or both be differences. Determining the correct signs is an important aspect of factoring trinomials. We suggest the following guidelines:

Sign Rules for the Trial-and-Error Method

Given the trinomial $ax^2 + bx + c$, $(a > 0)$, the signs can be determined as follows:

- If *c is positive*, then the signs in the binomials must be the same (either both positive or both negative). The correct choice is determined by the middle term. If the middle term is positive, then both signs must be positive. If the middle term is negative, then both signs must be negative.

  c is positive: $20x^2 + 43x + 21$ → $(4x + 3)(5x + 7)$ — Same signs

  c is positive: $20x^2 - 43x + 21$ → $(4x - 3)(5x - 7)$ — Same signs

- If *c is negative*, then the signs in the binomial must be different. The middle term in the trinomial determines which factor gets the positive sign and which gets the negative sign.

  c is negative: $x^2 + 3x - 28$ → $(x + 7)(x - 4)$ — Different signs

  c is negative: $x^2 - 3x - 28$ → $(x - 7)(x + 4)$ — Different signs

TIP: Look at the sign on the third term. If it is a sum, the signs will be the same in the two binomials. If it is a difference, the signs in the two binomials will be different: sum–same sign; difference–different signs.

Answer

1. $(3b + 2)(b + 2)$

Example 2 Factoring a Trinomial by the Trial-and-Error Method

Factor the trinomial. $13y - 6 + 8y^2$

Solution:

$13y - 6 + 8y^2$

$= 8y^2 + 13y - 6$ Write the polynomial in descending order.

$(\square y\ \ \square)(\square y\ \ \square)$ **Step 1:** The GCF is 1.

Step 2: List the positive factors of 8 and positive factors of 6. Consider the reverse order in one list of factors.

Factors of 8	Factors of 6
$1 \cdot 8$	$1 \cdot 6$
$2 \cdot 4$	$2 \cdot 3$
	$3 \cdot 2$ (reverse order)
	$6 \cdot 1$ (reverse order)

Step 3: Construct all possible binomial factors using different combinations of the factors of 8 and 6.

$(1y\ \ 1)(8y\ \ 6)$
$(1y\ \ 3)(8y\ \ 2)$
$(2y\ \ 1)(4y\ \ 6)$
$(2y\ \ 2)(4y\ \ 3)$
$(2y\ \ 3)(4y\ \ 2)$
$(2y\ \ 6)(4y\ \ 1)$

Without regard to signs, these factorizations cannot work because the terms in the binomials share a common factor greater than 1.

Test the remaining factorizations. Keep in mind that to produce a product of -6, the signs within the parentheses must be opposite (one positive and one negative). Also, the sum of the products of the inner terms and outer terms must be combined to form $13y$.

$(1y\ \ 6)(8y\ \ 1)$ *Incorrect.* Wrong middle term. Regardless of the signs, the product of inner terms, $48y$, and the product of outer terms, $1y$, cannot be combined to form the middle term $13y$.

$(1y\ \ 2)(8y\ \ 3)$ *Correct.* The terms $16y$ and $3y$ can be combined to form the middle term $13y$, provided the signs are applied correctly. We require $+16y$ and $-3y$.

The correct factorization of $8y^2 + 13y - 6$ is $(y + 2)(8y - 3)$.

Skill Practice Factor.

2. $-25w + 6w^2 + 4$

Remember that the first step in any factoring problem is to remove the GCF. By removing the GCF, the remaining terms of the trinomial will be simpler and may have smaller coefficients.

Answer

2. $(6w - 1)(w - 4)$

Example 3 Factoring a Trinomial by the Trial-and-Error Method

Factor the trinomial by the trial-and-error method. $40x^3 - 104x^2 + 10x$

Solution:

$40x^3 - 104x^2 + 10x$

$= 2x(20x^2 - 52x + 5)$ **Step 1:** The GCF is $2x$.

$= 2x(\square x \quad \square)(\square x \quad \square)$ **Step 2:** List the factors of 20 and factors of 5. Consider the reverse order in one list of factors.

> **TIP:** Notice that when the GCF, $2x$, is removed from the original trinomial, the new trinomial has smaller coefficients. This makes the factoring process simpler. It is easier to list the factors of 20 and 5 than the factors of 40 and 10.

Factors of 20	Factors of 5
$1 \cdot 20$	$1 \cdot 5$
$2 \cdot 10$	$5 \cdot 1$
$4 \cdot 5$	

Step 3: Construct all possible binomial factors using different combinations of the factors of 20 and factors of 5. The signs in the parentheses must both be negative.

$= 2x(1x - 1)(20x - 5)$
$= 2x(2x - 1)(10x - 5)$
$= 2x(4x - 1)(5x - 5)$

Incorrect. Once the GCF has been removed from the original polynomial, the binomial factors cannot contain a GCF greater than 1.

$= 2x(1x - 5)(20x - 1)$ *Incorrect.* Wrong middle term.

$2x(x - 5)(20x - 1)$
$= 2x(20x^2 - 1x - 100x + 5)$
$= 2x(20x^2 - 101x + 5)$

$= 2x(4x - 5)(5x - 1)$ *Incorrect.* Wrong middle term.

$2x(4x - 5)(5x - 1)$
$= 2x(20x^2 - 4x - 25x + 5)$
$= 2x(20x^2 - 29x + 5)$

$= 2x(2x - 5)(10x - 1)$ *Correct.*

$2x(2x - 5)(10x - 1)$
$= 2x(20x^2 - 2x - 50x + 5)$
$= 2x(20x^2 - 52x + 5)$
$= 40x^3 - 104x^2 + 10x$

The correct factorization is $2x(2x - 5)(10x - 1)$.

Skill Practice Factor.

3. $8t^3 + 38t^2 + 24t$

Often it is easier to factor a trinomial when the leading coefficient is positive. If the leading coefficient is negative, consider factoring out the opposite of the GCF.

Answer

3. $2t(4t + 3)(t + 4)$

Example 4 Factoring a Trinomial by the Trial-and-Error Method

Factor. $-45x^2 - 3xy + 18y^2$

Solution:

$-45x^2 - 3xy + 18y^2$

$= -3(15x^2 + xy - 6y^2)$ **Step 1:** Factor out -3 to make the leading coefficient positive.

$= -3(\Box x \quad \Box y)(\Box x \quad \Box y)$ **Step 2:** List the factors of 15 and 6.

Factors of 15	Factors of 6
$1 \cdot 15$	$1 \cdot 6$
$3 \cdot 5$	$2 \cdot 3$
	$3 \cdot 2$
	$6 \cdot 1$

Step 3: We will construct all binomial combinations, without regard to signs first.

$-3(x \quad y)(15x \quad 6y)$
$-3(x \quad 2y)(15x \quad 3y)$
$-3(3x \quad 3y)(5x \quad 2y)$
$-3(3x \quad 6y)(5x \quad y)$

Incorrect. The binomials contain a common factor.

Test the remaining factorizations. The signs within parentheses must be opposite to produce a product of $-6y^2$. Also, the sum of the products of the inner terms and outer terms must be combined to form $1xy$.

$-3(x \quad 3y)(15x \quad 2y)$ *Incorrect.* Regardless of signs, $45xy$ and $2xy$ cannot be combined to equal xy.

$-3(x \quad 6y)(15x \quad y)$ *Incorrect.* Regardless of signs, $90xy$ and xy cannot be combined to equal xy.

$-3(3x \quad y)(5x \quad 6y)$ *Incorrect.* Regardless of signs, $5xy$ and $18xy$ cannot be combined to equal xy.

$-3(3x \quad 2y)(5x \quad 3y)$ *Correct.* The terms $10xy$ and $9xy$ can be combined to form xy provided that the signs are applied correctly. We require $10xy$ and $-9xy$.

The correct factored form is $-3(3x + 2y)(5x - 3y)$.

Avoiding Mistakes

Do not forget to write the GCF in the final answer.

Skill Practice Factor.

4. $-4x^2 + 26xy - 40y^2$

Recall that a prime polynomial is a polynomial whose only factors are itself and 1. Not every trinomial is factorable by the methods presented in this text.

Answer

4. $-2(2x - 5y)(x - 4y)$

For Exercises 29–36, factor completely. Be sure to factor out the GCF first. **(See Examples 3–4.)**

29. $2m^2 - 12m - 80$
30. $3c^2 - 33c + 72$
31. $2y^5 + 13y^4 + 6y^3$
32. $3u^8 - 13u^7 + 4u^6$
33. $-a^2 - 15a + 34$
34. $-x^2 - 7x - 10$
35. $-80m^2 + 100mp + 30p^2$
36. $-60w^2 - 550wz + 500z^2$

For Exercises 37–42, factor the higher degree polynomial. **(See Example 6.)**

37. $x^4 + 10x^2 + 9$
38. $y^4 + 4y^2 - 21$
39. $w^4 + 2w^2 - 15$
40. $p^4 - 13p^2 + 40$
41. $2x^4 - 7x^2 - 15$
42. $5y^4 + 11y^2 + 2$

Mixed Exercises

For Exercises 43–82, factor each trinomial completely.

43. $20z - 18 - 2z^2$
44. $25t - 5t^2 - 30$
45. $42 - 13q + q^2$
46. $-5w - 24 + w^2$
47. $6t^2 + 7t - 3$
48. $4p^2 - 9p + 2$
49. $4m^2 - 20m + 25$
50. $16r^2 + 24r + 9$
51. $5c^2 - c + 2$
52. $7s^2 + 2s + 9$
53. $6x^2 - 19xy + 10y^2$
54. $15p^2 + pq - 2q^2$
55. $12m^2 + 11mn - 5n^2$
56. $4a^2 + 5ab - 6b^2$
57. $30r^2 + 5r - 10$
58. $36x^2 - 18x - 4$
59. $4s^2 - 8st + t^2$
60. $6u^2 - 10uv + 5v^2$
61. $10t^2 - 23t - 5$
62. $16n^2 + 14n + 3$
63. $14w^2 + 13w - 12$
64. $12x^2 - 16x + 5$
65. $a^2 - 10a - 24$
66. $b^2 + 6b - 7$
67. $x^2 + 9xy + 20y^2$
68. $p^2 - 13pq + 36q^2$
69. $a^2 + 21ab + 20b^2$
70. $x^2 - 17xy - 18y^2$
71. $t^2 - 10t + 21$
72. $z^2 - 15z + 36$
73. $5d^3 + 3d^2 - 10d$
74. $3y^3 - y^2 + 12y$
75. $4b^3 - 4b^2 - 80b$
76. $2w^2 + 20w + 42$
77. $x^2y^2 - 13xy^2 + 30y^2$
78. $p^2q^2 - 14pq^2 + 33q^2$
79. $-12u^3 - 22u^2 + 20u$
80. $-18z^4 + 15z^3 + 12z^2$
81. $8x^4 + 14x^2 + 3$
82. $6y^4 - 5y^2 - 4$

83. A rock is thrown straight upward from the top of a 40-ft building. Its height in feet after t seconds is given by the polynomial $-16t^2 + 12t + 40$.

a. Calculate the height of the rock after 1 s. $(t = 1)$

b. Write $-16t^2 + 12t + 40$ in factored form. Then evaluate the factored form of the polynomial for $t = 1$. Is the result the same as from part (a)?

84. A baseball is thrown straight downward from the top of a 120-ft building. Its height in feet after t seconds is given by $-16t^2 - 8t + 120$.

a. Calculate the height of the ball after 2 s. $(t = 2)$

b. Write $-16t^2 - 8t + 120$ in factored form. Then evaluate the factored form of the polynomial for $t = 2$. Is the result the same as from part (a)?

Expanding Your Skills

For Exercises 85–88, each pair of trinomials looks similar but differs by one sign. Factor each trinomial and see how their factored forms differ.

85. **a.** $x^2 - 10x - 24$
b. $x^2 - 10x + 24$

86. **a.** $x^2 - 13x - 30$
b. $x^2 - 13x + 30$

87. **a.** $x^2 - 5x - 6$
b. $x^2 - 5x + 6$

88. **a.** $x^2 - 10x + 9$
b. $x^2 + 10x + 9$

Factoring Trinomials: AC-Method

Section 6.4

Concept

1. **Factoring Trinomials by the AC-Method**

In Section 6.2, we factored trinomials with a leading coefficient of 1. In Section 6.3, we learned the trial-and-error method to factor the more general case in which the leading coefficient is any integer. In this section, we provide an alternative method to factor trinomials, called the ac-method.

1. Factoring Trinomials by the AC-Method

The product of two binomials results in a four-term expression that can sometimes be simplified to a trinomial. To factor the trinomial, we want to reverse the process.

Multiply:

Multiply the binomials. Add the middle terms.

$$(2x + 3)(x + 2) = \longrightarrow 2x^2 + 4x + 3x + 6 = \longrightarrow 2x^2 + 7x + 6$$

Factor:

$$2x^2 + 7x + 6 = \longrightarrow 2x^2 + 4x + 3x + 6 = \longrightarrow (2x + 3)(x + 2)$$

Rewrite the middle term as a sum or difference of terms. Factor by grouping.

To factor a quadratic trinomial, $ax^2 + bx + c$, by the ac-method, we rewrite the middle term, bx, as a sum or difference of terms. The goal is to produce a four-term polynomial that can be factored by grouping. The process is outlined as follows.

AC-Method: Factoring $ax^2 + bx + c$ $(a \neq 0)$

Step 1 Factor out the GCF from all terms.

Step 2 Multiply the coefficients of the first and last terms (ac).

Step 3 Find two integers whose product is ac and whose sum is b. (If no pair of integers can be found, then the trinomial cannot be factored further and is a *prime polynomial.*)

Step 4 Rewrite the middle term, bx, as the sum of two terms whose coefficients are the integers found in step 3.

Step 5 Factor the polynomial by grouping.

The ac-method for factoring trinomials is illustrated in Example 1. However, before we begin, keep these two important guidelines in mind:

- For any factoring problem you encounter, always factor out the GCF from all terms first.
- To factor a trinomial, write the trinomial in the form $ax^2 + bx + c$.

Example 1 Factoring a Trinomial by the AC-Method

Factor the trinomial by the ac-method. $2x^2 + 7x + 6$

Solution:

$2x^2 + 7x + 6$

Step 1: Factor out the GCF from all terms. In this case, the GCF is 1. The trinomial is written in the form $ax^2 + bx + c$.

$a = 2, b = 7, c = 6$

Step 2: Find the product $ac = (2)(6) = 12$.

12	**12**
$1 \cdot 12$	$(-1)(-12)$
$2 \cdot 6$	$(-2)(-6)$
$3 \cdot 4$	$(-3)(-4)$

Step 3: List all factors of ac and search for the pair whose sum equals the value of b. That is, list the factors of 12 and find the pair whose sum equals 7.

The numbers 3 and 4 satisfy both conditions: $3 \cdot 4 = 12$ and $3 + 4 = 7$.

$2x^2 + 7x + 6$

$= 2x^2 + 3x + 4x + 6$

Step 4: Write the middle term of the trinomial as the sum of two terms whose coefficients are the selected pair of numbers: 3 and 4.

$= 2x^2 + 3x \mid + 4x + 6$

Step 5: Factor by grouping.

$= x(2x + 3) + 2(2x + 3)$

$= (2x + 3)(x + 2)$

Check: $(2x + 3)(x + 2) = 2x^2 + 4x + 3x + 6$

$= 2x^2 + 7x + 6$ ✔

Skill Practice Factor by the ac-method.

1. $2x^2 + 5x + 3$

TIP: One frequently asked question is whether the order matters when we rewrite the middle term of the trinomial as two terms (step 4). The answer is no. From the previous example, the two middle terms in step 4 could have been reversed to obtain the same result:

$$2x^2 + 7x + 6$$
$$= 2x^2 + 4x + 3x + 6$$
$$= 2x(x + 2) + 3(x + 2)$$
$$= (x + 2)(2x + 3)$$

This example also points out that the order in which two factors are written does not matter. The expression $(x + 2)(2x + 3)$ is equivalent to $(2x + 3)(x + 2)$ because multiplication is a commutative operation.

Answer

1. $(x + 1)(2x + 3)$

Example 2 Factoring a Trinomial by the AC-Method

Factor the trinomial by the ac-method. $-2x + 8x^2 - 3$

Solution:

$-2x + 8x^2 - 3$ First rewrite the polynomial in the form $ax^2 + bx + c$.

$= 8x^2 - 2x - 3$ **Step 1:** The GCF is 1.

$a = 8, b = -2, c = -3$ **Step 2:** Find the product $ac = (8)(-3) = -24$.

Step 3: List all the factors of -24 and find the pair of factors whose sum equals -2.

−24	**−24**
$-1 \cdot 24$	$-24 \cdot 1$
$-2 \cdot 12$	$-12 \cdot 2$
$-3 \cdot 8$	$-8 \cdot 3$
$-4 \cdot 6$	$-6 \cdot 4$

The numbers -6 and 4 satisfy both conditions: $(-6)(4) = -24$ and $-6 + 4 = -2$.

$= 8x^2 - 2x - 3$ **Step 4:** Write the middle term of the trinomial as two terms whose coefficients are the selected pair of numbers, -6 and 4.

$= 8x^2 - 6x + 4x - 3$

$= 8x^2 - 6x \,\vdots\, + 4x - 3$ **Step 5:** Factor by grouping.

$= 2x(4x - 3) + 1(4x - 3)$

$= (4x - 3)(2x + 1)$

Check: $(4x - 3)(2x + 1) = 8x^2 + 4x - 6x - 3$

$= 8x^2 - 2x - 3$ ✔

Avoiding Mistakes

Before factoring a trinomial, be sure to write the trinomial in descending order. That is, write it in the form $ax^2 + bx + c$.

Skill Practice Factor by the ac-method.

2. $13w + 6w^2 + 6$

Example 3 Factoring a Trinomial by the AC-Method

Factor the trinomial by the ac-method. $10x^3 - 85x^2 + 105x$

Solution:

$10x^3 - 85x^2 + 105x$ **Step 1:** Factor out the GCF of $5x$.

$= 5x(2x^2 - 17x + 21)$ The trinomial is in the form $ax^2 + bx + c$.

$a = 2, b = -17, c = 21$ **Step 2:** Find the product $ac = (2)(21) = 42$.

Step 3: List all the factors of 42 and find the pair whose sum equals -17.

42	**42**
$1 \cdot 42$	$(-1)(-42)$
$2 \cdot 21$	$(-2)(-21)$
$3 \cdot 14$	$(-3)(-14)$
$6 \cdot 7$	$(-6)(-7)$

The numbers -3 and -14 satisfy both conditions: $(-3)(-14) = 42$ and $-3 + (-14) = -17$.

Answer

2. $(2w + 3)(3w + 2)$

$= 5x(2x^2 - 17x + 21)$ **Step 4:** Write the middle term of the trinomial as two terms whose coefficients are the selected pair of numbers, −3 and −14.

$= 5x(2x^2 - 3x - 14x + 21)$

$= 5x(2x^2 - 3x \mid - 14x + 21)$ **Step 5:** Factor by grouping.

$= 5x[x(2x - 3) - 7(2x - 3)]$

$= 5x(2x - 3)(x - 7)$

Avoiding Mistakes

Be sure to bring down the GCF in each successive step as you factor.

TIP: Notice when the GCF is removed from the original trinomial, the new trinomial has smaller coefficients. This makes the factoring process simpler because the product ac is smaller. It is much easier to list the factors of 42 than the factors of 1050.

Original trinomial	**With the GCF factored out**
$10x^3 - 85x^2 + 105x$	$5x(2x^2 - 17x + 21)$
$ac = (10)(105) = 1050$	$ac = (2)(21) = 42$

Skill Practice Factor by the ac-method.

3. $9y^3 - 30y^2 + 24y$

In most cases, it is easier to factor a trinomial with a positive leading coefficient.

Example 4 Factoring a Trinomial by the AC-Method

Factor the trinomial by the ac-method. $-18x^2 + 21xy + 15y^2$

Solution:

$-18x^2 + 21xy + 15y^2$ **Step 1:** Factor out the GCF.

$= -3(6x^2 - 7xy - 5y^2)$ Factor out −3 to make the leading term positive.

Step 2: The product $ac = (6)(-5) = -30$.

Step 3: The numbers −10 and 3 have a product of −30 and a sum of −7.

$= -3[6x^2 - 10xy + 3xy - 5y^2]$ **Step 4:** Rewrite the middle term, $-7xy$ as $-10xy + 3xy$.

$= -3[6x^2 - 10xy \mid + 3xy - 5y^2]$ **Step 5:** Factor by grouping.

$= -3[2x(3x - 5y) + y(3x - 5y)]$

$= -3(3x - 5y)(2x + y)$ Factored form

Skill Practice Factor.

4. $-8x^2 - 8xy + 30y^2$

Answers

3. $3y(3y - 4)(y - 2)$
4. $-2(2x - 3y)(2x + 5y)$

Recall that a prime polynomial is a polynomial whose only factors are itself and 1. It also should be noted that not every trinomial is factorable by the methods presented in this text.

Example 5 **Factoring a Trinomial by the AC-Method**

Factor the trinomial by the ac-method. $2p^2 - 8p + 3$

Solution:

$2p^2 - 8p + 3$ **Step 1:** The GCF is 1.

Step 2: The product $ac = 6$.

6	6
$1 \cdot 6$	$(-1)(-6)$
$2 \cdot 3$	$(-2)(-3)$

Step 3: List the factors of 6. Notice that no pair of factors has a sum of -8. Therefore, the trinomial cannot be factored.

The trinomial $2p^2 - 8p + 3$ is a prime polynomial.

Skill Practice Factor.

5. $4x^2 + 5x + 2$

In Example 6, we use the ac-method to factor a higher degree trinomial.

Example 6 **Factoring a Higher Degree Trinomial**

Factor the trinomial by the ac-method. $2x^4 + 5x^2 + 2$

Solution:

$2x^4 + 5x^2 + 2$ **Step 1:** The GCF is 1.

$a = 2, b = 5, c = 2$ **Step 2:** Find the product $ac = (2)(2) = 4$.

Step 3: The numbers 1 and 4 have a product of 4 and a sum of 5.

$= 2x^4 + x^2 + 4x^2 + 2$ **Step 4:** Rewrite the middle term, $5x^2$, as $x^2 + 4x^2$.

$= 2x^4 + x^2 \mid + 4x^2 + 2$ **Step 5:** Factor by grouping.

$= x^2(2x^2 + 1) + 2(2x^2 + 1)$

$= (2x^2 + 1)(x^2 + 2)$ Factored form

Skill Practice Factor.

6. $3y^4 + 2y^2 - 8$

Answers

5. Prime

6. $(3y^2 - 4)(y^2 + 2)$

Section 6.4 Practice Exercises

Vocabulary and Key Concepts

1. **a.** Which is the correct factored form of $10x^2 - 13x - 3$? The product $(5x + 1)(2x - 3)$ or $(2x - 3)(5x + 1)$?
   b. Which is the complete factorization of $12x^2 - 15x - 18$? The product $(4x + 3)(3x - 6)$ or $3(4x + 3)(x - 2)$?

Review Exercises

For Exercises 2–4, factor completely.

2. $5x(x - 2) - 2(x - 2)$
3. $8(y + 5) + 9y(y + 5)$
4. $6ab + 24b - 12a - 48$

Concept 1: Factoring Trinomials by the AC-Method

For Exercises 5–12, find the pair of integers whose product and sum are given.

5. Product: 12 Sum: 13
6. Product: 12 Sum: 7
7. Product: 8 Sum: −9
8. Product: −4 Sum: −3
9. Product: −20 Sum: 1
10. Product: −6 Sum: −1
11. Product: −18 Sum: 7
12. Product: −72 Sum: −6

For Exercises 13–30, factor the trinomials using the ac-method. **(See Examples 1, 2, and 5.)**

13. $3x^2 + 13x + 4$
14. $2y^2 + 9y + 9$
15. $4w^2 - 9w + 2$
16. $2p^2 - 3p - 2$
17. $x^2 + 7x - 18$
18. $y^2 - 6y - 40$
19. $2m^2 + 5m - 3$
20. $6n^2 + 7n - 3$
21. $8k^2 - 6k - 9$
22. $9h^2 - 3h - 2$
23. $4k^2 - 20k + 25$
24. $16h^2 + 24h + 9$
25. $5x^2 + x + 7$
26. $4y^2 - y + 2$
27. $10 + 9z^2 - 21z$
28. $13x + 4x^2 - 12$
29. $12y^2 + 8yz - 15z^2$
30. $20a^2 + 3ab - 9b^2$

For Exercises 31–38, factor completely. Be sure to factor out the GCF first. **(See Examples 3–4.)**

31. $50y + 24 + 14y^2$
32. $-24 + 10w + 4w^2$
33. $-15w^2 + 22w + 5$
34. $-16z^2 + 34z + 15$
35. $-12x^2 + 20xy - 8y^2$
36. $-6p^2 - 21pq - 9q^2$
37. $18y^3 + 60y^2 + 42y$
38. $8t^3 - 4t^2 - 40t$

For Exercises 39–44, factor the higher degree polynomial. **(See Example 6.)**

39. $a^4 + 5a^2 + 6$
40. $y^4 - 2y^2 - 35$
41. $6x^4 - x^2 - 15$
42. $8t^4 + 2t^2 - 3$
43. $8p^4 + 37p^2 - 15$
44. $2a^4 + 11a^2 + 14$

Mixed Exercises

For Exercises 45–80, factor completely.

45. $20p^2 - 19p + 3$

46. $4p^2 + 5pq - 6q^2$

47. $6u^2 - 19uv + 10v^2$

48. $15m^2 + mn - 2n^2$

49. $12a^2 + 11ab - 5b^2$

50. $3r^2 - rs - 14s^2$

51. $3h^2 + 19hk - 14k^2$

52. $2u^2 + uv - 15v^2$

53. $2x^2 - 13xy + y^2$

54. $3p^2 + 20pq - q^2$

55. $3 - 14z + 16z^2$

56. $10w + 1 + 16w^2$

57. $b^2 + 16 - 8b$

58. $1 + q^2 - 2q$

59. $25x - 5x^2 - 30$

60. $20a - 18 - 2a^2$

61. $-6 - t + t^2$

62. $-6 + m + m^2$

63. $v^2 + 2v + 15$

64. $x^2 - x - 1$

65. $72x^2 + 18x - 2$

66. $20y^2 - 78y - 8$

67. $p^3 - 6p^2 - 27p$

68. $w^5 - 11w^4 + 28w^3$

69. $3x^3 + 10x^2 + 7x$

70. $4r^3 + 3r^2 - 10r$

71. $2p^3 - 38p^2 + 120p$

72. $4q^3 - 4q^2 - 80q$

73. $x^2y^2 + 14x^2y + 33x^2$

74. $a^2b^2 + 13ab^2 + 30b^2$

75. $-k^2 - 7k - 10$

76. $-m^2 - 15m + 34$

77. $-3n^2 - 3n + 90$

78. $-2h^2 + 28h - 90$

79. $x^4 - 7x^2 + 10$

80. $m^4 + 10m^2 + 21$

81. Is the expression $(2x + 4)(x - 7)$ factored completely? Explain why or why not.

82. Is the expression $(3x + 1)(5x - 10)$ factored completely? Explain why or why not.

83. Colleen noticed that the number of tables placed in her restaurant affects the number of customers who eat at the restaurant. The number of customers each night is given by $-2x^2 + 40x - 72$, where x is the number of tables set up in the room, and $2 \le x \le 18$.

a. Calculate the number of customers when there are 10 tables set up. $(x = 10)$

b. Write $-2x^2 + 40x - 72$ in factored form. Then evaluate the factored form of the polynomial for $x = 10$. Is the result the same as from part (a)?

84. Roland sells skins for smartphones online. He noticed that for every dollar he discounts the price, he sells two more skins per week. His income in dollars each week is given by $-2d^2 + 30d + 200$, where d is the dollar amount of discount in price.

a. Calculate his income if his discount is \$2. $(d = 2)$

b. Write $-2d^2 + 30d + 200$ in factored form. Then evaluate the factored form of the polynomial for $d = 2$. Is the result the same as from part (a)?

85. A formula for finding the sum of the first n even integers is given by $n^2 + n$.

a. Find the sum of the first 6 even integers $(2 + 4 + 6 + 8 + 10 + 12)$ by evaluating the expression for $n = 6$.

b. Write the polynomial in factored form. Then evaluate the factored form of the expression for $n = 6$. Is the result the same as part (a)?

86. A formula for finding the sum of the squares of the first n integers is given by $\dfrac{2n^3 + 3n^2 + n}{6}$.

a. Find the sum of the squares of the first 4 integers $(1^2 + 2^2 + 3^2 + 4^2)$ by evaluating the expression for $n = 4$.

b. Write the polynomial in the numerator of the expression in factored form. Then evaluate the factored form of the expression for $n = 4$. Is the result the same as part (a)?

Section 6.5 Difference of Squares and Perfect Square Trinomials

Concepts

1. Factoring a Difference of Squares
2. Factoring Perfect Square Trinomials

1. Factoring a Difference of Squares

Up to this point, we have learned several methods of factoring, including:

- Factoring out the greatest common factor from a polynomial
- Factoring a four-term polynomial by grouping
- Factoring trinomials by the ac-method or by the trial-and-error method

In this section, we begin by factoring a special binomial called a difference of squares. Recall from Section 5.6 that the product of two conjugates results in a **difference of squares**:

$$(a + b)(a - b) = a^2 - b^2$$

Therefore, to factor a difference of squares, the process is reversed. Identify a and b and construct the conjugate factors.

Factored Form of a Difference of Squares

$$a^2 - b^2 = (a + b)(a - b)$$

To help recognize a difference of squares, we recommend that you become familiar with the first several perfect squares.

Perfect Squares	Perfect Squares	Perfect Squares
$1 = (1)^2$	$36 = (6)^2$	$121 = (11)^2$
$4 = (2)^2$	$49 = (7)^2$	$144 = (12)^2$
$9 = (3)^2$	$64 = (8)^2$	$169 = (13)^2$
$16 = (4)^2$	$81 = (9)^2$	$196 = (14)^2$
$25 = (5)^2$	$100 = (10)^2$	$225 = (15)^2$

It is also important to recognize that a variable expression is a perfect square if its exponent is a multiple of 2. For example:

Perfect Squares
$x^2 = (x)^2$
$x^4 = (x^2)^2$
$x^6 = (x^3)^2$
$x^8 = (x^4)^2$
$x^{10} = (x^5)^2$

Example 1 **Factoring Differences of Squares**

Factor the binomials.

a. $y^2 - 25$ **b.** $49s^2 - 4t^4$ **c.** $18w^2z - 2z$

Solution:

a. $y^2 - 25$ The binomial is a difference of squares.

$= (y)^2 - (5)^2$ Write in the form: $a^2 - b^2$, where $a = y$, $b = 5$.

$= (y + 5)(y - 5)$ Factor as $(a + b)(a - b)$.

b. $49s^2 - 4t^4$ The binomial is a difference of squares.

$= (7s)^2 - (2t^2)^2$ Write in the form $a^2 - b^2$, where $a = 7s$ and $b = 2t^2$.

$= (7s + 2t^2)(7s - 2t^2)$ Factor as $(a + b)(a - b)$.

c. $18w^2z - 2z$ The GCF is $2z$.

$= 2z(9w^2 - 1)$ $(9w^2 - 1)$ is a difference of squares.

$= 2z[(3w)^2 - (1)^2]$ Write in the form: $a^2 - b^2$, where $a = 3w$, $b = 1$.

$= 2z(3w - 1)(3w + 1)$ Factor as $(a - b)(a + b)$.

TIP: Recall that multiplication is commutative. Therefore,

$a^2 - b^2 = (a + b)(a - b)$

or $(a - b)(a + b)$.

Skill Practice Factor the binomials.

1. $a^2 - 64$ **2.** $25q^2 - 49w^2$ **3.** $98m^3n - 50mn$

The difference of squares $a^2 - b^2$ factors as $(a + b)(a - b)$. However, the *sum* of squares is not factorable.

Sum of Squares

Suppose a and b have no common factors. Then the **sum of squares** $a^2 + b^2$ is *not* factorable over the real numbers.

That is, $a^2 + b^2$ is prime over the real numbers.

To see why $a^2 + b^2$ is not factorable, consider the product of binomials:

$(a + b)(a - b) = a^2 - b^2$ Wrong sign

$(a + b)(a + b) = a^2 + 2ab + b^2$ Wrong middle term

$(a - b)(a - b) = a^2 - 2ab + b^2$ Wrong middle term

After exhausting all possibilities, we see that if a and b share no common factors, then the sum of squares $a^2 + b^2$ is a prime polynomial.

Example 2 **Factoring Binomials**

Factor the binomials, if possible. **a.** $p^2 - 9$ **b.** $p^2 + 9$

Solution:

a. $p^2 - 9$ Difference of squares

$= (p - 3)(p + 3)$ Factor as $a^2 - b^2 = (a - b)(a + b)$.

b. $p^2 + 9$ Sum of squares

Prime (cannot be factored)

Answers

1. $(a + 8)(a - 8)$
2. $(5q + 7w)(5q - 7w)$
3. $2mn(7m + 5)(7m - 5)$

Skill Practice Factor the binomials, if possible.

4. $t^2 - 144$ **5.** $t^2 + 144$

Some factoring problems require several steps. Always be sure to factor completely.

Example 3 Factoring a Difference of Squares

Factor completely. $w^4 - 81$

Solution:

$w^4 - 81$ — The GCF is 1. $w^4 - 81$ is a difference of squares.

$= (w^2)^2 - (9)^2$ — Write in the form: $a^2 - b^2$, where $a = w^2$, $b = 9$.

$= (w^2 + 9)(w^2 - 9)$ — Factor as $(a + b)(a - b)$.

$= (w^2 + 9)(w + 3)(w - 3)$ — Note that $w^2 - 9$ can be factored further as a difference of squares. (The binomial $w^2 + 9$ is a sum of squares and cannot be factored further.)

Skill Practice Factor completely.

6. $y^4 - 1$

Example 4 Factoring a Polynomial

Factor completely. $y^3 - 5y^2 - 4y + 20$

Solution:

$y^3 - 5y^2 - 4y + 20$ — The GCF is 1. The polynomial has four terms. Factor by grouping.

$= y^3 - 5y^2 \,\vdots\, - 4y + 20$

$= y^2(y - 5) - 4(y - 5)$

$= (y - 5)(y^2 - 4)$ — The expression $y^2 - 4$ is a difference of squares and can be factored further as $(y - 2)(y + 2)$.

$= (y - 5)(y - 2)(y + 2)$

Check: $(y - 5)(y - 2)(y + 2) = (y - 5)(y^2 - 2y + 2y - 4)$

$= (y - 5)(y^2 - 4)$

$= (y^3 - 4y - 5y^2 + 20)$

$= y^3 - 5y^2 - 4y + 20$ ✔

Skill Practice Factor completely.

7. $p^3 + 7p^2 - 9p - 63$

2. Factoring Perfect Square Trinomials

Recall from Section 5.6 that the square of a binomial always results in a **perfect square trinomial**.

$$(a + b)^2 = (a + b)(a + b) \xrightarrow{\text{Multiply.}} = a^2 + 2ab + b^2$$

$$(a - b)^2 = (a - b)(a - b) \xrightarrow{\text{Multiply.}} = a^2 - 2ab + b^2$$

Answers

4. $(t - 12)(t + 12)$
5. Prime
6. $(y + 1)(y - 1)(y^2 + 1)$
7. $(p - 3)(p + 3)(p + 7)$

For example, $(3x + 5)^2 = (3x)^2 + 2(3x)(5) + (5)^2$

$= 9x^2 + 30x + 25$ (perfect square trinomial)

We now want to reverse this process by factoring a perfect square trinomial. The trial-and-error method or the ac-method can always be used; however, if we recognize the pattern for a perfect square trinomial, we can use one of the following formulas to reach a quick solution.

Factored Form of a Perfect Square Trinomial

$$a^2 + 2ab + b^2 = (a + b)^2$$

$$a^2 - 2ab + b^2 = (a - b)^2$$

For example, $4x^2 + 36x + 81$ is a perfect square trinomial with $a = 2x$ and $b = 9$. Therefore, it factors as

$$4x^2 + 36x + 81 = (2x)^2 + 2(2x)(9) + (9)^2 = (2x + 9)^2$$

$$\uparrow \quad \uparrow \quad \uparrow \quad \uparrow \quad \uparrow \quad \uparrow$$

$$a^2 + 2\,(a)\,(b) + (b)^2 = (a + b)^2$$

To apply the formula to factor a perfect square trinomial, we must first be sure that the trinomial is indeed a perfect square trinomial.

Checking for a Perfect Square Trinomial

Step 1 Determine whether the first and third terms are both perfect squares and have positive coefficients.

Step 2 If this is the case, identify a and b and determine if the middle term equals $2ab$ or $-2ab$.

Example 5 Factoring Perfect Square Trinomials

Factor the trinomials completely.

a. $x^2 + 14x + 49$ **b.** $25y^2 - 20y + 4$

Solution:

a. $x^2 + 14x + 49$ The GCF is 1.

- The first and third terms are positive.
- The first term is a perfect square: $x^2 = (x)^2$.
- The third term is a perfect square: $49 = (7)^2$.
- The middle term is twice the product of x and 7: $14x = 2(x)(7)$.

Perfect squares

$x^2 + 14x + 49$

$= (x)^2 + 2(x)(7) + (7)^2$ The trinomial is in the form $a^2 + 2ab + b^2$, where $a = x$ and $b = 7$.

$= (x + 7)^2$ Factor as $(a + b)^2$.

TIP: The sign of the middle term in a perfect square trinomial determines the sign within the binomial of the factored form.

$a^2 + 2ab + b^2 = (a + b)^2$

$a^2 - 2ab + b^2 = (a - b)^2$

b. $25y^2 - 20y + 4$ — The GCF is 1.

Perfect squares

$25y^2 - 20y + 4$

$= (5y)^2 - 2(5y)(2) + (2)^2$

$= (5y - 2)^2$

- The first and third terms are positive.
- The first term is a perfect square: $25y^2 = (5y)^2$.
- The third term is a perfect square: $4 = (2)^2$.
- In the middle: $20y = 2(5y)(2)$

Factor as $(a - b)^2$.

Skill Practice Factor completely.

8. $x^2 - 6x + 9$ **9.** $81w^2 + 72w + 16$

Example 6 Factoring Perfect Square Trinomials

Factor the trinomials completely.

a. $18c^3 - 48c^2d + 32cd^2$ **b.** $5w^2 + 50w + 45$

Solution:

a. $18c^3 - 48c^2d + 32cd^2$

$= 2c(9c^2 - 24cd + 16d^2)$ — The GCF is $2c$.

Perfect squares

$= 2c(9c^2 - 24cd + 16d^2)$

$= 2c[(3c)^2 - 2(3c)(4d) + (4d)^2]$

$= 2c(3c - 4d)^2$

- The first and third terms are positive.
- The first term is a perfect square: $9c^2 = (3c)^2$.
- The third term is a perfect square: $16d^2 = (4d)^2$.
- In the middle: $24cd = 2(3c)(4d)$

Factor as $(a - b)^2$.

b. $5w^2 + 50w + 45$

$= 5(w^2 + 10w + 9)$ — The GCF is 5.

Perfect squares

$= 5(w^2 + 10w + 9)$

The first and third terms are perfect squares.

$w^2 = (w)^2$ and $9 = (3)^2$

However, the middle term is not 2 times the product of w and 3. Therefore, this is not a perfect square trinomial.

$10w \neq 2(w)(3)$

$= 5(w + 9)(w + 1)$ — To factor, use the trial-and-error method.

Skill Practice Factor completely.

10. $5z^3 + 20z^2w + 20zw^2$ **11.** $40x^2 + 130x + 90$

TIP: If you do not recognize that a trinomial is a perfect square trinomial, you can still use the trial-and-error method or ac-method to factor it.

Answers

8. $(x - 3)^2$
9. $(9w + 4)^2$
10. $5z(z + 2w)^2$
11. $10(4x + 9)(x + 1)$

Section 6.5 Practice Exercises

Vocabulary and Key Concepts

1. **a.** The binomial $x^2 - 16$ is an example of a ___________ of squares. After factoring out the GCF, we factor a difference of squares $a^2 - b^2$ as ___________.

   b. The binomial $y^2 + 121$ is an example of a ___________ of squares.

   c. A sum of squares with greatest common factor 1 (is/is not) factorable over the real numbers.

   d. The square of a binomial always results in a perfect ___________ trinomial.

   e. A perfect square trinomial $a^2 + 2ab + b^2$ factors as ___________. Likewise, $a^2 - 2ab + b^2$ factors as ___________.

Review Exercises

For Exercises 2–10, factor completely.

2. $3x^2 + x - 10$ **3.** $6x^2 - 17x + 5$ **4.** $6a^2b + 3a^3b$

5. $15x^2y^5 - 10xy^6$ **6.** $5p^2q + 20p^2 - 3pq - 12p$ **7.** $ax + ab - 6x - 6b$

8. $-6x + 5 + x^2$ **9.** $6y - 40 + y^2$ **10.** $a^2 + 7a + 1$

Concept 1: Factoring a Difference of Squares

11. What binomial factors as $(x - 5)(x + 5)$? **12.** What binomial factors as $(n - 3)(n + 3)$?

13. What binomial factors as $(2p - 3q)(2p + 3q)$? **14.** What binomial factors as $(7x - 4y)(7x + 4y)$?

For Exercises 15–38, factor each binomial completely. **(See Examples 1–3.)**

15. $x^2 - 36$ **16.** $r^2 - 81$ **17.** $3w^2 - 300$ **18.** $t^3 - 49t$

19. $4a^2 - 121b^2$ **20.** $9x^2 - y^2$ **21.** $49m^2 - 16n^2$ **22.** $100a^2 - 49b^2$

23. $9q^2 + 16$ **24.** $36 + s^2$ **25.** $y^2 - 4z^2$ **26.** $b^2 - 144c^2$

27. $a^2 - b^4$ **28.** $y^4 - x^2$ **29.** $25p^2q^2 - 1$ **30.** $81s^2t^2 - 1$

31. $c^2 - \frac{1}{25}$ **32.** $z^2 - \frac{1}{4}$ **33.** $50 - 32t^2$ **34.** $63 - 7h^2$

35. $x^4 - 256$ **36.** $y^4 - 625$ **37.** $16 - z^4$ **38.** $81 - a^4$

For Exercises 39–46, factor each polynomial completely. **(See Example 4.)**

39. $x^3 + 5x^2 - 9x - 45$ **40.** $y^3 + 6y^2 - 4y - 24$ **41.** $c^3 - c^2 - 25c + 25$ **42.** $t^3 + 2t^2 - 16t - 32$

43. $2x^2 - 18 + x^2y - 9y$ **44.** $5a^2 - 5 + a^2b - b$ **45.** $x^2y^2 - 9x^2 - 4y^2 + 36$ **46.** $w^2z^2 - w^2 - 25z^2 + 25$

Concept 2: Factoring Perfect Square Trinomials

47. Multiply. $(3x + 5)^2$ **48.** Multiply. $(2y - 7)^2$

49. **a.** Which trinomial is a perfect square trinomial? $x^2 + 4x + 4$ or $x^2 + 5x + 4$

b. Factor the trinomials from part (a).

50. **a.** Which trinomial is a perfect square trinomial? $x^2 + 13x + 36$ or $x^2 + 12x + 36$

b. Factor the trinomials from part (a).

For Exercises 51–68, factor completely. (*Hint:* Look for the pattern of a perfect square trinomial.) **(See Examples 5–6.)**

51. $x^2 + 18x + 81$

52. $y^2 - 8y + 16$

53. $25z^2 - 20z + 4$

54. $36p^2 + 60p + 25$

55. $49a^2 + 42ab + 9b^2$

56. $25m^2 - 30mn + 9n^2$

57. $-2y + y^2 + 1$

58. $4 + w^2 - 4w$

59. $80z^2 + 120zw + 45w^2$

60. $36p^2 - 24pq + 4q^2$

61. $9y^2 + 78y + 25$

62. $4y^2 + 20y + 9$

63. $2a^2 - 20a + 50$

64. $3t^2 + 18t + 27$

65. $4x^2 + x + 9$

66. $c^2 - 4c + 16$

67. $4x^2 + 4xy + y^2$

68. $100y^2 + 20yz + z^2$

69. The volume of the box shown is given as $3x^3 - 6x^2 + 3x$. Write the polynomial in factored form.

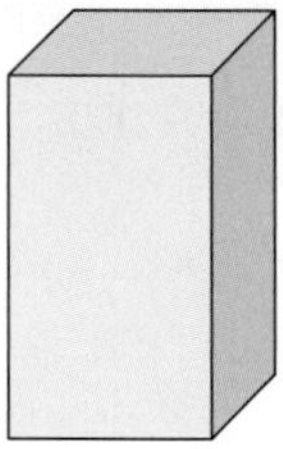

70. The volume of the box shown is given as $20y^3 + 20y^2 + 5y$. Write the polynomial in factored form.

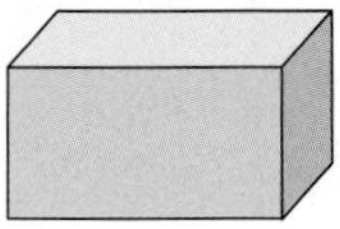

Expanding Your Skills

For Exercises 71–78, factor the difference of squares.

71. $(y - 3)^2 - 9$

72. $(x - 2)^2 - 4$

73. $(2p + 1)^2 - 36$

74. $(4q + 3)^2 - 25$

75. $16 - (t + 2)^2$

76. $81 - (a + 5)^2$

77. $(2a - 5)^2 - 100b^2$

78. $(3k + 7)^2 - 49m^2$

79. **a.** Write a polynomial that represents the area of the shaded region in the figure.

b. Factor the expression from part (a).

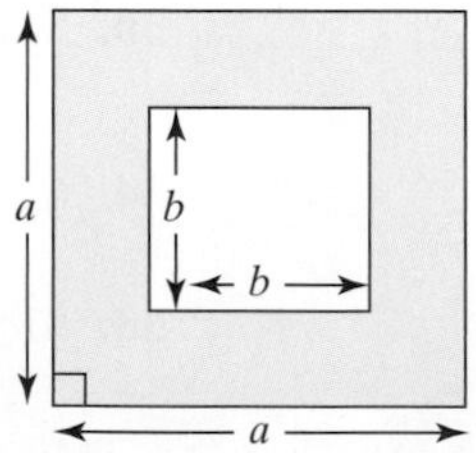

80. **a.** Write a polynomial that represents the area of the shaded region in the figure.

b. Factor the expression from part (a).

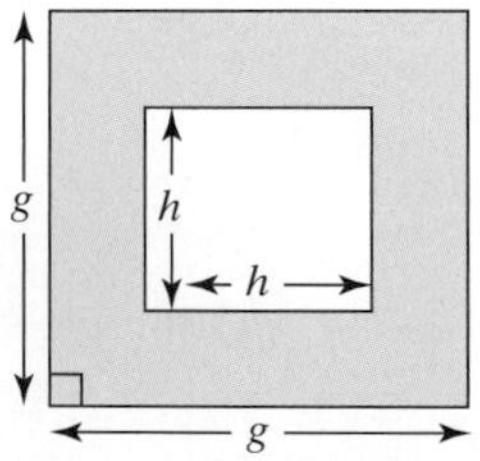

Section 6.6 Sum and Difference of Cubes

Concepts

1. **Factoring a Sum or Difference of Cubes**
2. **Factoring Binomials: A Summary**

1. Factoring a Sum or Difference of Cubes

A binomial $a^2 - b^2$ is a difference of squares and can be factored as $(a - b)(a + b)$. Furthermore, if a and b share no common factors, then a sum of squares $a^2 + b^2$ is not factorable over the real numbers. In this section, we will learn that both a difference of cubes, $a^3 - b^3$, and a sum of cubes, $a^3 + b^3$, are factorable.

Factored Form of a Sum or Difference of Cubes

Sum of Cubes: $a^3 + b^3 = (a + b)(a^2 - ab + b^2)$

Difference of Cubes: $a^3 - b^3 = (a - b)(a^2 + ab + b^2)$

Multiplication can be used to confirm the formulas for factoring a sum or difference of cubes:

$$(a + b)(a^2 - ab + b^2) = a^3 - \cancel{a^2b} + \cancel{ab^2} + \cancel{a^2b} - \cancel{ab^2} + b^3 = a^3 + b^3 \checkmark$$

$$(a - b)(a^2 + ab + b^2) = a^3 + \cancel{a^2b} + \cancel{ab^2} - \cancel{a^2b} - \cancel{ab^2} - b^3 = a^3 - b^3 \checkmark$$

To help you remember the formulas for factoring a sum or difference of cubes, keep the following guidelines in mind:

- The factored form is the product of a binomial and a trinomial.
- The first and third terms in the trinomial are the squares of the terms within the binomial factor.
- Without regard to signs, the middle term in the trinomial is the product of terms in the binomial factor.

Square the first term of the binomial. Product of terms in the binomial

$$x^3 + 8 = (x)^3 + (2)^3 = (x + 2)[(x)^2 - (x)(2) + (2)^2]$$

Square the last term of the binomial.

- The sign within the binomial factor is the same as the sign of the original binomial.
- The first and third terms in the trinomial are always positive.
- The sign of the middle term in the trinomial is opposite the sign within the binomial.

Same sign Positive

$$x^3 + 8 = (x)^3 + (2)^3 = (x + 2)[(x)^2 - (x)(2) + (2)^2]$$

Opposite signs

TIP: To help remember the placement of the signs in factoring the sum or difference of cubes, remember SOAP: **S**ame sign, **O**pposite signs, **A**lways **P**ositive.

To help you recognize a sum or difference of cubes, we recommend that you familiarize yourself with the first several perfect cubes:

Perfect Cubes	Perfect Cubes
$1 = (1)^3$	$216 = (6)^3$
$8 = (2)^3$	$343 = (7)^3$
$27 = (3)^3$	$512 = (8)^3$
$64 = (4)^3$	$729 = (9)^3$
$125 = (5)^3$	$1000 = (10)^3$

It is also helpful to recognize that a variable expression is a perfect cube if its exponent is a multiple of 3. For example:

Perfect Cubes
$x^3 = (x)^3$
$x^6 = (x^2)^3$
$x^9 = (x^3)^3$
$x^{12} = (x^4)^3$

Example 1 **Factoring a Sum of Cubes**

Factor. $w^3 + 64$

Solution:

$w^3 + 64$ — w^3 and 64 are perfect cubes.

$= (w)^3 + (4)^3$ — Write as $a^3 + b^3$, where $a = w$, $b = 4$.

$a^3 + b^3 = (a + b)(a^2 - ab + b^2)$ — Apply the formula for a sum of cubes.

$(w)^3 + (4)^3 = (w + 4)[(w)^2 - (w)(4) + (4)^2]$

$= (w + 4)(w^2 - 4w + 16)$ — Simplify.

Skill Practice Factor.

1. $p^3 + 125$

Example 2 **Factoring a Difference of Cubes**

Factor. $27p^3 - 1000q^3$

Solution:

$27p^3 - 1000q^3$ — $27p^3$ and $1000q^3$ are perfect cubes.

$= (3p)^3 - (10q)^3$ — Write as $a^3 - b^3$, where $a = 3p$, $b = 10q$.

$a^3 - b^3 = (a - b)(a^2 + ab + b^2)$ — Apply the formula for a difference of cubes.

$(3p)^3 - (10q)^3 = (3p - 10q)[(3p)^2 + (3p)(10q) + (10q)^2]$

$= (3p - 10q)(9p^2 + 30pq + 100q^2)$ — Simplify.

Skill Practice Factor.

2. $8y^3 - 27z^3$

2. Factoring Binomials: A Summary

After removing the GCF, the next step in any factoring problem is to recognize what type of pattern it follows. Exponents that are divisible by 2 are perfect squares and those divisible by 3 are perfect cubes. The formulas for factoring binomials are summarized in the following box:

Factored Forms of Binomials

Difference of Squares: $a^2 - b^2 = (a + b)(a - b)$

Difference of Cubes: $a^3 - b^3 = (a - b)(a^2 + ab + b^2)$

Sum of Cubes: $a^3 + b^3 = (a + b)(a^2 - ab + b^2)$

Example 3 **Factoring Binomials**

Factor completely.

a. $27y^3 + 1$ **b.** $\frac{1}{25}m^2 - \frac{1}{4}$ **c.** $z^6 - 8w^3$

Answers

1. $(p + 5)(p^2 - 5p + 25)$
2. $(2y - 3z)(4y^2 + 6yz + 9z^2)$

Solution:

a. $27y^3 + 1$ — Sum of cubes: $27y^3 = (3y)^3$ and $1 = (1)^3$.

$= (3y)^3 + (1)^3$ — Write as $a^3 + b^3$, where $a = 3y$ and $b = 1$.

$= (3y + 1)[(3y)^2 - (3y)(1) + (1)^2]$ — Apply the formula $a^3 + b^3 = (a + b)(a^2 - ab + b^2)$.

$= (3y + 1)(9y^2 - 3y + 1)$ — Simplify.

b. $\frac{1}{25}m^2 - \frac{1}{4}$ — Difference of squares

$= \left(\frac{1}{5}m\right)^2 - \left(\frac{1}{2}\right)^2$ — Write as $a^2 - b^2$, where $a = \frac{1}{5}m$ and $b = \frac{1}{2}$.

$= \left(\frac{1}{5}m + \frac{1}{2}\right)\left(\frac{1}{5}m - \frac{1}{2}\right)$ — Apply the formula $a^2 - b^2 = (a + b)(a - b)$.

c. $z^6 - 8w^3$ — Difference of cubes: $z^6 = (z^2)^3$ and $8w^3 = (2w)^3$

$= (z^2)^3 - (2w)^3$ — Write as $a^3 - b^3$, where $a = z^2$ and $b = 2w$.

$= (z^2 - 2w)[(z^2)^2 + (z^2)(2w) + (2w)^2]$ — Apply the formula $a^3 - b^3 = (a - b)(a^2 + ab + b^2)$.

$= (z^2 - 2w)(z^4 + 2z^2w + 4w^2)$ — Simplify.

Each factorization in this example can be checked by multiplying.

Skill Practice Factor completely.

3. $1000x^3 + 1$ **4.** $25p^2 - \frac{1}{9}$ **5.** $27a^6 - b^3$

Some factoring problems require more than one method of factoring. In general, when factoring a polynomial, be sure to factor completely.

Example 4 Factoring a Polynomial

Factor completely. $3y^4 - 48$

Solution:

$3y^4 - 48$

$= 3(y^4 - 16)$ — Factor out the GCF. The binomial is a difference of squares.

$= 3[(y^2)^2 - (4)^2]$ — Write as $a^2 - b^2$, where $a = y^2$ and $b = 4$.

$= 3(y^2 + 4)(y^2 - 4)$ — Apply the formula $a^2 - b^2 = (a + b)(a - b)$.

$y^2 + 4$ is a sum of squares and cannot be factored.

$= 3(y^2 + 4)(y + 2)(y - 2)$ — $y^2 - 4$ is a difference of squares and can be factored further.

Skill Practice Factor completely.

6. $2x^4 - 2$

Answers

3. $(10x + 1)(100x^2 - 10x + 1)$
4. $\left(5p - \frac{1}{3}\right)\left(5p + \frac{1}{3}\right)$
5. $(3a^2 - b)(9a^4 + 3a^2b + b^2)$
6. $2(x^2 + 1)(x - 1)(x + 1)$

Concept 2: Factoring Binomials: A Summary

For Exercises 31–66, factor completely. **(See Examples 3–6.)**

31. $x^4 - 4$ **32.** $b^4 - 25$ **33.** $a^2 + 9$ **34.** $w^2 + 36$

35. $t^3 + 64$ **36.** $u^3 + 27$ **37.** $g^3 - 4$ **38.** $h^3 - 25$

39. $4b^3 + 108$ **40.** $3c^3 - 24$ **41.** $5p^2 - 125$ **42.** $2q^4 - 8$

43. $\frac{1}{64} - 8h^3$ **44.** $\frac{1}{125} + k^6$ **45.** $x^4 - 16$ **46.** $p^4 - 81$

47. $\frac{4}{9}x^2 - w^2$ **48.** $\frac{16}{25}y^2 - x^2$ **49.** $q^6 - 64$ **50.** $a^6 - 1$

(*Hint:* Factor using the difference of squares first.)

51. $x^9 + 64y^3$ **52.** $125w^3 - z^9$ **53.** $2x^3 + 3x^2 - 2x - 3$ **54.** $3x^3 + x^2 - 12x - 4$

55. $16x^4 - y^4$ **56.** $1 - t^4$ **57.** $81y^4 - 16$ **58.** $u^5 - 256u$

59. $a^3 + b^6$ **60.** $u^6 - v^3$ **61.** $x^4 - y^4$ **62.** $a^4 - b^4$

63. $k^3 + 4k^2 - 9k - 36$ **64.** $w^3 - 2w^2 - 4w + 8$ **65.** $2t^3 - 10t^2 - 2t + 10$ **66.** $9a^3 + 27a^2 - 4a - 12$

Expanding Your Skills

For Exercises 67–70, factor completely.

67. $\frac{64}{125}p^3 - \frac{1}{8}q^3$ **68.** $\frac{1}{1000}r^3 + \frac{8}{27}s^3$ **69.** $a^{12} + b^{12}$ **70.** $a^9 - b^9$

Use Exercises 71–72 to investigate the relationship between division and factoring.

71. a. Use long division to divide $x^3 - 8$ by $(x - 2)$.

b. Factor $x^3 - 8$.

72. a. Use long division to divide $y^3 + 27$ by $(y + 3)$.

b. Factor $y^3 + 27$.

73. What trinomial multiplied by $(x - 4)$ gives a difference of cubes?

74. What trinomial multiplied by $(p + 5)$ gives a sum of cubes?

75. Write a binomial that when multiplied by $(4x^2 - 2x + 1)$ produces a sum of cubes.

76. Write a binomial that when multiplied by $(9y^2 + 15y + 25)$ produces a difference of cubes.

Problem Recognition Exercises

Factoring Strategy

Factoring Strategy

Step 1 Factor out the GCF (Section 6.1).

Step 2 Identify whether the polynomial has two terms, three terms, or more than three terms.

Step 3 If the polynomial has more than three terms, try factoring by grouping (Section 6.1).

Step 4 If the polynomial has three terms, check first for a perfect square trinomial (Section 6.5). Otherwise, factor the trinomial with the trial-and-error method or the ac-method (Sections 6.3 or 6.4).

Step 5 If the polynomial has two terms, determine if it fits the pattern for

- A difference of squares: $a^2 - b^2 = (a - b)(a + b)$ (Section 6.5)
- A sum of squares: $a^2 + b^2$ is prime.
- A difference of cubes: $a^3 - b^3 = (a - b)(a^2 + ab + b^2)$ (Section 6.6)
- A sum of cubes: $a^3 + b^3 = (a + b)(a^2 - ab + b^2)$ (Section 6.6)

Step 6 Be sure to factor the polynomial completely.

Step 7 Check by multiplying.

1. What is meant by a prime polynomial?

2. What is the first step in factoring any polynomial?

3. When factoring a binomial, what patterns can you look for?

4. What technique should be considered when factoring a four-term polynomial?

For Exercises 5–73,

a. Factor out the GCF from each polynomial. Then identify the category in which the remaining polynomial best fits. Choose from

- difference of squares
- sum of squares
- difference of cubes
- sum of cubes
- trinomial (perfect square trinomial)
- trinomial (nonperfect square trinomial)
- four terms-grouping
- none of these

b. Factor the polynomial completely.

5. $2a^2 - 162$

6. $y^2 + 4y + 3$

7. $6w^2 - 6w$

8. $16z^4 - 81$

9. $3t^2 + 13t + 4$

10. $5r^3 + 5$

11. $3ac + ad - 3bc - bd$

12. $x^3 - 125$

13. $y^3 + 8$

14. $7p^2 - 29p + 4$

15. $3q^2 - 9q - 12$

16. $-2x^2 + 8x - 8$

17. $18a^2 + 12a$

18. $54 - 2y^3$

19. $4t^2 - 100$

20. $4t^2 - 31t - 8$

21. $10c^2 + 10c + 10$

22. $2xw - 10x + 3yw - 15y$

23. $x^3 + 0.001$

24. $4q^2 - 9$

25. $64 + 16k + k^2$

26. $s^2t + 5t + 6s^2 + 30$

27. $2x^2 + 2x - xy - y$

28. $w^3 + y^3$

29. $a^3 - c^3$

30. $3y^2 + y + 1$

31. $c^2 + 8c + 9$

32. $a^2 + 2a + 1$

33. $b^2 + 10b + 25$

34. $-t^2 - 4t + 32$

35. $-p^3 - 5p^2 - 4p$

36. $x^2y^2 - 49$

37. $6x^2 - 21x - 45$

38. $20y^2 - 14y + 2$

39. $5a^2bc^3 - 7abc^2$

40. $8a^2 - 50$

41. $t^2 + 2t - 63$

42. $b^2 + 2b - 80$

43. $ab + ay - b^2 - by$

44. $6x^3y^4 + 3x^2y^5$

45. $14u^2 - 11uv + 2v^2$

46. $9p^2 - 36pq + 4q^2$

47. $4q^2 - 8q - 6$

48. $9w^2 + 3w - 15$

49. $9m^2 + 16n^2$

50. $5b^2 - 30b + 45$

51. $6r^2 + 11r + 3$

52. $4s^2 + 4s - 15$

53. $16a^4 - 1$

54. $p^3 + p^2c - 9p - 9c$

55. $81u^2 - 90uv + 25v^2$

56. $4x^2 + 16$

57. $x^2 - 5x - 6$

58. $q^2 + q - 7$

59. $2ax - 6ay + 4bx - 12by$

60. $8m^3 - 10m^2 - 3m$

61. $21x^4y + 41x^3y + 10x^2y$

62. $2m^4 - 128$

63. $8uv - 6u + 12v - 9$

64. $4t^2 - 20t + st - 5s$

65. $12x^2 - 12x + 3$

66. $p^2 + 2pq + q^2$

67. $6n^3 + 5n^2 - 4n$

68. $4k^3 + 4k^2 - 3k$

69. $64 - y^2$

70. $36b - b^3$

71. $b^2 - 4b + 10$

72. $y^2 + 6y + 8$

73. $c^4 - 12c^2 + 20$

Section 6.7 Solving Equations Using the Zero Product Rule

Concepts

1. **Definition of a Quadratic Equation**
2. **Zero Product Rule**
3. **Solving Equations by Factoring**

1. Definition of a Quadratic Equation

In Section 2.1, we solved linear equations in one variable. These are equations of the form $ax + b = c$ $(a \neq 0)$. A linear equation in one variable is sometimes called a first-degree polynomial equation because the highest degree of all its terms is 1. A second-degree polynomial equation in one variable is called a quadratic equation.

A Quadratic Equation in One Variable

If a, b, and c are real numbers such that $a \neq 0$, then a **quadratic equation** is an equation that can be written in the form

$$ax^2 + bx + c = 0.$$

The following equations are quadratic because they can each be written in the form $ax^2 + bx + c = 0$, $(a \neq 0)$.

$-4x^2 + 4x = 1$	$x(x - 2) = 3$	$(x - 4)(x + 4) = 9$
$-4x^2 + 4x - 1 = 0$	$x^2 - 2x = 3$	$x^2 - 16 = 9$
	$x^2 - 2x - 3 = 0$	$x^2 - 25 = 0$
		$x^2 + 0x - 25 = 0$

2. Zero Product Rule

One method for solving a quadratic equation is to factor and apply the zero product rule. The **zero product rule** states that if the product of two factors is zero, then one or both of its factors is zero.

Zero Product Rule

If $ab = 0$, then $a = 0$ or $b = 0$.

Example 1 Applying the Zero Product Rule

Solve the equation by using the zero product rule. $(x - 4)(x + 3) = 0$

Solution:

$(x - 4)(x + 3) = 0$	Apply the zero product rule.
$x - 4 = 0$ or $x + 3 = 0$	Set each factor equal to zero.
$x = 4$ or $x = -3$	Solve each equation for x.
Check: $x = 4$	Check: $x = -3$
$(4 - 4)(4 + 3) \stackrel{?}{=} 0$	$(-3 - 4)(-3 + 3) \stackrel{?}{=} 0$
$(0)(7) \stackrel{?}{=} 0$ ✔	$(-7)(0) \stackrel{?}{=} 0$ ✔

The solution set is $\{4, -3\}$.

Skill Practice Solve.

1. $(x + 1)(x - 8) = 0$

Answer

1. $\{-1, 8\}$

Example 2 **Applying the Zero Product Rule**

Solve the equation by using the zero product rule. $(x + 8)(4x + 1) = 0$

Solution:

$(x + 8)(4x + 1) = 0$	Apply the zero product rule.
$x + 8 = 0 \quad \text{or} \quad 4x + 1 = 0$	Set each factor equal to zero.
$x = -8 \quad \text{or} \quad 4x = -1$	Solve each equation for x.
$x = -8 \quad \text{or} \quad x = -\frac{1}{4}$	The solutions check in the original equation.

The solution set is $\left\{-8, -\frac{1}{4}\right\}$.

Skill Practice Solve.

2. $(4x - 5)(x + 6) = 0$

Example 3 **Applying the Zero Product Rule**

Solve the equation using the zero product rule. $x(3x - 7) = 0$

Solution:

$x(3x - 7) = 0$	Apply the zero product rule.
$x = 0 \quad \text{or} \quad 3x - 7 = 0$	Set each factor equal to zero.
$x = 0 \quad \text{or} \quad 3x = 7$	Solve each equation for x.
$x = 0 \quad \text{or} \quad x = \frac{7}{3}$	The solutions check in the original equation.

The solution set is $\left\{0, \frac{7}{3}\right\}$.

Skill Practice Solve.

3. $x(4x + 9) = 0$

3. Solving Equations by Factoring

Quadratic equations, like linear equations, arise in many applications in mathematics, science, and business. The following steps summarize the factoring method for solving a quadratic equation.

Solving a Quadratic Equation by Factoring

Step 1 Write the equation in the form: $ax^2 + bx + c = 0$.

Step 2 Factor the quadratic expression completely.

Step 3 Apply the zero product rule. That is, set each factor equal to zero and solve the resulting equations.

Note: The solution(s) found in step 3 may be checked by substitution in the original equation.

Answers

2. $\left\{\frac{5}{4}, -6\right\}$ **3.** $\left\{0, -\frac{9}{4}\right\}$

Example 4 Solving a Quadratic Equation

Solve the quadratic equation. $2x^2 - 9x = 5$

Solution:

$2x^2 - 9x = 5$

$2x^2 - 9x - 5 = 0$ Write the equation in the form $ax^2 + bx + c = 0$.

$(2x + 1)(x - 5) = 0$ Factor the polynomial completely.

$2x + 1 = 0$ or $x - 5 = 0$ Set each factor equal to zero.

$2x = -1$ or $x = 5$ Solve each equation.

$x = -\frac{1}{2}$ or $x = 5$

Check: $x = -\frac{1}{2}$

$2x^2 - 9x = 5$

$2\left(-\frac{1}{2}\right)^2 - 9\left(-\frac{1}{2}\right) \stackrel{?}{=} 5$

$2\left(\frac{1}{4}\right) + \frac{9}{2} \stackrel{?}{=} 5$

$\frac{1}{2} + \frac{9}{2} \stackrel{?}{=} 5$

$\frac{10}{2} \stackrel{?}{=} 5$ ✔

Check: $x = 5$

$2x^2 - 9x = 5$

$2(5)^2 - 9(5) \stackrel{?}{=} 5$

$2(25) - 45 \stackrel{?}{=} 5$

$50 - 45 \stackrel{?}{=} 5$ ✔

The solution set is $\left\{-\frac{1}{2}, 5\right\}$.

Skill Practice Solve the quadratic equation.

4. $2y^2 + 19y = -24$

Example 5 Solving a Quadratic Equation

Solve the quadratic equation. $4x^2 + 24x = 0$

Solution:

$4x^2 + 24x = 0$ The equation is already in the form $ax^2 + bx + c = 0$. (Note that $c = 0$.)

$4x(x + 6) = 0$ Factor completely.

$4x = 0$ or $x + 6 = 0$ Set each factor equal to zero.

$x = 0$ or $x = -6$ The solutions check in the original equation.

The solution set is $\{0, -6\}$.

Skill Practice Solve the quadratic equation.

5. $5s^2 = 45$

Answers

4. $\left\{-8, -\frac{3}{2}\right\}$ **5.** $\{3, -3\}$

Concept 1: Definition of a Quadratic Equation

For Exercises 8–13, identify the equations as linear, quadratic, or neither.

8. $4 - 5x = 0$

9. $5x^3 + 2 = 0$

10. $3x - 6x^2 = 0$

11. $1 - x + 2x^2 = 0$

12. $7x^4 + 8 = 0$

13. $3x + 2 = 0$

Concept 2: Zero Product Rule

For Exercises 14–22, solve each equation using the zero product rule. **(See Examples 1–3.)**

14. $(x - 5)(x + 1) = 0$

15. $(x + 3)(x - 1) = 0$

16. $(3x - 2)(3x + 2) = 0$

17. $(2x - 7)(2x + 7) = 0$

18. $2(x - 7)(x - 7) = 0$

19. $3(x + 5)(x + 5) = 0$

20. $(3x - 2)(2x - 3) = 0$

21. $x(5x - 1) = 0$

22. $x(3x + 8) = 0$

23. For a quadratic equation of the form $ax^2 + bx + c = 0$, what must be done before applying the zero product rule?

24. What are the requirements needed to use the zero product rule to solve a quadratic equation or higher degree polynomial equation?

Concept 3: Solving Equations by Factoring

For Exercises 25–72, solve each equation. **(See Examples 4–8.)**

25. $p^2 - 2p - 15 = 0$

26. $y^2 - 7y - 8 = 0$

27. $z^2 + 10z - 24 = 0$

28. $w^2 - 10w + 16 = 0$

29. $2q^2 - 7q = 4$

30. $4x^2 - 11x = 3$

31. $0 = 9x^2 - 4$

32. $4a^2 - 49 = 0$

33. $2k^2 - 28k + 96 = 0$

34. $0 = 2t^2 + 20t + 50$

35. $0 = 2m^3 - 5m^2 - 12m$

36. $3n^3 + 4n^2 + n = 0$

37. $5(3p + 1)(p - 3)(p + 6) = 0$

38. $4(2x - 1)(x - 10)(x + 7) = 0$

39. $x(x - 4)(2x + 3) = 0$

40. $x(3x + 1)(x + 1) = 0$

41. $-5x(2x + 9)(x - 11) = 0$

42. $-3x(x + 7)(3x - 5) = 0$

43. $x^3 - 16x = 0$

44. $t^3 - 36t = 0$

45. $3x^2 + 18x = 0$

46. $2y^2 - 20y = 0$

47. $16m^2 = 9$

48. $9n^2 = 1$

49. $2y^3 + 14y^2 = -20y$

50. $3d^3 - 6d^2 = 24d$

51. $5t - 2(t - 7) = 0$

52. $8h = 5(h - 9) + 6$

53. $2c(c - 8) = -30$

54. $3q(q - 3) = 12$

55. $b^3 = -4b^2 - 4b$

56. $x^3 + 36x = 12x^2$

57. $3(a^2 + 2a) = 2a^2 - 9$

58. $9(k - 1) = -4k^2$

59. $2n(n + 2) = 6$

60. $3p(p - 1) = 18$

61. $x(2x + 5) - 1 = 2x^2 + 3x + 2$

62. $3z(z - 2) - z = 3z^2 + 4$

63. $27q^2 = 9q$

64. $21w^2 = 14w$

65. $3(c^2 - 2c) = 0$

66. $2(4d^2 + d) = 0$

67. $y^3 - 3y^2 - 4y + 12 = 0$

68. $t^3 + 2t^2 - 16t - 32 = 0$

69. $(x - 1)(x + 2) = 18$

70. $(w + 5)(w - 3) = 20$

71. $(p + 2)(p + 3) = 1 - p$

72. $(k - 6)(k - 1) = -k - 2$

Problem Recognition Exercises

Polynomial Expressions Versus Polynomial Equations

For Exercises 1–36, factor each expression or solve each equation.

1. a. $x^2 + 6x - 7$
b. $x^2 + 6x - 7 = 0$

2. a. $c^2 + 8c + 12$
b. $c^2 + 8c + 12 = 0$

3. a. $2y^2 + 7y + 3$
b. $2y^2 + 7y + 3 = 0$

4. a. $3x^2 - 8x + 5$
b. $3x^2 - 8x + 5 = 0$

5. a. $5q^2 + q - 4 = 0$
b. $5q^2 + q - 4$

6. a. $6a^2 - 7a - 3 = 0$
b. $6a^2 - 7a - 3$

7. a. $a^2 - 64 = 0$
b. $a^2 - 64$

8. a. $v^2 - 100 = 0$
b. $v^2 - 100$

9. a. $4b^2 - 81$
b. $4b^2 - 81 = 0$

10. a. $36t^2 - 49$
b. $36t^2 - 49 = 0$

11. a. $8x^2 + 16x + 6 = 0$
b. $8x^2 + 16x + 6$

12. a. $12y^2 + 40y + 32 = 0$
b. $12y^2 + 40y + 32$

13. a. $x^3 - 8x^2 - 20x$
b. $x^3 - 8x^2 - 20x = 0$

14. a. $k^3 + 5k^2 - 14k$
b. $k^3 + 5k^2 - 14k = 0$

15. a. $b^3 + b^2 - 9b - 9 = 0$
b. $b^3 + b^2 - 9b - 9$

16. a. $x^3 - 8x^2 - 4x + 32 = 0$
b. $x^3 - 8x^2 - 4x + 32$

17. $2s^2 - 6s + rs - 3r$

18. $6t^2 + 3t + 10tu + 5u$

19. $8x^3 - 2x = 0$

20. $2b^3 - 50b = 0$

21. $2x^3 - 4x^2 + 2x = 0$

22. $3t^3 + 18t^2 + 27t = 0$

23. $7c^2 - 2c + 3 = 7(c^2 + c)$

24. $3z(2z + 4) = -7 + 6z^2$

25. $8w^3 + 27$

26. $1000q^3 - 1$

27. $5z^2 + 2z = 7$

28. $4h^2 + 25h = -6$

29. $3b(b + 6) = b - 10$

30. $3y^2 + 1 = y(y - 3)$

31. $5(2x - 3) - 2(3x + 1) = 4 - 3x$

32. $11 - 6a = -4(2a - 3) - 1$

33. $4s^2 = 64$

34. $81v^2 = 36$

35. $(x - 3)(x - 4) = 6$

36. $(x + 5)(x + 9) = 21$

Section 6.8 Applications of Quadratic Equations

Concepts

1. Applications of Quadratic Equations
2. Pythagorean Theorem

1. Applications of Quadratic Equations

In this section we solve applications using the Problem-Solving Strategies outlined in Section 2.4.

Example 1 Translating to a Quadratic Equation

The product of two consecutive integers is 14 more than 6 times the smaller integer.

Solution:

Let x represent the first (smaller) integer.

Then $x + 1$ represents the second (larger) integer. — Label the variables.

(Smaller integer)(larger integer) $= 6 \cdot$ (smaller integer) $+ 14$ — Verbal model

$x(x + 1) = 6(x) + 14$ — Algebraic equation

$x^2 + x = 6x + 14$ — Simplify.

$x^2 + x - 6x - 14 = 0$ — Set one side of the equation equal to zero.

$x^2 - 5x - 14 = 0$

$(x - 7)(x + 2) = 0$ — Factor.

$x - 7 = 0$ or $x + 2 = 0$ — Set each factor equal to zero.

$x = 7$ or $x = -2$ — Solve for x.

Recall that x represents the smaller integer. Therefore, there are two possibilities for the pairs of consecutive integers.

If $x = 7$, then the larger integer is $x + 1$ or $7 + 1 = 8$.

If $x = -2$, then the larger integer is $x + 1$ or $-2 + 1 = -1$.

The integers are 7 and 8, or -2 and -1.

Skill Practice

1. The product of two consecutive odd integers is 9 more than 10 times the smaller integer. Find the pair of integers.

Example 2 Using a Quadratic Equation in a Geometry Application

A rectangular sign has an area of 40 ft^2. If the width is 3 ft shorter than the length, what are the dimensions of the sign?

Solution:

Let x represent the length of the sign. Then $x - 3$ represents the width (Figure 6-1).

The problem gives information about the length of the sides and about the area. Therefore, we can form a relationship by using the formula for the area of a rectangle.

Label the variables.

Figure 6-1

Answer

1. The integers are 9 and 11 or -1 and 1.

$A = l \cdot w$	Area equals length times width.
$40 = x(x - 3)$	Set up an algebraic equation.
$40 = x^2 - 3x$	Clear parentheses.
$0 = x^2 - 3x - 40$	Write the equation in the form, $ax^2 + bx + c = 0$.
$0 = (x - 8)(x + 5)$	Factor.
$0 = x - 8$ or $0 = x + 5$	Set each factor equal to zero.
$8 = x$ or $-5 \neq x$	Because x represents the length of a rectangle, reject the negative solution.

The variable x represents the length of the sign. The length is 8 ft.

The expression $x - 3$ represents the width. The width is 8 ft − 3 ft, or 5 ft.

Skill Practice

2. The length of a rectangle is 5 ft more than the width. The area is 36 ft^2. Find the length and width.

Example 3 Using a Quadratic Equation in an Application

A stone is dropped off a 64-ft cliff and falls into the ocean below. The height of the stone above sea level is given by the equation

$h = -16t^2 + 64$ where h is the stone's height in feet, and t is the time in seconds.

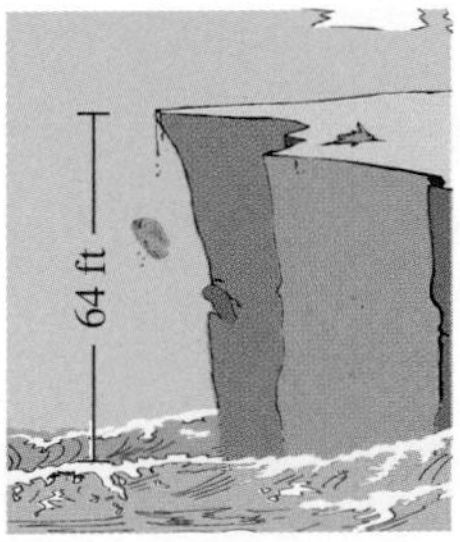

Find the time required for the stone to hit the water.

Solution:

When the stone hits the water, its height is zero. Therefore, substitute $h = 0$ into the equation.

$h = -16t^2 + 64$	The equation is quadratic.
$0 = -16t^2 + 64$	Substitute $h = 0$.
$0 = -16(t^2 - 4)$	Factor out the GCF.
$0 = -16(t - 2)(t + 2)$	Factor as a difference of squares.
$-16 \neq 0$ or $t - 2 = 0$ or $t + 2 = 0$	Set each factor to zero.
No solution, $t = 2$ or $t \neq -2$	Solve for t.

The negative value of t is rejected because the stone cannot fall for a negative time. Therefore, the stone hits the water after 2 sec.

Skill Practice

3. An object is launched into the air from the ground and its height is given by $h = -16t^2 + 144t$, where h is the height in feet after t seconds. Find the time required for the object to hit the ground.

Answers

2. The width is 4 ft, and the length is 9 ft.
3. The object hits the ground in 9 sec.

2. Pythagorean Theorem

Recall that a right triangle is a triangle that contains a 90° angle. Furthermore, the sum of the squares of the two legs (the shorter sides) of a right triangle equals the square of the hypotenuse (the longest side). This important fact is known as the Pythagorean theorem. The Pythagorean theorem is an enduring landmark of mathematical history from which many mathematical ideas have been built. Although the theorem is named after Pythagoras (sixth century B.C.E.), a Greek mathematician and philosopher, it is thought that the ancient Babylonians were familiar with the principle more than a thousand years earlier.

For the right triangle shown in Figure 6-2, the **Pythagorean theorem** is stated as:

$$a^2 + b^2 = c^2$$

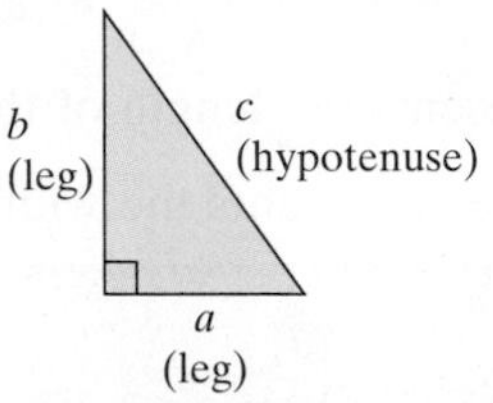

Figure 6-2

In this formula, a and b are the legs of the right triangle and c is the hypotenuse. Notice that the hypotenuse is the longest side of the right triangle and is opposite the 90° angle.

The triangle shown below is a right triangle. Notice that the lengths of the sides satisfy the Pythagorean theorem.

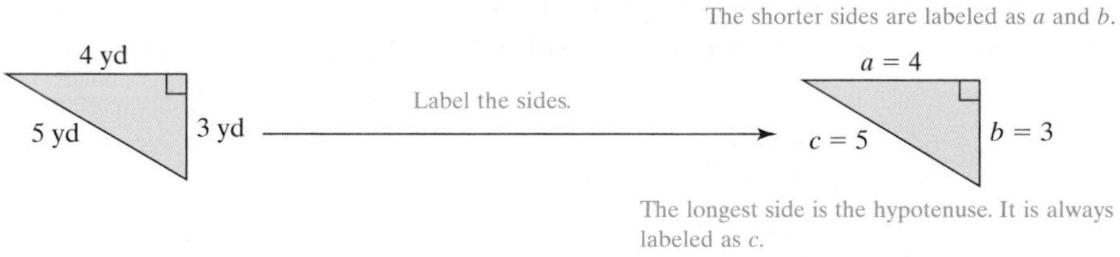

$a^2 + b^2 = c^2$	Apply the Pythagorean theorem.
$(4)^2 + (3)^2 = (5)^2$	Substitute $a = 4$, $b = 3$, and $c = 5$.
$16 + 9 = 25$	
$25 = 25$ ✔	

Example 4 Applying the Pythagorean Theorem

Find the length of the missing side of the right triangle.

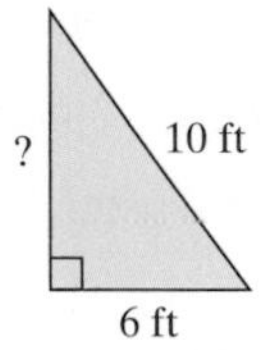

Solution:

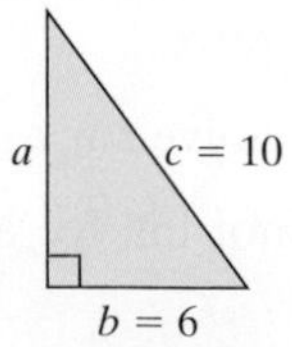

Label the triangle.

$a^2 + b^2 = c^2$	Apply the Pythagorean theorem.
$a^2 + 6^2 = 10^2$	Substitute $b = 6$ and $c = 10$.
$a^2 + 36 = 100$	Simplify.
	The equation is quadratic. Set the equation equal to zero.

$a^2 + 36 - 100 = 100 - 100$	Subtract 100 from both sides.
$a^2 - 64 = 0$	
$(a + 8)(a - 8) = 0$	Factor.
$a + 8 = 0$ or $a - 8 = 0$	Set each factor equal to zero.
$a \cancel{=} -8$ or $a = 8$	Because x represents the length of a side of a triangle, reject the negative solution.

The third side is 8 ft.

Skill Practice

4. Find the length of the missing side.

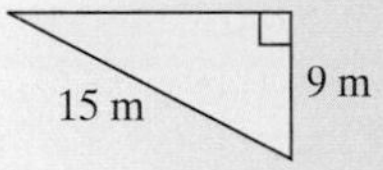

Example 5 Using a Quadratic Equation in an Application

A 13-ft board is used as a ramp to unload furniture off a loading platform. If the distance between the top of the board and the ground is 7 ft less than the distance between the bottom of the board and the base of the platform, find both distances.

Solution:

Let x represent the distance between the bottom of the board and the base of the platform. Then $x - 7$ represents the distance between the top of the board and the ground (Figure 6-3).

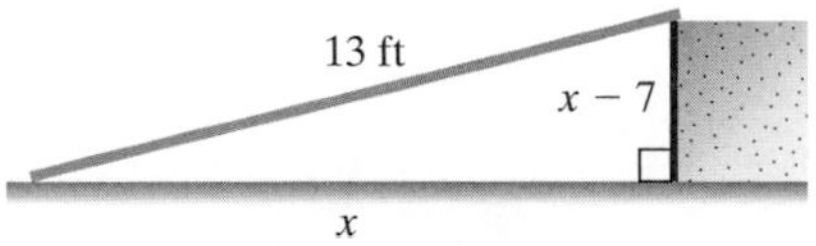

Figure 6-3

$a^2 + b^2 = c^2$	Pythagorean theorem
$x^2 + (x - 7)^2 = (13)^2$	
$x^2 + (x)^2 - 2(x)(7) + (7)^2 = 169$	
$x^2 + x^2 - 14x + 49 = 169$	
$2x^2 - 14x + 49 = 169$	Combine *like* terms.
$2x^2 - 14x + 49 - 169 = 169 - 169$	Set the equation equal to zero.
$2x^2 - 14x - 120 = 0$	Write the equation in the form $ax^2 + bx + c = 0$.
$2(x^2 - 7x - 60) = 0$	Factor.
$2(x - 12)(x + 5) = 0$	
$2 \cancel{=} 0$ or $x - 12 = 0$ or $x + 5 = 0$	Set each factor equal to zero.
$x = 12$ or $x \cancel{=} -5$	Solve both equations for x.

Avoiding Mistakes

Recall that the square of a binomial results in a perfect square trinomial.

$$(a - b)^2 = a^2 - 2ab + b^2$$
$$(x - 7)^2 = x^2 - 2(x)(7) + 7^2$$
$$= x^2 - 14x + 49$$

Don't forget the middle term.

Answer

4. The length of the third side is 12 m.

Recall that x represents the distance between the bottom of the board and the base of the platform. We reject the negative value of x because a distance cannot be negative. Therefore, the distance between the bottom of the board and the base of the platform is 12 ft. The distance between the top of the board and the ground is $x - 7 = 5$ ft.

Skill Practice

5. A 5-yd ladder leans against a wall. The distance from the bottom of the wall to the top of the ladder is 1 yd more than the distance from the bottom of the wall to the bottom of the ladder. Find both distances.

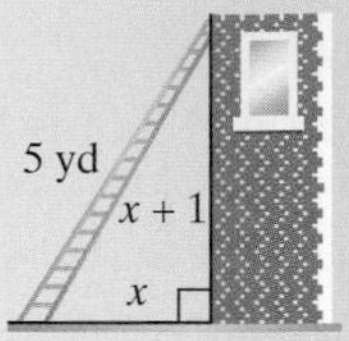

Answer

5. The distance along the wall to the top of the ladder is 4 yd. The distance on the ground from the ladder to the wall is 3 yd.

Section 6.8 Practice Exercises

Vocabulary and Key Concepts

1. a. If x is the smaller of two consecutive integers, then _______ represents the next greater integer.
   b. If x is the smaller of two consecutive odd integers, then _______ represents the next greater odd integer.
   c. If x is the smaller of two consecutive even integers, then _______ represents the next greater even integer.
   d. The area of a rectangle of length L and width W is given by $A =$ _______.
   e. The area of a triangle with base b and height h is given by the formula $A =$ _______.
   f. Given a right triangle with legs a and b and hypotenuse c, the Pythagorean theorem is stated as ___________.

Review Exercises

For Exercises 2–7, solve the quadratic equations.

2. $(6x + 1)(x + 4) = 0$
3. $9x(3x + 2) = 0$
4. $4x^2 - 1 = 0$
5. $x^2 - 5x = 6$
6. $x(x - 20) = -100$
7. $6x^2 - 7x - 10 = 0$
8. Explain what is wrong with the following problem: $(x - 3)(x + 2) = 5$
   $x - 3 = 5$ or $x + 2 = 5$

Concept 1: Applications of Quadratic Equations

9. If eleven is added to the square of a number, the result is sixty. Find all such numbers.
10. If a number is added to two times its square, the result is thirty-six. Find all such numbers.
11. If twelve is added to six times a number, the result is twenty-eight less than the square of the number. Find all such numbers.
12. The square of a number is equal to twenty more than the number. Find all such numbers.
13. The product of two consecutive odd integers is sixty-three. Find all such integers. **(See Example 1.)**
14. The product of two consecutive even integers is forty-eight. Find all such integers.
15. The sum of the squares of two consecutive integers is sixty-one. Find all such integers.
16. The sum of the squares of two consecutive even integers is fifty-two. Find all such integers.

17. *Las Meninas* (Spanish for *The Maids of Honor*) is a famous painting by Spanish painter Diego Velazquez. This work is regarded as one of the most important paintings in western art history. The height of the painting is approximately 2 ft more than its width. If the total area is 99 ft^2, determine the dimensions of the painting. **(See Example 2.)**

18. The width of a rectangular painting is 2 in. less than the length. The area is 120 in.^2 Find the length and width.

19. The width of a rectangular slab of concrete is 3 m less than the length. The area is 28 m^2.

a. What are the dimensions of the rectangle?

b. What is the perimeter of the rectangle?

20. The width of a rectangular picture is 7 in. less than the length. The area of the picture is 78 in.^2

a. What are the dimensions of the picture?

b. What is the perimeter of the picture?

21. The base of a triangle is 3 ft more than the height. If the area is 14 ft^2, find the base and the height.

22. The height of a triangle is 15 cm more than the base. If the area is 125 cm^2, find the base and the height.

23. The height of a triangle is 7 cm less than 3 times the base. If the area is 20 cm^2, find the base and the height.

24. The base of a triangle is 2 ft less than 4 times the height. If the area is 6 ft^2, find the base and the height.

25. In a physics experiment, a ball is dropped off a 144-ft platform. The height of the ball above the ground is given by the equation

$h = -16t^2 + 144$ where h is the ball's height in feet, and t is the time in seconds after the ball is dropped ($t \geq 0$).

Find the time required for the ball to hit the ground. (*Hint:* Let $h = 0$.) **(See Example 3.)**

26. A stone is dropped off a 256-ft cliff. The height of the stone above the ground is given by the equation

$h = -16t^2 + 256$ where h is the stone's height in feet, and t is the time in seconds after the stone is dropped ($t \geq 0$).

Find the time required for the stone to hit the ground.

27. An object is shot straight up into the air from ground level with an initial speed of 24 ft/sec. The height of the object (in feet) is given by the equation

$h = -16t^2 + 24t$ where t is the time in seconds after launch ($t \geq 0$).

Find the time(s) when the object is at ground level.

28. A rocket is launched straight up into the air from the ground with initial speed of 64 ft/sec. The height of the rocket (in feet) is given by the equation

$h = -16t^2 + 64t$ where t is the time in seconds after launch ($t \geq 0$).

Find the time(s) when the rocket is at ground level.

Concept 2: Pythagorean Theorem

29. Sketch a right triangle and label the sides with the words *leg* and *hypotenuse.*

30. State the Pythagorean theorem.

For Exercises 31–34, find the length of the missing side of the right triangle. **(See Example 4.)**

31.

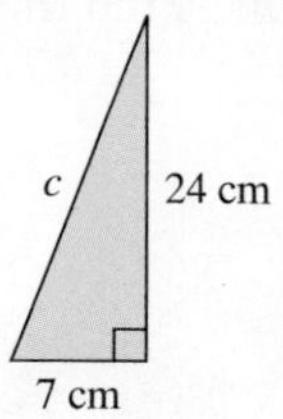

32.

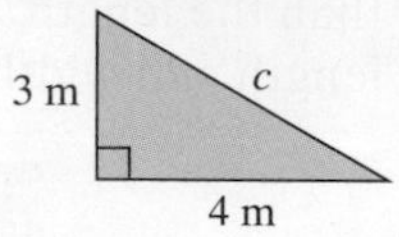

33.

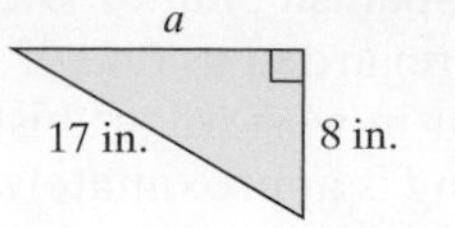

34.

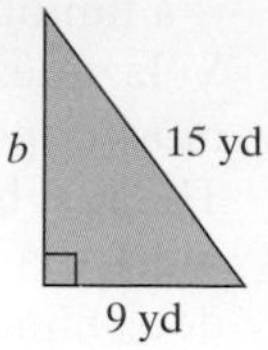

35. Find the length of the supporting brace.

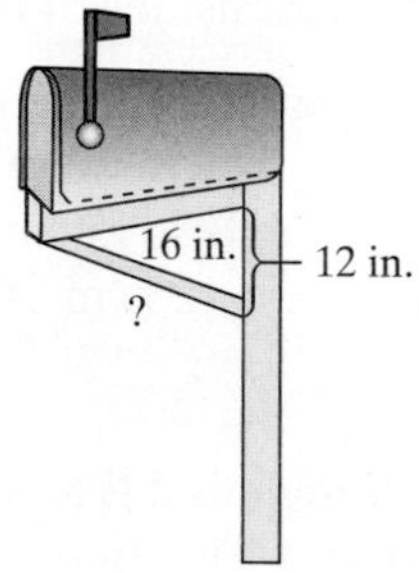

36. Find the height of the airplane above the ground.

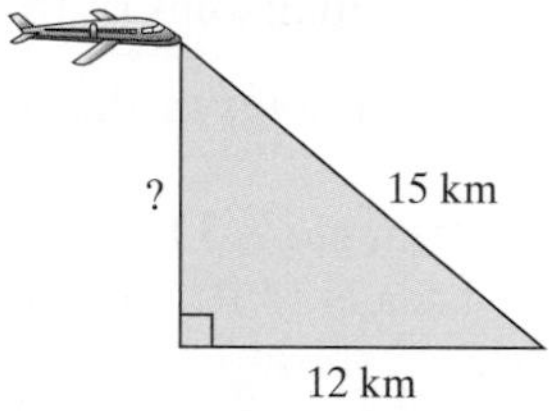

37. Darcy holds the end of a kite string 3 ft (1 yd) off the ground and wants to estimate the height of the kite. Her friend Jenna is 24 yd away from her, standing directly under the kite as shown in the figure. If Darcy has 30 yd of string out, find the height of the kite (ignore the sag in the string).

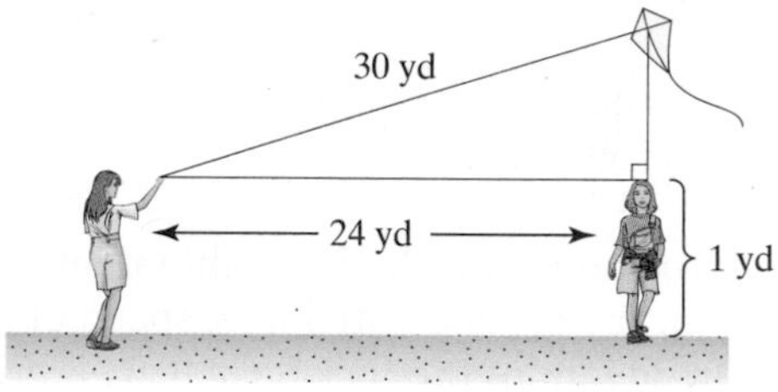

38. Two cars leave the same point at the same time, one traveling north and the other traveling east. After an hour, one car has traveled 48 mi and the other has traveled 64 mi. How many miles apart were they at that time?

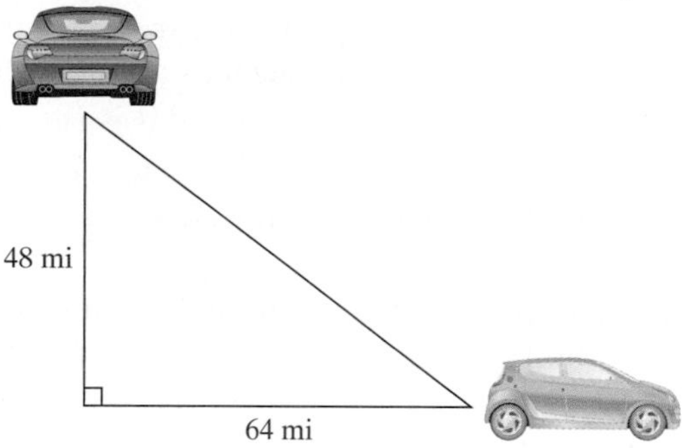

39. A 17-ft ladder rests against the side of a house. The distance between the top of the ladder and the ground is 7 ft more than the distance between the base of the ladder and the bottom of the house. Find both distances. **(See Example 5.)**

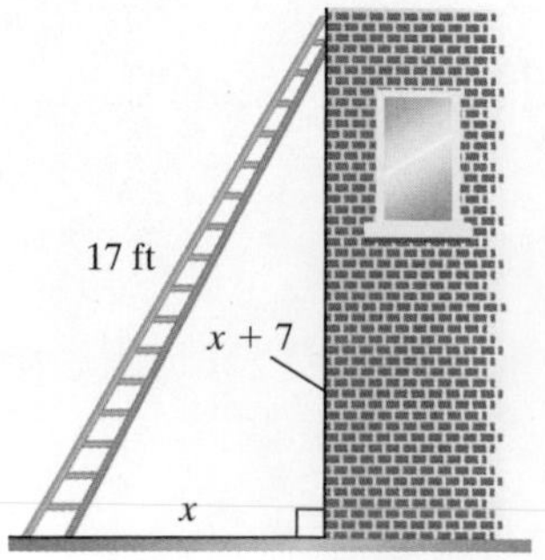

40. Two boats leave a marina. One travels east, and the other travels south. After 30 min, the second boat has traveled 1 mi farther than the first boat and the distance between the boats is 5 mi. Find the distance each boat traveled.

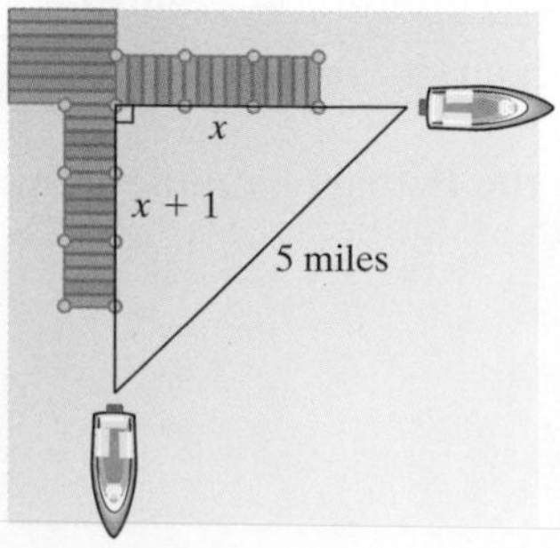

41. One leg of a right triangle is 4 m less than the hypotenuse. The other leg is 2 m less than the hypotenuse. Find the length of the hypotenuse.

42. The longer leg of a right triangle is 1 cm less than twice the shorter leg. The hypotenuse is 1 cm greater than twice the shorter leg. Find the length of the shorter leg.

Group Activity

Building a Factoring Test

Estimated Time: 30–45 minutes

Group Size: 3

In this activity, each group will make a test for this chapter. Then the groups will trade papers and take the test.

For Exercises 1–8, write a polynomial that has the given conditions. Do not use reference materials such as the textbook or your notes.

1. A trinomial with a GCF not equal to 1. The GCF should include a constant and at least one variable. **1.** ____________

2. A four-term polynomial that is factorable by grouping. **2.** ____________

3. A factorable trinomial with a leading coefficient of 1. (The trinomial should factor as a product of two binomials.) **3.** ____________

4. A factorable trinomial with a leading coefficient not equal to 1. (The trinomial should factor as a product of two binomials.) **4.** ____________

5. A trinomial that requires the GCF to be removed. The resulting trinomial should factor as a product of two binomials. **5.** ____________

6. A difference of squares. **6.** ____________

7. A difference of cubes. **7.** ____________

8. A sum of cubes. **8.** ____________

9. Write a quadratic *equation* that has solution set $\{4, -7\}$. **9.** ____________

10. Write a quadratic *equation* that has solution set $\left\{0, -\frac{2}{3}\right\}$. **10.** ____________

Chapter 6 Summary

Section 6.1 Greatest Common Factor and Factoring by Grouping

Key Concepts

The **greatest common factor** (GCF) is the greatest factor common to all terms of a polynomial. To factor out the GCF from a polynomial, use the distributive property.

A four-term polynomial may be factorable by grouping.

Steps to Factoring by Grouping

1. Identify and factor out the GCF from all four terms.
2. Factor out the GCF from the first pair of terms. Factor out the GCF or its opposite from the second pair of terms.
3. If the two terms share a common binomial factor, factor out the binomial factor.

Examples

Example 1

$3x(a + b) - 5(a + b)$ Greatest common factor is $(a + b)$.

$= (a + b)(3x - 5)$

Example 2

$60xa - 30xb - 80ya + 40yb$

$= 10[6xa - 3xb - 8ya + 4yb]$ Factor out GCF.

$= 10[3x(2a - b) - 4y(2a - b)]$ Factor by grouping.

$= 10(2a - b)(3x - 4y)$

Section 6.2 Factoring Trinomials of the Form $x^2 + bx + c$

Key Concepts

Factoring a Trinomial with a Leading Coefficient of 1

A trinomial of the form $x^2 + bx + c$ factors as

$$x^2 + bx + c = (x \quad \square)(x \quad \square)$$

where the remaining terms are given by two integers whose product is c and whose sum is b.

Example

Example 1

$x^2 - 14x + 45$ The integers -5 and -9 have a product of 45 and a sum of -14.

$= (x \quad \square)(x \quad \square)$

$= (x - 5)(x - 9)$

Section 6.3 Factoring Trinomials: Trial-and-Error Method

Key Concepts

Trial-and-Error Method for Factoring Trinomials in the Form $ax^2 + bx + c$ (where $a \neq 0$)

1. Factor out the GCF from all terms.
2. List the pairs of factors of a and the pairs of factors of c. Consider the reverse order in one of the lists.
3. Construct two binomials of the form

Factors of a

$$(\square x \quad \square)(\square x \quad \square)$$

Factors of c

4. Test each combination of factors and signs until the product forms the correct trinomial.
5. If no combination of factors produces the correct product, then the trinomial is prime.

Example

Example 1

$10y^2 + 35y - 20$

$= 5(2y^2 + 7y - 4)$

The pairs of factors of 2 are: $2 \cdot 1$

The pairs of factors of -4 are:

$-1(4) \quad 1(-4)$

$-2(2) \quad 2(-2)$

$-4(1) \quad 4(-1)$

$(2y - 2)(y + 2) = 2y^2 + 2y - 4$	No
$(2y - 4)(y + 1) = 2y^2 - 2y - 4$	No
$(2y + 1)(y - 4) = 2y^2 - 7y - 4$	No
$(2y + 2)(y - 2) = 2y^2 - 2y - 4$	No
$(2y + 4)(y - 1) = 2y^2 + 2y - 4$	No
$(2y - 1)(y + 4) = 2y^2 + 7y - 4$	Yes

$10y^2 + 35y - 20 = 5(2y - 1)(y + 4)$

Section 6.4 Factoring Trinomials: AC-Method

Key Concepts

AC-Method for Factoring Trinomials of the Form $ax^2 + bx + c$ (where $a \neq 0$)

1. Factor out the GCF from all terms.
2. Find the product ac.
3. Find two integers whose product is ac and whose sum is b. (If no pair of integers can be found, then the trinomial is prime.)
4. Rewrite the middle term (bx) as the sum of two terms whose coefficients are the integers found in step 3.
5. Factor the polynomial by grouping.

Example

Example 1

$10y^2 + 35y - 20$

$= 5(2y^2 + 7y - 4)$ First factor out GCF.

Identify the product $ac = (2)(-4) = -8$.

Find two integers whose product is -8 and whose sum is 7. The numbers are 8 and -1.

$5[2y^2 + 8y - 1y - 4]$

$= 5[2y(y + 4) - 1(y + 4)]$

$= 5(y + 4)(2y - 1)$

Section 6.5 Difference of Squares and Perfect Square Trinomials

Key Concepts

Factoring a Difference of Squares

$a^2 - b^2 = (a + b)(a - b)$

Factoring a Perfect Square Trinomial

The factored form of a **perfect square trinomial** is the square of a binomial:

$a^2 + 2ab + b^2 = (a + b)^2$

$a^2 - 2ab + b^2 = (a - b)^2$

Examples

Example 1

$25z^2 - 4y^2$

$= (5z + 2y)(5z - 2y)$

Example 2

Factor: $25y^2 + 10y + 1$

$= (5y)^2 + 2(5y)(1) + (1)^2$

$= (5y + 1)^2$

Section 6.6 Sum and Difference of Cubes

Key Concepts

Factoring a Sum or Difference of Cubes

$a^3 + b^3 = (a + b)(a^2 - ab + b^2)$

$a^3 - b^3 = (a - b)(a^2 + ab + b^2)$

Examples

Example 1

$x^6 + 8y^3$

$= (x^2)^3 + (2y)^3$

$= (x^2 + 2y)(x^4 - 2x^2y + 4y^2)$

Example 2

$m^3 - 64$

$= (m)^3 - (4)^3$

$= (m - 4)(m^2 + 4m + 16)$

Section 6.7 Solving Equations Using the Zero Product Rule

Key Concepts

An equation of the form $ax^2 + bx + c = 0$, where $a \neq 0$, is a **quadratic equation**.

The zero product rule states that if $ab = 0$, then $a = 0$ or $b = 0$. The zero product rule can be used to solve a quadratic equation or a higher degree polynomial equation that is factored and set to zero.

Examples

Example 1

The equation $2x^2 - 17x + 30 = 0$ is a quadratic equation.

Example 2

$3w(w - 4)(2w + 1) = 0$

$3w = 0$ or $w - 4 = 0$ or $2w + 1 = 0$

$w = 0$ or $w = 4$ or $w = -\dfrac{1}{2}$

The solution set is $\left\{0, 4, -\dfrac{1}{2}\right\}$.

Example 3

$4x^2 = 34x - 60$

$4x^2 - 34x + 60 = 0$

$2(2x^2 - 17x + 30) = 0$

$2(2x - 5)(x - 6) = 0$

$2 \neq 0$ or $2x - 5 = 0$ or $x - 6 = 0$

$x = \dfrac{5}{2}$ or $x = 6$

The solution set is $\left\{\dfrac{5}{2}, 6\right\}$.

Section 6.8 Applications of Quadratic Equations

Key Concepts

Use the zero product rule to solve applications.

Some applications involve the Pythagorean theorem.

$a^2 + b^2 = c^2$

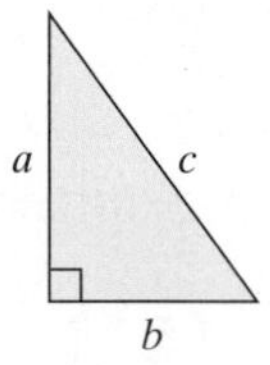

Examples

Example 1

Find two consecutive integers such that the sum of their squares is 61.

Let x represent one integer.
Let $x + 1$ represent the next consecutive integer.

$$x^2 + (x + 1)^2 = 61$$
$$x^2 + x^2 + 2x + 1 = 61$$
$$2x^2 + 2x - 60 = 0$$
$$2(x^2 + x - 30) = 0$$
$$2(x - 5)(x + 6) = 0$$
$$x = 5 \quad \text{or} \quad x = -6$$

If $x = 5$, then the next consecutive integer is 6.
If $x = -6$, then the next consecutive integer is -5.
The integers are 5 and 6, or -6 and -5.

Example 2

Find the length of the missing side.

$$x^2 + (7)^2 = (25)^2$$
$$x^2 + 49 = 625$$
$$x^2 - 576 = 0$$
$$(x - 24)(x + 24) = 0$$
$$x = 24 \quad \text{or} \quad x \cancel{=} -24$$

The length of the side is 24 ft.

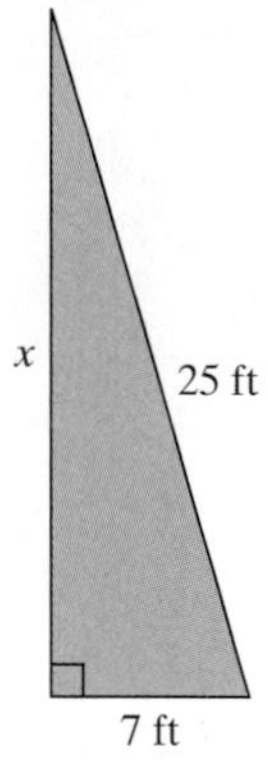

Chapter 6 Review Exercises

Section 6.1

For Exercises 1–4, identify the greatest common factor for each group of terms.

1. $15a^2b^4, 30a^3b, 9a^5b^3$

2. $3(x + 5), x(x + 5)$

3. $2c^3(3c - 5), 4c(3c - 5)$

4. $-2wyz, -4xyz$

For Exercises 5–10, factor out the greatest common factor.

5. $6x^2 + 2x^4 - 8x$

6. $11w^3y^3 - 44w^2y^5$

7. $-t^2 + 5t$

8. $-6u^2 - u$

9. $3b(b + 2) - 7(b + 2)$

10. $2(5x + 9) + 8x(5x + 9)$

For Exercises 11–14, factor by grouping.

11. $7w^2 + 14w + wb + 2b$

12. $b^2 - 2b + yb - 2y$

13. $60y^2 - 45y - 12y + 9$

14. $6a - 3a^2 - 2ab + a^2b$

Section 6.2

For Exercises 15–24, factor completely.

15. $x^2 - 10x + 21$

16. $y^2 - 19y + 88$

17. $-6z + z^2 - 72$

18. $-39 + q^2 - 10q$

19. $3p^2w + 36pw + 60w$

20. $2m^4 + 26m^3 + 80m^2$

21. $-t^2 + 10t - 16$

22. $-w^2 - w + 20$

23. $a^2 + 12ab + 11b^2$

24. $c^2 - 3cd - 18d^2$

Section 6.3

For Exercises 25–28, let a, b, and c represent positive integers.

25. When factoring a polynomial of the form $ax^2 - bx - c$, should the signs of the binomials be both positive, both negative, or different?

26. When factoring a polynomial of the form $ax^2 - bx + c$, should the signs of the binomials be both positive, both negative, or different?

27. When factoring a polynomial of the form $ax^2 + bx + c$, should the signs of the binomials be both positive, both negative, or different?

28. When factoring a polynomial of the form $ax^2 + bx - c$, should the signs of the binomials be both positive, both negative, or different?

For Exercises 29–42, factor each trinomial using the trial-and-error method.

29. $2y^2 - 5y - 12$

30. $4w^2 - 5w - 6$

31. $10z^2 + 29z + 10$

32. $8z^2 + 6z - 9$

33. $2p^2 - 5p + 1$

34. $5r^2 - 3r + 7$

35. $10w^2 - 60w - 270$

36. $-3y^2 + 18y + 48$

37. $9c^2 - 30cd + 25d^2$

38. $x^2 + 12x + 36$

39. $6g^2 + 7gh + 2h^2$

40. $12m^2 - 32mn + 5n^2$

41. $v^4 - 2v^2 - 3$

42. $x^4 + 7x^2 + 10$

Section 6.4

For Exercises 43–44, find a pair of integers whose product and sum are given.

43. Product: -5 sum: 4

44. Product: 15 sum: -8

For Exercises 45–58, factor each trinomial using the ac-method.

45. $3c^2 - 5c - 2$

46. $4y^2 + 13y + 3$

47. $t^2 + 13tw + 12w^2$

48. $4x^4 + 17x^2 - 15$

49. $w^4 + 7w^2 + 10$

50. $p^2 - 8pq + 15q^2$

51. $-40v^2 - 22v + 6$

52. $40s^2 + 30s - 100$

53. $a^3b - 10a^2b^2 + 24ab^3$

54. $2z^6 + 8z^5 - 42z^4$

55. $m + 9m^2 - 2$

56. $2 + 6p^2 + 19p$

57. $49x^2 + 140x + 100$

58. $9w^2 - 6wz + z^2$

Section 6.5

For Exercises 59–60, write the formula to factor each binomial, if possible.

59. $a^2 - b^2$

60. $a^2 + b^2$

For Exercises 61–76, factor completely.

61. $a^2 - 49$

62. $d^2 - 64$

63. $100 - 81t^2$

64. $4 - 25k^2$

65. $x^2 + 16$

66. $y^2 + 121$

67. $y^2 + 12y + 36$

68. $t^2 + 16t + 64$

69. $9a^2 - 12a + 4$

70. $25x^2 - 40x + 16$

71. $-3v^2 - 12v - 12$

72. $-2x^2 + 20x - 50$

73. $2c^4 - 18$

74. $72x^2 - 2y^2$

75. $p^3 + 3p^2 - 16p - 48$

76. $4k - 8 - k^3 + 2k^2$

Section 6.6

For Exercises 77–78, write the formula to factor each binomial, if possible.

77. $a^3 + b^3$

78. $a^3 - b^3$

For Exercises 79–92, factor completely using the factoring strategy found on page 461.

79. $64 + a^3$

80. $125 - b^3$

81. $p^6 + 8$

82. $q^6 - \frac{1}{27}$

83. $6x^3 - 48$

84. $7y^3 + 7$

85. $x^3 - 36x$

86. $q^4 - 64q$

87. $8h^2 + 20$

88. $m^2 - 8m$

89. $x^3 + 4x^2 - x - 4$

90. $5p^4q - 20q^3$

91. $8n + n^4$

92. $14m^3 - 14$

Section 6.7

93. For which of the following equations can the zero product rule be applied directly? Explain.

$(x - 3)(2x + 1) = 0$ or $(x - 3)(2x + 1) = 6$

For Exercises 94–109, solve each equation using the zero product rule.

94. $(4x - 1)(3x + 2) = 0$

95. $(a - 9)(2a - 1) = 0$

96. $3w(w + 3)(5w + 2) = 0$

97. $6u(u - 7)(4u - 9) = 0$

98. $7k^2 - 9k - 10 = 0$

99. $4h^2 - 23h - 6 = 0$

100. $q^2 - 144 = 0$

101. $r^2 = 25$

102. $5v^2 - v = 0$

103. $x(x - 6) = -8$

104. $36t^2 + 60t = -25$

105. $9s^2 + 12s = -4$

106. $3(y^2 + 4) = 20y$

107. $2(p^2 - 66) = -13p$

108. $2y^3 - 18y^2 = -28y$

109. $x^3 - 4x = 0$

Section 6.8

110. The base of a parallelogram is 1 ft longer than twice the height. If the area is 78 ft^2, what are the base and height of the parallelogram?

111. A ball is tossed into the air from ground level with initial speed of 16 ft/sec. The height of the ball is given by the equation

$h = -16t^2 + 16t \quad (t \geq 0)$ where h is the ball's height in feet, and t is the time in seconds.

Find the time(s) when the ball is at ground level.

112. Find the length of the ramp.

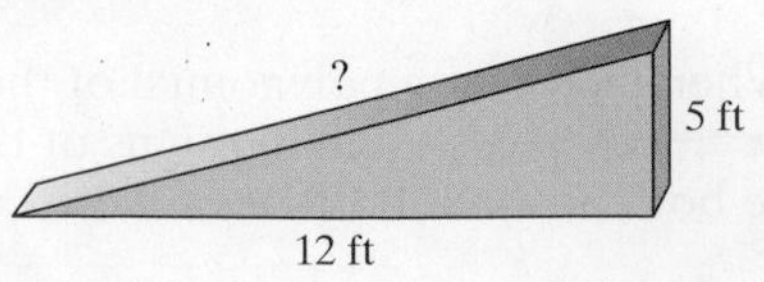

113. A right triangle has one leg that is 2 ft longer than the other leg. The hypotenuse is 2 ft less than twice the shorter leg. Find the lengths of all sides of the triangle.

114. If the square of a number is subtracted from 60, the result is -4. Find all such numbers.

115. The product of two consecutive integers is 44 more than 14 times their sum. Find all such integers.

116. The base of a triangle is 1 m longer than twice the height. If the area of the triangle is 18 m^2, find the base and height.

Chapter 6 Test

1. Factor out the GCF. $15x^4 - 3x + 6x^3$

2. Factor by grouping. $7a - 35 - a^2 + 5a$

3. Factor the trinomial. $6w^2 - 43w + 7$

4. Factor the difference of squares. $169 - p^2$

5. Factor the perfect square trinomial. $q^2 - 16q + 64$

6. Factor the sum of cubes. $8 + t^3$

For Exercises 7–26, factor completely.

7. $a^2 + 12a + 32$

8. $x^2 + x - 42$

9. $2y^2 - 17y + 8$

10. $6z^2 + 19z + 8$

11. $9t^2 - 100$

12. $v^2 - 81$

13. $3a^2 + 27ab + 54b^2$

14. $c^4 - 1$

15. $xy - 7x + 3y - 21$

16. $49 + p^2$

17. $-10u^2 + 30u - 20$

18. $12t^2 - 75$

19. $5y^2 - 50y + 125$

20. $21q^2 + 14q$

21. $2x^3 + x^2 - 8x - 4$

22. $y^3 - 125$

23. $m^2n^2 - 81$

24. $16a^2 - 64b^2$

25. $64x^3 - 27y^6$

26. $3x^2y - 6xy - 24y$

For Exercises 27–31, solve the equation.

27. $(2x - 3)(x + 5) = 0$

28. $x^2 - 7x = 0$

29. $x^2 - 6x = 16$

30. $x(5x + 4) = 1$

31. $y^3 + 10y^2 - 9y - 90 = 0$

32. A tennis court has an area of 312 yd^2. If the length is 2 yd more than twice the width, find the dimensions of the court.

33. The product of two consecutive odd integers is 35. Find the integers.

34. The height of a triangle is 5 in. less than the length of the base. The area is 42 in^2. Find the length of the base and the height of the triangle.

35. The hypotenuse of a right triangle is 2 ft less than three times the shorter leg. The longer leg is 3 ft less than three times the shorter leg. Find the length of the shorter leg.

36. A stone is dropped off a 64-ft cliff. The height of the stone above the ground is given in the equation

$h = -16t^2 + 64$ where h is the stone's height in feet, and t is the time in seconds after the stone is dropped ($t \geq 0$).

Find the time required for the stone to hit the ground.

Chapters 1–6 Cumulative Review Exercises

1. Simplify. $\dfrac{|4 - 25 \div (-5) \cdot 2|}{\sqrt{8^2 + 6^2}}$

2. Solve. $5 - 2(t + 4) = 3t + 12$

3. Solve for y. $3x - 2y = 8$

4. A child's piggy bank has 17 coins in quarters and dimes. The number of dimes is three less than the number of quarters. How many of each type of coin is in the piggy bank?

5. Solve the inequality. Graph the solution on a number line and write the solution set in interval notation.

$$-\frac{5}{12}x \le \frac{5}{3}$$

6. Given the equation $y = x + 4$,
   - **a.** Is the equation linear?
   - **b.** Identify the slope.
   - **c.** Identify the y-intercept.
   - **d.** Identify the x-intercept.
   - **e.** Graph the line.

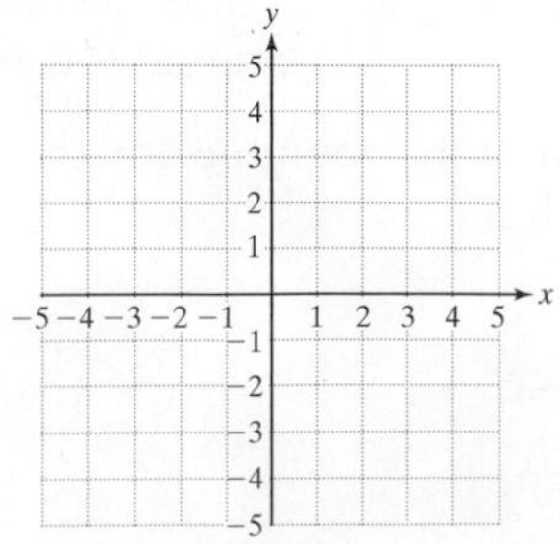

7. Consider the equation $x = 5$,
   - **a.** Does the equation represent a horizontal or vertical line?
   - **b.** Determine the slope of the line, if it exists.
   - **c.** Identify the x-intercept, if it exists.
   - **d.** Identify the y-intercept, if it exists.

8. Solve the system. $\begin{aligned} 2x - 3y &= 4 \\ 5x - 6y &= 13 \end{aligned}$

9. Solve the system. $\begin{aligned} 3x + y - 5z &= 18 \\ -x + z &= -2 \\ x - 2y + 4z &= -24 \end{aligned}$

For Exercises 10–13, perform the indicated operations.

10. $2\left(\frac{1}{3}y^3 - \frac{3}{2}y^2 - 7\right) - \left(\frac{2}{3}y^3 + \frac{1}{2}y^2 + 5y\right)$

11. $(4p^2 - 5p - 1)(2p - 3)$

12. $(2w - 7)^2$

13. $(r^4 + 2r^3 - 5r + 1) \div (r - 3)$

14. Simplify. $\dfrac{c^{12}c^{-5}}{c^3}$

15. Simplify. $\left(\dfrac{6a^2b^{-4}}{2a^4b^{-5}}\right)^{-2}$

16. Divide. Write the final answer in scientific notation. $\dfrac{8 \times 10^{-3}}{5 \times 10^{-6}}$

For Exercises 17–19, factor completely.

17. $w^4 - 16$

18. $2ax + 10bx - 3ya - 15yb$

19. $4x^2 - 8x - 5$

20. Solve. $4x(2x - 1)(x + 5) = 0$

Rational Expressions and Equations

7

CHAPTER OUTLINE

7.1 Introduction to Rational Expressions 488

7.2 Multiplication and Division of Rational Expressions 498

7.3 Least Common Denominator 505

7.4 Addition and Subtraction of Rational Expressions 511

Problem Recognition Exercises: Operations on Rational Expressions 521

7.5 Complex Fractions 522

7.6 Rational Equations 530

Problem Recognition Exercises: Comparing Rational Equations and Rational Expressions 540

7.7 Applications of Rational Equations and Proportions 541

Group Activity: Computing Monthly Mortgage Payments 552

Chapter 7

In this chapter, we define a rational expression as a ratio of two polynomials. Then we perform operations on rational expressions and solve rational equations.

Are You Prepared?

It will be helpful to review operations with fractions before you begin this chapter (see Section 1.1). Try the matching problems, then record the letter of the answer in the spaces below to complete the sentence.

1. Add. $\frac{7}{4}+\frac{5}{3}+\frac{1}{2}$

2. Multiply. $\frac{5}{3}\cdot\frac{11}{4}$

3. Fraction that is not in lowest terms.

4. In this expression, a common denominator is not required.

5. Fractions can be eliminated from this equation by multiplying by the LCD.

a. $\frac{7}{8}x+\frac{2}{3}=\frac{1}{2}$

t. $\frac{45}{12}$

r. $\frac{47}{12}$

p. $\frac{34}{3}\cdot\frac{1}{4}$

n. $\frac{7}{8}+\frac{1}{3}-\frac{1}{2}$

o. $\frac{55}{12}$

e. $\frac{7}{8}$

f. $\frac{1}{8}+\frac{7}{9}$

The enemy of a good student is $\underset{4}{\_}\ \underset{1}{\_}\ \underset{2}{\_}\ \text{c}\ \underset{1}{\_}\ \underset{5}{\_}\ \text{s}\ \underset{3}{\_}\ \text{i}\ \text{n}\ \underset{5}{\_}\ \underset{3}{\_}\ \text{i}\ \underset{2}{\_}\ \text{n}$.

Section 7.1 Introduction to Rational Expressions

Concepts

1. Definition of a Rational Expression
2. Evaluating Rational Expressions
3. Restricted Values of a Rational Expression
4. Simplifying Rational Expressions
5. Simplifying a Ratio of −1

1. Definition of a Rational Expression

In Section 1.2, we defined a rational number as the ratio of two integers, $\frac{p}{q}$, where $q \neq 0$.

Examples of rational numbers: $\frac{2}{3}, -\frac{1}{5}, 9$

In a similar way, we define a **rational expression** as the ratio of two polynomials, $\frac{p}{q}$, where $q \neq 0$.

Examples of rational expressions: $\frac{3x - 6}{x^2 - 4}, \quad \frac{3}{4}, \quad \frac{6r^5 + 2r}{7r^3}$

2. Evaluating Rational Expressions

Example 1 Evaluating Rational Expressions

Evaluate the rational expression (if possible) for the given values of x. $\frac{x}{x - 3}$

a. $x = 6$ **b.** $x = -3$ **c.** $x = 0$ **d.** $x = 3$

Solution:

Substitute the given value for the variable. Use order of operations to simplify.

a. $\frac{x}{x - 3}$

$\frac{(6)}{(6) - 3}$ Substitute $x = 6$.

$= \frac{6}{3}$

$= 2$

b. $\frac{x}{x - 3}$

$\frac{(-3)}{(-3) - 3}$ Substitute $x = -3$.

$= \frac{-3}{-6}$

$= \frac{1}{2}$

c. $\frac{x}{x - 3}$

$\frac{(0)}{(0) - 3}$ Substitute $x = 0$.

$= \frac{0}{-3}$

$= 0$

Avoiding Mistakes

The numerator is 0, therefore the fraction is equal to 0.

d. $\frac{x}{x - 3}$

$\frac{(3)}{(3) - 3}$ Substitute $x = 3$.

$= \frac{3}{0}$ Undefined.

Recall that division by zero is undefined.

Avoiding Mistakes

The denominator is 0, therefore the fraction is undefined.

Skill Practice Evaluate the expression for the given values of x. $\frac{x - 3}{x + 5}$

1. $x = 2$ **2.** $x = 0$ **3.** $x = 3$ **4.** $x = -5$

Answers

1. $-\frac{1}{7}$ 2. $-\frac{3}{5}$
3. 0 4. Undefined

3. Restricted Values of a Rational Expression

From Example 1 we see that not all values of x can be substituted into a rational expression. The values that make the denominator zero must be restricted. The expression $\frac{x}{x-3}$ is undefined for $x = 3$, so we call $x = 3$ a restricted value. **Restricted values of a rational expression** are all values that make the expression undefined, that is, make the denominator equal to zero.

Finding the Restricted Values of a Rational Expression

- Set the denominator equal to zero and solve the resulting equation.
- The restricted values are the solutions to the equation.

Example 2 Finding the Restricted Values of Rational Expressions

Identify the restricted values for each expression.

a. $\frac{y-3}{2y+7}$ **b.** $\frac{-5}{x}$

Solution:

a. $\frac{y-3}{2y+7}$

$2y + 7 = 0$ Set the denominator equal to zero.

$2y = -7$ Solve the equation.

$\frac{2y}{2} = \frac{-7}{2}$

$y = -\frac{7}{2}$ The restricted value is $y = -\frac{7}{2}$.

b. $\frac{-5}{x}$

$x = 0$ Set the denominator equal to zero.

The restricted value is $x = 0$.

Skill Practice Identify the restricted values.

5. $\frac{a+2}{2a-8}$ **6.** $\frac{2}{t}$

Answers

5. $a = 4$ **6.** $t = 0$

Example 3 Finding the Restricted Values of Rational Expressions

Identify the restricted values for each expression.

a. $\dfrac{a + 10}{a^2 - 25}$ **b.** $\dfrac{2x^3 + 5}{x^2 + 9}$

Solution:

a. $\dfrac{a + 10}{a^2 - 25}$

$a^2 - 25 = 0$ Set the denominator equal to zero. The equation is quadratic.

$(a - 5)(a + 5) = 0$ Factor.

$a - 5 = 0$ or $a + 5 = 0$ Set each factor equal to zero.

$a = 5$ or $a = -5$

The restricted values are $a = 5$ and $a = -5$.

b. $\dfrac{2x^3 + 5}{x^2 + 9}$

$x^2 + 9 = 0$

$x^2 = -9$

The quantity x^2 cannot be negative for any real number, x, so the denominator $x^2 + 9$ cannot equal zero. Therefore, there are no restricted values.

Skill Practice Identify the restricted values.

7. $\dfrac{w - 4}{w^2 - 9}$ **8.** $\dfrac{8}{z^4 + 1}$

4. Simplifying Rational Expressions

In many cases, it is advantageous to simplify or reduce a fraction to lowest terms. The same is true for rational expressions.

The method for simplifying rational expressions mirrors the process for simplifying fractions. In each case, factor the numerator and denominator. Common factors in the numerator and denominator form a ratio of 1 and can be reduced.

Simplifying a fraction: $\dfrac{21}{35} \xrightarrow{\text{Factor}} \dfrac{3 \cdot \overset{1}{\cancel{7}}}{5 \cdot \cancel{7}} = \dfrac{3}{5} \cdot (1) = \dfrac{3}{5}$

Simplifying a rational expression: $\dfrac{2x - 6}{x^2 - 9} \xrightarrow{\text{Factor}} \dfrac{2\overset{1}{\cancel{(x - 3)}}}{(x + 3)\cancel{(x - 3)}} = \dfrac{2}{(x + 3)}(1) = \dfrac{2}{x + 3}$

Informally, to simplify a rational expression, we simplify the ratio of common factors to 1. Formally, this is accomplished by applying the fundamental principle of rational expressions.

Answers

7. $w = 3, w = -3$
8. There are no restricted values.

Fundamental Principle of Rational Expressions

Let p, q, and r represent polynomials where $q \neq 0$ and $r \neq 0$. Then

$$\frac{pr}{qr} = \frac{p}{q} \cdot \frac{r}{r} = \frac{p}{q} \cdot 1 = \frac{p}{q}$$

Example 4 Simplifying a Rational Expression

Given the expression $\dfrac{2p - 14}{p^2 - 49}$

a. Factor the numerator and denominator.

b. Identify the restricted values.

c. Simplify the rational expression.

Solution:

a. $\dfrac{2p - 14}{p^2 - 49}$ Factor out the GCF in the numerator.

$= \dfrac{2(p - 7)}{(p + 7)(p - 7)}$ Factor the denominator as a difference of squares.

b. $(p + 7)(p - 7) = 0$ To find the restricted values, set the denominator equal to zero. The equation is quadratic.

$p + 7 = 0$ or $p - 7 = 0$ Set each factor equal to 0.

$p = -7$ or $p = 7$ The restricted values are -7 and 7.

c. $\dfrac{2\overset{1}{\cancel{(p - 7)}}}{(p + 7)\cancel{(p - 7)}}$ Simplify the ratio of common factors to 1.

$= \dfrac{2}{p + 7}$ (provided $p \neq 7$ and $p \neq -7$)

Avoiding Mistakes

The restricted values of a rational expression are always determined *before* simplifying the expression.

Skill Practice Given $\dfrac{5z + 25}{z^2 + 3z - 10}$

9. Factor the numerator and the denominator.

10. Identify the restricted values. **11.** Simplify the rational expression.

In Example 4, it is important to note that the expressions

$$\frac{2p - 14}{p^2 - 49} \quad \text{and} \quad \frac{2}{p + 7}$$

are equal for all values of p that make each expression a real number. Therefore,

$$\frac{2p - 14}{p^2 - 49} = \frac{2}{p + 7}$$

for all values of p except $p = 7$ and $p = -7$. (At $p = 7$ and $p = -7$, the original expression is undefined.) This is why the restricted values are determined before the expression is simplified.

Answers

9. $\dfrac{5(z + 5)}{(z + 5)(z - 2)}$

10. $z = -5, z = 2$

11. $\dfrac{5}{z - 2}$ $(z \neq 2, z \neq -5)$

From this point forward, we will write statements of equality between two rational expressions with the assumption that they are equal for all values of the variable for which each expression is defined.

Example 5 Simplifying a Rational Expression

Simplify the rational expression. $\dfrac{18a^4}{9a^5}$

Solution:

$$\frac{18a^4}{9a^5}$$

$$= \frac{2 \cdot 3 \cdot 3 \cdot a \cdot a \cdot a \cdot a}{3 \cdot 3 \cdot a \cdot a \cdot a \cdot a \cdot a} \quad \text{Factor the numerator and denominator.}$$

$$= \frac{2 \cdot \overset{1}{\cancel{(3 \cdot 3 \cdot a \cdot a \cdot a \cdot a)}}}{\cancel{(3 \cdot 3 \cdot a \cdot a \cdot a \cdot a)} \cdot a} \quad \text{Simplify common factors.}$$

$$= \frac{2}{a}$$

TIP: The expression $\dfrac{18a^4}{9a^5}$ can also be simplified using the properties of exponents.

$$\frac{18a^4}{9a^5} = 2a^{4-5} = 2a^{-1} = \frac{2}{a}$$

Skill Practice Simplify the rational expression.

12. $\dfrac{15q^3}{9q^2}$

Example 6 Simplifying a Rational Expression

Simplify the rational expression. $\dfrac{2c - 8}{10c^2 - 80c + 160}$

Solution:

$$\frac{2c - 8}{10c^2 - 80c + 160}$$

$$= \frac{2(c - 4)}{10(c^2 - 8c + 16)} \quad \text{Factor out the GCF.}$$

$$= \frac{2(c - 4)}{10(c - 4)^2} \quad \text{Factor the denominator.}$$

$$= \frac{\overset{1}{\cancel{2}}\overset{1}{\cancel{(c - 4)}}}{2 \cdot 5\cancel{(c - 4)}(c - 4)} \quad \text{Simplify the ratio of common factors to 1.}$$

$$= \frac{1}{5(c - 4)}$$

Avoiding Mistakes

Given the expression

$$\frac{2c - 8}{10c^2 - 80c + 160}$$

do not be tempted to reduce before factoring. The terms $2c$ and $10c^2$ cannot be "canceled" because they are *terms* not factors.

The numerator and denominator must be in factored form before simplifying.

Skill Practice Simplify the rational expression.

13. $\dfrac{x^2 - 1}{2x^2 - x - 3}$

Answers

12. $\dfrac{5q}{3}$ 13. $\dfrac{x - 1}{2x - 3}$

The process to simplify a rational expression is based on the identity property of multiplication. Therefore, this process applies only to factors (remember that factors are multiplied). For example:

$$\frac{3x}{3y} = \frac{3 \cdot x}{3 \cdot y} = \frac{\overset{1}{\cancel{3}}}{\cancel{3}} \cdot \frac{x}{y} = 1 \cdot \frac{x}{y} = \frac{x}{y}$$

Simplify

Terms that are added or subtracted cannot be reduced to lowest terms. For example:

$$\frac{x+3}{y+3}$$

Cannot be simplified

The objective of simplifying a rational expression is to create an equivalent expression that is simpler to use. Consider the rational expression from Example 6 in its original form and in its reduced form. If we substitute a value c into each expression, we see that the reduced form is easier to evaluate. For example, substitute $c = 3$:

	Original Expression	**Simplified Expression**
	$\frac{2c-8}{10c^2-80c+160}$	$\frac{1}{5(c-4)}$
Substitute $c = 3$	$=\frac{2(3)-8}{10(3)^2-80(3)+160}$	$=\frac{1}{5(3-4)}$
	$=\frac{6-8}{10(9)-240+160}$	$=\frac{1}{5(-1)}$
	$=\frac{-2}{90-240+160}$	$=-\frac{1}{5}$
	$=\frac{-2}{10}$ or $-\frac{1}{5}$	

5. Simplifying a Ratio of −1

When two factors are identical in the numerator and denominator, they form a ratio of 1 and can be reduced. Sometimes we encounter two factors that are opposites and form a ratio of −1. For example:

Simplified Form	**Details/Notes**
$\frac{-5}{5} = -1$	The ratio of a number and its opposite is −1.
$\frac{100}{-100} = -1$	The ratio of a number and its opposite is −1.
$\frac{x+7}{-x-7} = -1$	$\frac{x+7}{-x-7} = \frac{x+7}{-1(x+7)} = \frac{\overset{1}{\cancel{x+7}}}{-1(\cancel{x+7})} = \frac{1}{-1} = -1$ (factor out −1)
$\frac{2-x}{x-2} = -1$	$\frac{2-x}{x-2} = \frac{-1(-2+x)}{x-2} = \frac{-1(\overset{1}{\cancel{x-2}})}{\cancel{x-2}} = \frac{-1}{1} = -1$

Recognizing factors that are opposites is useful when simplifying rational expressions.

Avoiding Mistakes

While the expression $2 - x$ and $x - 2$ are opposites, the expressions $2 - x$ and $2 + x$ are *not*.

Therefore $\frac{2-x}{2+x}$ does not simplify to −1.

Example 7 Simplifying a Rational Expression

Simplify the rational expression. $\dfrac{3c - 3d}{d - c}$

Solution:

$\dfrac{3c - 3d}{d - c}$

$= \dfrac{3(c - d)}{d - c}$ Factor the numerator and denominator.

Notice that $(c - d)$ and $(d - c)$ are opposites and form a ratio of -1.

$= \dfrac{3(\overset{-1}{\cancel{c - d}})}{\cancel{d - c}}$ Details: $\dfrac{3(c - d)}{d - c} = \dfrac{3(c - d)}{-1(-d + c)} = \dfrac{3(c - d)}{-1(c - d)}$

$= 3(-1)$ $= \dfrac{3}{-1} = -3$

$= -3$

Skill Practice Simplify the rational expression.

14. $\dfrac{2t - 12}{6 - t}$

TIP: It is important to recognize that a rational expression can be written in several equivalent forms. In particular, two numbers with opposite signs form a negative quotient. Therefore, a number such as $-\frac{3}{4}$ can be written as:

$$-\frac{3}{4} \quad \text{or} \quad \frac{-3}{4} \quad \text{or} \quad \frac{3}{-4}$$

The negative sign can be written in the numerator, in the denominator, or out in front of the fraction. We demonstrate this concept in Example 8.

Example 8 Simplifying a Rational Expression

Simplify the rational expression. $\dfrac{5 - y}{y^2 - 25}$

Solution:

$\dfrac{5 - y}{y^2 - 25}$

$= \dfrac{5 - y}{(y - 5)(y + 5)}$ Factor the numerator and denominator.

Notice that $5 - y$ and $y - 5$ are opposites and form a ratio of -1.

Answer

14. -2

$$= \frac{\overset{-1}{\cancel{5 - y}}}{\cancel{(y - 5)}(y + 5)} \qquad \underline{\text{Details:}} \quad \frac{5 - y}{(y - 5)(y + 5)} = \frac{-1(-5 + y)}{(y - 5)(y + 5)}$$

$$= \frac{-1(y - 5)}{(y - 5)(y + 5)} = \frac{-1}{y + 5}$$

$$= \frac{-1}{y + 5} \quad \text{or} \quad \frac{1}{-(y + 5)} \quad \text{or} \quad -\frac{1}{y + 5}$$

Skill Practice Simplify the rational expression.

15. $\dfrac{b - a}{a^2 - b^2}$

Answer

15. $\dfrac{-1}{a + b}$

Section 7.1 Practice Exercises

Study Skills Exercise

Review Section 1.1 in this text. Write an example of how to simplify (reduce) a fraction, multiply two fractions, divide two fractions, add two fractions, and subtract two fractions. Then as you learn about rational expressions, compare the operations on rational expressions with those on fractions. This is a great place to use 3 × 5 cards again. Write an example of an operation with fractions on one side and the same operation with rational expressions on the other side.

Vocabulary and Key Concepts

1. **a.** A ____________ expression is the ratio of two polynomials, $\frac{p}{q}$, where $q \neq 0$.

   b. Restricted values of a rational expression are all values that make the ____________ equal to ____________.

   c. For polynomials p, q, and r, where ($q \neq 0$ and $r \neq 0$), $\dfrac{pr}{qr} =$ ____________.

   d. The ratio $\dfrac{a - b}{a - b} =$ ____________ whereas the ratio $\dfrac{a - b}{b - a} =$ ____________ provided that $a \neq b$.

Concept 2: Evaluating Rational Expressions

For Exercises 2–10, substitute the given number into the expression and simplify (if possible). **(See Example 1.)**

2. $\dfrac{5}{y - 4}$; $y = 6$

3. $\dfrac{t - 2}{t^2 - 4t + 8}$; $t = 2$

4. $\dfrac{4x}{x - 7}$; $x = 8$

5. $\dfrac{1}{x - 6}$; $x = -2$

6. $\dfrac{w - 10}{w + 6}$; $w = 0$

7. $\dfrac{w - 4}{2w + 8}$; $w = 0$

8. $\dfrac{y - 8}{2y^2 + y - 1}$; $y = 8$

9. $\dfrac{(a - 7)(a + 1)}{(a - 2)(a + 5)}$; $a = 2$

10. $\dfrac{(a + 4)(a + 1)}{(a - 4)(a - 1)}$; $a = 1$

11. A bicyclist rides 24 mi against a wind and returns 24 mi with the same wind. His average speed for the return trip traveling with the wind is 8 mph faster than his speed going out against the wind. If x represents the bicyclist's speed going out against the wind, then the total time, t, required for the round trip is given by

$$t = \frac{24}{x} + \frac{24}{x + 8} \quad \text{where } t \text{ is measured in hours.}$$

a. Find the time required for the round trip if the cyclist rides 12 mph against the wind.

b. Find the time required for the round trip if the cyclist rides 24 mph against the wind.

12. The manufacturer of mountain bikes has a fixed cost of \$56,000, plus a variable cost of \$140 per bike. The average cost per bike, y (in dollars), is given by the equation:

$$y = \frac{56{,}000 + 140x}{x} \quad \text{where } x \text{ represents the number of bikes produced.}$$

a. Find the average cost per bike if the manufacturer produces 1000 bikes.

b. Find the average cost per bike if the manufacturer produces 2000 bikes.

c. Find the average cost per bike if the manufacturer produces 10,000 bikes.

Concept 3: Restricted Values of a Rational Expression

For Exercises 13–24, identify the restricted values. **(See Examples 2–3.)**

13. $\dfrac{5}{k + 2}$ **14.** $\dfrac{-3}{h - 4}$ **15.** $\dfrac{x + 5}{(2x - 5)(x + 8)}$

16. $\dfrac{4y + 1}{(3y + 7)(y + 3)}$ **17.** $\dfrac{m + 12}{m^2 + 5m + 6}$ **18.** $\dfrac{c - 11}{c^2 - 5c - 6}$

19. $\dfrac{x - 4}{x^2 + 9}$ **20.** $\dfrac{x + 1}{x^2 + 4}$ **21.** $\dfrac{y^2 - y - 12}{12}$

22. $\dfrac{z^2 + 10z + 9}{9}$ **23.** $\dfrac{t - 5}{t}$ **24.** $\dfrac{2w + 7}{w}$

25. Construct a rational expression that is undefined for $x = 2$. (Answers will vary.)

26. Construct a rational expression that is undefined for $x = 5$. (Answers will vary.)

27. Construct a rational expression that is undefined for $x = -3$ and $x = 7$. (Answers will vary.)

28. Construct a rational expression that is undefined for $x = -1$ and $x = 4$. (Answers will vary.)

29. Evaluate the expressions for $x = -1$.

a. $\dfrac{3x^2 - 2x - 1}{6x^2 - 7x - 3}$ **b.** $\dfrac{x - 1}{2x - 3}$

30. Evaluate the expressions for $x = 4$.

a. $\dfrac{(x + 5)^2}{x^2 + 6x + 5}$ **b.** $\dfrac{x + 5}{x + 1}$

31. Evaluate the expressions for $x = 1$.

a. $\dfrac{5x + 5}{x^2 - 1}$ **b.** $\dfrac{5}{x - 1}$

32. Evaluate the expressions for $x = -3$.

a. $\dfrac{2x^2 - 4x - 6}{2x^2 - 18}$ **b.** $\dfrac{x + 1}{x + 3}$

Concept 4: Simplifying Rational Expressions

For Exercises 33–42,

a. Identify the restricted values. **b.** Simplify the rational expression. **(See Example 4.)**

33. $\dfrac{3y + 6}{6y + 12}$

34. $\dfrac{8x - 8}{4x - 4}$

35. $\dfrac{t^2 - 1}{t + 1}$

36. $\dfrac{r^2 - 4}{r - 2}$

37. $\dfrac{7w}{21w^2 - 35w}$

38. $\dfrac{12a^2}{24a^2 - 18a}$

39. $\dfrac{9x^2 - 4}{6x + 4}$

40. $\dfrac{8n - 20}{4n^2 - 25}$

41. $\dfrac{a^2 + 3a - 10}{a^2 + a - 6}$

42. $\dfrac{t^2 + 3t - 10}{t^2 + t - 20}$

For Exercises 43–72, simplify the rational expression. **(See Examples 5–6.)**

43. $\dfrac{7b^2}{21b}$

44. $\dfrac{15c^3}{3c^5}$

45. $\dfrac{-24x^2y^5z}{8xy^4z^3}$

46. $\dfrac{60rs^4t^2}{-12r^4s^2t^3}$

47. $\dfrac{(p - 3)(p + 5)}{(p + 5)(p + 4)}$

48. $\dfrac{(c + 4)(c - 1)}{(c + 4)(c + 2)}$

49. $\dfrac{m + 11}{4(m + 11)(m - 11)}$

50. $\dfrac{n - 7}{9(n + 2)(n - 7)}$

51. $\dfrac{x(2x + 1)^2}{4x^3(2x + 1)}$

52. $\dfrac{(p + 2)(p - 3)^4}{(p + 2)^2(p - 3)^2}$

53. $\dfrac{5}{20a - 25}$

54. $\dfrac{7}{14c - 21}$

55. $\dfrac{3x^2 - 6x}{9xy + 18x}$

56. $\dfrac{6p^2 + 12p}{2pq - 4p}$

57. $\dfrac{2x + 4}{x^2 - 3x - 10}$

58. $\dfrac{5z + 15}{z^2 - 4z - 21}$

59. $\dfrac{a^2 - 49}{a - 7}$

60. $\dfrac{b^2 - 64}{b - 8}$

61. $\dfrac{q^2 + 25}{q + 5}$

62. $\dfrac{r^2 + 36}{r + 6}$

63. $\dfrac{y^2 + 6y + 9}{2y^2 + y - 15}$

64. $\dfrac{h^2 + h - 6}{h^2 + 2h - 8}$

65. $\dfrac{5q^2 + 5}{q^4 - 1}$

66. $\dfrac{4t^2 + 16}{t^4 - 16}$

67. $\dfrac{ac - ad + 2bc - 2bd}{2ac + ad + 4bc + 2bd}$ (*Hint:* Factor by grouping.)

68. $\dfrac{3pr - ps - 3qr + qs}{3pr - ps + 3qr - qs}$ (*Hint:* Factor by grouping.)

69. $\dfrac{5x^3 + 4x^2 - 45x - 36}{x^2 - 9}$

70. $\dfrac{x^2 - 1}{ax^3 - bx^2 - ax + b}$

71. $\dfrac{2x^2 - xy - 3y^2}{2x^2 - 11xy + 12y^2}$

72. $\dfrac{2c^2 + cd - d^2}{5c^2 + 3cd - 2d^2}$

Concept 5: Simplifying a Ratio of −1

73. What is the relationship between $x - 2$ and $2 - x$?

74. What is the relationship between $w + p$ and $-w - p$?

For Exercises 75–86, simplify the rational expressions. **(See Examples 7–8.)**

75. $\dfrac{x - 5}{5 - x}$

76. $\dfrac{8 - p}{p - 8}$

77. $\dfrac{-4 - y}{4 + y}$

78. $\dfrac{z + 10}{-z - 10}$

79. $\dfrac{3y - 6}{12 - 6y}$

80. $\dfrac{4q - 4}{12 - 12q}$

81. $\dfrac{k + 5}{5 - k}$

82. $\dfrac{2 + n}{2 - n}$

83. $\dfrac{10x - 12}{10x + 12}$

84. $\dfrac{4t - 16}{16 + 4t}$

85. $\dfrac{x^2 - x - 12}{16 - x^2}$

86. $\dfrac{49 - b^2}{b^2 - 10b + 21}$

Mixed Exercises

For Exercises 87–100, simplify the rational expressions.

87. $\dfrac{3x^2 + 7x - 6}{x^2 + 7x + 12}$ **88.** $\dfrac{y^2 - 5y - 14}{2y^2 - y - 10}$ **89.** $\dfrac{3(m - 2)}{6(2 - m)}$ **90.** $\dfrac{8(1 - x)}{4(x - 1)}$

91. $\dfrac{w^2 - 4}{8 - 4w}$ **92.** $\dfrac{15 - 3x}{x^2 - 25}$ **93.** $\dfrac{18st^5}{12st^3}$ **94.** $\dfrac{20a^4b^2}{25ab^2}$

95. $\dfrac{4r^2 - 4rs + s^2}{s^2 - 4r^2}$ **96.** $\dfrac{y^2 - 9z^2}{3z^2 + 2yz - y^2}$ **97.** $\dfrac{3y - 3x}{2x^2 - 4xy + 2y^2}$ **98.** $\dfrac{49p^2 - 28pq + 4q^2}{4q - 14p}$

99. $\dfrac{2t^2 - 3t}{2t^4 - 13t^3 + 15t^2}$ **100.** $\dfrac{4m^3 + 3m^2}{4m^3 + 7m^2 + 3m}$

Expanding Your Skills

For Exercises 101–104, factor and simplify.

101. $\dfrac{w^3 - 8}{w^2 + 2w + 4}$ **102.** $\dfrac{y^3 + 27}{y^2 - 3y + 9}$ **103.** $\dfrac{z^2 - 16}{z^3 - 64}$ **104.** $\dfrac{x^2 - 25}{x^3 + 125}$

Section 7.2 Multiplication and Division of Rational Expressions

Concepts

1. **Multiplication of Rational Expressions**
2. **Division of Rational Expressions**

1. Multiplication of Rational Expressions

Recall from Section 1.1 that to multiply fractions, we multiply the numerators and multiply the denominators. The same is true for multiplying rational expressions.

Multiplication of Rational Expressions

Let p, q, r, and s represent polynomials, such that $q \neq 0, s \neq 0$. Then,

$$\frac{p}{q} \cdot \frac{r}{s} = \frac{pr}{qs}$$

For example:

<u>**Multiply the Fractions**</u>	<u>**Multiply the Rational Expressions**</u>
$\dfrac{2}{3} \cdot \dfrac{5}{7} = \dfrac{10}{21}$	$\dfrac{2x}{3y} \cdot \dfrac{5z}{7} = \dfrac{10xz}{21y}$

Sometimes it is possible to simplify a ratio of common factors to 1 *before* multiplying. To do so, we must first factor the numerators and denominators of each fraction.

$$\frac{15}{14} \cdot \frac{21}{10} = \frac{3 \cdot \overset{1}{\cancel{5}}}{2 \cdot \cancel{7}} \cdot \frac{3 \cdot \overset{1}{\cancel{7}}}{2 \cdot \cancel{5}} = \frac{9}{4}$$

The same process is also used to multiply rational expressions.

Multiplying Rational Expressions

Step 1 Factor the numerators and denominators of all rational expressions.

Step 2 Simplify the ratios of common factors to 1 and opposite factors to −1.

Step 3 Multiply the remaining factors in the numerator, and multiply the remaining factors in the denominator.

Example 1 Multiplying Rational Expressions

Multiply. $\dfrac{5a^2b}{2} \cdot \dfrac{6a}{10b}$

Solution:

$$\frac{5a^2b}{2} \cdot \frac{6a}{10b}$$

$$= \frac{5 \cdot a \cdot a \cdot b}{2} \cdot \frac{2 \cdot 3 \cdot a}{2 \cdot 5 \cdot b} \quad \text{Factor into prime factors.}$$

$$= \frac{\overset{1}{\cancel{5}} \cdot a \cdot a \cdot \overset{1}{\cancel{b}}}{2} \cdot \frac{\overset{1}{\cancel{2}} \cdot 3 \cdot a}{\cancel{2} \cdot \cancel{5} \cdot \cancel{b}} \quad \text{Simplify.}$$

$$= \frac{3a^3}{2} \quad \text{Multiply remaining factors.}$$

Skill Practice Multiply.

1. $\dfrac{7a}{3b} \cdot \dfrac{15b}{14a^2}$

Example 2 Multiplying Rational Expressions

Multiply. $\dfrac{3c - 3d}{6c} \cdot \dfrac{2}{c^2 - d^2}$

Solution:

$$\frac{3c - 3d}{6c} \cdot \frac{2}{c^2 - d^2}$$

$$= \frac{3(c - d)}{2 \cdot 3 \cdot c} \cdot \frac{2}{(c - d)(c + d)} \quad \text{Factor.}$$

$$= \frac{\overset{1}{\cancel{3}}\overset{1}{\cancel{(c - d)}}}{\cancel{2} \cdot \cancel{3} \cdot c} \cdot \frac{\overset{1}{\cancel{2}}}{\cancel{(c - d)}(c + d)} \quad \text{Simplify.}$$

$$= \frac{1}{c(c + d)} \quad \text{Multiply remaining factors.}$$

Avoiding Mistakes

If all the factors in the numerator reduce to a ratio of 1, a factor of 1 is left in the numerator.

Skill Practice Multiply.

2. $\dfrac{4x - 8}{x + 6} \cdot \dfrac{x^2 + 6x}{2x}$

Answers

1. $\dfrac{5}{2a}$ 2. $2(x - 2)$

Example 3 **Multiplying Rational Expressions**

Multiply. $\dfrac{35-5x}{5x+5} \cdot \dfrac{x^2+5x+4}{x^2-49}$

Solution:

$$\frac{35-5x}{5x+5} \cdot \frac{x^2+5x+4}{x^2-49}$$

$$= \frac{5(7-x)}{5(x+1)} \cdot \frac{(x+4)(x+1)}{(x-7)(x+7)}$$ Factor the numerators and denominators completely.

$$= \frac{\overset{1}{\cancel{5}}\overset{-1}{\cancel{(7-x)}}}{\cancel{5}\cancel{(x+1)}} \cdot \frac{(x+4)\overset{1}{\cancel{(x+1)}}}{\cancel{(x-7)}(x+7)}$$ Simplify the ratios of common factors to 1 or −1.

$$= \frac{-1(x+4)}{x+7}$$ Multiply remaining factors.

$$= \frac{-(x+4)}{x+7} \quad \text{or} \quad \frac{x+4}{-(x+7)} \quad \text{or} \quad -\frac{x+4}{x+7}$$

TIP: The ratio $\frac{7-x}{x-7} = -1$ because $7 - x$ and $x - 7$ are opposites.

Skill Practice Multiply.

3. $\dfrac{p^2+4p+3}{5p+10} \cdot \dfrac{p^2-p-6}{9-p^2}$

2. Division of Rational Expressions

Recall that to divide two fractions, multiply the first fraction by the reciprocal of the second.

$$\frac{21}{10} \div \frac{49}{15} \xrightarrow[\text{of the second fraction}]{\text{Multiply by the reciprocal}} \frac{21}{10} \cdot \frac{15}{49} \xrightarrow{\text{Factor}} \frac{3 \cdot \overset{1}{\cancel{7}}}{2 \cdot \cancel{5}} \cdot \frac{3 \cdot \overset{1}{\cancel{5}}}{\cancel{7} \cdot 7} = \frac{9}{14}$$

The same process is used to divide rational expressions.

Division of Rational Expressions

Let p, q, r, and s represent polynomials, such that $q \neq 0, r \neq 0, s \neq 0$. Then,

$$\frac{p}{q} \div \frac{r}{s} = \frac{p}{q} \cdot \frac{s}{r} = \frac{ps}{qr}$$

Example 4 **Dividing Rational Expressions**

Divide. $\dfrac{5t-15}{2} \div \dfrac{t^2-9}{10}$

Solution:

$$\frac{5t-15}{2} \div \frac{t^2-9}{10}$$

$$= \frac{5t-15}{2} \cdot \frac{10}{t^2-9}$$ Multiply the first fraction by the reciprocal of the second.

Avoiding Mistakes

When dividing rational expressions, take the reciprocal of the second fraction and change to multiplication *before* reducing like factors.

Answer

3. $\dfrac{-(p+1)}{5}$ or $\dfrac{p+1}{-5}$ or $-\dfrac{p+1}{5}$

$$= \frac{5(t-3)}{2} \cdot \frac{2 \cdot 5}{(t-3)(t+3)}$$ Factor each polynomial.

$$= \frac{5\overset{1}{\cancel{(t-3)}}}{\cancel{2}} \cdot \frac{\overset{1}{\cancel{2}} \cdot 5}{\cancel{(t-3)}(t+3)}$$ Simplify the ratio of common factors to 1.

$$= \frac{25}{t+3}$$

Skill Practice Divide.

4. $\dfrac{7y-14}{y+1} \div \dfrac{y^2+2y-8}{2y+2}$

Example 5 Dividing Rational Expressions

Divide. $\dfrac{p^2-11p+30}{10p^2-250} \div \dfrac{30p-5p^2}{2p+4}$

Solution:

$$\frac{p^2-11p+30}{10p^2-250} \div \frac{30p-5p^2}{2p+4}$$

$$= \frac{p^2-11p+30}{10p^2-250} \cdot \frac{2p+4}{30p-5p^2}$$ Multiply the first fraction by the reciprocal of the second.

Factor the trinomial.
$p^2 - 11p + 30 = (p-5)(p-6)$

$$= \frac{(p-5)(p-6)}{2 \cdot 5(p-5)(p+5)} \cdot \frac{2(p+2)}{5p(6-p)}$$

Factor out the GCF.
$2p + 4 = 2(p+2)$

Factor out the GCF. Then factor the difference of squares.
$10p^2 - 250 = 10(p^2-25)$
$= 2 \cdot 5(p-5)(p+5)$

Factor out the GCF.
$30p - 5p^2 = 5p(6-p)$

$$= \frac{\overset{1}{\cancel{(p-5)}}\overset{-1}{\cancel{(p-6)}}}{\cancel{2} \cdot 5\cancel{(p-5)}(p+5)} \cdot \frac{\overset{1}{\cancel{2}}(p+2)}{5p\cancel{(6-p)}}$$ Simplify the ratio of common factors to 1 or -1.

$$= -\frac{(p+2)}{25p(p+5)}$$

Skill Practice Divide.

5. $\dfrac{4x^2-9}{2x^2-x-3} \div \dfrac{20x+30}{x^2+7x+6}$

Answers

4. $\dfrac{14}{y+4}$ 5. $\dfrac{x+6}{10}$

Example 6 Dividing Rational Expressions

Divide. $\dfrac{\dfrac{3x}{4y}}{\dfrac{5x}{6y}}$

Solution:

$\dfrac{\dfrac{3x}{4y}}{\dfrac{5x}{6y}}$ ← This fraction bar denotes division (÷).

$= \dfrac{3x}{4y} \div \dfrac{5x}{6y}$

$= \dfrac{3x}{4y} \cdot \dfrac{6y}{5x}$ Multiply by the reciprocal of the second fraction.

$= \dfrac{3 \cdot \overset{1}{\cancel{x}}}{\cancel{2} \cdot 2 \cdot \cancel{y}} \cdot \dfrac{\overset{1}{\cancel{2}} \cdot 3 \cdot \overset{1}{\cancel{y}}}{5 \cdot \cancel{x}}$ Simplify the ratio of common factors to 1.

$= \dfrac{9}{10}$

Skill Practice Divide.

6. $\dfrac{\dfrac{a^3b}{9c}}{\dfrac{4ab}{3c^3}}$

Sometimes multiplication and division of rational expressions appear in the same problem. In such a case, apply the order of operations by multiplying or dividing in order from left to right.

Example 7 Multiplying and Dividing Rational Expressions

Perform the indicated operations. $\dfrac{4}{c^2 - 9} \div \dfrac{6}{c - 3} \cdot \dfrac{3c}{8}$

Solution:

In this example, division occurs first, before multiplication. Parentheses may be inserted to reinforce the proper order.

$\left(\dfrac{4}{c^2 - 9} \div \dfrac{6}{c - 3}\right) \cdot \dfrac{3c}{8}$

$= \left(\dfrac{4}{c^2 - 9} \cdot \dfrac{c - 3}{6}\right) \cdot \dfrac{3c}{8}$ Multiply the first fraction by the reciprocal of the second.

Answer

6. $\dfrac{a^2c^2}{12}$

$$= \left(\frac{2 \cdot 2}{(c-3)(c+3)} \cdot \frac{c-3}{2 \cdot 3}\right) \cdot \frac{3 \cdot c}{2 \cdot 2 \cdot 2}$$

Now that each operation is written as multiplication, factor the polynomials and reduce the common factors.

$$= \frac{\overset{1}{\cancel{2}} \cdot \overset{1}{\cancel{2}}}{\cancel{(c-3)}(c+3)} \cdot \frac{\overset{1}{\cancel{(c-3)}}}{2 \cdot \cancel{3}} \cdot \frac{\overset{1}{\cancel{3}} \cdot c}{2 \cdot 2 \cdot 2}$$

$$= \frac{c}{4(c+3)}$$

Simplify.

Skill Practice Perform the indicated operations.

7. $\dfrac{v}{v+2} \div \dfrac{5v^2}{v^2-4} \cdot \dfrac{v}{10}$

Answer

7. $\dfrac{v-2}{50}$

Section 7.2 Practice Exercises

Review Exercises

For Exercises 1–8, multiply or divide the fractions.

1. $\dfrac{3}{5} \cdot \dfrac{1}{2}$

2. $\dfrac{6}{7} \cdot \dfrac{5}{12}$

3. $\dfrac{3}{4} \div \dfrac{3}{8}$

4. $\dfrac{18}{5} \div \dfrac{2}{5}$

5. $6 \cdot \dfrac{5}{12}$

6. $\dfrac{7}{25} \cdot 5$

7. $\dfrac{\frac{21}{4}}{\frac{7}{5}}$

8. $\dfrac{\frac{9}{2}}{\frac{3}{4}}$

Concept 1: Multiplication of Rational Expressions

For Exercises 9–24, multiply. **(See Examples 1–3.)**

9. $\dfrac{2xy}{5x^2} \cdot \dfrac{15}{4y}$

10. $\dfrac{7s}{t^2} \cdot \dfrac{t^2}{14s^2}$

11. $\dfrac{6x^3}{9x^6y^2} \cdot \dfrac{18x^4y^7}{4y}$

12. $\dfrac{10a^2b}{15b^2} \cdot \dfrac{30b}{2a^3}$

13. $\dfrac{4x-24}{20x} \cdot \dfrac{5x}{8}$

14. $\dfrac{5a+20}{a} \cdot \dfrac{3a}{10}$

15. $\dfrac{3y+18}{y^2} \cdot \dfrac{4y}{6y+36}$

16. $\dfrac{2p-4}{6p} \cdot \dfrac{4p^2}{8p-16}$

17. $\dfrac{10}{2-a} \cdot \dfrac{a-2}{16}$

18. $\dfrac{w-3}{6} \cdot \dfrac{20}{3-w}$

19. $\dfrac{b^2-a^2}{a-b} \cdot \dfrac{a}{a^2-ab}$

20. $\dfrac{(x-y)^2}{x^2+xy} \cdot \dfrac{x}{y-x}$

21. $\dfrac{y^2+2y+1}{5y-10} \cdot \dfrac{y^2-3y+2}{y^2-1}$

22. $\dfrac{6a^2-6}{a^2+6a+5} \cdot \dfrac{a^2+5a}{12a}$

23. $\dfrac{10x}{2x^2+3x+1} \cdot \dfrac{x^2+7x+6}{5x}$

24. $\dfrac{p-3}{p^2+p-12} \cdot \dfrac{4p+16}{p+1}$

Concept 2: Division of Rational Expressions

For Exercises 25–38, divide. **(See Examples 4–6.)**

25. $\dfrac{4x}{7y} \div \dfrac{2x^2}{21xy}$

26. $\dfrac{6cd}{5d^2} \div \dfrac{8c^3}{10d}$

27. $\dfrac{\dfrac{8m^4n^5}{5n^6}}{\dfrac{24mn}{15m^3}}$

28. $\dfrac{\dfrac{10a^3b}{3a}}{\dfrac{5b}{9ab}}$

29. $\dfrac{4a + 12}{6a - 18} \div \dfrac{3a + 9}{5a - 15}$

30. $\dfrac{8m - 16}{3m + 3} \div \dfrac{5m - 10}{2m + 2}$

31. $\dfrac{3x - 21}{6x^2 - 42x} \div \dfrac{7}{12x}$

32. $\dfrac{4a^2 - 4a}{9a - 9} \div \dfrac{5}{12a}$

33. $\dfrac{m^2 - n^2}{9} \div \dfrac{3n - 3m}{27m}$

34. $\dfrac{9 - t^2}{15t + 15} \div \dfrac{t - 3}{5t}$

35. $\dfrac{3p + 4q}{p^2 + 4pq + 4q^2} \div \dfrac{4}{p + 2q}$

36. $\dfrac{x^2 + 2xy + y^2}{2x - y} \div \dfrac{x + y}{5}$

37. $\dfrac{p^2 - 2p - 3}{p^2 - p - 6} \div \dfrac{p^2 - 1}{p^2 + 2p}$

38. $\dfrac{4t^2 - 1}{t^2 - 5t} \div \dfrac{2t^2 + 5t + 2}{t^2 - 3t - 10}$

Mixed Exercises

For Exercises 39–64, multiply or divide as indicated.

39. $(w + 3) \cdot \dfrac{w}{2w^2 + 5w - 3}$

40. $\dfrac{5t + 1}{5t^2 - 31t + 6} \cdot (t - 6)$

41. $(r - 5) \cdot \dfrac{4r}{2r^2 - 7r - 15}$

42. $\dfrac{q + 1}{5q^2 - 28q - 12} \cdot (5q + 2)$

43. $\dfrac{\dfrac{5t - 10}{12}}{\dfrac{4t - 8}{8}}$

44. $\dfrac{\dfrac{6m + 6}{5}}{\dfrac{3m + 3}{10}}$

45. $\dfrac{2a^2 + 13a - 24}{8a - 12} \div (a + 8)$

46. $\dfrac{3y^2 + 20y - 7}{5y + 35} \div (3y - 1)$

47. $\dfrac{y^2 + 5y - 36}{y^2 - 2y - 8} \cdot \dfrac{y + 2}{y - 6}$

48. $\dfrac{z^2 - 11z + 28}{z - 1} \cdot \dfrac{z + 1}{z^2 - 6z - 7}$

49. $\dfrac{2t^2 + t - 1}{t^2 + 3t + 2} \cdot \dfrac{t + 2}{2t - 1}$

50. $\dfrac{3p^2 - 2p - 8}{3p^2 - 5p - 12} \cdot \dfrac{p - 3}{p - 2}$

51. $(5t - 1) \div \dfrac{5t^2 + 9t - 2}{3t + 8}$

52. $(2q - 3) \div \dfrac{2q^2 + 5q - 12}{q - 7}$

53. $\dfrac{x^2 + 2x - 3}{x^2 - 3x + 2} \cdot \dfrac{x^2 + 2x - 8}{x^2 + 4x + 3}$

54. $\dfrac{y^2 + y - 12}{y^2 - y - 20} \cdot \dfrac{y^2 + y - 30}{y^2 - 2y - 3}$

55. $\dfrac{\dfrac{w^2 - 6w + 9}{8}}{\dfrac{9 - w^2}{4w + 12}}$

56. $\dfrac{\dfrac{p^2 - 6p + 8}{24}}{\dfrac{16 - p^2}{6p + 6}}$

57. $\dfrac{5k^2 + 7k + 2}{k^2 + 5k + 4} \div \dfrac{5k^2 + 17k + 6}{k^2 + 10k + 24}$

58. $\dfrac{4h^2 - 5h + 1}{h^2 + h - 2} \div \dfrac{6h^2 - 7h + 2}{2h^2 + 3h - 2}$

59. $\dfrac{ax + a + bx + b}{2x^2 + 4x + 2} \cdot \dfrac{4x + 4}{a^2 + ab}$

60. $\dfrac{3my + 9m + ny + 3n}{9m^2 + 6mn + n^2} \cdot \dfrac{30m + 10n}{5y^2 + 15y}$

61. $\dfrac{y^4 - 1}{2y^2 - 3y + 1} \div \dfrac{2y^2 + 2}{8y^2 - 4y}$

62. $\dfrac{x^4 - 16}{6x^2 + 24} \div \dfrac{x^2 - 2x}{3x}$

63. $\dfrac{x^2 - xy - 2y^2}{x + 2y} \div \dfrac{x^2 - 4xy + 4y^2}{x^2 - 4y^2}$

64. $\dfrac{4m^2 - 4mn - 3n^2}{8m^2 - 18n^2} \div \dfrac{3m + 3n}{6m^2 + 15mn + 9n^2}$

For Exercises 65–70, multiply or divide as indicated. **(See Example 7.)**

65. $\dfrac{y^3 - 3y^2 + 4y - 12}{y^4 - 16} \cdot \dfrac{3y^2 + 5y - 2}{3y^2 - 10y + 3} \div \dfrac{3}{6y - 12}$

66. $\dfrac{x^2 - 25}{3x^2 + 3xy} \cdot \dfrac{x^2 + 4x + xy + 4y}{x^2 + 9x + 20} \div \dfrac{x - 5}{x}$

67. $\dfrac{a^2 - 5a}{a^2 + 7a + 12} \div \dfrac{a^3 - 7a^2 + 10a}{a^2 + 9a + 18} \div \dfrac{a + 6}{a + 4}$

68. $\dfrac{t^2 + t - 2}{t^2 + 5t + 6} \div \dfrac{t - 1}{t} \div \dfrac{5t - 5}{t + 3}$

69. $\dfrac{p^3 - q^3}{p - q} \cdot \dfrac{p + q}{2p^2 + 2pq + 2q^2}$

70. $\dfrac{r^3 + s^3}{r - s} \div \dfrac{r^2 + 2rs + s^2}{r^2 - s^2}$

Least Common Denominator

Section 7.3

Concepts

1. **Least Common Denominator**
2. **Writing Rational Expressions with the Least Common Denominator**

1. Least Common Denominator

In Sections 7.1 and 7.2, we learned how to simplify, multiply, and divide rational expressions. Our next goal is to add and subtract rational expressions. As with fractions, rational expressions may be added or subtracted only if they have the same denominator.

The **least common denominator (LCD)** of two or more rational expressions is defined as the least common multiple of the denominators. For example, consider the fractions $\frac{1}{20}$ and $\frac{1}{8}$. By inspection, you can probably see that the least common denominator is 40. To understand why, find the prime factorization of both denominators:

$$20 = 2^2 \cdot 5 \qquad \text{and} \qquad 8 = 2^3$$

A common multiple of 20 and 8 must be a multiple of 5, a multiple of 2^2, and a multiple of 2^3. However, any number that is a multiple of $2^3 = 8$ is automatically a multiple of $2^2 = 4$. Therefore, it is sufficient to construct the least common denominator as the product of unique prime factors, in which each factor is raised to its highest power.

$$\text{The LCD of } \frac{1}{20} \text{ and } \frac{1}{8} \text{ is } 2^3 \cdot 5 = 40.$$

Finding the Least Common Denominator of Two or More Rational Expressions

Step 1 Factor all denominators completely.

Step 2 The LCD is the product of unique prime factors from the denominators, in which each factor is raised to the highest power to which it appears in any denominator.

Example 1 Finding the Least Common Denominator

Find the LCD of the rational expressions.

a. $\frac{5}{14}; \frac{3}{49}; \frac{1}{8}$ **b.** $\frac{5}{3x^2z}; \frac{7}{x^5y^3}$

Solution:

a. $\frac{5}{14}; \frac{3}{49}; \frac{1}{8}$

$= \frac{5}{2 \cdot 7}; \frac{3}{7^2}; \frac{1}{2^3}$ Factor the denominators.

The LCD is $7^2 \cdot 2^3 = 392$. The LCD is the product of unique factors, each raised to its highest power.

b. $\frac{5}{3x^2z}; \frac{7}{x^5y^3}$

$= \frac{5}{3 \cdot x^2 \cdot z^1}; \frac{7}{x^5 \cdot y^3}$ The denominators are in factored form.

The LCD is the product of $3 \cdot x^5 \cdot y^3 \cdot z^1$ or simply $3x^5y^3z$.

Skill Practice Find the LCD for each set of expressions.

1. $\frac{3}{8}; \frac{7}{10}; \frac{1}{15}$ **2.** $\frac{1}{5a^3b^2}; \frac{1}{10a^4b}$

Example 2 Finding the Least Common Denominator

Find the LCD for each pair of rational expressions.

a. $\frac{a+b}{a^2-25}; \frac{1}{2a-10}$ **b.** $\frac{x-5}{x^2-2x}; \frac{1}{x^2-4x+4}$

Solution:

a. $\frac{a+b}{a^2-25}; \frac{1}{2a-10}$

$= \frac{a+b}{(a-5)(a+5)}; \frac{1}{2(a-5)}$ Factor the denominators.

The LCD is $2(a-5)(a+5)$. The LCD is the product of unique factors, each raised to its highest power.

b. $\frac{x-5}{x^2-2x}; \frac{1}{x^2-4x+4}$

$= \frac{x-5}{x(x-2)}; \frac{1}{(x-2)^2}$ Factor the denominators.

The LCD is $x(x-2)^2$. The LCD is the product of unique factors, each raised to its highest power.

Answers

1. 120

2. $10a^4b^2$

Skill Practice Find the LCD.

3. $\dfrac{x}{x^2-16};\ \dfrac{2}{3x+12}$ 4. $\dfrac{6}{t^2+5t-14};\ \dfrac{8}{t^2-3t+2}$

2. Writing Rational Expressions with the Least Common Denominator

To add or subtract two rational expressions, the expressions must have the same denominator. Therefore, we must first practice the skill of converting each rational expression into an equivalent expression with the LCD as its denominator.

Writing Equivalent Fractions with Common Denominators

Step 1 Identify the LCD for the expressions.

Step 2 Multiply the numerator and denominator of each fraction by the factors from the LCD that are missing from the original denominators.

Example 3 Converting to the Least Common Denominator

Find the LCD of each pair of rational expressions. Then convert each expression to an equivalent fraction with the denominator equal to the LCD.

a. $\dfrac{3}{2ab};\ \dfrac{6}{5a^2}$ **b.** $\dfrac{4}{x+1};\ \dfrac{7}{x-4}$

Solution:

a. $\dfrac{3}{2ab};\ \dfrac{6}{5a^2}$ The LCD is $10a^2b$.

$$\frac{3}{2ab}=\frac{3\cdot 5a}{2ab\cdot 5a}=\frac{15a}{10a^2b}$$

The first expression is missing the factor $5a$ from the denominator.

$$\frac{6}{5a^2}=\frac{6\cdot 2b}{5a^2\cdot 2b}=\frac{12b}{10a^2b}$$

The second expression is missing the factor $2b$ from the denominator.

b. $\dfrac{4}{x+1};\ \dfrac{7}{x-4}$ The LCD is $(x+1)(x-4)$.

$$\frac{4}{x+1}=\frac{4(x-4)}{(x+1)(x-4)}=\frac{4x-16}{(x+1)(x-4)}$$

The first expression is missing the factor $(x-4)$ from the denominator.

$$\frac{7}{x-4}=\frac{7(x+1)}{(x-4)(x+1)}=\frac{7x+7}{(x-4)(x+1)}$$

The second expression is missing the factor $(x+1)$ from the denominator.

Skill Practice For each pair of expressions, find the LCD, and then convert each expression to an equivalent fraction with the denominator equal to the LCD.

5. $\dfrac{2}{rs^2};\ \dfrac{-1}{r^3s}$ 6. $\dfrac{5}{x-3};\ \dfrac{x}{x+1}$

Answers

3. $3(x-4)(x+4)$
4. $(t+7)(t-2)(t-1)$
5. $\dfrac{2}{rs^2}=\dfrac{2r^2}{r^3s^2};\ \dfrac{-1}{r^3s}=\dfrac{-s}{r^3s^2}$
6. $\dfrac{5}{x-3}=\dfrac{5x+5}{(x-3)(x+1)}$; $\dfrac{x}{x+1}=\dfrac{x^2-3x}{(x+1)(x-3)}$

Example 4 Converting to the Least Common Denominator

Find the LCD of the pair of rational expressions. Then convert each expression to an equivalent fraction with the denominator equal to the LCD.

$$\frac{w+2}{w^2-w-12}; \frac{1}{w^2-9}$$

Solution:

$$\frac{w+2}{w^2-w-12}; \frac{1}{w^2-9}$$ To find the LCD, factor each denominator.

$$\frac{w+2}{(w-4)(w+3)}; \frac{1}{(w-3)(w+3)}$$ The LCD is $(w-4)(w+3)(w-3)$.

$$\frac{w+2}{(w-4)(w+3)} = \frac{(w+2)(w-3)}{(w-4)(w+3)(w-3)}$$ The first expression is missing the factor $(w-3)$ from the denominator.

$$= \frac{w^2-w-6}{(w-4)(w+3)(w-3)}$$

$$\frac{1}{(w-3)(w+3)} = \frac{1(w-4)}{(w-3)(w+3)(w-4)}$$ The second expression is missing the factor $(w-4)$ from the denominator.

$$= \frac{w-4}{(w-3)(w+3)(w-4)}$$

Skill Practice Find the LCD. Then convert each expression to an equivalent expression with the denominator equal to the LCD.

7. $\frac{z}{z^2-4}; \frac{-3}{z^2-z-2}$

Example 5 Converting to the Least Common Denominator

Convert each expression to an equivalent expression with the denominator equal to the LCD.

$$\frac{3}{x-7} \quad \text{and} \quad \frac{1}{7-x}$$

TIP: In Example 5, the expressions

$$\frac{3}{x-7} \quad \text{and} \quad \frac{1}{7-x}$$

have opposite factors in the denominators. In such a case, you do not need to include *both* factors in the LCD.

Solution:

Notice that the expressions $x-7$ and $7-x$ are opposites and differ by a factor of -1. Therefore, we may use either $x-7$ or $7-x$ as a common denominator. Each case is shown below.

Converting to the Denominator $x - 7$

$$\frac{3}{x-7}; \frac{1}{7-x}$$ Leave the first fraction unchanged because it has the desired LCD.

$$\frac{1}{7-x} = \frac{(-1)1}{(-1)(7-x)}$$ Multiply the *second* rational expression by the ratio $\frac{-1}{-1}$ to change its denominator to $x-7$.

$$= \frac{-1}{-7+x}$$ Apply the distributive property.

$$= \frac{-1}{x-7}$$

Answer

7. $\frac{z^2+z}{(z-2)(z+2)(z+1)}; \frac{-3z-6}{(z-2)(z+2)(z+1)}$

Converting to the Denominator $7 - x$

$\dfrac{3}{x-7}; \dfrac{1}{7-x}$ — Leave the second fraction unchanged because it has the desired LCD.

$\dfrac{3}{x-7} = \dfrac{(-1)3}{(-1)(x-7)};$ — Multiply the *first* rational expression by the ratio $\frac{-1}{-1}$ to change its denominator to $7 - x$.

$= \dfrac{-3}{-x+7}$ — Apply the distributive property.

$= \dfrac{-3}{7-x}$

Skill Practice

8. a. Find the LCD of the expressions. $\dfrac{9}{w-2}; \dfrac{11}{2-w}$

b. Convert each expression to an equivalent fraction with denominator equal to the LCD.

Answers

8. a. The LCD is $(w - 2)$ or $(2 - w)$.

b. $\dfrac{9}{w-2} = \dfrac{9}{w-2};$ $\dfrac{11}{2-w} = \dfrac{-11}{w-2}$

or

$\dfrac{9}{w-2} = \dfrac{-9}{2-w};$ $\dfrac{11}{2-w} = \dfrac{11}{2-w}$

Section 7.3 Practice Exercises

Vocabulary and Key Concepts

1. The least common denominator (LCD) of two rational expressions is defined as the least common ____________ of the ____________.

Review Exercises

2. Evaluate the expression for the given values of x. $\dfrac{2x}{x+5}$

a. $x = 1$ **b.** $x = 5$ **c.** $x = -5$

For Exercises 3–4, identify the restricted values. Then simplify the expression.

3. $\dfrac{3x+3}{5x^2-5}$

4. $\dfrac{x+2}{x^2-3x-10}$

For Exercises 5–8, multiply or divide as indicated.

5. $\dfrac{a+3}{a+7} \cdot \dfrac{a^2+3a-10}{a^2+a-6}$

6. $\dfrac{6(a+2b)}{2(a-3b)} \cdot \dfrac{4(a+3b)(a-3b)}{9(a+2b)(a-2b)}$

7. $\dfrac{16y^2}{9y+36} \div \dfrac{8y^3}{3y+12}$

8. $\dfrac{5w^2+6w+1}{w^2+5w+6} \div (5w+1)$

9. Which of the expressions are equivalent to $-\dfrac{5}{x-3}$? Circle all that apply.

a. $\dfrac{-5}{x-3}$ **b.** $\dfrac{5}{-x+3}$ **c.** $\dfrac{5}{3-x}$ **d.** $\dfrac{5}{-(x-3)}$

Example 1 **Adding and Subtracting Rational Expressions with the Same Denominator**

Add or subtract as indicated. **a.** $\frac{1}{12} + \frac{7}{12}$ **b.** $\frac{2}{5p} - \frac{7}{5p}$

Solution:

a. $\frac{1}{12} + \frac{7}{12}$ The fractions have the same denominator.

$= \frac{1 + 7}{12}$ Add the terms in the numerators, and write the result over the common denominator.

$= \frac{\overset{2}{\cancel{8}}}{\underset{3}{\cancel{12}}}$

$= \frac{2}{3}$ Simplify.

b. $\frac{2}{5p} - \frac{7}{5p}$ The rational expressions have the same denominator.

$= \frac{2 - 7}{5p}$ Subtract the terms in the numerators, and write the result over the common denominator.

$= \frac{-5}{5p}$

$= \frac{\overset{-1}{-\cancel{5}}}{\cancel{5}p}$ Simplify.

$= -\frac{1}{p}$

Skill Practice Add or subtract as indicated.

1. $\frac{3}{14} + \frac{4}{14}$ **2.** $\frac{2}{7d} - \frac{9}{7d}$

Example 2 **Adding and Subtracting Rational Expressions with the Same Denominator**

Add or subtract as indicated.

a. $\frac{2}{3d + 5} + \frac{7d}{3d + 5}$ **b.** $\frac{x^2}{x - 3} - \frac{-5x + 24}{x - 3}$

Solution:

a. $\frac{2}{3d + 5} + \frac{7d}{3d + 5}$ The rational expressions have the same denominator.

$= \frac{2 + 7d}{3d + 5}$ Add the terms in the numerators, and write the result over the common denominator.

$= \frac{7d + 2}{3d + 5}$ Because the numerator and denominator share no common factors, the expression is in lowest terms.

Answers

1. $\frac{1}{2}$ **2.** $-\frac{1}{d}$

b. $\dfrac{x^2}{x-3} - \dfrac{-5x+24}{x-3}$ The rational expressions have the same denominator.

$= \dfrac{x^2 - (-5x+24)}{x-3}$ Subtract the terms in the numerators, and write the result over the common denominator.

$= \dfrac{x^2 + 5x - 24}{x-3}$ Simplify the numerator.

$= \dfrac{(x+8)(x-3)}{(x-3)}$ Factor the numerator and denominator to determine if the rational expression can be simplified.

$= \dfrac{(x+8)\overset{1}{\cancel{(x-3)}}}{\cancel{(x-3)}}$ Simplify.

$= x + 8$

Avoiding Mistakes

When subtracting rational expressions, use parentheses to group the terms in the numerator that follow the subtraction sign. This will help you remember to apply the distributive property.

Skill Practice Add or subtract as indicated.

3. $\dfrac{x^2+2}{x+3} + \dfrac{4x+1}{x+3}$ **4.** $\dfrac{4t-9}{2t+1} - \dfrac{t-5}{2t+1}$

2. Addition and Subtraction of Rational Expressions with Different Denominators

To add or subtract two rational expressions with unlike denominators, we must convert the expressions to equivalent expressions with the same denominator. For example, consider adding

$$\frac{1}{10} + \frac{12}{5y}$$

The LCD is $10y$. For each expression, identify the factors from the LCD that are missing from the denominator. Then multiply the numerator and denominator of the expression by thc missing factor(s).

$$\frac{1}{\underbrace{10}_{\text{Missing } y}} + \frac{12}{\underbrace{5y}_{\text{Missing } 2}}$$

$= \dfrac{1 \cdot y}{10 \cdot y} + \dfrac{12 \cdot 2}{5y \cdot 2}$

$= \dfrac{y}{10y} + \dfrac{24}{10y}$ The rational expressions now have the same denominators.

$= \dfrac{y+24}{10y}$ Add the numerators.

Avoiding Mistakes

In the expression $\frac{y+24}{10y}$, notice that you cannot reduce the 24 and 10 because 24 is not a factor in the numerator, it is a term. Only factors can be reduced—not terms.

After successfully adding or subtracting two rational expressions, always check to see if the final answer is simplified. If necessary, factor the numerator and denominator, and reduce common factors. The expression

$$\frac{y+24}{10y}$$

is in lowest terms because the numerator and denominator do not share any common factors.

Answers

3. $x+1$ **4.** $\dfrac{3t-4}{2t+1}$

Adding or Subtracting Rational Expressions

Step 1 Factor the denominators of each rational expression.

Step 2 Identify the LCD.

Step 3 Rewrite each rational expression as an equivalent expression with the LCD as its denominator.

Step 4 Add or subtract the numerators, and write the result over the common denominator.

Step 5 Simplify.

Example 3 Subtracting Rational Expressions with Different Denominators

Subtract. $\dfrac{4}{7k} - \dfrac{3}{k^2}$

Solution:

$\dfrac{4}{7k} - \dfrac{3}{k^2}$

Step 1: The denominators are already factored.

Step 2: The LCD is $7k^2$.

$= \dfrac{4 \cdot k}{7k \cdot k} - \dfrac{3 \cdot 7}{k^2 \cdot 7}$ **Step 3:** Write each expression with the LCD.

$= \dfrac{4k}{7k^2} - \dfrac{21}{7k^2}$

Avoiding Mistakes

Do not reduce after rewriting the fractions with the LCD. You will revert back to the original expression.

$= \dfrac{4k - 21}{7k^2}$ **Step 4:** Subtract the numerators, and write the result over the LCD.

Step 5: The expression is in lowest terms because the numerator and denominator share no common factors.

Skill Practice Subtract.

5. $\dfrac{4}{3x} - \dfrac{1}{2x^2}$

Example 4 Subtracting Rational Expressions with Different Denominators

Subtract. $\dfrac{2q - 4}{3} - \dfrac{q + 1}{2}$

Solution:

$\dfrac{2q - 4}{3} - \dfrac{q + 1}{2}$

Step 1: The denominators are already factored.

Step 2: The LCD is 6.

$= \dfrac{2(2q - 4)}{2 \cdot 3} - \dfrac{3(q + 1)}{3 \cdot 2}$ **Step 3:** Write each expression with the LCD.

Answer

5. $\dfrac{8x - 3}{6x^2}$

$= \dfrac{2(2q - 4) - 3(q + 1)}{6}$ **Step 4:** Subtract the numerators, and write the result over the LCD.

$= \dfrac{4q - 8 - 3q - 3}{6}$

$= \dfrac{q - 11}{6}$ **Step 5:** The expression is in lowest terms because the numerator and denominator share no common factors.

Skill Practice Subtract.

6. $\dfrac{t}{12} - \dfrac{t - 2}{4}$

Example 5 Adding Rational Expressions with Different Denominators

Add. $\dfrac{1}{x - 5} + \dfrac{-10}{x^2 - 25}$

Solution:

$\dfrac{1}{x - 5} + \dfrac{-10}{x^2 - 25}$

$= \dfrac{1}{x - 5} + \dfrac{-10}{(x - 5)(x + 5)}$ **Step 1:** Factor the denominators.

Step 2: The LCD is $(x - 5)(x + 5)$.

$= \dfrac{1(x + 5)}{(x - 5)(x + 5)} + \dfrac{-10}{(x - 5)(x + 5)}$ **Step 3:** Write each expression with the LCD.

$= \dfrac{1(x + 5) + (-10)}{(x - 5)(x + 5)}$ **Step 4:** Add the numerators, and write the result over the LCD.

$= \dfrac{x + 5 - 10}{(x - 5)(x + 5)}$

$= \dfrac{\overset{1}{\cancel{x - 5}}}{\cancel{(x - 5)}(x + 5)}$ **Step 5:** Simplify.

$= \dfrac{1}{x + 5}$

Skill Practice Add.

7. $\dfrac{1}{x - 4} + \dfrac{-8}{x^2 - 16}$

Answers

6. $\dfrac{-t + 3}{6}$ **7.** $\dfrac{1}{x + 4}$

Example 6 **Subtracting Rational Expressions with Different Denominators**

Subtract. $\dfrac{p+2}{p-1} - \dfrac{2}{p+6} - \dfrac{14}{p^2+5p-6}$

Solution:

$$\frac{p+2}{p-1} - \frac{2}{p+6} - \frac{14}{p^2+5p-6}$$

$$= \frac{p+2}{p-1} - \frac{2}{p+6} - \frac{14}{(p-1)(p+6)}$$

Step 1: Factor the denominators.

Step 2: The LCD is $(p-1)(p+6)$.

Step 3: Write each expression with the LCD.

$$= \frac{(p+2)(p+6)}{(p-1)(p+6)} - \frac{2(p-1)}{(p+6)(p-1)} - \frac{14}{(p-1)(p+6)}$$

$$= \frac{(p+2)(p+6) - 2(p-1) - 14}{(p-1)(p+6)}$$

Step 4: Combine the numerators, and write the result over the LCD.

$$= \frac{p^2 + 6p + 2p + 12 - 2p + 2 - 14}{(p-1)(p+6)}$$

Step 5: Clear parentheses in the numerator.

$$= \frac{p^2 + 6p}{(p-1)(p+6)}$$

Combine *like* terms.

$$= \frac{p(p+6)}{(p-1)(p+6)}$$

Factor the numerator to determine if the expression is in lowest terms.

$$= \frac{p\cancel{(p+6)}^{1}}{(p-1)\cancel{(p+6)}}$$

Simplify.

$$= \frac{p}{p-1}$$

Skill Practice Subtract.

8. $\dfrac{2y}{y-1} - \dfrac{1}{y} - \dfrac{2y+1}{y^2-y}$

When the denominators of two rational expressions are opposites, we can produce identical denominators by multiplying one of the expressions by the ratio $\frac{-1}{-1}$. This is demonstrated in Example 7.

Example 7 **Adding Rational Expressions with Different Denominators**

Add the rational expressions. $\dfrac{1}{d-7} + \dfrac{5}{7-d}$

Answer

8. $\dfrac{2y-3}{y-1}$

Solution:

$$\frac{1}{d-7}+\frac{5}{7-d}$$

The expressions $d - 7$ and $7 - d$ are opposites and differ by a factor of -1. Therefore, multiply the numerator and denominator of *either* expression by -1 to obtain a common denominator.

$$=\frac{1}{d-7}+\frac{(-1)5}{(-1)(7-d)}$$

Note that $-1(7 - d) = -7 + d$ or $d - 7$.

$$=\frac{1}{d-7}+\frac{-5}{d-7}$$

Simplify.

$$=\frac{1+(-5)}{d-7}$$

Add the terms in the numerators, and write the result over the common denominator.

$$=\frac{-4}{d-7}$$

Skill Practice Add.

9. $\dfrac{3}{p-8}+\dfrac{1}{8-p}$

3. Using Rational Expressions in Translations

Example 8 Using Rational Expressions in Translations

Write the English phrase as a mathematical expression. Then simplify by combining the rational expressions.

The difference of the reciprocal of n and the quotient of n and 3

Solution:

The difference of the reciprocal of n and the quotient of n and 3

The difference of

$$\left(\frac{1}{n}\right)-\left(\frac{n}{3}\right)$$

The reciprocal of n — The quotient of n and 3

$$\frac{1}{n}-\frac{n}{3}$$

The LCD is $3n$.

$$=\frac{3\cdot 1}{3\cdot n}-\frac{n\cdot n}{3\cdot n}$$

Write each expression with the LCD.

$$=\frac{3-n^2}{3n}$$

Subtract the numerators.

Skill Practice Write the English phrase as a mathematical expression. Then simplify by combining the rational expressions.

10. The sum of 1 and the quotient of 2 and a

Answers

9. $\dfrac{2}{p-8}$ or $\dfrac{-2}{8-p}$

10. $1+\dfrac{2}{a}$; $\dfrac{a+2}{a}$

Example 3 **Simplifying a Complex Fraction (Method I)**

Simplify the expression. $\dfrac{\dfrac{1}{x}+\dfrac{1}{y}}{x-\dfrac{y^2}{x}}$

Solution:

$\dfrac{\dfrac{1}{x}+\dfrac{1}{y}}{x-\dfrac{y^2}{x}}$ The LCD in the numerator is xy. The LCD in the denominator is x.

$=\dfrac{\dfrac{1\cdot y}{x\cdot y}+\dfrac{1\cdot x}{y\cdot x}}{\dfrac{x\cdot x}{1\cdot x}-\dfrac{y^2}{x}}$ Rewrite the expressions using common denominators.

$=\dfrac{\dfrac{y}{xy}+\dfrac{x}{xy}}{\dfrac{x^2}{x}-\dfrac{y^2}{x}}$

$=\dfrac{\dfrac{y+x}{xy}}{\dfrac{x^2-y^2}{x}}$ Form single fractions in the numerator and denominator.

$=\dfrac{y+x}{xy}\cdot\dfrac{x}{x^2-y^2}$ Multiply the numerator by the reciprocal of the denominator.

$=\dfrac{\overset{1}{\cancel{y+x}}}{\cancel{x}y}\cdot\dfrac{\overset{1}{\cancel{x}}}{\cancel{(x+y)}(x-y)}$ Factor and reduce. Note that $(y+x)=(x+y)$.

$=\dfrac{1}{y(x-y)}$ Simplify.

Skill Practice Simplify the expression.

3. $\dfrac{1-\dfrac{1}{p}}{\dfrac{p}{w}+\dfrac{w}{p}}$

2. Simplifying Complex Fractions (Method II)

We will now simplify the expressions from Examples 2 and 3 again using a second method to simplify complex fractions (Method II). Recall that multiplying the numerator and denominator of a rational expression by the same quantity does not change the value of the expression because we are multiplying by a number equivalent to 1. This is the basis for Method II.

Answer

3. $\dfrac{w(p-1)}{p^2+w^2}$

Simplifying a Complex Fraction (Method II)

Step 1 Multiply the numerator and denominator of the complex fraction by the LCD of *all* individual fractions within the expression.

Step 2 Apply the distributive property, and simplify the numerator and denominator.

Step 3 Simplify to lowest terms if possible.

Example 4 Simplifying a Complex Fraction (Method II)

Simplify the expression. $\dfrac{1 + \dfrac{3}{4} - \dfrac{1}{6}}{\dfrac{1}{2} + \dfrac{1}{3}}$

Solution:

$$\frac{1 + \frac{3}{4} - \frac{1}{6}}{\frac{1}{2} + \frac{1}{3}}$$

The LCD of the expressions $1, \frac{3}{4}, \frac{1}{6}, \frac{1}{2}$, and $\frac{1}{3}$ is 12.

$$= \frac{12\left(1 + \frac{3}{4} - \frac{1}{6}\right)}{12\left(\frac{1}{2} + \frac{1}{3}\right)}$$

Step 1: Multiply the numerator and denominator of the complex fraction by 12.

$$= \frac{12 \cdot 1 + 12 \cdot \frac{3}{4} - 12 \cdot \frac{1}{6}}{12 \cdot \frac{1}{2} + 12 \cdot \frac{1}{3}}$$

Step 2: Apply the distributive property.

$$= \frac{12 \cdot 1 + \overset{3}{\cancel{12}} \cdot \frac{3}{\cancel{4}} - \overset{2}{\cancel{12}} \cdot \frac{1}{\cancel{6}}}{\overset{6}{\cancel{12}} \cdot \frac{1}{\cancel{2}} + \overset{4}{\cancel{12}} \cdot \frac{1}{\cancel{3}}}$$

Simplify each term.

$$= \frac{12 + 9 - 2}{6 + 4}$$

$$= \frac{19}{10}$$

Step 3: Simplify.

TIP: In step 1, we are multiplying the original expression by $\frac{12}{12}$, which equals 1.

Skill Practice Simplify the expression.

4. $\dfrac{1 - \dfrac{3}{5}}{\dfrac{1}{4} - \dfrac{7}{10} + 1}$

Answer

4. $\frac{8}{11}$

Example 5 Simplifying a Complex Fraction (Method II)

Simplify the expression. $\dfrac{\dfrac{1}{x}+\dfrac{1}{y}}{x-\dfrac{y^2}{x}}$

Solution:

$$\dfrac{\dfrac{1}{x}+\dfrac{1}{y}}{x-\dfrac{y^2}{x}}$$

The LCD of the expressions $\frac{1}{x}$, $\frac{1}{y}$, x, and $\frac{y^2}{x}$ is xy.

$$=\dfrac{xy\left(\dfrac{1}{x}+\dfrac{1}{y}\right)}{xy\left(x-\dfrac{y^2}{x}\right)}$$

Step 1: Multiply numerator and denominator of the complex fraction by xy.

$$=\dfrac{xy\cdot\dfrac{1}{x}+xy\cdot\dfrac{1}{y}}{xy\cdot x-xy\cdot\dfrac{y^2}{x}}$$

Step 2: Apply the distributive property, and simplify each term.

$$=\dfrac{y+x}{x^2y-y^3}$$

$$=\dfrac{y+x}{y(x^2-y^2)}$$

Step 3: Factor completely, and reduce common factors.

$$=\dfrac{\overset{1}{\cancel{y+x}}}{y\cancel{(x+y)}(x-y)}$$

Note that $(y+x)=(x+y)$.

$$=\dfrac{1}{y(x-y)}$$

Skill Practice Simplify the expression.

5. $\dfrac{\dfrac{z}{3}-\dfrac{3}{z}}{1+\dfrac{3}{z}}$

Answer

5. $\dfrac{z-3}{3}$

Example 6 **Simplifying a Complex Fraction (Method II)**

Simplify the expression. $\dfrac{\dfrac{1}{k+1}-1}{\dfrac{1}{k+1}+1}$

Solution:

$$\frac{\dfrac{1}{k+1}-1}{\dfrac{1}{k+1}+1}$$

The LCD of $\dfrac{1}{k+1}$ and 1 is $(k+1)$.

$$=\frac{(k+1)\left(\dfrac{1}{k+1}-1\right)}{(k+1)\left(\dfrac{1}{k+1}+1\right)}$$

Step 1: Multiply numerator and denominator of the complex fraction by $(k+1)$.

$$=\frac{(k+1)\cdot\dfrac{1}{(k+1)}-(k+1)\cdot 1}{(k+1)\cdot\dfrac{1}{(k+1)}+(k+1)\cdot 1}$$

Step 2: Apply the distributive property.

$$=\frac{1-(k+1)}{1+(k+1)}$$

Simplify.

$$=\frac{1-k-1}{1+k+1}$$

$$=\frac{-k}{k+2}$$

Step 3: The expression is already in lowest terms.

Skill Practice Simplify the expression.

6. $\dfrac{\dfrac{4}{p-3}+1}{1+\dfrac{2}{p-3}}$

Answer

6. $\dfrac{p+1}{p-1}$

Section 7.5 Practice Exercises

Vocabulary and Key Concepts

1. A ___________ fraction is an expression containing one or more fractions in the numerator, denominator, or both.

Review Exercises

For Exercises 2–3, simplify the expression.

2. $\dfrac{y(2y+9)}{y^2(2y+9)}$

3. $\dfrac{a+5}{2a^2+7a-15}$

For Exercises 4–6, perform the indicated operations.

4. $\dfrac{2}{w-2}+\dfrac{3}{w}$

5. $\dfrac{6}{5}-\dfrac{3}{5k-10}$

6. $\dfrac{x^2-2xy+y^2}{x^4-y^4}\div\dfrac{3x^2y-3xy^2}{x^2+y^2}$

Concepts 1–2: Simplifying Complex Fractions (Methods I and II)

For Exercises 7–34, simplify the complex fractions using either method. **(See Examples 1–6.)**

7. $\dfrac{\dfrac{7}{18y}}{\dfrac{2}{9}}$

8. $\dfrac{\dfrac{a^2}{2a-3}}{\dfrac{5a}{8a-12}}$

9. $\dfrac{\dfrac{3x+2y}{2y}}{\dfrac{6x+4y}{2}}$

10. $\dfrac{\dfrac{2x-10}{4}}{\dfrac{x^2-5x}{3x}}$

11. $\dfrac{\dfrac{8a^4b^3}{3c}}{\dfrac{a^7b^2}{9c}}$

12. $\dfrac{\dfrac{12x^2}{5y}}{\dfrac{8x^6}{9y^2}}$

13. $\dfrac{\dfrac{4r^3s}{t^5}}{\dfrac{2s^7}{r^2t^9}}$

14. $\dfrac{\dfrac{5p^4q}{w^4}}{\dfrac{10p^2}{qw^2}}$

15. $\dfrac{\dfrac{1}{8}+\dfrac{4}{3}}{\dfrac{1}{2}-\dfrac{5}{12}}$

16. $\dfrac{\dfrac{8}{9}-\dfrac{1}{3}}{\dfrac{7}{6}+\dfrac{1}{9}}$

17. $\dfrac{\dfrac{1}{h}+\dfrac{1}{k}}{\dfrac{1}{hk}}$

18. $\dfrac{\dfrac{1}{b}+1}{\dfrac{1}{b}}$

19. $\dfrac{\dfrac{n+1}{n^2-9}}{\dfrac{2}{n+3}}$

20. $\dfrac{\dfrac{5}{k-5}}{\dfrac{k+1}{k^2-25}}$

21. $\dfrac{2+\dfrac{1}{x}}{4+\dfrac{1}{x}}$

22. $\dfrac{6+\dfrac{6}{k}}{1+\dfrac{1}{k}}$

23. $\dfrac{\dfrac{m}{7}-\dfrac{7}{m}}{\dfrac{1}{7}+\dfrac{1}{m}}$

24. $\dfrac{\dfrac{2}{p}+\dfrac{p}{2}}{\dfrac{p}{3}-\dfrac{3}{p}}$

25. $\dfrac{\dfrac{1}{5}-\dfrac{1}{y}}{\dfrac{7}{10}+\dfrac{1}{y^2}}$

26. $\dfrac{\dfrac{1}{m^2}+\dfrac{2}{3}}{\dfrac{1}{m}-\dfrac{5}{6}}$

27. $\dfrac{\dfrac{8}{a+4}+2}{\dfrac{12}{a+4}-2}$

28. $\dfrac{\dfrac{2}{w+1}+3}{\dfrac{3}{w+1}+4}$

29. $\dfrac{1-\dfrac{4}{t^2}}{1-\dfrac{2}{t}-\dfrac{8}{t^2}}$

30. $\dfrac{1-\dfrac{9}{p^2}}{1-\dfrac{1}{p}-\dfrac{6}{p^2}}$

31. $\dfrac{t+4+\dfrac{3}{t}}{t-4-\dfrac{5}{t}}$

32. $\dfrac{\dfrac{9}{4m}+\dfrac{9}{2m^2}}{\dfrac{3}{2}+\dfrac{3}{m}}$

33. $\dfrac{\dfrac{1}{k-6}-1}{\dfrac{2}{k-6}-2}$

34. $\dfrac{\dfrac{3}{y-3}+4}{8+\dfrac{6}{y-3}}$

For Exercises 35–38, write the English phrases as algebraic expressions. Then simplify the expressions.

35. The sum of one-half and two-thirds, divided by five

36. The quotient of ten and the difference of two-fifths and one-fourth

37. The quotient of three and the sum of two-thirds and three-fourths

38. The difference of three-fifths and one-half, divided by four

39. In electronics, resistors oppose the flow of current. For two resistors in parallel, the total resistance is given by

$$R = \frac{1}{\dfrac{1}{R_1} + \dfrac{1}{R_2}}$$

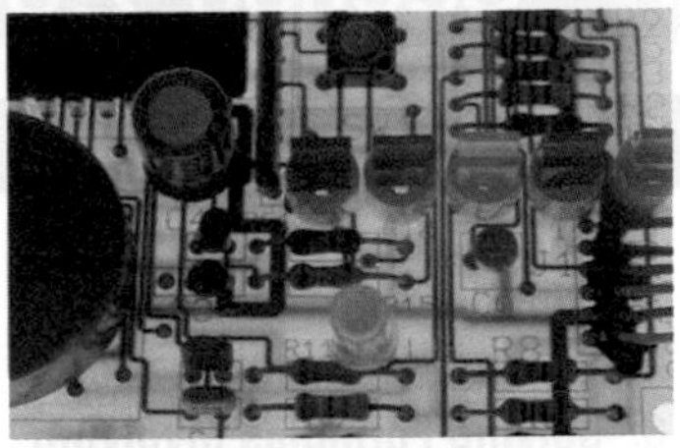

a. Find the total resistance if $R_1 = 2\ \Omega$ (ohms) and $R_2 = 3\ \Omega$.

b. Find the total resistance if $R_1 = 10\ \Omega$ and $R_2 = 15\ \Omega$.

40. Suppose that Joëlle makes a round trip to a location that is d miles away. If the average rate going to the location is r_1 and the average rate on the return trip is given by r_2, the average rate of the entire trip, R, is given by

$$R = \frac{2d}{\dfrac{d}{r_1} + \dfrac{d}{r_2}}$$

a. Find the average rate of a trip to a destination 30 mi away when the average rate going there was 60 mph and the average rate returning home was 45 mph. (Round to the nearest tenth of a mile per hour.)

b. Find the average rate of a trip to a destination that is 50 mi away if the driver travels at the same rates as in part (a). (Round to the nearest tenth of a mile per hour.)

c. Compare your answers from parts (a) and (b) and explain the results in the context of the problem.

Expanding Your Skills

For Exercises 41–50, simplify the complex fractions using either method.

41. $\dfrac{x^{-1} - y^{-1}}{x^{-2} - y^{-2}}$

42. $\dfrac{a^{-2} - 1}{a^{-1} - 1}$

43. $\dfrac{2x^{-1} + 8y^{-1}}{4x^{-1}}$ $\left(\textit{Hint: } 2x^{-1} = \dfrac{2}{x}\right)$

44. $\dfrac{6a^{-1} + 4b^{-1}}{8b^{-1}}$

45. $\dfrac{(mn)^{-2}}{m^{-2} + n^{-2}}$

46. $\dfrac{(xy)^{-1}}{2x^{-1} + 3y^{-1}}$

47. $\dfrac{\dfrac{1}{z^2 - 9} + \dfrac{2}{z + 3}}{\dfrac{3}{z - 3}}$

48. $\dfrac{\dfrac{5}{w^2 - 25} - \dfrac{3}{w + 5}}{\dfrac{4}{w - 5}}$

49. $\dfrac{\dfrac{2}{x - 1} + 2}{\dfrac{2}{x + 1} - 2}$

50. $\dfrac{\dfrac{1}{y - 3} + 1}{\dfrac{2}{y + 3} - 1}$

For Exercises 51–52, simplify the complex fractions. (*Hint:* Use the order of operations and begin with the fraction on the lower right.)

51. $1 + \dfrac{1}{1 + 1}$

52. $1 + \dfrac{1}{1 + \dfrac{1}{1 + 1}}$

Example 3 **Solving a Rational Equation**

Solve the equation. $1 + \frac{3a}{a - 2} = \frac{6}{a - 2}$

Solution:

$$1 + \frac{3a}{a - 2} = \frac{6}{a - 2}$$ The LCD of all the expressions is $a - 2$. The restricted value is $a = 2$.

$$(a - 2)\left(1 + \frac{3a}{a - 2}\right) = (a - 2)\left(\frac{6}{a - 2}\right)$$ Multiply by the LCD.

$$(a - 2)1 + \overset{1}{(a - 2)}\left(\frac{3a}{a - 2}\right) = \overset{1}{(a - 2)}\left(\frac{6}{a - 2}\right)$$ Apply the distributive property.

$$a - 2 + 3a = 6$$ Solve the resulting equation (linear).

$$4a - 2 = 6$$

$$4a = 8$$

$$a = 2$$ 2 is a restricted value.

Check: $1 + \frac{3a}{a - 2} = \frac{6}{a - 2}$

$$1 + \frac{3(2)}{(2) - 2} \stackrel{?}{=} \frac{6}{(2) - 2}$$

$$1 + \frac{6}{0} \stackrel{?}{=} \frac{6}{0}$$

The denominator is 0 when $a = 2$.

Because the value $a = 2$ makes the denominator zero in one (or more) of the rational expressions within the equation, the equation is undefined for $a = 2$. No other potential solutions exist for the equation, therefore, the solution set is { }.

Skill Practice Solve the equation.

3. $\frac{x}{x + 1} - 2 = \frac{-1}{x + 1}$

Examples 1–3 show that the steps to solve a rational equation mirror the process of clearing fractions from Section 2.3. However, there is one significant difference. The solutions of a rational equation must not make the denominator equal to zero for any expression within the equation.

Answer

3. { } (The value -1 does not check.)

The steps to solve a rational equation are summarized as follows.

Solving a Rational Equation

Step 1 Factor the denominators of all rational expressions. Identify the restricted values.

Step 2 Identify the LCD of all expressions in the equation.

Step 3 Multiply both sides of the equation by the LCD.

Step 4 Solve the resulting equation.

Step 5 Check potential solutions in the original equation.

After multiplying by the LCD and then simplifying, the rational equation will be either a linear equation or higher degree equation.

Example 4 Solving a Rational Equation

Solve the equation. $1 - \frac{4}{p} = -\frac{3}{p^2}$

Solution:

$1 - \frac{4}{p} = -\frac{3}{p^2}$ **Step 1:** The denominators are already factored. The restricted value is $p = 0$.

Step 2: The LCD of all expressions is p^2.

$p^2\left(1 - \frac{4}{p}\right) = p^2\left(-\frac{3}{p^2}\right)$ **Step 3:** Multiply by the LCD.

$p^2(1) - \overset{p}{\cancel{p^2}}\left(\frac{4}{\cancel{p}}\right) = \overset{1}{\cancel{p^2}}\left(-\frac{3}{\cancel{p^2}}\right)$ Apply the distributive property.

$p^2 - 4p = -3$ **Step 4:** Solve the resulting quadratic equation.

$p^2 - 4p + 3 = 0$ Set the equation equal to zero and factor.

$(p - 3)(p - 1) = 0$

$p - 3 = 0 \quad \text{or} \quad p - 1 = 0$ Set each factor equal to zero.

$p = 3 \quad \text{or} \quad p = 1$ **Step 5:** Check: $p = 3$ Check: $p = 1$

3 and 1 are not restricted values.

Check: $p = 3$	Check: $p = 1$
$1 - \frac{4}{p} = -\frac{3}{p^2}$	$1 - \frac{4}{p} = -\frac{3}{p^2}$
$1 - \frac{4}{(3)} \stackrel{?}{=} -\frac{3}{(3)^2}$	$1 - \frac{4}{(1)} \stackrel{?}{=} -\frac{3}{(1)^2}$
$\frac{3}{3} - \frac{4}{3} \stackrel{?}{=} -\frac{3}{9}$	$1 - 4 \stackrel{?}{=} -3$
$-\frac{1}{3} \stackrel{?}{=} -\frac{1}{3}$ ✔	$-3 \stackrel{?}{=} -3$ ✔

The solution set is $\{3, 1\}$.

Skill Practice Solve the equation.

4. $\frac{z}{2} - \frac{1}{2z} = \frac{12}{z}$

Answer

4. $\{5, -5\}$

Example 5 Solving a Rational Equation

Solve the equation. $\dfrac{6}{t^2 - 7t + 12} + \dfrac{2t}{t - 3} = \dfrac{3t}{t - 4}$

Solution:

$$\frac{6}{t^2 - 7t + 12} + \frac{2t}{t - 3} = \frac{3t}{t - 4}$$

$$\frac{6}{(t - 3)(t - 4)} + \frac{2t}{t - 3} = \frac{3t}{t - 4}$$

Step 1: Factor the denominators. The restricted values are $t = 3$ and $t = 4$.

Step 2: The LCD is $(t - 3)(t - 4)$.

Step 3: Multiply by the LCD on both sides.

$$(t - 3)(t - 4)\left(\frac{6}{(t - 3)(t - 4)} + \frac{2t}{t - 3}\right) = (t - 3)(t - 4)\left(\frac{3t}{t - 4}\right)$$

$$(t - 3)(t - 4)\left(\frac{6}{(t - 3)(t - 4)}\right) + (t - 3)(t - 4)\left(\frac{2t}{t - 3}\right) = (t - 3)(t - 4)\left(\frac{3t}{t - 4}\right)$$

$$6 + 2t(t - 4) = 3t(t - 3)$$

$$6 + 2t^2 - 8t = 3t^2 - 9t$$

Step 4: Solve the resulting equation.

$$0 = 3t^2 - 2t^2 - 9t + 8t - 6$$

Because the resulting equation is quadratic, set the equation equal to zero and factor.

$$0 = t^2 - t - 6$$

$$0 = (t - 3)(t + 2)$$

$$t - 3 = 0 \quad \text{or} \quad t + 2 = 0$$

Set each factor equal to zero.

$$t = 3 \quad \text{or} \quad t = -2$$

3 is a restricted value, but -2 is not restricted.

Step 5: Check the potential solutions in the original equation.

Check: $t = 3$

3 cannot be a solution to the equation because it will make the denominator zero in the original equation.

$$\frac{6}{t^2 - 7t + 12} + \frac{2t}{t - 3} = \frac{3t}{t - 4}$$

$$\frac{6}{(3)^2 - 7(3) + 12} + \frac{2(3)}{(3) - 3} \stackrel{?}{=} \frac{3(3)}{(3) - 4}$$

$$\frac{6}{0} + \frac{6}{0} \stackrel{?}{=} \frac{9}{-1}$$

Zero in the denominator

Check: $t = -2$

$$\frac{6}{t^2 - 7t + 12} + \frac{2t}{t - 3} = \frac{3t}{t - 4}$$

$$\frac{6}{(-2)^2 - 7(-2) + 12} + \frac{2(-2)}{(-2) - 3} \stackrel{?}{=} \frac{3(-2)}{(-2) - 4}$$

$$\frac{6}{4 + 14 + 12} + \frac{-4}{-5} \stackrel{?}{=} \frac{-6}{-6}$$

$$\frac{6}{30} + \frac{4}{5} \stackrel{?}{=} 1$$

$$\frac{1}{5} + \frac{4}{5} \stackrel{?}{=} 1 \checkmark \text{ (True)}$$

$t = -2$ is a solution.

The solution set is $\{-2\}$.

Skill Practice Solve the equation.

5. $\dfrac{-8}{x^2 + 6x + 8} + \dfrac{x}{x + 4} = \dfrac{2}{x + 2}$

Answer

5. $\{4\}$ (The value -4 does not check.)

Example 6 Translating to a Rational Equation

Ten times the reciprocal of a number is added to four. The result is equal to the quotient of twenty-two and the number. Find the number.

Solution:

Let x represent the number.

10 times → 10; the reciprocal of a number → $\left(\frac{1}{x}\right)$; the quotient of 22 and the number → $\frac{22}{x}$

$$4 + 10\left(\frac{1}{x}\right) = \frac{22}{x}$$

is added to four → $+$; the result is equal to → $=$

$$4 + \frac{10}{x} = \frac{22}{x}$$

Step 1: The denominators are already factored. The restricted value is $x = 0$.

Step 2: The LCD is x.

$$x\left(4 + \frac{10}{x}\right) = x\left(\frac{22}{x}\right)$$

Step 3: Multiply both sides by the LCD.

$$4x + 10 = 22$$

Apply the distributive property.

$$4x = 12$$

Step 4: Solve the resulting linear equation.

$x = 3$ is a potential solution.

Step 5: 3 is not a restricted value. Substituting $x = 3$ into the original equation verifies that it is a solution.

The number is 3.

Skill Practice

6. The quotient of ten and a number is two less than four times the reciprocal of the number. Find the number.

3. Solving Formulas Involving Rational Expressions

A rational equation may have more than one variable. To solve for a specific variable within a rational equation, we can still apply the principle of clearing fractions.

Answer

6. The number is -3.

Example 7 Solving Formulas Involving Rational Equations

Solve for k. $F = \dfrac{ma}{k}$

Solution:

To solve for k, we must clear fractions so that k no longer appears in the denominator.

$$F = \frac{ma}{k}$$ The LCD is k.

$$k \cdot (F) = k \cdot \left(\frac{ma}{k}\right)$$ Multiply both sides of the equation by the LCD.

$$kF = ma$$ Clear fractions.

$$\frac{kF}{F} = \frac{ma}{F}$$ Divide both sides by F.

$$k = \frac{ma}{F}$$

Skill Practice

7. Solve for t. $C = \dfrac{rt}{d}$

Example 8 Solving Formulas Involving Rational Equations

A formula to find the height of a trapezoid given its area and the lengths of the two parallel sides is $h = \dfrac{2A}{B + b}$. Solve for b, the length of one of the parallel sides.

Solution:

To solve for b, we must clear fractions so that b no longer appears in the denominator.

$$h = \frac{2A}{B + b}$$ The LCD is $(B + b)$.

$$h(B + b) = \left(\frac{2A}{B + b}\right) \cdot (B + b)$$ Multiply both sides of the equation by the LCD.

$$hB + hb = 2A$$ Apply the distributive property.

$$hb = 2A - hB$$ Subtract hB from both sides to isolate the b term.

$$\frac{hb}{h} = \frac{2A - hB}{h}$$ Divide by h.

$$b = \frac{2A - hB}{h}$$

Avoiding Mistakes

Algebra is case-sensitive. The variables B and b represent different values.

Skill Practice

8. Solve the formula for x. $y = \dfrac{3}{x - 2}$

Answers

7. $t = \dfrac{Cd}{r}$

8. $x = \dfrac{3 + 2y}{y}$ or $x = \dfrac{3}{y} + 2$

TIP: The solution to Example 8 can be written in several forms. The quantity

$$\frac{2A - hB}{h}$$

can be left as a single rational expression or can be split into two fractions and simplified.

$$b = \frac{2A - hB}{h} = \frac{2A}{h} - \frac{hB}{h} = \frac{2A}{h} - B$$

Example 9 Solving Formulas Involving Rational Equations

Solve for z. $\quad y = \dfrac{x - z}{x + z}$

Solution:

To solve for z, we must clear fractions so that z no longer appears in the denominator.

$y = \dfrac{x - z}{x + z}$	LCD is $(x + z)$.
$y(x + z) = \left(\dfrac{x - z}{x + z}\right)(x + z)$	Multiply both sides of the equation by the LCD.
$yx + yz = x - z$	Apply the distributive property.
$yz + z = x - yx$	Collect z terms on one side of the equation and collect terms not containing z on the other side.
$z(y + 1) = x - yx$	Factor out z.
$z = \dfrac{x - yx}{y + 1}$	Divide by $y + 1$ to solve for z.

Skill Practice

9. Solve for h. $\quad \dfrac{b}{x} = \dfrac{a}{h} + 1$

Answer

9. $h = \dfrac{ax}{b - x}$ or $\dfrac{-ax}{x - b}$

Section 7.6 Practice Exercises

Vocabulary and Key Concepts

1. a. The equation $4x + 7 = -18$ is an example of a ____________ equation, whereas $3y^2 - 4y - 7 = 0$ is an example of a ____________ equation.

   b. The equation $\dfrac{6}{x + 2} + \dfrac{1}{4} = \dfrac{2}{3}$ is an example of a ____________ equation.

   c. After solving a rational equation, check each potential solution to determine if it makes the ____________ equal to zero in one or more of the rational expressions. If so, that potential solution is not part of the solution set.

Example 4 Using Similar Triangles in an Application

A tree that is 20 ft from a house is to be cut down. Use the following information and similar triangles to find the height of the tree to determine if it will hit the house.

The shadow cast by a yardstick is 2 ft long. The shadow cast by the tree is 11 ft long.

Solution:

Let x represent the height of the tree. **Step 1:** Read the problem. **Step 2:** Label the variables.

We will assume that the measurements were taken at the same time of day. Therefore, the angle of the Sun is the same on both objects, and we can set up similar triangles (Figure 7-3).

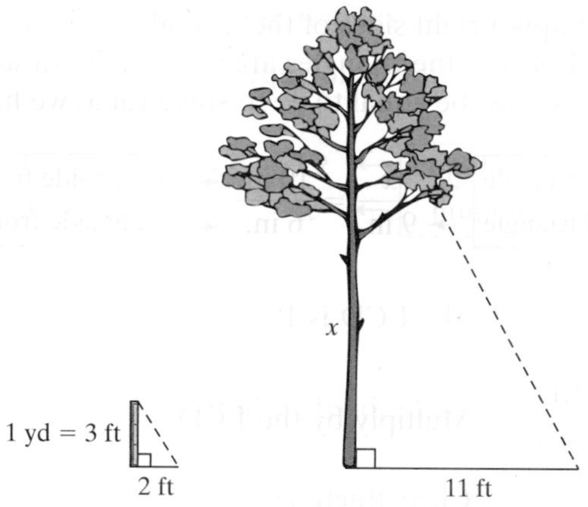

Figure 7-3

Step 3: Create a verbal model.

$$\frac{\text{Height of yardstick}}{\text{height of tree}} \rightarrow \frac{3\text{ ft}}{x} = \frac{2\text{ ft}}{11\text{ ft}} \leftarrow \frac{\text{Length of yardstick's shadow}}{\text{length of tree's shadow}}$$

$$\frac{3}{x} = \frac{2}{11}$$ **Step 4:** Write a mathematical equation.

$$11x\left(\frac{3}{x}\right) = \left(\frac{2}{11}\right)11x$$ **Step 5:** Multiply by the LCD.

$$33 = 2x$$ Solve the equation.

$$\frac{33}{2} = \frac{2x}{2}$$

$$16.5 = x$$ **Step 6:** Interpret the results, and write the answer in words.

The tree is 16.5 ft high. The tree is less than 20 ft high so it will not hit the house.

Skill Practice

4. The Sun casts a 3.2-ft shadow of a 6-ft man. At the same time, the Sun casts a 80-ft shadow of a building. How tall is the building?

Answer

4. The building is 150 ft tall.

3. Distance, Rate, and Time Applications

In Sections 2.7 and 4.4 we presented applications involving the relationship among the variables distance, rate, and time. Recall that $d = rt$.

Example 5 Using a Rational Equation in a Distance, Rate, and Time Application

A small plane flies 440 mi with the wind from Memphis, TN, to Oklahoma City, OK. In the same amount of time, the plane flies 340 miles against the wind from Oklahoma City to Little Rock, AR (see Figure 7-4). If the wind speed is 30 mph, find the speed of the plane in still air.

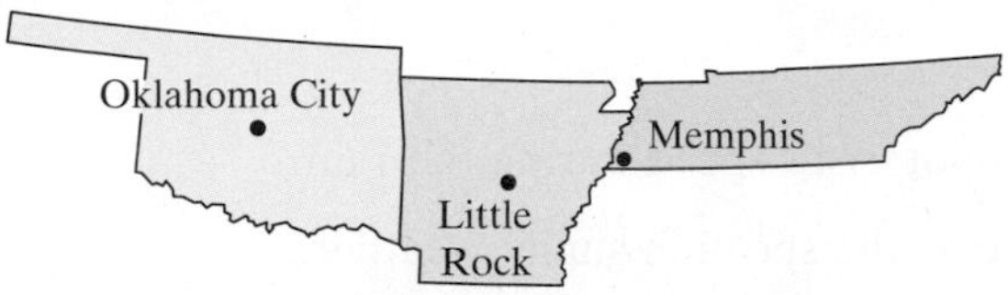

Figure 7-4

Solution:

Let x represent the speed of the plane in still air.

Then $x + 30$ is the speed of the plane with the wind.

$x - 30$ is the speed of the plane against the wind.

Organize the given information in a chart.

	Distance	Rate	Time
With the wind	440	$x + 30$	$\frac{440}{x+30}$
Against the wind	340	$x - 30$	$\frac{340}{x-30}$

Because $d = rt$, then $t = \frac{d}{r}$

The plane travels with the wind for the same amount of time as it travels against the wind, so we can equate the two expressions for time.

$$\begin{pmatrix}\text{Time with}\\ \text{the wind}\end{pmatrix} = \begin{pmatrix}\text{time against}\\ \text{the wind}\end{pmatrix}$$

$$\frac{440}{x+30} = \frac{340}{x-30}$$ The LCD is $(x + 30)(x - 30)$.

$$\cancel{(x+30)}(x-30) \cdot \frac{440}{\cancel{x+30}} = (x+30)\cancel{(x-30)} \cdot \frac{340}{\cancel{x-30}}$$

$$440(x - 30) = 340(x + 30)$$

$$440x - 13{,}200 = 340x + 10{,}200$$ Solve the resulting linear equation.

$$100x = 23{,}400$$

$$x = 234$$

The plane's speed in still air is 234 mph.

TIP: The equation

$$\frac{440}{x+30} = \frac{340}{x-30}$$

is a proportion. The fractions can also be cleared by equating the cross products.

$$\frac{440}{x+30} \times \frac{340}{x-30}$$

$$440(x - 30) = 340(x + 30)$$

Skill Practice

5. Alison paddles her kayak in a river where the current of the water is 2 mph. She can paddle 20 mi with the current in the same time that she can paddle 10 mi against the current. Find the speed of the kayak in still water.

Example 6 Using a Rational Equation in a Distance, Rate, and Time Application

A motorist drives 100 mi between two cities in a bad rainstorm. For the return trip in sunny weather, she averages 10 mph faster and takes $\frac{1}{2}$ hr less time. Find the average speed of the motorist in the rainstorm and in sunny weather.

Solution:

Let x represent the motorist's speed during the rain.

Then $x + 10$ represents the speed in sunny weather.

	Distance	Rate	Time
Trip during rainstorm	100	x	$\frac{100}{x}$
Trip during sunny weather	100	$x + 10$	$\frac{100}{x + 10}$

Because $d = rt$, then $t = \frac{d}{r}$

Because the same distance is traveled in $\frac{1}{2}$ hr less time, the difference between the time of the trip during the rainstorm and the time during sunny weather is $\frac{1}{2}$ hr.

Avoiding Mistakes

The equation

$$\frac{100}{x} - \frac{100}{x + 10} = \frac{1}{2}$$

is not a proportion because the left-hand side has more than one fraction. Do not try to multiply the cross products. Instead, multiply by the LCD to clear fractions.

$$\begin{pmatrix}\text{Time during}\\ \text{the rainstorm}\end{pmatrix} - \begin{pmatrix}\text{time during}\\ \text{sunny weather}\end{pmatrix} = \left(\frac{1}{2}\text{ hr}\right)$$ Verbal model

$$\frac{100}{x} - \frac{100}{x + 10} = \frac{1}{2}$$ Mathematical equation

$$2x(x + 10)\left(\frac{100}{x} - \frac{100}{x + 10}\right) = 2x(x + 10)\left(\frac{1}{2}\right)$$ Multiply by the LCD.

$$2x(x + 10)\left(\frac{100}{x}\right) - 2x(x + 10)\left(\frac{100}{x + 10}\right) = 2x(x + 10)\left(\frac{1}{2}\right)$$ Apply the distributive property.

$$200(x + 10) - 200x = x(x + 10)$$ Clear fractions.

$$200x + 2000 - 200x = x^2 + 10x$$ Solve the resulting equation (quadratic).

$$2000 = x^2 + 10x$$

$$0 = x^2 + 10x - 2000$$ Set the equation equal to zero.

$$0 = (x - 40)(x + 50)$$ Factor.

$$x = 40 \quad \text{or} \quad x \neq -50$$

Answer

5. The speed of the kayak is 6 mph.

Because a rate of speed cannot be negative, reject $x = -50$. Therefore, the speed of the motorist in the rainstorm is 40 mph. Because $x + 10 = 40 + 10 = 50$, the average speed for the return trip in sunny weather is 50 mph.

Skill Practice

6. Harley rode his mountain bike 12 mi to the top of the mountain and the same distance back down. His speed going up was 8 mph slower than coming down. The ride up took 2 hr longer than the ride coming down. Find his speeds.

4. Work Applications

Example 7 demonstrates how work rates are related to a portion of a job that can be completed in one unit of time.

Example 7 Using a Rational Equation in a Work Problem

A new printing press can print the morning edition in 2 hr, whereas the old printer required 4 hr. How long would it take to print the morning edition if both printers were working together?

Solution:

One method to solve this problem is to add rates.

Let x represent the time required for both printers working together to complete the job.

$$\begin{pmatrix}\text{Rate}\\ \text{of old printer}\end{pmatrix} + \begin{pmatrix}\text{rate}\\ \text{of new printer}\end{pmatrix} = \begin{pmatrix}\text{rate of}\\ \text{both working together}\end{pmatrix}$$

$$\frac{1\text{ job}}{4\text{ hr}} + \frac{1\text{ job}}{2\text{ hr}} = \frac{1\text{ job}}{x\text{ hr}}$$

$$\frac{1}{4} + \frac{1}{2} = \frac{1}{x}$$

$$4x\left(\frac{1}{4} + \frac{1}{2}\right) = 4x\left(\frac{1}{x}\right)$$ The LCD is $4x$.

$$\overset{1}{\cancel{4}}x \cdot \frac{1}{\cancel{4}} + \overset{2}{\cancel{4}}x \cdot \frac{1}{\cancel{2}} = \overset{1}{4\cancel{x}} \cdot \frac{1}{\cancel{x}}$$ Apply the distributive property.

$$x + 2x = 4$$ Solve the resulting linear equation.

$$3x = 4$$

$$x = \frac{4}{3}$$ The time required to print the morning edition using both printers is $1\frac{1}{3}$ hr.

Skill Practice

7. The computer at a bank can process and prepare the bank statements in 30 hr. A new faster computer can do the job in 20 hr. If the bank uses both computers together, how long will it take to process the statements?

Answers

6. Uphill speed was 4 mph; downhill speed was 12 mph.
7. 12 hr

An alternative approach to Example 7 is to determine the portion of the job that each printer can complete in 1 hr and extend that rate to the portion of the job completed in x hours.

- The old printer can perform the job in 4 hr. Therefore, it completes $\frac{1}{4}$ of the job in 1 hr and $\frac{1}{4}x$ jobs in x hours.
- The new printer can perform the job in 2 hr. Therefore, it completes $\frac{1}{2}$ of the job in 1 hr and $\frac{1}{2}x$ jobs in x hours.

The sum of the portions of the job completed by each printer must equal one whole job.

$$\begin{pmatrix}\text{Portion of job}\\ \text{completed by}\\ \text{old printer}\end{pmatrix} + \begin{pmatrix}\text{portion of job}\\ \text{completed by}\\ \text{new printer}\end{pmatrix} = \begin{pmatrix}1\\ \text{whole}\\ \text{job}\end{pmatrix}$$

$$\frac{1}{4}x + \frac{1}{2}x = 1 \qquad \text{The LCD is 4.}$$

$$4\left(\frac{1}{4}x + \frac{1}{2}x\right) = 4(1) \qquad \text{Multiply by the LCD.}$$

$$x + 2x = 4 \qquad \text{Solve the resulting linear equation.}$$

$$3x = 4$$

$$x = \frac{4}{3} \qquad \text{The time required using both printers is } 1\tfrac{1}{3}\text{ hr.}$$

Section 7.7 Practice Exercises

Vocabulary and Key Concepts

1. a. An equation that equates two ratios is called a ____________.

b. Given similar triangles, the lengths of corresponding sides are ____________.

Review Exercises

For Exercises 2–7, determine whether each of the following is an equation or an expression. If it is an equation, solve it. If it is an expression, perform the indicated operation.

2. $\frac{b}{5} + 3 = 9$

3. $\frac{m}{m-1} - \frac{2}{m+3}$

4. $\frac{2}{a+5} + \frac{5}{a^2-25}$

5. $\frac{3y+6}{20} \div \frac{4y+8}{8}$

6. $\frac{z^2+z}{24} \cdot \frac{8}{z+1}$

7. $\frac{3}{p+3} = \frac{12p+19}{p^2+7p+12} - \frac{5}{p+4}$

8. Determine whether 1 is a solution to the equation. $\frac{1}{x-1} + \frac{1}{2} = \frac{2}{x^2-1}$

Concept 1: Solving Proportions

For Exercises 9–22, solve the proportions. **(See Example 1.)**

9. $\dfrac{8}{5} = \dfrac{152}{p}$

10. $\dfrac{6}{7} = \dfrac{96}{y}$

11. $\dfrac{19}{76} = \dfrac{z}{4}$

12. $\dfrac{15}{135} = \dfrac{w}{9}$

13. $\dfrac{5}{3} = \dfrac{a}{8}$

14. $\dfrac{b}{14} = \dfrac{3}{8}$

15. $\dfrac{2}{1.9} = \dfrac{x}{38}$

16. $\dfrac{16}{1.3} = \dfrac{30}{p}$

17. $\dfrac{y+1}{2y} = \dfrac{2}{3}$

18. $\dfrac{w-2}{4w} = \dfrac{1}{6}$

19. $\dfrac{9}{2z-1} = \dfrac{3}{z}$

20. $\dfrac{1}{t} = \dfrac{1}{4-t}$

21. $\dfrac{8}{9a-1} = \dfrac{5}{3a+2}$

22. $\dfrac{4p+1}{3} = \dfrac{2p-5}{6}$

23. Charles' law describes the relationship between the initial and final temperature and volume of a gas held at a constant pressure.

$$\frac{V_i}{V_f} = \frac{T_i}{T_f}$$

a. Solve the equation for V_f.

b. Solve the equation for T_f.

24. The relationship between the area, height, and base of a triangle is given by the proportion

$$\frac{A}{b} = \frac{h}{2}$$

a. Solve the equation for A.

b. Solve the equation for b.

Concept 2: Applications of Proportions and Similar Triangles

For Exercises 25–32, solve using proportions.

25. Toni drives her Honda Civic 132 mi on the highway on 4 gal of gas. At this rate how many miles can she drive on 9 gal of gas? **(See Example 2.)**

26. Tim takes his pulse for 10 sec and counts 12 beats. How many beats per minute is this?

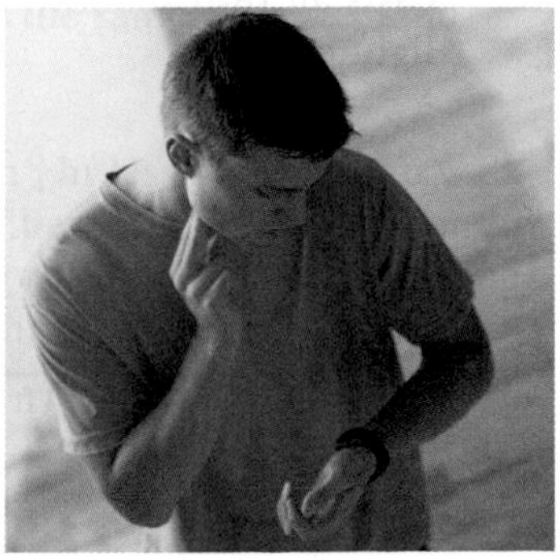

27. It is recommended that 7.8 mL of Grow-It-Right plant food be mixed with 2 L of water for feeding house plants. How much plant food should be mixed with 1 gal of water to maintain the same concentration? (1 gal ≈ 3.8 L.) Express the answer in milliliters.

28. According to the website for the state of Virginia, 0.8 million tons of clothing is reused or recycled out of 7 million tons of clothing discarded. If 17.5 million tons of clothing is discarded, how many tons will be reused or recycled?

29. Andrew is on a low-carbohydrate diet. If his diet book tells him that an 8-oz serving of pineapple contains 19.2 g of carbohydrate, how many grams of carbohydrate does a 5-oz serving contain?

30. Cooking oatmeal requires 1 cup of water for every $\frac{1}{2}$ cup of oats. How many cups of water will be required for $\frac{3}{4}$ cup of oats?

31. According to a building code, a wheelchair ramp must be at least 12 ft long for each foot of height. If the height of a newly constructed ramp is to be $1\frac{2}{3}$ ft, find the minimum acceptable length.

32. A map has a scale of 50 mi/in. If two cities measure 6.5 in. apart, how many miles does this represent?

Method II

1. Multiply the numerator and denominator of the complex fraction by the LCD of all individual fractions within the expression.
2. Apply the distributive property, and simplify the result.
3. Simplify to lowest terms, if possible.

Example 2

Simplify. $\dfrac{1 - \dfrac{4}{w^2}}{1 - \dfrac{1}{w} - \dfrac{6}{w^2}} = \dfrac{w^2\left(1 - \dfrac{4}{w^2}\right)}{w^2\left(1 - \dfrac{1}{w} - \dfrac{6}{w^2}\right)}$

$$= \frac{w^2 - 4}{w^2 - w - 6} = \frac{(w-2)\overset{1}{\cancel{(w+2)}}}{(w-3)\cancel{(w+2)}}$$

$$= \frac{w-2}{w-3}$$

Section 7.6 Rational Equations

Key Concepts

An equation with one or more rational expressions is called a **rational equation**.

Steps to Solve a Rational Equation

1. Factor the denominators of all rational expressions. Identify the restricted values.
2. Identify the LCD of all expressions in the equation.
3. Multiply both sides of the equation by the LCD.
4. Solve the resulting equation.
5. Check each potential solution in the original equation.

Examples

Example 1

Solve. $\dfrac{1}{w} - \dfrac{1}{2w-1} = \dfrac{-2w}{2w-1}$ The restricted values are $w = 0$ and $w = \frac{1}{2}$.

The LCD is $w(2w - 1)$.

$$\cancel{w}(2w-1)\frac{1}{\cancel{w}} - w\cancel{(2w-1)}\frac{1}{\cancel{2w-1}} = w\cancel{(2w-1)}\frac{-2w}{\cancel{2w-1}}$$

$$(2w-1)(1) - w(1) = w(-2w)$$

$$2w - 1 - w = -2w^2 \quad \text{Quadratic equation}$$

$$2w^2 + w - 1 = 0$$

$$(2w-1)(w+1) = 0$$

$w \cancel{=} \frac{1}{2}$ (Does not check.) or $w = -1$ (Checks.)

The solution set is $\{-1\}$.

Example 2

Solve for I. $q = \dfrac{VQ}{I}$

$$I \cdot q = \frac{VQ}{\cancel{I}} \cdot \cancel{I}$$

$$Iq = VQ$$

$$I = \frac{VQ}{q}$$

Section 7.7 Applications of Rational Equations and Proportions

Key Concepts and Examples

Solving Proportions

An equation that equates two rates or ratios is called a **proportion**:

$$\frac{a}{b} = \frac{c}{d} \quad (b \neq 0, d \neq 0)$$

To solve a proportion, multiply both sides of the equation by the LCD.

Examples

Example 1

A 90-g serving of a particular ice cream contains 10 g of fat. How much fat does 400 g of the same ice cream contain?

$$\frac{10 \text{ g fat}}{90 \text{ g ice cream}} = \frac{x \text{ grams fat}}{400 \text{ g ice cream}}$$

$$\frac{10}{90} = \frac{x}{400}$$

$$\overset{40}{\cancel{3600}} \cdot \left(\frac{10}{\cancel{90}}\right) = \left(\frac{x}{\cancel{400}}\right) \cdot \overset{9}{\cancel{3600}}$$

$$400 = 9x$$

$$x = \frac{400}{9} \approx 44.4 \text{ g}$$

Examples 2 and 3 give applications of rational equations.

Example 2

Two cars travel from Los Angeles to Las Vegas. One car travels an average of 8 mph faster than the other car. If the faster car travels 189 mi in the same time as the slower car travels 165 mi, what is the average speed of each car?

Let r represent the speed of the slower car.
Let $r + 8$ represent the speed of the faster car.

	Distance	Rate	Time
Slower car	165	r	$\frac{165}{r}$
Faster car	189	$r + 8$	$\frac{189}{r+8}$

$$\frac{165}{r} = \frac{189}{r + 8}$$

$$165(r + 8) = 189r$$

$$165r + 1320 = 189r$$

$$1320 = 24r$$

$$55 = r$$

The slower car travels 55 mph, and the faster car travels $55 + 8 = 63$ mph.

Example 3

Beth and Cecelia have a house cleaning business. Beth can clean a particular house in 5 hr by herself. Cecelia can clean the same house in 4 hr. How long would it take if they cleaned the house together?

Let x be the number of hours it takes for both Beth and Cecelia to clean the house.

Beth's rate is $\frac{1 \text{ job}}{5 \text{ hr}}$. Cecelia's rate is $\frac{1 \text{ job}}{4 \text{ hr}}$.

The rate together is $\frac{1 \text{ job}}{x \text{ hr}}$.

$$\frac{1}{5} + \frac{1}{4} = \frac{1}{x} \qquad \text{Add the rates.}$$

$$20x\left(\frac{1}{5} + \frac{1}{4}\right) = 20x\left(\frac{1}{x}\right)$$

$$4x + 5x = 20$$

$$9x = 20$$

$$x = \frac{20}{9}$$

It takes $\frac{20}{9}$ hr or $2\frac{2}{9}$ hr working together.

3. Applications Involving Relations

Example 5 Analyzing a Relation

The data in Table 8-3 depict the length of a woman's femur and her corresponding height. Based on these data, a forensics specialist can find a linear relationship between height y (in inches) and femur length x (in centimeters):

$$y = 0.91x + 24 \qquad 40 \le x \le 55$$

From this type of relationship, the height of a woman can be inferred based on skeletal remains.

a. Find the height of a woman whose femur is 46.0 cm.

b. Find the height of a woman whose femur is 51.0 cm.

c. Why is the domain restricted to $40 \le x \le 55$?

Table 8-3

Length of Femur (cm) x	Height (in.) y
45.5	65.5
48.2	68.0
41.8	62.2
46.0	66.0
50.4	70.0

Solution:

a. $y = 0.91x + 24$

$= 0.91(46.0) + 24$ Substitute $x = 46.0$ cm.

$= 65.86$ The woman is approximately 65.9 in. tall.

b. $y = 0.91x + 24$

$= 0.91(51.0) + 24$ Substitute $x = 51.0$ cm.

$= 70.41$ The woman is approximately 70.4 in. tall.

c. The domain restricts femur length to values between 40 cm and 55 cm inclusive. These values are within the normal lengths for an adult female and are in the proximity of the observed data (Figure 8-4).

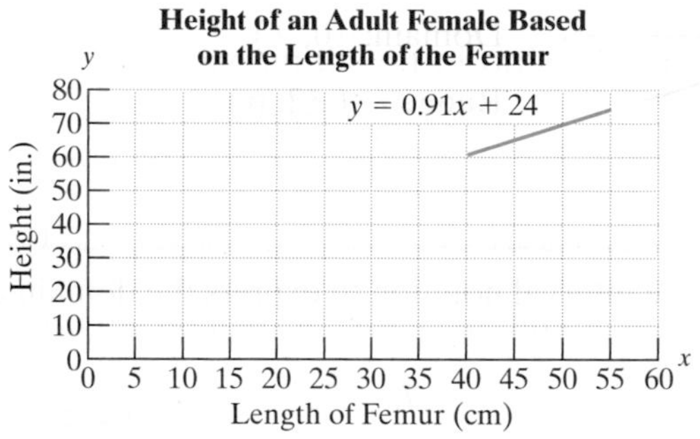

Figure 8-4

Skill Practice The linear equation, $y = -0.014x + 64.5$, for $1500 \le x \le 4000$, relates the weight of a car, x (in pounds), to its gas mileage, y (in mpg).

8. Find the gas mileage in miles per gallon for a car weighing 2550 lb.

9. Find the gas mileage for a car weighing 2850 lb.

10. Why is the domain restricted to $1500 \le x \le 4000$?

Answers

8. 28.8 mpg **9.** 24.6 mpg

10. The relation is valid only for cars weighing between 1500 lb and 4000 lb, inclusive.

Section 8.1 Practice Exercises

Vocabulary and Key Concepts

1. **a.** A set of ordered pairs (x, y) is called a ____________ in x and y.

   b. The ____________ of a relation is the set of first components in the ordered pairs.

   c. The ____________ of a relation is the set of second components in the ordered pairs.

Concept 2: Domain and Range of a Relation

2. Explain how to determine the domain and range of a relation represented by a set of ordered pairs.

For Exercises 3–14,

a. Write the relation as a set of ordered pairs.

b. Determine the domain and range. **(See Examples 1–3.)**

3.

Region	Number living in poverty (thousands)
Northeast	54.1
Midwest	65.6
South	110.7
West	70.7

4.

x	y
0	3
-2	$\frac{1}{2}$
-7	1
-2	8
5	1

5.

Country	Year of First Man or Woman in Space
USSR	1961
USA	1962
Poland	1978
Vietnam	1980
Cuba	1980

6.

State, x	Year of Statehood, y
Maine	1820
Nebraska	1823
Utah	1847
Hawaii	1959
Alaska	1959

7.

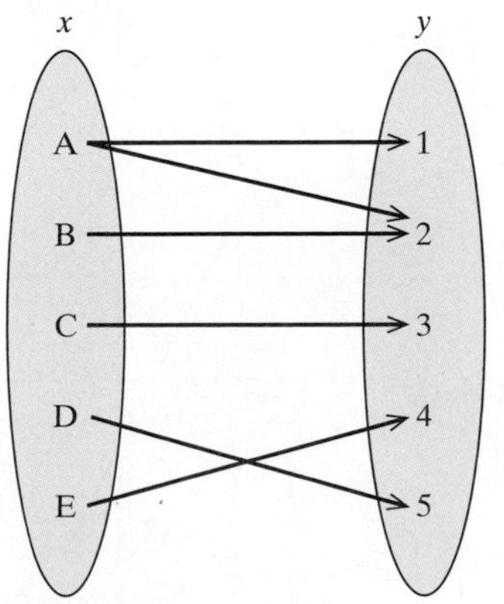

8.

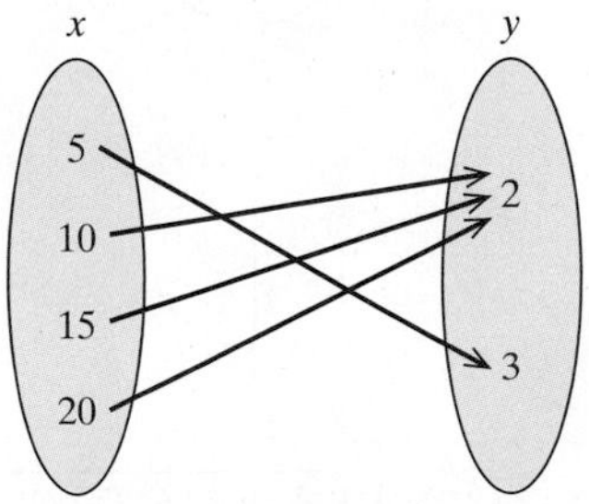

9.

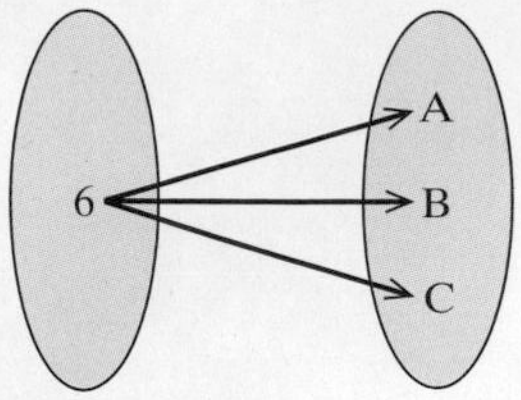

10.

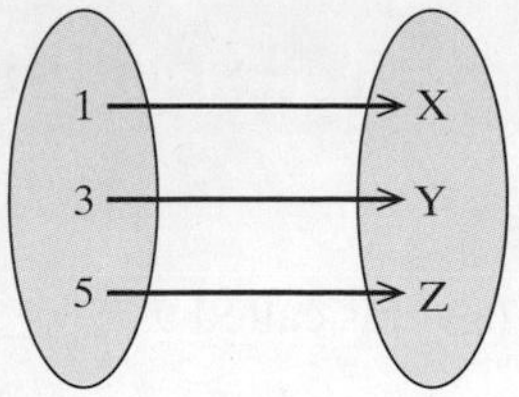

11.

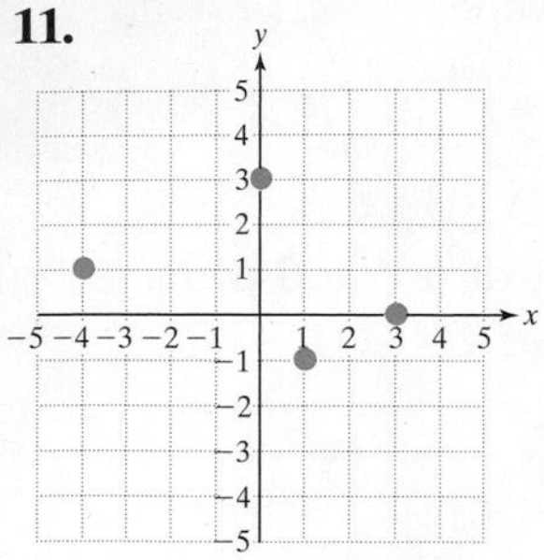

12.

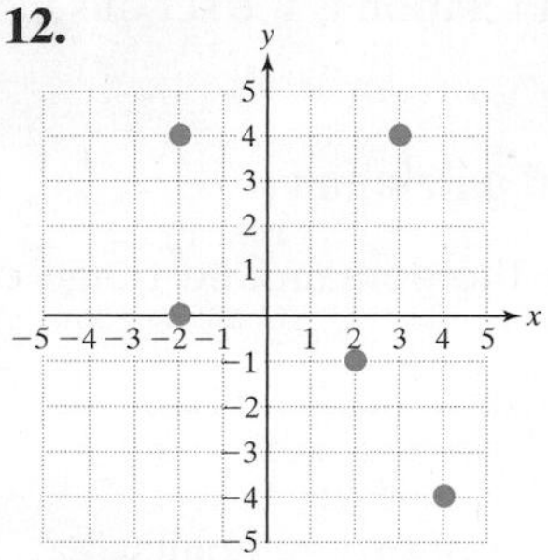

13.

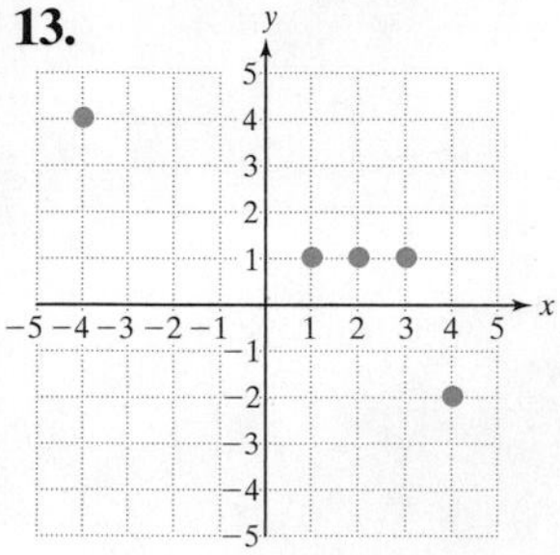

14.

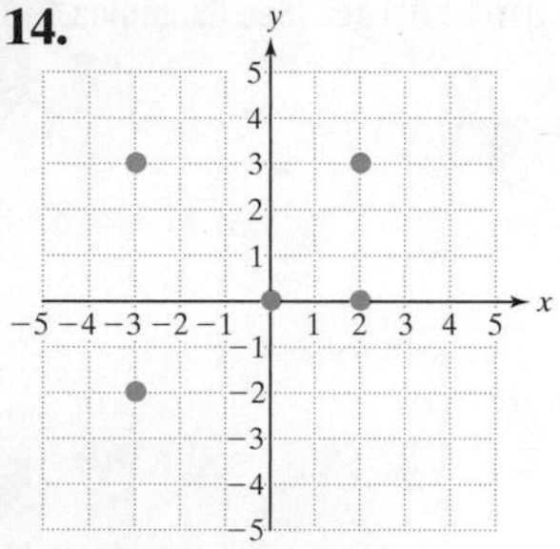

For Exercises 15–30, find the domain and range of the relations. Use interval notation where appropriate. **(See Example 4.)**

15.

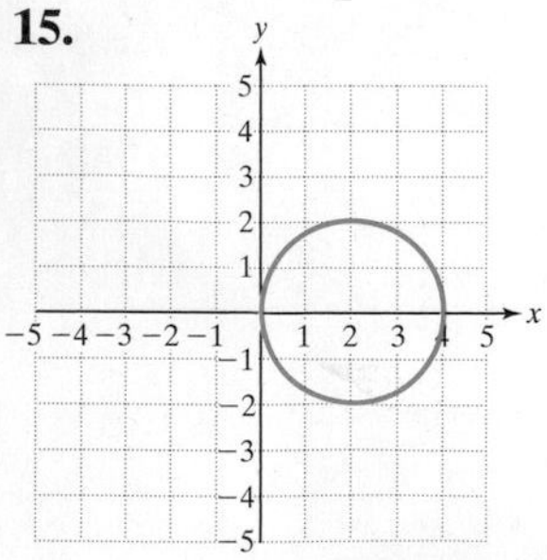

16.

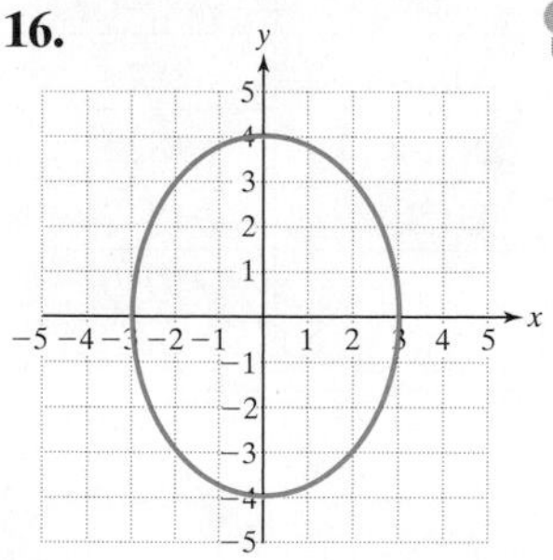

17.

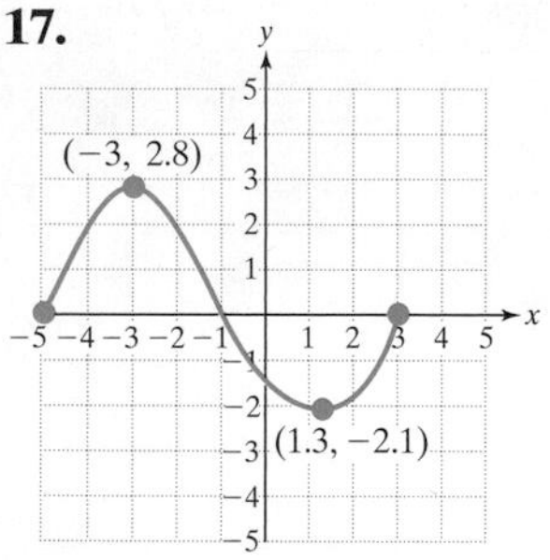

18.

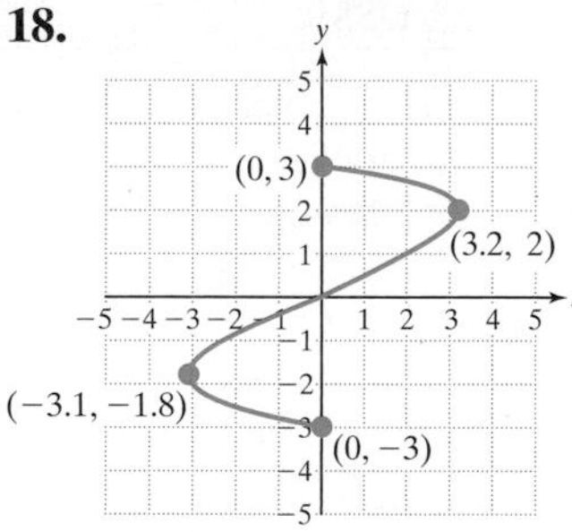

19.

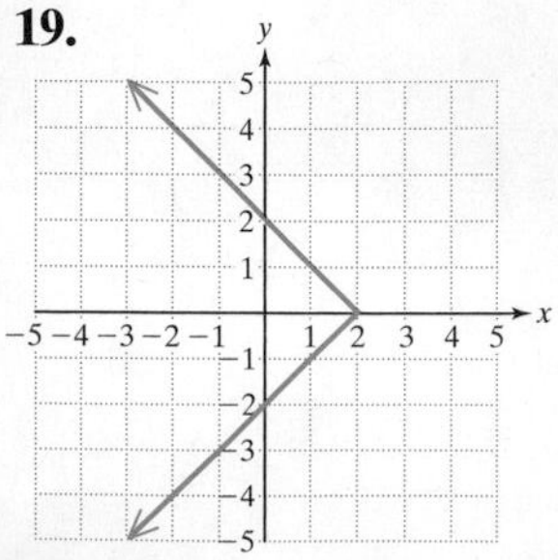

20.

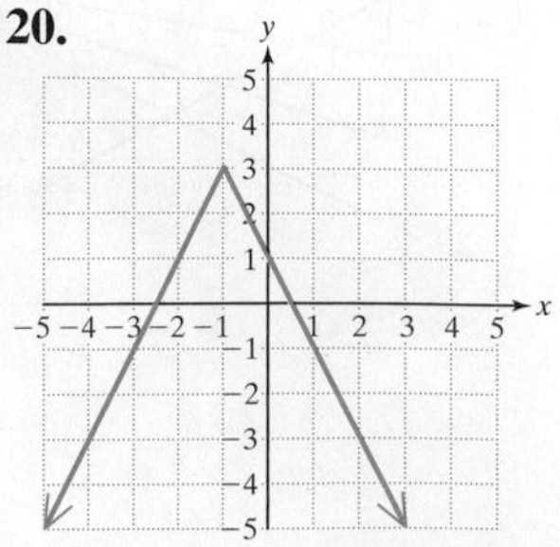

21.

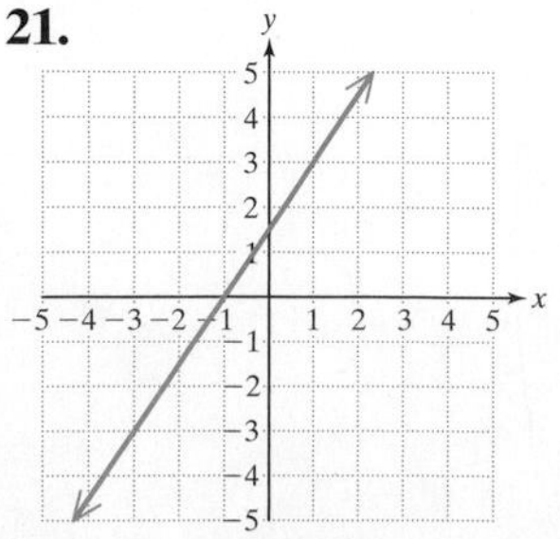

22.

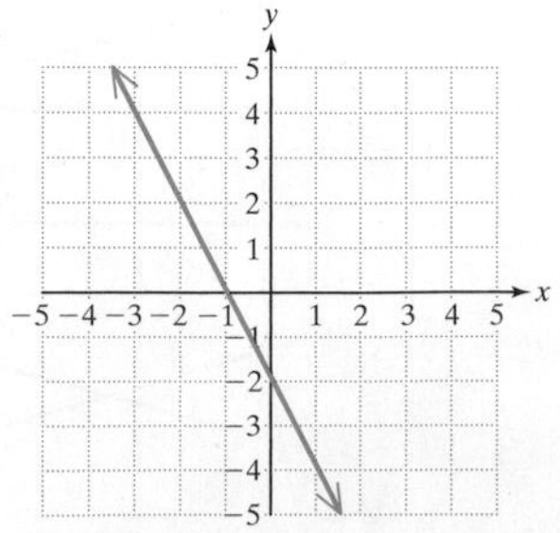

23.
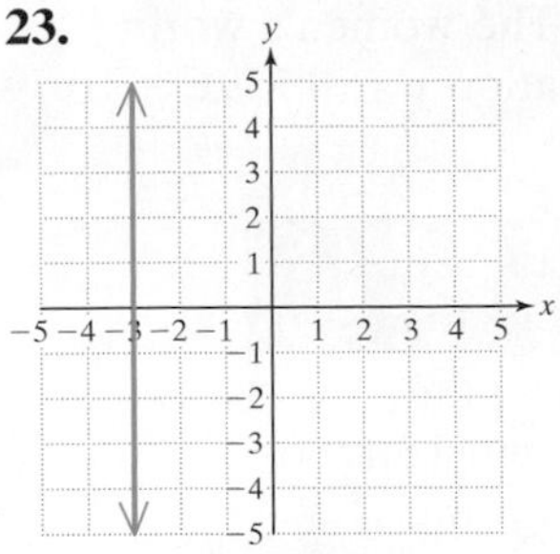

24.
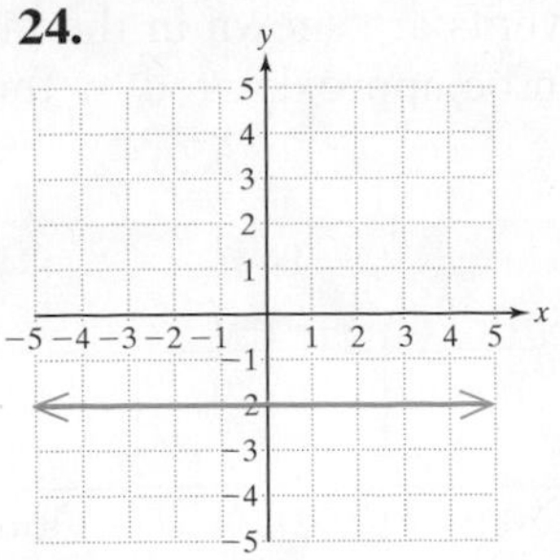

25.
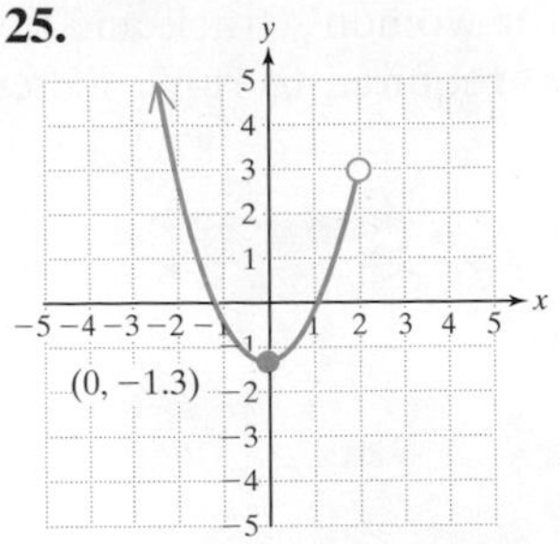

26.
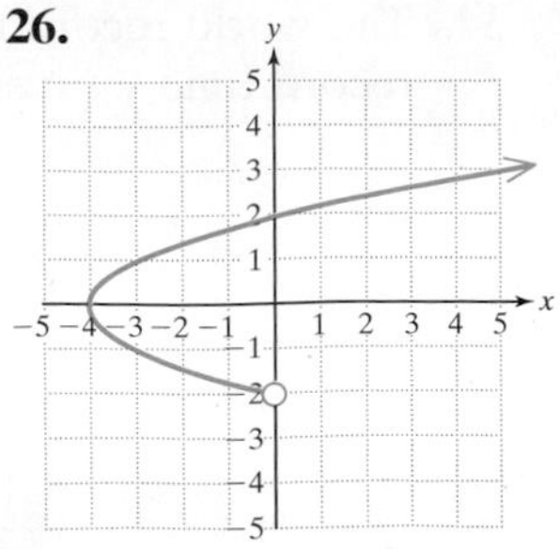

27.
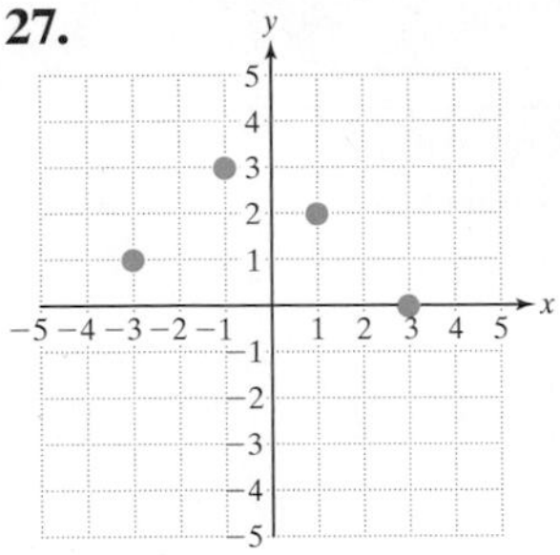

28.
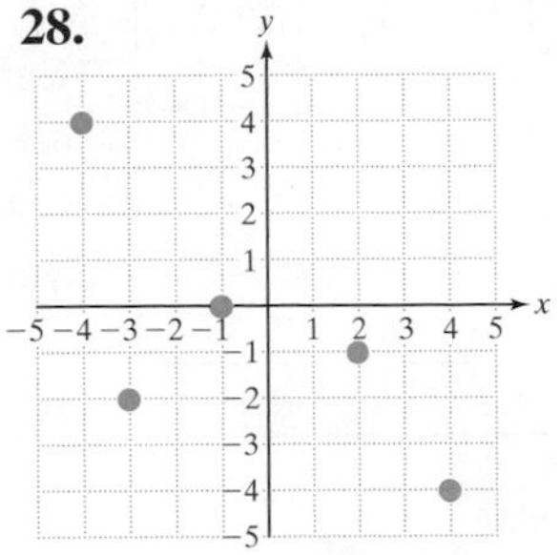

29.
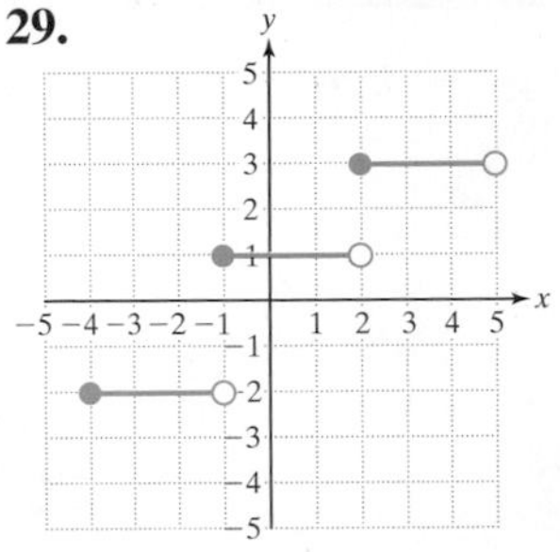

30.
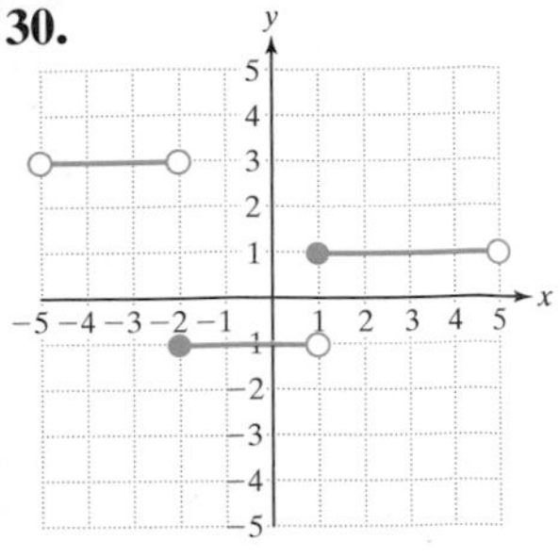

Concept 3: Applications Involving Relations

31. The table gives a relation between the month of the year and the average precipitation for that month for Miami, Florida. **(See Example 5.)**

Month x	Precipitation (in.) y	Month x	Precipitation (in.) y
Jan.	2.01	July	5.70
Feb.	2.08	Aug.	7.58
Mar.	2.39	Sept.	7.63
Apr.	2.85	Oct.	5.64
May	6.21	Nov.	2.66
June	9.33	Dec.	1.83

Source: U.S. National Oceanic and Atmospheric Administration

a. What is the range element corresponding to April?

b. What is the range element corresponding to June?

c. Which element in the domain corresponds to the least value in the range?

d. Complete the ordered pair: (, 2.66)

e. Complete the ordered pair: (Sept.,)

f. What is the domain of this relation?

32. The table gives a relation between a person's age and the person's maximum recommended heart rate.

Age (years) x	Maximum Recommended Heart Rate (Beats per Minute) y
20	200
30	190
40	180
50	170
60	160

a. What is the domain?

b. What is the range?

c. The range element 200 corresponds to what element in the domain?

d. Complete the ordered pair: (50,)

e. Complete the ordered pair: (, 190)

33. The population of Canada, y (in millions), can be approximated by the relation $y = 0.276x + 31$, where x represents the number of years since 2000.

a. Approximate the population of Canada in the year 2009.

b. In what year will the population of Canada reach approximately 35,140,000?

34. The world record times for women's track and field events are shown in the table. The women's world record time y (in seconds) required to run x meters can be approximated by the relation $y = 0.159x - 10.79$.

Distance (m)	Time (sec)	Winner's Name and Country
100	10.49	Florence Griffith Joyner (United States)
200	21.34	Florence Griffith Joyner (United States)
400	47.60	Marita Koch (East Germany)
800	113.28	Jarmila Kratochvilova (Czechoslovakia)
1000	148.98	Svetlana Masterkova (Russia)
1500	230.46	Qu Yunxia (China)

a. Predict the time required for a 500-m race.

b. Use this model to predict the time for a 1000-m race. Is this value exactly the same as the data value given in the table? Explain.

Expanding Your Skills

35. a. Define a relation with four ordered pairs such that the first element of the ordered pair is the name of a friend and the second element is your friend's place of birth.

b. State the domain and range of this relation.

36. a. Define a relation with four ordered pairs such that the first element is a state and the second element is its capital.

b. State the domain and range of this relation.

37. Use a mathematical equation to define a relation whose second component y is 1 less than 2 times the first component x.

38. Use a mathematical equation to define a relation whose second component y is 3 more than the first component x.

39. Use a mathematical equation to define a relation whose second component is the square of the first component.

40. Use a mathematical equation to define a relation whose second component is one-fourth the first component.

Introduction to Functions

Section 8.2

Concepts

1. **Definition of a Function**
2. **Vertical Line Test**
3. **Function Notation**
4. **Finding Function Values from a Graph**
5. **Domain of a Function**

1. Definition of a Function

In this section, we introduce a special type of relation called a function.

Definition of a Function

Given a relation in x and y, we say "y is a **function** of x" if, for each element x in the domain, there is exactly one value of y in the range.

Note: This means that no two ordered pairs may have the same first coordinate and different second coordinates.

To understand the difference between a relation that is a function and a relation that is not a function, consider Example 1.

Example 1 **Determining Whether a Relation Is a Function**

Determine which of the relations define y as a function of x.

a. **b.** **c.**

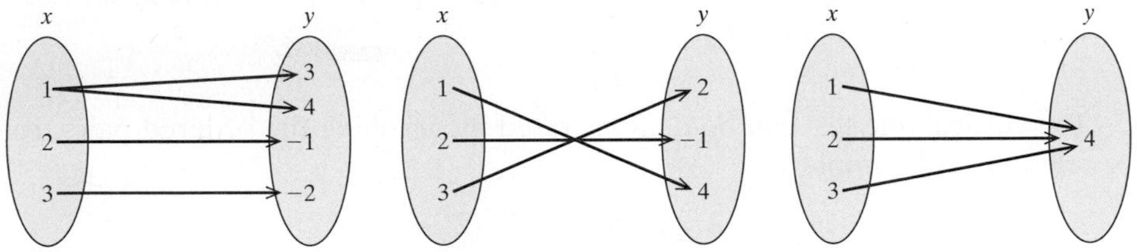

Solution:

a. This relation is defined by the set of ordered pairs

same x

$$\{(1, 3), (1, 4), (2, -1), (3, -2)\}$$

different y-values

When $x = 1$, there are *two* possible range elements: $y = 3$ and $y = 4$. Therefore, this relation is *not* a function.

b. This relation is defined by the set of ordered pairs $\{(1, 4), (2, -1), (3, 2)\}$.

Notice that no two ordered pairs have the same value of x but different values of y. Therefore, this relation *is* a function.

c. This relation is defined by the set of ordered pairs $\{(1, 4), (2, 4), (3, 4)\}$.

Notice that no two ordered pairs have the same value of x but different values of y. Therefore, this relation *is* a function.

Skill Practice Determine if the relations define y as a function of x.

1.

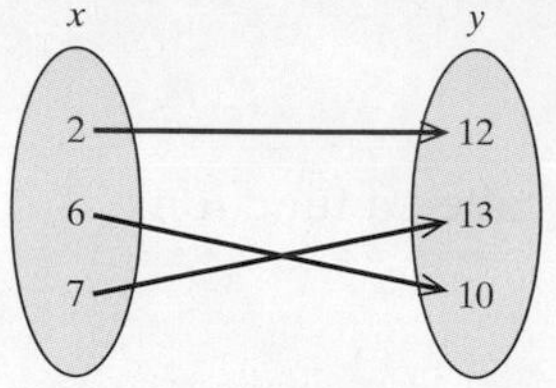

2. $\{(4, 2), (-5, 4), (0, 0), (8, 4)\}$

3. $\{(-1, 6), (8, 9), (-1, 4), (-3, 10)\}$

2. Vertical Line Test

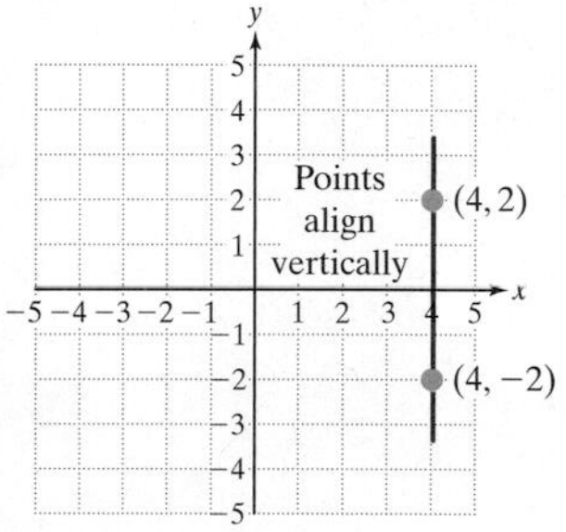

Figure 8-5

A relation that is not a function has at least one domain element x paired with more than one range value y. For example, the set $\{(4, 2), (4, -2)\}$ does not define a function because two different y-values correspond to the same x. These two points are aligned vertically in the xy-plane, and a vertical line drawn through one point also intersects the other point (see Figure 8-5). If a vertical line drawn through a graph of a relation intersects the graph in more than one point, the relation cannot be a function. This idea is stated formally as the **vertical line test**.

The Vertical Line Test

Consider a relation defined by a set of points (x, y) in a rectangular coordinate system. The graph defines y as a function of x if no vertical line intersects the graph in more than one point.

The vertical line test can be demonstrated by graphing the ordered pairs from the relations in Example 1.

a. $\{(1, 3), (1, 4), (2, -1), (3, -2)\}$ **b.** $\{(1, 4), (2, -1), (3, 2)\}$

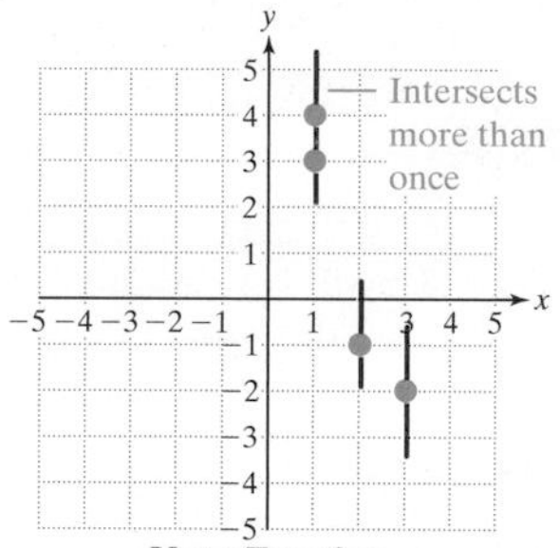

Not a Function
A vertical line intersects in more than one point.

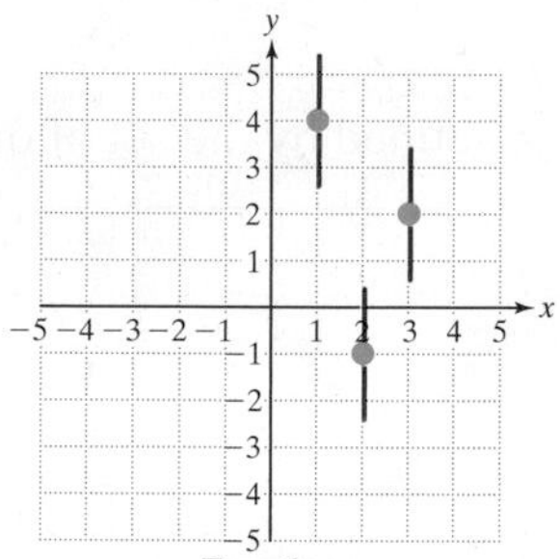

Function
No vertical line intersects more than once.

Example 2 Using the Vertical Line Test

Use the vertical line test to determine whether the relations define y as a function of x.

a.

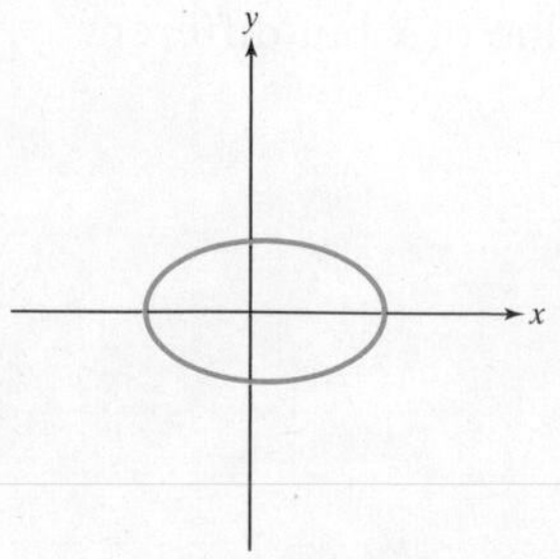

b.

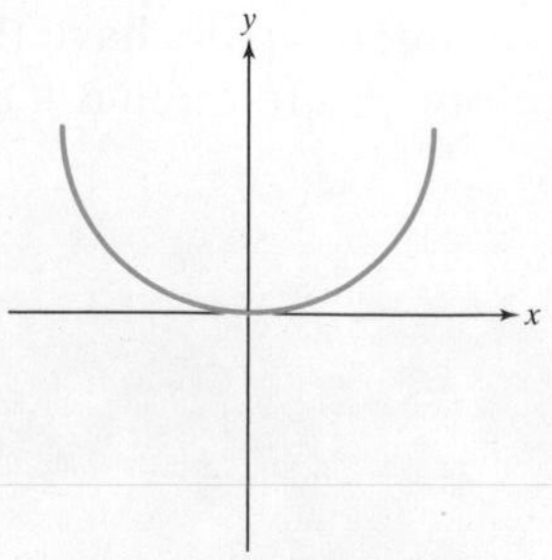

Answers
1. Yes **2.** Yes **3.** No

Solution:

a.

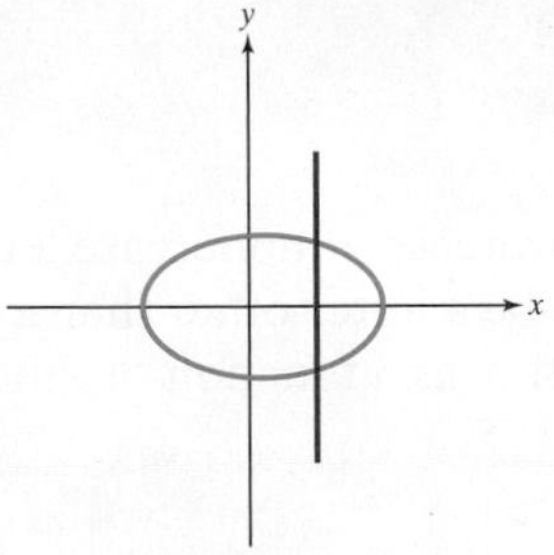

Not a Function
A vertical line intersects in more than one point.

b.

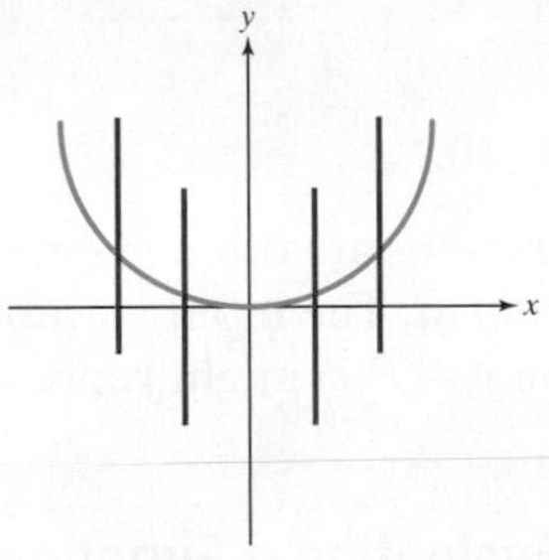

Function
No vertical line intersects in more than one point.

Skill Practice Use the vertical line test to determine whether the relations define y as a function of x.

4.

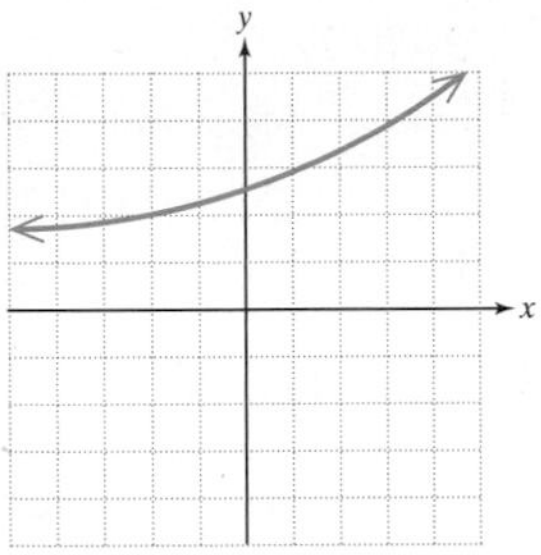

5.

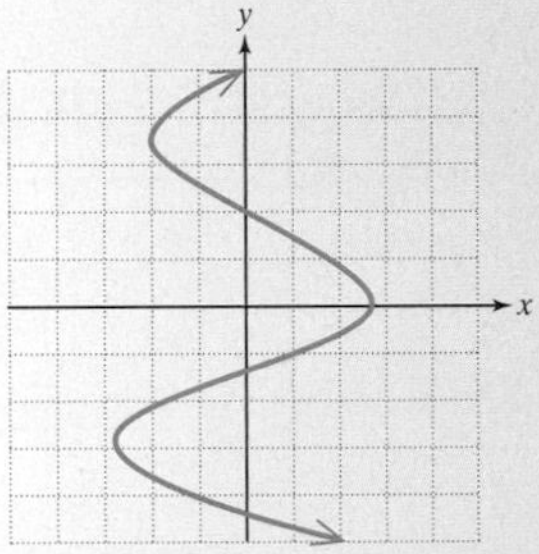

3. Function Notation

A function is defined as a relation with the added restriction that each value in the domain must have only one corresponding y value in the range. In mathematics, functions are often given by rules or equations to define the relationship between two or more variables. For example, the equation $y = 2x$ defines the set of ordered pairs such that the y value is twice the x value.

When a function is defined by an equation, we often use **function notation**. For example, the equation $y = 2x$ may be written in function notation as

$f(x) = 2x$

- f is the name of the function.
- x is an input value from the domain of the function.
- $f(x)$ is the function value (y value) corresponding to x.

The notation $f(x)$ is read as "f of x" or "the value of the function f at x."

A function may be evaluated at different values of x by substituting x-values from the domain into the function. For example, to evaluate the function defined by $f(x) = 2x$ at $x = 5$, substitute $x = 5$ into the function.

$$f(x) = 2x$$
$$\downarrow \qquad \downarrow$$
$$f(5) = 2(5)$$
$$f(5) = 10$$

TIP: $f(5) = 10$ can be written as the ordered pair $(5, 10)$.

Avoiding Mistakes

Be sure to note that $f(x)$ is *not* $f \cdot x$.

Answers

4. Yes **5.** No

Thus, when $x = 5$, the corresponding function value is 10. We say:

- f of 5 is 10.
- f at 5 is 10.
- f evaluated at 5 is 10.

The names of functions are often given by either lowercase or uppercase letters, such as f, g, h, p, K, and M. The input variable may also be a letter other than x. For example, the function $y = P(t)$ might represent population as a function of time.

Example 3 Evaluating a Function

Given the function defined by $g(x) = \frac{1}{2}x - 1$, find the function values.

a. $g(0)$ **b.** $g(2)$ **c.** $g(4)$ **d.** $g(-2)$

Solution:

a. $g(x) = \dfrac{1}{2}x - 1$

$g(0) = \dfrac{1}{2}(0) - 1$

$= 0 - 1$

$= -1$

We say that "g of 0 is -1." This is equivalent to the ordered pair $(0, -1)$.

b. $g(x) = \dfrac{1}{2}x - 1$

$g(2) = \dfrac{1}{2}(2) - 1$

$= 1 - 1$

$= 0$

We say that "g of 2 is 0." This is equivalent to the ordered pair $(2, 0)$.

c. $g(x) = \dfrac{1}{2}x - 1$

$g(4) = \dfrac{1}{2}(4) - 1$

$= 2 - 1$

$= 1$

We say that "g of 4 is 1." This is equivalent to the ordered pair $(4, 1)$.

d. $g(x) = \dfrac{1}{2}x - 1$

$g(-2) = \dfrac{1}{2}(-2) - 1$

$= -1 - 1$

$= -2$

We say that "g of -2 is -2." This is equivalent to the ordered pair $(-2, -2)$.

Skill Practice Given the function defined by $f(x) = -2x - 3$, find the function values.

6. $f(1)$ **7.** $f(0)$ **8.** $f(-3)$ **9.** $f\left(\dfrac{1}{2}\right)$

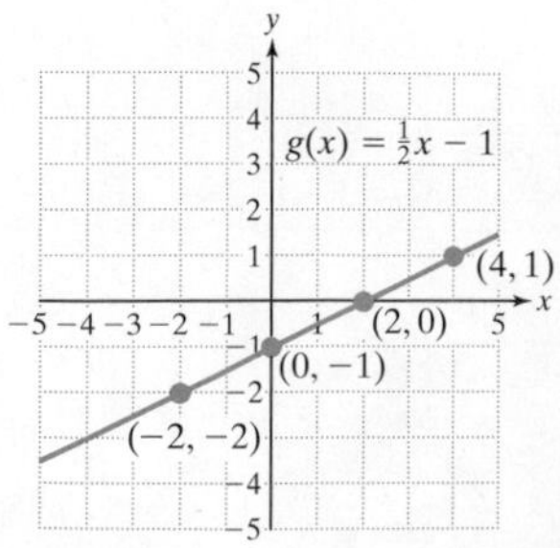

Figure 8-6

Answers

6. -5 **7.** -3 **8.** 3 **9.** -4

In Example 3, notice that $g(0)$, $g(2)$, $g(4)$, and $g(-2)$ correspond to the ordered pairs $(0, -1)$, $(2, 0)$, $(4, 1)$, and $(-2, -2)$. In the graph, these points "line up." The graph of *all* ordered pairs defined by this function is a line with a slope of $\frac{1}{2}$ and y-intercept of $(0, -1)$ (Figure 8-6). This should not be surprising because the function defined by $g(x) = \frac{1}{2}x - 1$ is equivalent to $y = \frac{1}{2}x - 1$.

Calculator Connections

Topic: Using the *Table* and *Value* Features

The values of $g(x)$ in Example 3 can be found using a *Table* feature.

$$Y_1 = \frac{1}{2}x - 1$$

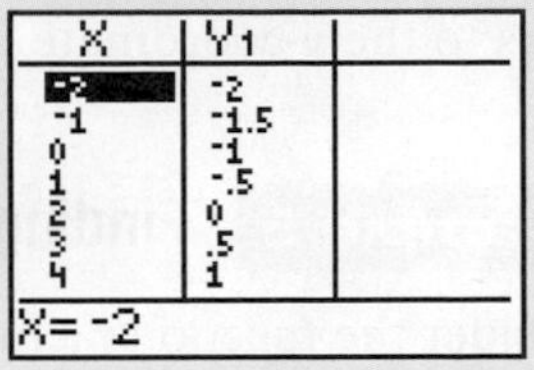

Function values can also be evaluated by using a *Value* feature. The value of $g(4)$ is shown here.

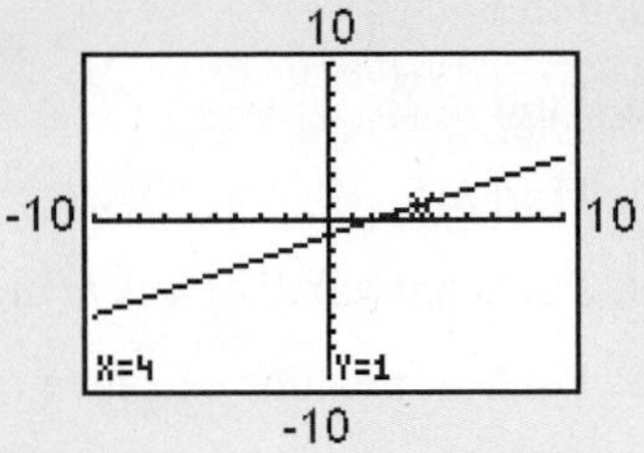

A function may be evaluated at numerical values or at algebraic expressions, as shown in Example 4.

Example 4 Evaluating Functions

Given the functions defined by $f(x) = x^2 - 2x$ and $g(x) = 3x + 5$, find the function values.

a. $f(t)$ **b.** $g(w + 4)$ **c.** $f(-t)$

Solution:

a. $f(x) = x^2 - 2x$

$f(t) = (t)^2 - 2(t)$ Substitute $x = t$ for all values of x in the function.

$= t^2 - 2t$ Simplify.

b. $g(x) = 3x + 5$

$g(w + 4) = 3(w + 4) + 5$ Substitute $x = w + 4$ for all values of x in the function.

$= 3w + 12 + 5$

$= 3w + 17$ Simplify.

c. $f(x) = x^2 - 2x$ Substitute $-t$ for x.

$f(-t) = (-t)^2 - 2(-t)$

$= t^2 + 2t$ Simplify.

Skill Practice Given the function defined by $g(x) = 4x - 3$, find the function values.

10. $g(a)$ **11.** $g(x + h)$ **12.** $g(-x)$

Answers

10. $4a - 3$ **11.** $4x + 4h - 3$
12. $-4x - 3$

4. Finding Function Values from a Graph

We can find function values by looking at a graph of the function. The value of $f(a)$ refers to the y-coordinate of a point with x-coordinate a.

Example 5 Finding Function Values from a Graph

Consider the function pictured in Figure 8-7.

a. Find $h(-1)$.

b. Find $h(2)$.

c. Find $h(5)$.

d. For what value of x is $h(x) = 3$?

e. For what values of x is $h(x) = 0$?

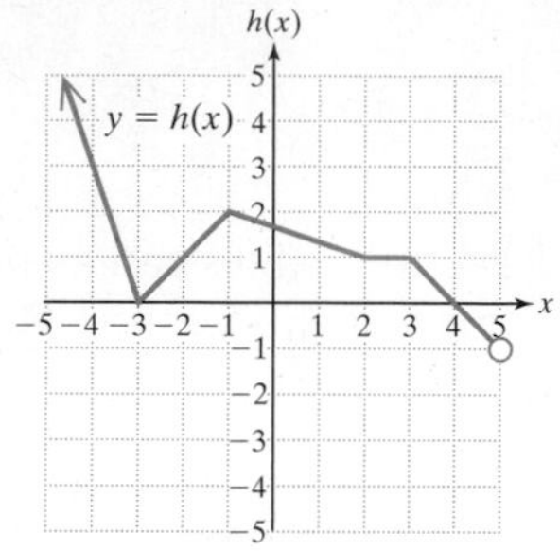

Figure 8-7

Solution:

a. $h(-1) = 2$ This corresponds to the ordered pair $(-1, 2)$.

b. $h(2) = 1$ This corresponds to the ordered pair $(2, 1)$.

c. $h(5)$ is not defined. The value 5 is not in the domain.

d. $h(x) = 3$ for $x = -4$ This corresponds to the ordered pair $(-4, 3)$.

e. $h(x) = 0$ for $x = -3$ and $x = 4$ These are the ordered pairs $(-3, 0)$ and $(4, 0)$.

Skill Practice Refer to the function graphed here.

13. Find $f(0)$.

14. Find $f(-2)$.

15. Find $f(5)$.

16. For what value(s) of x is $f(x) = 0$?

17. For what value(s) of x is $f(x) = -4$?

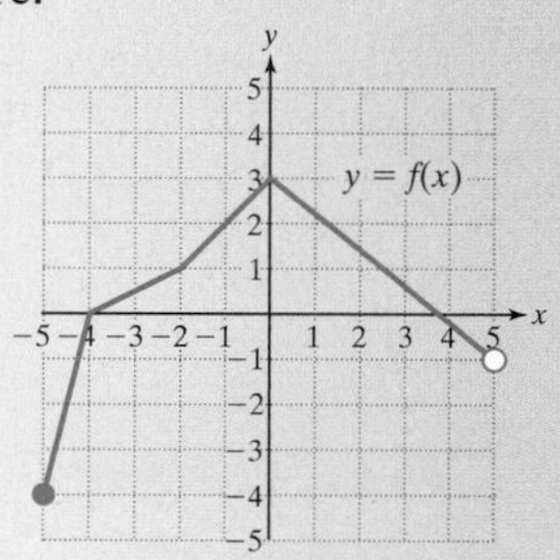

5. Domain of a Function

A function is a relation, and it is often necessary to determine its domain and range. Consider a function defined by the equation $y = f(x)$. The **domain** of f is the set of all x-values that when substituted into the function produce a real number. The **range** of f is the set of all y-values corresponding to the values of x in the domain.

To find the domain of a function defined by $y = f(x)$, keep these guidelines in mind.

- Exclude values of x that make the denominator of a fraction zero.
- Exclude values of x that make the expression within a square root negative.

Answers

13. 3 **14.** 1
15. not defined
16. $x = -4$ and $x = 4$
17. $x = -5$

Example 6 Finding the Domain of a Function

Write the domain in interval notation.

a. $f(x) = \dfrac{x + 7}{2x - 1}$ **b.** $h(x) = \dfrac{x - 4}{x^2 + 9}$

c. $k(t) = \sqrt{t + 4}$ **d.** $g(t) = t^2 - 3t$

Solution:

a. $f(x) = \frac{x+7}{2x-1}$ will not be a real number when the denominator is zero, that is, when

$$2x - 1 = 0$$
$$2x = 1$$
$$x = \frac{1}{2}$$ The value $x = \frac{1}{2}$ must be *excluded* from the domain.

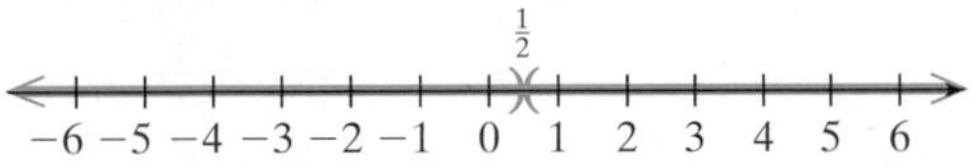

The number line indicates that the domain consists of two intervals, $(-\infty, \frac{1}{2})$ and $(\frac{1}{2}, \infty)$. We use the notation $\cup$ to combine the two intervals. The symbol $\cup$ stands for union. The union of two intervals consists of all the numbers in the first interval, along with all the numbers in the second. This will be discussed further in Section 9.1.

Interval notation: $\left(-\infty, \dfrac{1}{2}\right) \cup \left(\dfrac{1}{2}, \infty\right)$

b. For $h(x) = \frac{x-4}{x^2+9}$ the quantity x^2 is greater than or equal to 0 for all real numbers x, and the number 9 is positive. The sum $x^2 + 9$ must be *positive* for all real numbers x. The denominator will never be zero; therefore, the domain is the set of all real numbers.

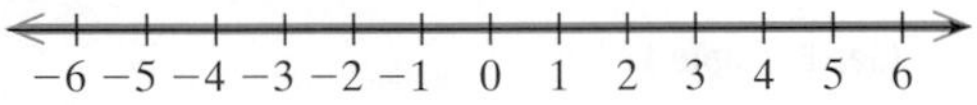

Interval notation: $(-\infty, \infty)$

c. The value of the function defined by $k(t) = \sqrt{t + 4}$ will not be a real number when the expression within the square root is negative. Therefore, the domain is the set of all t values that make $t + 4$ greater than or equal to zero.

$$t + 4 \geq 0$$
$$t \geq -4$$

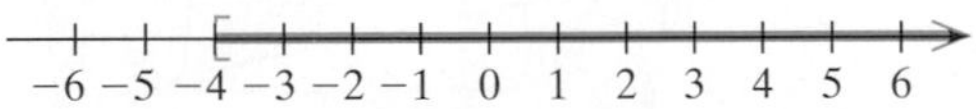

Interval notation: $[-4, \infty)$

d. The function defined by $g(t) = t^2 - 3t$ has no restrictions on its domain because any real number substituted for t will produce a real number. The domain is the set of all real numbers.

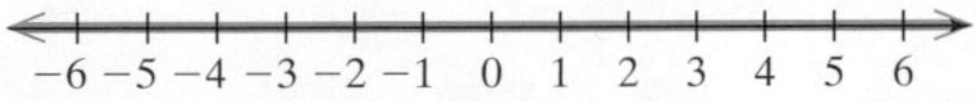

Interval notation: $(-\infty, \infty)$

Skill Practice Write the domain in interval notation.

18. $f(x) = \dfrac{2x + 1}{x - 9}$ **19.** $k(x) = \dfrac{-5}{4x^2 + 1}$

20. $g(x) = \sqrt{x - 2}$ **21.** $h(x) = x + 6$

Answers

18. $(-\infty, 9) \cup (9, \infty)$ **19.** $(-\infty, \infty)$
20. $[2, \infty)$ **21.** $(-\infty, \infty)$

Section 8.2 Practice Exercises

Vocabulary and Key Concepts

1. **a.** Given a relation in x and y, we say that y is a ____________ of x if for each element x in the domain, there is exactly one value of y in the range.

   b. If a ____________ line intersects the graph of a relation in more than one point, the relation is not a function.

   c. Function notation for the equation $y = 2x + 1$ is $f(x) =$ ____________.

   d. Given a function defined by $y = f(x)$, the set of all ____________ that produce a real number when substituted into a function is called the domain of the function.

   e. The set of all ____________ corresponding to x values in the domain is called the range.

   f. To find the domain of a function defined by $y = f(x)$, exclude any values of x that make the ____________ of a fraction equal to zero.

   g. To find the domain of a function defined by $y = f(x)$, exclude any values of x that make the expression within a square root ____________.

Review Exercises

For Exercises 2–4, **a.** write the relation as a set of ordered pairs, **b.** identify the domain, and **c.** identify the range.

2.

Parent, x	Child, y
Kevin	Kayla
Kevin	Kira
Kathleen	Katie
Kathleen	Kira

3.

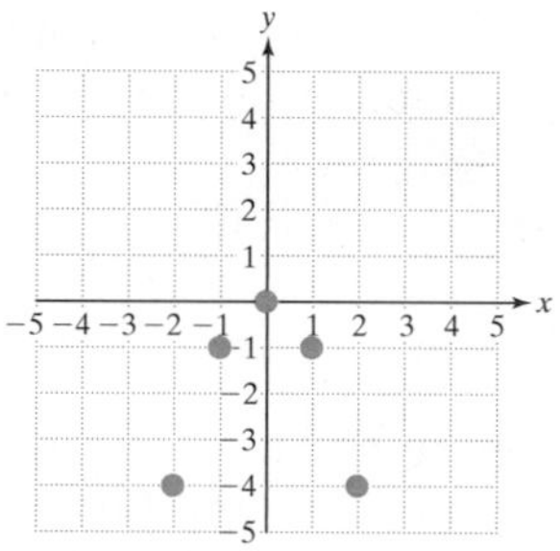

4.

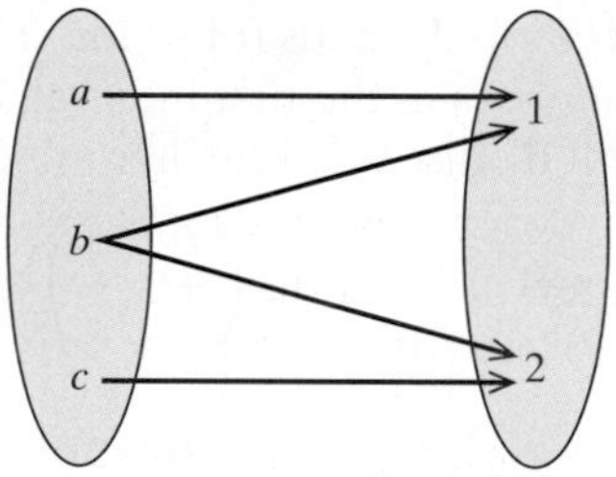

Concept 1: Definition of a Function

For Exercises 5–10, determine if the relation defines y as a function of x. **(See Example 1.)**

5.

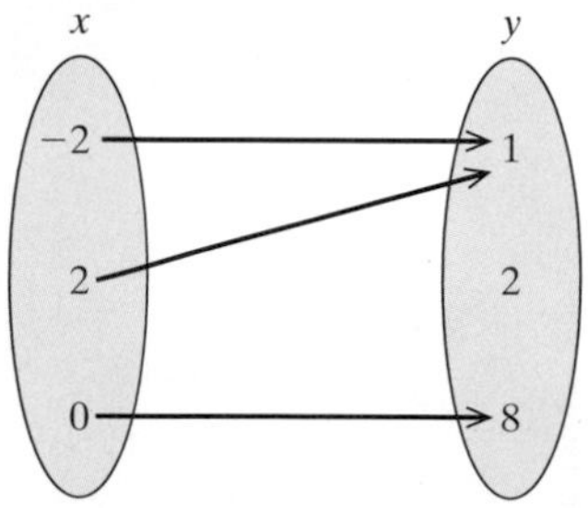

6.

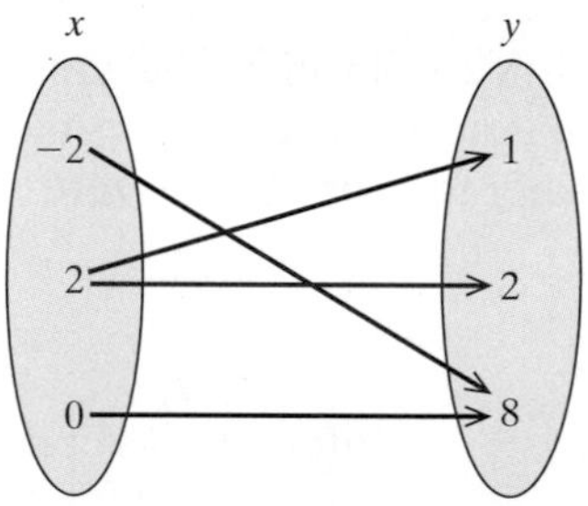

7.

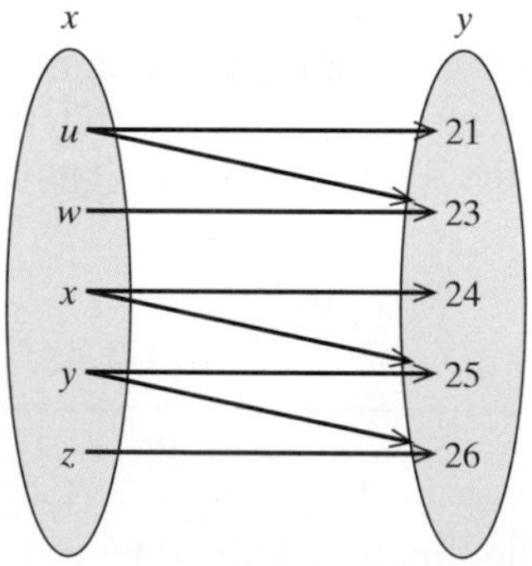

8.

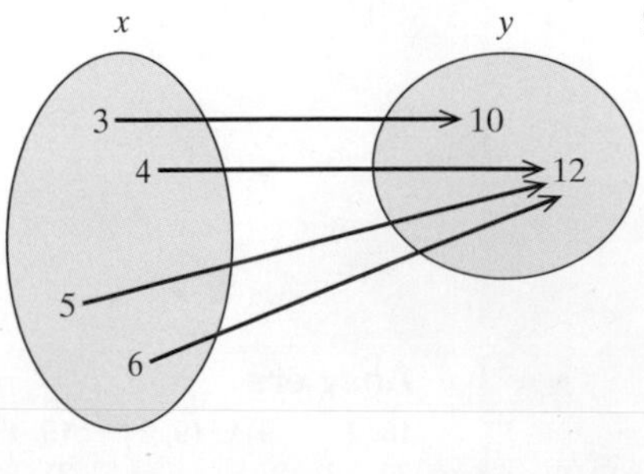

9. $\{(1, 2), (3, 4), (5, 4), (-9, 3)\}$

10. $\left\{(0, -1.1), \left(\frac{1}{2}, 8\right), (1.1, 8), \left(4, \frac{1}{2}\right)\right\}$

Concept 2: Vertical Line Test

For Exercises 11–16, use the vertical line test to determine whether the relation defines y as a function of x. **(See Example 2.)**

11.

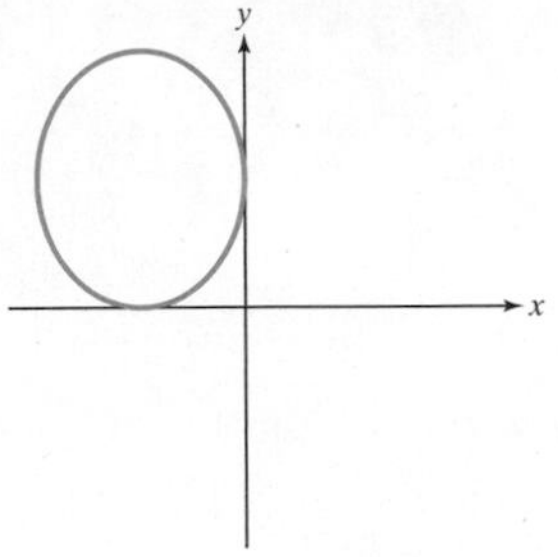

12.

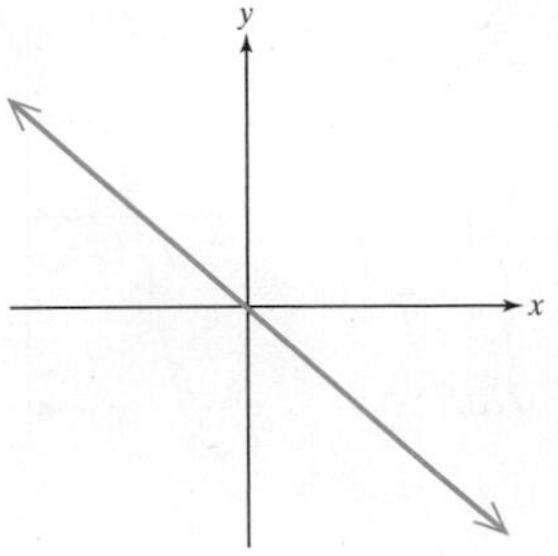

13.

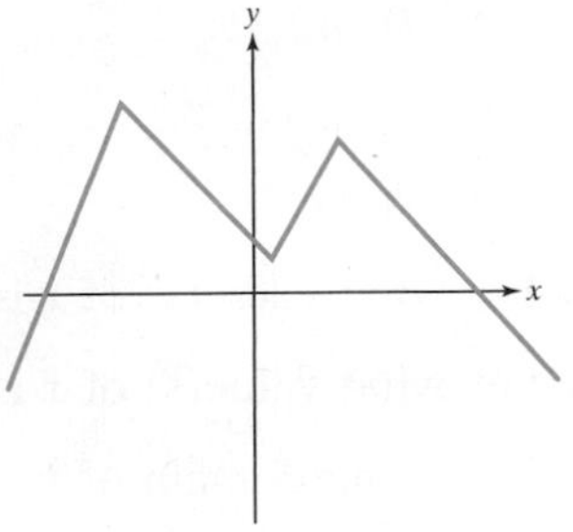

14.

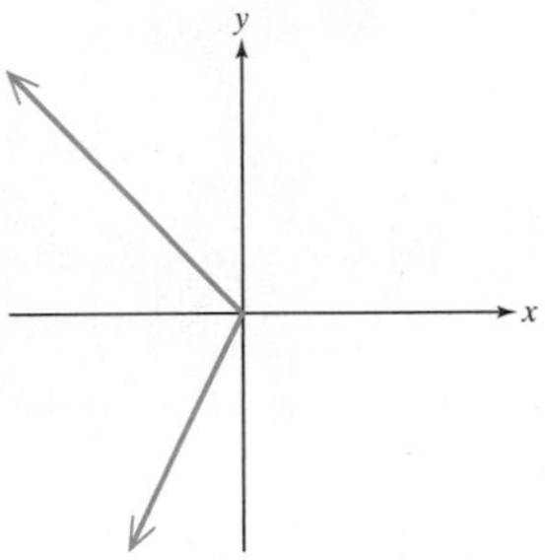

15.

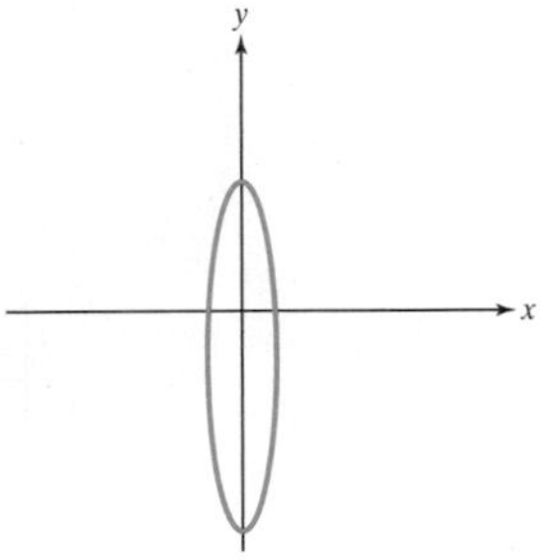

16.

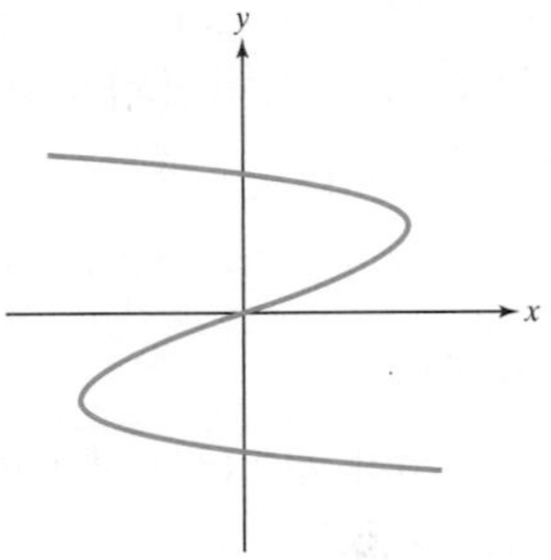

Concept 3: Function Notation

For Exercises 17–20, consider a function defined by $y = f(x)$.

17. Interpret the meaning of $f(2) = 5$.

18. Interpret the meaning of $f(-7) = 8$.

19. Write the ordered pair represented by $f(0) = -2$.

20. Write the ordered pair represented by $f(-10) = 11$.

Consider the functions defined by $f(x) = 6x - 2$, $g(x) = -x^2 - 4x + 1$, $h(x) = 7$, and $k(x) = |x - 2|$. For Exercises 21–52, find the following. **(See Examples 3–4.)**

21. $g(2)$ **22.** $k(2)$ **23.** $g(0)$ **24.** $h(0)$

25. $k(0)$ **26.** $f(0)$ **27.** $f(t)$ **28.** $g(a)$

29. $h(u)$ **30.** $k(v)$ **31.** $g(-3)$ **32.** $h(-5)$

33. $k(-2)$ **34.** $f(-6)$ **35.** $f(x + 1)$ **36.** $h(x + 1)$

37. $g(2x)$ **38.** $k(x - 3)$ **39.** $g(-\pi)$ **40.** $g(a^2)$

41. $h(a + b)$ **42.** $f(x + h)$ **43.** $f(-a)$ **44.** $g(-b)$

45. $k(-c)$ **46.** $h(-x)$ **47.** $f\left(\frac{1}{2}\right)$ **48.** $g\left(\frac{1}{4}\right)$

49. $h\left(\frac{1}{7}\right)$ **50.** $k\left(\frac{3}{2}\right)$ **51.** $f(-2.8)$ **52.** $k(-5.4)$

Consider the functions $p = \{(\frac{1}{2}, 6), (2, -7), (1, 0), (3, 2\pi)\}$ and $q = \{(6, 4), (2, -5), (\frac{3}{4}, \frac{1}{5}), (0, 9)\}$. For Exercises 53–60, find the function values.

53. $p(2)$ **54.** $p(1)$ **55.** $p(3)$ **56.** $p\left(\frac{1}{2}\right)$

57. $q(2)$ **58.** $q\left(\frac{3}{4}\right)$ **59.** $q(6)$ **60.** $q(0)$

Concept 4: Finding Function Values from a Graph

61. The graph of $y = f(x)$ is given. **(See Example 5.)**

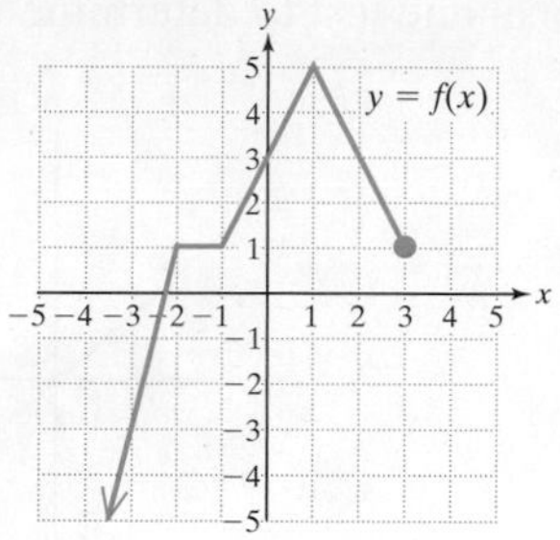

a. Find $f(0)$.

b. Find $f(3)$.

c. Find $f(-2)$.

d. For what value(s) of x is $f(x) = -3$?

e. For what value(s) of x is $f(x) = 3$?

f. Write the domain of f.

g. Write the range of f.

62. The graph of $y = g(x)$ is given.

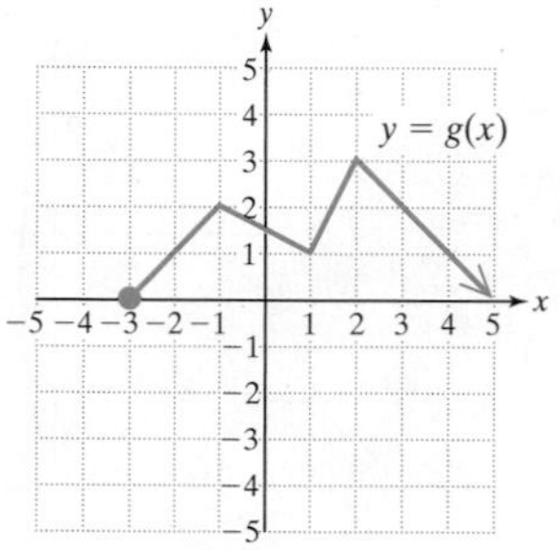

a. Find $g(-1)$.

b. Find $g(1)$.

c. Find $g(4)$.

d. For what value(s) of x is $g(x) = 3$?

e. For what value(s) of x is $g(x) = 0$?

f. Write the domain of g.

g. Write the range of g.

63. The graph of $y = H(x)$ is given.

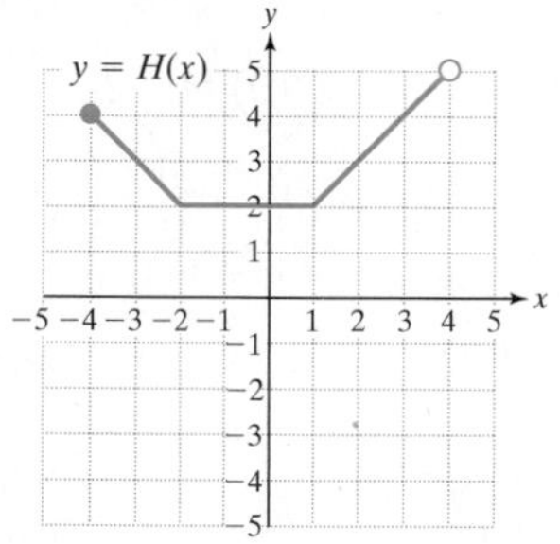

a. Find $H(-3)$.

b. Find $H(4)$.

c. Find $H(3)$.

d. For what value(s) of x is $H(x) = 3$?

e. For what value(s) of x is $H(x) = 2$?

f. Write the domain of H.

g. Write the range of H.

64. The graph of $y = K(x)$ is given.

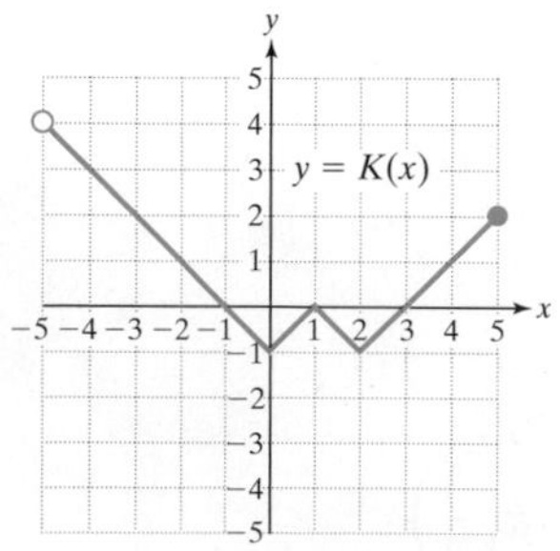

a. Find $K(0)$.

b. Find $K(-5)$.

c. Find $K(1)$.

d. For what value(s) of x is $K(x) = 0$?

e. For what value(s) of x is $K(x) = 3$?

f. Write the domain of K.

g. Write the range of K.

65. The graph of $y = p(x)$ is given.

a. Find $p(2)$.

b. Find $p(-1)$.

c. Find $p(1)$.

d. For what value(s) of x is $p(x) = 0$?

e. For what value(s) of x is $p(x) = -2$?

f. Write the domain of p.

g. Write the range of p.

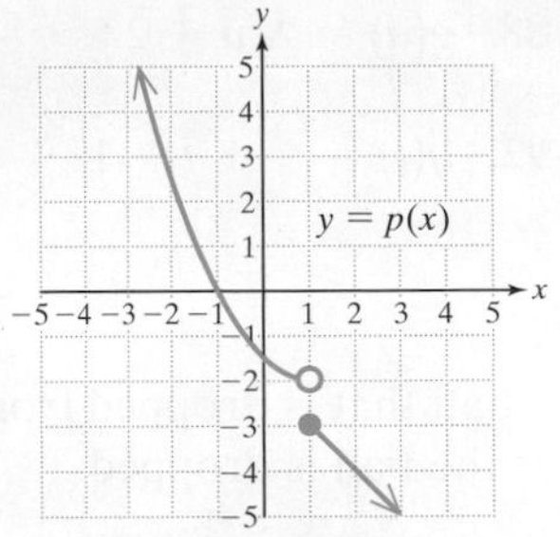

66. The graph of $y = q(x)$ is given.

a. Find $q(3)$.

b. Find $q(-1)$.

c. Find $q(2)$.

d. For what value(s) of x is $q(x) = -4$?

e. For what value(s) of x is $q(x) = 3$?

f. Write the domain of q.

g. Write the range of q.

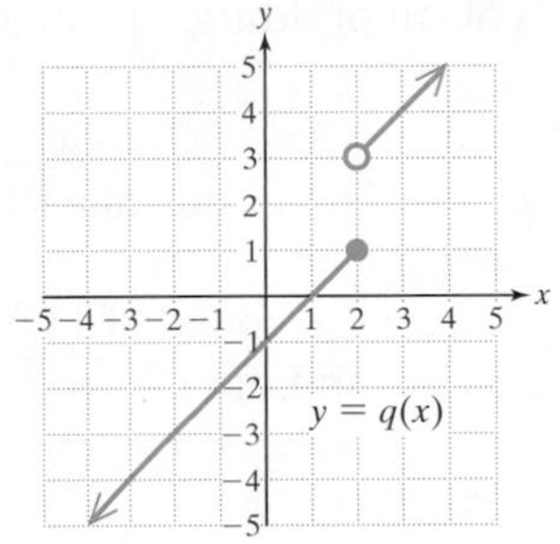

For Exercises 67–76, refer to the functions $y = f(x)$ and $y = g(x)$, defined as follows:

$$f = \{(-3, 5), (-7, -3), (-\tfrac{3}{2}, 4), (1.2, 5)\}$$

$$g = \{(0, 6), (2, 6), (6, 0), (1, 0)\}$$

67. Identify the domain of f.

68. Identify the range of f.

69. Identify the range of g.

70. Identify the domain of g.

71. For what value(s) of x is $f(x) = 5$?

72. For what value(s) of x is $f(x) = -3$?

73. For what value(s) of x is $g(x) = 0$?

74. For what value(s) of x is $g(x) = 6$?

75. Find $f(-7)$.

76. Find $g(0)$.

Concept 5: Domain of a Function

77. Explain how to determine the domain of the function defined by $f(x) = \dfrac{x + 6}{x - 2}$.

78. Explain how to determine the domain of the function defined by $g(x) = \sqrt{x - 3}$.

For Exercises 79–94, find the domain. Write the answers in interval notation. **(See Example 6.)**

79. $k(x) = \dfrac{x - 3}{x + 6}$

80. $m(x) = \dfrac{x - 1}{x - 4}$

81. $f(t) = \dfrac{5}{t}$

82. $g(t) = \dfrac{t - 7}{t}$

83. $h(p) = \dfrac{p - 4}{p^2 + 1}$

84. $n(p) = \dfrac{p + 8}{p^2 + 2}$

85. $h(t) = \sqrt{t + 7}$

86. $k(t) = \sqrt{t - 5}$

87. $f(a) = \sqrt{a - 3}$ **88.** $g(a) = \sqrt{a + 2}$ **89.** $m(x) = \sqrt{1 - 2x}$ **90.** $n(x) = \sqrt{12 - 6x}$

91. $p(t) = 2t^2 + t - 1$ **92.** $q(t) = t^3 + t - 1$ **93.** $f(x) = x + 6$ **94.** $g(x) = 8x - \pi$

Mixed Exercises

95. The height (in feet) of a ball that is dropped from an 80-ft building is given by $h(t) = -16t^2 + 80$, where t is the time in seconds after the ball is dropped.

a. Find $h(1)$ and $h(1.5)$

b. Interpret the meaning of the function values found in part (a).

96. A ball is dropped from a 50-m building. The height (in meters) after t sec is given by $h(t) = -4.9t^2 + 50$.

a. Find $h(1)$ and $h(1.5)$.

b. Interpret the meaning of the function values found in part (a).

97. If Alicia rides a bike at an average speed of 11.5 mph, the distance that she rides can be represented by $d(t) = 11.5t$, where t is the time in hours.

a. Find $d(1)$ and $d(1.5)$.

b. Interpret the meaning of the function values found in part (a).

98. Brian's score on an exam is a function of the number of hours he spends studying. The function defined by $P(x) = \dfrac{100x^2}{50 + x^2}$ $(x \geq 0)$ indicates that he will achieve a score of $P\%$ if he studies for x hours.

Evaluate $P(0)$, $P(5)$, $P(10)$, $P(15)$, $P(20)$, and $P(25)$ and confirm the values on the graph. (Round to one decimal place.) Interpret $P(25)$ in the context of this problem.

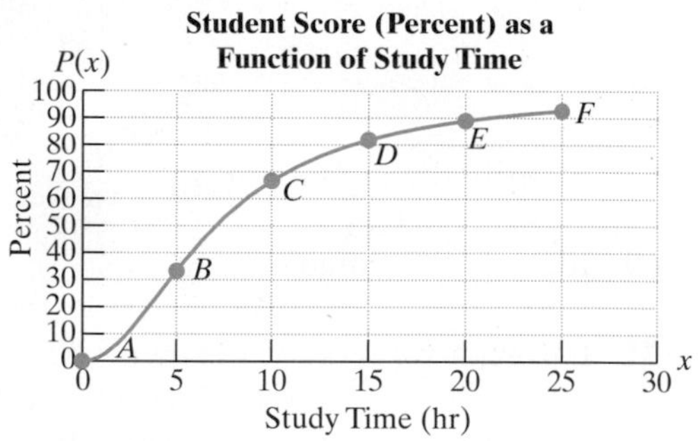

For Exercises 99–102, write a function defined by $y = f(x)$ subject to the conditions given.

99. The value of $f(x)$ is three more than two times x.

100. The value of $f(x)$ is four less than the square of x.

101. The value of $f(x)$ is ten less than the absolute value of x.

102. The value of $f(x)$ is sixteen times the square root of x.

Expanding Your Skills

For Exercises 103–104, write the domain in interval notation.

103. $q(x) = \dfrac{2}{\sqrt{x + 2}}$

104. $p(x) = \dfrac{8}{\sqrt{x - 4}}$

Graphing Calculator Exercises

105. Graph $k(t) = \sqrt{t - 5}$. Use the graph to support your answer to Exercise 86.

106. Graph $h(t) = \sqrt{t + 7}$. Use the graph to support your answer to Exercise 85.

Graphs of Functions

Section 8.3

Concepts

1. Linear and Constant Functions
2. Graphs of Basic Functions
3. Definition of a Quadratic Function
4. Finding the x- and y-Intercepts of a Graph Defined by $y = f(x)$

1. Linear and Constant Functions

A function may be expressed as a mathematical equation that relates two or more variables. In this section, we will look at several elementary functions.

Recall from Section 3.2 that an equation in the form $y = k$, where k is a constant, is a horizontal line. In function notation, this can be written as $f(x) = k$. For example, the graph of the function defined by $f(x) = 3$ is a horizontal line, as shown in Figure 8-8.

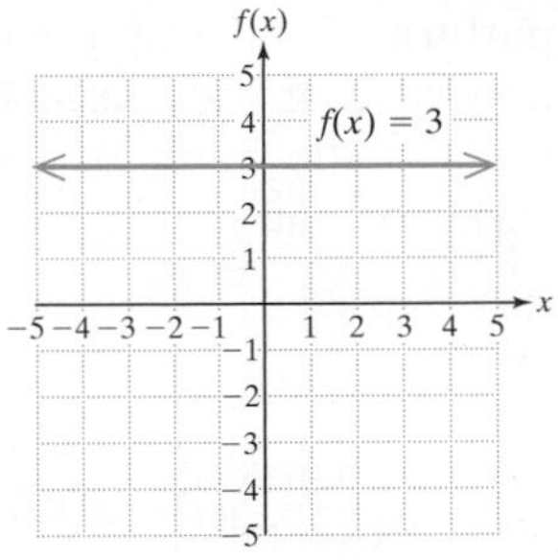

Figure 8-8

We say that a function defined by $f(x) = k$ is a constant function because for any value of x, the function value is constant.

An equation of the form $y = mx + b$ is represented graphically by a line with slope m and y-intercept $(0, b)$. In function notation, this may be written as $f(x) = mx + b$. A function in this form is called a linear function. For example, the function defined by $f(x) = 2x - 3$ is a linear function with slope $m = 2$ and y-intercept $(0, -3)$ (Figure 8-9).

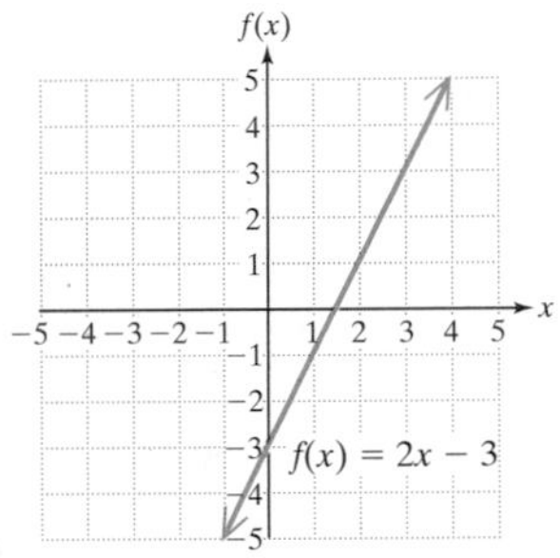

Figure 8-9

Linear Functions and Constant Functions

Let m and b represent real numbers such that $m \neq 0$. Then:

A function that can be written in the form $f(x) = mx + b$ is a **linear function**.

A function that can be written in the form $f(x) = b$ is a **constant function**.

Note: The graphs of linear and constant functions are lines.

2. Graphs of Basic Functions

At this point, we are able to recognize the equations and graphs of linear and constant functions. In addition to linear and constant functions, the following equations define six basic functions that will be encountered in the study of algebra:

Equation	(equivalent function notation)	Function Notation	Type of Function
$y = x$		$f(x) = x$	Identity function
$y = x^2$		$f(x) = x^2$	Quadratic function
$y = x^3$		$f(x) = x^3$	Cubic function
$y = \lvert x \rvert$	equivalent function notation →	$f(x) = \lvert x \rvert$	Absolute value function
$y = \sqrt{x}$		$f(x) = \sqrt{x}$	Square root function
$y = \frac{1}{x}$		$f(x) = \frac{1}{x}$	Reciprocal function

The graph of the function defined by $f(x) = x$ is linear, with slope $m = 1$ and y-intercept $(0, 0)$ (Figure 8-10).

To determine the shapes of the other basic functions, we can plot several points to establish the pattern of the graph. Analyzing the equation itself may also provide insight to the domain, range, and shape of the graph. To demonstrate this, we will graph $f(x) = x^2$ and $g(x) = \frac{1}{x}$.

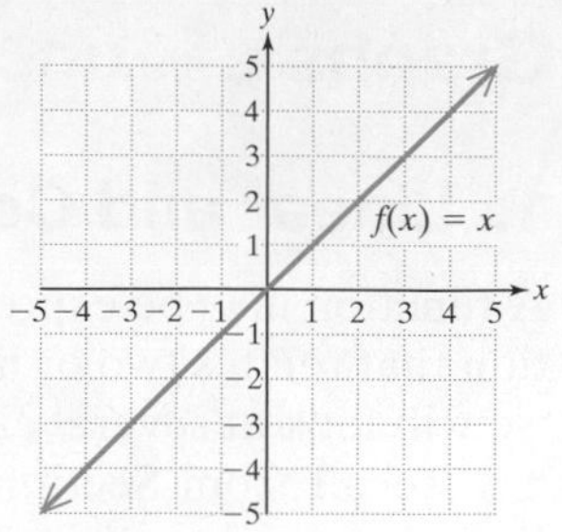

Figure 8-10

Example 1 Graphing Basic Functions

Graph the function defined by $f(x) = x^2$.

Solution:

The domain of the function given by $f(x) = x^2$ (or equivalently $y = x^2$) is all real numbers.

To graph the function, choose arbitrary values of x within the domain of the function. Be sure to choose values of x that are positive and values that are negative to determine the behavior of the function to the right and left of the origin (Table 8-4). The graph of $f(x) = x^2$ is shown in Figure 8-11.

The function values are equated to the square of x, so $f(x)$ will always be greater than or equal to zero. Hence, the y-coordinates on the graph will never be negative. The range of the function is $[0, \infty)$. The arrows on each branch of the graph imply that the pattern continues indefinitely.

Table 8-4

x	$f(x) = x^2$
0	0
1	1
2	4
3	9
−1	1
−2	4
−3	9

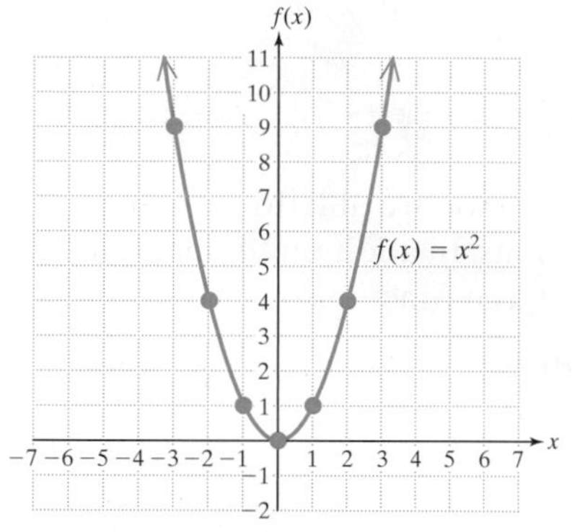

Figure 8-11

Skill Practice

1. Graph $f(x) = -x^2$ by first making a table of points.

Answer

1.

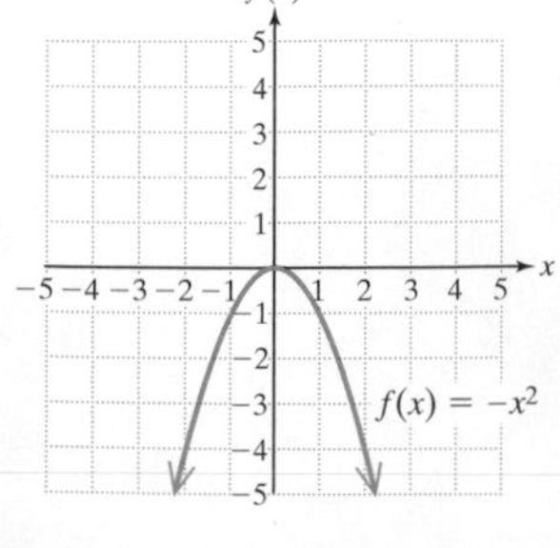

Example 2 **Graphing Basic Functions**

Graph the function defined by $g(x) = \frac{1}{x}$.

Solution:

$g(x) = \frac{1}{x}$ Notice that $x = 0$ is not in the domain of the function. From the equation $y = \frac{1}{x}$, the y values will be the reciprocal of the x-values. The graph defined by $g(x) = \frac{1}{x}$ is shown in Figure 8-12.

x	$g(x) = \frac{1}{x}$
1	1
2	$\frac{1}{2}$
3	$\frac{1}{3}$
−1	−1
−2	$-\frac{1}{2}$
−3	$-\frac{1}{3}$

x	$g(x) = \frac{1}{x}$
$\frac{1}{2}$	2
$\frac{1}{3}$	3
$\frac{1}{4}$	4
$-\frac{1}{2}$	−2
$-\frac{1}{3}$	−3
$-\frac{1}{4}$	−4

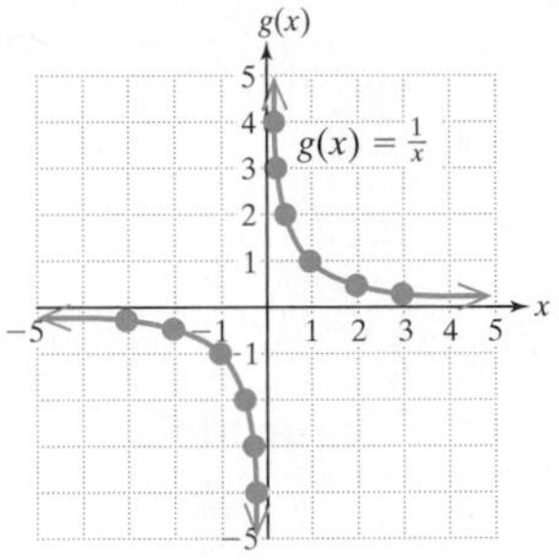

Figure 8-12

Notice that as x approaches ∞ and $-\infty$, the y values approach zero, and the graph approaches the x-axis. In this case, the x-axis is called a *horizontal asymptote*. Similarly, the graph of the function approaches the y-axis as x gets close to zero. In this case, the y-axis is called a *vertical asymptote*. In general terms, an asymptote is a line that a curve approaches more and more closely but never reaches.

Skill Practice

2. Graph $h(x) = |x| - 1$ by first making a table of points.

Calculator Connections

Topic: Graphing Nonlinear Functions

To enter a function, let $f(x) = y$. That is, to graph $f(x) = x^2$, enter $Y_1 = x^2$.

To graph $g(x) = \frac{1}{x}$, enter $Y_1 = 1/x$.

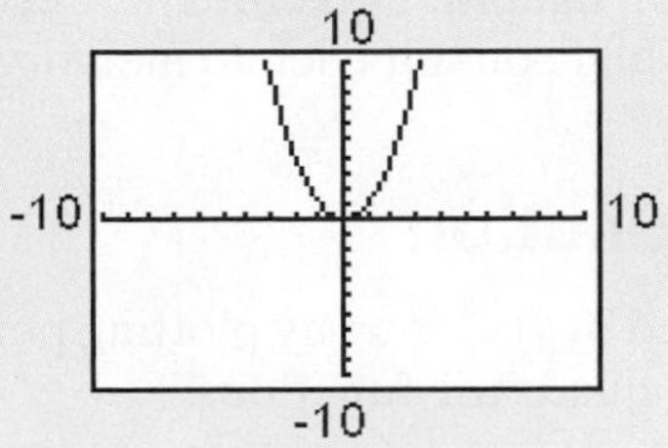

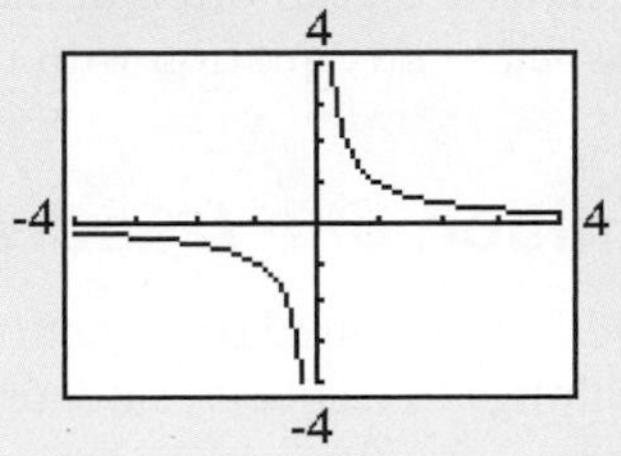

Answer

2.

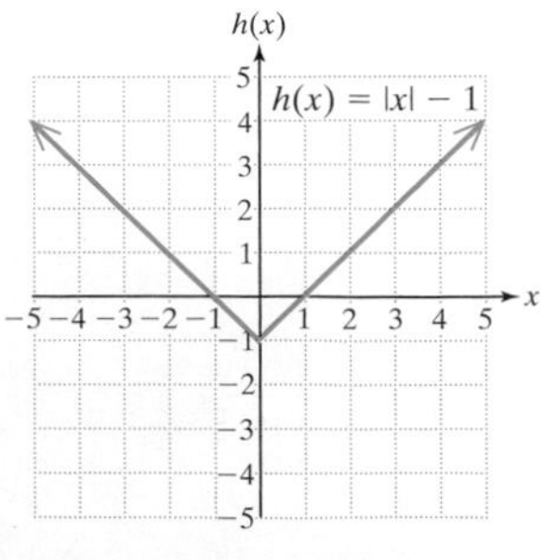

Summary of Six Basic Functions and Their Graphs

Function | **Graph** | **Domain and Range**

1. $f(x) = x$

Identity function

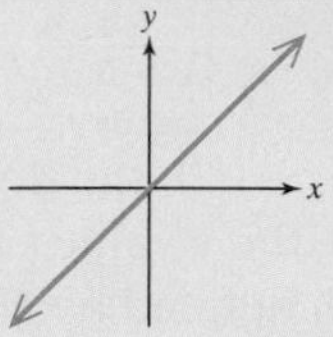

Domain $(-\infty, \infty)$

Range $(-\infty, \infty)$

2. $f(x) = x^2$

Quadratic function

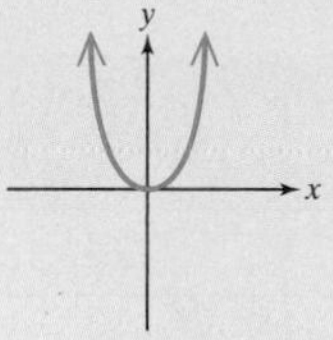

Domain $(-\infty, \infty)$

Range $[0, \infty)$

3. $f(x) = x^3$

Cubic function

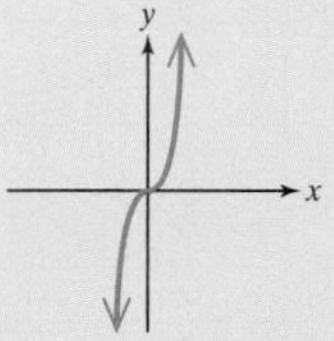

Domain $(-\infty, \infty)$

Range $(-\infty, \infty)$

4. $f(x) = |x|$

Absolute value function

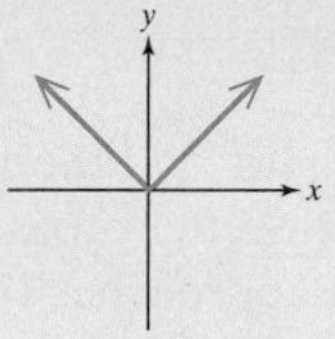

Domain $(-\infty, \infty)$

Range $[0, \infty)$

5. $f(x) = \sqrt{x}$

Square root function

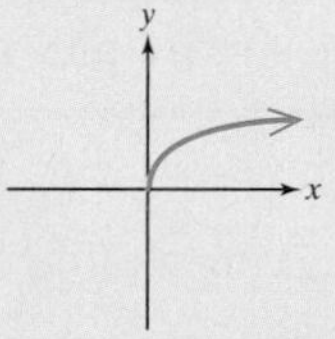

Domain $[0, \infty)$

Range $[0, \infty)$

6. $f(x) = \dfrac{1}{x}$

Reciprocal function

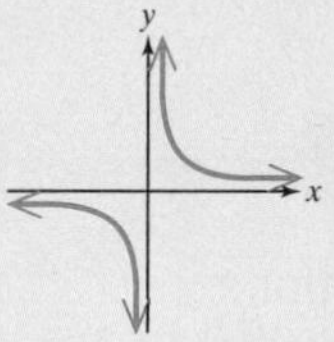

Domain $(-\infty, 0) \cup (0, \infty)$

Range $(-\infty, 0) \cup (0, \infty)$

TIP: Recall that the symbol $\cup$ means the combination (or union) of the two intervals.

The shapes of these six graphs will be developed in the homework exercises. These functions are used often in the study of algebra. Therefore, we recommend that you associate an equation with its graph and commit each to memory.

3. Definition of a Quadratic Function

In Example 1 we graphed the function defined by $f(x) = x^2$ by plotting points. This function belongs to a special category called quadratic functions.

Definition of a Quadratic Function

A **quadratic function** is a function defined by

$$f(x) = ax^2 + bx + c \qquad \text{where } a, b, \text{ and } c \text{ are real numbers and } a \neq 0.$$

The graph of a quadratic function is in the shape of a **parabola**. The leading coefficient, a, determines the direction of the parabola.

- If $a > 0$, then the parabola opens upward, and the vertex is the minimum point on the parabola. For example, the graph of $f(x) = x^2$ is shown in Figure 8-13.
- If $a < 0$, then the parabola opens downward, and the vertex is the maximum point on the parabola. For example, the graph of $f(x) = -x^2$ is shown in Figure 8-14.

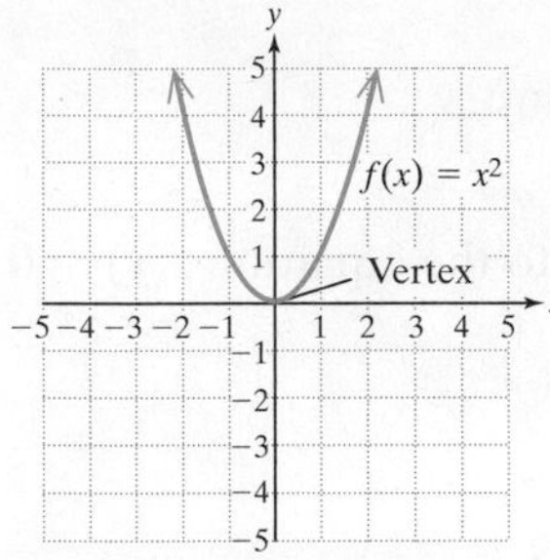

Figure 8-13

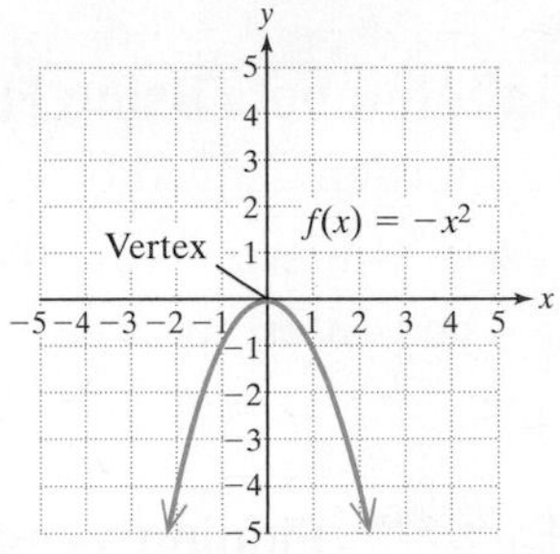

Figure 8-14

Example 3 Identifying Functions

Identify each function as linear, constant, quadratic, or none of these.

a. $f(x) = -4$ **b.** $f(x) = x^2 + 3x + 2$ **c.** $f(x) = 7 - 2x$

d. $f(x) = \dfrac{4x + 8}{8}$ **e.** $f(x) = \dfrac{6}{x} + 2$

Solution:

a. $f(x) = -4$ is a constant function. It is in the form $f(x) = b$, where $b = -4$.

b. $f(x) = x^2 + 3x + 2$ is a quadratic function. It is in the form $f(x) = ax^2 + bx + c$, where $a \neq 0$.

c. $f(x) = 7 - 2x$ is linear. Writing it in the form $f(x) = mx + b$, we get $f(x) = -2x + 7$, where $m = -2$ and $b = 7$.

d. $f(x) = \dfrac{4x + 8}{8}$ is linear. Writing it in the form $f(x) = mx + b$, we get

$$f(x) = \frac{4x}{8} + \frac{8}{8}$$

$$= \frac{1}{2}x + 1, \text{ where } m = \frac{1}{2} \text{ and } b = 1.$$

e. $f(x) = \dfrac{6}{x} + 2$ fits none of these categories.

Skill Practice Identify each function as constant, linear, quadratic, or none of these.

3. $m(x) = -2x^2 - 3x + 7$ **4.** $n(x) = -6$

5. $W(x) = \dfrac{4}{3}x - \dfrac{1}{2}$ **6.** $R(x) = \dfrac{4}{3x} - \dfrac{1}{2}$

Answers

3. Quadratic
4. Constant
5. Linear
6. None of these

4. Finding the x- and y-Intercepts of a Graph Defined by $y = f(x)$

In Section 3.2, we learned that to find the x-intercept, we substitute $y = 0$ and solve the equation for x. Using function notation, this is equivalent to finding the real solutions of the equation $f(x) = 0$. To find the y-intercept, substitute $x = 0$ and solve the equation for y. In function notation, this is equivalent to finding $f(0)$.

Finding Intercepts Using Function Notation

Given a function defined by $y = f(x)$,

Step 1 The x-intercepts are the real solutions to the equation $f(x) = 0$.

Step 2 The y-intercept is given by $f(0)$.

Example 4 Finding x- and y-Intercepts

Given the function defined by $f(x) = 2x - 4$:

a. Find the x-intercept(s).

b. Find the y-intercept.

c. Graph the function.

Solution:

a. To find the x-intercept(s), find the real solutions to the equation $f(x) = 0$.

$f(x) = 2x - 4$

$0 = 2x - 4$ Substitute $f(x) = 0$.

$4 = 2x$

$2 = x$ The x-intercept is $(2, 0)$.

b. To find the y-intercept, evaluate $f(0)$.

$f(0) = 2(0) - 4$ Substitute $x = 0$.

$f(0) = -4$ The y-intercept is $(0, -4)$.

c. This function is linear, with a y-intercept of $(0, -4)$, an x-intercept of $(2, 0)$, and a slope of 2 (Figure 8-15).

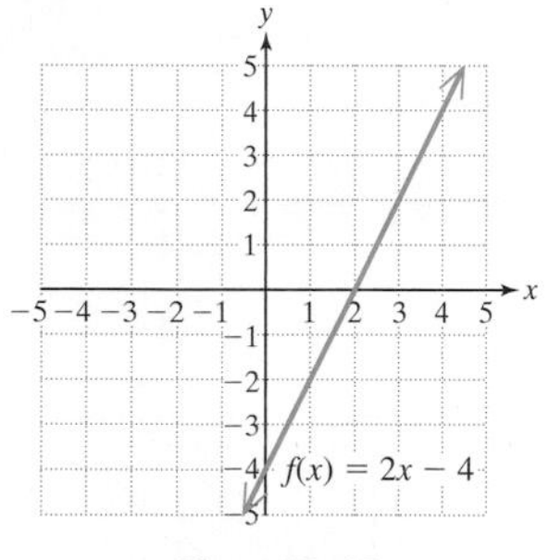

Figure 8-15

Skill Practice Consider $f(x) = -5x + 1$.

7. Find the x-intercept.

8. Find the y-intercept.

9. Graph the function.

Answers

7. $(\frac{1}{5}, 0)$ **8.** $(0, 1)$

9.

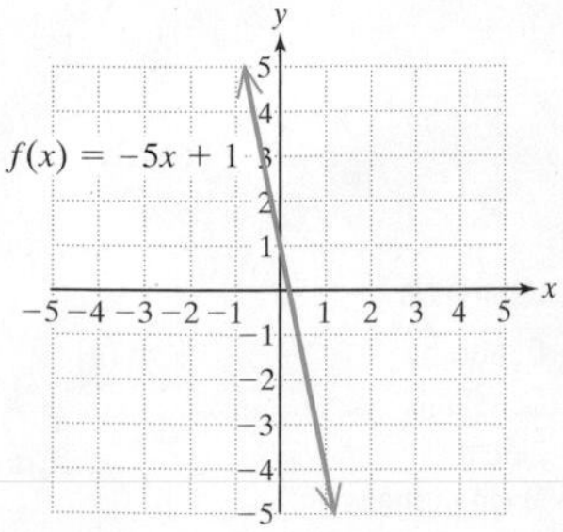

Calculator Connections

Topic: Finding *x*- and *y*-Intercepts

Refer to Example 4 with $f(x) = 2x - 4$. To find the *y*-intercept, let $x = 0$. We can do this using the *Value* key.

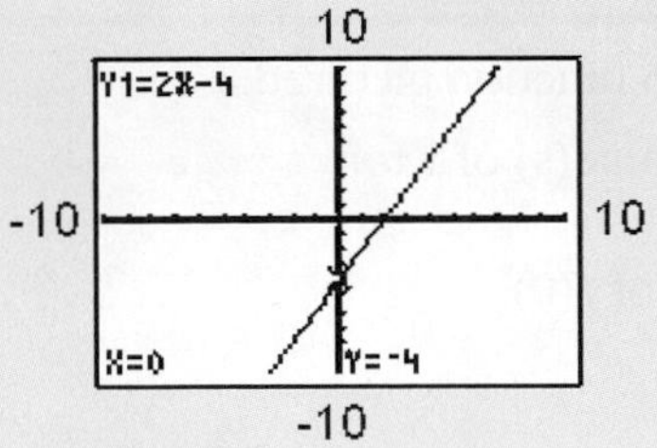

To find the *x*-intercept, use the *Zero* feature. To use this feature you must give bounds for the *x*-intercept. To find a left bound, place the curser to the left of the *x*-intercept and press Enter. For the right bound, place the curser to the right of the *x*-intercept and press Enter.

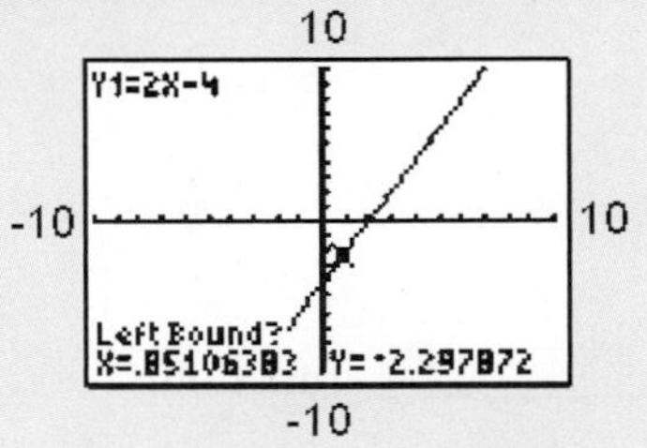

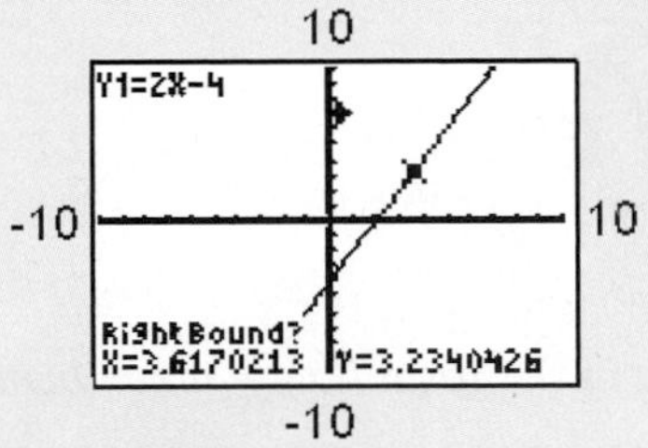

Then make a guess by placing the curser near the *x*-intercept. Press Enter and the *x*-intercept will be displayed.

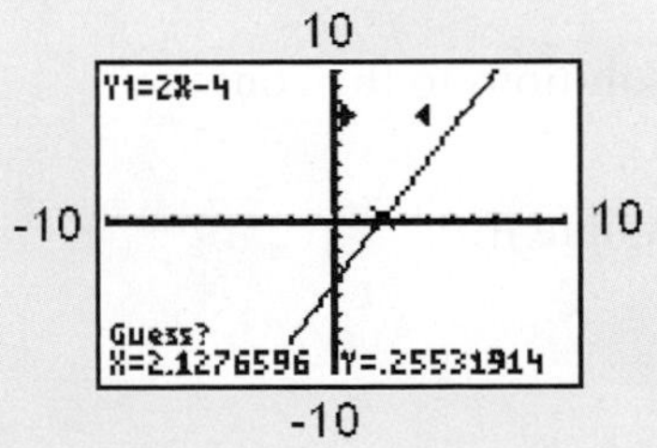

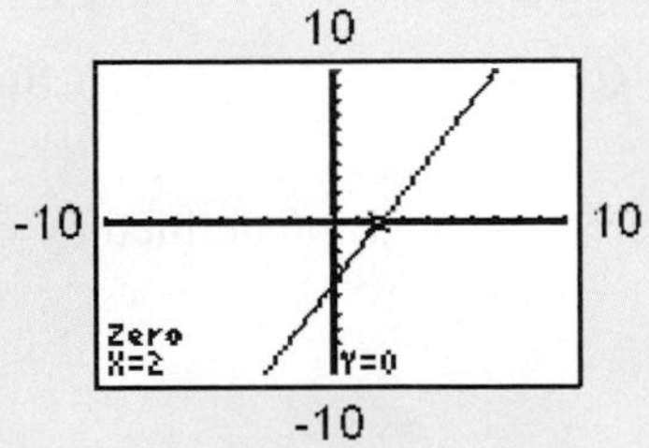

Example 5 **Finding *x*- and *y*-Intercepts**

For the function pictured in Figure 8-16, estimate

a. The real values of *x* for which $f(x) = 0$.

b. The value of $f(0)$.

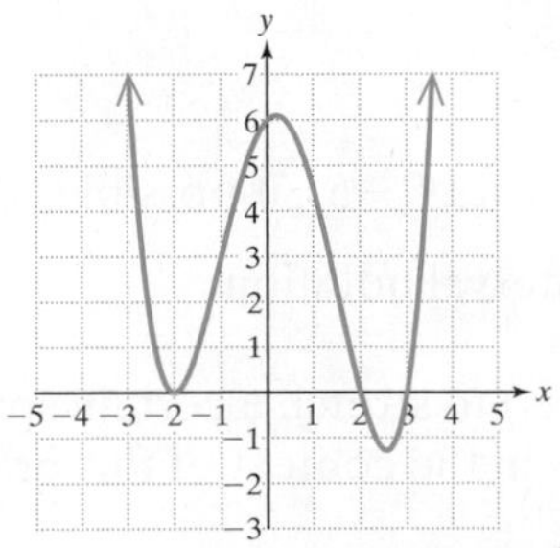

Figure 8-16

Solution:

a. The real values of x for which $f(x) = 0$ are the x-intercepts of the function. For this graph, the x-intercepts are located at $x = -2$, $x = 2$, and $x = 3$.

b. The value of $f(0)$ is the value of y at $x = 0$. That is, $f(0)$ is the y-intercept, $f(0) = 6$.

Skill Practice Use the function pictured.

10. a. Estimate the real value(s) of x for which $f(x) = 0$

b. Estimate the value of $f(0)$.

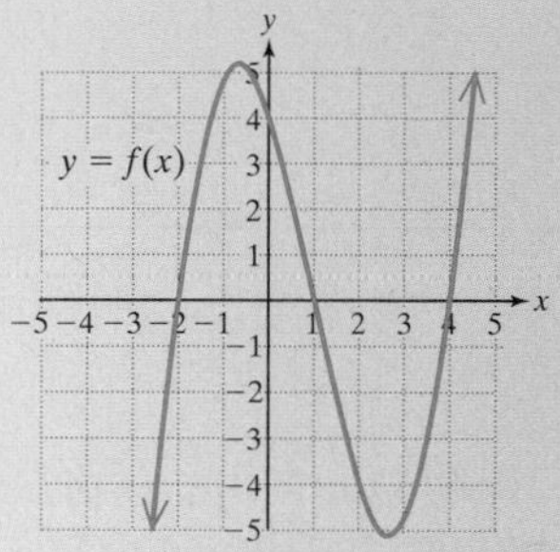

Answer

10. a. $x = -2$, $x = 1$, and $x = 4$
 b. $f(0) = 4$

Section 8.3 Practice Exercises

Vocabulary and Key Concepts

1. **a.** A function that can be written in the form $f(x) = mx + b, m \neq 0$, is a ____________ function.
 b. A function that can be written in the form $f(x) = b$ is a ____________ function.
 c. A function that can be written in the form $f(x) = ax^2 + bx + c, a \neq 0$, is a ____________ function.
 d. The graph of a quadratic function is in the shape of a ____________.
 e. To find the x-intercept(s) of a graph defined by $y = f(x)$, find the real solutions to the equation $f(x) =$ ____________.
 f. To find the ____________-intercept of a graph defined by $y = f(x)$, evaluate $f(0)$.

Review Exercises

2. Given: $g = \{(6, 1), (5, 2), (4, 3), (3, 4)\}$
 a. Is this relation a function?
 b. List the elements in the domain.
 c. List the elements in the range.

3. Given: $f = \{(7, 3), (2, 3), (-5, 3)\}$
 a. Is this relation a function?
 b. List the elements in the domain.
 c. List the elements in the range.

4. Given: $f(x) = \sqrt{x + 4}$
 a. Evaluate $f(0)$, $f(-3)$, $f(-4)$, and $f(-5)$, if possible.
 b. Write the domain of f in interval notation.

5. The force (measured in pounds) to stretch a certain spring x inches is given by $f(x) = 3x$. Evaluate $f(3)$ and $f(10)$, and interpret the results in the context of this problem.

6. The velocity (in feet per second) of a falling object is given by $V(t) = -32t$, where t is the time in seconds after the object was released. Evaluate $V(2)$ and interpret the results in the context of this problem.

Concept 1: Linear and Constant Functions

7. Fill in the blank with the word *vertical* or *horizontal.* The graph of a constant function is a ______ line.

8. For the linear function defined by $f(x) = mx + b$, identify the slope and y-intercept.

9. Graph the constant function $f(x) = 2$. Then use the graph to identify the domain and range of f.

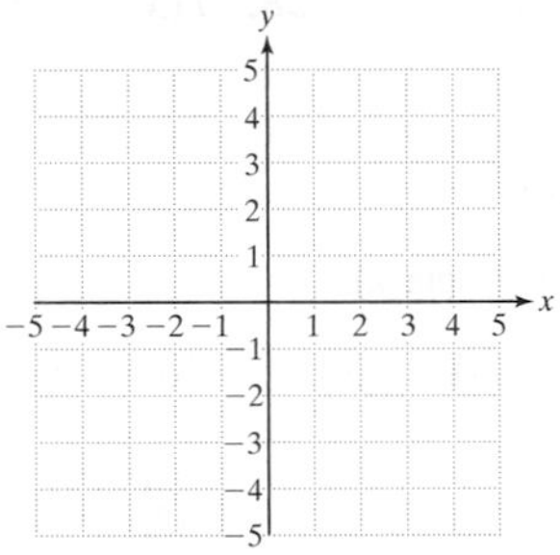

10. Graph the linear function $g(x) = -2x + 1$. Then use the graph to identify the domain and range of g.

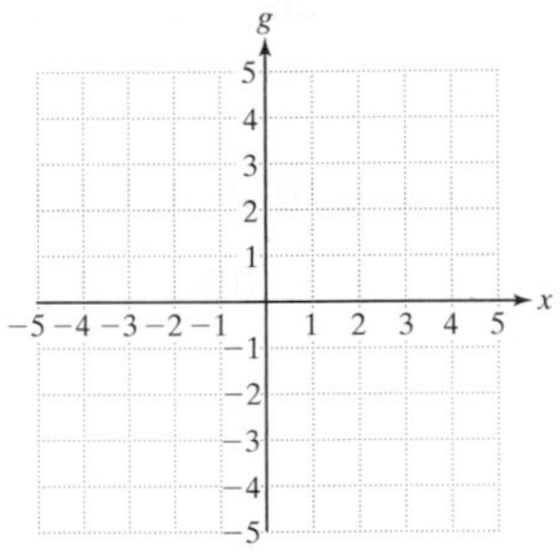

Concept 2: Graphs of Basic Functions

For Exercises 11–16, sketch a graph by completing the table and plotting the points. **(See Examples 1–2.)**

11. $f(x) = \dfrac{1}{x}$

Animation

x	$f(x)$
-2	
-1	
$-\frac{1}{2}$	
$-\frac{1}{4}$	

x	$f(x)$
$\frac{1}{4}$	
$\frac{1}{2}$	
1	
2	

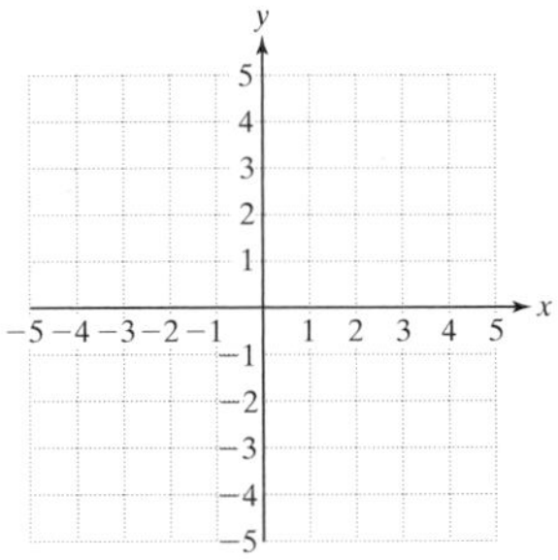

12. $g(x) = |x|$

x	$g(x)$
-2	
-1	
0	
1	
2	

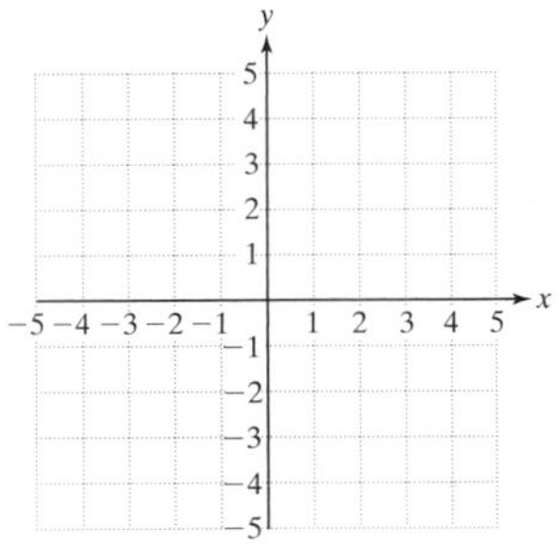

13. $h(x) = x^3$

x	$h(x)$
-2	
-1	
0	
1	
2	

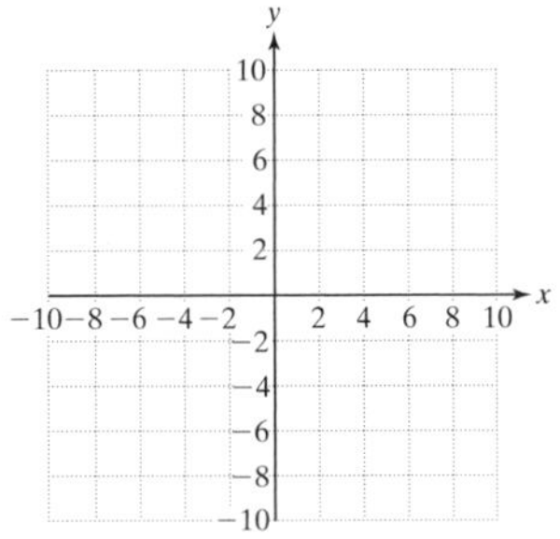

14. $k(x) = x$

x	$k(x)$
-2	
-1	
0	
1	
2	

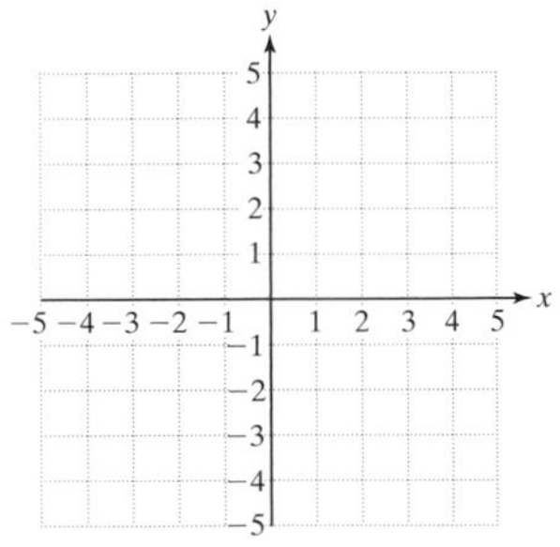

15. $q(x) = x^2$

x	$q(x)$
-2	
-1	
0	
1	
2	

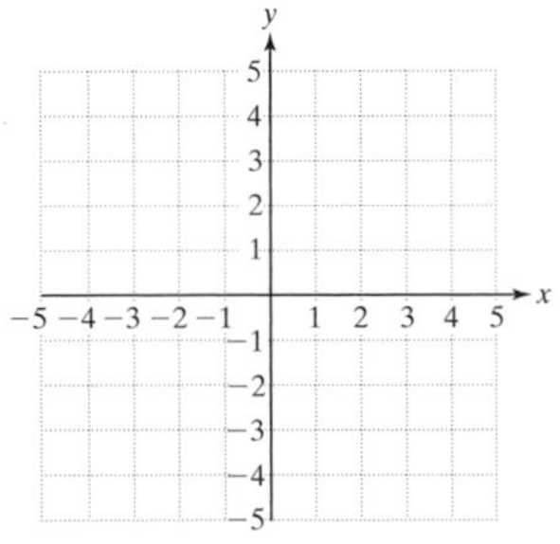

16. $p(x) = \sqrt{x}$

x	$p(x)$
0	
1	
4	
9	
16	

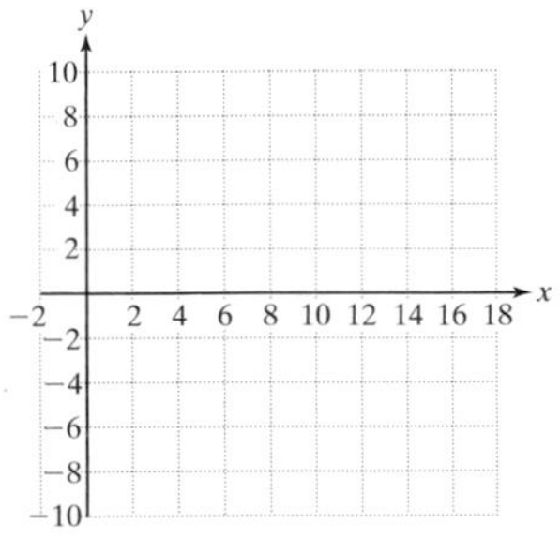

v.

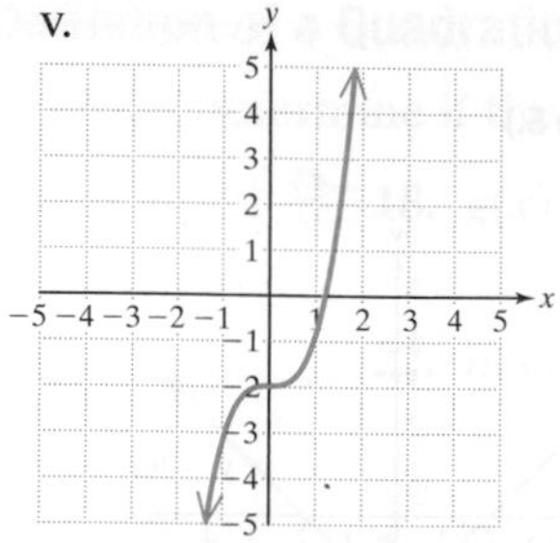

vi.

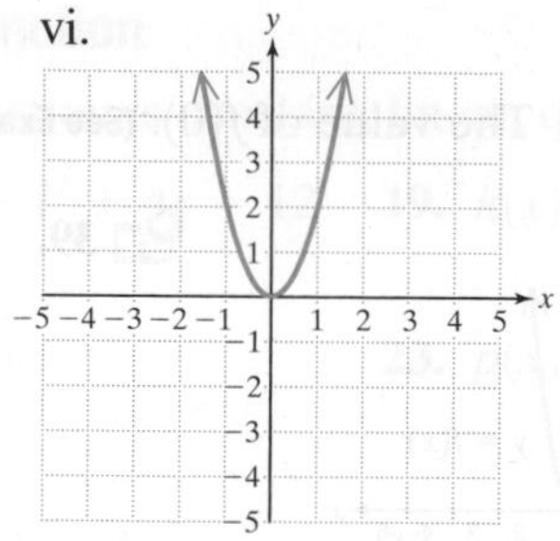

vii.

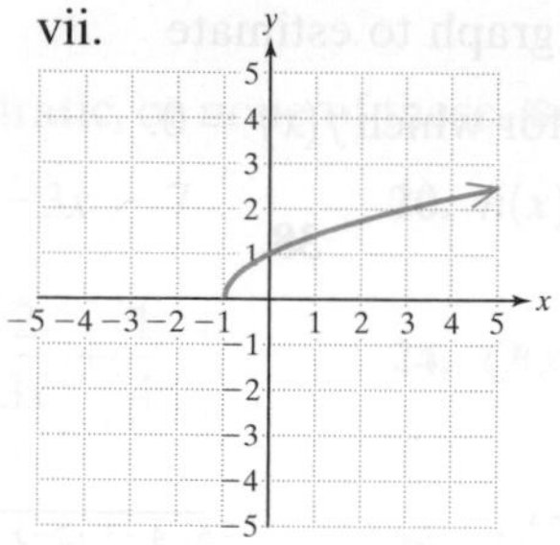

viii.

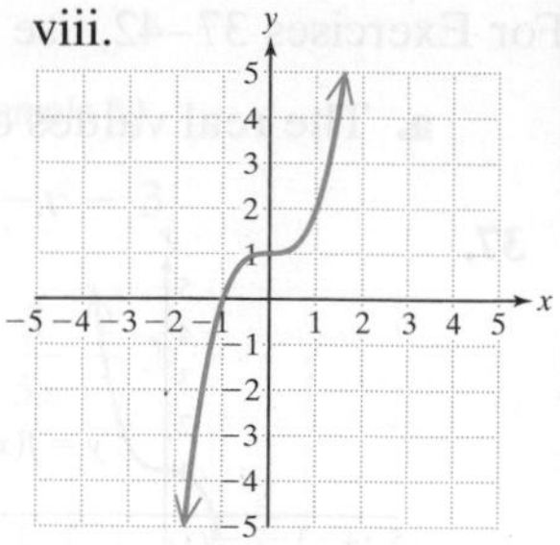

ix.

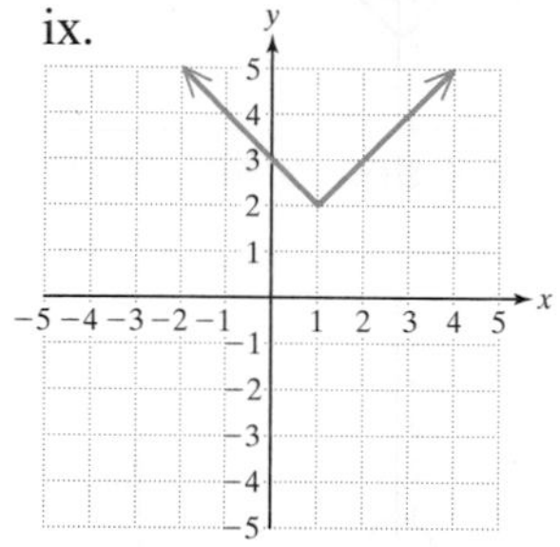

x.

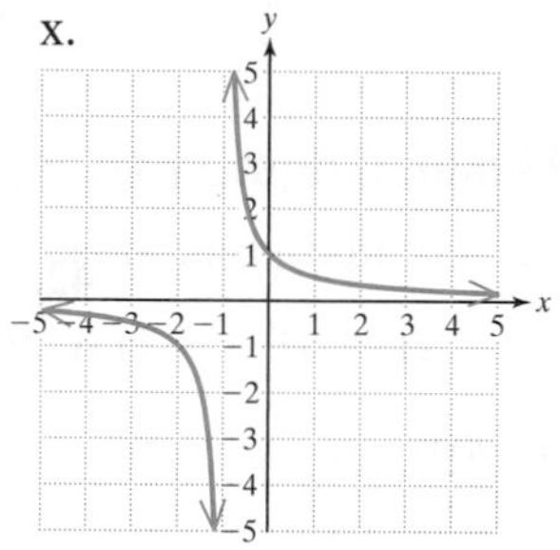

53. Suppose that a student has an 80% average on all of her chapter tests in her Intermediate Algebra class. This counts as $\frac{3}{4}$ of the student's overall grade. The final exam grade counts as the remaining $\frac{1}{4}$ of the student's overall grade. The student's overall course grade, $G(x)$, can be computed by

$$G(x) = \frac{3}{4}(80) + \frac{1}{4}x, \text{ where } x \text{ is the student's grade on the final exam.}$$

a. Is this function linear, quadratic, or neither?

b. Evaluate $G(90)$ and interpret its meaning in the context of the problem.

c. Evaluate $G(50)$ and interpret its meaning in the context of the problem.

54. The median weekly earnings, $E(x)$ in dollars, for women 16 yr and older working full time can be approximated by $E(x) = 0.14x^2 + 7.8x + 540$. For this function, x represents the number of years since 2000. (*Source:* U.S. Department of Labor)

a. Is this function linear, quadratic, or neither?

b. Evaluate $E(5)$ and interpret its meaning in the context of this problem.

c. Evaluate $E(10)$ and interpret its meaning in the context of this problem.

For Exercises 55–60, write a function defined by $y = f(x)$ under the given conditions.

55. The value of $f(x)$ is two more than the square of x.

56. The value of $f(x)$ is the square of the sum of two and x.

57. The function f is a constant function passing through the point $(4, 3)$.

58. The function f is a constant function with y-intercept $(0, 5)$.

59. The function f is a linear function with slope $\frac{1}{2}$ and y-intercept $(0, -2)$.

60. The function f is a linear function with slope -4 and y-intercept $(0, \frac{1}{3})$.

Graphing Calculator Exercises

For Exercises 61–66, use a graphing calculator to graph the basic functions. Verify your answers from the table on page 588.

61. $f(x) = x$ **62.** $f(x) = x^2$ **63.** $f(x) = x^3$

64. $f(x) = |x|$ **65.** $f(x) = \sqrt{x}$ **66.** $f(x) = \frac{1}{x}$

For Exercises 67–70, find the x- and y-intercepts using a graphing calculator and the *Value* and *Zero* features.

67. $y = -\frac{1}{8}x + 1$

68. $y = -\frac{1}{2}x - 3$

69. $y = \frac{4}{5}x + 4$

70. $y = \frac{7}{2}x - 7$

Problem Recognition Exercises

Characteristics of Relations

Exercises 1–15 refer to the sets of points (x, y) described in a–h.

a. $\{(0, 8), (1, 4), (\frac{1}{2}, 4), (-3, 5), (2, 1)\}$

b. $\{(-6, 4), (2, 3), (-9, 6), (2, 1), (0, 10)\}$

c. $c(x) = 3x^2 - 2x - 1$

d. $d(x) = 5x - 9$

e.

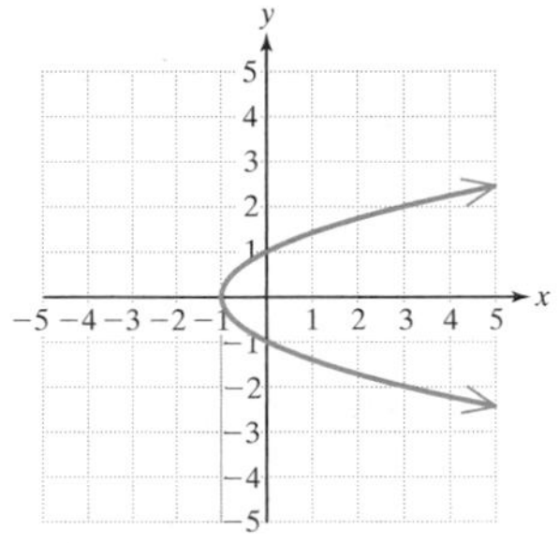

f.

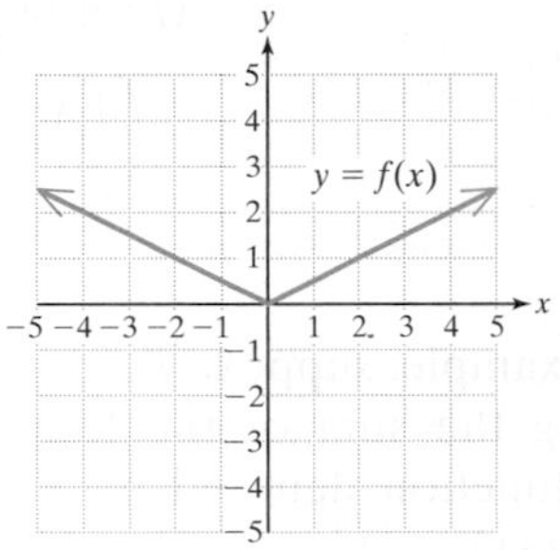

g.

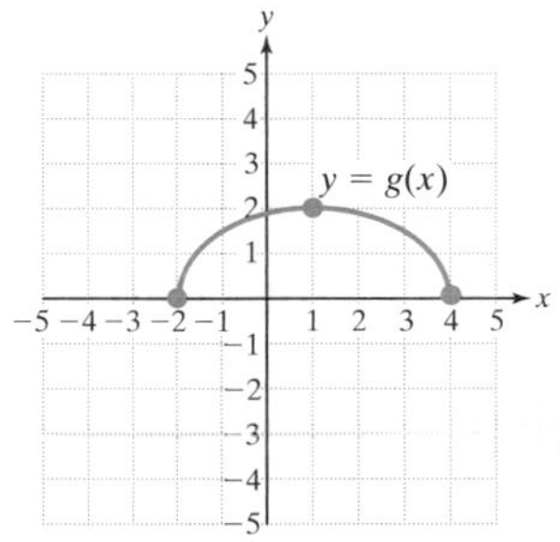

h.

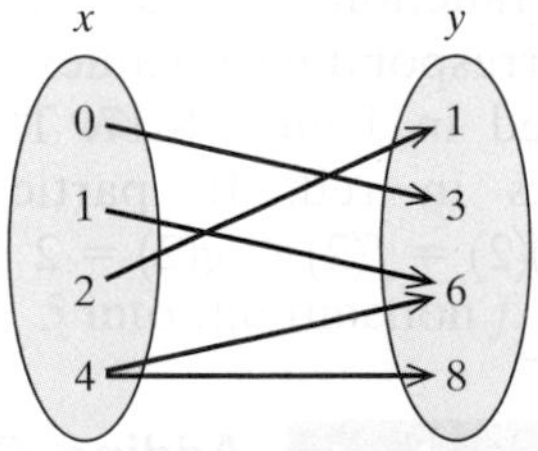

1. Which relations define y as a function of x?

2. Which relations contain the point $(2, 1)$?

3. Use relation (c) to find $c(-1)$.

4. Use relation (f) to find $f(-4)$.

5. Find the domain of relation (a).

6. Find the range of relation (b).

7. Find the domain of relation (g).

8. Find the range of relation (f).

9. Use relation (h) to complete the ordered pair (__, 3).

10. Find the x-intercept(s) of the graph of relation (d).

11. Find the y-intercept(s) of the graph shown in relation (e).

12. Use relation (g) to determine the value of x such that $g(x) = 2$.

13. Which relation describes a quadratic function?

14. Which relation describes a linear function?

15. Use relation (d) to find the value of x such that $d(x) = 6$.

Solution:

a. $(f \circ g)(x) = f(g(x))$

$= f(x^2)$ Evaluate the function f at x^2.

$= (x^2) - 5$ Replace x by x^2 in the function f.

$= x^2 - 5$

b. $(g \circ f)(x) = g(f(x))$

$= g(x - 5)$ Evaluate the function g at $(x - 5)$.

$= (x - 5)^2$ Replace x by $(x - 5)$ in function g.

$= x^2 - 10x + 25$ Simplify.

c. $(n \circ f)(x) = n(f(x))$

$= n(x - 5)$ Evaluate the function n at $x - 5$.

$= \sqrt{(x - 5) + 2}$ Replace x by the quantity $(x - 5)$ in function n.

$= \sqrt{x - 3}$

TIP: Examples 2(a) and 2(b) illustrate that the order in which two functions are composed may result in different functions. That is, $f \circ g$ does not necessarily equal $g \circ f$.

Skill Practice Given $f(x) = 2x^2$, $g(x) = x + 3$, and $h(x) = \sqrt{x - 1}$, find

5. $(f \circ g)(x)$ **6.** $(g \circ f)(x)$ **7.** $(h \circ g)(x)$

3. Operations on Functions

Example 3 Combining Functions

Given the functions defined by $f(x) = x - 7$ and $h(x) = 2x^3$, find the function values, if possible.

a. $(f \cdot h)(3)$ **b.** $\left(\frac{h}{f}\right)(7)$ **c.** $(h \circ f)(2)$

Solution:

a. $(f \cdot h)(3) = f(3) \cdot h(3)$ $(f \cdot h)(3)$ is a product (not a composition).

$= (3 - 7) \cdot 2(3)^3$

$= (-4) \cdot 2(27)$

$= -216$

b. $\left(\frac{h}{f}\right)(7) = \frac{h(7)}{f(7)} = \frac{2(7)^3}{7 - 7}$

The value $x = 7$ will make the denominator equal to 0. Therefore, $\left(\frac{h}{f}\right)(7)$ is undefined.

c. $(h \circ f)(2) = h(f(2))$ Evaluate $f(2)$ first. $f(2) = 2 - 7 = -5$.

$= h(-5)$ Substitute the result into function h.

$= 2(-5)^3$

$= 2(-125)$

$= -250$

Answers

5. $2x^2 + 12x + 18$ **6.** $2x^2 + 3$

7. $\sqrt{x + 2}$

Skill Practice Given $h(x) = x + 4$ and $k(x) = x^2 - 3$, find

8. $(h \cdot k)(-2)$ **9.** $\left(\frac{k}{h}\right)(-4)$ **10.** $(k \circ h)(1)$

Example 4 Finding Function Values from a Graph

For the functions f and g pictured, find the function values if possible.

a. $g(2)$

b. $(f - g)(-3)$

c. $\left(\frac{g}{f}\right)(5)$

d. $(f \circ g)(4)$

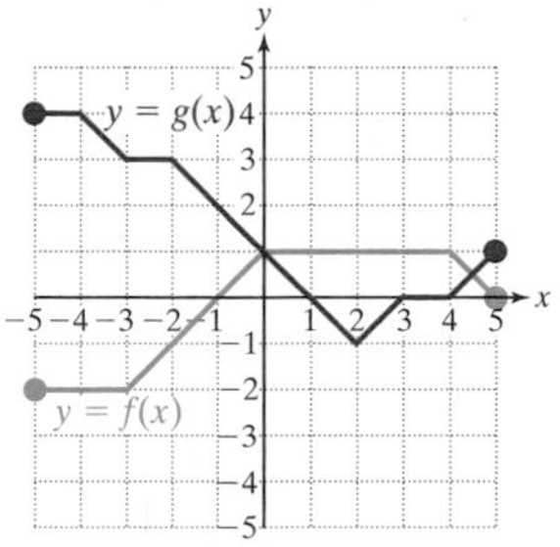

Solution:

a. $g(2) = -1$

The value $g(2)$ represents the y-value of $y = g(x)$ (the red graph) when $x = 2$. Because the point $(2, -1)$ lies on the graph, $g(2) = -1$.

b. $(f - g)(-3) = f(-3) - g(-3)$ Evaluate the difference of $f(-3)$ and $g(-3)$.

$= -2 - (3)$ Estimate function values from the graph.

$= -5$

c. $\left(\frac{g}{f}\right)(5) = \frac{g(5)}{f(5)}$ Evaluate the quotient of $g(5)$ and $f(5)$.

$= \frac{1}{0}$ (undefined)

The function $\frac{g}{f}$ is undefined at 5 because the denominator is zero.

d. $(f \circ g)(4) = f(g(4))$ From the red graph, find the value of $g(4)$ first. We see that $g(4) = 0$.

$= f(0)$ From the blue graph, find the value of f at $x = 0$.

$= 1$

Skill Practice Find the values from the graph.

11. $g(3)$

12. $(f + g)(-4)$

13. $\left(\frac{f}{g}\right)(2)$

14. $(g \circ f)(-2)$

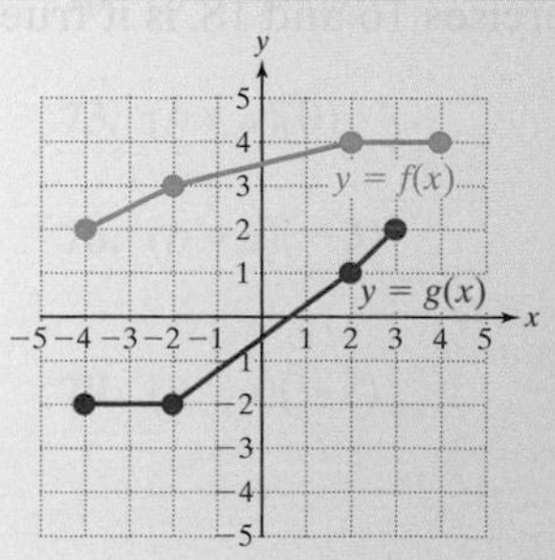

Answers

8. 2 **9.** undefined **10.** 22
11. 2 **12.** 0 **13.** 4 **14.** 2

81. The cost in dollars of producing x toy cars is $C(x) = 2.2x + 1$. The revenue received is $R(x) = 5.98x$. To calculate profit, subtract the cost from the revenue.

a. Write and simplify a function P that represents profit in terms of x.

b. Find the profit of producing 50 toy cars.

82. The cost in dollars of producing x lawn chairs is $C(x) = 2.5x + 10.1$. The revenue for selling x lawn chairs is $R(x) = 6.99x$. To calculate profit, subtract the cost from the revenue.

a. Write and simplify a function P that represents profit in terms of x.

b. Find the profit in producing 100 lawn chairs.

83. The functions defined by $D(t) = 0.925t + 26.958$ and $R(t) = 0.725t + 20.558$ approximate the amount of child support (in billions of dollars) that was due and the amount of child support actually received in the United States since 2000. In each case, $t = 0$ corresponds to the year 2000.

a. Find the function F defined by $F(t) = D(t) - R(t)$. What does F represent in the context of this problem?

b. Find $F(4)$. What does this function value represent in the context of this problem?

Difference Between Child Support Due and Child Support Paid, United States

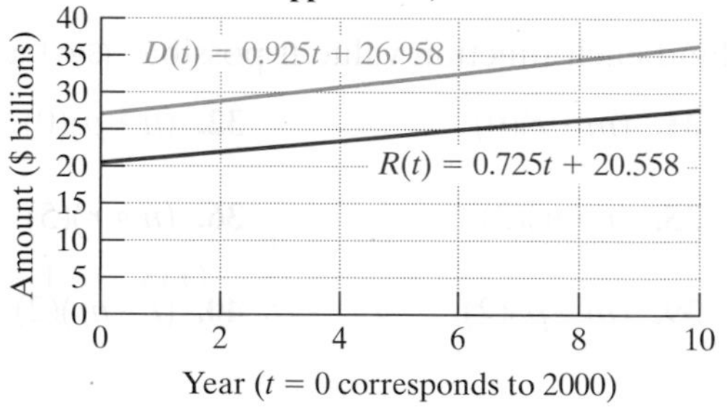

Source: U.S. Bureau of the Census

84. The rural and urban populations in the South (in the United States) between the years 1900 and 1970 can be modeled by the following:

$$r(t) = -3.497t^2 + 266.2t + 20{,}220$$

$$u(t) = 0.0566t^3 + 0.952t^2 + 177.8t + 4593$$

The variable t represents the number of years since 1900, $r(t)$ represents the rural population in thousands, and $u(t)$ represents the urban population in thousands.

Rural and Urban Populations in the South, United States, 1900–1970

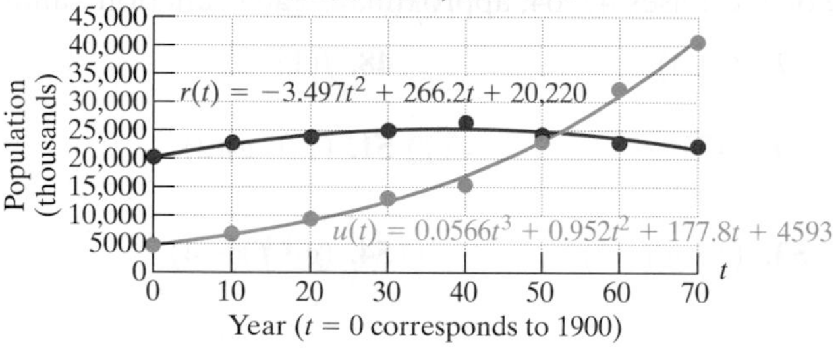

Source: Historical Abstract of the United States

a. Find the function T defined by $T(t) = r(t) + u(t)$. What does the function T represent in the context of this problem?

b. Use the function T to approximate the total population in the South for the year 1940.

85. Joe rides a bicycle and his wheels revolve at 80 revolutions per minute (rpm). Therefore, the total number of revolutions, r, is given by $r(t) = 80t$, where t is the time in minutes. For each revolution of the wheels of the bike, he travels approximately 7 ft. Therefore, the total distance he travels, D, depends on the total number of revolutions, r, according to the function $D(r) = 7r$.

a. Find $(D \circ r)(t)$ and interpret its meaning in the context of this problem.

b. Find Joe's total distance in feet after 10 min.

86. The area of a square is given by the function $a(x) = x^2$, where x is the length of the sides of the square. If carpeting costs \$9.95 per square yard, then the cost, C, to carpet a square room is given by $C(a) = 9.95a$, where a is the area of the room in square yards.

a. Find $(C \circ a)(x)$ and interpret its meaning in the context of this problem.

b. Find the cost to carpet a square room if its floor dimensions are 15 yd by 15 yd.

Variation

Section 8.5

Concepts

1. **Definition of Direct and Inverse Variation**
2. **Translations Involving Variation**
3. **Applications of Variation**

1. Definition of Direct and Inverse Variation

In this section, we introduce the concept of variation. Direct and inverse variation models can show how one quantity varies in proportion to another.

Definition of Direct and Inverse Variation

Let k be a nonzero constant real number. Then,

1. y varies **directly** as x.
   y is directly proportional to x. $\Big\}\quad y = kx$
2. y varies **inversely** as x.
   y is inversely proportional to x. $\Big\}\quad y = \dfrac{k}{x}$

Note: The value of k is called the constant of variation.

For a car traveling 30 mph, the equation $d = 30t$ indicates that the distance traveled is *directly proportional* to the time of travel. For positive values of k, when two variables are directly related, as one variable increases, the other variable will also increase. Likewise, if one variable decreases, the other will decrease. In the equation $d = 30t$, the longer the time of the trip, the greater the distance traveled. The shorter the time of the trip, the shorter the distance traveled.

For positive values of k, when two positive variables are *inversely related*, as one variable increases, the other will decrease, and vice versa. Consider a car traveling between Toronto and Montreal, a distance of 500 km. The time required to make the trip is inversely proportional to the speed of travel: $t = 500/r$. As the rate of speed, r, increases, the quotient $500/r$ will decrease. Thus, the time will decrease. Similarly, as the rate of speed decreases, the trip will take longer.

2. Translations Involving Variation

The first step in using a variation model is to write an English phrase as an equivalent mathematical equation.

Example 1 Translating to a Variation Model

Write each expression as an equivalent mathematical model.

a. The circumference of a circle varies directly as the radius.

b. At a constant temperature, the volume of a gas varies inversely as the pressure.

c. The length of time of a meeting is directly proportional to the *square* of the number of people present.

Example 4 Solving an Application Involving Direct Variation

The speed of a racing canoe in still water varies directly as the square root of the length of the canoe.

a. If a 16-ft canoe can travel 6.2 mph in still water, find a variation model that relates the speed of a canoe to its length.

b. Find the speed of a 25-ft canoe.

Solution:

a. Let s represent the speed of the canoe and L represent the length. The general variation model is $s = k\sqrt{L}$. To solve for k, substitute the known values for s and L.

$$s = k\sqrt{L}$$

$$6.2 = k\sqrt{16} \qquad \text{Substitute } s = 6.2 \text{ mph and } L = 16 \text{ ft.}$$

$$6.2 = k \cdot 4$$

$$\frac{6.2}{4} = \frac{4k}{4} \qquad \text{Solve for } k.$$

$$k = 1.55$$

$$s = 1.55\sqrt{L} \qquad \text{Substitute } k = 1.55 \text{ into the model } s = k\sqrt{L}.$$

b. $s = 1.55\sqrt{L}$

$= 1.55\sqrt{25}$ Find the speed when $L = 25$ ft.

$= 7.75$ mph The speed is 7.75 mph.

Skill Practice

9. The amount of water needed by a mountain hiker varies directly as the time spent hiking. The hiker needs 2.4 L for a 4-hr hike. How much water will be needed for a 5-hr hike?

Example 5 Solving an Application Involving Inverse Variation

The loudness of sound measured in decibels (dB) varies inversely as the square of the distance between the listener and the source of the sound. If the loudness of sound is 17.92 dB at a distance of 10 ft from a home theater speaker, what is the decibel level 20 ft from the speaker?

Solution:

Let L represent the loudness of sound in decibels and d represent the distance in feet. The inverse relationship between decibel level and the square of the distance is modeled by

Answer

9. 3 L

$$L = \frac{k}{d^2}$$

$$17.92 = \frac{k}{(10)^2}$$ Substitute $L = 17.92$ dB and $d = 10$ ft.

$$17.92 = \frac{k}{100}$$

$$(17.92)100 = \frac{k}{100} \cdot 100$$ Solve for k (clear fractions).

$$k = 1792$$

$$L = \frac{1792}{d^2}$$ Substitute $k = 1792$ into the original model $L = \frac{k}{d^2}$.

With the value of k known, we can find L for any value of d.

$$L = \frac{1792}{(20)^2}$$ Find the loudness when $d = 20$ ft.

$$= 4.48 \text{ dB}$$ The loudness is 4.48 dB.

Notice that the loudness of sound is 17.92 dB at a distance 10 ft from the speaker. When the distance from the speaker is increased to 20 ft, the decibel level decreases to 4.48 dB. This is consistent with an inverse relationship. For $k > 0$, as one variable is increased, the other is decreased. It also seems reasonable that the further one moves away from the source of a sound, the softer the sound becomes.

Skill Practice

10. The yield on a bond varies inversely as the price. The yield on a particular bond is 5% when the price is \$100. Find the yield when the price is \$125.

Example 6 Solving an Application Involving Joint Variation

The kinetic energy of an object varies jointly as the weight of the object at sea level and as the square of its velocity. During a hurricane, a 0.5-lb stone traveling at 60 mph has 81 J (joules) of kinetic energy. Suppose the wind speed doubles to 120 mph. Find the kinetic energy.

Solution:

Let E represent the kinetic energy, let w represent the weight, and let v represent the velocity of the stone. The variation model is

$$E = kwv^2$$

$$81 = k(0.5)(60)^2$$ Substitute $E = 81$ J, $w = 0.5$ lb, and $v = 60$ mph.

$$81 = k(0.5)(3600)$$ Simplify exponents.

$$81 = k(1800)$$

$$\frac{81}{1800} = \frac{k(1800)}{1800}$$ Divide by 1800.

$$0.045 = k$$ Solve for k.

Answer

10. 4%

With the value of k known, the model $E = kwv^2$ can now be written as $E = 0.045wv^2$. We now find the kinetic energy of a 0.5-lb stone traveling at 120 mph.

$$E = 0.045(0.5)(120)^2$$
$$= 324$$

The kinetic energy of a 0.5-lb stone traveling at 120 mph is 324 J.

Skill Practice

11. The amount of simple interest earned in an account varies jointly as the interest rate and time of the investment. An account earns $72 in 4 years at 2% interest. How much interest would be earned in 3 years at a rate of 5%?

Answer

11. $135

In Example 6, when the velocity increased by 2 times, the kinetic energy increased by 4 times (note that 324 J = 4 · 81 J). This factor of 4 occurs because the kinetic energy is proportional to the *square* of the velocity. When the velocity increased by 2 times, the kinetic energy increased by 2^2 times.

Section 8.5 Practice Exercises

Vocabulary and Key Concepts

1. a. Let k be a nonzero constant. If y varies directly as x, then $y =$ ____________, where k is the constant of variation.

b. Let k be a nonzero constant. If y varies inversely as x, then $y =$ ____________, where k is the constant of variation.

c. Let k be a nonzero constant. If y varies jointly as x and w, then $y =$ ____________, where k is the constant of variation.

Review Exercises

For Exercises 2–7, refer to the functions defined below.

$$f(x) = x^2 \qquad g(x) = x - 2 \qquad h(x) = \sqrt{2 - x}$$

Find the indicated functions or function values.

2. $(f + g)(2)$

3. $(f \circ g)(x)$

4. $(g - f)(3)$

5. $(g \circ f)(x)$

6. $(f \cdot g)(x)$

7. $\left(\frac{g}{h}\right)(1)$

Concept 1: Definition of Direct and Inverse Variation

8. In the equation $r = kt$, does r vary directly or inversely as t?

9. In the equation $w = \frac{k}{v}$, does w vary directly or inversely as v?

10. In the equation $P = \frac{k \cdot c}{v}$, does P vary directly or inversely as v?

Concept 2: Translations Involving Variation

For Exercises 11–22, write a variation model. Use k as the constant of variation. **(See Examples 1–2.)**

11. T varies directly as q.

12. W varies directly as z.

13. b varies inversely as c.

14. m varies inversely as t.

15. Q is directly proportional to x and inversely proportional to y.

16. d is directly proportional to p and inversely proportional to n.

17. c varies jointly as s and t.

18. w varies jointly as p and f.

19. L varies jointly as w and the square root of v.

20. q varies jointly as v and the square root of w.

21. x varies directly as the square of y and inversely as z.

22. a varies directly as n and inversely as the square of d.

Concept 3: Applications of Variation

For Exercises 23–28, find the constant of variation, k. **(See Example 3.)**

23. y varies directly as x and when x is 4, y is 18.

24. m varies directly as x and when x is 8, m is 22.

25. p varies inversely as q and when q is 16, p is 32.

26. T varies inversely as x and when x is 40, T is 200.

27. y varies jointly as w and v. When w is 50 and v is 0.1, y is 8.75.

28. N varies jointly as t and p. When t is 1 and p is 7.5, N is 330.

Solve Exercises 29–40 using the steps found on page 607. **(See Example 3.)**

29. x varies directly as p. If $x = 50$ when $p = 10$, find x when p is 14.

30. y is directly proportional to z. If $y = 12$ when $z = 36$, find y when z is 21.

31. b is inversely proportional to c. If b is 4 when c is 3, find b when $c = 2$.

32. q varies inversely as w. If q is 8 when w is 50, find q when w is 125.

33. Z varies directly as the square of w. If $Z = 14$ when $w = 4$, find Z when $w = 8$.

34. m varies directly as the square of x. If $m = 200$ when $x = 20$, find m when x is 32.

35. Q varies inversely as the square of p. If $Q = 4$ when $p = 3$, find Q when $p = 2$.

36. z is inversely proportional to the square of t. If $z = 15$ when $t = 4$, find z when $t = 10$.

37. L varies jointly as a and the square root of b. If $L = 72$ when $a = 8$ and $b = 9$, find L when $a = \frac{1}{2}$ and $b = 36$.

38. Y varies jointly as the cube of x and the square root of w. $Y = 128$ when $x = 2$ and $w = 16$. Find Y when $x = \frac{1}{2}$ and $w = 64$.

39. B varies directly as m and inversely as n. $B = 20$ when $m = 10$ and $n = 3$. Find B when $m = 15$ and $n = 12$.

40. R varies directly as s and inversely as t. $R = 14$ when $s = 2$ and $t = 9$. Find R when $s = 4$ and $t = 3$.

For Exercises 41–58, use a variation model to solve for the unknown value. **(See Examples 4–6.)**

41. The weight of a person's heart varies directly as the person's actual weight. For a 150-lb man, his heart would weigh 0.75 lb.

a. Approximate the weight of a 184-lb man's heart.

b. How much does your heart weigh?

42. The number of calories, C, in beer varies directly with the number of ounces, n. If 12 oz of beer contains 153 calories, how many calories are in 40 oz of beer?

43. The amount of medicine that a physician prescribes for a patient varies directly as the weight of the patient. A physician prescribes 3 g of a medicine for a 150-lb person.

a. How many grams should be prescribed for a 180-lb person?

b. How many grams should be prescribed for a 225-lb person?

c. How many grams should be prescribed for a 120-lb person?

44. The number of turkeys needed for a banquet is directly proportional to the number of guests that must be fed. Master Chef Rico knows that he needs to cook 3 turkeys to feed 42 guests.

a. How many turkeys should he cook to feed 70 guests?

b. How many turkeys should he cook to feed 140 guests?

c. How many turkeys should be cooked to feed 700 guests at an inaugural ball?

d. How many turkeys should be cooked for a wedding with 100 guests?

45. The unit cost of producing CDs is inversely proportional to the number of CDs produced. If 5000 CDs are produced, the cost per CD is \$0.48.

a. What would be the unit cost if 6000 CDs were produced?

b. What would be the unit cost if 8000 CDs were produced?

c. What would be the unit cost if 2400 CDs were produced?

46. An author self-publishes a book and finds that the number of books she can sell per month varies inversely as the price of the book. The author can sell 1500 books per month when the price is set at \$8 per book.

a. How many books would she expect to sell if the price were \$12?

b. How many books would she expect to sell if the price were \$15?

c. How many books would she expect to sell if the price were \$6?

47. The amount of pollution entering the atmosphere over a given time varies directly as the number of people living in an area. If 80,000 people create 56,800 tons of pollutants, how many tons enter the atmosphere in a city with a population of 500,000?

48. The area of a picture projected on a wall varies directly as the square of the distance from the projector to the wall. If a 10-ft distance produces a 16-ft^2 picture, what is the area of a picture produced when the projection unit is moved to a distance 20 ft from the wall?

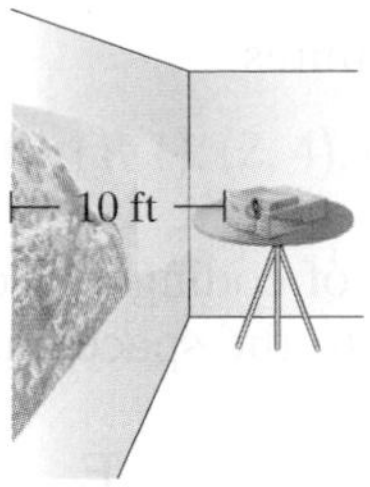

49. The stopping distance of a car varies directly as the square of the speed of the car. If a car traveling at 40 mph has a stopping distance of 109 ft, find the stopping distance of a car that is traveling at 25 mph. (Round your answer to one decimal place.)

50. The intensity of a light source varies inversely as the square of the distance from the source. If the intensity of a light bulb is 400 lumen/m^2 (lux) at a distance of 5 m, determine the intensity at 8 m.

51. The power in an electric circuit varies jointly as the current and the square of the resistance. If the power is 144 W (watts) when the current is 4 A (amperes) and the resistance is 6 Ω, find the power when the current is 3 A and the resistance is 10 Ω.

52. Some body-builders claim that, within safe limits, the number of repetitions that a person can complete on a given weight-lifting exercise is inversely proportional to the amount of weight lifted. Roxanne can bench press 45 lb for 15 repetitions.

a. How many repetitions can Roxanne bench with 60 lb of weight?

b. How many repetitions can Roxanne bench with 75 lb of weight?

c. How many repetitions can Roxanne bench with 100 lb of weight?

53. The current in a wire varies directly as the voltage and inversely as the resistance. If the current is 9 A when the voltage is 90 V (volts) and the resistance is 10 Ω (ohms), find the current when the voltage is 185 V and the resistance is 10 Ω.

54. The resistance of a wire varies directly as its length and inversely as the square of its diameter. A 40-ft wire 0.1 in. in diameter has a resistance of 4 Ω. What is the resistance of a 50-ft wire with a diameter of 0.2 in.?

55. The weight of a medicine ball varies directly as the cube of its radius. A ball with a radius of 3 in. weighs 4.32 lb. How much would a medicine ball weigh if its radius is 5 in.?

56. The area of an equilateral triangle varies directly as the square of the length of the sides. For an equilateral triangle with 7-cm sides, the area is 21.22 cm^2. What is the area of an equilateral triangle with 17-cm sides? Round to the nearest whole unit.

57. The amount of simple interest earned in an account varies jointly as the amount of principal invested and the amount of time the money is invested. If $2500 in principal earns $500 in interest after 4 years, then how much interest will be earned on $7000 invested for 10 years?

58. The amount of simple interest earned in an account varies jointly as the amount of principal invested and the amount of time the money is invested. If $6000 in principal earns $840 in interest after 2 years, then how much interest will be earned on $4500 invested for 8 years?

Function Notation

$f(x)$ is the value of the function f at x.

The domain of a function defined by $y = f(x)$ is the set of x-values that when substituted into the function produces a real number. In particular,

- Exclude values of x that make the denominator of a fraction zero.
- Exclude values of x that make the expression within a square root negative.

Example 3

Given $f(x) = -3x^2 + 5x$, find $f(-2)$.

$$\begin{aligned} f(-2) &= -3(-2)^2 + 5(-2) \\ &= -12 - 10 \\ &= -22 \end{aligned}$$

Example 4

Find the domain.

1. $f(x) = \dfrac{x+4}{x-5}$; Domain: $(-\infty, 5) \cup (5, \infty)$
2. $f(x) = \sqrt{x-3}$; Domain: $[3, \infty)$
3. $f(x) = 3x^2 - 5$; Domain: $(-\infty, \infty)$

Section 8.3 Graphs of Functions

Key Concepts

A function of the form $f(x) = mx + b$ $(m \neq 0)$ is a **linear function**. Its graph is a line with slope m and y-intercept $(0, b)$.

A function of the form $f(x) = k$ is a **constant function**. Its graph is a horizontal line.

A function of the form $f(x) = ax^2 + bx + c$ $(a \neq 0)$ is a **quadratic function**. Its graph is a **parabola**.

Graphs of basic functions:

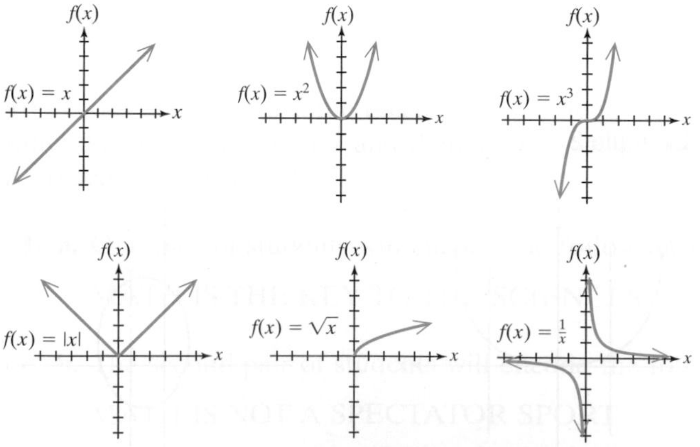

The x-intercepts of a function are determined by finding the real solutions to the equation $f(x) = 0$.

The y-intercept of a function is at $f(0)$.

Examples

Example 1

$f(x) = 2x - 3$

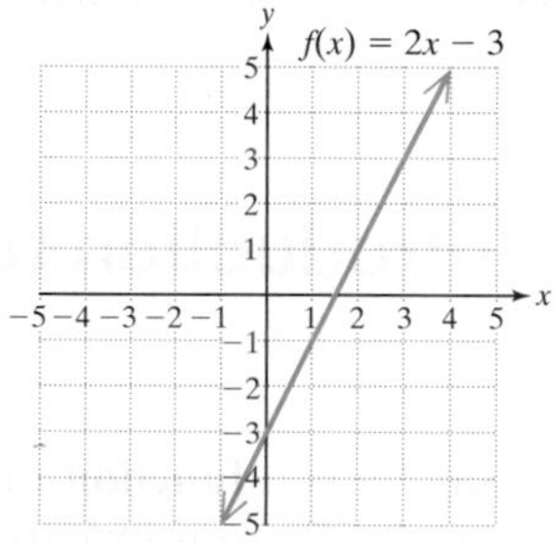

$f(x) = 3$

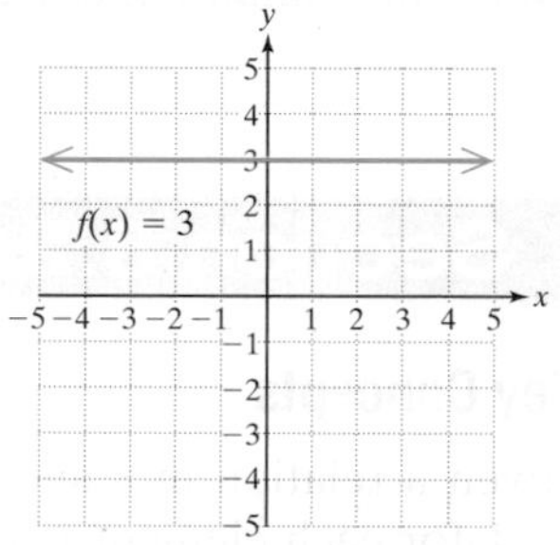

Example 2

Find the x- and y-intercepts for the function pictured.

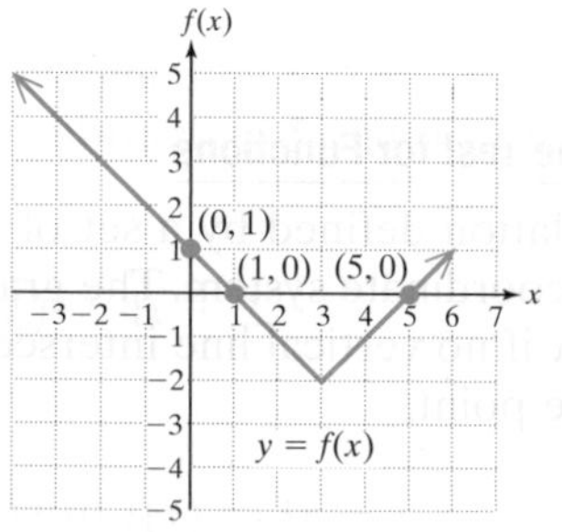

$f(x) = 0$, when $x = 1$ and $x = 5$.

The x-intercepts are $(1, 0)$ and $(5, 0)$.

$f(0) = 1$. The y-intercept is $(0, 1)$.

Section 8.4 Algebra of Functions and Composition

Key Concepts

The Algebra of Functions

Given two functions f and g, the functions $f + g, f - g, f \cdot g$, and $\frac{f}{g}$ are defined as

$$(f + g)(x) = f(x) + g(x)$$
$$(f - g)(x) = f(x) - g(x)$$
$$(f \cdot g)(x) = f(x) \cdot g(x)$$
$$\left(\frac{f}{g}\right)(x) = \frac{f(x)}{g(x)} \quad \text{provided } g(x) \neq 0$$

Composition of Functions

The **composition** of f and g, denoted $f \circ g$, is defined by the rule

$(f \circ g)(x) = f(g(x))$ provided that $g(x)$ is in the domain of f

Examples

Example 1

Let $g(x) = 5x + 1$ and $h(x) = x^3$. Find:

1. $(g + h)(3) = g(3) + h(3) = 16 + 27 = 43$
2. $(g \cdot h)(-1) = g(-1) \cdot h(-1) = (-4) \cdot (-1) = 4$
3. $(g - h)(x) = 5x + 1 - x^3$
4. $\left(\frac{g}{h}\right)(x) = \frac{5x + 1}{x^3}, x \neq 0$

Example 2

Find $(f \circ g)(x)$ given the functions defined by $f(x) = 4x + 3$ and $g(x) = 7x$.

$$\begin{aligned}(f \circ g)(x) &= f(g(x)) \\ &= f(7x) \\ &= 4(7x) + 3 \\ &= 28x + 3\end{aligned}$$

Section 8.5 Variation

Key Concepts

Direct Variation

y varies directly as x.
y is directly proportional to x. } $y = kx$

Inverse Variation

y varies inversely as x.
y is inversely proportional to x. } $y = \frac{k}{x}$

Examples

Example 1

t varies directly as the square root of x.

$t = k\sqrt{x}$

Example 2

W is inversely proportional to the cube of x.

$W = \frac{k}{x^3}$

For Exercises 32–33, sketch the functions.

32. $q(x) = 3$

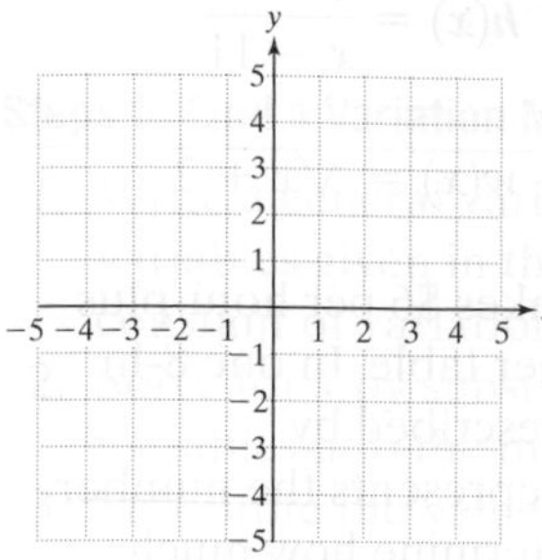

33. $k(x) = 2x + 1$

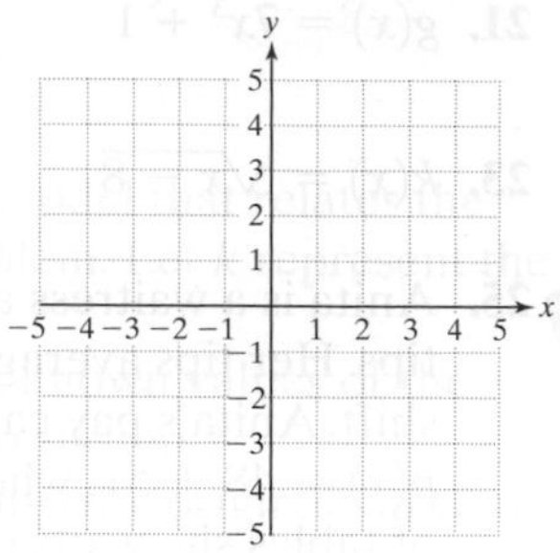

34. Given: $s(x) = (x - 2)^2$

a. Find $s(4), s(-3), s(2), s(1)$, and $s(0)$.

b. What is the domain of s?

35. Given: $r(x) = 2\sqrt{x - 4}$

a. Find $r(2), r(4), r(5)$, and $r(8)$.

b. What is the domain of r?

36. Given: $h(x) = \dfrac{3}{x - 3}$

a. Find $h(-3), h(0), h(2)$, and $h(5)$.

b. What is the domain of h?

37. Given: $k(x) = -|x + 3|$

a. Find $k(-5), k(-4), k(-3)$, and $k(2)$.

b. What is the domain of k?

For Exercises 38–39, find the x- and y-intercepts.

38. $p(x) = 4x - 7$

39. $q(x) = -2x + 9$

40. The function defined by $b(t) = 0.7t + 4.5$ represents the per capita consumption of bottled water in the United States since 1985. The values of $b(t)$ are measured in gallons, and $t = 0$ corresponds to the year 1985. (*Source:* U.S. Department of Agriculture)

a. Evaluate $b(0)$ and $b(7)$ and interpret the results in the context of this problem.

b. Determine the slope and interpret its meaning in the context of this problem.

For Exercises 41–46, refer to the graph.

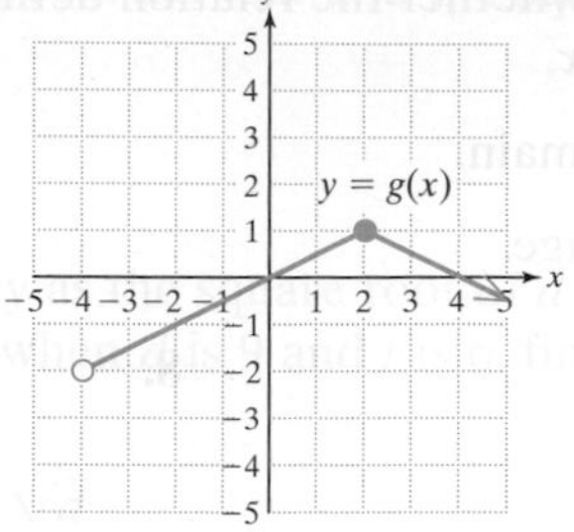

41. Find $g(-2)$. **42.** Find $g(4)$.

43. For what value(s) of x is $g(x) = 0$?

44. For what value(s) of x is $g(x) = 4$?

45. Write the domain of g.

46. Write the range of g.

Section 8.4

For Exercises 47–54, refer to the functions defined here.

$$f(x) = x - 7 \qquad g(x) = -2x^3 - 8x$$
$$m(x) = x^2 \qquad n(x) = \frac{1}{x - 2}$$

Find the indicated functions.

47. $(f - g)(x)$ **48.** $(f + g)(x)$

49. $(f \cdot n)(x)$ **50.** $(f \cdot m)(x)$

51. $\left(\dfrac{f}{g}\right)(x)$ **52.** $\left(\dfrac{g}{f}\right)(x)$

53. $(m \circ f)(x)$ **54.** $(n \circ f)(x)$

For Exercises 55–58, refer to the functions defined for Exercises 47–54. Find the function values, if possible.

55. $(m \circ g)(-1)$ **56.** $(n \circ g)(-1)$

57. $(f \circ g)(4)$ **58.** $(g \circ f)(8)$

59. Given $f(x) = 2x + 1$ and $g(x) = x^2$

a. Find $(g \circ f)(x)$.

b. Find $(f \circ g)(x)$.

c. Based on your answers to part (a), is $f \circ g$ equal to $g \circ f$?

For Exercises 60–65, refer to the graph. Approximate the function values, if possible.

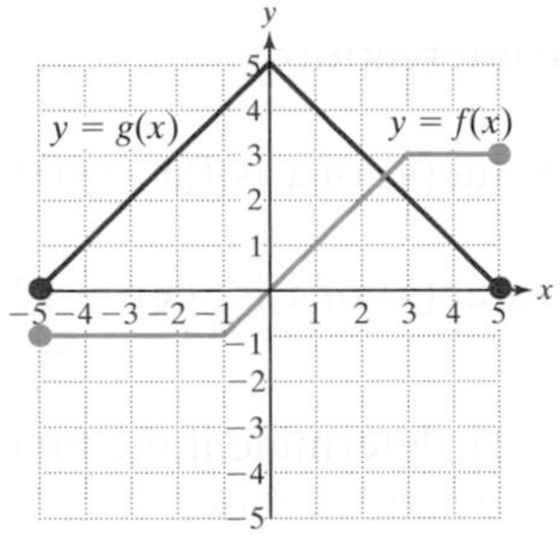

60. $\left(\frac{f}{g}\right)(1)$

61. $(f \cdot g)(-2)$

62. $(f + g)(-4)$

63. $(f - g)(2)$

64. $(g \circ f)(-3)$

65. $(f \circ g)(4)$

Section 8.5

66. The force applied to a spring varies directly with the distance that the spring is stretched.

 a. Write a variation model using k as the constant of variation.

 b. When 6 lb of force is applied, the spring stretches 2 ft. Find k.

 c. How much force is required to stretch the spring 4.2 ft?

67. Suppose y varies inversely with the cube of x, and $y = 9$ when $x = 2$. Find y when $x = 3$.

68. Suppose y varies jointly with x and the square root of z, and $y = 3$ when $x = 3$ and $z = 4$. Find y when $x = 8$ and $z = 9$.

69. The distance, d, that one can see to the horizon varies directly as the square root of the height above sea level. If a person 25 m above sea level can see 30 km, how far can a person see if she is 64 m above sea level?

Chapter 8 Test

For Exercises 1–2, **a.** determine if the relation defines y as a function of x, **b.** identify the domain, and **c.** identify the range.

1.

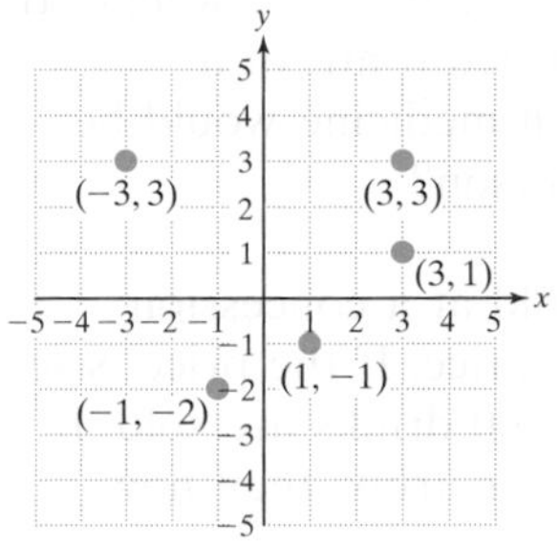

2.

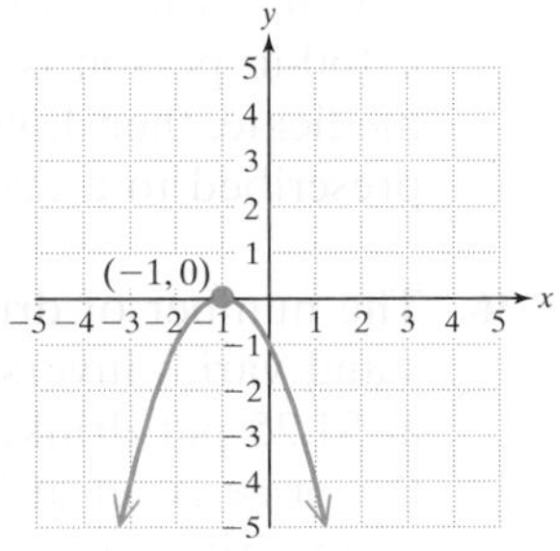

3. Explain how to find the x- and y-intercepts of the graph defined by $y = f(x)$.

For Exercises 4–7, graph the functions.

4. $f(x) = -3x - 1$

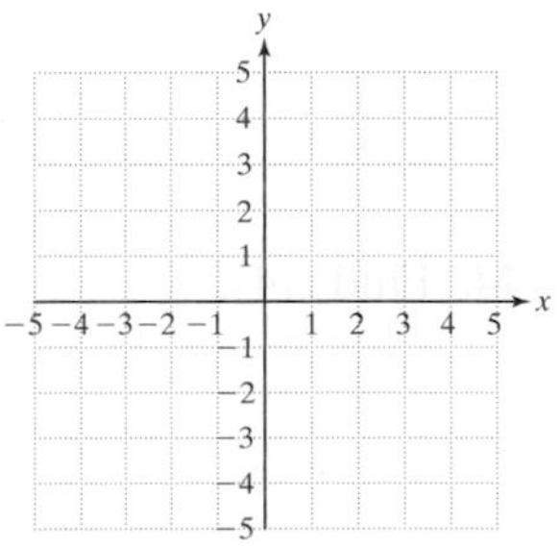

5. $k(x) = -2$

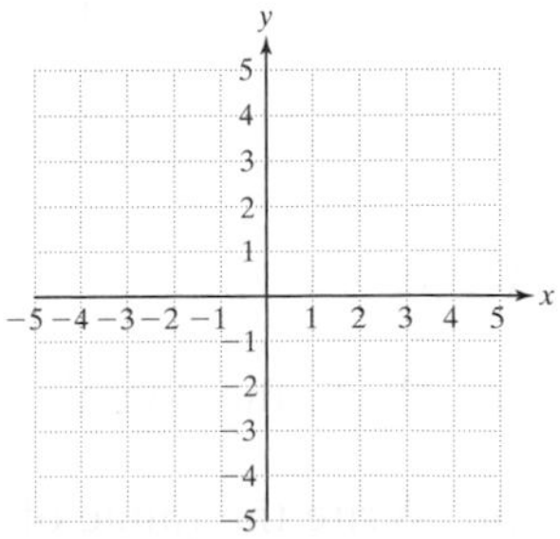

For Exercises 8–10, write the domain in interval notation.

8. $f(x) = \frac{x - 5}{x + 7}$

9. $f(x) =$ [illegible]

10. $h(x) = (x - 7)(x - 6)$

11. Given $r(x) = x^2 - 2x + 1$

a. Find $r(-2)$, $r(0)$, and $r(3)$.

b. What is the domain of r?

12. The function defined by [illegible] approximates the per capita consumption of bottled water in the United States [illegible] The value of [illegible] corresponds to the year [illegible] $s(7)$ and [illegible] this problem.

For Exercises 13–16, refer to the graph.

13. Find $f(1)$.

14. Find $f(4)$.

15. Write the domain of f.

16. Write the range of f.

18. Find the [illegible]

19. For what value(s) of x is $f(x) = 0$?

20. For what value(s) of x is $f(x) = 12$?

For Exercises 21–24, determine if the function is constant, linear, quadratic, or none of these.

21. $f(x) =$ [illegible]

23. $h(x) =$ [illegible]

25. Find the x- and y-intercepts for $f(x) =$ [illegible]

For Exercises 26–34, refer to these functions.

[illegible]

Find the indicated functions or function values.

26. [illegible]

28. [illegible]

29. [illegible]

32. [illegible]

33. [illegible]

34. [illegible]

35. [illegible] If the person is prescribed [illegible] medicine, then how much medicine [illegible] prescribed to a 220-lb person?

36. The number of drinks sold at a concession stand varies inversely as price. If the price is set at \$1.25 per drink, then 400 drinks are sold. If the price is set at \$2.50 per drink, then how many drinks are sold?

More Equations and Inequalities

9

CHAPTER OUTLINE

9.1 Compound Inequalities 626
9.2 Polynomial and Rational Inequalities 638
9.3 Absolute Value Equations 649
9.4 Absolute Value Inequalities 656
Problem Recognition Exercises: Equations and Inequalities 666
9.5 Linear Inequalities and Systems of Linear Inequalities in Two Variables 667
Group Activity: Recognizing Inequality Types 680

Chapter 9

In this chapter we will solve different types of inequalities including polynomial, rational, and absolute value inequalities.

Are You Prepared?

To prepare for this section, practice solving linear inequalities in one variable that were first presented in Section 2.8. Match the inequality on the left with the correct solution set on the right.

1. $5(x + 1) > 20$	**a.** $(-\infty, 3)$
2. $9x + 1 \le -x + 31$	**b.** $(3, \infty)$
3. $2x + 5 < 4x + 11$	**c.** $[-3, \infty)$
4. $5(2x + 1) < -x + 38$	**d.** $(-\infty, -3]$
5. $7 \ge -x + 10$	**e.** $[3, \infty)$
6. $2(x + 2) \ge -2$	**f.** $(-3, \infty)$
7. $-7x + 8 \ge 29$	**g.** $(-\infty, 3]$
8. $-4x + 32 > 44$	**h.** $(-\infty, -3)$

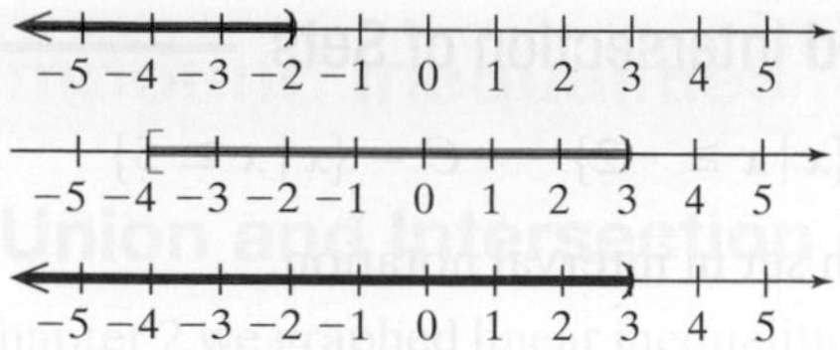

$(-\infty, -2)$

$[-4, 3)$

The union consists of all real numbers in the red interval along with the real numbers in the blue interval: $(-\infty, 3)$

The union is $(-\infty, 3)$.

b. $(-\infty, -2) \cap [-4, 3)$

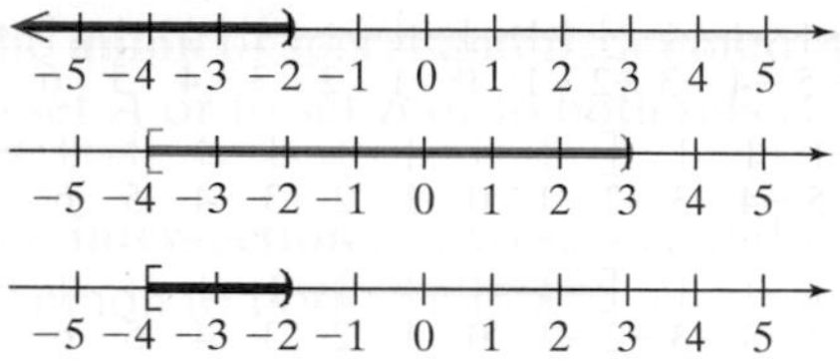

$(-\infty, -2)$

$[-4, 3)$

The intersection is the "overlap" of the two intervals: $[-4, -2)$.

The intersection is $[-4, -2)$.

Skill Practice Find the union or intersection. Write the answer in interval notation.

6. $(-\infty, -5] \cup (-7, 0)$ **7.** $(-\infty, -5] \cap (-7, 0)$

2. Solving Compound Inequalities: And

The solution to two inequalities joined by the word *and* is the intersection of their solution sets.

Solving a Compound Inequality: And

Step 1 Solve and graph each inequality separately.

Step 2 If the inequalities are joined by the word *and*, find the intersection of the two solution sets.

Step 3 Express the solution set in interval notation or in set-builder notation.

As you work through the examples in this section, remember that multiplying or dividing an inequality by a negative factor reverses the direction of the inequality sign.

Example 4 Solving a Compound Inequality: And

Solve the compound inequality.

$$-2x < 6 \quad \text{and} \quad x + 5 \leq 7$$

Solution:

$-2x < 6$ and $x + 5 \leq 7$ Solve each inequality separately.

$\dfrac{-2x}{-2} > \dfrac{6}{-2}$ and $x \leq 2$ Reverse the first inequality sign.

$x > -3$ and $x \leq 2$

Answers

6. $(-\infty, 0)$ **7.** $(-7, -5]$

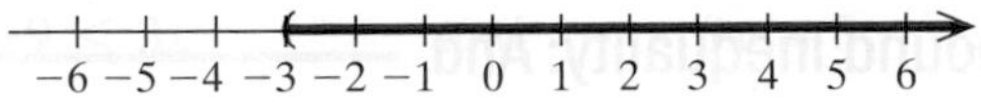

$\{x \mid x > -3\}$

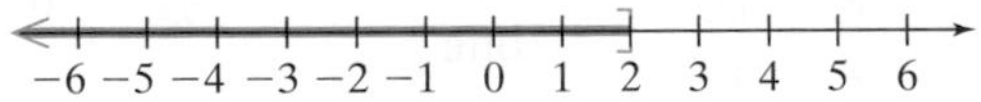

$\{x \mid x \le 2\}$

Identify the intersection of the solution sets: $\{x \mid -3 < x \le 2\}$

The solution is $\{x \mid -3 < x \le 2\}$, or equivalently in interval notation, $(-3, 2]$.

Skill Practice Solve the compound inequality.

8. $5x + 2 \ge -8$ and $-4x > -24$

Example 5 Solving a Compound Inequality: And

Solve the compound inequality.

$$4.4a + 3.1 < -12.3 \quad \text{and} \quad -2.8a + 9.1 < -6.3$$

Solution:

$$4.4a + 3.1 < -12.3 \quad \text{and} \quad -2.8a + 9.1 < -6.3$$

$$4.4a < -15.4 \quad \text{and} \quad -2.8a < -15.4$$

Solve each inequality separately.

$$\frac{4.4a}{4.4} < \frac{-15.4}{4.4} \quad \text{and} \quad \frac{-2.8a}{-2.8} > \frac{-15.4}{-2.8}$$

Reverse the second inequality sign.

$$a < -3.5 \quad \text{and} \quad a > 5.5$$

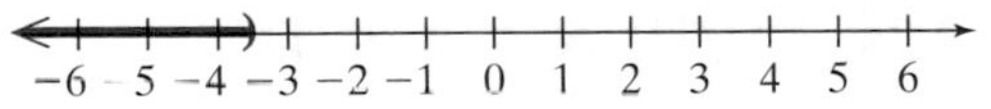

$\{a \mid a < -3.5\}$

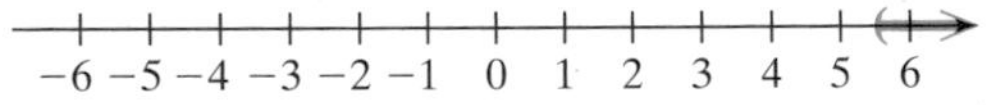

$\{a \mid a > 5.5\}$

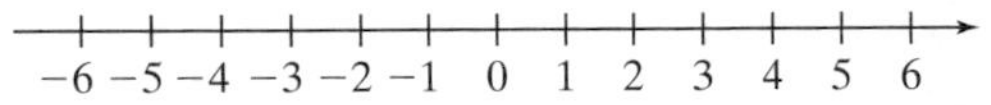

The intersection of the solution sets is the empty set: { }

There are no real numbers that are simultaneously less than -3.5 and greater than 5.5. There is no solution.

The solution set is { }.

Skill Practice Solve the compound inequality.

9. $3.2y - 2.4 > 16.8$ and $-4.1y \ge 8.2$

Answers

8. $\{x \mid -2 \le x < 6\}$; $[-2, 6)$

9. { }

Solving a Compound Inequality: Or

Step 1 Solve and graph each inequality separately.

Step 2 If the inequalities are joined by the word *or*, find the union of the two solution sets.

Step 3 Express the solution set in interval notation or in set-builder notation.

Example 9 Solving a Compound Inequality: Or

Solve the compound inequality.

$$-3y - 5 > 4 \quad \text{or} \quad 4 - y \le 6$$

Solution:

$-3y - 5 > 4$ or $4 - y \le 6$

$-3y > 9$ or $-y \le 2$ Solve each inequality separately.

$\dfrac{-3y}{-3} < \dfrac{9}{-3}$ or $\dfrac{-y}{-1} \ge \dfrac{2}{-1}$ Reverse the inequality signs.

$y < -3$ or $y \ge -2$

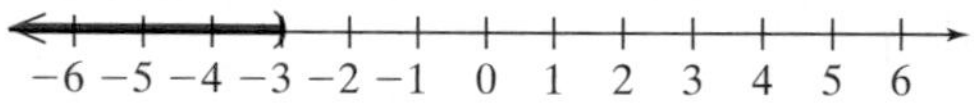

$\{y \mid y < -3\}$

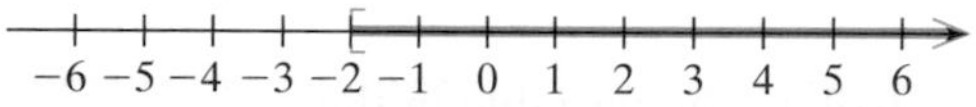

$\{y \mid y \ge -2\}$

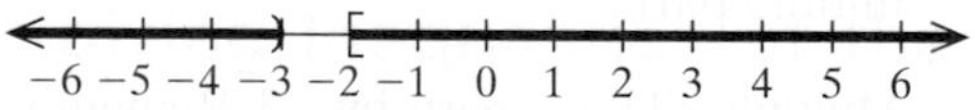

Identify the union of the solution sets: $\{y \mid y < -3 \text{ or } y \ge -2\}$

The solution is $\{y \mid y < -3 \text{ or } y \ge -2\}$ or, equivalently in interval notation, $(-\infty, -3) \cup [-2, \infty)$.

Skill Practice Solve the compound inequality.

13. $-10t - 8 \ge 12$ or $3t - 6 > 3$

Example 10 Solving a Compound Inequality: Or

Solve the compound inequality.

$$4x + 3 < 16 \quad \text{or} \quad -2x < 3$$

Answer

13. $\{t \mid t \le -2 \text{ or } t > 3\}$; $(-\infty, -2] \cup (3, \infty)$

Solution:

$4x + 3 < 16 \quad \text{or} \quad -2x < 3$

$4x < 13 \quad \text{or} \quad x > -\frac{3}{2}$ Solve each inequality separately.

$x < \frac{13}{4} \quad \text{or} \quad x > -\frac{3}{2}$

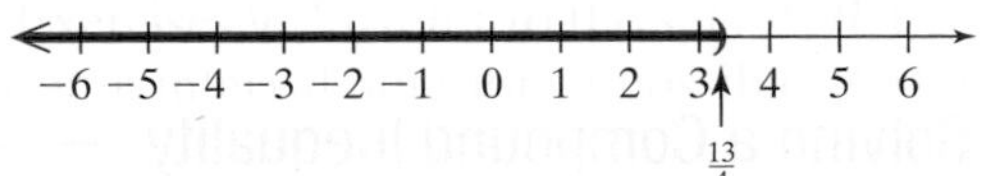

$\{x \mid x < \frac{13}{4}\}$

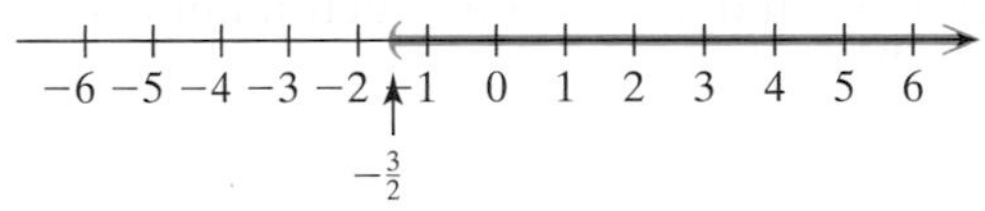

$\{x \mid x > -\frac{3}{2}\}$

Identify the union of the solution sets.

The union of the solution sets is $\{x \mid x$ is a real number$\}$, or equivalently, $(-\infty, \infty)$.

Skill Practice Solve the compound inequality.

14. $x - 7 > -2$ or $-6x > -48$

5. Applications of Compound Inequalities

Compound inequalities are used in many applications, as shown in Examples 11 and 12.

Example 11 **Translating Compound Inequalities**

The normal level of thyroid-stimulating hormone (TSH) for adults ranges from 0.4 to 4.8 microunits per milliliter (μU/mL), inclusive. Let x represent the amount of TSH measured in microunits per milliliter.

a. Write an inequality representing the normal range of TSH, inclusive.

b. Write a compound inequality representing abnormal TSH levels.

Solution:

a. $0.4 \le x \le 4.8$ **b.** $x < 0.4$ or $x > 4.8$

Skill Practice The length of a normal human pregnancy, w, is from 37 to 41 weeks, inclusive.

15. Write an inequality representing the normal length of a pregnancy.

16. Write a compound inequality representing an abnormal length for a pregnancy.

Answers

14. $\{x \mid x$ is a real number$\}$; $(-\infty, \infty)$

15. $37 \le w \le 41$

16. $w < 37$ or $w > 41$

Concept 3: Solving Inequalities of the Form $a < x < b$

37. Write $-4 \le t < \frac{3}{4}$ as two separate inequalities.

38. Write $-2.8 < y \le 15$ as two separate inequalities.

39. Explain why $6 < x < 2$ has no solution.

40. Explain why $4 < t < 1$ has no solution.

41. Explain why $-5 > y > -2$ has no solution.

42. Explain why $-3 > w > -1$ has no solution.

For Exercises 43–54, solve the compound inequality and graph the solution set. Write the answer in interval notation. **(See Examples 7–8.)**

43. $0 \le 2b - 5 < 9$

44. $-6 < 3k - 9 \le 0$

45. $-1 < \frac{a}{6} \le 1$

46. $-3 \le \frac{1}{2}x < 0$

47. $-\frac{2}{3} < \frac{y - 4}{-6} < \frac{1}{3}$

48. $\frac{1}{3} > \frac{t - 4}{-3} > -2$

49. $5 \le -3x - 2 \le 8$

50. $-1 < -2x + 4 \le 5$

51. $12 > 6x + 3 \ge 0$

52. $-4 \ge 2x - 5 > -7$

53. $-0.2 < 2.6 + 7t < 4$

54. $-1.5 < 0.1x \le 8.1$

Concept 4: Solving Compound Inequalities: Or

For Exercises 55–64, solve the compound inequality and graph the solution set. Write the answer in interval notation. **(See Examples 9–10.)**

55. $2y - 1 \ge 3$ or $y < -2$

56. $x < 0$ or $3x + 1 \ge 7$

57. $1 > 6z - 8$ or $8z - 6 \le 10$

58. $22 > 4t - 10$ or $7 > 2t - 5$

59. $5(x - 1) \ge -5$ or $5 - x \le 11$

60. $-p + 7 \ge 10$ or $3(p - 1) \le 12$

61. $\frac{5}{3}v \le 5$ or $-v - 6 < 1$

62. $\frac{3}{8}u + 1 > 0$ or $-2u \ge -4$

63. $0.5w + 5 < 2.5w - 4$ or $0.3w \le -0.1w - 1.6$

64. $1.25a + 3 \le 0.5a - 6$ or $2.5a - 1 \ge 9 - 1.5a$

Mixed Exercises

For Exercises 65–74, solve the compound inequality. Write the answer in interval notation.

65. **a.** $3x - 5 < 19$ and $-2x + 3 < 23$
    b. $3x - 5 < 19$ or $-2x + 3 < 23$

66. **a.** $0.5(6x + 8) > 0.8x - 7$ and $4(x + 1) < 7.2$
    b. $0.5(6x + 8) > 0.8x - 7$ or $4(x + 1) < 7.2$

67. **a.** $8x - 4 \ge 6.4$ or $0.3(x + 6) \le -0.6$
    b. $8x - 4 \ge 6.4$ and $0.3(x + 6) \le -0.6$

68. **a.** $-2r + 4 \le -8$ or $3r + 5 \le 8$
    b. $-2r + 4 \le -8$ and $3r + 5 \le 8$

69. $-4 \le \dfrac{2-4x}{3} < 8$

70. $-1 < \dfrac{3-x}{2} \le 0$

71. $5 \ge -4(t-3) + 3t$ or $6 < 12t + 8(4-t)$

72. $3 > -(w-3) + 4w$ or $-5 \ge -3(w-5) + 6w$

73. $\dfrac{-x+3}{2} > \dfrac{4+x}{5}$ or $\dfrac{1-x}{4} > \dfrac{2-x}{3}$

74. $\dfrac{y-7}{-3} < \dfrac{1}{4}$ or $\dfrac{y+1}{-2} > -\dfrac{1}{3}$

Concept 5: Applications of Compound Inequalities

75. The normal number of white blood cells for human blood is between 4800 and 10,800 cells per cubic millimeter, inclusive. Let x represent the number of white blood cells per cubic millimeter. **(See Example 11.)**

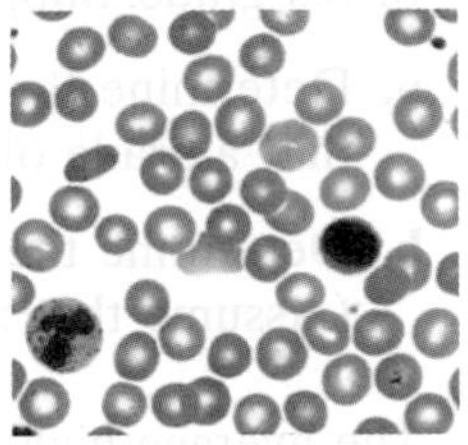

a. Write an inequality representing the normal range of white blood cells per cubic millimeter.

b. Write a compound inequality representing abnormal levels of white blood cells per cubic millimeter.

76. Normal hemoglobin levels in human blood for adult males are between 13 and 16 grams per deciliter (g/dL), inclusive. Let x represent the level of hemoglobin measured in grams per deciliter.

a. Write an inequality representing normal hemoglobin levels for adult males.

b. Write a compound inequality representing abnormal levels of hemoglobin for adult males.

77. A polling company estimates that a certain candidate running for office will receive between 44% and 48% of the votes. Let x represent the percentage of votes for this candidate.

a. Write a strict inequality representing the expected percentage of votes for this candidate.

b. Write a compound inequality representing the percentage of votes that would fall outside the polling company's prediction.

78. A machine is calibrated to cut a piece of wood between 2.4 in. thick and 2.6 in. thick. Let x represent the thickness of the wood after it is cut.

a. Write a strict inequality representing the expected range of thickness of the wood after it has been cut.

b. Write a compound inequality representing the thickness of wood that would fall outside the normal range for this machine.

79. Twice a number is between -3 and 12. Find all such numbers. **(See Example 12.)**

80. The difference of a number and 6 is between 0 and 8. Find all such numbers.

81. One plus twice a number is either greater than 5 or less than -1. Find all such numbers.

82. One-third of a number is either less than -2 or greater than 5. Find all such numbers.

Notice that $x = 1$ and $x = 5$ are the boundaries of the solution set to the inequalities in Example 1. These values are the solutions to the related equation $x^2 - 6x + 5 = 0$.

Definition of Boundary Points

The **boundary points** of an inequality consist of the real solutions to the related equation and the points where the inequality is undefined.

Testing points in intervals bounded by these points is the basis of the **test point method** to solve inequalities.

Solving Inequalities by Using the Test Point Method

Step 1 Find the boundary points of the inequality.

Step 2 Plot the boundary points on the number line. This divides the number line into intervals.

Step 3 Select a test point from each interval and substitute it into the original inequality.
- If a test point makes the original inequality true, then that interval is part of the solution set.

Step 4 Test the boundary points in the original inequality.
- If the original inequality is strict ($<$ or $>$), do not include the boundary points in the solution set.
- If the original inequality is defined using $\leq$ or $\geq$, then include the boundary points that are well defined within the inequality.

Note: Any boundary point that makes an expression within the inequality undefined must *always* be excluded from the solution set.

Example 2 Solving a Quadratic Inequality by Using the Test Point Method

Solve the inequality by using the test point method.

$$2x^2 + 5x < 12$$

Solution:

$2x^2 + 5x < 12$ **Step 1:** Find the boundary points. Because polynomials are defined for all values of x, the only boundary points are the real solutions to the related equation.

$2x^2 + 5x = 12$ Solve the related equation.

$2x^2 + 5x - 12 = 0$

$(2x - 3)(x + 4) = 0$

$x = \frac{3}{2} \quad x = -4$ The boundary points are $\frac{3}{2}$ and -4.

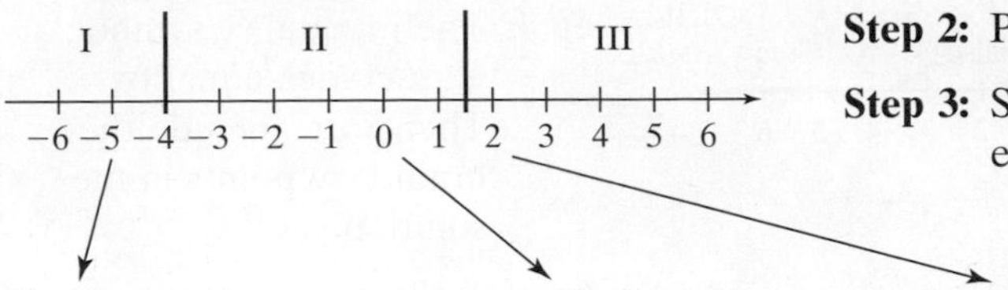

Step 2: Plot the boundary points.

Step 3: Select a test point from each interval.

Test $x = -5$	**Test $x = 0$**	**Test $x = 2$**
$2x^2 + 5x < 12$	$2x^2 + 5x < 12$	$2x^2 + 5x < 12$
$2(-5)^2 + 5(-5) \stackrel{?}{<} 12$	$2(0)^2 + 5(0) \stackrel{?}{<} 12$	$2(2)^2 + 5(2) \stackrel{?}{<} 12$
$50 - 25 \stackrel{?}{<} 12$	$0 \stackrel{?}{<} 12$	$8 + 10 \stackrel{?}{<} 12$
$25 \stackrel{?}{<} 12$ False	$0 \stackrel{?}{<} 12$ True	$18 \stackrel{?}{<} 12$ False

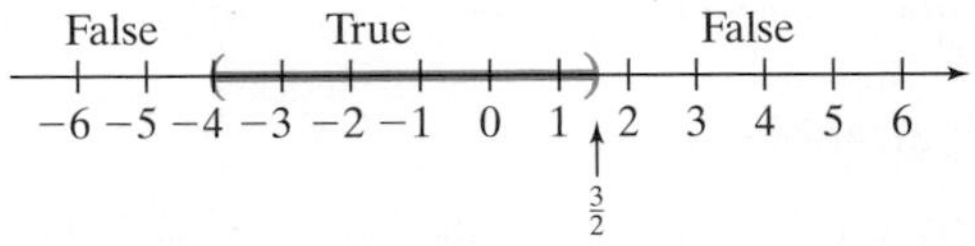

Step 4: Test the boundary points. The strict inequality excludes values of x for which $2x^2 + 5x = 12$. Therefore, the boundary points are *not* included in the solution set.

The solution is $\{x \mid -4 < x < \frac{3}{2}\}$ or equivalently in interval notation $\left(-4, \frac{3}{2}\right)$.

Skill Practice Solve the inequality.

3. $x^2 + x > 6$

Calculator Connections

Topic: Analyzing a Quadratic Inequality Graphically

Graph $Y_1 = 2x^2 + 5x$ and $Y_2 = 12$. Notice that $Y_1 < Y_2$ for $\{x \mid -4 < x < \frac{3}{2}\}$.

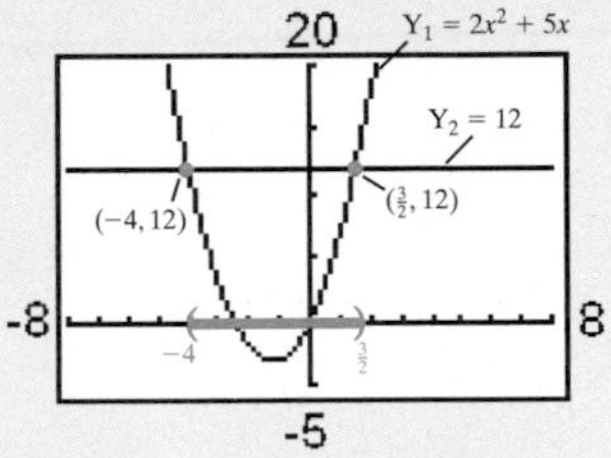

Example 3 Solving a Polynomial Inequality by Using the Test Point Method

Solve the inequality by using the test point method.

$$x(x + 4)^2(x - 4) \geq 0$$

Solution:

$x(x + 4)^2(x - 4) \geq 0$

$x(x + 4)^2(x - 4) = 0$ **Step 1:** Find the boundary points.

$x = 0 \qquad x = -4 \qquad x = 4$

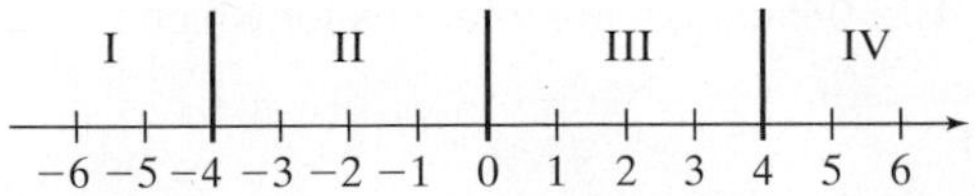

Step 2: Plot the boundary points.

Step 3: Select a test point from each interval.

Test $x = -5$: $-5(-5 + 4)^2(-5 - 4) \stackrel{?}{\geq} 0$ $\qquad 45 \stackrel{?}{\geq} 0$ True

Test $x = -1$: $-1(-1 + 4)^2(-1 - 4) \stackrel{?}{\geq} 0$ $\qquad 45 \stackrel{?}{\geq} 0$ True

Test $x = 1$: $1(1 + 4)^2(1 - 4) \stackrel{?}{\geq} 0$ $\qquad -75 \stackrel{?}{\geq} 0$ False

Test $x = 5$: $5(5 + 4)^2(5 - 4) \stackrel{?}{\geq} 0$ $\qquad 405 \stackrel{?}{\geq} 0$ True

Answer

3. $(-\infty, -3) \cup (2, \infty)$

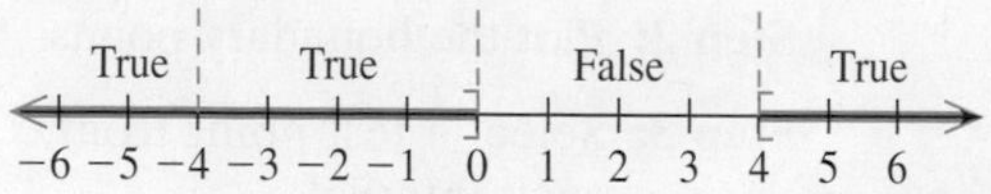

Step 4: The inequality symbol, $\geq$, includes equality. Therefore, include the boundary points in the solution set.

The solution is $\{x \mid x \leq 0 \text{ and } x \geq 4\}$, or equivalently in interval notation, $(-\infty, 0] \cup [4, \infty)$.

Skill Practice Solve the inequality.

4. $t(t-5)(t+2)^2 > 0$

Calculator Connections

Topic: Analyzing a Polynomial Inequality Graphically

Graph $Y_1 = x(x+4)^2(x-4)$. Y_1 is positive (above the x-axis) for $\{x \mid x \leq 0 \text{ and } x \geq 4\}$ or equivalently $(-\infty, 0] \cup [4, \infty)$.

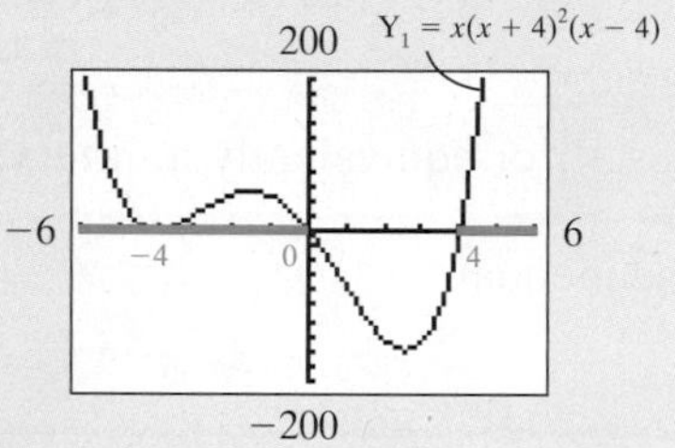

TIP: In Example 3, one side of the inequality is factored, and the other side is zero. For inequalities written in this form, we can use a sign chart to determine the sign of each factor. Then the sign of the product (bottom row) is easily determined.

Sign of x	−	−	+	+
Sign of $(x+4)^2$	+	+	+	+
Sign of $(x-4)$	−	−	−	+
Sign of $x(x+4)^2(x-4)$	+	+	−	+
	−4	0	4	

The solution to the inequality $x(x+4)^2(x-4) \geq 0$ includes the intervals for which the product is positive (shown in blue).

The solution is $(-\infty, 0] \cup [4, \infty)$.

2. Solving Rational Inequalities

The test point method can be used to solve rational inequalities. A **rational inequality** is an inequality in which one or more terms is a rational expression. The solution set to a rational inequality must exclude all values of the variable that make the inequality undefined. That is, exclude all values that make the denominator equal to zero for any rational expression in the inequality.

Answer

4. $(-\infty, -2) \cup (-2, 0) \cup (5, \infty)$

Example 4 Solving a Rational Inequality by Using the Test Point Method

Solve the inequality. $\dfrac{3}{x-1} > 0$

Solution:

$$\frac{3}{x-1} > 0$$

Step 1: Find the boundary points. Note that the inequality is undefined for $x = 1$, so $x = 1$ is a boundary point. To find any other boundary points, solve the related equation.

$$\frac{3}{x-1} = 0$$

$$\cancel{(x-1)} \cdot \left(\frac{3}{\cancel{x-1}}\right) = (x-1) \cdot 0$$

Clear fractions.

$$3 = 0$$

There is no solution to the related equation.

The only boundary point is $x = 1$.

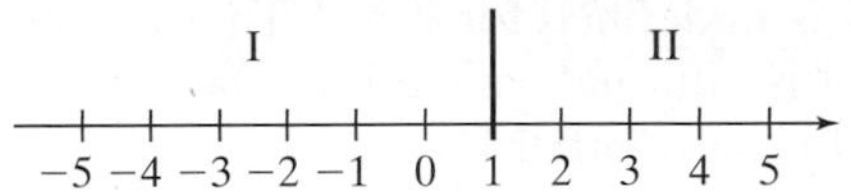

Step 2: Plot boundary points.

Step 3: Select test points.

Test $x = 0$:

$$\frac{3}{(0)-1} \stackrel{?}{>} 0$$

$$\frac{3}{-1} \stackrel{?}{>} 0 \quad \text{False}$$

Test $x = 2$:

$$\frac{3}{(2)-1} \stackrel{?}{>} 0$$

$$\frac{3}{1} > 0 \quad \text{True}$$

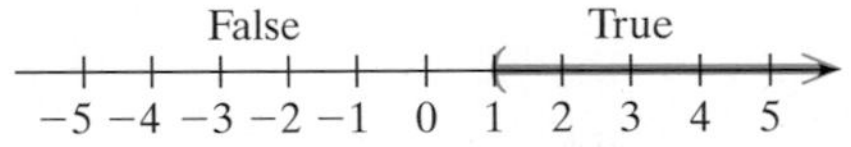

Step 4: The boundary point $x = 1$ cannot be included in the solution set because it is undefined in the original inequality.

The solution is $\{x \mid x > 1\}$ or equivalently in interval notation, $(1, \infty)$.

Skill Practice Solve the inequality.

5. $\dfrac{-5}{y+2} < 0$

TIP: Using a sign chart we see that the quotient of the factors 3 and $(x - 1)$ is positive on the interval $(1, \infty)$.

Therefore, the solution to the inequality $\dfrac{3}{x-1} > 0$ is $(1, \infty)$.

Sign of 3	+	+
Sign of $(x - 1)$	−	+
Sign of $\dfrac{3}{x-1}$	−	+

1 (undefined)

Answer

5. $(-2, \infty)$

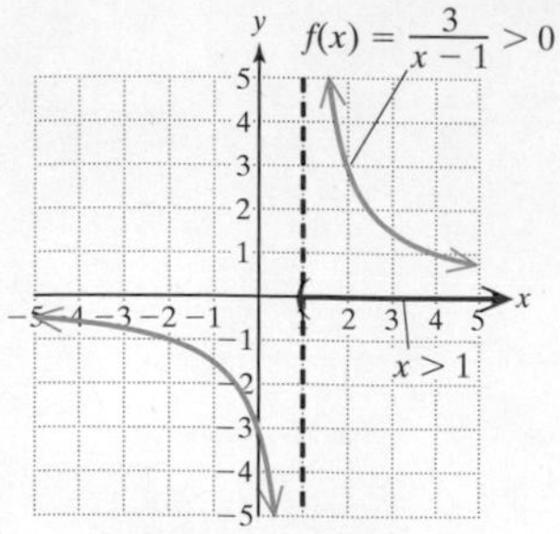

Figure 9-4

The solution to the inequality $\frac{3}{x-1} > 0$ can be confirmed from the graph of the related rational function, $f(x) = \frac{3}{x-1}$ (see Figure 9-4).

- The graph is above the x-axis where $f(x) = \frac{3}{x-1} > 0$ for $x > 1$ (shaded red).
- Also note that $x = 1$ cannot be included in the solution set because 1 is not in the domain of f.

Example 5 Solving a Rational Inequality by Using the Test Point Method

Solve the inequality by using the test point method. $\frac{x+2}{x-4} \le 3$

Solution:

$$\frac{x+2}{x-4} \le 3$$

Step 1: Find the boundary points. Note that the inequality is undefined for $x = 4$. Therefore, $x = 4$ is automatically a boundary point. To find any other boundary points, solve the related equation.

$$\frac{x+2}{x-4} = 3$$

$$(x-4)\left(\frac{x+2}{x-4}\right) = (x-4)(3)$$ Clear fractions.

$$x + 2 = 3(x - 4)$$ Solve for x.

$$x + 2 = 3x - 12$$

$$-2x = -14$$

$$x = 7$$

The solution to the related equation is $x = 7$, and the inequality is undefined for $x = 4$. Therefore, the boundary points are $x = 4$ and $x = 7$.

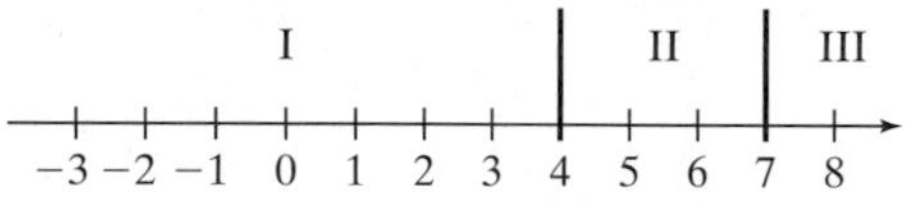

Step 2: Plot boundary points.

Step 3: Select test points.

Test $x = 0$		**Test $x = 5$**		**Test $x = 8$**	
$\frac{x+2}{x-4} \le 3$		$\frac{x+2}{x-4} \le 3$		$\frac{x+2}{x-4} \le 3$	
$\frac{0+2}{0-4} \stackrel{?}{\le} 3$		$\frac{5+2}{5-4} \stackrel{?}{\le} 3$		$\frac{8+2}{8-4} \stackrel{?}{\le} 3$	
$-\frac{1}{2} \stackrel{?}{\le} 3$	True	$\frac{7}{1} \stackrel{?}{\le} 3$	False	$\frac{10}{4} \stackrel{?}{\le} 3$	
				$\frac{5}{2} \stackrel{?}{\le} 3$	True

Test $x = 4$:

$\dfrac{x+2}{x-4} \le 3$

$\dfrac{4+2}{4-4} \overset{?}{\le} 3$

$\dfrac{6}{0} \overset{?}{\le} 3$ Undefined

Test $x = 7$:

$\dfrac{x+2}{x-4} \le 3$

$\dfrac{7+2}{7-4} \overset{?}{\le} 3$

$\dfrac{9}{3} \overset{?}{\le} 3$ True

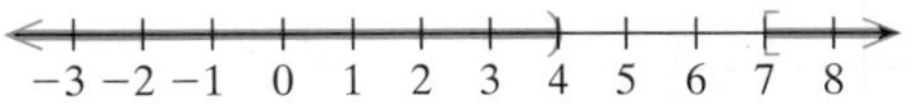

Step 4: Test the boundary points.

The boundary point $x = 4$ cannot be included in the solution set, because it is undefined in the inequality. The boundary point $x = 7$ makes the original inequality true and must be included in the solution set.

The solution is $\{x \mid x < 4 \text{ or } x \ge 7\}$, or equivalently in interval notation, $(-\infty, 4) \cup [7, \infty)$.

Skill Practice Solve the inequality.

6. $\dfrac{x-5}{x+4} \le -1$

Answer

6. $\left(-4, \dfrac{1}{2}\right]$

Section 9.2 Practice Exercises

Vocabulary and Key Concepts

1. **a.** An inequality of the form $ax^2 + bx + c > 0$ or $ax^2 + bx + c < 0$ is an example of a __________ inequality.
   b. The boundary points of an inequality consist of the real __________ to the related equation and the points where the inequality is __________.
   c. In solving an inequality by using the __________ __________ method, a point is selected from each interval formed by the boundary points and substituted into the original inequality.
   d. If a test point makes the original inequality __________, then that interval is part of the solution set.
   e. The inequality $\dfrac{4}{x+7} > 0$ is an example of a __________ inequality.
   f. The solution set to a rational inequality must exclude all values that make the denominator equal to __________ for any rational expression in the inequality.

Review Exercises

For Exercises 2–8, solve the compound inequalities. Write the solutions in interval notation.

2. $6x - 10 > 8$ or $8x + 2 < 5$

3. $3(a - 1) + 2 > 0$ or $2a > 5a + 12$

4. $5(k - 2) > -25$ and $7(1 - k) > 7$

5. $2y + 4 \ge 10$ and $5y - 3 \le 13$

6. $0 < 3(x + 1) \le 4$

7. $6 \ge 4 - 2x \ge -2$

8. $-4 > 5 - x > -6$

Mixed Exercises

For Exercises 57–76, identify the inequality as one of the following types: linear, quadratic, rational, or polynomial (degree > 2). Then solve the inequality and write the answer in interval notation.

57. $2y^2 - 8 \le 24$

58. $8p^2 - 18 > 0$

59. $(5x + 2)^2 > 4$

60. $(7x - 4)^2 < 9$

61. $4(x - 2) < 6x - 3$

62. $-7(3 - y) > 4 + 2y$

63. $\dfrac{2x + 3}{x + 1} \le 2$

64. $\dfrac{5x - 1}{x + 3} \ge 5$

65. $4x^3 - 40x^2 + 100x > 0$

66. $2y^3 - 12y^2 + 18y < 0$

67. $2p^3 > 4p^2$

68. $w^3 \le 5w^2$

69. $-3(x + 4)^2(x - 5) \ge 0$

70. $5x(x - 2)(x - 6)^2 \ge 0$

71. $x^2 - 4 < 0$

72. $y^2 - 9 > 0$

73. $\dfrac{a + 2}{a - 5} \ge 0$

74. $\dfrac{t + 1}{t - 2} \le 0$

75. $2 \ge t - 3$

76. $-5p + 8 < p$

Expanding Your Skills

The solution to an inequality is often one or more intervals on the real number line. Sometimes, however, the solution to an inequality may be a single point on the number line, the empty set, or the set of all real numbers. We call these "special case" solution sets.

For Exercises 77–92, solve the inequalities involving "special case" solution sets.

77. $x^2 + 10x + 25 \ge 0$

78. $x^2 + 6x + 9 < 0$

79. $x^2 + 2x + 1 < 0$

80. $x^2 + 8x + 16 \ge 0$

81. $x^4 + 3x^2 \le 0$

82. $x^4 + 2x^2 \le 0$

83. $x^2 + 12x + 36 < 0$

84. $x^2 + 12x + 36 \ge 0$

85. $x^2 + 3x + 5 < 0$

86. $2x^2 + 3x + 3 > 0$

87. $-5x^2 + x < 1$

88. $-3x^2 - x > 6$

89. $x^2 + 22x + 121 > 0$

90. $y^2 - 24y + 144 > 0$

91. $4t^2 - 12t \le -9$

92. $4t^2 - 12t > -9$

Graphing Calculator Exercises

93. To solve the inequality $\dfrac{x}{x - 2} > 0$ enter Y_1 as $x/(x - 2)$ and determine where the graph is above the x-axis. Write the solution in interval notation.

94. To solve the inequality $\dfrac{x}{x - 2} < 0$ enter Y_1 as $x/(x - 2)$ and determine where the graph is below the x-axis. Write the solution in interval notation.

95. To solve the inequality $x^2 - 1 < 0$, enter Y_1 as $x^2 - 1$ and determine where the graph is below the x-axis. Write the solution in interval notation.

96. To solve the inequality $x^2 - 1 > 0$, enter Y_1 as $x^2 - 1$ and determine where the graph is above the x-axis. Write the solution in interval notation.

For Exercises 97–100, determine the solution by graphing the inequalities.

97. $x^2 + 10x + 25 \le 0$

98. $-x^2 + 10x - 25 \ge 0$

99. $\dfrac{8}{x^2 + 2} < 0$

100. $\dfrac{-6}{x^2 + 3} > 0$

Absolute Value Equations

Section 9.3

Concepts

1. Solving Absolute Value Equations
2. Solving Equations Containing Two Absolute Values

1. Solving Absolute Value Equations

An equation of the form $|x| = a$ is called an **absolute value equation**. The solution includes all real numbers whose absolute value equals a. For example, the solutions to the equation $|x| = 4$ are 4 as well as -4, because $|4| = 4$ and $|-4| = 4$. In Chapter 1, we introduced a geometric interpretation of $|x|$. The absolute value of a number is its distance from zero on the number line (Figure 9-5). Therefore, the solutions to the equation $|x| = 4$ are the values of x that are 4 units away from zero.

$|x| = 4$

$x = -4$ or $x = 4$

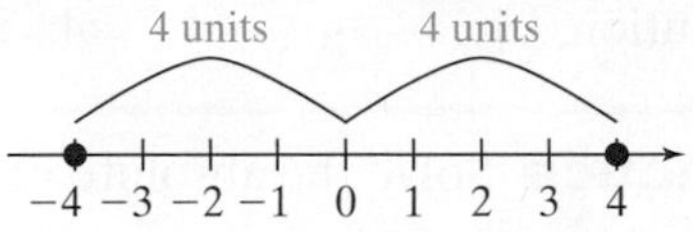

Figure 9-5

Solving Absolute Value Equations of the Form $|x| = a$

If a is a real number, then

- If $a \geq 0$, the solutions to the equation $|x| = a$ are $x = a$ and $x = -a$.
- If $a < 0$, there is no solution to the equation $|x| = a$.

To solve an absolute value equation of the form $|x| = a$ $(a \geq 0)$, rewrite the equation as $x = a$ or $x = -a$.

Example 1 Solving Absolute Value Equations

Solve the absolute value equations.

a. $|x| = 5$ **b.** $|w| - 2 = 12$ **c.** $|p| = 0$ **d.** $|x| = -6$

Solution:

a. $|x| = 5$ The equation is in the form $|x| = a$, where $a = 5$.

$x = 5$ or $x = -5$ Rewrite the equation as $x = a$ or $x = -a$.

The solution set is $\{5, -5\}$.

b. $|w| - 2 = 12$ Isolate the absolute value to write the equation in the form $|x| = a$.

$|w| = 14$

$w = 14$ or $w = -14$ Rewrite the equation as $w = a$ or $w = -a$.

The solution set is $\{14, -14\}$.

c. $|p| = 0$

$p = 0$ or $p = -0$

The solution set is {0}.

Rewrite as two equations. Notice that the second equation $p = -0$ is the same as the first equation. Intuitively, $p = 0$ is the only number whose absolute value equals 0.

d. $|x| = -6$

No solution, { }

The equation is of the form $|x| = a$, but a is negative. There is no number whose absolute value is negative.

Skill Practice Solve the absolute value equations.

1. $|y| = 7$ **2.** $|v| + 6 = 10$ **3.** $|w| = 0$ **4.** $|z| = -12$

We have solved absolute value equations of the form $|x| = a$. Notice that x can represent any algebraic quantity. For example, to solve the equation $|2w - 3| = 5$, we still rewrite the absolute value equation as two equations. In this case, we set the quantity $2w - 3$ equal to 5 and to -5, respectively.

$$|2w - 3| = 5$$

$$2w - 3 = 5 \quad \text{or} \quad 2w - 3 = -5$$

Solving an Absolute Value Equation

Step 1 Isolate the absolute value. That is, write the equation in the form $|x| = a$, where a is a real number.

Step 2 If $a < 0$, there is no solution.

Step 3 Otherwise, if $a \geq 0$, rewrite the absolute value equation as $x = a$ or $x = -a$.

Step 4 Solve the individual equations from step 3.

Step 5 Check the answers in the original absolute value equation.

Example 2 Solving an Absolute Value Equation

Solve the equation. $|2w - 3| = 5$

Solution:

$|2w - 3| = 5$ — The equation is already in the form $|x| = a$, where $x = 2w - 3$.

$2w - 3 = 5$ or $2w - 3 = -5$ — Rewrite as two equations.

$2w = 8$ or $2w = -2$ — Solve each equation.

$w = 4$ or $w = -1$

Answers

1. {7, −7}
2. {4, −4}
3. {0} 4. { }

Check: $w = 4$	Check: $w = -1$	Check the solutions in the original equation.
$\|2w - 3\| = 5$	$\|2w - 3\| = 5$	
$\|2(4) - 3\| \stackrel{?}{=} 5$	$\|2(-1) - 3\| \stackrel{?}{=} 5$	
$\|8 - 3\| \stackrel{?}{=} 5$	$\|-2 - 3\| \stackrel{?}{=} 5$	
$\|5\| \stackrel{?}{=} 5$ ✔	$\|-5\| \stackrel{?}{=} 5$ ✔	

The solution set is $\{4, -1\}$.

Skill Practice Solve the equation.

5. $|4x + 1| = 9$

Calculator Connections

Topic: Analyzing an Absolute Value Equation Graphically

To confirm the answers to Example 2, graph $Y_1 = \text{abs}(2x - 3)$ and $Y_2 = 5$. The solutions to the equation $|2x - 3| = 5$ are the x-coordinates of the points of intersection $(4, 5)$ and $(-1, 5)$.

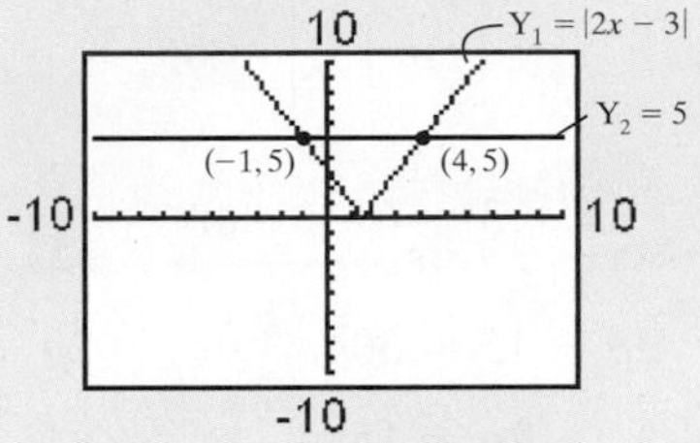

Example 3 Solving an Absolute Value Equation

Solve the equation. $|2c - 5| + 6 = 2$

Solution:

$|2c - 5| + 6 = 2$

$|2c - 5| = -4$ Isolate the absolute value. The equation is in the form $|x| = a$, where $x = 2c - 5$ and $a = -4$. Because $a < 0$, there is no solution.

No solution, { } There are no numbers c that will make an absolute value equal to a negative number.

Avoiding Mistakes

Always isolate the absolute value first. Otherwise you will get answers that do not check.

Skill Practice Solve the equation.

6. $|3z + 10| + 3 = 1$

Calculator Connections

Topic: Analyzing an Absolute Value Equation with No Solution

To confirm the answer in Example 3, note that the graphs of $Y_1 = \text{abs}(2x - 5) + 6$ and $Y_2 = 2$ do not intersect.

Therefore, there is no solution to the equation $|2x - 5| + 6 = 2$.

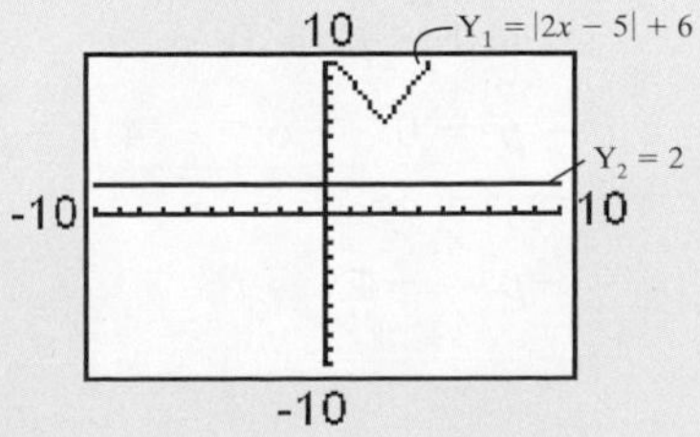

Answers

5. $\left\{2, -\frac{5}{2}\right\}$ **6.** { }

Example 4 Solving an Absolute Value Equation

Solve the equation. $-2\left|\frac{2}{5}p + 3\right| - 7 = -19$

Solution:

$$-2\left|\frac{2}{5}p + 3\right| - 7 = -19$$

$$-2\left|\frac{2}{5}p + 3\right| = -12 \qquad \text{Isolate the absolute value.}$$

$$\frac{-2\left|\frac{2}{5}p + 3\right|}{-2} = \frac{-12}{-2}$$

$$\left|\frac{2}{5}p + 3\right| = 6$$

$$\frac{2}{5}p + 3 = 6 \quad \text{or} \quad \frac{2}{5}p + 3 = -6 \qquad \text{Rewrite as two equations.}$$

$$2p + 15 = 30 \quad \text{or} \quad 2p + 15 = -30 \qquad \text{Multiply by 5 to clear fractions.}$$

$$2p = 15 \quad \text{or} \quad 2p = -45$$

$$p = \frac{15}{2} \quad \text{or} \quad p = -\frac{45}{2} \qquad \text{Both values check in the original equation.}$$

The solution set is $\left\{\frac{15}{2}, -\frac{45}{2}\right\}$.

Skill Practice Solve the equation.

7. $3\left|\frac{3}{2}a + 1\right| + 2 = 14$

Example 5 Solving an Absolute Value Equation

Solve the equation. $6.9 = |4.1 - p| + 6.9$

Solution:

$$6.9 = |4.1 - p| + 6.9$$

$$|4.1 - p| + 6.9 = 6.9$$

First write the absolute value on the left. Then subtract 6.9 from both sides to write the equation in the form $|x| = a$.

$$|4.1 - p| = 0 \qquad \text{Isolate the absolute value.}$$

$$4.1 - p = 0 \quad \text{or} \quad 4.1 - p = -0$$

Rewrite as two equations. Notice that the equations are the same.

$$-p = -4.1 \qquad \text{Subtract 4.1 from both sides.}$$

Answer

7. $\left\{2, -\frac{10}{3}\right\}$

$p = 4.1$

Check: $p = 4.1$

$$|4.1 - p| + 6.9 = 6.9$$
$$|4.1 - 4.1| + 6.9 \stackrel{?}{=} 6.9$$
$$|0| + 6.9 \stackrel{?}{=} 6.9$$
$$6.9 \stackrel{?}{=} 6.9 \checkmark$$

The solution set is $\{4.1\}$.

Skill Practice Solve the equation.

8. $-3.5 = |1.2 + x| - 3.5$

2. Solving Equations Containing Two Absolute Values

Some equations have two absolute values such as $|x| = |y|$. If two quantities have the same absolute value, then the quantities are equal or the quantities are opposites.

Equality of Absolute Values

$|x| = |y|$ implies that $x = y$ or $x = -y$.

Example 6 Solving an Equation Having Two Absolute Values

Solve the equation. $|2w - 3| = |5w + 1|$

Solution:

$$|2w - 3| = |5w + 1|$$

$2w - 3 = 5w + 1$	or	$2w - 3 = -(5w + 1)$	Rewrite as two equations, $x = y$ or $x = -y$.
$2w - 3 = 5w + 1$	or	$2w - 3 = -5w - 1$	Solve for w.
$-3w - 3 = 1$	or	$7w - 3 = -1$	
$-3w = 4$	or	$7w = 2$	
$w = -\dfrac{4}{3}$	or	$w = \dfrac{2}{7}$	Both values check in the original equation.

The solution set is $\left\{-\dfrac{4}{3}, \dfrac{2}{7}\right\}$.

Avoiding Mistakes

To take the opposite of the quantity $5w + 1$, use parentheses and apply the distributive property.

Skill Practice Solve the equation.

9. $|3 - 2x| = |3x - 1|$

Answers

8. $\{-1.2\}$ **9.** $\left\{\dfrac{4}{5}, -2\right\}$

Section 9.4 Absolute Value Inequalities

Concepts

1. **Solving Absolute Value Inequalities by Definition**
2. **Solving Absolute Value Inequalities by the Test Point Method**
3. **Translating to an Absolute Value Expression**

1. Solving Absolute Value Inequalities by Definition

In Section 9.3, we studied absolute value equations in the form $|x| = a$. In this section, we will solve absolute value *inequalities*. An inequality in any of the forms $|x| < a$, $|x| \le a$, $|x| > a$, or $|x| \ge a$ is called an **absolute value inequality**.

Recall that an absolute value represents distance from zero on the real number line. Consider the following absolute value equation and inequalities.

1. $|x| = 3$

$x = 3$ or $x = -3$

Solution:

The set of all points 3 units from zero on the number line

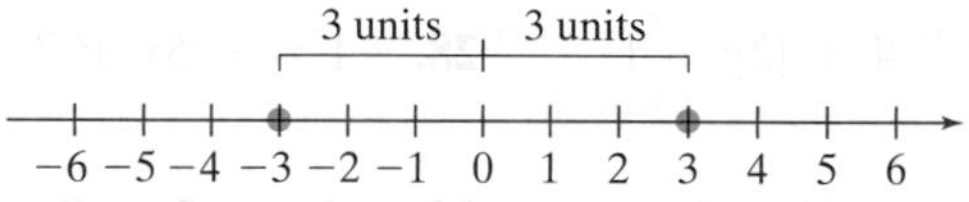

2. $|x| > 3$

$x < -3$ or $x > 3$

Solution:

The set of all points more than 3 units from zero

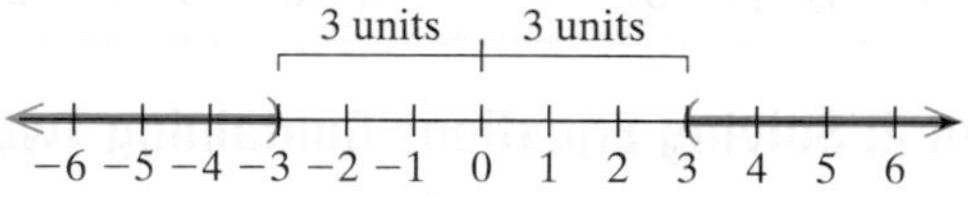

3. $|x| < 3$

$-3 < x < 3$

Solution:

The set of all points less than 3 units from zero

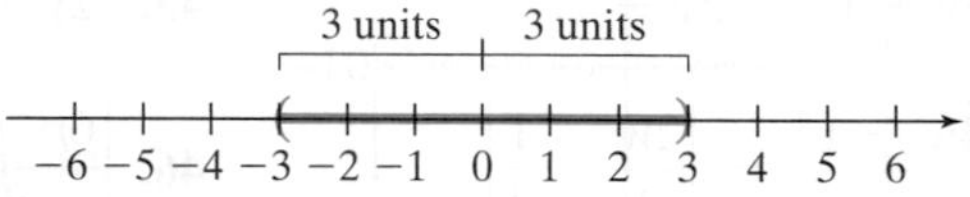

Solving Absolute Value Equations and Inequalities

Let a be a real number such that $a > 0$. Then

Equation/ Inequality	Solution (Equivalent Form)	Graph
$|x| = a$	$x = -a$ or $x = a$	
$|x| > a$	$x < -a$ or $x > a$	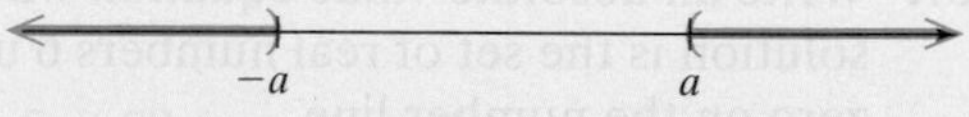
$|x| < a$	$-a < x < a$	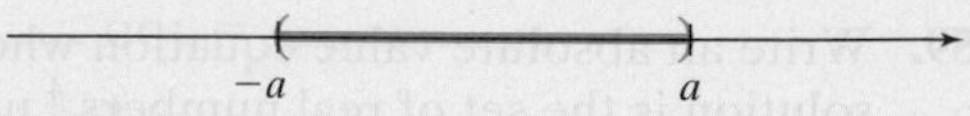

To solve an absolute value inequality, first isolate the absolute value and then rewrite the absolute value inequality in its equivalent form.

Example 1 Solving an Absolute Value Inequality

Solve the inequality. $|3w + 1| - 4 < 7$

Solution:

$|3w + 1| - 4 < 7$

$|3w + 1| < 11$ ⟵ Isolate the absolute value first.

The inequality is in the form $|x| < a$, where $x = 3w + 1$.

$-11 < 3w + 1 < 11$ Rewrite in the equivalent form $-a < x < a$.

$-12 < 3w < 10$ Solve for w.

$-4 < w < \frac{10}{3}$

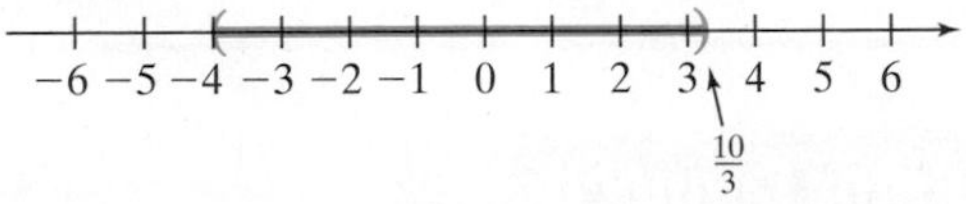

The solution is $\{w \mid -4 < w < \frac{10}{3}\}$, or equivalently in interval notation, $(-4, \frac{10}{3})$.

Skill Practice Solve the inequality. Write the solution in interval notation.

1. $|2t + 5| + 2 \le 11$

TIP: Recall that a strict inequality (using the symbols > and <) will have parentheses at the endpoints of the interval form of the solution.

Calculator Connections

Topic: Analyzing an Absolute Value Inequality Graphically

To confirm the answer in Example 1, graph $Y_1 = \text{abs}(3x + 1) - 4$ and $Y_2 = 7$. On the given display window, $Y_1 < Y_2$ (Y_1 is below Y_2) for $-4 < x < \frac{10}{3}$.

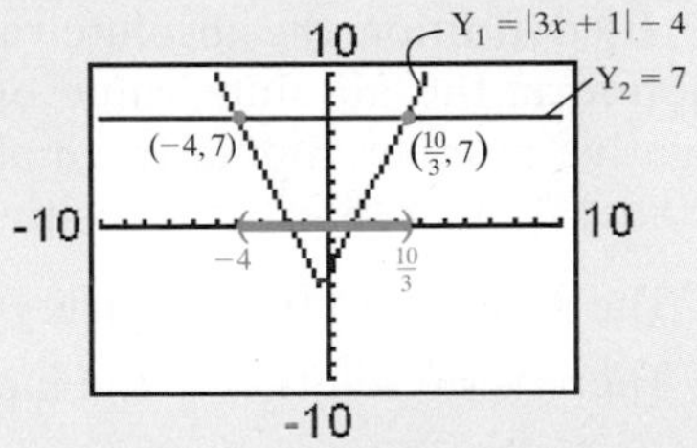

Example 2 Solving an Absolute Value Inequality

Solve the inequality. $3 \le 1 + \left|\frac{1}{2}t - 5\right|$

Solution:

$3 \le 1 + \left|\frac{1}{2}t - 5\right|$

$1 + \left|\frac{1}{2}t - 5\right| \ge 3$ Write the inequality with the absolute value on the left.

$\left|\frac{1}{2}t - 5\right| \ge 2$ Isolate the absolute value.

The inequality is in the form $|x| \ge a$, where $x = \frac{1}{2}t - 5$.

$\frac{1}{2}t - 5 \le -2$ or $\frac{1}{2}t - 5 \ge 2$ Rewrite in the equivalent form $x \le -a$ or $x \ge a$.

TIP: It is generally easier to solve an absolute value inequality if the absolute value appears on the left-hand side of the inequality.

Answer

1. $[-7, 2]$

$\frac{1}{2}t \leq 3$ or $\frac{1}{2}t \geq 7$ Solve the compound inequality.

$2\left(\frac{1}{2}t\right) \leq 2(3)$ or $2\left(\frac{1}{2}t\right) \geq 2(7)$ Clear fractions.

$t \leq 6$ or $t \geq 14$

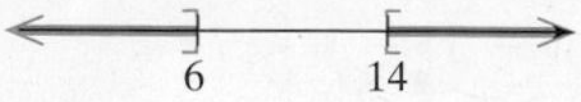

The solution is $\{t \mid t \leq 6 \text{ or } t \geq 14\}$ or, equivalently in interval notation, $(-\infty, 6] \cup [14, \infty)$.

Skill Practice Solve the inequality. Write the solution in interval notation.

2. $5 < 1 + \left|\frac{1}{3}c - 1\right|$

Calculator Connections

Topic: Analyzing an Absolute Value Inequality Graphically

To confirm the answer in Example 2, graph $Y_1 = \text{abs}((1/2)x - 5) + 1$ and $Y_2 = 3$. On the given display window, $Y_1 \geq Y_2$ for $x \leq 6$ or $x \geq 14$.

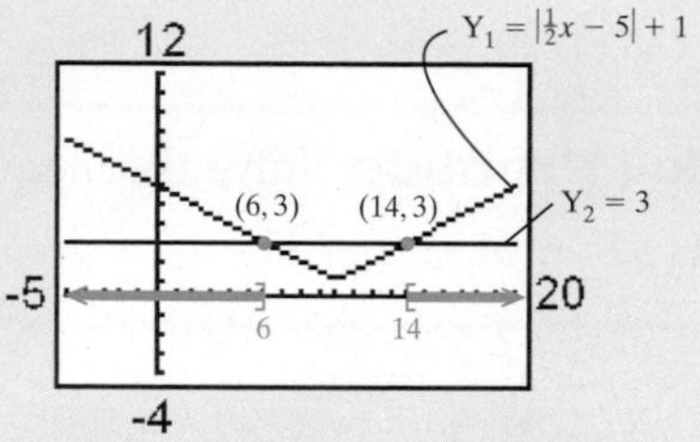

By definition, the absolute value of a real number will always be nonnegative. Therefore, the absolute value of any expression will always be greater than a negative number. Similarly, an absolute value can never be less than a negative number. Let a represent a positive real number. Then

- The solution to the inequality $|x| > -a$ is all real numbers, $(-\infty, \infty)$.
- There is no solution to the inequality $|x| < -a$.

Example 3 Solving Absolute Value Inequalities

Solve the inequalities.

a. $|3d - 5| + 7 < 4$ **b.** $|3d - 5| + 7 > 4$

Solution:

a. $|3d - 5| + 7 < 4$

$|3d - 5| < -3$

Isolate the absolute value. An absolute value expression cannot be less than a negative number. Therefore, there is no solution.

No solution, { }

b. $|3d - 5| + 7 > 4$

$|3d - 5| > -3$

Isolate the absolute value. The inequality is in the form $|x| > a$, where a is negative. An absolute value of any real number is greater than a negative number. Therefore, the solution is all real numbers.

All real numbers, $(-\infty, \infty)$

Skill Practice Solve the inequalities.

3. $|4p + 2| + 6 < 2$ **4.** $|4p + 2| + 6 > 2$

Answers

2. $(-\infty, -9) \cup (15, \infty)$
3. { }
4. All real numbers; $(-\infty, \infty)$

Calculator Connections

Topic: Analyzing an Absolute Value Inequality Graphically

By graphing $Y_1 = \text{abs}(3x - 5) + 7$ and $Y_2 = 4$ from Example 3, we see that $Y_1 > Y_2$ (Y_1 is above Y_2) for all real numbers x on the given display window.

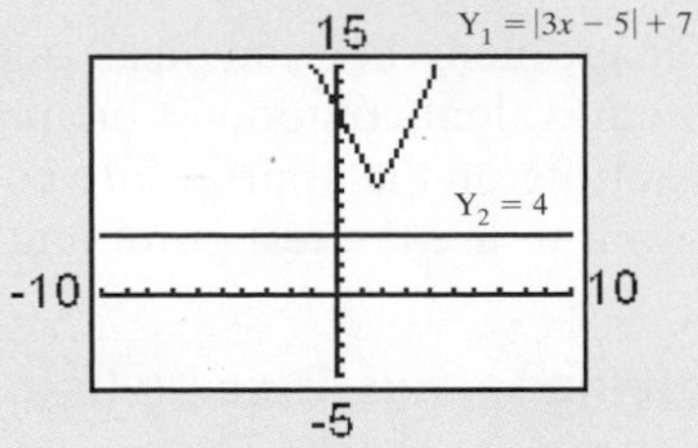

Example 4 Solving Absolute Value Inequalities

Solve the inequalities.

a. $|4x + 2| \geq 0$ **b.** $|4x + 2| > 0$ **c.** $|4x + 2| \leq 0$

Solution:

a. $|4x + 2| \geq 0$ ← The absolute value is already isolated.

The absolute value of any real number is nonnegative. Therefore, the solution is all real numbers, $(-\infty, \infty)$.

b. $|4x + 2| > 0$

An absolute value will be greater than zero at all points *except where it is equal to zero*. That is, the point(s) for which $|4x + 2| = 0$ must be excluded from the solution set.

$|4x + 2| = 0$

$4x + 2 = 0$ or $4x + 2 = -0$ The second equation is the same as the first.

$4x = -2$

$x = -\dfrac{1}{2}$ Therefore, exclude $x = -\frac{1}{2}$ from the solution.

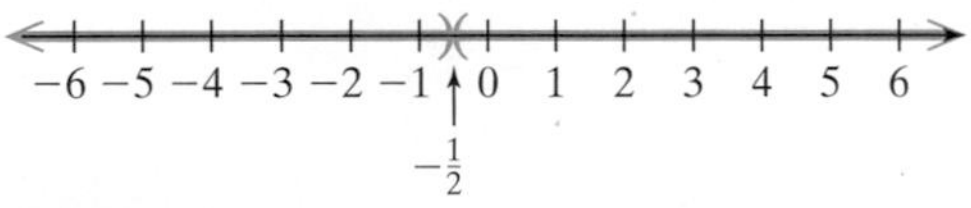

The solution is $\{x \mid x \neq -\frac{1}{2}\}$ or equivalently in interval notation, $(-\infty, -\frac{1}{2}) \cup (-\frac{1}{2}, \infty)$.

c. $|4x + 2| \leq 0$

An absolute value of a number cannot be less than zero. However, it can be *equal* to zero. Therefore, the only solutions to this inequality are the solutions to the related equation:

$|4x + 2| = 0$ From part (b), we see that the solution set is $\left\{-\dfrac{1}{2}\right\}$.

Skill Practice Solve the inequalities.

5. $|3x - 1| \geq 0$ **6.** $|3x - 1| > 0$ **7.** $|3x - 1| \leq 0$

Calculator Connections

Topic: Analyzing an Absolute Value Inequality Graphically

From Example 4, graph $Y_1 = \text{abs}(4x + 2)$. From the graph, $Y_1 = 0$ at $x = -\frac{1}{2}$ (the x-intercept). On the given display window, $Y_1 > 0$ for $x < -\frac{1}{2}$ or $x > -\frac{1}{2}$.

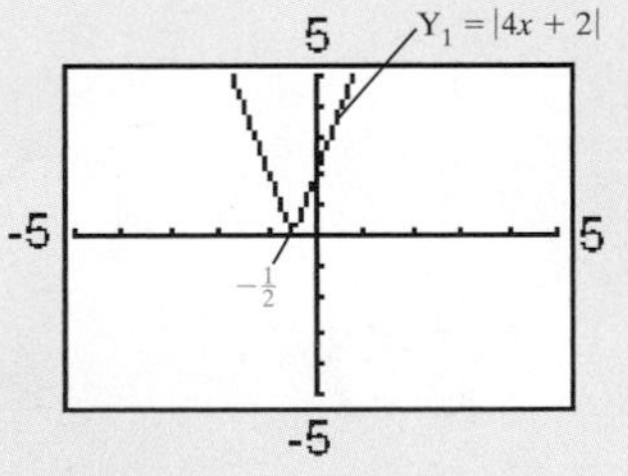

Answers

5. $(-\infty, \infty)$

6. $\left\{x \mid x \neq \dfrac{1}{3}\right\}$ or $\left(-\infty, \dfrac{1}{3}\right) \cup \left(\dfrac{1}{3}, \infty\right)$

7. $\left\{\dfrac{1}{3}\right\}$

2. Solving Absolute Value Inequalities by the Test Point Method

For the problems in Examples 1 and 2, the absolute value inequality was converted to an equivalent compound inequality. However, sometimes students have difficulty setting up the appropriate compound inequality. To avoid this problem, you may want to use the test point method to solve absolute value inequalities.

Solving Inequalities by Using the Test Point Method

Step 1 Find the boundary points of the inequality. (Boundary points are the real solutions to the related equation and points where the inequality is undefined.)

Step 2 Plot the boundary points on the number line. This divides the number line into intervals.

Step 3 Select a test point from each interval and substitute it into the original inequality.

- If a test point makes the original inequality true, then that interval is part of the solution set.

Step 4 Test the boundary points in the original inequality.

- If the original inequality is strict ($<$ or $>$), do not include the boundary points in the solution set.
- If the original inequality is defined using $\leq$ or $\geq$, then include the boundary points that are well defined within the inequality.

Note: Any boundary point that makes an expression within the inequality undefined must *always* be excluded from the solution set.

To demonstrate the use of the test point method, we will repeat the absolute value inequalities from Examples 1 and 2. Notice that regardless of the method used, the absolute value is always isolated *first* before any further action is taken.

Example 5 Solving an Absolute Value Inequality by the Test Point Method

Solve the inequality by using the test point method. $|3w + 1| - 4 < 7$

Solution:

$|3w + 1| - 4 < 7$

$|3w + 1| < 11$ ← Isolate the absolute value.

$|3w + 1| = 11$ **Step 1:** Solve the related equation.

$3w + 1 = 11$ or $3w + 1 = -11$ Write as an equivalent system of two equations.

$3w = 10$ or $3w = -12$

$w = \frac{10}{3}$ or $w = -4$ These are the only boundary points.

Step 2: Plot the boundary points.

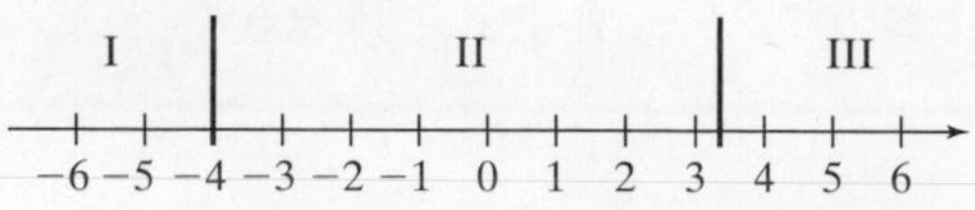

Step 3: Select a test point from each interval.

Test $w = -5$:

$$|3(-5) + 1| - 4 \stackrel{?}{<} 7$$
$$|-14| - 4 \stackrel{?}{<} 7$$
$$14 - 4 \stackrel{?}{<} 7$$
$$10 \stackrel{?}{<} 7 \text{ False}$$

Test $w = 0$:

$$|3(0) + 1| - 4 \stackrel{?}{<} 7$$
$$|1| - 4 \stackrel{?}{<} 7$$
$$-3 \stackrel{?}{<} 7 \text{ True}$$

Test $w = 4$:

$$|3(4) + 1| - 4 \stackrel{?}{<} 7$$
$$|13| - 4 \stackrel{?}{<} 7$$
$$13 - 4 \stackrel{?}{<} 7$$
$$9 \stackrel{?}{<} 7 \text{ False}$$

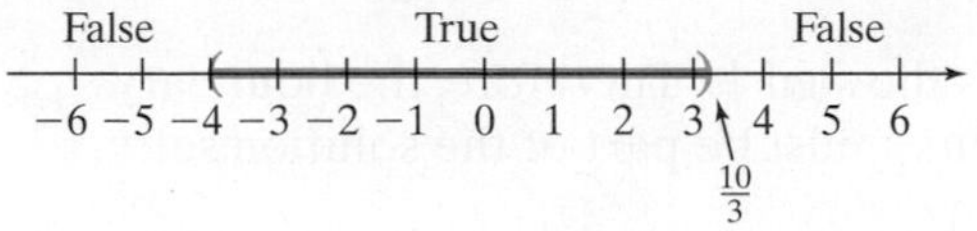

Step 4: Because the original inequality is a strict inequality, the boundary points (where equality occurs) are not included.

The solution is $\{w \mid -4 < w < \frac{10}{3}\}$ or, equivalently in interval notation, $(-4, \frac{10}{3})$.

Skill Practice Solve the inequality.

8. $6 + |3t - 4| \leq 10$

Example 6 Solving an Absolute Value Inequality by the Test Point Method

Solve the inequality by using the test point method. $3 \leq 1 + \left|\frac{1}{2}t - 5\right|$

Solution:

$$3 \leq 1 + \left|\frac{1}{2}t - 5\right|$$

$$1 + \left|\frac{1}{2}t - 5\right| \geq 3$$ Write the inequality with the absolute value on the left.

$$\left|\frac{1}{2}t - 5\right| \geq 2$$ Isolate the absolute value.

$$\left|\frac{1}{2}t - 5\right| = 2$$ **Step 1:** Solve the related equation.

$$\frac{1}{2}t - 5 = 2 \quad \text{or} \quad \frac{1}{2}t - 5 = -2$$ Write as an equivalent system of two equations.

$$\frac{1}{2}t = 7 \quad \text{or} \quad \frac{1}{2}t = 3$$

$$t = 14 \quad \text{or} \quad t = 6$$ These are the boundary points.

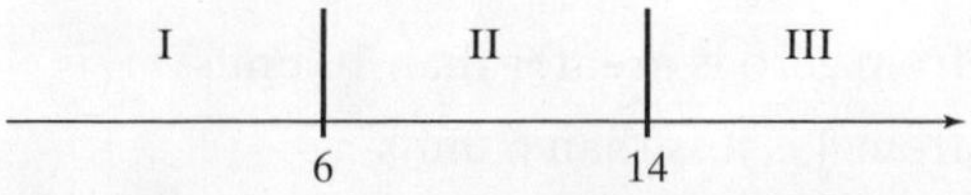

Step 2: Plot the boundary points.

Step 3: Select a test point from each interval.

Answer

8. $\left[0, \frac{8}{3}\right]$

Test $t = 0$:	**Test $t = 10$:**	**Test $t = 16$:**
$3 \overset{?}{\leq} 1 + \left\lvert \frac{1}{2}(0) - 5 \right\rvert$	$3 \overset{?}{\leq} 1 + \left\lvert \frac{1}{2}(10) - 5 \right\rvert$	$3 \overset{?}{\leq} 1 + \left\lvert \frac{1}{2}(16) - 5 \right\rvert$
$3 \overset{?}{\leq} 1 + \lvert 0 - 5 \rvert$	$3 \overset{?}{\leq} 1 + \lvert 5 - 5 \rvert$	$3 \overset{?}{\leq} 1 + \lvert 8 - 5 \rvert$
$3 \overset{?}{\leq} 1 + \lvert -5 \rvert$	$3 \overset{?}{\leq} 1 + \lvert 0 \rvert$	$3 \overset{?}{\leq} 1 + \lvert 3 \rvert$
$3 \overset{?}{\leq} 6$ True	$3 \overset{?}{\leq} 1$ False	$3 \overset{?}{\leq} 4$ True

Step 4: The original inequality uses the sign $\geq$. Therefore, the boundary points (where equality occurs) must be part of the solution set.

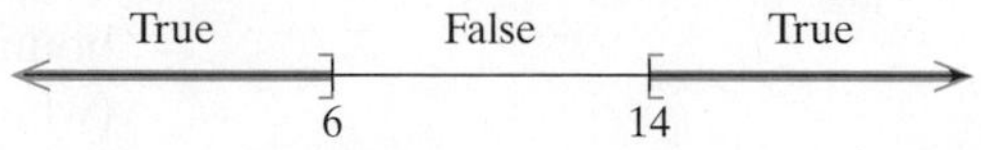

The solution is $\{t \mid t \leq 6 \text{ or } t \geq 14\}$ or, equivalently in interval notation, $(-\infty, 6] \cup [14, \infty)$.

Skill Practice Solve the inequality.

9. $\left\lvert \frac{1}{2}c + 4 \right\rvert + 1 > 6$

3. Translating to an Absolute Value Expression

Absolute value expressions can be used to describe distances. The distance between c and d is given by $\lvert c - d \rvert$. For example, the distance between -2 and 3 on the number line is $\lvert (-2) - 3 \rvert = 5$ as expected.

Example 7 Expressing Distances with Absolute Value

Write an absolute value inequality to represent the following phrases.

a. All real numbers x, whose distance from zero is greater than 5 units

b. All real numbers x, whose distance from -7 is less than 3 units

Solution:

a. All real numbers x, whose distance from zero is greater than 5 units

$\lvert x - 0 \rvert > 5$ or simply $\lvert x \rvert > 5$

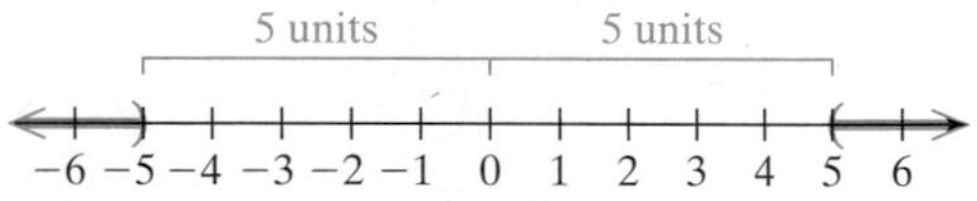

b. All real numbers x, whose distance from -7 is less than 3 units

$\lvert x - (-7) \rvert < 3$ or simply $\lvert x + 7 \rvert < 3$

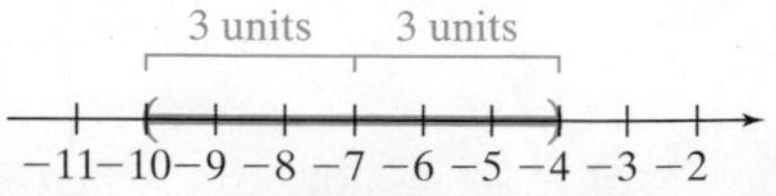

Skill Practice Write an absolute value inequality to represent the following phrases.

10. All real numbers whose distance from zero is greater than 10 units

11. All real numbers whose distance from 4 is less than 6 units

Answers

9. $(-\infty, -18) \cup (2, \infty)$
10. $\lvert x \rvert > 10$
11. $\lvert x - 4 \rvert < 6$

Absolute value expressions can also be used to describe boundaries for measurement error.

Example 8 Expressing Measurement Error with Absolute Value

Latoya measured a certain compound on a scale in the chemistry lab at school. She measured 8 g of the compound, but the scale is only accurate to ± 0.1 g. Write an absolute value inequality to express an interval for the true mass, x, of the compound she measured.

Solution:

Because the scale is only accurate to ± 0.1 g, the true mass, x, of the compound may deviate by as much as 0.1 g above or below 8 g. This may be expressed as an absolute value inequality:

$|x - 8.0| \le 0.1$ or equivalently $7.9 \le x \le 8.1$

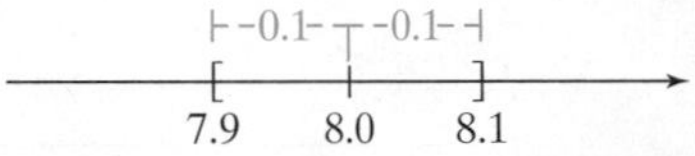

Skill Practice

12. Vonzell molded a piece of metal in her machine shop. She measured the thickness at 12 mm. Her machine is accurate to ± 0.05 mm. Write an absolute value inequality to express an interval for the true measurement of the thickness, t, of the metal.

Answer

12. $|t - 12| \le 0.05$

Section 9.4 Practice Exercises

Vocabulary and Key Concepts

1. a. If a is a positive real number, then the inequality $|x| < a$ is equivalent to ________ $< x <$ ________.

b. If a is a positive real number, then the inequality $|x| > a$ is equivalent to $x <$ ________ or x ________ a.

c. The solution set to the inquality $|x + 2| < -6$ is ________, whereas the solution set to the inequality $|x + 2| > -6$ is ________.

d. The solution set to the inequality $|x + 4| \le 0$ (includes/excludes) -4, whereas the solution set to the inequality $|x + 4| < 0$ (includes/excludes) -4.

Review Exercises

For Exercises 2–4, solve the equations.

2. $|10x - 6| = -5$

3. $2 = |5 - 7x| + 1$

4. $|3x - 12| + 4 = 6 - 2$

For Exercises 5–8, solve the inequalities and graph the solution set. Write the solution in interval notation.

5. $-15 < 3w - 6 \le -9$

6. $5 - 2y \le 1$ and $3y + 2 \ge 14$

7. $m - 7 \le -5$ or $m - 7 \ge -10$

8. $3b - 2 < 7$ or $b - 2 > 4$

Concepts 1 and 2: Solving Absolute Value Inequalities

For Exercises 9–20, solve the equations and inequalities. For each inequality, graph the solution set and express the solution in interval notation. **(See Examples 1–6.)**

9. a. $|x| = 5$
b. $|x| > 5$
c. $|x| < 5$

10. a. $|a| = 4$
b. $|a| > 4$
c. $|a| < 4$

11. a. $|x - 3| = 7$
b. $|x - 3| > 7$
c. $|x - 3| < 7$

12. a. $|w + 2| = 6$
b. $|w + 2| > 6$
c. $|w + 2| < 6$

13. a. $|p| = -2$
b. $|p| > -2$
c. $|p| < -2$

14. a. $|x| = -14$
b. $|x| > -14$
c. $|x| < -14$

15. a. $|y + 1| = -6$
b. $|y + 1| > -6$
c. $|y + 1| < -6$

16. a. $|z - 4| = -3$
b. $|z - 4| > -3$
c. $|z - 4| < -3$

17. a. $|x| = 0$
b. $|x| > 0$
c. $|x| < 0$

18. a. $|p + 3| = 0$
b. $|p + 3| > 0$
c. $|p + 3| < 0$

19. a. $|k - 7| = 0$
b. $|k - 7| > 0$
c. $|k - 7| < 0$

20. a. $|2x + 4| + 3 = 2$
b. $|2x + 4| + 3 > 2$
c. $|2x + 4| + 3 < 2$

For Exercises 21–50, solve the absolute value inequalities. Graph the solution set and write the solution in interval notation. **(See Examples 1–6.)**

21. $|x| > 6$

22. $|x| \le 6$

23. $|t| \le 3$

24. $|p| > 3$

25. $|y + 2| \ge 0$

26. $0 \le |7n + 2|$

27. $5 \le |2x - 1|$

28. $|x - 2| \ge 7$

29. $|k - 7| < -3$

30. $|h + 2| < -9$

31. $\left|\dfrac{w - 2}{3}\right| - 3 \le 1$

32. $\left|\dfrac{x + 3}{2}\right| - 2 \ge 4$

33. $12 \le |9 - 4y| - 2$

34. $5 > |2m - 7| + 4$

35. $4 > -1 + \left|\dfrac{2x + 1}{4}\right|$

36. $9 \ge 2 + \left|\dfrac{x - 4}{5}\right|$

37. $8 < |4 - 3x| + 12$

38. $-16 < |5x - 1| - 1$

39. $5 - |2m + 1| > 5$

40. $3 - |5x + 3| > 3$

41. $|p + 5| \leq 0$

42. $|y + 1| - 4 \leq -4$

43. $|z - 6| + 5 > 5$

44. $|2c - 1| - 4 > -4$

45. $5|2y - 6| + 3 \geq 13$

46. $7|y + 1| - 3 \geq 11$

47. $-3|6 - t| + 1 > -5$

48. $-4|8 - x| + 2 > -14$

49. $|0.02x + 0.06| - 0.1 < 0.05$

50. $|0.05x - 0.04| - 0.01 < 0.11$

Concept 3: Translating to an Absolute Value Expression

For Exercises 51–54, write an absolute value inequality equivalent to the expression given. **(See Example 7.)**

51. All real numbers whose distance from 0 is greater than 7

52. All real numbers whose distance from -3 is less than 4

53. All real numbers whose distance from 2 is at most 13

54. All real numbers whose distance from 0 is at least 6

55. A 32-oz jug of orange juice may not contain exactly 32 oz of juice. The possibility of measurement error exists when the jug is filled in the factory. If the maximum measurement error is ± 0.05 oz, write an absolute value inequality representing the range of volumes, x, in which the orange juice jug may be filled. **(See Example 8.)**

56. The length of a board is measured to be 32.3 in. The maximum measurement error is ± 0.2 in. Write an absolute value inequality that represents the range for the length of the board, x.

57. A bag of potato chips states that its weight is $6\frac{3}{4}$ oz. The maximum measurement error is $\pm\frac{1}{8}$ oz. Write an absolute value inequality that represents the range for the weight, x, of the bag of chips.

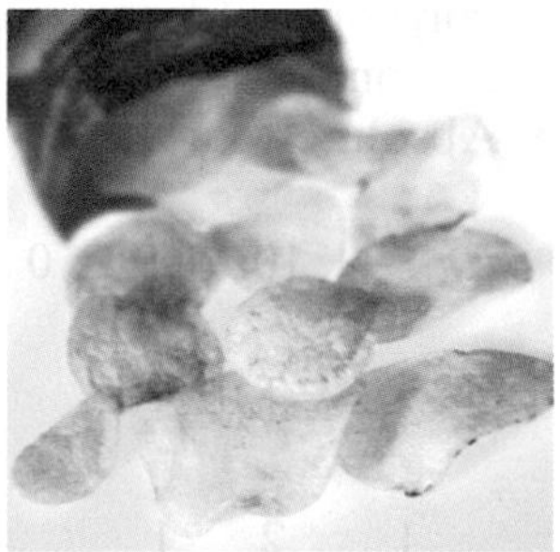

58. A $\frac{7}{8}$-in. bolt varies in length by at most $\pm\frac{1}{16}$ in. Write an absolute value inequality that represents the range for the length, x, of the bolt.

59. The width, w, of a bolt is supposed to be 2 cm but may have a 0.01-cm margin of error. Solve $|w - 2| \leq 0.01$, and interpret the solution to the inequality in the context of this problem.

60. In a political poll, the front-runner was projected to receive 53% of the votes with a margin of error of 3%. Solve $|p - 0.53| \leq 0.03$ and interpret the solution in the context of this problem.

Expanding Your Skills

For Exercises 61–64, match the graph with the inequality.

61.

62.

63.

64.

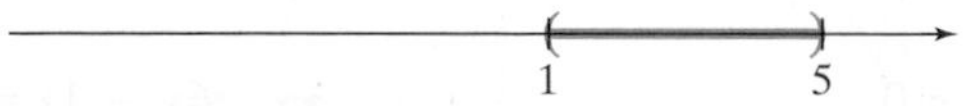

a. $|x - 2| < 4$ **b.** $|x - 1| > 4$ **c.** $|x - 3| < 2$ **d.** $|x - 5| > 1$

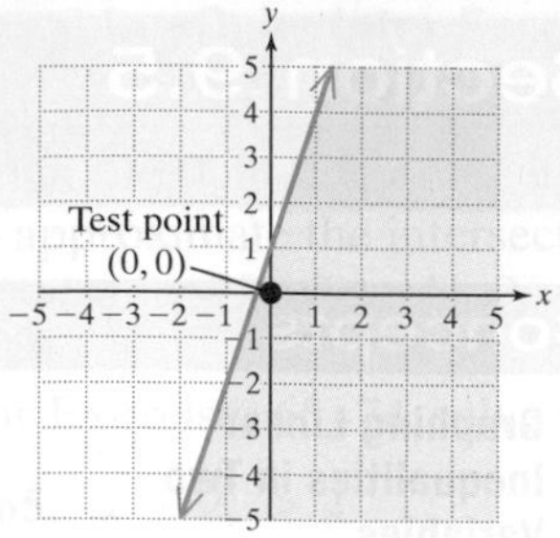

Figure 9-7

After graphing the solution to a linear inequality, we can verify that we have shaded the correct side of the line by using test points. In Example 1, we can pick an arbitrary ordered pair within the shaded region. Then substitute the x- and y-coordinates in the original inequality. If the result is a true statement, then that ordered pair is a solution to the inequality and suggests that other points from the same region are also solutions.

For example, the point (0, 0) lies within the shaded region (Figure 9-7).

$-3x + y \le 1$ Substitute (0, 0) in the original inequality.

$-3(0) + (0) \overset{?}{\le} 1$

$0 + 0 \overset{?}{\le} 1$ ✔ True The point (0, 0) from the shaded region is a solution.

In Example 2, we will graph the solution set to a strict inequality. A strict inequality does not include equality and therefore, is expressed with the symbols $<$ or $>$. In such a case, the boundary line will be drawn as a dashed line. This indicates that the boundary itself is *not* part of the solution set.

Example 2 Graphing a Linear Inequality in Two Variables

Graph the solution set. $-4y < 5x$

Solution:

$-4y < 5x$

$\dfrac{-4y}{-4} > \dfrac{5x}{-4}$ Solve for y. Recall that when we divide both sides by a negative number, reverse the inequality sign.

$y > -\dfrac{5}{4}x$

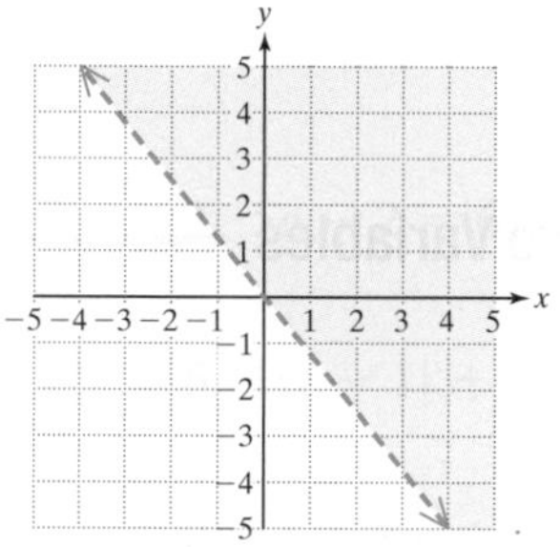

Figure 9-8

Graph the line defined by the related equation, $y = -\frac{5}{4}x$. The boundary line is drawn as a dashed line because the inequality is strict. Also note that the line passes through the origin.

Because the inequality is of the form $y > mx + b$, the solution to the inequality is the region *above* the line. See Figure 9-8.

Skill Practice Graph the solution set.

2. $-3y < x$

Answer

2.

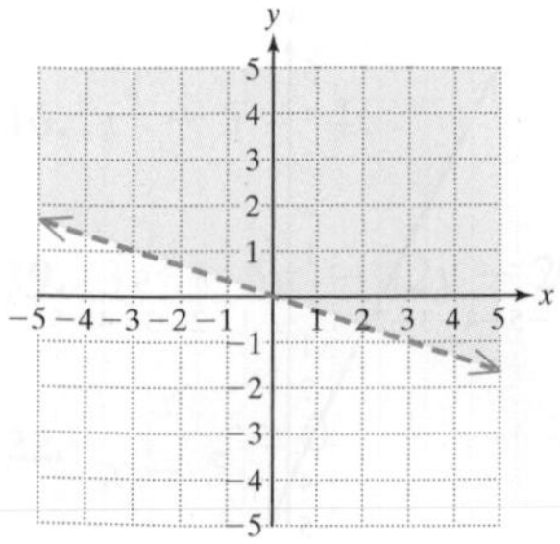

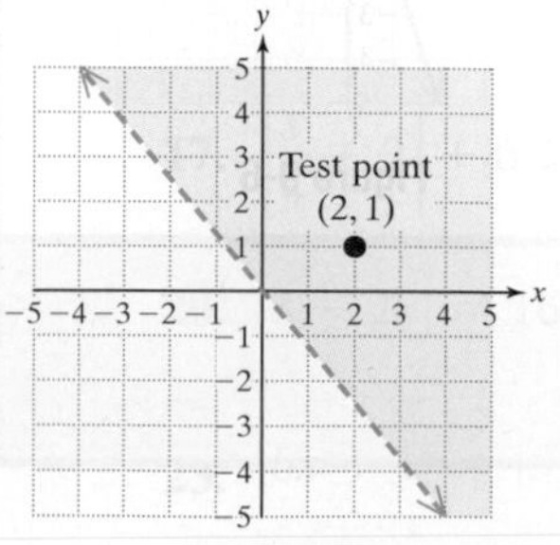

Figure 9-9

In Example 2, we cannot use the origin as a test point, because the point (0, 0) is on the boundary line. Be sure to select a test point strictly within the shaded region. In this case, we choose (2, 1). See Figure 9-9.

$-4y < 5x$

$-4(1) \overset{?}{<} 5(2)$ Substitute (2, 1) in the original inequality.

$-4 \overset{?}{<} 10$ ✔ True The point (2, 1) from the shaded region is a solution to the original inequality.

In Example 3, we encounter a situation in which we cannot solve for the y-variable.

Example 3 Graphing a Linear Inequality in Two Variables

Graph the solution set. $4x \geq -12$

Solution:

$4x \geq -12$

$x \geq -3$

In this inequality, there is no y-variable. However, we can simplify the inequality by solving for x.

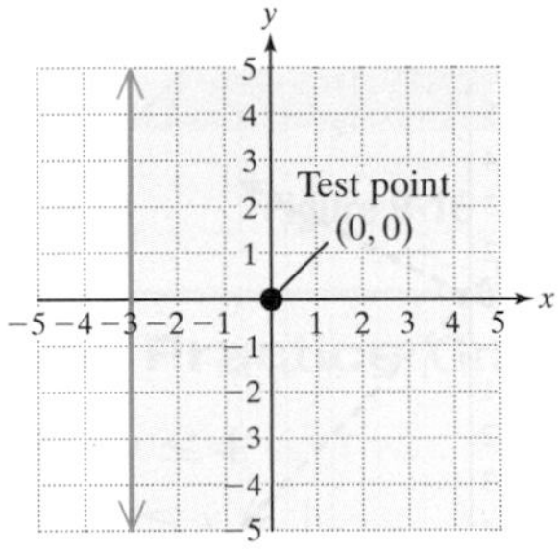

Figure 9-10

Graph the related equation $x = -3$. This is a vertical line. The boundary is drawn as a solid line, because the inequality is not strict, $\geq$.

To shade the appropriate region, refer to the inequality, $x \geq -3$. The points for which x is greater than -3 are to the right of $x = -3$. Therefore, shade the region to the *right* of the line (Figure 9-10).

Selecting a test point such as (0, 0) from the shaded region indicates that we have shaded the correct side of the line.

$4x \geq -12$ Substitute $x = 0$.

$4(0) \overset{?}{\geq} -12$ ✔ True

Skill Practice Graph the solution set.

3. $-2x \geq 2$

2. Systems of Linear Inequalities in Two Variables

Some applications require us to find the solutions to a system of linear inequalities.

Example 4 Graphing a System of Linear Inequalities

Graph the solution set.

$$y > \tfrac{1}{2}x + 1$$
$$x + y < 1$$

Solution:

Solve each inequality for y.

<u>First inequality</u>

$y > \frac{1}{2}x + 1$

The inequality is of the form $y > mx + b$. Shade *above* the boundary line. See Figure 9-11.

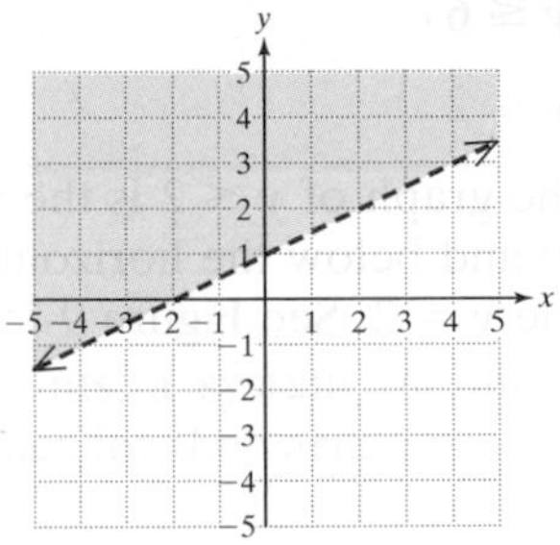

Figure 9-11

Answer

3.

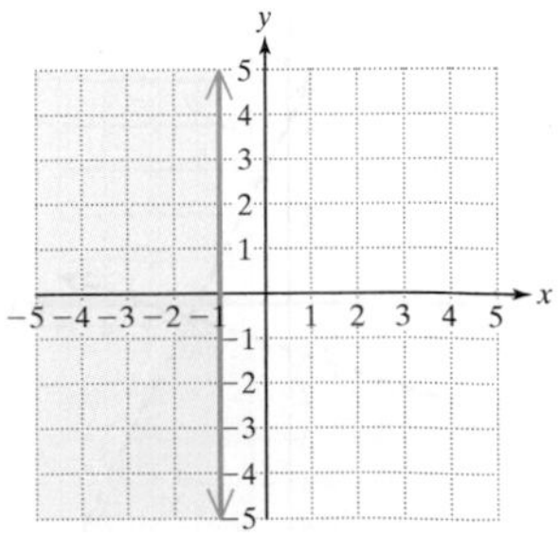

Example 7 Graphing a Feasible Region

Susan has two tests on Friday: one in chemistry and one in psychology. Because the two classes meet in consecutive hours, she has no study time between tests. Susan estimates that she has a maximum of 12 hr of study time before the tests, and she must divide her time between chemistry and psychology.

Let x represent the number of hours Susan spends studying chemistry.

Let y represent the number of hours Susan spends studying psychology.

a. Find a set of inequalities to describe the constraints on Susan's study time.

b. Graph the constraints to find the feasible region defining Susan's study time.

Solution:

a. Because Susan cannot study chemistry or psychology for a negative period of time, we have $x \geq 0$ and $y \geq 0$. Furthermore, her total time studying cannot exceed 12 hr: $x + y \leq 12$.

A system of inequalities that defines the constraints on Susan's study time is:

$$x \geq 0$$
$$y \geq 0$$
$$x + y \leq 12$$

b. The first two conditions $x \geq 0$ and $y \geq 0$ represent the set of points in the first quadrant. The third condition $x + y \leq 12$ represents the set of points below and including the line $x + y = 12$ (Figure 9-18).

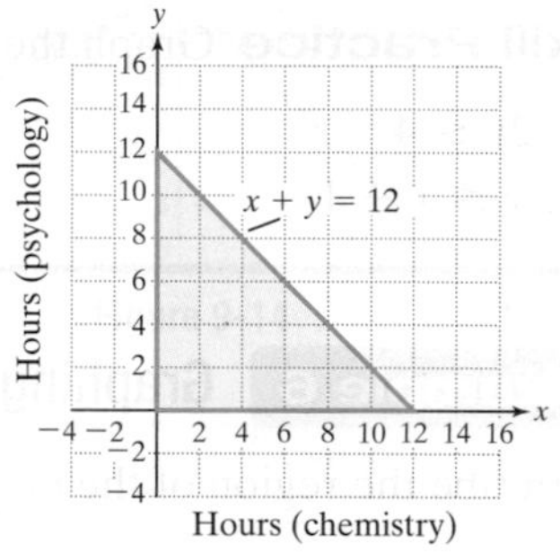

Figure 9-18

Discussion:

1. Refer to the feasible region drawn in Example 7(b). Is the ordered pair (8, 5) part of the feasible region?

   No. The ordered pair (8, 5) indicates that Susan spent 8 hr studying chemistry and 5 hr studying psychology. This is a total of 13 hr, which exceeds the constraint that Susan only had 12 hr to study. The point (8, 5) lies outside the feasible region, above the line $x + y = 12$ (Figure 9-19).

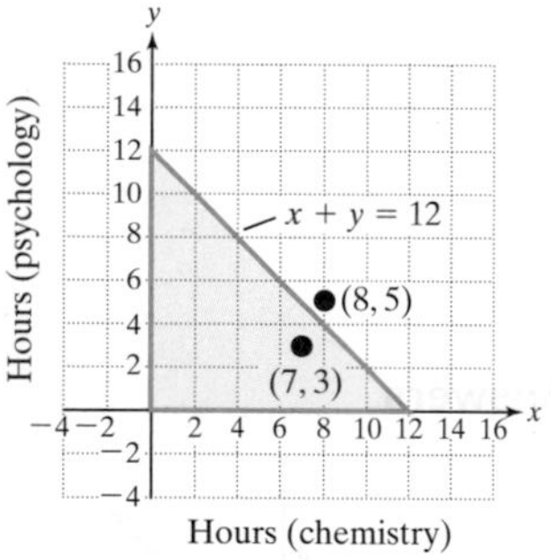

Figure 9-19

2. Is the ordered pair (7, 3) part of the feasible region?

   Yes. The ordered pair (7, 3) indicates that Susan spent 7 hr studying chemistry and 3 hr studying psychology.

   This point lies within the feasible region and satisfies all three constraints.

$x \geq 0 \longrightarrow$	$7 \geq 0$	True
$y \geq 0 \longrightarrow$	$3 \geq 0$	True
$x + y \leq 12 \longrightarrow$	$(7) + (3) \leq 12$	True

   Notice that the ordered pair (7, 3) corresponds to a point where Susan is not making full use of the 12 hr of study time.

3. Suppose there was one additional constraint imposed on Susan's study time. She knows she needs to spend at least twice as much time studying chemistry as she does studying psychology. Graph the feasible region with this additional constraint.

Because the time studying chemistry must be at least twice the time studying psychology, we have $x \geq 2y$.

This inequality may also be written as $y \leq \frac{1}{2}x$.

Figure 9-20 shows the first quadrant with the constraint $y \leq \frac{1}{2}x$.

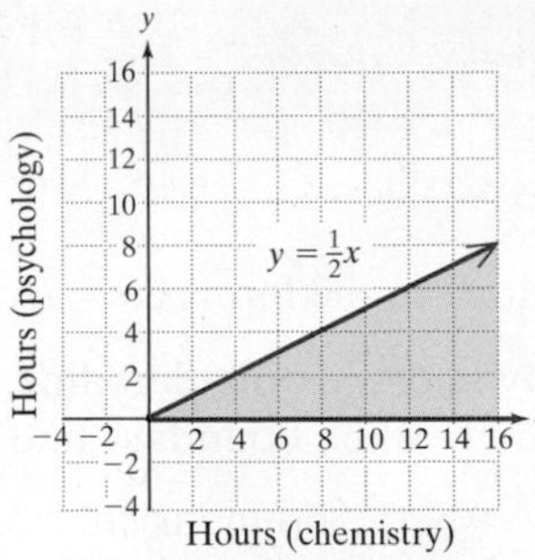

Figure 9-20

4. At what point in the feasible region is Susan making the most efficient use of her time for both classes?

First and foremost, Susan must make use of *all* 12 hr. This occurs for points along the line $x + y = 12$. Susan will also want to study for both classes with approximately twice as much time devoted to chemistry. Therefore, Susan will be deriving the maximum benefit at the point of intersection of the line

$x + y = 12$ and the line $y = \frac{1}{2}x$.

Using the substitution method, replace $y = \frac{1}{2}x$ into the equation $x + y = 12$.

$x + \frac{1}{2}x = 12$

$2x + x = 24$ Clear fractions.

$3x = 24$

$x = 8$ Solve for x.

$y = \dfrac{(8)}{2}$ To solve for y, substitute $x = 8$ into the equation $y = \frac{1}{2}x$.

$y = 4$

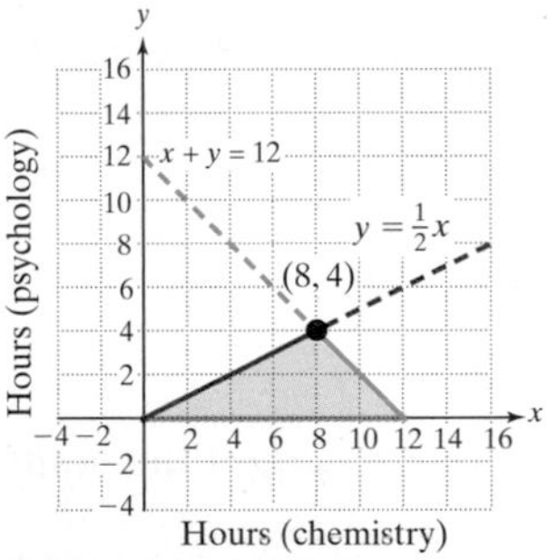

Therefore, Susan should spend 8 hr studying chemistry and 4 hr studying psychology.

Skill Practice

7. A local pet rescue group has a total of 30 cages that can be used to hold cats and dogs. Let x represent the number of cages used for cats, and let y represent the number used for dogs.

a. Write a set of inequalities to express the fact that the number of cat and dog cages cannot be negative.

b. Write an inequality to describe the constraint on the total number of cages for cats and dogs.

c. Graph the system of inequalities to find the feasible region describing the available cages.

Answer

7a. $x \geq 0$ and $y \geq 0$

b. $x + y \leq 30$

c.

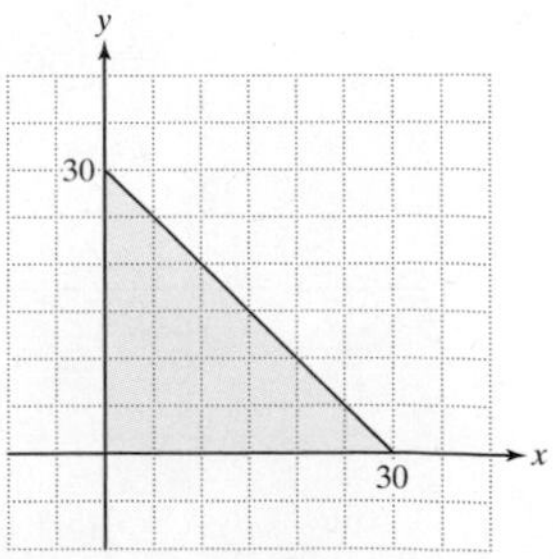

Section 9.5 Practice Exercises

Vocabulary and Key Concepts

1. **a.** An inequality that can be written in the form $Ax + By > C$ is called a ________ inequality in two variables.

   b. Given the inequality $3x - 4y < 6$, the boundary line $3x - 4y = 6$ (is/is not) included in the solution set. However, given $3x - 4y \leq 6$, then the boundary line (is/is not) included in the solution set.

   c. Given the inequality $5x + y > 5$, the boundary line $5x + y = 5$ should be drawn as a (solid/dashed) line to indicate that the line (is/is not) part of the solution set.

   d. Given the inequality $y \geq -x + 4$, the boundary line $y = -x + 4$ should be drawn as a (solid/dashed) line to indicate that the line (is/is not) part of the solution set.

Review Exercises

For Exercises 2–5, solve the inequalities. Write the solution set in interval notation.

2. $5 < x + 1$ and $-2x + 6 \geq -6$

3. $5 - x \leq 4$ and $6 > 3x - 3$

4. $4 - y < 3y + 12$ or $-2(y + 3) \geq 12$

5. $-2x < 4$ or $3x - 1 \leq -13$

Concept 1: Graphing Linear Inequalities in Two Variables

For Exercises 6–9, determine if the given point is a solution to the inequality.

6. $2x - y > 8$

   a. $(3, -5)$ **b.** $(-1, -10)$ **c.** $(4, -2)$ **d.** $(0, 0)$

7. $3y + x < 5$

   a. $(-1, 7)$ **b.** $(5, 0)$ **c.** $(0, 0)$ **d.** $(2, -3)$

8. $y \leq -2$

   a. $(5, -3)$ **b.** $(-4, -2)$ **c.** $(0, 0)$ **d.** $(3, 2)$

9. $x \geq 5$

   a. $(4, 5)$ **b.** $(5, -1)$ **c.** $(8, 8)$ **d.** $(0, 0)$

10. When should you use a dashed line to graph the solution to a linear inequality?

For Exercises 11–16, decide which inequality symbol should be used $(<, >, \geq, \leq)$ by looking at the graph.

11.
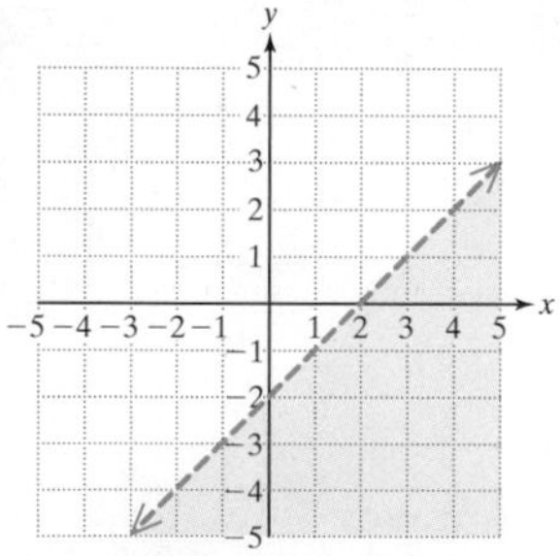

$x - y$ ____ 2

12.
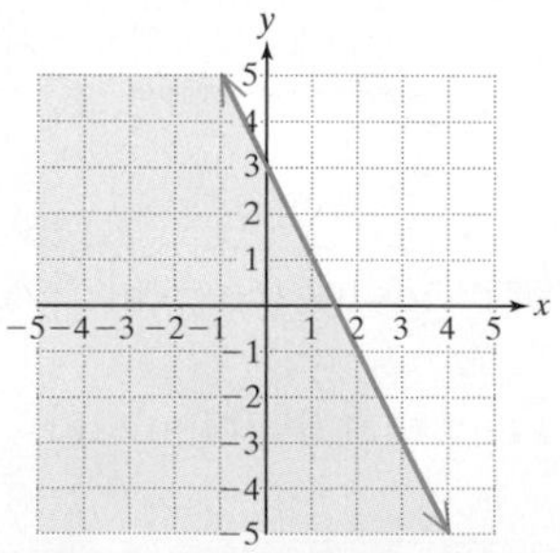

y ____ $-2x + 3$

13.
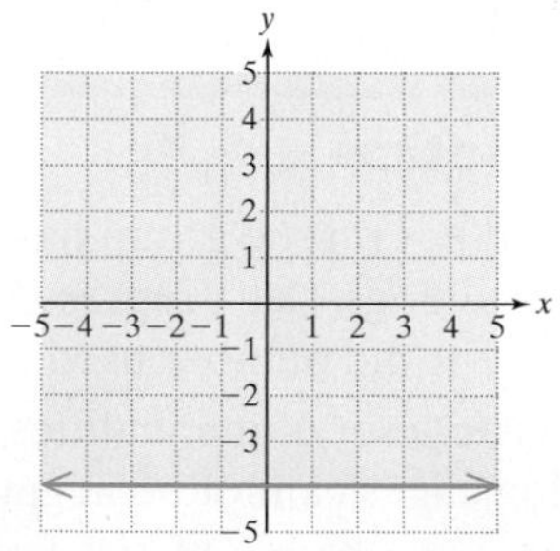

y ____ -4

14.
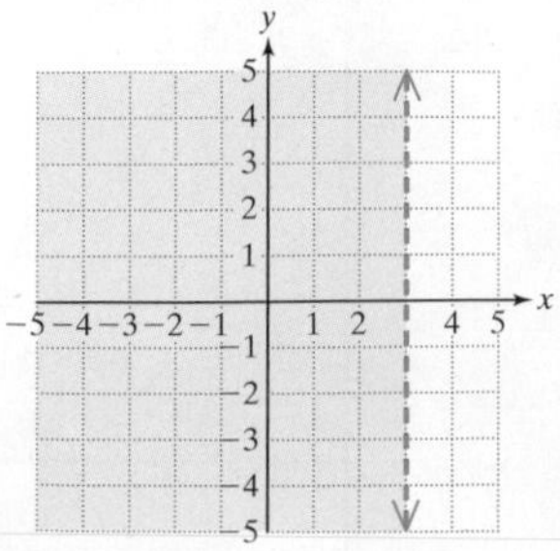

x ____ 3

15.
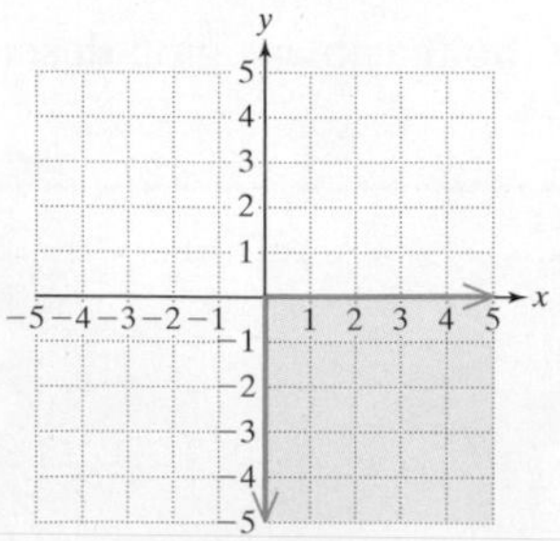

x ____ 0 and y ____ 0

16.
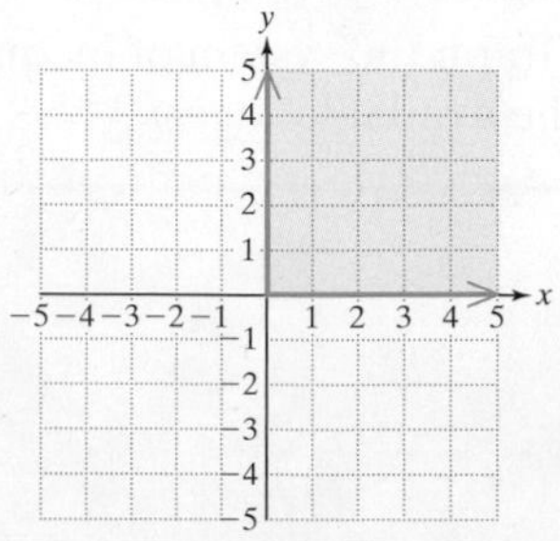

x ____ 0 and y ____ 0

For Exercises 17–40, graph the solution set. **(See Examples 1–3.)**

17. $x - 2y > 4$

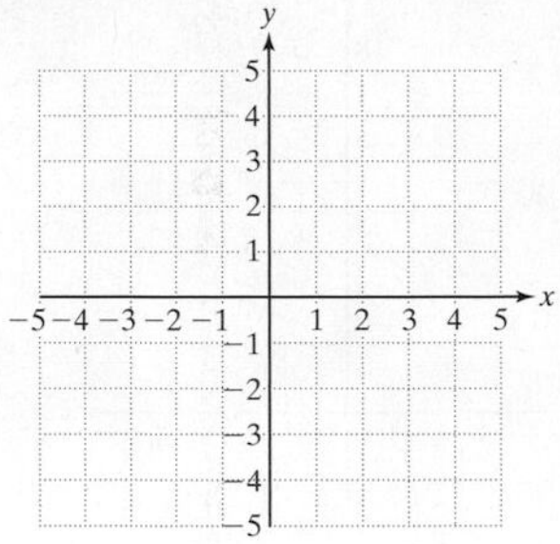

18. $x - 3y \geq 6$

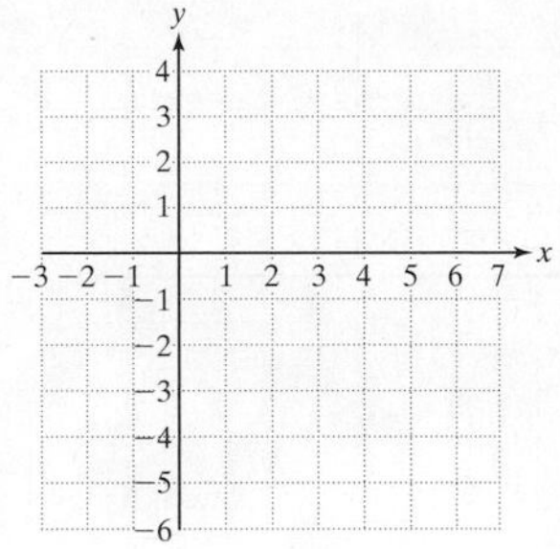

19. $5x - 2y < 10$

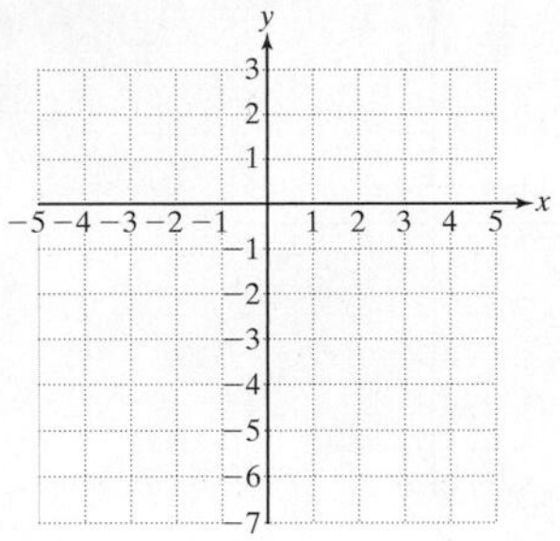

20. $x - 3y < 8$

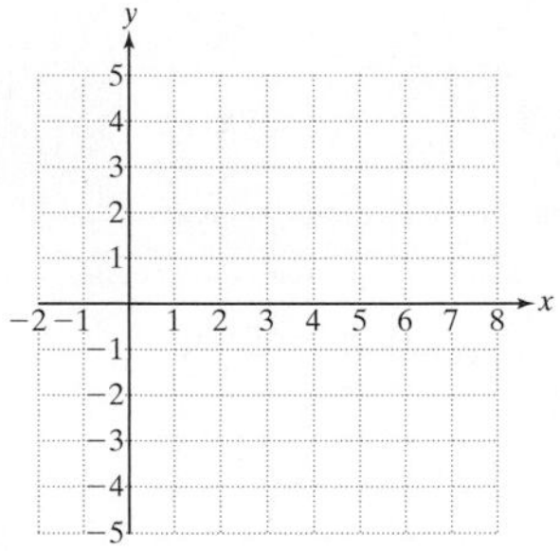

21. $2x \leq -6y + 12$

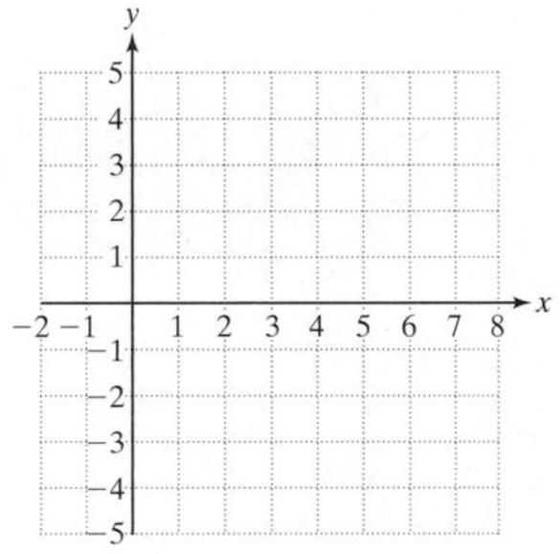

22. $4x < 3y + 12$

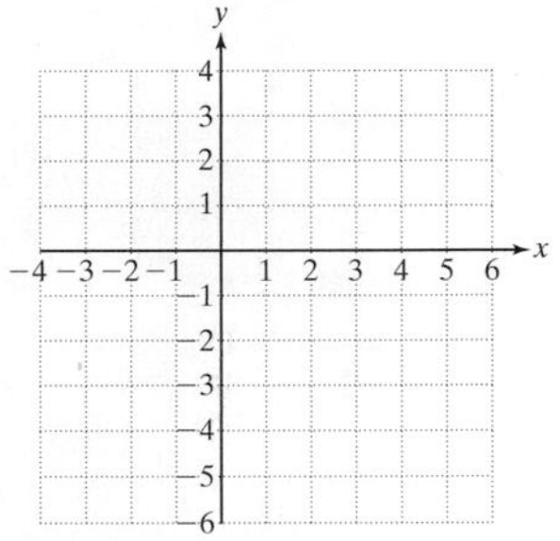

23. $2y \leq 4x$

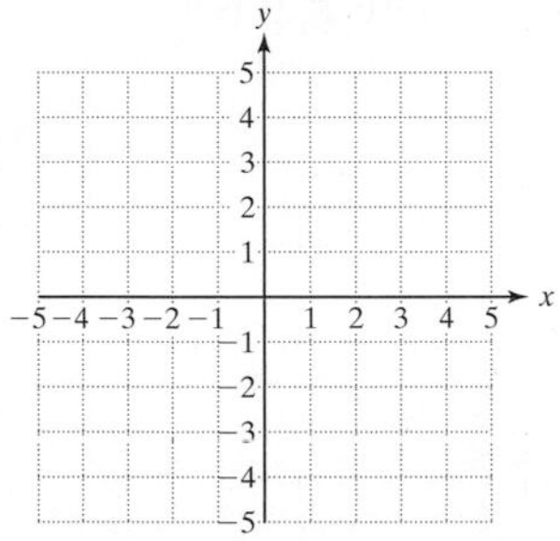

24. $-6x < 2y$

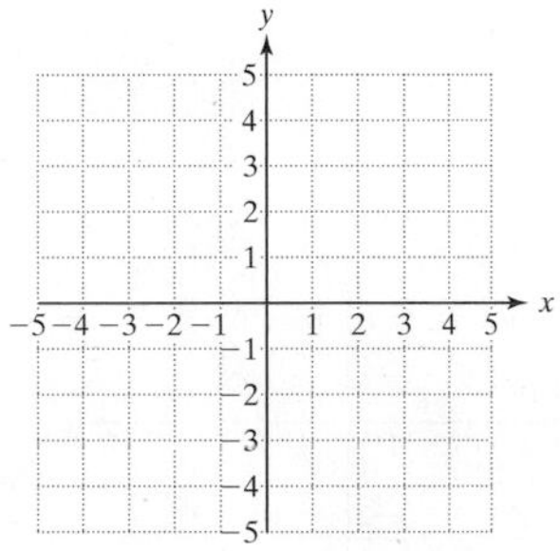

25. $y \geq -2$

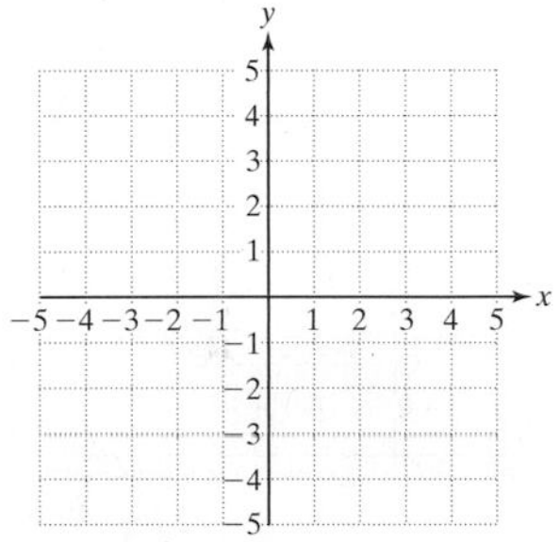

26. $y \geq 5$

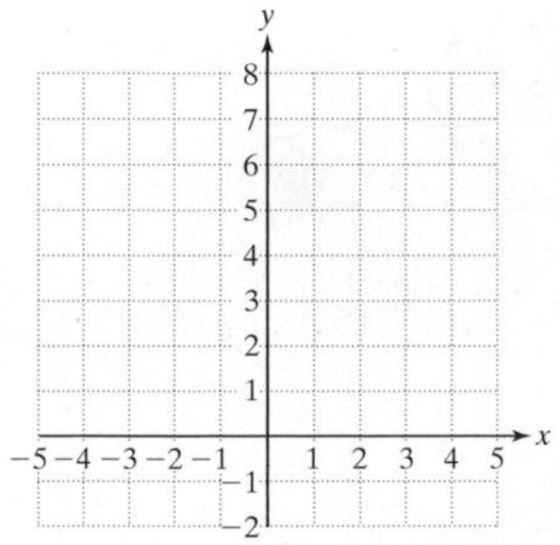

27. $4x < 5$

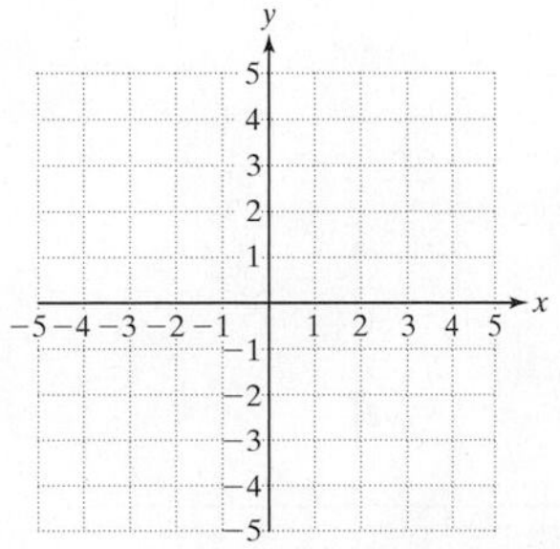

28. $x + 6 < 7$

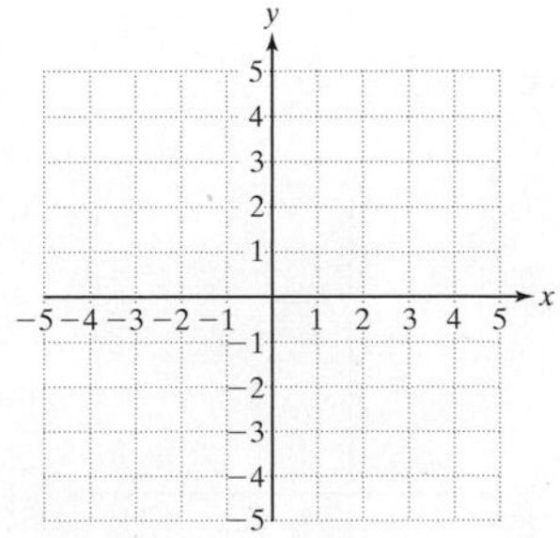

29. $y \geq \frac{2}{5}x - 4$

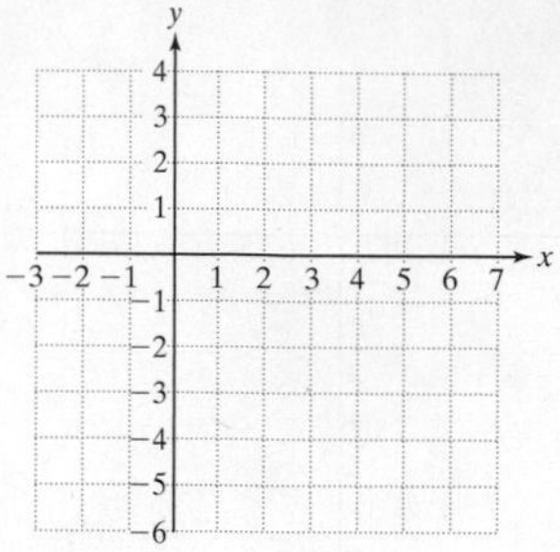

30. $y \geq -\frac{5}{2}x - 4$

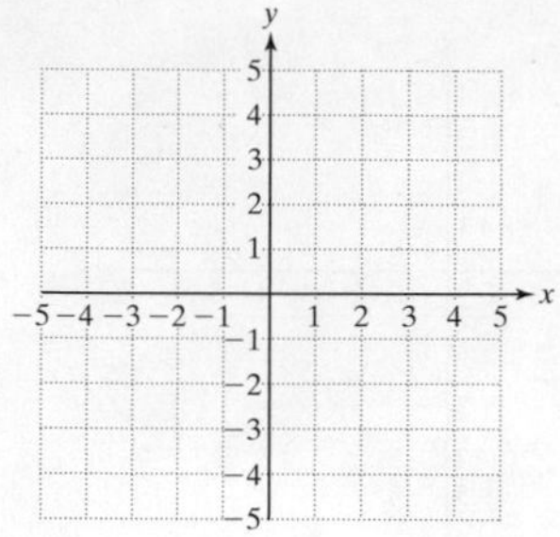

31. $y \leq \frac{1}{3}x + 6$

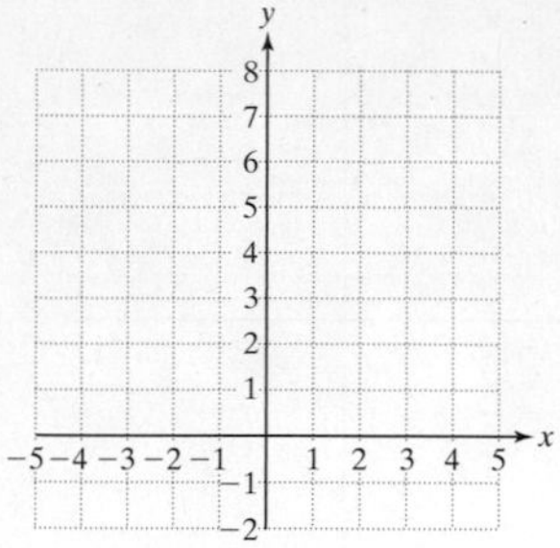

32. $y \leq -\frac{1}{4}x + 2$

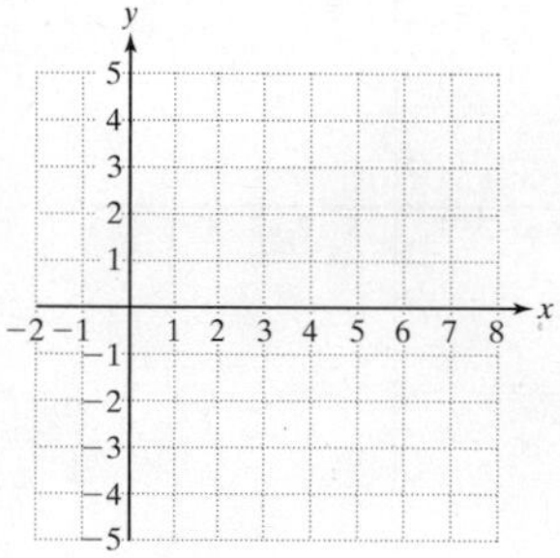

33. $y - 5x > 0$

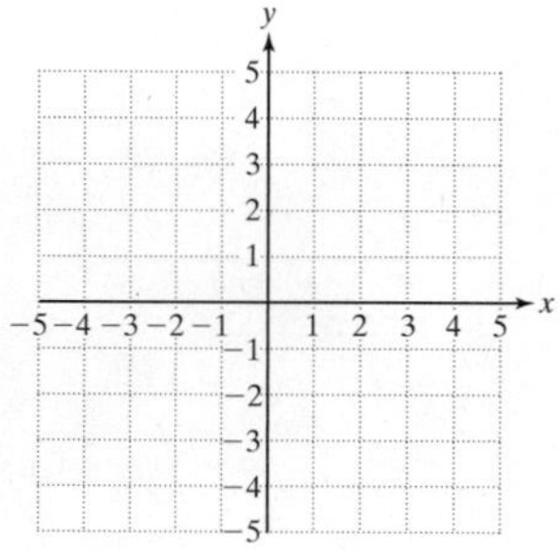

34. $y - \frac{1}{2}x > 0$

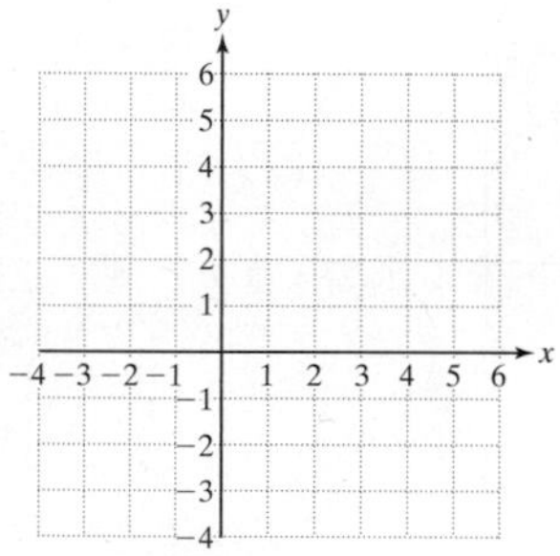

35. $\frac{x}{5} + \frac{y}{4} < 1$

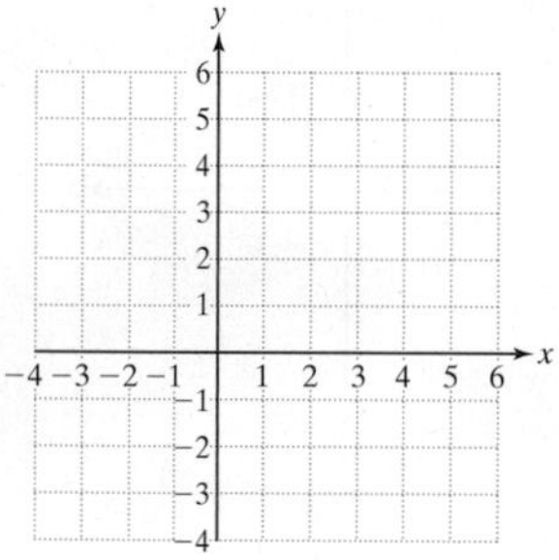

36. $x + \frac{y}{2} \geq 2$

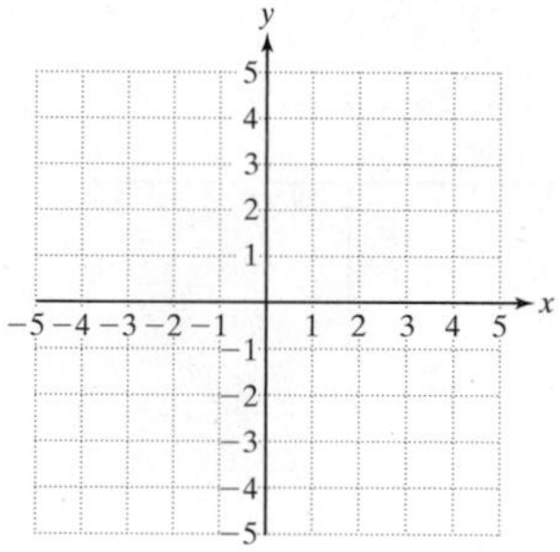

37. $0.1x + 0.2y \leq 0.6$

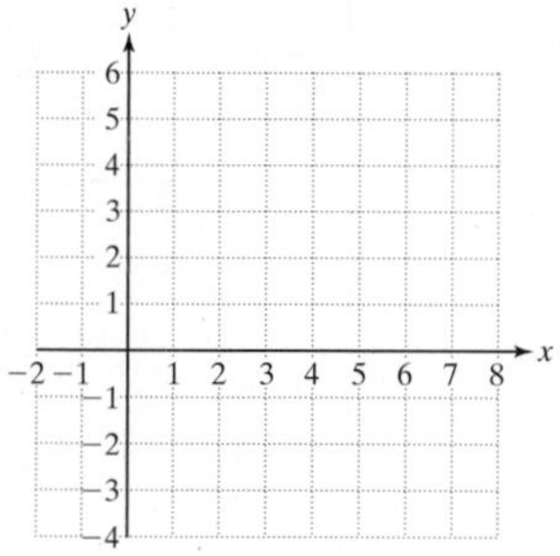

38. $0.3x - 0.2y < 0.6$

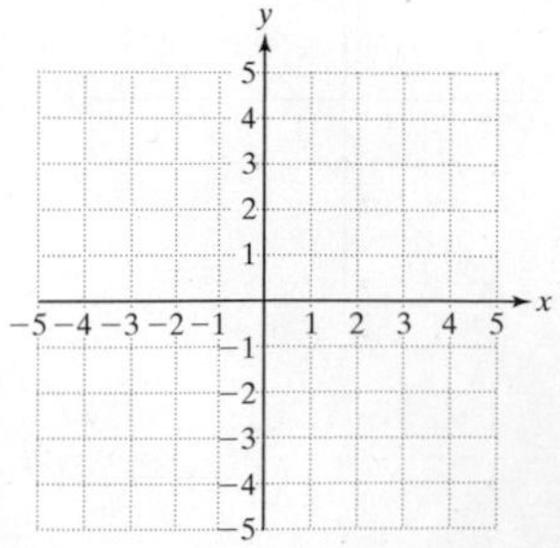

39. $x \leq -\frac{2}{3}y$

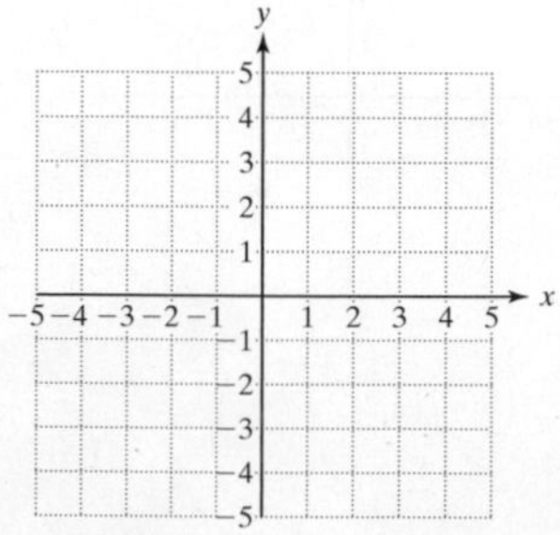

40. $x \geq -\frac{5}{4}y$

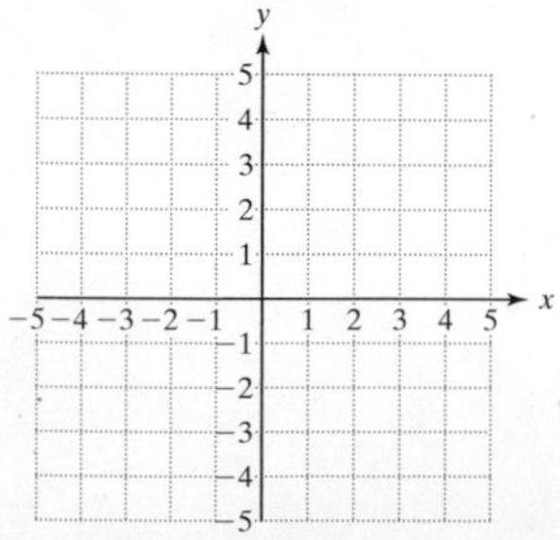

Chapter 9 Summary

Section 9.1 Compound Inequalities

Key Concepts

$A \cup B$ is the **union** of A and B. This is the set of elements that belong to set A or set B or both sets A and B.

$A \cap B$ is the **intersection** of A and B. This is the set of elements common to both A and B.

- Solve two or more inequalities joined by *and* by finding the intersection of their solution sets.
- Solve two or more inequalities joined by *or* by finding the union of their solution sets.

Examples

Example 1

Union

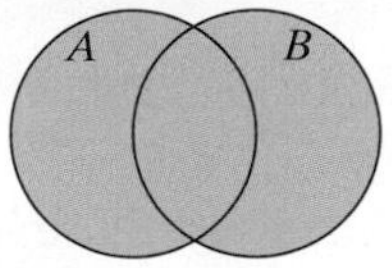

$A \cup B$

Intersection

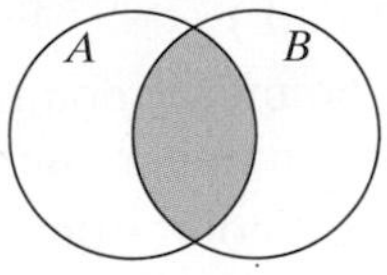

$A \cap B$

Example 2

$-7x + 3 \geq -11$	and	$1 - x < 4.5$
$-7x \geq -14$	and	$-x < 3.5$
$x \leq 2$	and	$x > -3.5$

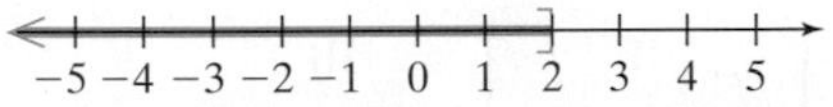

$x \leq 2$

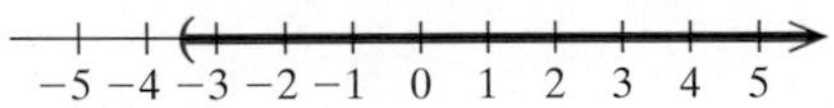

$x > -3.5$

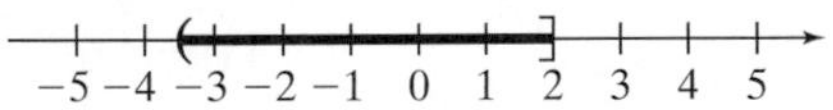

The solution is $\{x \mid -3.5 < x \leq 2\}$ or equivalently $(-3.5, 2]$.

Inequalities of the form $a < x < b$:

The inequality $a < x < b$ is represented by

or, in interval notation, (a, b).

Example 3

$5y + 1 \geq 6$	or	$2y - 5 \leq -11$
$5y \geq 5$	or	$2y \leq -6$
$y \geq 1$	or	$y \leq -3$

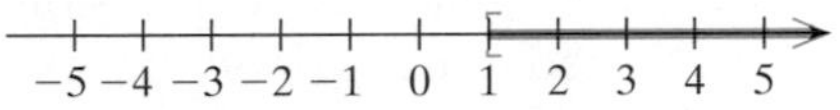

$y \geq 1$

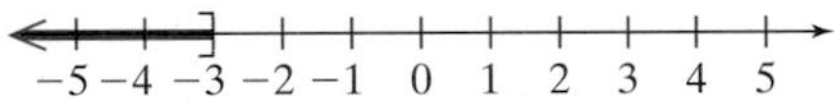

$y \leq -3$

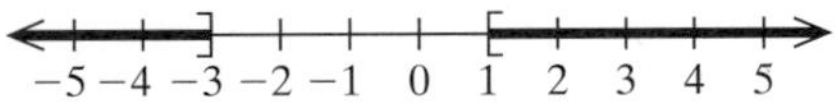

The solution is $\{y \mid y \geq 1 \text{ or } y \leq -3\}$ or equivalently $(-\infty, -3] \cup [1, \infty)$.

Example 4

Solve.

$$-13 \leq 3x - 1 < 5$$
$$-13 + 1 \leq 3x - 1 + 1 < 5 + 1$$
$$-12 \leq 3x < 6$$
$$\frac{-12}{3} \leq \frac{3x}{3} < \frac{6}{3}$$
$$-4 \leq x < 2$$

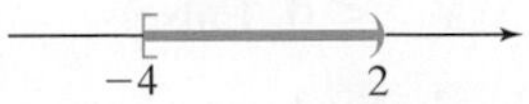

Interval notation: $[-4, 2)$

Section 9.2 Polynomial and Rational Inequalities

Key Concepts

The Test Point Method to Solve Polynomial and Rational Inequalities

1. Find the boundary points of the inequality. (Boundary points are the real solutions to the related equation and points where the inequality is undefined.)
2. Plot the boundary points on the number line. This divides the number line into intervals.
3. Select a test point from each interval and substitute it into the original inequality.
   - If a test point makes the original inequality true, then that interval is part of the solution set.
4. Test the boundary points in the original inequality.
   - If the original inequality is strict ($<$ or $>$), do not include the boundary points in the solution set.
   - If the original inequality is defined using $\leq$ or $\geq$, then include the boundary points that are well defined within the inequality.

Note: Any boundary point that makes an expression within the inequality undefined must *always* be excluded from the solution set.

Example 1

$4x^2 - 7x - 2 < 0$

$(4x + 1)(x - 2) = 0$ Related equation

$4x + 1 = 0 \quad x - 2 = 0$

$x = -\dfrac{1}{4} \quad x = 2$ The boundaries are $-\dfrac{1}{4}$ and 2.

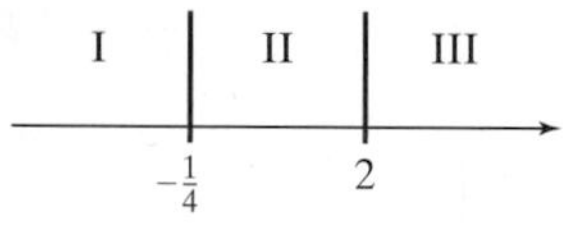

Interval I: Test $x = -1$: $4(-1)^2 - 7(-1) - 2 \overset{?}{<} 0$ False

Interval II: Test $x = 0$: $4(0)^2 - 7(0) - 2 \overset{?}{<} 0$ True

Interval III: Test $x = 3$: $4(3)^2 - 7(3) - 2 \overset{?}{<} 0$ False

The strict inequality excludes the boundary points as solutions.

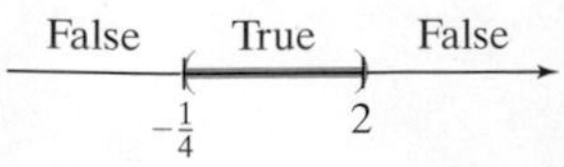

The solution is $\left(-\dfrac{1}{4}, 2\right)$.

Examples

Example 2

$\dfrac{28}{2x - 3} \leq 4$ The inequality is undefined for $x = \frac{3}{2}$. Find other possible boundary points by solving the related equation.

$\dfrac{28}{2x - 3} = 4$ Related equation

$(2x - 3) \cdot \dfrac{28}{2x - 3} = (2x - 3) \cdot 4$

$28 = 8x - 12$

$40 = 8x$

$x = 5$

The boundaries are $x = \dfrac{3}{2}$ and $x = 5$.

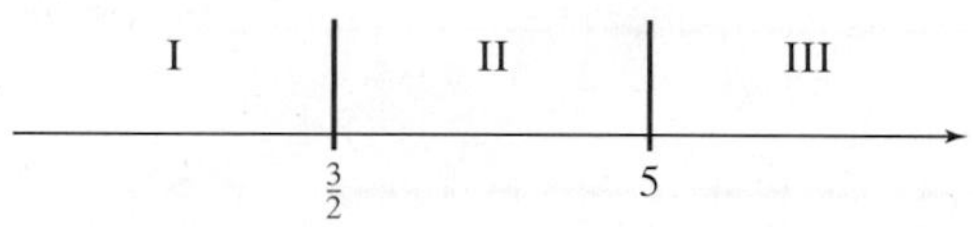

Interval I: Test $x = 1$: $\dfrac{28}{2(1) - 3} \overset{?}{\leq} 4$ True

Interval II: Test $x = 2$: $\dfrac{28}{2(2) - 3} \overset{?}{\leq} 4$ False

Interval III: Test $x = 6$: $\dfrac{28}{2(6) - 3} \overset{?}{\leq} 4$ True

The boundary point $x = \frac{3}{2}$ is not included because $\dfrac{28}{2x - 3}$ is undefined there. The boundary $x = 5$ does check in the original inequality.

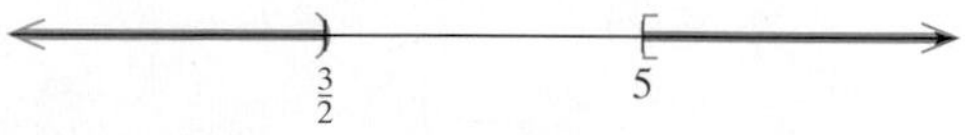

The solution is $(-\infty, \frac{3}{2}) \cup [5, \infty)$.

Section 9.3 Absolute Value Equations

Key Concepts

The equation $|x| = a$ is an absolute value equation. For $a \geq 0$, the solution to the equation $|x| = a$ is $x = a$ or $x = -a$.

Steps to Solve an Absolute Value Equation

1. Isolate the absolute value to write the equation in the form $|x| = a$.
2. If $a < 0$, there is no solution.
3. Otherwise, rewrite the equation $|x| = a$ as $x = a$ or $x = -a$.
4. Solve the equations from step 3.
5. Check answers in the original equation.

The equation $|x| = |y|$ implies $x = y$ or $x = -y$.

Examples

Example 1

$|2x - 3| + 5 = 10$

$|2x - 3| = 5$ Isolate the absolute value.

$2x - 3 = 5$ or $2x - 3 = -5$

$2x = 8$ or $2x = -2$

$x = 4$ or $x = -1$

The solution set is $\{4, -1\}$.

Example 2

$|x + 2| + 5 = 1$

$|x + 2| = -4$ There is no solution, $\{\ \}$.

Example 3

$|2x - 1| = |x + 4|$

$2x - 1 = x + 4$ or $2x - 1 = -(x + 4)$

$x = 5$ or $2x - 1 = -x - 4$

or $3x = -3$

or $x = -1$

The solution set is $\{5, -1\}$.

Section 9.4 Absolute Value Inequalities

Key Concepts

Solutions to Absolute Value Inequalities

For $a > 0$, we have:

$|x| > a \Rightarrow x < -a$ or $x > a$

$|x| < a \Rightarrow -a < x < a$

Test Point Method to Solve Inequalities

1. Find the boundary points of the inequality. (Boundary points are the real solutions to the related equation and points where the inequality is undefined.)
2. Plot the boundary points on the number line. This divides the number line into intervals.
3. Select a test point from each interval and substitute it into the original inequality.
   - If a test point makes the original inequality true, then that interval is part of the solution set.
4. Test the boundary points in the original inequality.
   - If the original inequality is strict ($<$ or $>$), do not include the boundary in the solution set.
   - If the original inequality is defined using $\leq$ or $\geq$, then include the boundary points that are well defined within the inequality.

Note: Any boundary point that makes an expression within the inequality undefined must *always* be excluded from the solution set.

If *a* is *negative* ($a < 0$), then

1. $|x| < a$ has no solution.
2. $|x| > a$ is true for all real numbers.

Examples

Example 1

$$|5x - 2| < 12$$
$$-12 < 5x - 2 < 12$$
$$-10 < 5x < 14$$
$$-2 < x < \frac{14}{5}$$

The solution is $\left(-2, \frac{14}{5}\right)$.

Example 2

$|x - 3| + 2 \geq 7$

$|x - 3| \geq 5$ Isolate the absolute value.

$|x - 3| = 5$ Solve the related equation.

$x - 3 = 5$ or $x - 3 = -5$

$x = 8$ or $x = -2$ Boundary points

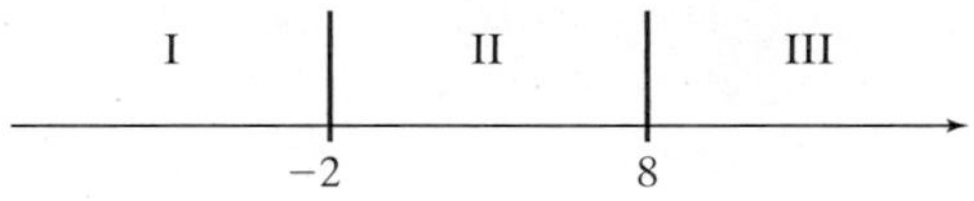

Interval I: Test $x = -3$: $|(-3) - 3| + 2 \stackrel{?}{\geq} 7$ True

Interval II: Test $x = 0$: $|(0) - 3| + 2 \stackrel{?}{\geq} 7$ False

Interval III: Test $x = 9$: $|(9) - 3| + 2 \stackrel{?}{\geq} 7$ True

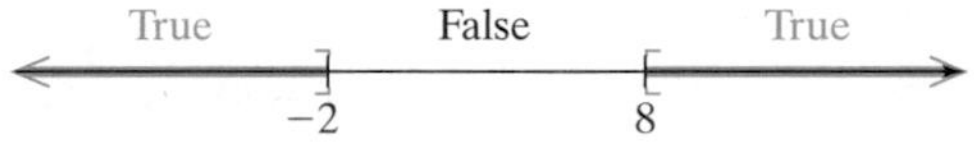

The solution is $(-\infty, -2] \cup [8, \infty)$.

Example 3

$|x + 5| > -2$

The solution is all real numbers because an absolute value will always be greater than a negative number.

$(-\infty, \infty)$

77. Suppose a farmer has 100 acres of land on which to grow oranges and grapefruit. Furthermore, because of demand from his customers, he wants to plant at least 4 times as many acres of orange trees as grapefruit trees.

Let x represent the number of acres of orange trees.

Let y represent the number of acres of grapefruit trees.

a. Write two inequalities that express the fact that the farmer cannot use a negative number of acres to plant orange and grapefruit trees.

b. Write an inequality that expresses the fact that the total number of acres used for growing orange and grapefruit trees is at most 100.

c. Write an inequality that expresses the fact that the farmer wants to plant at least 4 times as many orange trees as grapefruit trees.

d. Sketch the inequalities in parts (a)–(c) to find the feasible region for the farmer's distribution of orange and grapefruit trees.

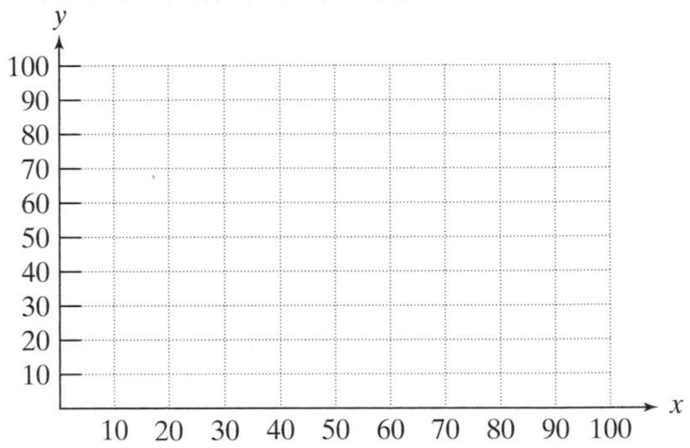

Chapter 9 Test

For Exercises 1–5, solve the compound inequalities. Write the answers in interval notation.

1. $-2 \le 3x - 1 \le 5$

2. $-\frac{3}{5}x - 1 \le 8$ or $-\frac{2}{3}x \ge 16$

3. $-2x - 3 > -3$ and $x + 3 \ge 0$

4. $5x + 1 \le 6$ or $2x + 4 > -6$

5. $2x - 3 > 1$ and $x + 4 < -1$

6. The normal range in humans of the enzyme adenosine deaminase (ADA), is between 9 and 33 IU (international units), inclusive. Let x represent the ADA level in international units.

a. Write an inequality representing the normal range for ADA.

b. Write a compound inequality representing abnormal ranges for ADA.

For Exercises 7–12, solve the polynomial and rational inequalities.

7. $50 - 2a^2 > 0$

8. $y^3 + 3y^2 - 4y - 12 < 0$

9. $5x^2 - 2x + 2 < 0$

10. $t^2 + 22t + 121 \le 0$

11. $\frac{2x - 1}{x - 6} \le 0$

12. $\frac{3}{w + 3} > 2$

For Exercises 13–14, solve the absolute value equations.

13. $\left|\frac{1}{2}x + 3\right| - 4 = 4$

14. $|3x + 4| = |x - 12|$

For Exercises 15–18, solve the absolute value inequalities. Write the answers in interval notation.

15. $|3 - 2x| + 6 < 2$

16. $|3x - 8| > 9$

16. Find the x- and y-intercepts and slope (if they exist) of the lines. Then graph the lines.

a. $3x + 5 = 8$

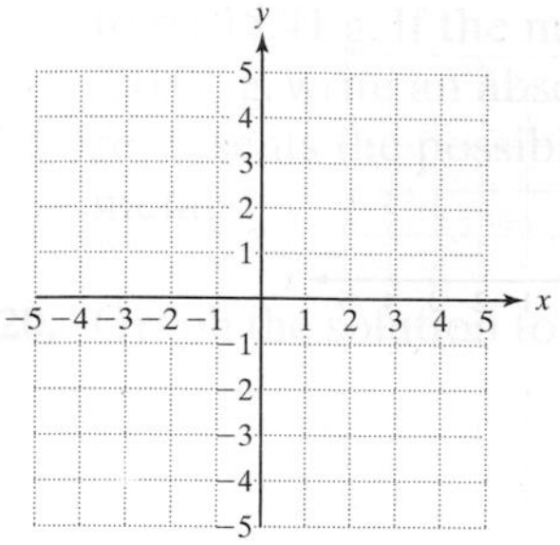

b. $\frac{1}{2}x + y = 4$

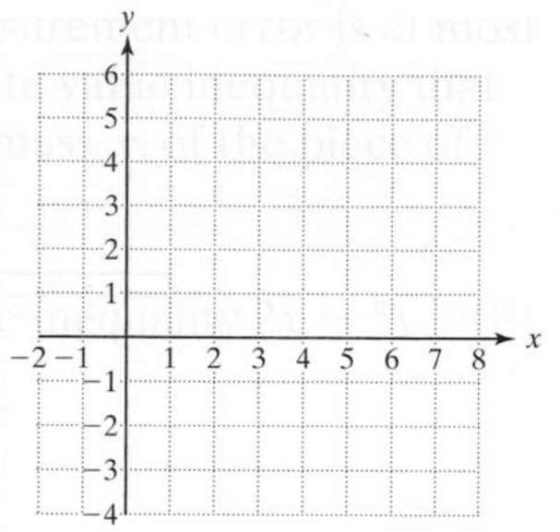

17. Find an equation of the line with slope $-\frac{2}{3}$ passing through the point $(4, -7)$. Write the final answer in slope-intercept form.

18. Solve the system of equations.

$$3x + y = z + 2$$
$$y = 1 - 2x$$
$$3z = -2y$$

19. Simplify. $\left(\frac{5x^2y^5}{30x^{-2}y^0}\right)^{-1}$

20. Against a headwind, a plane can travel 6240 mi in 13 hr. On the return trip flying with the same wind, the plane can fly 6240 mi in 12 hr. Find the wind speed and the speed of the plane in still air.

21. The profit that a company makes manufacturing computer desks is given by

$$P(x) = -\tfrac{1}{5}(x - 20)(x - 650) \qquad x \geq 0$$

where x is the number of desks produced and $P(x)$ is the profit in dollars.

a. Is this function constant, linear, or quadratic?

b. Find $P(0)$ and interpret the result in the context of this problem.

c. Find the values of x where $P(x) = 0$. Interpret the results in the context of this problem.

22. Factor the expression. $3x^3 - 6x^2 - 12x + 24$

23. Simplify completely. $\dfrac{x^{-1} - y^{-1}}{y^{-2} - x^{-2}}$

24. Divide. $\dfrac{a^3 + 64}{16 - a^2} \div \dfrac{a^3 - 4a^2 + 16a}{a^2 - 3a - 4}$

25. Perform the indicated operations.

$$\frac{1}{x^2 - 7x + 10} + \frac{1}{x^2 + 8x - 20}$$

Radicals and Complex Numbers

10

CHAPTER OUTLINE

10.1 Definition of an *n*th Root 694

10.2 Rational Exponents 706

10.3 Simplifying Radical Expressions 713

10.4 Addition and Subtraction of Radicals 720

10.5 Multiplication of Radicals 726

Problem Recognition Exercises: Simplifying Radical Expressions 734

10.6 Division of Radicals and Rationalization 734

10.7 Solving Radical Equations 744

10.8 Complex Numbers 754

Group Activity: Margin of Error of Survey Results 764

Chapter 10

In this chapter, we study radical expressions. This includes operations on square roots, cube roots, fourth roots, and so on. We also revisit the Pythagorean theorem and its applications as well as introduce the set of complex numbers.

Are You Prepared?

Take a minute to review your knowledge of square roots and operations on polynomials. These skills will help you be successful in this chapter.

For Exercises 1–10, perform the indicated operations. Then write the letter corresponding to each answer in the space at the bottom of the page.

1. $(4x - 3)(x + 5)$ **2.** $4x^2(3x^2 + 5x + 1)$ **3.** $(4x - 3)(4x + 3)$ **4.** $(4x - 3)^2$

5. $\sqrt{4}$ **6.** 4^2 **7.** $\sqrt{-4}$ **8.** $\sqrt{10^2 - 6^2}$

9. $(-3x^4 + 9x^2 - 15x) - (-3x^4 - 7x^2 + 9x + 9)$ **10.** $(2x)(6x^3)$

R	16	N	$16x^2 - 9$	I	$16x^2 - 24x + 9$	M	8
Y	$16x^2 - 24x - 9$	A	not a real number	E	$12x^4 + 20x^3 + 4x^2$	U	2
G	$4x^2 + 17x - 15$	B	$12x^4$				

In this chapter, we also introduce a new type of number called an

__ __ __ __ __ __ __ __ __   __ __ __ __ __ __.

4 8 7 1 4 3 7 6 9   3 5 8 10 2 6

Example 3 **Simplifying Square Roots**

Simplify the square roots, if possible.

a. $\sqrt{-144}$ **b.** $-\sqrt{144}$ **c.** $\sqrt{-0.01}$ **d.** $-\sqrt{\frac{1}{9}}$

Solution:

a. $\sqrt{-144}$ is *not* a real number. No real number when squared equals -144.

b. $-\sqrt{144}$

$= -1 \cdot \sqrt{144}$

$= -1 \cdot 12$

$= -12$

TIP: For the expression $-\sqrt{144}$, the factor of -1 is *outside* the radical.

c. $\sqrt{-0.01}$ is *not* a real number. No real number when squared equals -0.01.

d. $-\sqrt{\frac{1}{9}}$

$= -1 \cdot \sqrt{\frac{1}{9}}$

$= -1 \cdot \frac{1}{3}$

$= -\frac{1}{3}$

Skill Practice Simplify the square roots, if possible.

8. $\sqrt{-81}$ **9.** $-\sqrt{64}$ **10.** $-\sqrt{0.25}$ **11.** $\sqrt{-\frac{1}{4}}$

2. Definition of an *n*th Root

Finding a square root of a number is the reverse process of squaring a number. This concept can be extended to finding a third root (called a cube root), a fourth root, and in general an ***n*th root**.

Definition of an *n*th Root

b is an nth root of a if $b^n = a$.

Example: 2 is a square root of 4 because 2^2 is 4.

Example: 2 is a third root of 8 because 2^3 is 8.

Example: 2 is a fourth root of 16 because 2^4 is 16.

The radical sign $\sqrt{\ }$ is used to denote the principal square root of a number. The symbol $\sqrt[n]{\ }$ is used to denote the principal nth root of a number. In the expression $\sqrt[n]{a}$, n is called the **index** of the radical, and a is called the **radicand**. For a square root, the index is 2, but it is usually not written ($\sqrt[2]{a}$ is denoted simply as $\sqrt{a}$). A radical with an index of 3 is called a **cube root**, denoted by $\sqrt[3]{a}$.

Answers

8. Not a real number **9.** -8
10. -0.5 **11.** Not a real number

Evaluating $\sqrt[n]{a}$

1. If $n > 1$ is an *even* integer and $a > 0$, then $\sqrt[n]{a}$ is the principal (positive) *n*th root of *a*. Example: $\sqrt{9} = 3$
2. If $n > 1$ is an *odd* integer, then $\sqrt[n]{a}$ is the *n*th root of *a*.
   Example: $\sqrt[3]{8} = 2$, $\sqrt[3]{-8} = -2$
3. If $n > 1$ is an integer, then $\sqrt[n]{0} = 0$.

For the purpose of simplifying *n*th roots, it is helpful to know numbers that are perfect squares as well as the following common perfect cubes, fourth powers, and fifth powers.

Perfect Cubes	Perfect Fourth Powers	Perfect Fifth Powers
$1^3 = 1$	$1^4 = 1$	$1^5 = 1$
$2^3 = 8$	$2^4 = 16$	$2^5 = 32$
$3^3 = 27$	$3^4 = 81$	$3^5 = 243$
$4^3 = 64$	$4^4 = 256$	$4^5 = 1024$
$5^3 = 125$	$5^4 = 625$	$5^5 = 3125$

Example 4 Identifying the *n*th Root of a Real Number

Simplify the expressions, if possible.

a. $\sqrt{4}$ **b.** $\sqrt[3]{64}$ **c.** $\sqrt[5]{-32}$ **d.** $\sqrt[4]{81}$

e. $\sqrt[6]{1{,}000{,}000}$ **f.** $\sqrt{-100}$ **g.** $\sqrt[4]{-16}$

Solution:

a. $\sqrt{4} = 2$ because $(2)^2 = 4$

b. $\sqrt[3]{64} = 4$ because $(4)^3 = 64$

c. $\sqrt[5]{-32} = -2$ because $(-2)^5 = -32$

d. $\sqrt[4]{81} = 3$ because $(3)^4 = 81$

e. $\sqrt[6]{1{,}000{,}000} = 10$ because $(10)^6 = 1{,}000{,}000$

f. $\sqrt{-100}$ is not a real number. No real number when squared equals -100.

g. $\sqrt[4]{-16}$ is not a real number. No real number when raised to the fourth power equals -16.

Skill Practice Simplify if possible.

12. $\sqrt[4]{16}$ **13.** $\sqrt[3]{1000}$ **14.** $\sqrt[5]{-1}$ **15.** $\sqrt[5]{32}$

16. $\sqrt[5]{100{,}000}$ **17.** $\sqrt{-36}$ **18.** $\sqrt[3]{-27}$

Calculator Connections

Topic: Approximating *n*th Roots

A calculator can be used to approximate *n*th roots by using the $\sqrt[x]{\ }$ function. On most calculators, the index is entered first.

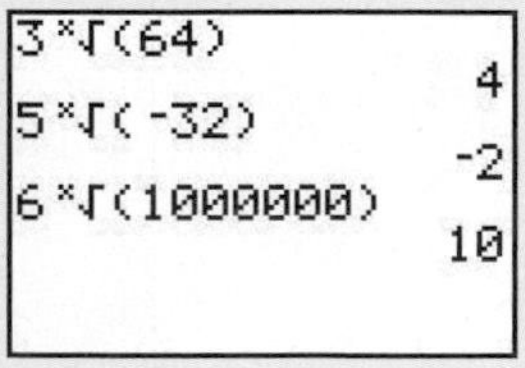

Examples 4(f) and 4(g) illustrate that an *n*th root of a negative quantity is not a real number if the index is even. This is because no real number raised to an even power is negative.

3. Roots of Variable Expressions

Finding an *n*th root of a variable expression is similar to finding an *n*th root of a numerical expression. For roots with an even index, however, particular care must be taken to obtain a nonnegative result.

Answers

12. 2 **13.** 10 **14.** -1
15. 2 **16.** 10
17. Not a real number **18.** -3

Evaluating $\sqrt[n]{a^n}$

1. If n is a positive *odd* integer, then $\sqrt[n]{a^n} = a$.
2. If n is a positive *even* integer, then $\sqrt[n]{a^n} = |a|$.

The absolute value bars are necessary for roots with an even index because the variable a may represent a positive quantity or a negative quantity. By using absolute value bars, $\sqrt[n]{a^n} = |a|$ is nonnegative and represents the principal nth root of a^n.

Example 5 Simplifying Expressions of the Form $\sqrt[n]{a^n}$

Simplify the expressions.

a. $\sqrt[4]{(-3)^4}$ **b.** $\sqrt[5]{(-3)^5}$ **c.** $\sqrt{(x+2)^2}$ **d.** $\sqrt[6]{(a+b)^3}$ **e.** $\sqrt{y^4}$

Solution:

a. $\sqrt[4]{(-3)^4} = |-3| = 3$ Because this is an *even*-indexed root, absolute value bars are necessary to make the answer positive.

b. $\sqrt[5]{(-3)^5} = -3$ This is an *odd*-indexed root, so absolute value bars are not necessary.

c. $\sqrt{(x+2)^2} = |x+2|$ Because this is an *even*-indexed root, absolute value bars are necessary. The sign of the quantity $x + 2$ is unknown; however, $|x + 2| \geq 0$ regardless of the value of x.

d. $\sqrt[3]{(a+b)^3} = a + b$ This is an *odd*-indexed root, so absolute value bars are not necessary.

e. $\sqrt{y^4} = \sqrt{(y^2)^2}$

$= |y^2|$ Because this is an even-indexed root, use absolute value bars.

$= y^2$ However, because y^2 is nonnegative, the absolute value bars are not necessary.

Skill Practice Simplify the expressions.

19. $\sqrt{(-4)^2}$ **20.** $\sqrt[3]{(-4)^3}$ **21.** $\sqrt{(y+9)^2}$ **22.** $\sqrt[3]{(t+1)^3}$ **23.** $\sqrt[4]{v^8}$

If n is an even integer, then $\sqrt[n]{a^n} = |a|$; however, if the variable a is assumed to be *nonnegative,* then the absolute value bars may be dropped. That is, $\sqrt[n]{a^n} = a$ provided $a \geq 0$. In many examples and exercises, we will make the assumption that the variables within a radical expression are positive real numbers. In such a case, the absolute value bars are not needed to evaluate $\sqrt[n]{a^n}$.

In Chapter 6 you became familiar with the patterns associated with perfect squares and perfect cubes. In general, any expression raised to an even power is a perfect square. An expression raised to a power that is a multiple of three is a perfect cube.

Perfect Squares	Perfect Cubes
$(x^1)^2 = x^2$	$(x^1)^3 = x^3$
$(x^2)^2 = x^4$	$(x^2)^3 = x^6$
$(x^3)^2 = x^6$	$(x^3)^3 = x^9$
$(x^4)^2 = x^8$	$(x^4)^3 = x^{12}$

These patterns may be extended to higher powers.

Answers

19. 4 **20.** −4 **21.** $|y + 9|$
22. $t + 1$ **23.** v^2

Example 6 Simplifying *n*th Roots

Simplify the expressions. Assume that all variables are positive real numbers.

a. $\sqrt{y^8}$ **b.** $\sqrt[3]{27a^3}$ **c.** $\sqrt[5]{\dfrac{a^5}{b^5}}$ **d.** $-\sqrt[4]{\dfrac{81x^4y^8}{16}}$

Solution:

a. $\sqrt{y^8} = \sqrt{(y^4)^2}$
$= y^4$

b. $\sqrt[3]{27a^3} = \sqrt[3]{(3a)^3}$
$= 3a$

c. $\sqrt[5]{\dfrac{a^5}{b^5}} = \sqrt[5]{\left(\dfrac{a}{b}\right)^5}$
$= \dfrac{a}{b}$

d. $-\sqrt[4]{\dfrac{81x^4y^8}{16}} = -\sqrt[4]{\left(\dfrac{3xy^2}{2}\right)^4}$
$= -\dfrac{3xy^2}{2}$

TIP: In Example 6, the variables are assumed to represent positive numbers. Therefore, absolute value bars are not necessary in the simplified form.

Skill Practice Simplify the expressions. Assume all variables represent positive real numbers.

24. $\sqrt{t^6}$ **25.** $\sqrt[3]{64y^{12}}$ **26.** $\sqrt[4]{\dfrac{x^4}{y^4}}$ **27.** $-\sqrt[5]{\dfrac{32a^5}{b^{10}}}$

4. Pythagorean Theorem

In Section 6.8, we used the Pythagorean theorem in several applications. For the triangle shown in Figure 10-1, the **Pythagorean theorem** may be stated as $a^2 + b^2 = c^2$. In this formula, a and b are the legs of the right triangle, and c is the hypotenuse.

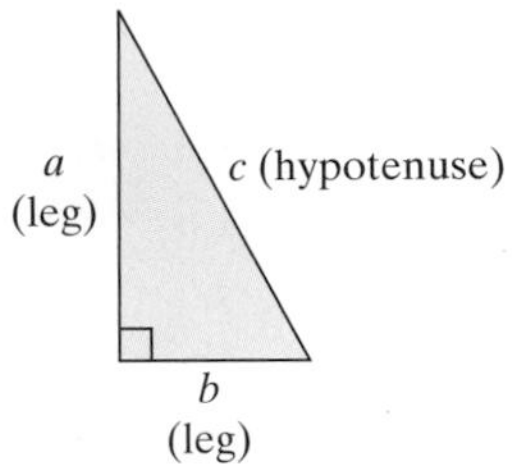

Figure 10-1

Example 7 Applying the Pythagorean Theorem

Use the Pythagorean theorem and the definition of the principal square root to find the length of the unknown side.

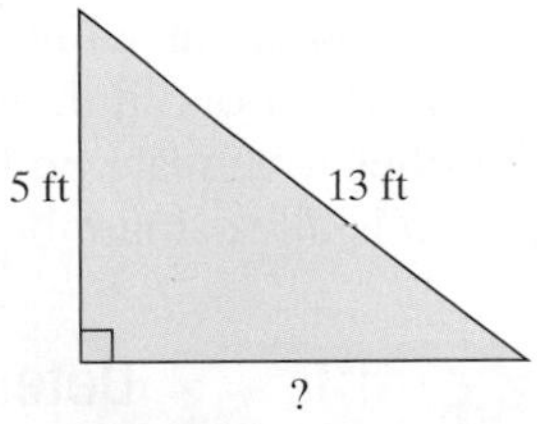

Solution:

Label the sides of the triangle.

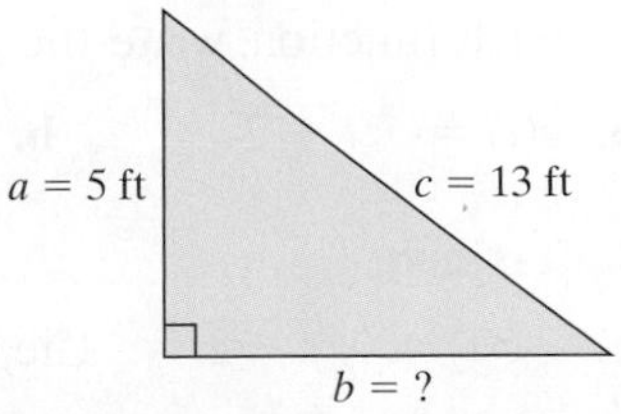

$a^2 + b^2 = c^2$	Apply the Pythagorean theorem.
$(5)^2 + b^2 = (13)^2$	
$25 + b^2 = 169$	Simplify.
$b^2 = 169 - 25$	Isolate b^2.
$b^2 = 144$	By definition, b must be one of the square roots of 144. Because b represents the length of a side of a triangle, choose the positive square root of 144.
$b = 12$	

The third side is 12 ft long.

Skill Practice Use the Pythagorean theorem and the definition of the principal square root to find the length of the unknown side of the right triangle.

28.

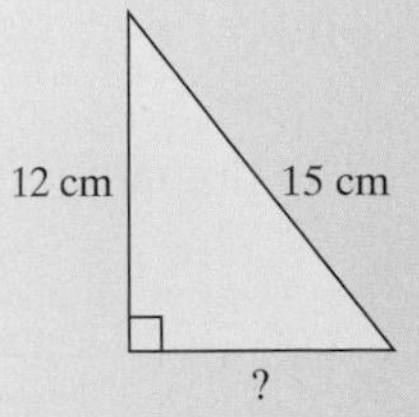

Answers

24. t^3 **25.** $4y^4$ **26.** $\dfrac{x}{y}$

27. $-\dfrac{2a}{b^2}$ **28.** 9 cm

Example 8 Applying the Pythagorean Theorem

Two boats leave a dock at 12:00 noon. One travels due north at 6 mph, and the other travels due east at 8 mph (Figure 10-2). How far apart are the two boats after 2 hr?

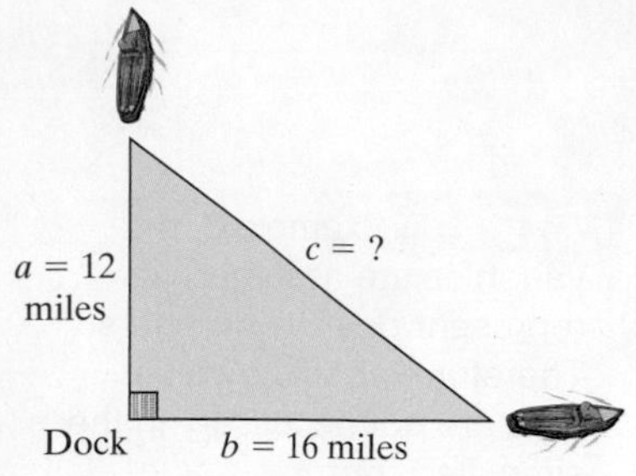

Figure 10-2

Solution:

The boat traveling north travels a distance of (6 mph)(2 hr) = 12 mi. The boat traveling east travels a distance of (8 mph)(2 hr) = 16 mi. The course of the boats forms a right triangle where the hypotenuse represents the distance between them.

$$a^2 + b^2 = c^2$$

$$(12)^2 + (16)^2 = c^2 \quad \text{Apply the Pythagorean theorem.}$$

$$144 + 256 = c^2 \quad \text{Simplify.}$$

$$400 = c^2$$

$$\sqrt{400} = c$$

$$20 = c$$

By definition, c must be one of the square roots of 400. Choose the positive square root of 400 to represent the distance between the two boats.

The boats are 20 mi apart.

Skill Practice

29. Two cars leave from the same place at the same time. One travels west at 40 mph, and the other travels north at 30 mph. How far apart are they after 2 hr?

5. Radical Functions

If n is an integer greater than 1, then a function written in the form $f(x) = \sqrt[n]{x}$ is called a **radical function**. Note that if n is an even integer, then the function will be a real number only if the radicand is nonnegative. Therefore, the domain is restricted to nonnegative real numbers, or equivalently, $[0, \infty)$. If n is an odd integer, then the domain is all real numbers.

Example 9 Determining the Domain of Radical Functions

For each function, write the domain in interval notation.

a. $g(t) = \sqrt[4]{t - 2}$ **b.** $h(a) = \sqrt[3]{a - 3}$ **c.** $k(x) = \sqrt{3 - 5x} + 2$

Solution:

a. $g(t) = \sqrt[4]{t - 2}$ The index is even. The radicand must be nonnegative.

$t - 2 \geq 0$ Set the radicand greater than or equal to zero.

$t \geq 2$ Solve for t.

The domain is $[2, \infty)$.

b. $h(a) = \sqrt[3]{a - 3}$ The index is odd; therefore, the domain is all real numbers.

The domain is $(-\infty, \infty)$.

Answer

29. 100 mi

c. $k(x) = \sqrt{3 - 5x} + 2$ The index is even; therefore, the radicand must be nonnegative.

$3 - 5x \geq 0$ Set the radicand greater than or equal to zero.

$-5x \geq -3$ Solve for x.

$\frac{-5x}{-5} \leq \frac{-3}{-5}$ Reverse the inequality sign.

$x \leq \frac{3}{5}$

The domain is $(-\infty, \frac{3}{5}]$.

Skill Practice For each function, write the domain in interval notation.

30. $f(x) = \sqrt{x + 5}$ **31.** $g(t) = \sqrt[3]{t - 9}$ **32.** $h(a) = \sqrt{1 - 2a}$

Calculator Connections

Topic: Graphing Radical Functions

We can graph the functions defined in Example 9. The graphs support the answers we obtained for the domain of each function.

$g(t) = \sqrt[4]{t - 2}$

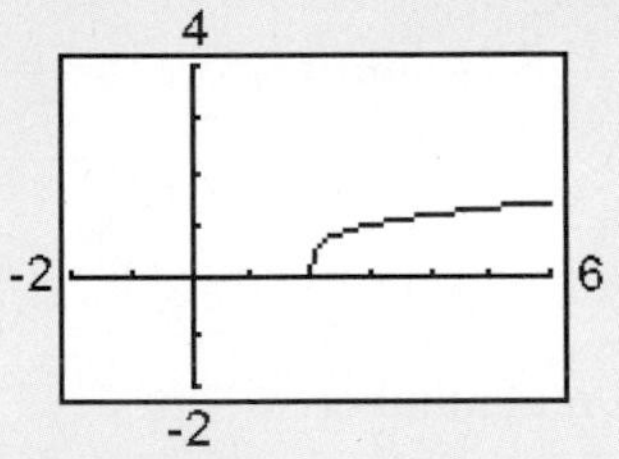

$h(a) = \sqrt[3]{a - 3}$

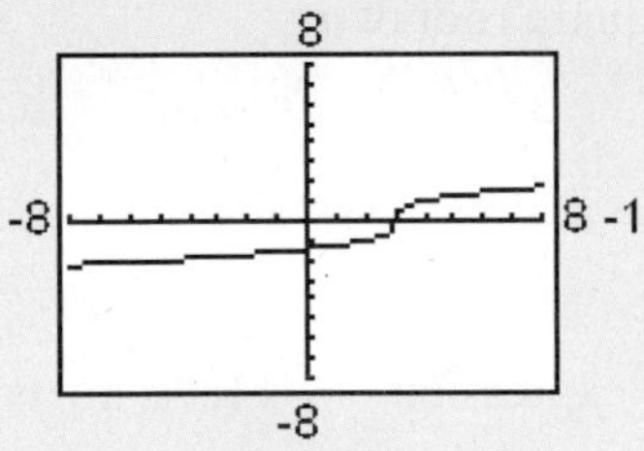

$k(x) = \sqrt{3 - 5x} + 2$

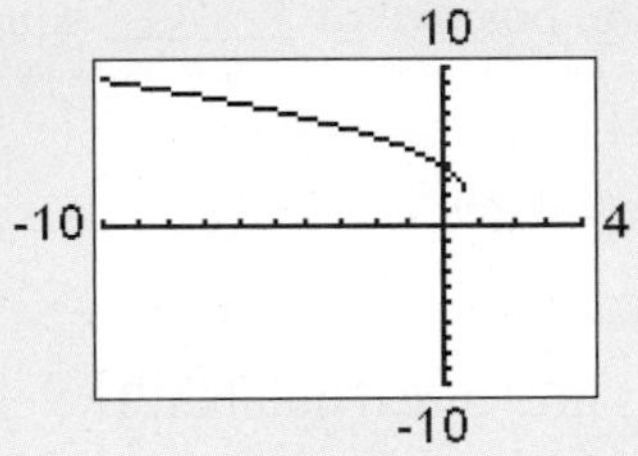

Example 10 Graphing a Radical Function

Given $f(x) = \sqrt{3 - x}$

a. Write the domain of f in interval notation.

b. Graph f by making a table of ordered pairs.

Solution:

a. $f(x) = \sqrt{3 - x}$

$3 - x \geq 0$ The index is even. The radicand must be greater than or equal to zero.

$-x \geq -3$

$x \leq 3$ Reverse the inequality sign.

The domain is $(-\infty, 3]$.

Answers

30. $[-5, \infty)$ **31.** $(-\infty, \infty)$

32. $(-\infty, \frac{1}{2}]$

b. Create a table of ordered pairs where x values are taken to be less than or equal to 3.

x	$f(x)$
3	0
2	1
−1	2
−6	3

$f(3) = \sqrt{3 - 3} = \sqrt{0} = 0$
$f(2) = \sqrt{3 - 2} = \sqrt{1} = 1$
$f(-1) = \sqrt{3 - (-1)} = \sqrt{4} = 2$
$f(-6) = \sqrt{3 - (-6)} = \sqrt{9} = 3$

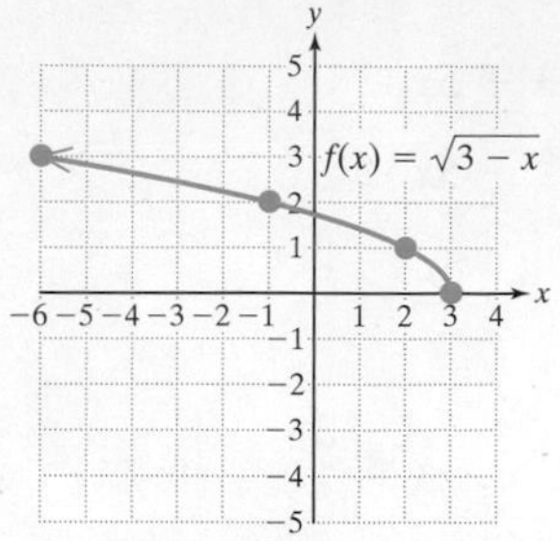

Skill Practice

33. Given $f(x) = \sqrt{x + 4}$
a. Write the domain of f in interval notation.
b. Graph f by making a table of ordered pairs.

Answers

33. a. $[-4, \infty)$
b.

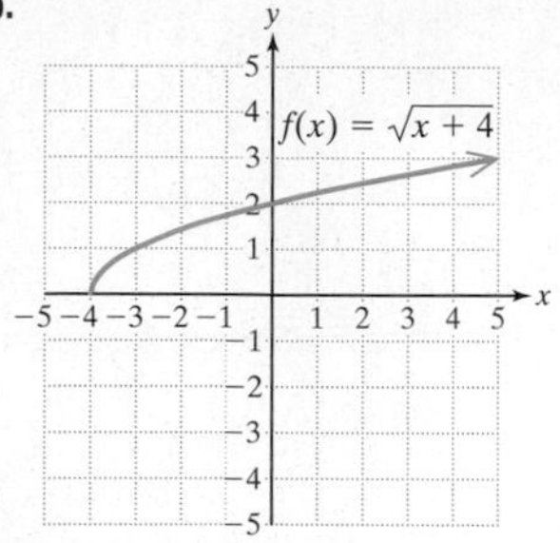

Section 10.1 Practice Exercises

Vocabulary and Key Concepts

1. a. If $b^2 = a$, then ________ is a square root of ________.

b. The symbol $\sqrt{a}$ denotes the positive or ________ square root of a.

c. b is an nth root of a if ________ = ________.

d. Given the symbol $\sqrt[n]{a}$, the value n is called the ________ and a is called the ________.

e. The symbol $\sqrt[3]{a}$ denotes the ________ root of a.

f. The expression $\sqrt{-4}$ (is/is not) a real number. The expression $-\sqrt{4}$ (is/is not) a real number.

g. The expression $\sqrt[n]{a^n} = |a|$ if n is (even/odd). The expression $\sqrt[n]{a^n} = a$ if n is (even/odd).

h. Given a right triangle with legs a and b and hypotenuse c, the ________ theorem is stated as $a^2 + b^2 =$ ________.

i. In interval notation, the domain of $f(x) = \sqrt{x}$ is ________, whereas the domain of $g(x) = \sqrt[3]{x}$ is ________.

j. Which of the following values of x are *not* in the domain of $h(x) = \sqrt{x + 3}$: $x = -5, x = -4, x = -3, x = -2, x = -1, x = 0$?

Concept 1: Definition of a Square Root

2. Simplify the expression $\sqrt[3]{8}$. Explain how you can check your answer.

3. a. Find the square roots of 64. **(See Example 1.)**
b. Find $\sqrt{64}$.
c. Explain the difference between the answers in part (a) and part (b).

4. a. Find the square roots of 121.
b. Find $\sqrt{121}$.
c. Explain the difference between the answers in part (a) and part (b).

5. a. What is the principal square root of 81?
b. What is the negative square root of 81?

6. a. What is the principal square root of 100?
b. What is the negative square root of 100?

7. Using the definition of a square root, explain why $\sqrt{-36}$ is not a real number.

For Exercises 8–19, evaluate the roots without using a calculator. Identify those that are not real numbers. **(See Examples 2–3.)**

8. $\sqrt{25}$ **9.** $\sqrt{49}$ **10.** $-\sqrt{25}$ **11.** $-\sqrt{49}$

12. $\sqrt{-25}$ **13.** $\sqrt{-49}$ **14.** $\sqrt{\frac{100}{121}}$ **15.** $\sqrt{\frac{64}{9}}$

16. $\sqrt{0.64}$ **17.** $\sqrt{0.81}$ **18.** $-\sqrt{0.0144}$ **19.** $-\sqrt{0.16}$

Concept 2: Definition of an *n*th Root

20. Using the definition of an *n*th root, explain why $\sqrt[4]{-16}$ is not a real number.

For Exercises 21–38, evaluate the roots without using a calculator. Identify those that are not real numbers. **(See Example 4.)**

21. a. $\sqrt{64}$ **b.** $\sqrt[3]{64}$ **c.** $-\sqrt{64}$
d. $-\sqrt[3]{64}$ **e.** $\sqrt{-64}$ **f.** $\sqrt[3]{-64}$

22. a. $\sqrt{16}$ **b.** $\sqrt[4]{16}$ **c.** $-\sqrt{16}$
d. $-\sqrt[4]{16}$ **e.** $\sqrt{-16}$ **f.** $\sqrt[4]{-16}$

23. $\sqrt[3]{-27}$ **24.** $\sqrt[3]{-125}$ **25.** $\sqrt[3]{\frac{1}{8}}$ **26.** $\sqrt[5]{\frac{1}{32}}$

27. $\sqrt[5]{32}$ **28.** $\sqrt[4]{1}$ **29.** $\sqrt[3]{-\frac{125}{64}}$ **30.** $\sqrt[3]{-\frac{8}{27}}$

31. $\sqrt[4]{-1}$ **32.** $\sqrt[6]{-1}$ **33.** $\sqrt[6]{1{,}000{,}000}$ **34.** $\sqrt[4]{10{,}000}$

35. $-\sqrt[3]{0.008}$ **36.** $-\sqrt[4]{0.0016}$ **37.** $\sqrt[4]{0.0625}$ **38.** $\sqrt[3]{0.064}$

Concept 3: Roots of Variable Expressions

For Exercises 39–58, simplify the radical expressions. **(See Example 5.)**

39. $\sqrt{a^2}$ **40.** $\sqrt[4]{a^4}$ **41.** $\sqrt[3]{a^3}$ **42.** $\sqrt[5]{a^5}$

43. $\sqrt[6]{a^6}$ **44.** $\sqrt[7]{a^7}$ **45.** $\sqrt{(x+1)^2}$ **46.** $\sqrt[3]{(y+3)^3}$

47. $\sqrt{x^2y^4}$ **48.** $\sqrt[3]{(u+v)^3}$ **49.** $-\sqrt[3]{\frac{x^3}{y^3}},\ y \neq 0$ **50.** $\sqrt[4]{\frac{a^4}{b^8}},\ b \neq 0$

51. $\frac{2}{\sqrt[4]{x^4}},\ x \neq 0$ **52.** $\sqrt{(-5)^2}$ **53.** $\sqrt[3]{(-92)^3}$ **54.** $\sqrt[6]{(50)^6}$

55. $\sqrt[10]{(-2)^{10}}$ **56.** $\sqrt[5]{(-2)^5}$ **57.** $\sqrt[7]{(-923)^7}$ **58.** $\sqrt[6]{(-417)^6}$

For Exercises 59–74, simplify the expressions. Assume all variables are positive real numbers. **(See Example 6.)**

59. $\sqrt{y^8}$ **60.** $\sqrt{x^4}$ **61.** $\sqrt{\frac{a^6}{b^2}}$ **62.** $\sqrt{\frac{w^2}{z^4}}$

63. $-\sqrt{\frac{25}{q^2}}$ **64.** $-\sqrt{\frac{p^6}{81}}$ **65.** $\sqrt{9x^2y^4z^2}$ **66.** $\sqrt{4a^4b^2c^6}$

67. $\sqrt{\dfrac{h^2k^4}{16}}$ **68.** $\sqrt{\dfrac{4x^2}{y^8}}$ **69.** $-\sqrt[3]{\dfrac{t^3}{27}}$ **70.** $\sqrt[4]{\dfrac{16}{w^4}}$

71. $\sqrt[5]{32y^{10}}$ **72.** $\sqrt[3]{64x^6y^3}$ **73.** $\sqrt[6]{64p^{12}q^{18}}$ **74.** $\sqrt[4]{16r^{12}s^8}$

Concept 4: Pythagorean Theorem

For Exercises 75–78, find the length of the third side of each triangle by using the Pythagorean theorem. **(See Example 7.)**

75.

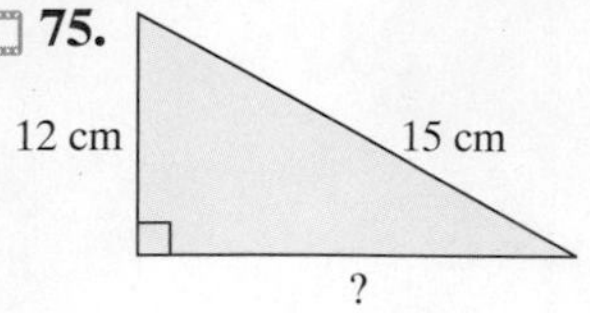

76.

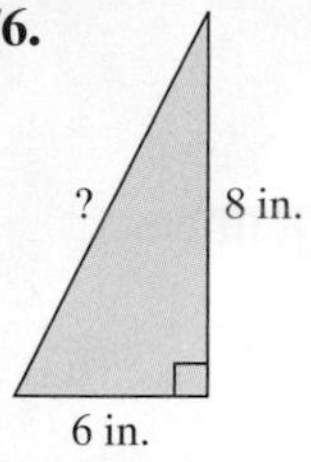

77.

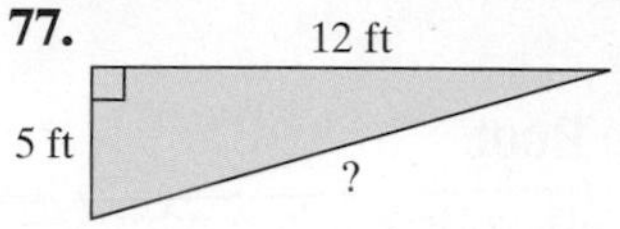

78.

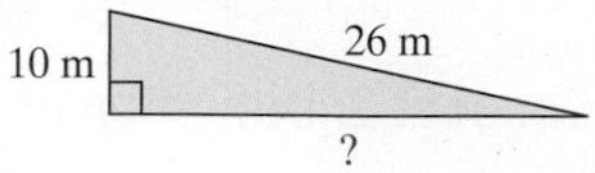

For Exercises 79–82, use the Pythagorean theorem.

79. Roberto and Sherona began running from the same place at the same time. They ran along two different paths that formed right angles with each other. Roberto ran 4 mi and stopped, while Sherona ran 3 mi and stopped. How far apart were they when they stopped? **(See Example 8.)**

80. Leine and Laura began hiking from their campground. Laura headed south while Leine headed east. Laura walked 12 mi and Leine walked 5 mi. How far apart were they when they stopped walking?

81. Two mountain bikers take off from the same place at the same time. One travels north at 4 mph, and the other travels east at 3 mph. How far apart are they after 5 hr?

82. Professor Ortiz leaves campus on her bike, heading west at 12 ft/sec. Professor Wilson leaves campus at the same time and walks south at 5 ft/sec. How far apart are they after 40 sec?

Concept 5: Radical Functions

For Exercises 83–86, evaluate the function for the given values of x. Then write the domain of the function in interval notation. **(See Example 9.)**

83. $h(x) = \sqrt{x - 2}$
- **a.** $h(0)$
- **b.** $h(1)$
- **c.** $h(2)$
- **d.** $h(3)$
- **e.** $h(6)$

84. $k(x) = \sqrt{x + 1}$
- **a.** $k(-3)$
- **b.** $k(-2)$
- **c.** $k(-1)$
- **d.** $k(0)$
- **e.** $k(3)$

85. $g(x) = \sqrt[3]{x - 2}$
- **a.** $g(-6)$
- **b.** $g(1)$
- **c.** $g(2)$
- **d.** $g(3)$

86. $f(x) = \sqrt[3]{x + 1}$
- **a.** $f(-9)$
- **b.** $f(-2)$
- **c.** $f(0)$
- **d.** $f(7)$

For each function defined in Exercises 87–94, write the domain in interval notation. **(See Example 9.)**

87. $f(x) = \sqrt{5 - 2x}$ **88.** $g(x) = \sqrt{3 - 4x}$ **89.** $k(x) = \sqrt[3]{4x - 7}$ **90.** $R(x) = \sqrt[3]{x + 1}$

91. $M(x) = \sqrt{x - 5} + 3$ **92.** $N(x) = \sqrt{x + 3} - 1$ **93.** $F(x) = \sqrt[3]{x + 7} - 2$ **94.** $G(x) = \sqrt[3]{x - 10} + 4$

For Exercises 95–102,

a. Write the domain of f in interval notation.

b. Graph f by making a table of ordered pairs. **(See Example 10.)**

95. $f(x) = \sqrt{1 - x}$

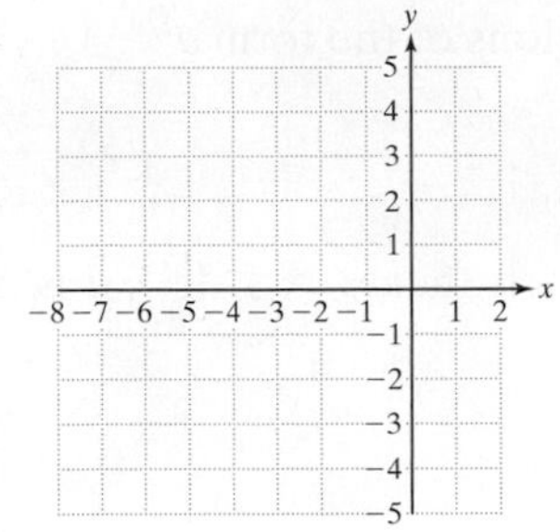

96. $f(x) = \sqrt{2 - x}$

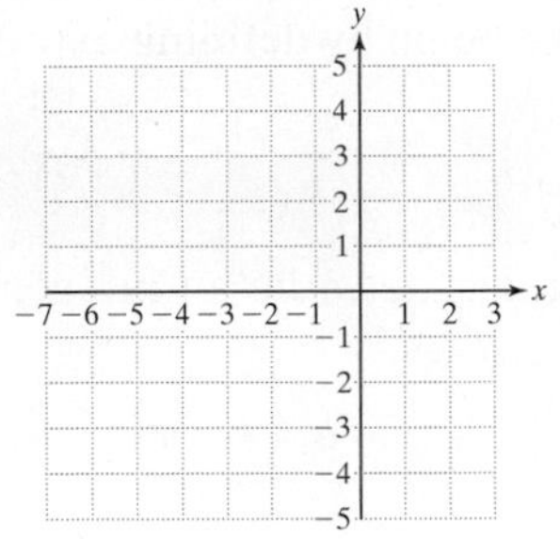

97. $f(x) = \sqrt{x + 3}$

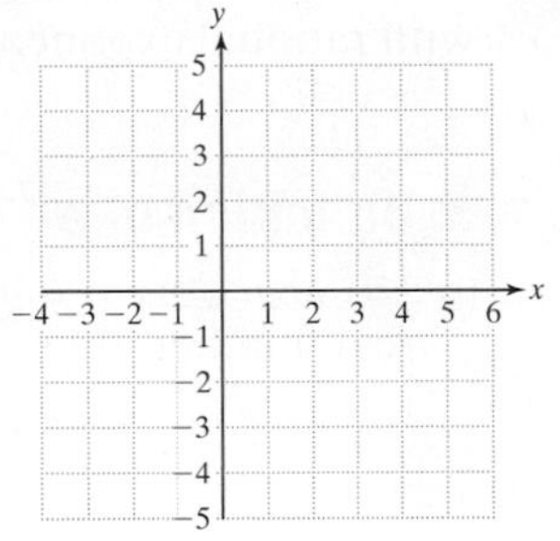

98. $f(x) = \sqrt{x + 1}$

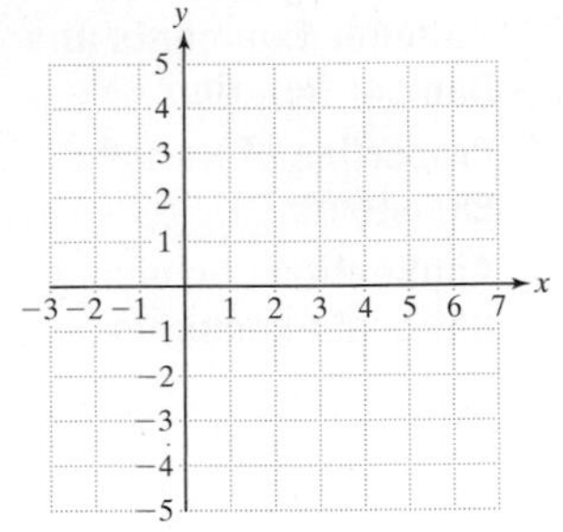

99. $f(x) = \sqrt{x} + 2$

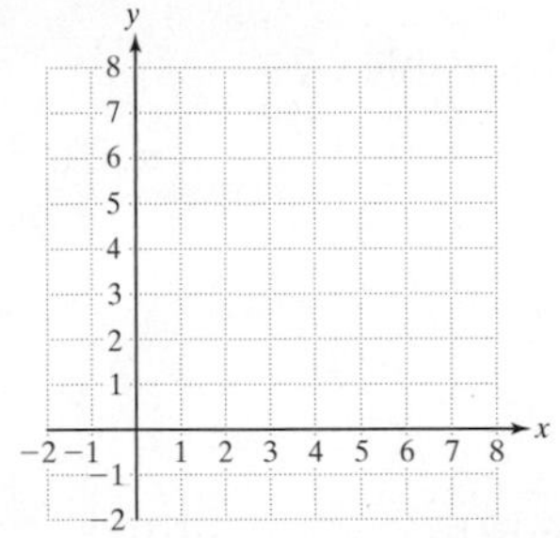

100. $f(x) = \sqrt{x} - 1$

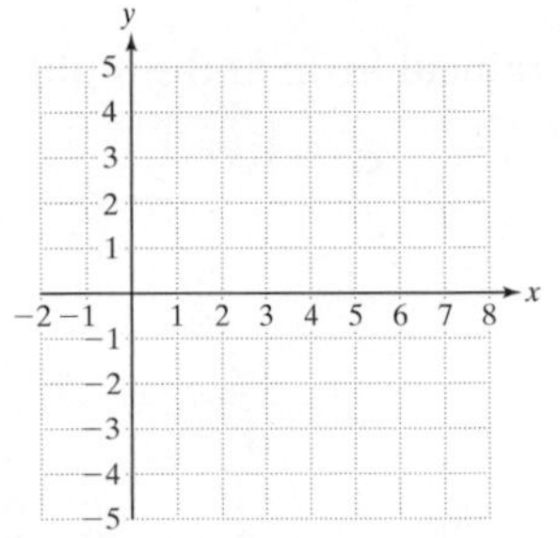

101. $f(x) = \sqrt[3]{x - 1}$

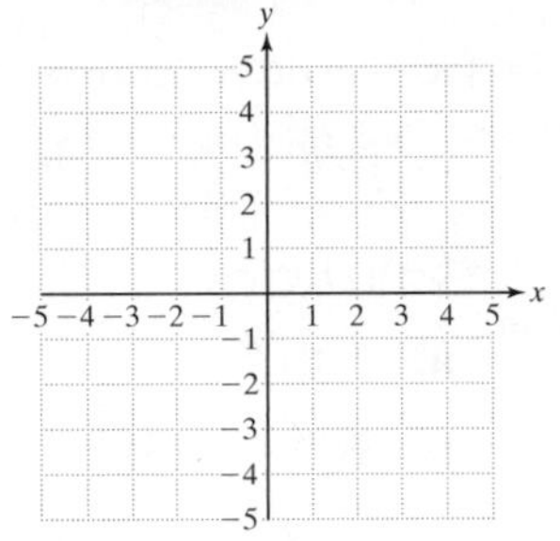

102. $f(x) = \sqrt[3]{x + 2}$

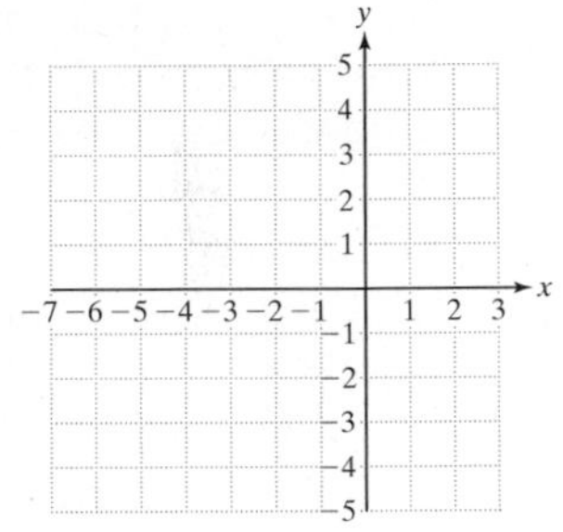

Mixed Exercises

For Exercises 103–106, write the English phrase as an algebraic expression.

103. The sum of q and the square of p

104. The product of 11 and the cube root of x

105. The quotient of 6 and the cube root of x

106. The difference of y and the principal square root of x

107. If a square has an area of 64 in.^{2}, then what are the lengths of the sides?

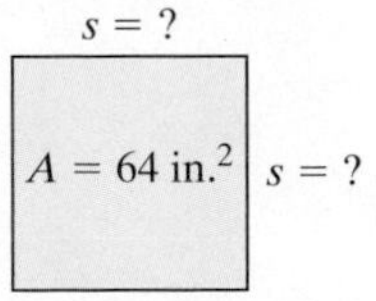

108. If a square has an area of 121 m^2, then what are the lengths of the sides?

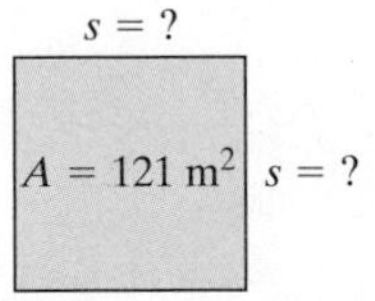

Graphing Calculator Exercises

For Exercises 109–116, use a calculator to evaluate the expressions to four decimal places.

109. $\sqrt{69}$

110. $\sqrt{5798}$

111. $2 + \sqrt[3]{5}$

112. $3 - 2\sqrt[4]{10}$

113. $7\sqrt[4]{25}$

114. $-3\sqrt[3]{9}$

115. $\dfrac{3 - \sqrt{19}}{11}$

116. $\dfrac{5 + 2\sqrt{15}}{12}$

117. Graph $h(x) = \sqrt{x - 2}$. Use the graph to confirm the domain found in Exercise 83.

118. Graph $k(x) = \sqrt{x + 1}$. Use the graph to confirm the domain found in Exercise 84.

119. Graph $g(x) = \sqrt[3]{x - 2}$. Use the graph to confirm the domain found in Exercise 85.

120. Graph $f(x) = \sqrt[3]{x + 1}$. Use the graph to confirm the domain found in Exercise 86.

Section 10.2 Rational Exponents

Concepts

1. Definition of $a^{1/n}$ and $a^{m/n}$
2. Converting Between Rational Exponents and Radical Notation
3. Properties of Rational Exponents
4. Applications Involving Rational Exponents

1. Definition of $a^{1/n}$ and $a^{m/n}$

In Section 5.1, the properties for simplifying expressions with integer exponents were presented. In this section, the properties are expanded to include expressions with rational exponents. We begin by defining expressions of the form $a^{1/n}$.

Definition of $a^{1/n}$

Let a be a real number, and let n be an integer such that $n > 1$. If $\sqrt[n]{a}$ is a real number, then

$$a^{1/n} = \sqrt[n]{a}$$

Example 1 Evaluating Expressions of the Form $a^{1/n}$

Convert the expression to radical form and simplify, if possible.

a. $(-8)^{1/3}$ **b.** $81^{1/4}$ **c.** $-100^{1/2}$ **d.** $(-100)^{1/2}$ **e.** $16^{-1/2}$

Solution:

a. $(-8)^{1/3} = \sqrt[3]{-8} = -2$

b. $81^{1/4} = \sqrt[4]{81} = 3$

c. $-100^{1/2} = -1 \cdot 100^{1/2}$ The exponent applies only to the base of 100.

$= -1\sqrt{100}$

$= -10$

d. $(-100)^{1/2}$ is not a real number because $\sqrt{-100}$ is not a real number.

e. $16^{-1/2} = \dfrac{1}{16^{1/2}}$ Write the expression with a positive exponent. Recall that $b^{-n} = \dfrac{1}{b^n}$.

$= \dfrac{1}{\sqrt{16}}$

$= \dfrac{1}{4}$

Skill Practice Convert the expression to radical form and simplify, if possible.

1. $(-64)^{1/3}$ **2.** $16^{1/4}$ **3.** $-36^{1/2}$ **4.** $(-36)^{1/2}$ **5.** $64^{-1/3}$

If $\sqrt[n]{a}$ is a real number, then we can define an expression of the form $a^{m/n}$ in such a way that the multiplication property of exponents still holds true. For example:

$$16^{3/4} \nearrow (16^{1/4})^3 = (\sqrt[4]{16})^3 = (2)^3 = 8$$

$$16^{3/4} \searrow (16^3)^{1/4} = \sqrt[4]{16^3} = \sqrt[4]{4096} = 8$$

Answers

1. −4 **2.** 2 **3.** −6

4. Not a real number **5.** $\frac{1}{4}$

Definition of $a^{m/n}$

Let a be a real number, and let m and n be positive integers such that m and n share no common factors and $n > 1$. If $\sqrt[n]{a}$ is a real number, then

$$a^{m/n} = (a^{1/n})^m = (\sqrt[n]{a})^m \qquad \text{and} \qquad a^{m/n} = (a^m)^{1/n} = \sqrt[n]{a^m}$$

The rational exponent in the expression $a^{m/n}$ is essentially performing two operations. The numerator of the exponent raises the base to the mth power. The denominator takes the nth root.

Example 2 Evaluating Expressions of the Form $a^{m/n}$

Convert each expression to radical form and simplify.

a. $8^{2/3}$ **b.** $100^{5/2}$ **c.** $\left(\frac{1}{25}\right)^{3/2}$ **d.** $4^{-3/2}$ **e.** $(-81)^{3/4}$

Solution:

a. $8^{2/3} = (\sqrt[3]{8})^2$ Take the cube root of 8 and square the result.

$= (2)^2$ Simplify.

$= 4$

b. $100^{5/2} = (\sqrt{100})^5$ Take the square root of 100 and raise the result to the fifth power.

$= (10)^5$ Simplify.

$= 100{,}000$

c. $\left(\frac{1}{25}\right)^{3/2} = \left(\sqrt{\frac{1}{25}}\right)^3$ Take the square root of $\frac{1}{25}$ and cube the result.

$= \left(\frac{1}{5}\right)^3$ Simplify.

$= \frac{1}{125}$

d. $4^{-3/2} = \left(\frac{1}{4}\right)^{3/2} = \frac{1}{4^{3/2}}$ Write the expression with positive exponents.

$= \frac{1}{(\sqrt{4})^3}$ Take the square root of 4 and cube the result.

$= \frac{1}{2^3}$ Simplify.

$= \frac{1}{8}$

e. $(-81)^{3/4}$ is not a real number because $\sqrt[4]{-81}$ is not a real number.

Calculator Connections

Topic: Evaluating Expressions with Rational Exponents

A calculator can be used to confirm the results of Example 2(a)–2(c).

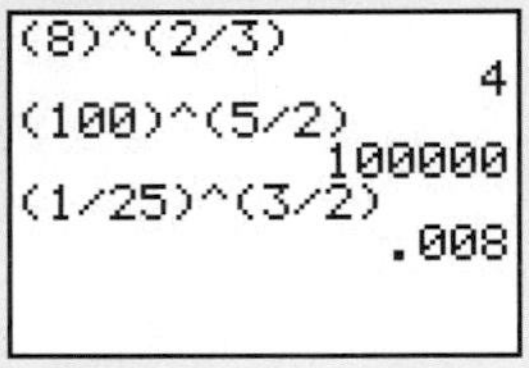

Skill Practice Convert each expression to radical form and simplify.

6. $9^{3/2}$ **7.** $8^{5/3}$ **8.** $\left(\frac{1}{27}\right)^{4/3}$ **9.** $32^{-4/5}$ **10.** $(-4)^{3/2}$

2. Converting Between Rational Exponents and Radical Notation

Example 3 Using Radical Notation and Rational Exponents

Convert each expression to radical notation. Assume all variables represent positive real numbers.

a. $a^{3/5}$ **b.** $5^{1/3}x^{2/3}$ **c.** $3y^{1/4}$ **d.** $9z^{-3/4}$

Solution:

a. $a^{3/5} = \sqrt[5]{a^3}$ or $\left(\sqrt[5]{a}\right)^3$

b. $5^{1/3}x^{2/3} = (5x^2)^{1/3} = \sqrt[3]{5x^2}$

c. $3y^{1/4} = 3\sqrt[4]{y}$ Note that the coefficient 3 is not raised to the $\frac{1}{4}$ power.

d. $9z^{-3/4} = 9 \cdot \dfrac{1}{z^{3/4}} = \dfrac{9}{\sqrt[4]{z^3}}$ Note that the coefficient 9 has an implied exponent of 1, not $-\frac{3}{4}$.

Skill Practice Convert each expression to radical notation. Assume all variables represent positive real numbers.

11. $t^{4/5}$ **12.** $2^{1/4}y^{3/4}$ **13.** $10p^{1/2}$ **14.** $11q^{-2/3}$

Example 4 Using Radical Notation and Rational Exponents

Convert each expression to an equivalent expression by using rational exponents. Assume that all variables represent positive real numbers.

a. $\sqrt[4]{b^3}$ **b.** $\sqrt{7a}$ **c.** $7\sqrt{a}$

Solution:

a. $\sqrt[4]{b^3} = b^{3/4}$ **b.** $\sqrt{7a} = (7a)^{1/2}$ **c.** $7\sqrt{a} = 7a^{1/2}$

Skill Practice Convert to an equivalent expression using rational exponents. Assume all variables represent positive real numbers.

15. $\sqrt[3]{x^2}$ **16.** $\sqrt{5y}$ **17.** $5\sqrt{y}$

3. Properties of Rational Exponents

In Sections 5.1–5.3, several properties and definitions were introduced to simplify expressions with integer exponents. These properties also apply to rational exponents.

Answers

6. 27 **7.** 32 **8.** $\frac{1}{81}$
9. $\frac{1}{16}$ **10.** Not a real number
11. $\sqrt[5]{t^4}$ **12.** $\sqrt[4]{2y^3}$ **13.** $10\sqrt{p}$
14. $\frac{11}{\sqrt[3]{q^2}}$ **15.** $x^{2/3}$ **16.** $(5y)^{1/2}$
17. $5y^{1/2}$

Definitions and Properties of Exponents

Let a and b be nonzero real numbers. Let m and n be rational numbers such that a^m, a^n, and b^m are real numbers.

Description	Property	Example
1. Multiplying like bases	$a^m a^n = a^{m+n}$	$x^{1/3}x^{4/3} = x^{5/3}$
2. Dividing like bases	$\dfrac{a^m}{a^n} = a^{m-n}$	$\dfrac{x^{3/5}}{x^{1/5}} = x^{2/5}$
3. The power rule	$(a^m)^n = a^{mn}$	$(2^{1/3})^{1/2} = 2^{1/6}$
4. Power of a product	$(ab)^m = a^m b^m$	$(9y)^{1/2} = 9^{1/2}y^{1/2} = 3y^{1/2}$
5. Power of a quotient	$\left(\dfrac{a}{b}\right)^m = \dfrac{a^m}{b^m}$	$\left(\dfrac{4}{25}\right)^{1/2} = \dfrac{4^{1/2}}{25^{1/2}} = \dfrac{2}{5}$

Description	Definition	Example
1. Negative exponents	$a^{-m} = \left(\dfrac{1}{a}\right)^m = \dfrac{1}{a^m}$	$(8)^{-1/3} = \left(\dfrac{1}{8}\right)^{1/3} = \dfrac{1}{2}$
2. Zero exponent	$a^0 = 1$	$5^0 = 1$

Example 5 Simplifying Expressions with Rational Exponents

Use the properties of exponents to simplify the expressions. Assume all variables represent positive real numbers.

a. $y^{2/5}y^{3/5}$ **b.** $\dfrac{6a^{-1/2}}{a^{3/2}}$ **c.** $\left(\dfrac{s^{1/2}t^{1/3}}{w^{3/4}}\right)^4$

Solution:

a. $y^{2/5}y^{3/5} = y^{(2/5)+(3/5)}$ Multiply like bases by adding exponents.

$= y^{5/5}$ Simplify.

$= y$

b. $\dfrac{6a^{-1/2}}{a^{3/2}}$ Divide like bases by subracting exponents.

$= 6a^{(-1/2)-(3/2)}$ Simplify: $-\dfrac{4}{2} = -2$

$= 6a^{-2}$

$= \dfrac{6}{a^2}$ Simplify the negative exponent.

c. $\left(\dfrac{s^{1/2}t^{1/3}}{w^{3/4}}\right)^4 = \dfrac{s^{(1/2)\cdot 4}t^{(1/3)\cdot 4}}{w^{(3/4)\cdot 4}}$ Apply the power rule. Multiply exponents.

$= \dfrac{s^2t^{4/3}}{w^3}$ Simplify.

Skill Practice Use the properties of exponents to simplify the expressions. Assume all variables represent positive real numbers.

18. $x^{1/2} \cdot x^{3/4}$ **19.** $\dfrac{4k^{-2/3}}{k^{1/3}}$ **20.** $\left(\dfrac{a^{1/3}b^{1/2}}{c^{5/8}}\right)^6$

Answers

18. $x^{5/4}$ **19.** $\dfrac{4}{k}$ **20.** $\dfrac{a^2b^3}{c^{15/4}}$

For Exercises 57–64, write each expression by using rational exponents rather than radical notation. **(See Example 4.)**

57. $\sqrt[3]{x}$ **58.** $\sqrt[4]{a}$ **59.** $10\sqrt{b}$ **60.** $-2\sqrt[3]{t}$

61. $\sqrt[3]{y^2}$ **62.** $\sqrt[6]{z^5}$ **63.** $\sqrt[4]{a^2b^3}$ **64.** $\sqrt{abc}$

Concept 3: Properties of Rational Exponents

For Exercises 65–88, simplify the expressions by using the properties of rational exponents. Write the final answer using positive exponents only. **(See Example 5.)**

65. $x^{1/4}x^{-5/4}$ **66.** $2^{2/3}2^{-5/3}$ **67.** $\dfrac{p^{5/3}}{p^{2/3}}$ **68.** $\dfrac{q^{5/4}}{q^{1/4}}$

69. $(y^{1/5})^{10}$ **70.** $(x^{1/2})^8$ **71.** $6^{-1/5}6^{3/5}$ **72.** $a^{-1/3}a^{2/3}$

73. $\dfrac{4t^{-1/3}}{t^{4/3}}$ **74.** $\dfrac{5s^{-1/3}}{s^{5/3}}$ **75.** $(a^{1/3}a^{1/4})^{12}$ **76.** $(x^{2/3}x^{1/2})^6$

77. $(5a^2c^{-1/2}d^{1/2})^2$ **78.** $(2x^{-1/3}y^2z^{5/3})^3$ **79.** $\left(\dfrac{x^{-2/3}}{y^{-3/4}}\right)^{12}$ **80.** $\left(\dfrac{m^{-1/4}}{n^{-1/2}}\right)^{-4}$

81. $\left(\dfrac{16w^{-2}z}{2wz^{-8}}\right)^{1/3}$ **82.** $\left(\dfrac{50p^{-1}q}{2pq^{-3}}\right)^{1/2}$ **83.** $(25x^2y^4z^6)^{1/2}$ **84.** $(8a^6b^3c^9)^{2/3}$

85. $(x^2y^{-1/3})^6(x^{1/2}yz^{2/3})^2$ **86.** $(a^{-1/3}b^{1/2})^4(a^{-1/2}b^{3/5})^{10}$ **87.** $\left(\dfrac{x^{3m}y^{2m}}{z^{5m}}\right)^{1/m}$ **88.** $\left(\dfrac{a^{4n}b^{3n}}{c^n}\right)^{1/n}$

Concept 4: Applications Involving Rational Exponents

89. If P dollars in principal grows to A dollars after t years with annual interest, then the interest rate is given by $r = \left(\dfrac{A}{P}\right)^{1/t} - 1$. **(See Example 6.)**

a. In one account, \$10,000 grows to \$16,802 after 5 yr. Compute the interest rate. Round your answer to a tenth of a percent.

b. In another account \$10,000 grows to \$18,000 after 7 yr. Compute the interest rate. Round your answer to a tenth of a percent.

c. Which account produced a higher average yearly return?

90. If the area A of a square is known, then the length of its sides, s, can be computed by the formula $s = A^{1/2}$.

a. Compute the length of the sides of a square having an area of 100 in.^{2}

b. Compute the length of the sides of a square having an area of 72 in.^{2} Round your answer to the nearest 0.1 in.

91. The radius r of a sphere of volume V is given by $r = \left(\dfrac{3V}{4\pi}\right)^{1/3}$. Find the radius of a sphere having a volume of 85 in.^{3} Round your answer to the nearest 0.1 in.

92. Is $(a + b)^{1/2}$ the same as $a^{1/2} + b^{1/2}$? If not, give a counterexample.

Expanding Your Skills

For Exercises 93–104, write the expression using rational exponents. Then simplify and convert back to radical notation.

Example: $\sqrt[15]{x^{10}} \xrightarrow[\text{exponents}]{\text{Rational}} x^{10/15} \xrightarrow{\text{Simplify}} x^{2/3} \xrightarrow[\text{notation}]{\text{Radical}} \sqrt[3]{x^2}$

93. $\sqrt[6]{y^3}$ **94.** $\sqrt[4]{w^2}$ **95.** $\sqrt[12]{z^3}$ **96.** $\sqrt[18]{t^3}$

97. $\sqrt[9]{x^6}$ **98.** $\sqrt[12]{p^9}$ **99.** $\sqrt[6]{x^3y^6}$ **100.** $\sqrt[8]{m^2p^8}$

101. $\sqrt{16x^8y^6}$ **102.** $\sqrt{81a^{12}b^{20}}$ **103.** $\sqrt[3]{8x^3y^2z}$ **104.** $\sqrt[3]{64m^2n^3p}$

For Exercises 105–108, write the expression as a single radical.

105. $\sqrt{\sqrt[3]{x}}$ **106.** $\sqrt[3]{\sqrt{x}}$ **107.** $\sqrt[5]{\sqrt[3]{w}}$ **108.** $\sqrt[3]{\sqrt[4]{w}}$

For Exercises 109–116, use a calculator to approximate the expressions. Round to four decimal places, if necessary.

109. $9^{1/2}$ **110.** $125^{-1/3}$ **111.** $50^{-1/4}$ **112.** $(172)^{3/5}$

113. $\sqrt[3]{5^2}$ **114.** $\sqrt[4]{6^3}$ **115.** $\sqrt{10^3}$ **116.** $\sqrt[3]{16}$

Simplifying Radical Expressions

Section 10.3

Concepts

1. **Multiplication Property of Radicals**
2. **Simplifying Radicals by Using the Multiplication Property of Radicals**
3. **Simplifying Radicals by Using the Order of Operations**

1. Multiplication Property of Radicals

You may have already noticed certain properties of radicals involving a product or quotient.

Multiplication Property of Radicals

Let a and b represent real numbers such that $\sqrt[n]{a}$ and $\sqrt[n]{b}$ are both real. Then

$$\sqrt[n]{ab} = \sqrt[n]{a} \cdot \sqrt[n]{b}$$

The multiplication property of radicals follows from the property of rational exponents.

$$\sqrt[n]{ab} = (ab)^{1/n} = a^{1/n}b^{1/n} = \sqrt[n]{a} \cdot \sqrt[n]{b}$$

The multiplication property of radicals indicates that a product within a radicand can be written as a product of radicals, provided the roots are real numbers. For example:

$$\sqrt{144} = \sqrt{16} \cdot \sqrt{9}$$

The reverse process is also true. A product of radicals can be written as a single radical provided the roots are real numbers and they have the same indices.

$$\sqrt{3} \cdot \sqrt{12} = \sqrt{36}$$

Calculator Connections

Topic: Verifying a Simplified Radical

A calculator can be used to support the solution to Example 3. The decimal approximation for $\sqrt{56}$ and $2\sqrt{14}$ agree for the first 10 digits. This in itself does not make $\sqrt{56} = 2\sqrt{14}$. It is the multiplication property of radicals that guarantees that the expressions are equal.

```
√(56)
          7.483314774
2*√(14)
          7.483314774
```

Example 4 **Using the Multiplication Property to Simplify Radicals**

Simplify. $6\sqrt{50}$

Solution:

$6\sqrt{50} = 6\sqrt{5^2 \cdot 2}$	Factor the radicand.
$= 6 \cdot \sqrt{5^2} \cdot \sqrt{2}$	Apply the multiplication property of radicals.
$= 6 \cdot 5 \cdot \sqrt{2}$	Simplify.
$= 30\sqrt{2}$	Simplify.

TIP: The radical can also be simplified as:

$$6\sqrt{50} = 6\sqrt{25 \cdot 2}$$
$$= 6\sqrt{25} \cdot \sqrt{2}$$
$$= 6 \cdot 5\sqrt{2}$$
$$= 30\sqrt{2}$$

Skill Practice Simplify.

5. $5\sqrt{18}$

Example 5 **Using the Multiplication Property to Simplify Radicals**

Simplify the expression. Assume that x, y, and z represent positive real numbers.

$\sqrt[3]{40x^3y^5z^7}$

Solution:

$\sqrt[3]{40x^3y^5z^7}$

$= \sqrt[3]{2^3 5x^3y^5z^7}$	Factor the radicand.	$2\,\lfloor 40$ $2\,\lfloor 20$ $2\,\lfloor 10$ 5
$= \sqrt[3]{(2^3x^3y^3z^6) \cdot (5y^2z)}$	$2^3x^3y^3z^6$ is the greatest perfect cube.	
$= \sqrt[3]{2^3x^3y^3z^6} \cdot \sqrt[3]{5y^2z}$	Apply the multiplication property of radicals.	
$= 2xyz^2\sqrt[3]{5y^2z}$	Simplify.	

TIP: In Example 5, the numerical coefficient within the radicand can be written $8 \cdot 5$ because 8 is the greatest perfect cube factor of 40:

$$\sqrt[3]{40x^3y^5z^7} = \sqrt[3]{8 \cdot 5x^3y^5z^7}$$
$$= \sqrt[3]{(8x^3y^3z^6)(5y^2z)}$$
$$= \sqrt[3]{8x^3y^3z^6} \cdot \sqrt[3]{5y^2z}$$
$$= 2xyz^2 \cdot \sqrt[3]{5y^2z}$$

Skill Practice Simplify. Assume that $a > 0$ and $b > 0$.

6. $\sqrt[4]{32a^{10}b^{19}}$

3. Simplifying Radicals by Using the Order of Operations

Often a radical can be simplified by applying the order of operations. In Example 6, the first step will be to simplify the expression within the radicand.

Answers

5. $15\sqrt{2}$ **6.** $2a^2b^4\sqrt[4]{2a^2b^3}$

Example 6 Using the Order of Operations to Simplify Radicals

Use the order of operations to simplify the expressions. Assume $a > 0$.

a. $\sqrt{\dfrac{a^7}{a^3}}$ **b.** $\sqrt[3]{\dfrac{3}{81}}$

Solution:

a. $\sqrt{\dfrac{a^7}{a^3}}$ The radicand contains a fraction. However, the fraction can be reduced to lowest terms.

$= \sqrt{a^4}$

$= a^2$ Simplify the radical.

b. $\sqrt[3]{\dfrac{3}{81}}$ The radical contains a fraction that can be simplified.

$= \sqrt[3]{\dfrac{1}{27}}$ Reduce to lowest terms.

$= \dfrac{1}{3}$ Simplify.

Skill Practice Use the order of operations to simplify the expressions. Assume $v > 0$.

7. $\sqrt{\dfrac{v^{21}}{v^5}}$ **8.** $\sqrt[5]{\dfrac{64}{2}}$

Example 7 Simplifying a Radical Expression

Simplify. $\dfrac{7\sqrt{50}}{10}$

Solution:

$\dfrac{7\sqrt{50}}{10} = \dfrac{7\sqrt{25 \cdot 2}}{10}$ 25 is the greatest perfect square in the radicand.

$= \dfrac{7 \cdot 5\sqrt{2}}{10}$ Simplify the radical.

$= \dfrac{7 \cdot \overset{1}{\cancel{5}}\sqrt{2}}{\underset{2}{\cancel{10}}}$ Simplify the fraction to lowest terms.

$= \dfrac{7\sqrt{2}}{2}$

Avoiding Mistakes

The expression $\frac{7\sqrt{2}}{2}$ cannot be simplified further because one factor of 2 is in the radicand and the other is outside the radical.

Skill Practice Simplify.

9. $\dfrac{2\sqrt{300}}{30}$

Answers

7. v^8 **8.** 2 **9.** $\dfrac{2\sqrt{3}}{3}$

81. On a baseball diamond, the bases are 90 ft apart. Find the exact distance from home plate to second base. Then round to the nearest tenth of a foot.

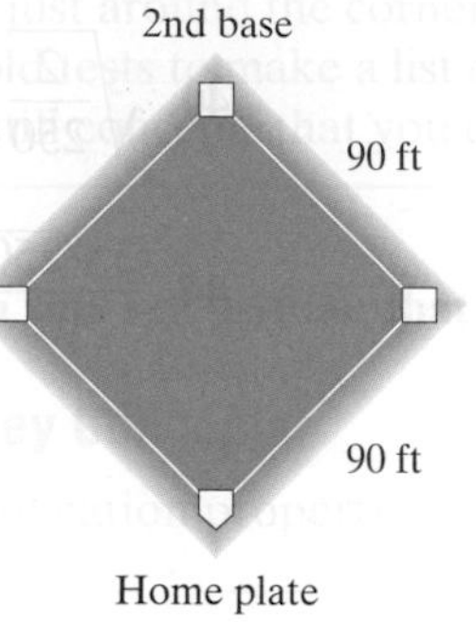

82. Linda is at the beach flying a kite. The kite is directly over a sand castle 60 ft away from Linda. If 100 ft of kite string is out (ignoring any sag in the string), how high is the kite? (Assume that Linda is 5 ft tall.) See figure.

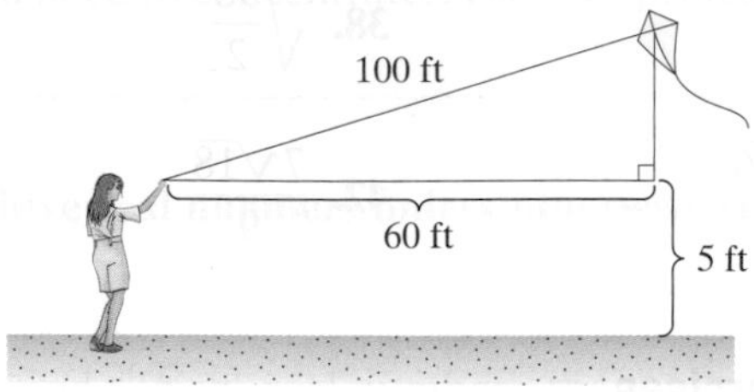

Expanding Your Skills

83. Tom has to travel from town A to town C across a small mountain range. He can travel one of two routes. He can travel on a four-lane highway from A to B and then from B to C at an average speed of 55 mph. Or he can travel on a two-lane road directly from town A to town C, but his average speed will be only 35 mph. If Tom is in a hurry, which route will take him to town C faster?

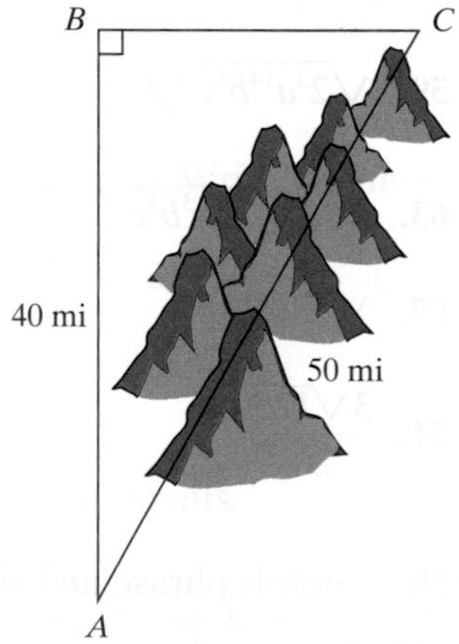

84. One side of a rectangular pasture is 80 ft in length. The diagonal distance is 110 yd. If fencing costs $3.29 per foot, how much will it cost to fence the pasture?

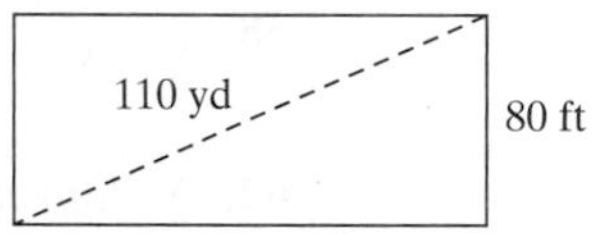

Section 10.4 Addition and Subtraction of Radicals

Concept

1. Addition and Subtraction of Radicals

1. Addition and Subtraction of Radicals

Definition of *Like* Radicals

Two radical terms are called ***like* radicals** if they have the same index and same radicand.

Like radicals can be added or subtracted by using the distributive property.

Same index; Distributive property

$$3\sqrt{x} + 7\sqrt{x} = (3 + 7)\sqrt{x} = 10\sqrt{x}$$

Same radicand

Example 1 Adding and Subtracting Radicals

Add or subtract as indicated.

a. $6\sqrt{11} - 2\sqrt{11}$ **b.** $\sqrt{3} + \sqrt{3}$

Solution:

a. $6\sqrt{11} - 2\sqrt{11}$

$= (6 - 2)\sqrt{11}$ Apply the distributive property.

$= 4\sqrt{11}$ Simplify.

b. $\sqrt{3} + \sqrt{3}$

$= 1\sqrt{3} + 1\sqrt{3}$ Note that $\sqrt{3} = 1\sqrt{3}$.

$= (1 + 1)\sqrt{3}$ Apply the distributive property.

$= 2\sqrt{3}$ Simplify.

Avoiding Mistakes

The process of adding *like* radicals with the distributive property is similar to adding *like* terms. The end result is that the numerical coefficients are added and the radical factor is unchanged.

$$\sqrt{3} + \sqrt{3} = 1\sqrt{3} + 1\sqrt{3} = 2\sqrt{3}$$

Be careful: $\sqrt{3} + \sqrt{3} \neq \sqrt{6}$

In general: $\sqrt{x} + \sqrt{y} \neq \sqrt{x + y}$

Skill Practice Add or subtract as indicated.

1. $5\sqrt{6} - 8\sqrt{6}$ **2.** $\sqrt{10} + \sqrt{10}$

Example 2 Adding and Subtracting Radicals

Add or subtract as indicated.

a. $-2\sqrt[3]{ab} + 7\sqrt[3]{ab} - \sqrt[3]{ab}$ **b.** $\frac{1}{4}x\sqrt{3y} - \frac{3}{2}x\sqrt{3y}$

Solution:

a. $-2\sqrt[3]{ab} + 7\sqrt[3]{ab} - \sqrt[3]{ab}$

$= (-2 + 7 - 1)\sqrt[3]{ab}$ Apply the distributive property.

$= 4\sqrt[3]{ab}$ Simplify.

b. $\frac{1}{4}x\sqrt{3y} - \frac{3}{2}x\sqrt{3y}$

$= \left(\frac{1}{4} - \frac{3}{2}\right)x\sqrt{3y}$ Apply the distributive property.

$= \left(\frac{1}{4} - \frac{6}{4}\right)x\sqrt{3y}$ Get a common denominator.

$= -\frac{5}{4}x\sqrt{3y}$ Simplify.

Answers

1. $-3\sqrt{6}$ **2.** $2\sqrt{10}$

Skill Practice Add or subtract as indicated.

3. $5\sqrt[3]{xy} - 3\sqrt[3]{xy} + 7\sqrt[3]{xy}$
4. $\frac{5}{6}y\sqrt{2} + \frac{1}{4}y\sqrt{2}$

Example 3 shows that it is often necessary to simplify radicals before adding or subtracting.

Example 3 Adding and Subtracting Radicals

Simplify the radicals and add or subtract as indicated. Assume all variables represent positive real numbers.

a. $3\sqrt{8} + \sqrt{2}$ **b.** $8\sqrt{x^3y^2} - 3y\sqrt{x^3}$

c. $\sqrt{50x^2y^5} - 13y\sqrt{2x^2y^3} + xy\sqrt{98y^3}$

Solution:

a. $3\sqrt{8} + \sqrt{2}$ — The radicands are different. Try simplifying the radicals first.

$= 3 \cdot 2\sqrt{2} + \sqrt{2}$ — Simplify: $\sqrt{8} = \sqrt{2^3} = 2\sqrt{2}$

$= 6\sqrt{2} + \sqrt{2}$

$= (6 + 1)\sqrt{2}$ — Apply the distributive property.

$= 7\sqrt{2}$ — Simplify.

b. $8\sqrt{x^3y^2} - 3y\sqrt{x^3}$ — The radicands are different. Simplify the radicals first.

$= 8xy\sqrt{x} - 3xy\sqrt{x}$ — Simplify $\sqrt{x^3y^2} = xy\sqrt{x}$ and $\sqrt{x^3} = x\sqrt{x}$.

$= (8 - 3)xy\sqrt{x}$ — Apply the distributive property.

$= 5xy\sqrt{x}$ — Simplify.

c. $\sqrt{50x^2y^5} - 13y\sqrt{2x^2y^3} + xy\sqrt{98y^3}$ — Simplify each radical.

$$\left\{\begin{aligned} \sqrt{50x^2y^5} &= \sqrt{25 \cdot 2x^2y^5} \\ &= 5xy^2\sqrt{2y} \\ -13y\sqrt{2x^2y^3} &= -13xy^2\sqrt{2y} \\ xy\sqrt{98y^3} &= xy\sqrt{49 \cdot 2y^3} \\ &= 7xy^2\sqrt{2y} \end{aligned}\right.$$

$= 5xy^2\sqrt{2y} - 13xy^2\sqrt{2y} + 7xy^2\sqrt{2y}$

$= (5 - 13 + 7)xy^2\sqrt{2y}$ — Apply the distributive property.

$= -xy^2\sqrt{2y}$

Skill Practice Simplify the radicals and add or subtract as indicated. Assume all variables represent positive real numbers.

5. $\sqrt{75} + 2\sqrt{3}$
6. $4\sqrt{a^2b} - 6a\sqrt{b}$
7. $-3\sqrt{2y^3} + 5y\sqrt{18y} - 2\sqrt{50y^3}$

Answers

3. $9\sqrt[3]{xy}$
4. $\frac{13}{12}y\sqrt{2}$
5. $7\sqrt{3}$
6. $-2a\sqrt{b}$
7. $2y\sqrt{2y}$

In some cases, when two radicals are added, the resulting sum is written in factored form. This is demonstrated in Example 4.

Example 4 **Adding Radical Expressions**

Add the radicals. Assume that $x \geq 0$. $3\sqrt{2x^2} + \sqrt{8}$

Solution:

$3\sqrt{2x^2} + \sqrt{8}$

$= 3x\sqrt{2} + 2\sqrt{2}$ Simplify each radical. Notice that the radicands are the same, but the terms are not *like* terms. The first term has a factor of x and the second does not.

$= (3x + 2)\sqrt{2}$ Apply the distributive property. The expression cannot be simplified further because $3x$ and 2 are not *like* terms.

Skill Practice Add the radicals. Assume that $y \geq 0$.

8. $4\sqrt{45} - \sqrt{5y^4}$

Answer

8. $(12 - y^2)\sqrt{5}$

Section 10.4 Practice Exercises

For the exercises in this set, assume that all variables represent positive real numbers, unless otherwise stated.

Vocabulary and Key Concepts

1. a. Two radical terms are called *like* radicals if they have the same ________ and the same ________.

b. The expression $\sqrt{3x} + \sqrt{3x}$ simplifies to ________.

c. The expression $\sqrt{2} + \sqrt{3}$ (can/cannot) be simplified further whereas the expression $\sqrt{2} \cdot \sqrt{3}$ (can/cannot) be simplified further.

d. The expression $\sqrt{2} + \sqrt{18}$ simplifies to ________.

Review Exercises

For Exercises 2–5, simplify the radicals.

2. $\sqrt[3]{-16s^4t^9}$

3. $-\sqrt[4]{x^7y^4}$

4. $\sqrt{36a^2b^3}$

5. $\sqrt[3]{\dfrac{7b^8}{56b^2}}$

6. Write $(4x^2)^{1/3}$ in radical notation.

7. Write $\sqrt[4]{x^3y}$ using rational exponents.

8. Simplify. $32^{-1/5}$

For Exercises 9–10, simplify the expressions. Write the answer with positive exponents only.

9. $y^{2/3}y^{1/4}$

10. $(x^{1/2}y^{-3/4})^{-4}$

Concept 1: Addition and Subtraction of Radicals

For Exercises 11–12, determine if the radical terms are *like.*

11. **a.** $\sqrt{2}$ and $\sqrt[3]{2}$
b. $\sqrt{2}$ and $3\sqrt{2}$
c. $\sqrt{2}$ and $\sqrt{5}$

12. **a.** $7\sqrt[3]{x}$ and $\sqrt[3]{x}$
b. $\sqrt[3]{x}$ and $\sqrt[4]{x}$
c. $2\sqrt[4]{x}$ and $x\sqrt[4]{2}$

13. Explain the similarities between the pairs of expressions.
a. $7\sqrt{5} + 4\sqrt{5}$ and $7x + 4x$
b. $-2\sqrt{6} - 9\sqrt{3}$ and $-2x - 9y$

14. Explain the similarities between the pairs of expressions.
a. $-4\sqrt{3} + 5\sqrt{3}$ and $-4z + 5z$
b. $13\sqrt{7} - 18$ and $13a - 18$

For Exercises 15–32, add or subtract the radical expressions, if possible. **(See Examples 1–2.)**

15. $3\sqrt{5} + 6\sqrt{5}$
16. $5\sqrt{a} + 3\sqrt{a}$
17. $3\sqrt[3]{tw} - 2\sqrt[3]{tw} + \sqrt[3]{tw}$
18. $6\sqrt[3]{7} - 2\sqrt[3]{7} + \sqrt[3]{7}$
19. $6\sqrt{10} - \sqrt{10}$
20. $13\sqrt{11} - \sqrt{11}$
21. $\sqrt[4]{3} + 7\sqrt[4]{3} - \sqrt[4]{14}$
22. $2\sqrt{11} + 3\sqrt{13} + 5\sqrt{11}$
23. $8\sqrt{x} + 2\sqrt{y} - 6\sqrt{x}$
24. $10\sqrt{10} - 8\sqrt{10} + \sqrt{2}$
25. $\sqrt[3]{ab} + a\sqrt[3]{b}$
26. $x\sqrt[4]{y} - y\sqrt[4]{x}$
27. $\sqrt{2t} + \sqrt[3]{2t}$
28. $\sqrt[4]{5c} + \sqrt[3]{5c}$
29. $\frac{5}{6}z\sqrt[3]{6} + \frac{7}{9}z\sqrt[3]{6}$
30. $\frac{3}{4}a\sqrt[4]{b} + \frac{1}{6}a\sqrt[4]{b}$
31. $0.81x\sqrt{y} - 0.11x\sqrt{y}$
32. $7.5\sqrt{pq} - 6.3\sqrt{pq}$

33. Explain the process for adding the two radicals. Then find the sum. $3\sqrt{2} + 7\sqrt{50}$

34. Explain the process for subtracting two radicals. Then find the difference. $\sqrt{12x} - \sqrt{75x}$

For Exercises 35–64, add or subtract the radical expressions as indicated. **(See Examples 3–4.)**

35. $\sqrt{36} + \sqrt{81}$
36. $3\sqrt{80} - 5\sqrt{45}$
37. $2\sqrt{12} + \sqrt{48}$
38. $5\sqrt{32} + 2\sqrt{50}$
39. $4\sqrt{7} + \sqrt{63} - 2\sqrt{28}$
40. $8\sqrt{3} - 2\sqrt{27} + \sqrt{75}$
41. $5\sqrt{18} + \sqrt{27} - 4\sqrt{50}$
42. $7\sqrt{40} - \sqrt{8} + 4\sqrt{50}$
43. $\sqrt[3]{81} - \sqrt[3]{24}$
44. $17\sqrt[3]{81} - 2\sqrt[3]{24}$
45. $3\sqrt{2a} - \sqrt{8a} - \sqrt{72a}$
46. $\sqrt{12t} - \sqrt{27t} + 5\sqrt{3t}$
47. $2s^2\sqrt[3]{s^2t^6} + 3t^2\sqrt[3]{8s^8}$
48. $4\sqrt[3]{x^4} - 2x\sqrt[3]{x}$
49. $7\sqrt[3]{x^4} - x\sqrt[3]{x}$
50. $6\sqrt[3]{y^{10}} - 3y^2\sqrt[3]{y^4}$
51. $5p\sqrt{20p^2} + p^2\sqrt{80}$
52. $2q\sqrt{48q^2} - \sqrt{27q^4}$
53. $\sqrt[3]{a^2b} - \sqrt[3]{8a^2b}$
54. $w\sqrt{80} - 3\sqrt{125w^2}$
55. $5x\sqrt{x} + 6\sqrt{x}$
56. $9y^2\sqrt{2} + 4\sqrt{2}$
57. $\sqrt{50x^2} - 3\sqrt{8}$
58. $\sqrt{9x^3} - \sqrt{25x}$
59. $11\sqrt[3]{54cd^3} - 2\sqrt[3]{2cd^3} + d\sqrt[3]{16c}$
60. $x\sqrt[3]{64x^5y^2} - x^2\sqrt[3]{x^2y^2} + 5\sqrt[3]{x^8y^2}$

61. $\frac{3}{2}ab\sqrt{24a^3} + \frac{4}{3}\sqrt{54a^5b^2} - a^2b\sqrt{150a}$

62. $mn\sqrt{72n} + \frac{2}{3}n\sqrt{8m^2n} - \frac{5}{6}\sqrt{50m^2n^3}$

63. $x\sqrt[3]{16} - 2\sqrt[3]{27x} + \sqrt[3]{54x^3}$

64. $5\sqrt[4]{y^5} - 2y\sqrt[4]{y} + \sqrt[4]{16y^7}$

Mixed Exercises

For Exercises 65–72, answer true or false. If an answer is false, explain why or give a counterexample.

65. $\sqrt{x} + \sqrt{y} = \sqrt{x + y}$

66. $\sqrt{x} + \sqrt{x} = 2\sqrt{x}$

67. $5\sqrt[3]{x} + 2\sqrt[3]{x} = 7\sqrt[3]{x}$

68. $6\sqrt{x} + 5\sqrt[3]{x} = 11\sqrt{x}$

69. $\sqrt{y} + \sqrt{y} = \sqrt{2y}$

70. $\sqrt{c^2 + d^2} = c + d$

71. $2w\sqrt{5} + 4w\sqrt{5} = 6w^2\sqrt{5}$

72. $7x\sqrt{3} - 2\sqrt{3} = (7x - 2)\sqrt{3}$

For Exercises 73–76, write the English phrase as an algebraic expression. Simplify each expression.

73. The sum of the principal square root of 48 and the principal square root of 12

74. The sum of the cube root of 16 and the cube root of 2

75. The difference of 5 times the cube root of x^6 and the square of x

76. The sum of the cube of y and the principal fourth root of y^{12}

For Exercises 77–80, write an English phrase that translates the mathematical expression. (Answers may vary.)

77. $\sqrt{18} - 5^2$

78. $4^3 - \sqrt[3]{4}$

79. $\sqrt[4]{x} + y^3$

80. $a^4 + \sqrt{a}$

For Exercises 81–82, find the exact value of the perimeter, and then approximate the value to one decimal place.

81.

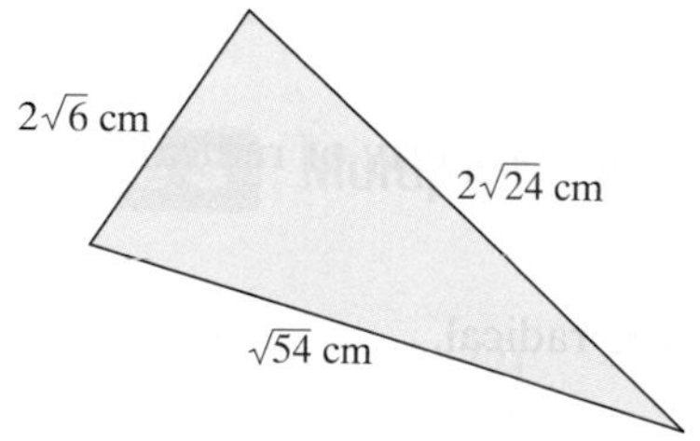

82.

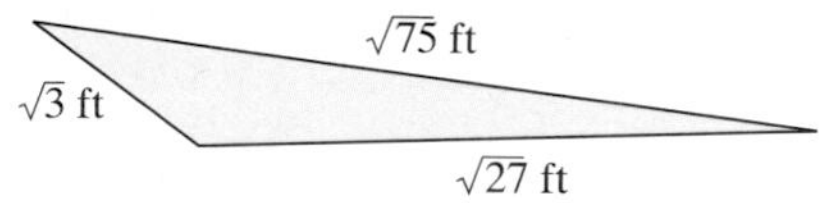

83. The figure has perimeter $14\sqrt{2}$ ft. Find the value of x.

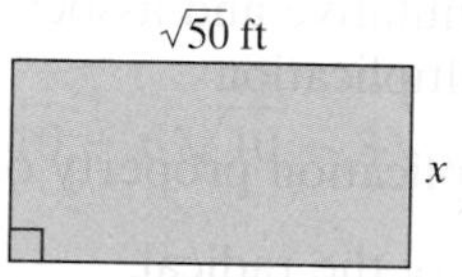

84. The figure has perimeter $12\sqrt{7}$ cm. Find the value of x.

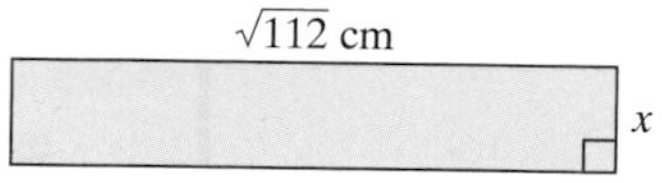

Expanding Your Skills

85. a. An irregularly shaped garden is shown in the figure. All distances are expressed in yards. Find the perimeter. (*Hint*: Use the Pythagorean theorem to find the length of each side.) Write the final answer in radical form.

b. Approximate your answer to two decimal places.

c. If edging costs \$1.49 per foot and sales tax is 6%, find the total cost of edging the garden.

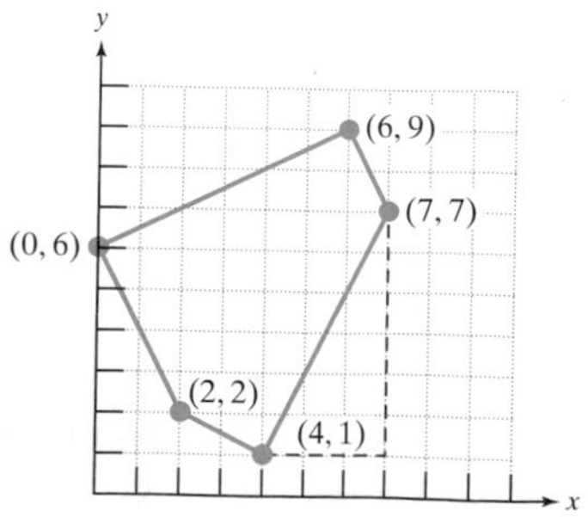

Concept 1: Multiplication Property of Radicals

For Exercises 9–44, multiply the radical expressions. **(See Examples 1–4.)**

9. $\sqrt[3]{7} \cdot \sqrt[3]{3}$

10. $\sqrt[4]{6} \cdot \sqrt[4]{2}$

11. $\sqrt{2} \cdot \sqrt{10}$

12. $\sqrt[3]{4} \cdot \sqrt[3]{12}$

13. $\sqrt[4]{16} \cdot \sqrt[4]{64}$

14. $\sqrt{5x^3} \cdot \sqrt{10x^4}$

15. $(4\sqrt[3]{4})(2\sqrt[3]{5})$

16. $(2\sqrt{5})(3\sqrt{7})$

17. $(8a\sqrt{b})(-3\sqrt{ab})$

18. $(p\sqrt[4]{q^3})(\sqrt[4]{pq})$

19. $\sqrt{30} \cdot \sqrt{12}$

20. $\sqrt{20} \cdot \sqrt{54}$

21. $\sqrt{6x} \cdot \sqrt{12x}$

22. $(\sqrt{3ab^2})(\sqrt{21a^2b})$

23. $\sqrt{5a^3b^2} \cdot \sqrt{20a^3b^3}$

24. $\sqrt[3]{m^2n^2} \cdot \sqrt[3]{48m^4n^2}$

25. $(4\sqrt{3xy^3})(-2\sqrt{6x^3y^2})$

26. $(2\sqrt[4]{3x})(4\sqrt[4]{27x^6})$

27. $(\sqrt[3]{4a^2b})(\sqrt[3]{2ab^3})(\sqrt[3]{54a^2b})$

28. $(\sqrt[3]{9x^3y})(\sqrt[3]{6xy})(\sqrt[3]{8x^2y^5})$

29. $\sqrt{3}(4\sqrt{3} - 6)$

30. $3\sqrt{5}(2\sqrt{5} + 4)$

31. $\sqrt{2}(\sqrt{6} - \sqrt{3})$

32. $\sqrt{5}(\sqrt{3} + \sqrt{7})$

33. $-\frac{1}{3}\sqrt{x}(6\sqrt{x} + 7)$

34. $-\frac{1}{2}\sqrt{y}(8 - 3\sqrt{y})$

35. $(\sqrt{3} + 2\sqrt{10})(4\sqrt{3} - \sqrt{10})$

36. $(8\sqrt{7} - \sqrt{5})(\sqrt{7} + 3\sqrt{5})$

37. $(\sqrt{x} + 4)(\sqrt{x} - 9)$

38. $(\sqrt{w} - 2)(\sqrt{w} - 9)$

39. $(\sqrt[3]{y} + 2)(\sqrt[3]{y} - 3)$

40. $(4 + \sqrt[5]{p})(5 + \sqrt[5]{p})$

41. $(\sqrt{a} - 3\sqrt{b})(9\sqrt{a} - \sqrt{b})$

42. $(11\sqrt{m} + 4\sqrt{n})(\sqrt{m} + \sqrt{n})$

43. $(\sqrt{p} + 2\sqrt{q})(8 + 3\sqrt{p} - \sqrt{q})$

44. $(5\sqrt{s} - \sqrt{t})(\sqrt{s} + 5 + 6\sqrt{t})$

Concept 2: Expressions of the Form $(\sqrt[n]{a})^n$

For Exercises 45–52, simplify the expressions. Assume all variables represent positive real numbers. **(See Example 5.)**

45. $(\sqrt{15})^2$

46. $(\sqrt{58})^2$

47. $(\sqrt{3y})^2$

48. $(\sqrt{19yz})^2$

49. $(\sqrt[3]{6})^3$

50. $(\sqrt[5]{24})^5$

51. $\sqrt{709} \cdot \sqrt{709}$

52. $\sqrt{401} \cdot \sqrt{401}$

Concept 3: Special Case Products

53. a. Write the formula for the product of two conjugates. $(x + y)(x - y) =$

    b. Multiply $(x + 5)(x - 5)$.

54. a. Write the formula for squaring a binomial. $(x + y)^2 =$

    b. Multiply $(x + 5)^2$.

For Exercises 55–66, multiply the radical expressions. **(See Examples 6–7.)**

55. $(\sqrt{13} + 4)^2$

56. $(6 - \sqrt{11})^2$

57. $(\sqrt{p} - \sqrt{7})^2$

58. $(\sqrt{q} + \sqrt{2})^2$

59. $(\sqrt{2a} - 3\sqrt{b})^2$

60. $(\sqrt{3w} + 4\sqrt{z})^2$

61. $(\sqrt{3} + x)(\sqrt{3} - x)$

62. $(y + \sqrt{6})(y - \sqrt{6})$

63. $(\sqrt{6} + \sqrt{2})(\sqrt{6} - \sqrt{2})$

64. $(\sqrt{15} + \sqrt{5})(\sqrt{15} - \sqrt{5})$

65. $\left(\frac{2}{3}\sqrt{x} + \frac{1}{2}\sqrt{y}\right)\left(\frac{2}{3}\sqrt{x} - \frac{1}{2}\sqrt{y}\right)$

66. $\left(\frac{1}{4}\sqrt{s} + \frac{1}{5}\sqrt{t}\right)\left(\frac{1}{4}\sqrt{s} - \frac{1}{5}\sqrt{t}\right)$

Skill Practice Solve using the square root property.

1. $25a^2 = 16$

For a quadratic equation, $ax^2 + bx + c = 0$, if $b = 0$, then the equation is easily solved by using the square root property. This is demonstrated in Example 2.

Example 2 **Solving a Quadratic Equation by Using the Square Root Property**

Use the square root property to solve the equation.

$$3x^2 + 75 = 0$$

Solution:

$3x^2 + 75 = 0$	Rewrite the equation to fit the form $x^2 = k$.
$3x^2 = -75$	
$x^2 = -25$	The equation is now in the form $x^2 = k$.
$x = \pm\sqrt{-25}$	Apply the square root property.
$= \pm 5i$	

Check: $x = 5i$	Check: $x = -5i$
$3x^2 + 75 = 0$	$3x^2 + 75 = 0$
$3(5i)^2 + 75 \stackrel{?}{=} 0$	$3(-5i)^2 + 75 \stackrel{?}{=} 0$
$3(25i^2) + 75 \stackrel{?}{=} 0$	$3(25i^2) + 75 \stackrel{?}{=} 0$
$3(-25) + 75 \stackrel{?}{=} 0$	$3(-25) + 75 \stackrel{?}{=} 0$
$-75 + 75 \stackrel{?}{=} 0$ ✔	$-75 + 75 \stackrel{?}{=} 0$ ✔

The solution set is $\{\pm 5i\}$.

Avoiding Mistakes

A common mistake is to forget the $\pm$ symbol when solving the equation $x^2 = k$:

$$x = \pm\sqrt{k}$$

Skill Practice Solve using the square root property.

2. $8x^2 + 72 = 0$

Example 3 **Solving a Quadratic Equation by Using the Square Root Property**

Use the square root property to solve the equation.

$$(w + 3)^2 = 20$$

Solution:

$(w + 3)^2 = 20$	The equation is in the form $x^2 = k$, where $x = (w + 3)$.
$w + 3 = \pm\sqrt{20}$	Apply the square root property.
$w + 3 = \pm\sqrt{4 \cdot 5}$	Simplify the radical.
$w + 3 = \pm 2\sqrt{5}$	
$w = -3 \pm 2\sqrt{5}$	Solve for w.

The solution set is $\{-3 \pm 2\sqrt{5}\}$.

TIP: Recall that $-3 \pm 2\sqrt{5}$ represents two solutions:

$-3 + 2\sqrt{5}$ and $-3 - 2\sqrt{5}$.

Skill Practice Solve using the square root property.

3. $(t - 5)^2 = 18$

Answers

1. $\left\{\frac{4}{5}, -\frac{4}{5}\right\}$ 2. $\{\pm 3i\}$
3. $\{5 \pm 3\sqrt{2}\}$

$x - 3 = \pm\sqrt{-4}$	**Step 4:**	Apply the square root property.
$x - 3 = \pm 2i$		Simplify the radical.
$x = 3 \pm 2i$		Solve for x.

The solutions are imaginary numbers and can be written as $3 + 2i$ and $3 - 2i$.

The solution set is $\{3 \pm 2i\}$.

Skill Practice Solve by completing the square and applying the square root property.

8. $z^2 - 4z + 26 = 0$

Example 6 Solving a Quadratic Equation by Completing the Square and Applying the Square Root Property

Solve by completing the square and applying the square root property.

$$2m^2 + 10m = 3$$

Solution:

$$2m^2 + 10m = 3$$ The variable terms are already isolated on one side of the equation.

$$\frac{2m^2}{2} + \frac{10m}{2} = \frac{3}{2}$$ Divide by the leading coefficient, 2.

$$m^2 + 5m = \frac{3}{2}$$

$$m^2 + 5m + \frac{25}{4} = \frac{3}{2} + \frac{25}{4}$$ Add $[\frac{1}{2}(5)]^2 = (\frac{5}{2})^2 = \frac{25}{4}$ to both sides.

$$\left(m + \frac{5}{2}\right)^2 = \frac{6}{4} + \frac{25}{4}$$ Factor the left side and write the terms on the right with a common denominator.

$$\left(m + \frac{5}{2}\right)^2 = \frac{31}{4}$$

$$m + \frac{5}{2} = \pm\sqrt{\frac{31}{4}}$$ Apply the square root property.

$$m = -\frac{5}{2} \pm \frac{\sqrt{31}}{2}$$ Subtract $\frac{5}{2}$ from both sides and simplify the radical.

The solution set is $\left\{-\frac{5}{2} \pm \frac{\sqrt{31}}{2}\right\}$. The solutions are irrational numbers.

TIP: The solutions to Example 6 can also be written as:

$$\frac{-5 \pm \sqrt{31}}{2}$$

Skill Practice Solve by completing the square and applying the square root property.

9. $4x^2 + 12x = 5$

Answers

8. $\{2 \pm i\sqrt{22}\}$

9. $\left\{-\frac{3}{2} \pm \frac{\sqrt{14}}{2}\right\}$

Example 7 Solving a Quadratic Equation by Completing the Square and Applying the Square Root Property

Solve by completing the square and applying the square root property.

$$2x(2x - 10) = -30 + 6x$$

Solution:

$2x(2x - 10) = -30 + 6x$

$4x^2 - 20x = -30 + 6x$ Clear parentheses.

$4x^2 - 26x + 30 = 0$ Write the equation in the form $ax^2 + bx + c = 0$.

$\frac{4x^2}{4} - \frac{26x}{4} + \frac{30}{4} = \frac{0}{4}$ **Step 1:** Divide both sides by the leading coefficient, 4.

$x^2 - \frac{13}{2}x + \frac{15}{2} = 0$

$x^2 - \frac{13}{2}x = -\frac{15}{2}$ **Step 2:** Isolate the variable terms on one side.

$x^2 - \frac{13}{2}x + \frac{169}{16} = -\frac{15}{2} + \frac{169}{16}$ **Step 3:** Add $[\frac{1}{2}(-\frac{13}{2})]^2 = (-\frac{13}{4})^2 = \frac{169}{16}$ to both sides.

$\left(x - \frac{13}{4}\right)^2 = -\frac{120}{16} + \frac{169}{16}$ Factor the perfect square trinomial. Rewrite the right-hand side with a common denominator.

$\left(x - \frac{13}{4}\right)^2 = \frac{49}{16}$

$x - \frac{13}{4} = \pm\sqrt{\frac{49}{16}}$ **Step 4:** Apply the square root property.

$x - \frac{13}{4} = \pm\frac{7}{4}$ Simplify the radical.

$x = \frac{13}{4} \pm \frac{7}{4}$

$x = \frac{13}{4} + \frac{7}{4} = \frac{20}{4} = 5$

$x = \frac{13}{4} - \frac{7}{4} = \frac{6}{4} = \frac{3}{2}$

The solution set is $\left\{5, \frac{3}{2}\right\}$. The solutions are rational numbers.

TIP: In general, if the solutions to a quadratic equation are rational numbers, the equation can be solved by factoring and using the zero product rule. Consider the equation from Example 7.

$$2x(2x - 10) = -30 + 6x$$
$$4x^2 - 20x = -30 + 6x$$
$$4x^2 - 26x + 30 = 0$$
$$2(2x^2 - 13x + 15) = 0$$
$$2(x - 5)(2x - 3) = 0$$
$$x = 5 \quad \text{or} \quad x = \frac{3}{2}$$

Avoiding Mistakes

When the solutions are rational, combine the *like* terms. That is, do not leave the solution with the $\pm$ sign.

Skill Practice Solve by completing the square and applying the square root property.

10. $2y(y - 1) = 3 - y$

Answer

10. $\left\{\frac{3}{2}, -1\right\}$

For Exercises 41–60, solve the quadratic equation by completing the square and applying the square root property. Write imaginary solutions in the form $a + bi$. **(See Examples 5–7.)**

41. $t^2 + 8t + 15 = 0$

42. $m^2 + 6m + 8 = 0$

43. $x^2 + 6x = -16$

44. $x^2 - 4x = -15$

45. $p^2 + 4p + 6 = 0$

46. $q^2 + 2q + 2 = 0$

47. $-3y - 10 = -y^2$

48. $-24 = -2y^2 + 2y$

49. $2a^2 + 4a + 5 = 0$

50. $3a^2 + 6a - 7 = 0$

51. $9x^2 - 36x + 40 = 0$

52. $9y^2 - 12y + 5 = 0$

53. $25p^2 - 10p = 2$

54. $9n^2 - 6n = 1$

55. $(2w + 5)(w - 1) = 2$

56. $(3p - 5)(p + 1) = -3$

57. $n(n - 4) = 7$

58. $m(m + 10) = 2$

59. $2x(x + 6) = 14$

60. $3x(x - 2) = 24$

Concept 3: Literal Equations

61. The distance (in feet) that an object falls in t sec is given by the equation $d = 16t^2$, where $t \geq 0$.

a. Solve the equation for t. **(See Example 8.)**

b. Using the equation from part (a), determine the amount of time required for an object to fall 1024 ft.

62. The volume of a can that is 4 in. tall is given by the equation $V = 4\pi r^2$, where r is the radius of the can, measured in inches.

a. Solve the equation for r. Do not rationalize the denominator.

b. Using the equation from part (a), determine the radius of a can with a volume of 12.56 in.^{3} Use 3.14 for π.

For Exercises 63–68, solve for the indicated variable.

63. $A = \pi r^2$ for r $(r > 0)$

64. $E = mc^2$ for c $(c > 0)$

65. $a^2 + b^2 + c^2 = d^2$ for a $(a > 0)$

66. $a^2 + b^2 = c^2$ for b $(b > 0)$

67. $V = \frac{1}{3}\pi r^2 h$ for r $(r > 0)$

68. $V = \frac{1}{3}s^2 h$ for s $(s > 0)$

69. A corner shelf is to be made from a triangular piece of plywood, as shown in the diagram. Find the distance x that the shelf will extend along the walls. Assume that the walls are at right angles. Round the answer to a tenth of a foot.

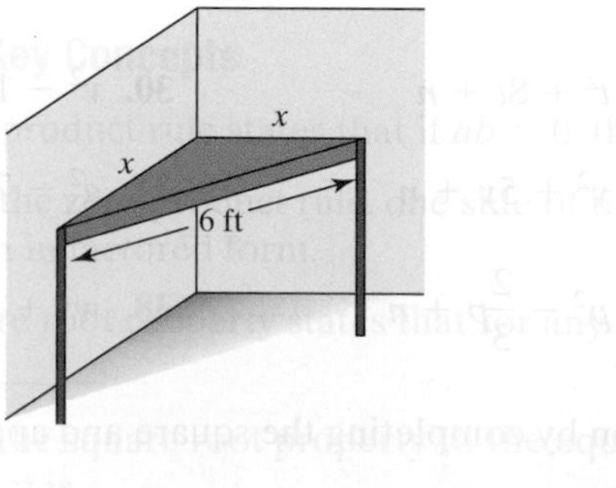

70. The volume of a box with a square bottom and a height of 4 in. is given by $V(x) = 4x^2$, where x is the length (in inches) of the sides of the bottom of the box.

a. If the volume of the box is 289 in.^{3}, find the dimensions of the box.

b. Are there two possible answers to part (a)? Why or why not?

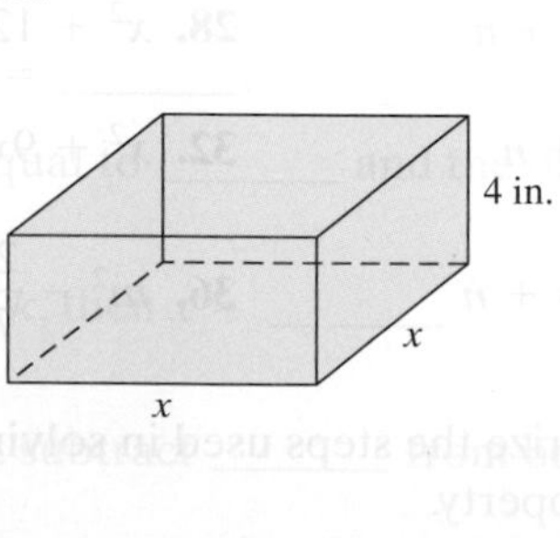

71. A square has an area of 50 in.^{2} What are the lengths of the sides? (Round to one decimal place.)

72. The amount of money A in an account with an interest rate r compounded annually is given by

$$A = P(1 + r)^t$$

where P is the initial principal and t is the number of years the money is invested.

a. If a \$10,000 investment grows to \$11,664 after 2 yr, find the interest rate.

b. If a \$6000 investment grows to \$7392.60 after 2 yr, find the interest rate.

c. Jamal wants to invest \$5000. He wants the money to grow to at least \$6500 in 2 yr to cover the cost of his son's first year at college. What interest rate does Jamal need for his investment to grow to \$6500 in 2 yr? Round to the nearest hundredth of a percent.

73. A textbook company has discovered that the profit for selling its books is given by

$$P(x) = -\frac{1}{8}x^2 + 5x$$

where x is the number of textbooks produced (in thousands) and $P(x)$ is the corresponding profit (in thousands of dollars). The graph of the function is shown at right.

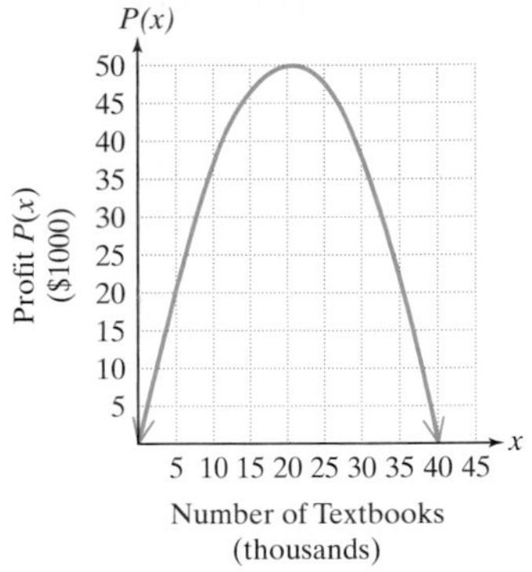

a. Approximate the number of books required to make a profit of \$20,000. [*Hint:* Let $P(x) = 20$. Then complete the square to solve for x.] Round to one decimal place.

b. Why are there two answers to part (a)?

74. If we ignore air resistance, the distance (in feet) that an object travels in free fall can be approximated by $d(t) = 16t^2$, where t is the time in seconds after the object was dropped.

a. If the CN Tower in Toronto is 1815 ft high, how long will it take an object to fall from the top of the building? Round to one decimal place.

b. If the Renaissance Tower in Dallas is 886 ft high, how long will it take an object to fall from the top of the building? Round to one decimal place.

$a = 1, b = -6, \text{ and } c = 11$ — Identify a, b, and c.

$$x = \frac{-b \pm \sqrt{b^2 - 4ac}}{2a}$$ Apply the quadratic formula.

$$= \frac{-(-6) \pm \sqrt{(-6)^2 - 4(1)(11)}}{2(1)}$$ Substitute $a = 1, b = -6, \text{ and } c = 11$.

$$= \frac{6 \pm \sqrt{36 - 44}}{2}$$ Simplify.

$$= \frac{6 \pm \sqrt{-8}}{2}$$

$$= \frac{6 \pm 2i\sqrt{2}}{2}$$ Simplify the radical.

$$= \frac{2(3 \pm i\sqrt{2})}{2}$$ Factor the numerator.

$$= \frac{2(3 \pm i\sqrt{2})}{2}$$ Simplify the fraction to lowest terms.

$$= 3 \pm i\sqrt{2} \quad \begin{cases} x = 3 + i\sqrt{2} \\ x = 3 - i\sqrt{2} \end{cases}$$ The solutions are imaginary numbers.

The solution set is $\{3 \pm i\sqrt{2}\}$.

Avoiding Mistakes

When identifying *a*, *b*, and *c*, use the coefficients only, not the variable.

Avoiding Mistakes

Always simplify the radical completely before trying to reduce the fraction to lowest terms.

Skill Practice Solve the equation by using the quadratic formula.

2. $-y(y + 4) = 12$

3. Using the Quadratic Formula in Applications

Example 3 Using the Quadratic Formula in an Application

A delivery truck travels south from Hartselle, Alabama, to Birmingham, Alabama, along Interstate 65. The truck then heads east to Atlanta, Georgia, along Interstate 20. The distance from Birmingham to Atlanta is 8 mi less than twice the distance from Hartselle to Birmingham. If the straight-line distance from Hartselle to Atlanta is 165 mi, find the distance from Hartselle to Birmingham and from Birmingham to Atlanta. (Round the answers to the nearest mile.)

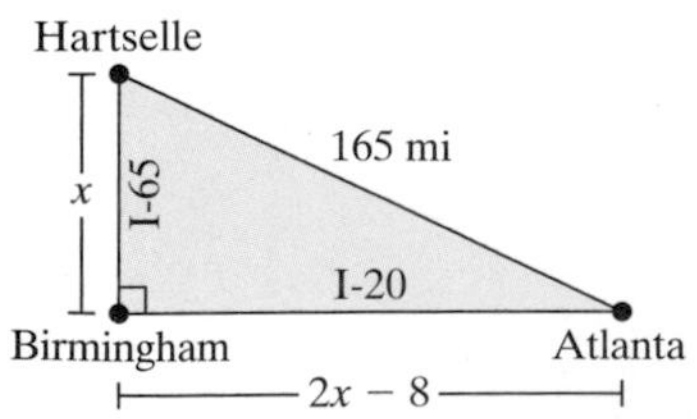

Figure 11-1

Solution:

The motorist travels due south and then due east. Therefore, the three cities form the vertices of a right triangle (Figure 11-1).

Let x represent the distance between Hartselle and Birmingham.

Then $2x - 8$ represents the distance between Birmingham and Atlanta.

Use the Pythagorean theorem to establish a relationship among the three sides of the triangle.

Answer

2. $\{-2 \pm 2i\sqrt{2}\}$

$$(x)^2 + (2x - 8)^2 = (165)^2$$

$$x^2 + 4x^2 - 32x + 64 = 27{,}225$$

$$5x^2 - 32x - 27{,}161 = 0$$ Write the equation in the form $ax^2 + bx + c = 0$.

$a = 5 \quad b = -32 \quad c = -27{,}161$ Identify a, b, and c.

$$x = \frac{-(-32) \pm \sqrt{(-32)^2 - 4(5)(-27{,}161)}}{2(5)}$$ Apply the quadratic formula.

$$= \frac{32 \pm \sqrt{1024 + 543{,}220}}{10}$$ Simplify.

$$= \frac{32 \pm \sqrt{544{,}244}}{10}$$

$$x = \frac{32 + \sqrt{544{,}244}}{10} \approx 76.97$$

$$x = \frac{32 - \sqrt{544{,}244}}{10} \approx -70.57$$

We reject the negative solution because distance cannot be negative. Rounding to the nearest whole unit, we have $x = 77$. Therefore, $2x - 8 = 2(77) - 8 = 146$.

The distance between Hartselle and Birmingham is 77 mi, and the distance between Birmingham and Atlanta is 146 mi.

Skill Practice

3. Steve and Tammy leave a campground, hiking on two different trails. Steve heads south and Tammy heads east. By lunchtime they are 9 mi apart. Steve walked 3 mi more than twice as many miles as Tammy. Find the distance each person hiked. (Round to the nearest tenth of a mile.)

Example 4 Analyzing a Quadratic Function

A model rocket is launched straight upward from the side of a 144-ft cliff (Figure 11-2). The initial velocity is 112 ft/sec. The height of the rocket $h(t)$ is given by

$$h(t) = -16t^2 + 112t + 144$$

where $h(t)$ is measured in feet and t is the time in seconds. Find the time(s) at which the rocket is 208 ft above the ground.

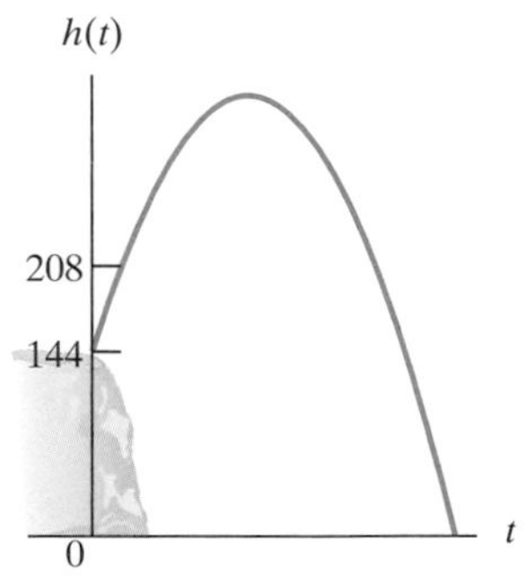

Figure 11-2

Solution:

$$h(t) = -16t^2 + 112t + 144$$

$$208 = -16t^2 + 112t + 144$$ Substitute 208 for $h(t)$.

$$16t^2 - 112t + 64 = 0$$ Write the equation in the form $at^2 + bt + c = 0$.

$$\frac{16t^2}{16} - \frac{112t}{16} + \frac{64}{16} = \frac{0}{16}$$ Divide by 16. This makes the coefficients smaller, and it is less cumbersome to solve.

$$t^2 - 7t + 4 = 0$$ The equation is not factorable. Apply the quadratic formula.

Answer

3. Tammy hiked 2.8 mi, and Steve hiked 8.6 mi.

$f(x) = x^2 - 2x + 1$

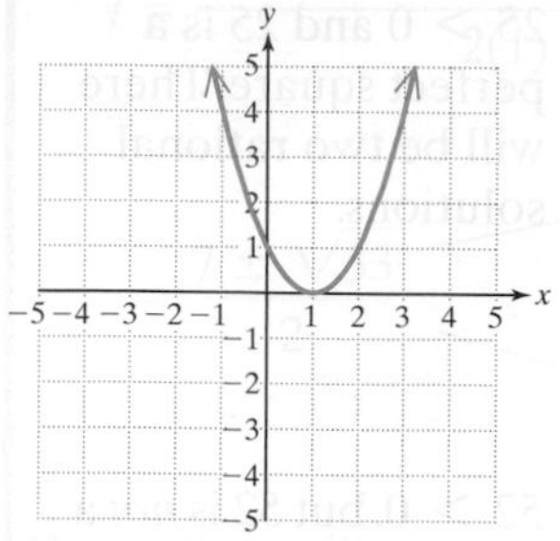

Use $x^2 - 2x + 1 = 0$ to find the value of the discriminant.

$$b^2 - 4ac = (-2)^2 - 4(1)(1) = 0$$

Since the discriminant is zero, there is one real solution to the quadratic equation. Therefore, there is one x-intercept to the corresponding quadratic function, (1, 0).

Example 6 Finding *x*- and *y*-Intercepts of a Quadratic Function

Given $f(x) = x^2 - 3x + 1$

a. Find the discriminant and use it to determine if there are any x-intercepts.

b. Find the x-intercept(s), if they exist.

c. Find the y-intercept.

Solution:

a. $a = 1, b = -3$, and $c = 1$.

The discriminant is $b^2 - 4ac = (-3)^2 - 4(1)(1) = 9 - 4 = 5$

Since $5 > 0$, there are two x-intercepts.

b. The x-intercepts are given by the real solutions to the equation $f(x) = 0$. In this case, we have

$f(x) = x^2 - 3x + 1 = 0$

$x^2 - 3x + 1 = 0$ The equation is in the form $ax^2 + bx + c = 0$.

$x = \dfrac{3 \pm \sqrt{(-3)^2 - (4)(1)(1)}}{2(1)}$ Apply the quadratic formula.

$= \dfrac{3 \pm \sqrt{5}}{2}$ → $x = \dfrac{3 + \sqrt{5}}{2} \approx 2.6$; $x = \dfrac{3 - \sqrt{5}}{2} \approx 0.4$

The solutions are $\dfrac{3 + \sqrt{5}}{2}$ and $\dfrac{3 - \sqrt{5}}{2}$. Therefore, the x-intercepts are $\left(\dfrac{3 + \sqrt{5}}{2}, 0\right)$ and $\left(\dfrac{3 - \sqrt{5}}{2}, 0\right)$.

c. To find the y-intercept, evaluate $f(0)$.

$f(0) = (0)^2 - 3(0) + 1 = 1$

The y-intercept is located at (0, 1).

The parabola is shown in the graph with the x- and y-intercepts labeled.

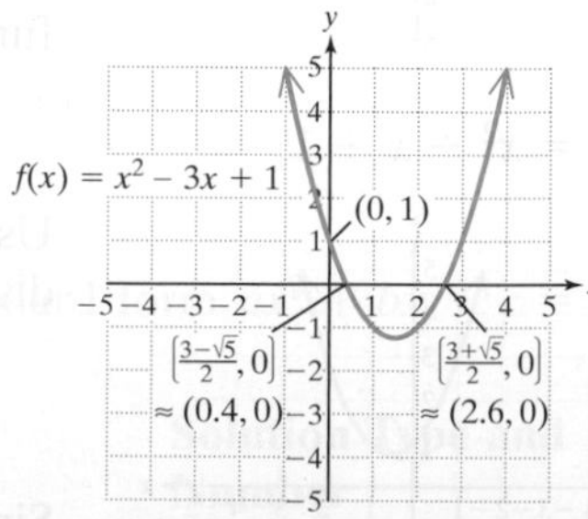

TIP: Recall that an x-intercept is a point $(a, 0)$ where the graph of a function intersects the x-axis. A y-intercept is a point $(0, b)$ where the graph intersects the y-axis.

Skill Practice Given $f(x) = x^2 + 5x + 2$,

9. Find the discriminant and use it to determine if there are any x-intercepts.

10. Find the x- and y-intercepts.

Answers

9. 17, there are two x-intercepts.

10. x-intercepts: $\left(\dfrac{-5 + \sqrt{17}}{2}, 0\right)$, $\left(\dfrac{-5 - \sqrt{17}}{2}, 0\right)$

y-intercept: (0, 2)

Example 7 Finding *x*- and *y*-Intercepts of a Quadratic Function

Given $f(x) = x^2 + x + 2$

a. Find the discriminant and use it to determine if there are any x-intercepts.

b. Find the x-intercept(s), if they exist.

c. Find the y-intercept.

Solution:

a. $a = 1, b = 1$, and $c = 2$.

The discriminant is $b^2 - 4ac = (1)^2 - 4(1)(2)$

$= 1 - 8$

$= -7$

Since $-7 < 0$, there are no x-intercepts.

b. There are no x-intercepts.

c. $f(0) = (0)^2 + (0) + 2$

$= 2$

The y-intercept is located at $(0, 2)$.

The parabola is shown. *Note:* The graph does not intersect the x-axis.

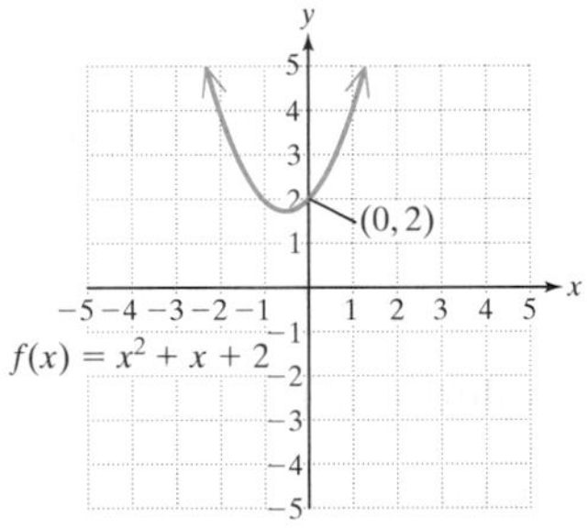

Skill Practice Given $f(x) = 2x^2 - 3x + 5$,

11. Find the discriminant and use it to determine if there are any x-intercepts.

12. Find the y-intercept.

5. Mixed Review: Methods to Solve a Quadratic Equation

Three methods have been presented to solve quadratic equations.

Methods to Solve a Quadratic Equation

Factor and use the zero product rule (Section 6.7). • This method works well if you can factor the equation easily.	Example: $x^2 + 8x + 15 = 0$ factors as $(x + 3)(x + 5) = 0$
Use the square root property. Complete the square if necessary (Section 11.1). This method is particularly good if • the equation is of the form $ax^2 + c = 0$ or • the equation is of the form $x^2 + bx + c = 0$, where b is even.	Examples: $4x^2 + 9 = 0$ $x^2 + 10x - 3 = 0$
Quadratic Formula (Section 11.2) • This method works in all cases—just be sure to write the equation in the form $ax^2 + bx + c = 0$ before applying the formula.	Example: $7x^2 - 3x + 11 = 0$

Answers

11. -31, there are no x-intercepts.

12. $(0, 5)$

Section 11.3 Equations in Quadratic Form

Concepts

1. **Solving Equations by Using Substitution**
2. **Solving Equations Reducible to a Quadratic**

1. Solving Equations by Using Substitution

We have learned to solve a variety of different types of equations, including linear, radical, rational, and polynomial equations. Sometimes, however, it is necessary to use a quadratic equation as a tool to solve other types of equations.

In Example 1, we will solve the equation $(2x^2 - 5)^2 - 16(2x^2 - 5) + 39 = 0$. Notice that the terms in the equation are written in descending order by degree. Furthermore, the first two terms have the same base, $2x^2 - 5$, and the exponent on the first term is exactly double the exponent on the second term. The third term is a constant. An equation in this pattern is called **quadratic in form**.

exponent is double   third term is constant

$$(2x^2 - 5)^2 - 16(2x^2 - 5)^1 + 39 = 0.$$

To solve this equation we will use substitution as demonstrated in Example 1.

Example 1 Solving an Equation in Quadratic Form

Solve the equation.

$$(2x^2 - 5)^2 - 16(2x^2 - 5) + 39 = 0$$

Solution:

$(2x^2 - 5)^2 - 16(2x^2 - 5) + 39 = 0$ — Substitute $u = (2x^2 - 5)$. Once the substitution is made, the equation becomes quadratic in the variable u.

$u^2 - 16u + 39 = 0$ — The equation is in the form $au^2 + bu + c = 0$.

$(u - 13)(u - 3) = 0$ — Factor.

$u = 13$ or $u = 3$ — Apply the zero product rule.

Reverse substitute.

$2x^2 - 5 = 13$ or $2x^2 - 5 = 3$ — Reverse substitute.

$2x^2 = 18$ or $2x^2 = 8$

$x^2 = 9$ or $x^2 = 4$ — Write the equations in the form $x^2 = k$.

$x = \pm\sqrt{9}$ or $x = \pm\sqrt{4}$ — Apply the square root property.

$= \pm 3$ or $= \pm 2$

The solution set is $\{3, -3, 2, -2\}$. — All solutions check in the original equation.

Avoiding Mistakes

When using substitution, it is critical to reverse substitute to solve the equation in terms of the original variable.

Skill Practice Solve the equation.

1. $(3t^2 - 10)^2 + 5(3t^2 - 10) - 14 = 0$

Answer

1. $\{1, -1, 2, -2\}$

For an equation written in descending order, notice that u was set equal to the variable factor on the middle term. This is generally the case.

Example 2 Solving an Equation in Quadratic Form

Solve the equation. $p^{2/3} - 2p^{1/3} = 8$

Solution:

$p^{2/3} - 2p^{1/3} = 8$

$p^{2/3} - 2p^{1/3} - 8 = 0$ Set the equation equal to zero.

$(p^{1/3})^2 - 2(p^{1/3})^1 - 8 = 0$ Make the substitution $u = p^{1/3}$.

Substitute $u = p^{1/3}$.

$u^2 - 2u - 8 = 0$ Then the equation is in the form $au^2 + bu + c = 0$.

$(u - 4)(u + 2) = 0$ Factor.

$u = 4$ or $u = -2$ Apply the zero product rule.

Reverse substitute.

$p^{1/3} = 4$ or $p^{1/3} = -2$

$\sqrt[3]{p} = 4$ or $\sqrt[3]{p} = -2$ The equations are radical equations.

$(\sqrt[3]{p})^3 = (4)^3$ or $(\sqrt[3]{p})^3 = (-2)^3$ Cube both sides.

$p = 64$ or $p = -8$

The solution set is $\{64, -8\}$. All solutions check in the original equation.

Skill Practice Solve the equation.

2. $y^{2/3} - y^{1/3} = 12$

Example 3 Solving an Equation in Quadratic Form

Solve the equation. $x - \sqrt{x} - 12 = 0$

Solution:

The equation can be solved by first isolating the radical and then squaring both sides (this is left as an exercise—see Exercise 25). However, this equation is also quadratic in form. By writing $\sqrt{x}$ as $x^{1/2}$, we see that the exponent on the first term is exactly double the exponent on the middle term.

$x^1 - x^{1/2} - 12 = 0$

$(x^{1/2})^2 - (x^{1/2})^1 - 12 = 0$ Let $u = x^{1/2}$.

$u^2 - u - 12 = 0$

$(u - 4)(u + 3) = 0$ Factor.

$u = 4$ or $u = -3$ Solve for u.

$x^{1/2} = 4$ or $x^{1/2} = -3$ Reverse substitute.

Answer

2. $\{64, -27\}$

9. a. Solve the quadratic equation by factoring. $u^2 + 10u + 24 = 0$
   b. Solve the equation by using substitution. $(y^2 + 5y)^2 + 10(y^2 + 5y) + 24 = 0$

10. a. Solve the quadratic equation by factoring. $u^2 - 2u - 35 = 0$
    b. Solve the equation by using substitution. $(w^2 - 6w)^2 - 2(w^2 - 6w) - 35 = 0$

For Exercises 11–24, solve the equation by using substitution. **(See Examples 1–3.)**

11. $(x^2 - 2x)^2 + 2(x^2 - 2x) = 3$
12. $(x^2 + x)^2 - 8(x^2 + x) = -12$
13. $(y^2 - 4y)^2 - (y^2 - 4y) = 20$
14. $(w^2 - 2w)^2 - 11(w^2 - 2w) = -24$
15. $m^{2/3} - m^{1/3} - 6 = 0$
16. $2n^{2/3} + 7n^{1/3} - 15 = 0$
17. $2t^{2/5} + 7t^{1/5} + 3 = 0$
18. $p^{2/5} + p^{1/5} - 2 = 0$
19. $y + 6\sqrt{y} = 16$
20. $p - 8\sqrt{p} = -15$
21. $2x + 3\sqrt{x} - 2 = 0$
22. $3t + 5\sqrt{t} - 2 = 0$
23. $16\left(\frac{x+6}{4}\right)^2 + 8\left(\frac{x+6}{4}\right) + 1 = 0$
24. $9\left(\frac{x+3}{2}\right)^2 - 6\left(\frac{x+3}{2}\right) + 1 = 0$

25. In Example 3, we solved the equation $x - \sqrt{x} - 12 = 0$ by using substitution. Now solve this equation by first isolating the radical and then squaring both sides. Don't forget to check the potential solutions in the original equation. Do you obtain the same solution as in Example 3?

Concept 2: Solving Equations Reducible to a Quadratic

For Exercises 26–36, solve the equations. **(See Examples 4–5.)**

26. $t^4 + t^2 - 12 = 0$
27. $w^4 + 4w^2 - 45 = 0$
28. $x^2(9x^2 + 7) = 2$
29. $y^2(4y^2 + 17) = 15$
30. $\frac{y}{10} - 1 = -\frac{12}{5y}$
31. $1 + \frac{5}{x} = -\frac{3}{x^2}$
32. $\frac{x+5}{x} + \frac{x}{2} = \frac{x+19}{4x}$
33. $\frac{3x}{x+1} - \frac{2}{x-3} = 1$
34. $\frac{2t}{t-3} - \frac{1}{t+4} = 1$
35. $\frac{x}{2x-1} = \frac{1}{x-2}$
36. $\frac{z}{3z+2} = \frac{2}{z+1}$

Mixed Exercises

For Exercises 37–60, solve the equations.

37. $x^4 - 16 = 0$
38. $t^4 - 625 = 0$
39. $(4x + 5)^2 + 3(4x + 5) + 2 = 0$
40. $2(5x + 3)^2 - (5x + 3) - 28 = 0$
41. $4m^4 - 9m^2 + 2 = 0$
42. $x^4 - 7x^2 + 12 = 0$
43. $x^6 - 9x^3 + 8 = 0$
44. $x^6 - 26x^3 - 27 = 0$
45. $\sqrt{x^2 + 20} = 3\sqrt{x}$
46. $\sqrt{x^2 + 60} = 4\sqrt{x}$
47. $\sqrt{4t + 1} = t + 1$
48. $\sqrt{t + 10} = t + 4$

49. $2\left(\frac{t-4}{3}\right)^2 - \left(\frac{t-4}{3}\right) - 3 = 0$

50. $\left(\frac{x+1}{5}\right)^2 - 3\left(\frac{x+1}{5}\right) - 10 = 0$

51. $x^{2/3} + x^{1/3} = 20$

52. $x^{2/5} - 3x^{1/5} = -2$

53. $m^4 + 2m^2 - 8 = 0$

54. $2c^4 + c^2 - 1 = 0$

55. $a^3 + 16a - a^2 - 16 = 0$
(*Hint:* Factor by grouping first.)

56. $b^3 + 9b - b^2 - 9 = 0$

57. $x^3 + 5x - 4x^2 - 20 = 0$

58. $y^3 + 8y - 3y^2 - 24 = 0$

59. $\left(\frac{2}{x-3}\right)^2 + 8\left(\frac{2}{x-3}\right) + 12 = 0$

60. $\left(\frac{5}{x+1}\right)^2 - 6\left(\frac{5}{x+1}\right) - 16 = 0$

Graphing Calculator Exercises

61. **a.** Solve the equation $x^4 + 4x^2 + 4 = 0$.

b. How many solutions are real and how many solutions are imaginary?

c. How many x-intercepts do you anticipate for the function defined by $y = x^4 + 4x^2 + 4$?

d. Graph $Y_1 = x^4 + 4x^2 + 4$ on a standard viewing window.

62. **a.** Solve the equation $x^4 - 2x^2 + 1 = 0$.

b. How many solutions are real and how many solutions are imaginary?

c. How many x-intercepts do you anticipate for the function defined by $y = x^4 - 2x^2 + 1$?

d. Graph $Y_1 = x^4 - 2x^2 + 1$ on a standard viewing window.

63. **a.** Solve the equation $x^4 - x^3 - 6x^2 = 0$.

b. How many solutions are real and how many solutions are imaginary?

c. How many x-intercepts do you anticipate for the function defined by $y = x^4 - x^3 - 6x^2$?

d. Graph $Y_1 = x^4 - x^3 - 6x^2$ on a standard viewing window.

64. **a.** Solve the equation $x^4 - 10x^2 + 9 = 0$.

b. How many solutions are real and how many solutions are imaginary?

c. How many x-intercepts do you anticipate for the function defined by $y = x^4 - 10x^2 + 9$?

d. Graph $Y_1 = x^4 - 10x^2 + 9$ on a standard viewing window.

Problem Recognition Exercises

Quadratic and Quadratic Type Equations

For Exercises 1–4, solve each equation by

a. Completing the square and applying the square root property.

b. Using the quadratic formula.

1. $x^2 + 10x + 3 = 0$

2. $v^2 - 16v + 5 = 0$

3. $3t^2 + t + 4 = 0$

4. $4y^2 + 3y + 5 = 0$

Graphs of $f(x) = x^2 + k$

A function of the type $f(x) = x^2 + k$ represents a vertical shift of the graph of $f(x) = x^2$.

If $k > 0$, then the graph of $f(x) = x^2 + k$ is the same as the graph of $f(x) = x^2$ shifted *up* k units.

If $k < 0$, then the graph of $f(x) = x^2 + k$ is the same as the graph of $f(x) = x^2$ shifted *down* $|k|$ units.

Calculator Connections

Topic: Investigating Vertical Shifts of a Function

Try experimenting with a graphing calculator by graphing functions of the form $y = x^2 + k$ for several values of k.

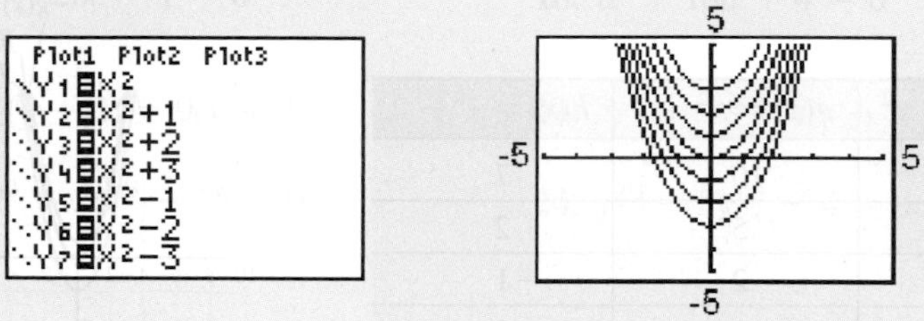

Example 2 Graphing Quadratic Functions of the Form $f(x) = x^2 + k$

Sketch the functions defined by

a. $m(x) = x^2 - 4$ **b.** $n(x) = x^2 + \frac{7}{2}$

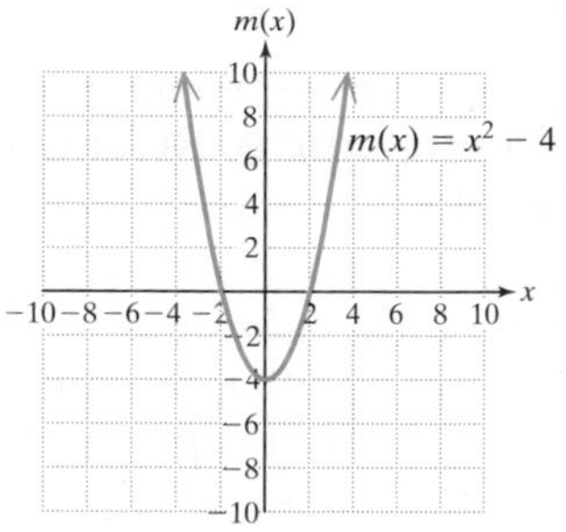

Figure 11-6

Solution:

a. $m(x) = x^2 - 4$

$m(x) = x^2 + (-4)$

Because $k = -4$, the graph is obtained by shifting the graph of $f(x) = x^2$ down $|-4|$ units (Figure 11-6).

b. $n(x) = x^2 + \frac{7}{2}$

Because $k = \frac{7}{2}$, the graph is obtained by shifting the graph of $f(x) = x^2$ up $\frac{7}{2}$ units (Figure 11-7).

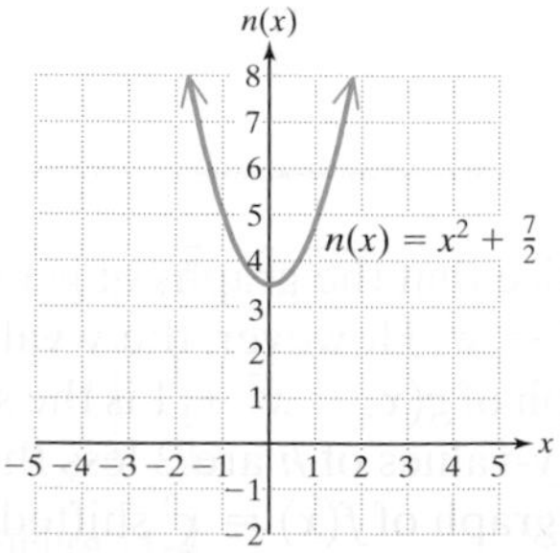

Figure 11-7

TIP: For more accuracy in the graph, plot one or two points near the vertex and use the symmetry of the curve to find additional points on the graph.

Skill Practice

2. Graph the functions f, g, and h on the same coordinate system.

$f(x) = x^2 \qquad g(x) = x^2 + 3 \qquad h(x) = x^2 - 5$

Answer

2.

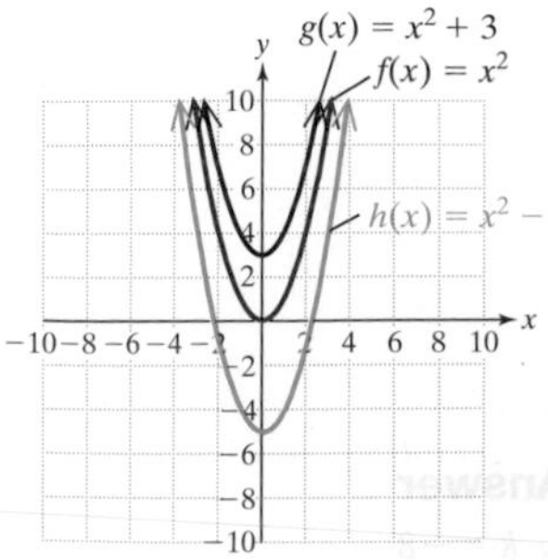

2. Quadratic Functions of the Form $f(x) = (x - h)^2$

The graph of $f(x) = x^2 + k$ represents a vertical shift (up or down) of the graph of $f(x) = x^2$. Example 3 shows that functions of the form $f(x) = (x - h)^2$ represent a horizontal shift (left or right) of the graph of $f(x) = x^2$.

Example 3 Graphing Quadratic Functions of the Form $f(x) = (x - h)^2$

Graph the functions f, g, and h on the same coordinate system.

$$f(x) = x^2 \qquad g(x) = (x + 1)^2 \qquad h(x) = (x - 2)^2$$

Solution:

Several function values for f, g, and h are shown in Table 11-2 for selected values of x. The corresponding graphs are pictured in Figure 11-8.

Table 11-2

x	$f(x) = x^2$	$g(x) = (x + 1)^2$	$h(x) = (x - 2)^2$
−4	16	9	36
−3	9	4	25
−2	4	1	16
−1	1	0	9
0	0	1	4
1	1	4	1
2	4	9	0
3	9	16	1
4	16	25	4
5	25	36	9

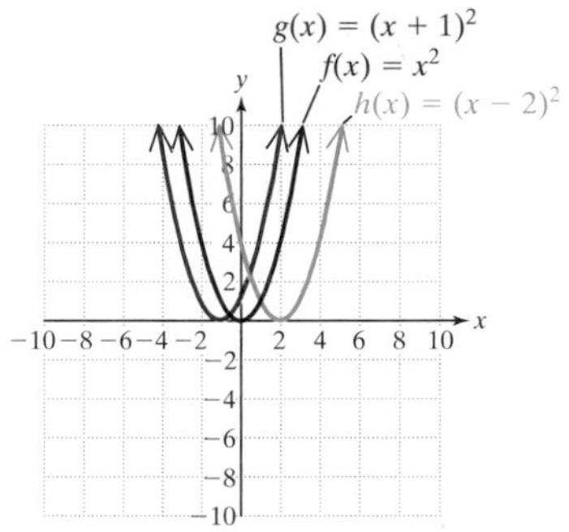

Figure 11-8

Skill Practice Refer to the graph of $f(x) = (x - h)^2$ to determine the value of h.

3.

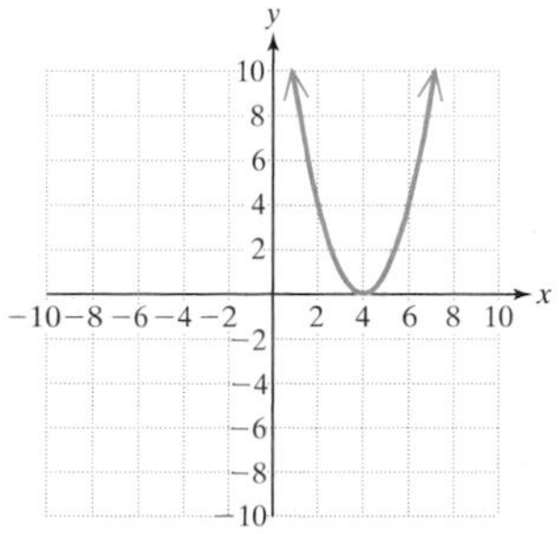

Example 3 illustrates the following properties of quadratic functions of the form $f(x) = (x - h)^2$.

Answer

3. $h = 4$

Chapter 11 Summary

Section 11.1 Square Root Property and Completing the Square

Key Concepts

The **square root property** states that

If $x^2 = k$ then $x = \pm\sqrt{k}$

Follow these steps to solve a quadratic equation in the form $ax^2 + bx + c = 0\ (a \neq 0)$ by completing the square and applying the square root property:

1. Divide both sides by a to make the leading coefficient 1.
2. Isolate the variable terms on one side of the equation.
3. Complete the square: Add the square of one-half the linear term coefficient to both sides of the equation. Then factor the resulting perfect square trinomial.
4. Apply the square root property and solve for x.

Examples

Example 1

$(x - 5)^2 = -13$

$x - 5 = \pm\sqrt{-13}$ (square root property)

$x = 5 \pm i\sqrt{13}$

The solution set is $\{5 \pm i\sqrt{13}\}$.

Example 2

$2x^2 - 12x - 16 = 0$

$\frac{2x^2}{2} - \frac{12x}{2} - \frac{16}{2} = \frac{0}{2}$

$x^2 - 6x - 8 = 0$

$x^2 - 6x = 8$

$x^2 - 6x + 9 = 8 + 9$ *Note:* $[\frac{1}{2}(-6)]^2 = 9$

$(x - 3)^2 = 17$

$x - 3 = \pm\sqrt{17}$

$x = 3 \pm \sqrt{17}$

The solution set is $\{3 \pm \sqrt{17}\}$.

Section 11.2 Quadratic Formula

Key Concepts

The solutions to a quadratic equation $ax^2 + bx + c = 0$ $(a \neq 0)$ are given by the **quadratic formula**

$$x = \frac{-b \pm \sqrt{b^2 - 4ac}}{2a}$$

The **discriminant** of a quadratic equation $ax^2 + bx + c = 0$ is $b^2 - 4ac$. If a, b, and c are rational numbers, then

1. If $b^2 - 4ac > 0$, then there will be two real solutions. Moreover,
   a. If $b^2 - 4ac$ is a perfect square, the solutions will be rational numbers.
   b. If $b^2 - 4ac$ is not a perfect square, the solutions will be irrational numbers.
2. If $b^2 - 4ac < 0$, then there will be two imaginary solutions.
3. If $b^2 - 4ac = 0$, then there will be one rational solution.

Three methods to solve a quadratic equation are

1. Factoring and applying the zero product rule.
2. Completing the square and applying the square root property.
3. Using the quadratic formula.

Example

Example 1

$$3x^2 - 2x + 4 = 0$$

$a = 3 \qquad b = -2 \qquad c = 4$

$$x = \frac{-(-2) \pm \sqrt{(-2)^2 - 4(3)(4)}}{2(3)}$$

$$= \frac{2 \pm \sqrt{4 - 48}}{6}$$

$$= \frac{2 \pm \sqrt{-44}}{6}$$

The discriminant is -44. Therefore, there will be two imaginary solutions.

$$= \frac{2 \pm 2i\sqrt{11}}{6}$$

$$= \frac{\overset{1}{\cancel{2}}(1 \pm i\sqrt{11})}{\underset{3}{\cancel{6}}}$$

$$= \frac{1 \pm i\sqrt{11}}{3}$$

$$= \frac{1}{3} \pm \frac{\sqrt{11}}{3}i$$

The solution set is $\left\{\frac{1}{3} \pm \frac{\sqrt{11}}{3}i\right\}$.

Section 11.3 Equations in Quadratic Form

Key Concepts

Substitution can be used to solve equations that are in quadratic form.

Example

Example 1

$x^{2/3} - x^{1/3} - 12 = 0 \quad$ Let $u = x^{1/3}$.

$$u^2 - u - 12 = 0$$

$$(u - 4)(u + 3) = 0$$

$u = 4 \quad$ or $\quad u = -3$

$x^{1/3} = 4 \quad$ or $\quad x^{1/3} = -3$

$x = 64 \quad$ or $\quad x = -27 \quad$ Cube both sides.

The solution set is $\{64, -27\}$.

Section 12.1 Inverse Functions

Concepts

1. **Introduction to Inverse Functions**
2. **Definition of a One-to-One Function**
3. **Definition of the Inverse of a Function**
4. **Finding an Equation of the Inverse of a Function**

1. Introduction to Inverse Functions

In Section 8.2, we defined a function as a set of ordered pairs (x, y) such that for every element x in the domain, there corresponds exactly one element y in the range. For example, the function f relates the weight of a package of deli meat, x, to its cost, y.

$$f = \{(1, 4), (2.5, 10), (4, 16)\}$$

That is, 1 lb of meat sells for \$4, 2.5 lb sells for \$10, and 4 lb sells for \$16. Now suppose we create a new function in which the values of x and y are interchanged. The new function, called the **inverse of *f***, denoted $\boldsymbol{f^{-1}}$, relates the price of meat, x, to its weight, y.

Avoiding Mistakes

f^{-1} denotes the inverse of a function. The -1 does not represent an exponent.

$$f^{-1} = \{(4, 1), (10, 2.5), (16, 4)\}$$

Notice that interchanging the x- and y-values has the following outcome. The domain of f is the same as the range of f^{-1}, and the range of f is the domain of f^{-1}.

2. Definition of a One-to-One Function

A necessary condition for a function f to have an inverse function is that no two ordered pairs in f have different x-coordinates and the same y-coordinate. A function that satisfies this condition is called a **one-to-one function**. The function relating the weight of a package of meat to its price is a one-to-one function. However, consider the function g defined by

$$g = \{(1, 4), (2, 3), (-2, 4)\}$$

same y

different x

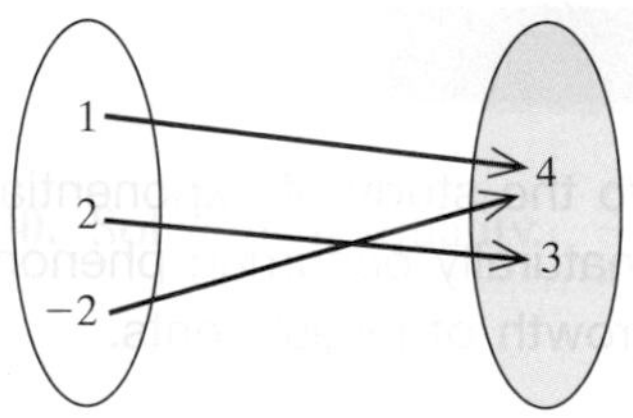

Not a one-to-one function because two different x values map to the same y value.

This function is not one-to-one because the range element 4 has two different x-coordinates, 1 and -2. Interchanging the x- and y-values produces a relation that violates the definition of a function.

$$\{(4, 1), (3, 2), (4, -2)\}$$

same x

different y

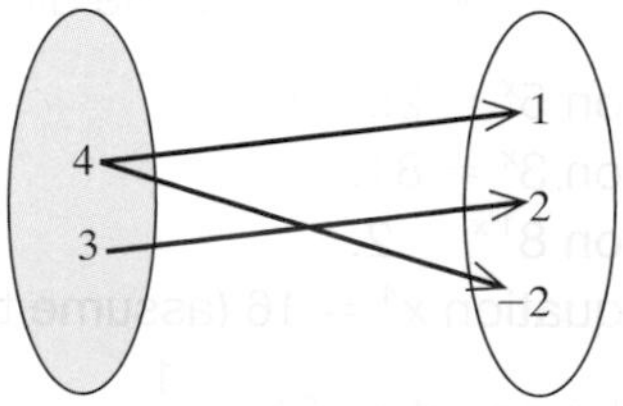

This relation is not a function because for $x = 4$, there are two different y-values.

In Section 8.2, you learned the vertical line test to determine visually if a graph represents a function. Similarly, we use a **horizontal line test** to determine whether a function is one-to-one.

Using the Horizontal Line Test

Consider a function defined by a set of points (x, y) in a rectangular coordinate system. Then y is a *one-to-one* function of x if no horizontal line intersects the graph in more than one point.

To understand the horizontal line test, consider the functions f and g.

$f = \{(1, 4), (2.5, 10), (4, 16)\}$ $g = \{(1, 4), (2, 3), (-2, 4)\}$

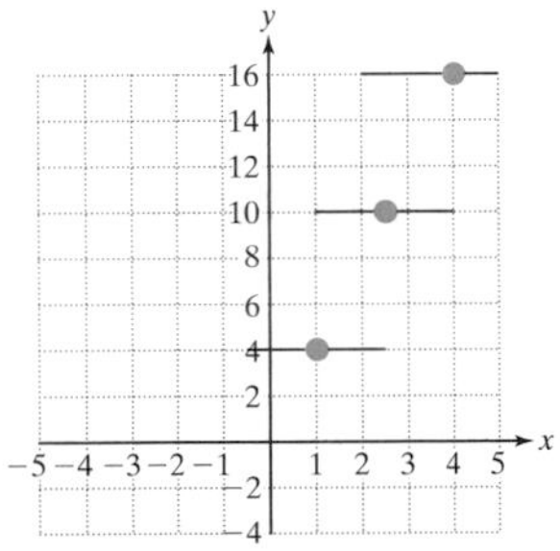

This function is one-to-one. No horizontal line intersects more than once.

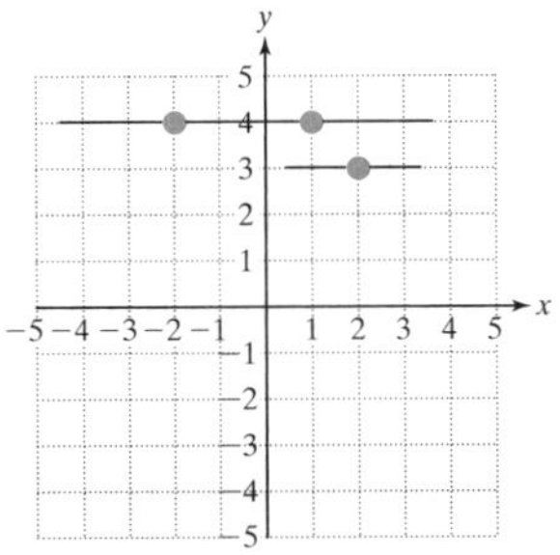

This function is *not* one-to-one. A horizontal line intersects more than once.

Example 1 Identifying a One-to-One Function

For each function, determine if the function is one-to-one.

a.

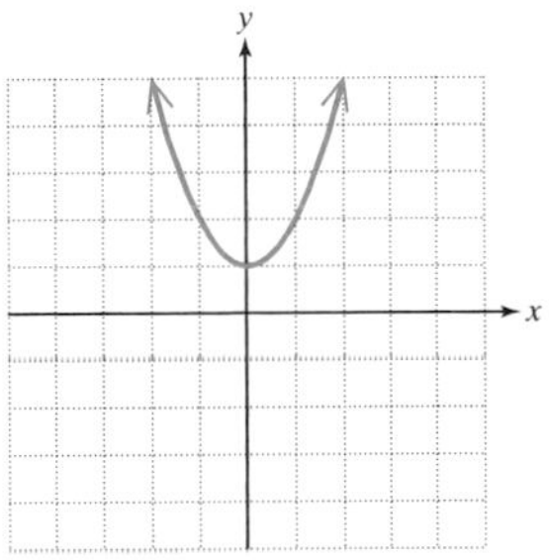

b.

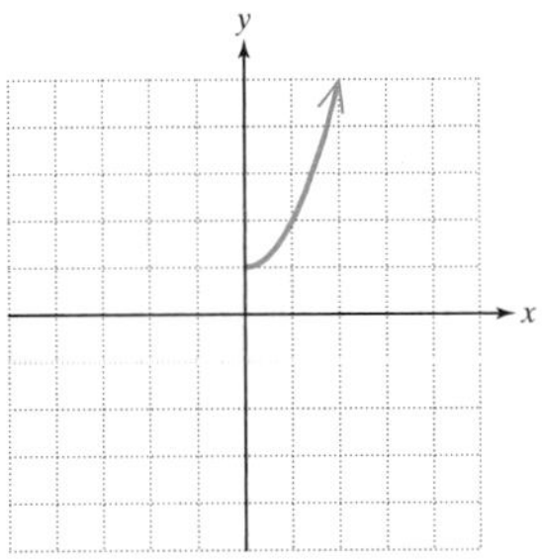

Solution:

a. Function is not one-to-one. A horizontal line intersects in more than one point.

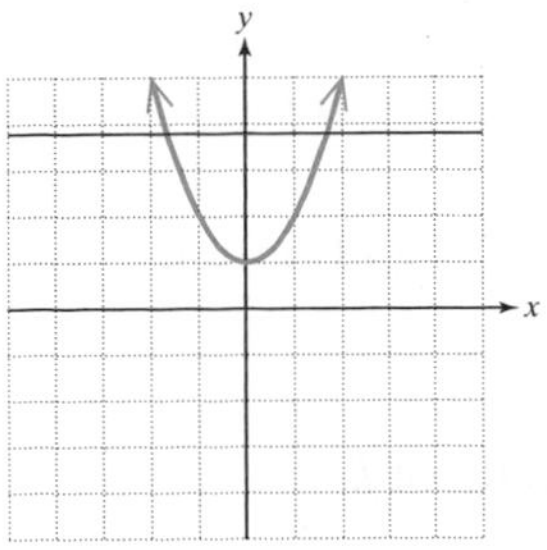

b. Function is one-to-one. No horizontal line intersects more than once.

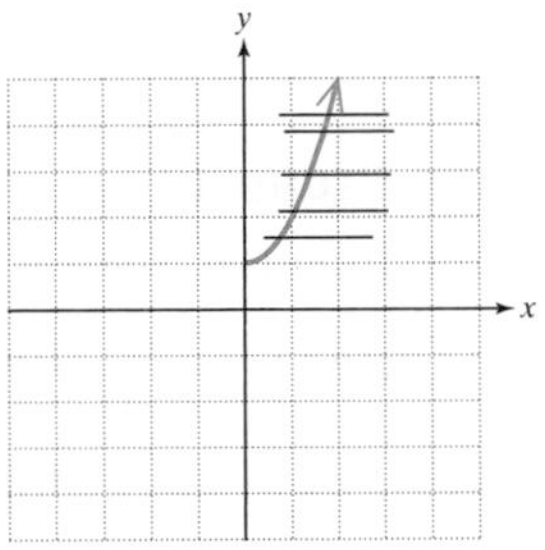

Solution:

	Logarithmic Form		Exponential Form
a.	$\log_2 32 = 5$	$\Leftrightarrow$	$2^5 = 32$
b.	$\log_{10}\left(\frac{1}{1000}\right) = -3$	$\Leftrightarrow$	$10^{-3} = \frac{1}{1000}$
c.	$\log_5 1 = 0$	$\Leftrightarrow$	$5^0 = 1$

Skill Practice Rewrite the logarithmic equations in exponential form.

1. $\log_3 9 = 2$ **2.** $\log_{10}\left(\frac{1}{100}\right) = -2$ **3.** $\log_8 1 = 0$

2. Evaluating Logarithmic Expressions

Example 2 Evaluating Logarithmic Expressions

Evaluate the logarithmic expressions.

a. $\log_8 64$ **b.** $\log_5\left(\frac{1}{125}\right)$ **c.** $\log_{1/2}\left(\frac{1}{8}\right)$

Solution:

a. $\log_8 64$ is the exponent to which 8 must be raised to obtain 64.

$y = \log_8 64$ Let y represent the value of the logarithm.

$8^y = 64$ Rewrite the expression in exponential form.

$8^y = 8^2$

$y = 2$ Therefore, $\log_8 64 = 2$.

b. $\log_5\left(\frac{1}{125}\right)$ is the exponent to which 5 must be raised to obtain $\frac{1}{125}$.

$y = \log_5\left(\frac{1}{125}\right)$ Let y represent the value of the logarithm.

$5^y = \frac{1}{125}$ Rewrite the expression in exponential form.

$5^y = \frac{1}{5^3} = 5^{-3}$

$y = -3$ Therefore, $\log_5\left(\frac{1}{125}\right) = -3$.

c. $\log_{1/2}\left(\frac{1}{8}\right)$ is the exponent to which $\frac{1}{2}$ must be raised to obtain $\frac{1}{8}$.

$y = \log_{1/2}\left(\frac{1}{8}\right)$ Let y represent the value of the logarithm.

$\left(\frac{1}{2}\right)^y = \frac{1}{8}$ Rewrite the expression in exponential form.

$\left(\frac{1}{2}\right)^y = \left(\frac{1}{2}\right)^3$

$y = 3$ Therefore, $\log_{1/2}\left(\frac{1}{8}\right) = 3$.

Skill Practice Evaluate the logarithmic expressions.

4. $\log_{10} 1000$ **5.** $\log_4\left(\frac{1}{16}\right)$ **6.** $\log_{1/3} 3$

Answers

1. $3^2 = 9$ **2.** $10^{-2} = \frac{1}{100}$
3. $8^0 = 1$ **4.** 3
5. -2 **6.** -1

Example 3 **Evaluating Logarithmic Expressions**

Evaluate the logarithmic expressions.

a. $\log_b b$ **b.** $\log_c c^7$ **c.** $\log_3 \sqrt[4]{3}$

Solution:

a. $\log_b b$ is the exponent to which b must be raised to obtain b.

$y = \log_b b$ Let y represent the value of the logarithm.

$b^y = b$ Rewrite the expression in exponential form.

$y = 1$ Therefore, $\log_b b = 1$.

b. $\log_c c^7$ is the exponent to which c must be raised to obtain c^7.

$y = \log_c c^7$ Let y represent the value of the logarithm.

$c^y = c^7$ Rewrite the expression in exponential form.

$y = 7$ Therefore, $\log_c c^7 = 7$.

c. $\log_3 \sqrt[4]{3} = \log_3 3^{1/4}$ is the exponent to which 3 must be raised to obtain $3^{1/4}$.

$y = \log_3 3^{1/4}$ Let y represent the value of the logarithm.

$3^y = 3^{1/4}$ Rewrite the expression in exponential form.

$y = \frac{1}{4}$ Therefore, $\log_3 \sqrt[4]{3} = \frac{1}{4}$.

Skill Practice Evaluate the logarithmic expressions.

7. $\log_x x$ **8.** $\log_b b^{10}$ **9.** $\log_5 \sqrt[3]{5}$

3. The Common Logarithmic Function

The logarithmic function with base 10 is called the **common logarithmic function** and is denoted by $y = \log x$. Notice that the base is not explicitly written but is understood to be 10. That is, $y = \log_{10} x$ is written simply as $y = \log x$.

Example 4 **Evaluating Common Logarithms**

Evaluate the logarithmic expressions.

a. $\log 100{,}000$ **b.** $\log 0.01$

Solution:

a. $\log 100{,}000$ is the exponent to which 10 must be raised to obtain 100,000.

$y = \log 100{,}000$ Let y represent the value of the logarithm.

$10^y = 100{,}000$ Rewrite the expression in exponential form.

$10^y = 10^5$

$y = 5$ Therefore, $\log 100{,}000 = 5$.

Answers

7. 1 **8.** 10 **9.** $\frac{1}{3}$

The general shape and important features of exponential and logarithmic functions are summarized as follows.

Graphs of Exponential and Logarithmic Functions

Exponential Functions

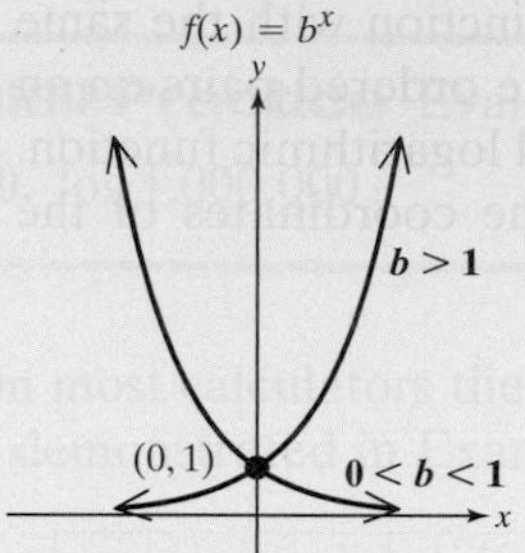

Domain: $(-\infty, \infty)$
Range: $(0, \infty)$
Horizontal asymptote: $y = 0$
Passes through $(0, 1)$
If $b > 1$, the function is increasing.
If $0 < b < 1$, the function is decreasing.

Logarithmic Functions

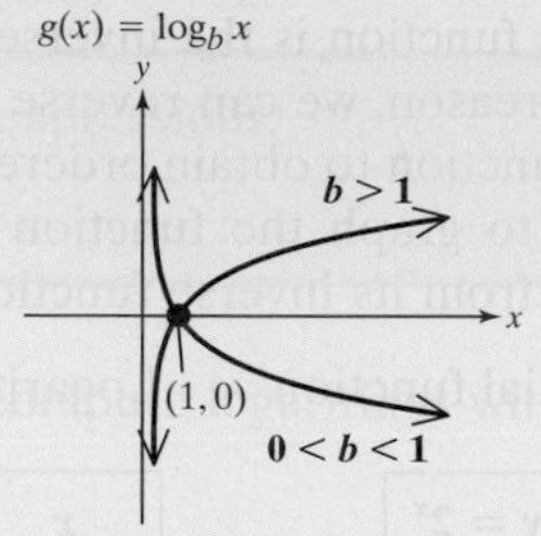

Domain: $(0, \infty)$
Range: $(-\infty, \infty)$
Vertical asymptote: $x = 0$
Passes through $(1, 0)$
If $b > 1$, the function is increasing.
If $0 < b < 1$, the function is decreasing.

Notice that the roles of x and y are interchanged for the functions $y = b^x$ and $b^y = x$. Therefore, it is not surprising that the domain and range are reversed between exponential and logarithmic functions. Moreover, an exponential function passes through $(0, 1)$, whereas a logarithmic function passes through $(1, 0)$. An exponential function has a horizontal asymptote at $y = 0$, whereas a logarithmic function has a vertical asymptote at $x = 0$.

When graphing a logarithmic equation, it is helpful to know its domain.

Example 7 Identifying the Domain of a Logarithmic Function

Find the domain of the functions.

a. $f(x) = \log(4 - x)$ **b.** $g(x) = \log(2x + 6)$

Solution:

The domain of the function $y = \log_b x$ is the set of all positive real numbers. That is, the argument x must be greater than zero: $x > 0$.

a. $f(x) = \log(4 - x)$	The argument is $4 - x$.
$4 - x > 0$	The argument of the logarithm must be greater than zero.
$-x > -4$	Solve for x.
$x < 4$	Divide by -1 and reverse the inequality sign.

The domain is $(-\infty, 4)$.

b. $g(x) = \log(2x + 6)$ The argument is $2x + 6$.

$2x + 6 > 0$ The argument of the logarithm must be greater than zero.

$2x > -6$

$x > -3$

The domain is $(-3, \infty)$.

Skill Practice Find the domain of the functions.

17. $f(x) = \log_3(x + 7)$ **18.** $g(x) = \log(4 - 8x)$

Calculator Connections

Topic: Graphing Common Logarithmic Functions

The graphs of $Y_1 = \log(4 - x)$ and $Y_2 = \log(2x + 6)$ are shown here and can be used to confirm the solutions to Example 7. Notice that each function has a vertical asymptote at the value of x where the argument equals zero.

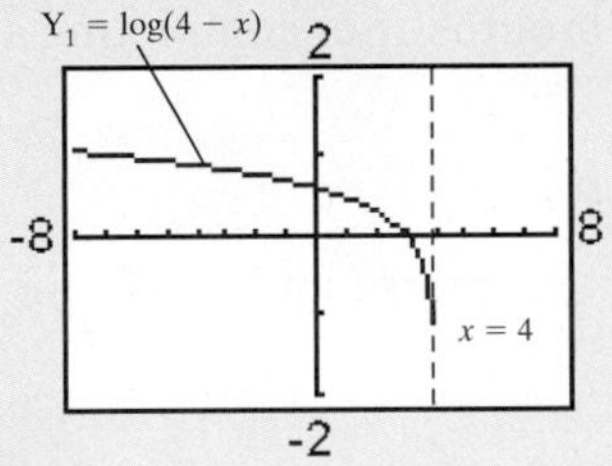

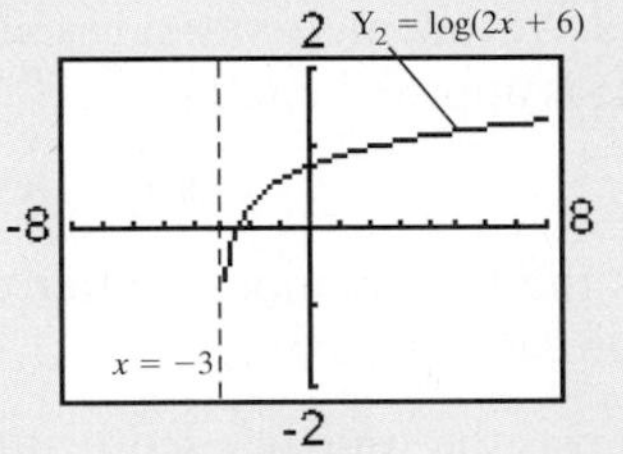

5. Applications of the Common Logarithmic Function

Example 8 Applying a Common Logarithm to Compute pH

The pH (hydrogen potential) of a solution is defined as

$$\text{pH} = -\log[\text{H}^+]$$

where $[\text{H}^+]$ represents the concentration of hydrogen ions in moles per liter (mol/L). The pH scale ranges from 0 to 14. The midpoint of this range, 7, represents a neutral solution. Values below 7 are progressively more acidic, and values above 7 are progressively more alkaline. Based on the equation $\text{pH} = -\log[\text{H}^+]$, a 1-unit change in pH means a 10-fold change in hydrogen ion concentration.

a. Normal rain has a pH of 5.6. However, in some areas of the northeastern United States the rainwater is more acidic. What is the pH of a rain sample for which the concentration of hydrogen ions is 0.0002 mol/L?

b. Find the pH of household ammonia if the concentration of hydrogen ions is 1.0×10^{-11} mol/L.

Solution:

a. $\text{pH} = -\log[\text{H}^+]$

$= -\log(0.0002)$ Substitute $[\text{H}^+] = 0.0002$.

≈ 3.7 The pH of the rain sample is 3.7. (To compare this value with a familiar substance, note that the pH of orange juice is roughly 3.5.)

Answers

17. Domain: $(-7, \infty)$

18. Domain: $\left(-\infty, \frac{1}{2}\right)$

b. $\text{pH} = -\log[\text{H}^+]$

$= -\log(1.0 \times 10^{-11})$ Substitute $[\text{H}^+] = 1.0 \times 10^{-11}$.

$= -\log(10^{-11})$

$= -(-11)$

$= 11$ The pH of household ammonia is 11.

Skill Practice

19. A new all-natural shampoo on the market claims its hydrogen ion concentration is 5.88×10^{-7} mol/L. Use the formula $\text{pH} = -\log[\text{H}^+]$ to calculate the pH level of the shampoo.

Example 9 Applying a Logarithmic Function to a Memory Model

One method of measuring a student's retention of material after taking a course is to retest the student at specified time intervals after the course has been completed. A student's score on a calculus test t months after completing a course in calculus is approximated by

$$S(t) = 85 - 25\log(t + 1)$$

where t is the time in months after completing the course and $S(t)$ is the student's score as a percent.

a. What was the student's score at $t = 0$?

b. What was the student's score after 2 months?

c. What was the student's score after 1 yr?

Solution:

a. $S(t) = 85 - 25\log(t + 1)$

$S(0) = 85 - 25\log(0 + 1)$ Substitute $t = 0$.

$= 85 - 25\log 1$ $\log 1 = 0$ because $10^0 = 1$.

$= 85 - 25(0)$

$= 85 - 0$

$= 85$ The student's score at the time the course was completed was 85%.

b. $S(t) = 85 - 25\log(t + 1)$

$S(2) = 85 - 25\log(2 + 1)$

$= 85 - 25\log 3$ Use a calculator to approximate log 3.

≈ 73.1 The student's score dropped to 73.1%.

c. $S(t) = 85 - 25\log(t + 1)$

$S(12) = 85 - 25\log(12 + 1)$

$= 85 - 25\log 13$ Use a calculator to approximate log 13.

≈ 57.2 The student's score dropped to 57.2%.

Answer

19. $\text{pH} \approx 6.23$

Skill Practice The memory model for a student's score on a statistics test t months after completion of the course in statistics is approximated by

$$S(t) = 92 - 28 \log (t + 1)$$

20. What was the student's score at the time the course was completed ($t = 0$)?
21. What was her score after 1 month?
22. What was the score after 2 months?

Answers
20. 92 **21.** 83.6 **22.** 78.6

Section 12.3 Practice Exercises

Vocabulary and Key Concepts

1. a. The function defined by $y = \log_b x$ is called the ______________ function with base ______________. The values of x and b are positive, and $b \neq 1$.

b. Given $y = \log_b x$, we call y the ______________, we call b the ______________, and we call x the ______________.

c. In interval notation, the domain of $y = \log_b x$ is ______________ and the range is ______________.

d. A logarithmic function base b is the inverse of the ______________ function base b.

e. The logarithmic function base 10 is called the ______________ logarithmic function and is denoted by $y = \log x$.

f. The graph of a logarithmic function is (increasing/decreasing) if the base $b > 1$, whereas the graph is (increasing/decreasing) if the base is between 0 and 1.

g. Which values of x are *not* in the domain of $y = \log(x - 4)$? $x = 2, x = 3, x = 4, x = 5, x = 6$

h. The graphs of a logarithmic function base b and an exponential function base b are symmetric with respect to the line ______________.

Review Exercises

2. For which graph of $y = b^x$ is $0 < b < 1$?

3. For which graph of $y = b^x$ is $b > 1$?

i.

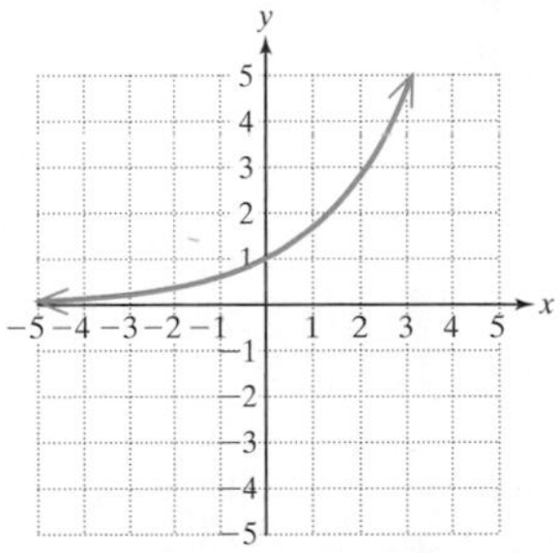

ii.

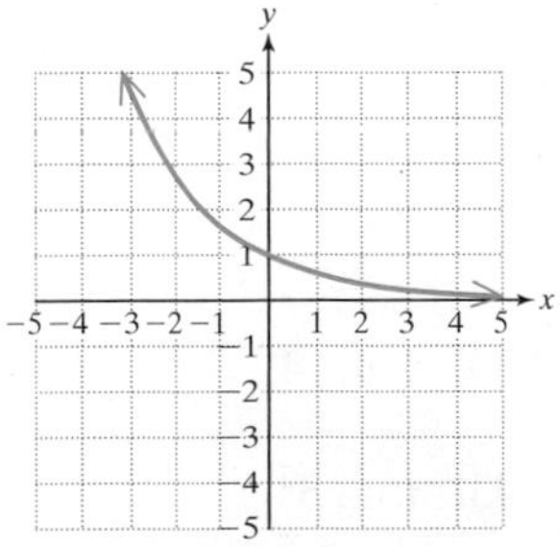

4. Let $f(x) = 6^x$.

a. Find $f(-2), f(-1), f(0), f(1)$, and $f(2)$.

b. Graph $y = f(x)$.

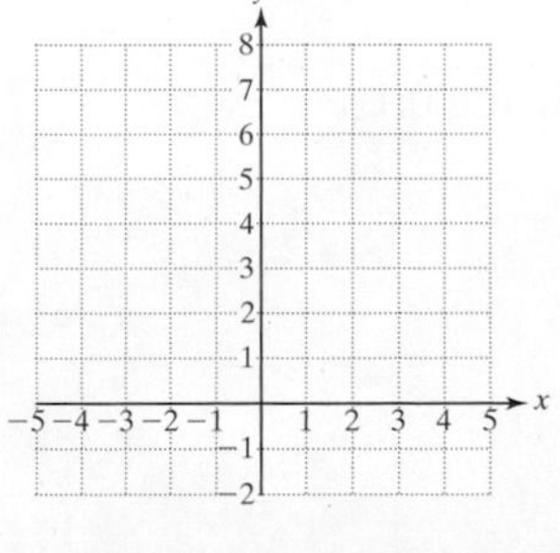

5. Let $s(x) = \left(\frac{2}{5}\right)^x$.

a. Find $s(-2), s(-1), s(0), s(1)$, and $s(2)$.

b. Graph $y = s(x)$.

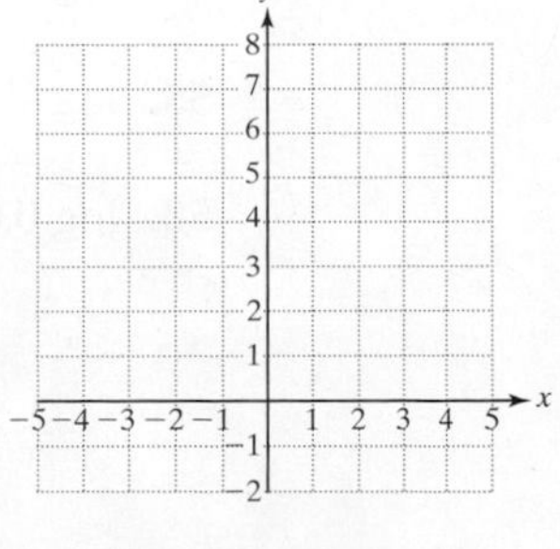

6. Let $r(x) = \left(\frac{3}{4}\right)^x$. Find $r(-2)$, $r(-1)$, $r(0)$, $r(1)$, and $r(2)$.

7. Let $g(x) = 3^x$. Find $g(-2)$, $g(-1)$, $g(0)$, $g(1)$, and $g(2)$.

Concept 1: Definition of a Logarithmic Function

8. For the equation $y = \log_b x$, identify the base, the argument, and the logarithm.

9. Rewrite the equation in exponential form. $y = \log_b x$

10. Write the equation in logarithmic form. $b^y = x$

For Exercises 11–22, write the equation in exponential form. **(See Example 1.)**

11. $\log_5 625 = 4$ **12.** $\log_{125} 25 = \frac{2}{3}$ **13.** $\log_{10} (0.0001) = -4$ **14.** $\log_{25}\left(\frac{1}{5}\right) = -\frac{1}{2}$

15. $\log_6 36 = 2$ **16.** $\log_2 128 = 7$ **17.** $\log_b 15 = x$ **18.** $\log_b 82 = y$

19. $\log_3 5 = x$ **20.** $\log_2 7 = x$ **21.** $\log_{1/4} x = 10$ **22.** $\log_{1/2} x = 6$

For Exercises 23–34, write the equation in logarithmic form.

23. $3^x = 81$ **24.** $10^3 = 1000$ **25.** $5^2 = 25$ **26.** $8^{1/3} = 2$

27. $7^{-1} = \frac{1}{7}$ **28.** $8^{-2} = \frac{1}{64}$ **29.** $b^x = y$ **30.** $b^y = x$

31. $e^x = y$ **32.** $e^y = x$ **33.** $\left(\frac{1}{3}\right)^{-2} = 9$ **34.** $\left(\frac{5}{2}\right)^{-1} = \frac{2}{5}$

Concept 2: Evaluating Logarithmic Expressions

For Exercises 35–50, evaluate the logarithms without the use of a calculator. **(See Examples 2–3.)**

35. $\log_7 49$ **36.** $\log_3 81$ **37.** $\log_{10} 0.1$ **38.** $\log_2\left(\frac{1}{16}\right)$

39. $\log_{16} 4$ **40.** $\log_8 2$ **41.** $\log_{7/2} 1$ **42.** $\log_{1/2} 2$

43. $\log_3 3^5$ **44.** $\log_9 9^3$ **45.** $\log_{10} 10$ **46.** $\log_7 1$

47. $\log_a a^3$ **48.** $\log_r r^4$ **49.** $\log_x \sqrt{x}$ **50.** $\log_y \sqrt[3]{y}$

Concept 3: The Common Logarithmic Function

For Exercises 51–58, evaluate the common logarithm without the use of a calculator. **(See Example 4.)**

51. $\log 10$ **52.** $\log 100$ **53.** $\log 1000$

54. $\log 10{,}000$ **55.** $\log (1.0 \times 10^6)$ **56.** $\log 0.1$

57. $\log 0.01$ **58.** $\log 0.001$

For Exercises 59–70, use a calculator to approximate the logarithms. Round to four decimal places. **(See Example 5.)**

59. $\log 6$ **60.** $\log 18$ **61.** $\log \pi$ **62.** $\log\left(\frac{1}{8}\right)$

63. $\log\left(\frac{1}{32}\right)$ **64.** $\log \sqrt{5}$ **65.** $\log 0.0054$ **66.** $\log 0.0000062$

67. $\log(3.4 \times 10^5)$ **68.** $\log(4.78 \times 10^9)$ **69.** $\log(3.8 \times 10^{-8})$ **70.** $\log(2.77 \times 10^{-4})$

71. Given: $\log 10 = 1$ and $\log 100 = 2$

a. Estimate $\log 93$.

b. Estimate $\log 12$.

c. Evaluate the logarithms in parts (a) and (b) on a calculator and compare to your estimates.

72. Given: $\log\left(\frac{1}{10}\right) = -1$ and $\log 1 = 0$

a. Estimate $\log\left(\frac{9}{10}\right)$.

b. Estimate $\log\left(\frac{1}{5}\right)$.

c. Evaluate the logarithms in parts (a) and (b) on a calculator and compare to your estimates.

Concept 4: Graphs of Logarithmic Functions

73. Let $f(x) = \log_4 x$.

a. Find the values of $f\left(\frac{1}{64}\right), f\left(\frac{1}{16}\right), f\left(\frac{1}{4}\right), f(1), f(4), f(16)$, and $f(64)$.

b. Graph $y = f(x)$. **(See Example 6.)**

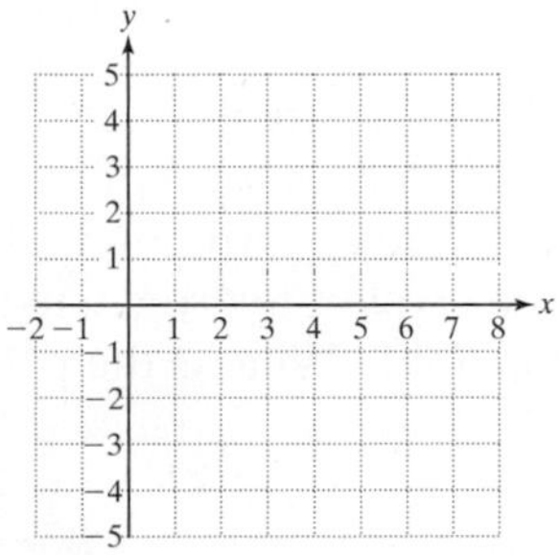

74. Let $g(x) = \log_2 x$.

a. Find the values of $g\left(\frac{1}{8}\right), g\left(\frac{1}{4}\right), g\left(\frac{1}{2}\right), g(1), g(2), g(4)$, and $g(8)$.

b. Graph $y = g(x)$.

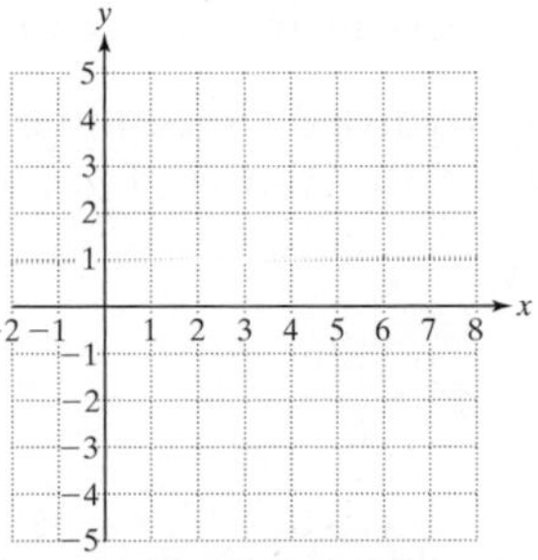

Graph the logarithmic functions in Exercises 75–78 by writing the function in exponential form and making a table of points.

75. $y = \log_3 x$

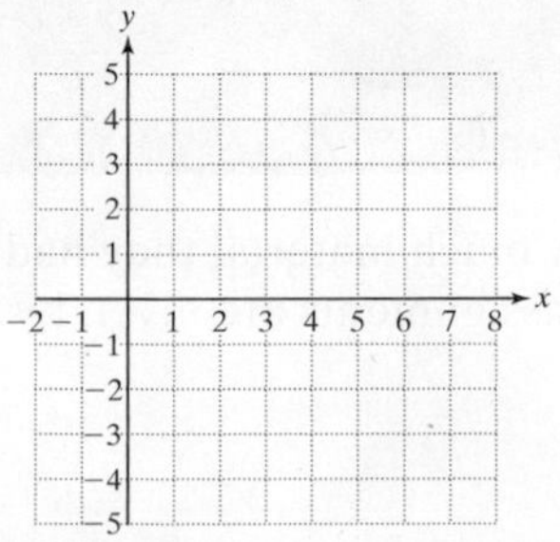

x	y

76. $y = \log_5 x$

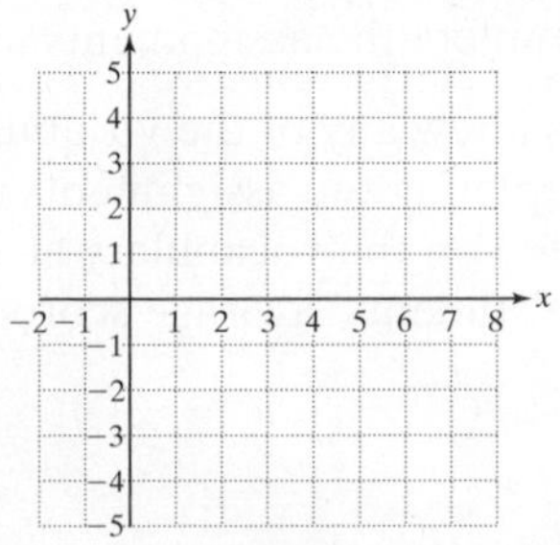

x	y

77. $y = \log_{1/2} x$ **(See Example 6.)**

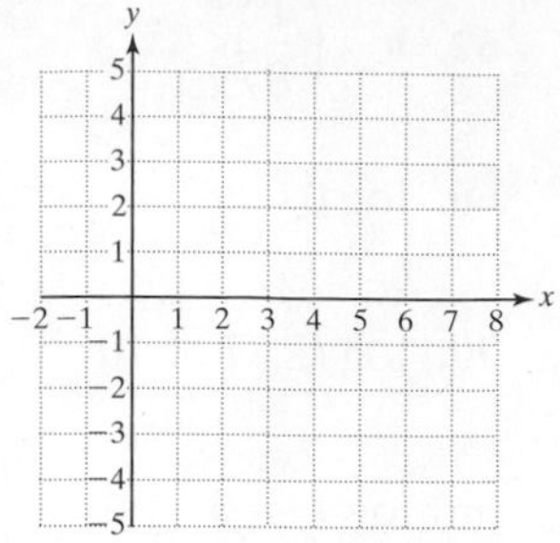

x	y

78. $y = \log_{1/3} x$

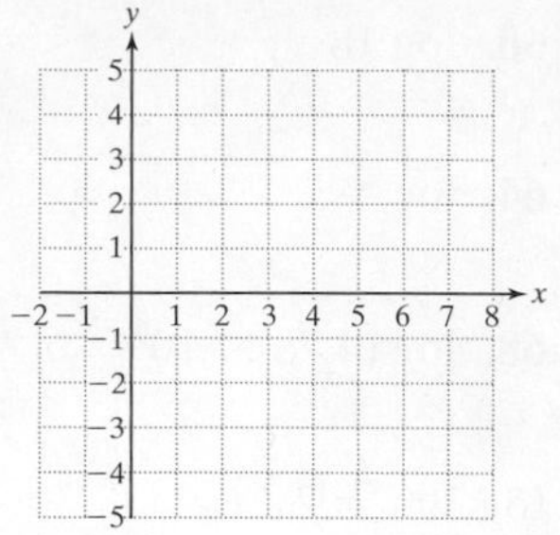

x	y

For Exercises 79–90, find the domain of the function and express the domain in interval notation. **(See Example 7.)**

79. $y = \log_7 (x - 5)$

80. $y = \log (x - 4)$

81. $g(x) = \log (2 - x)$

82. $f(x) = \log (1 - x)$

83. $y = \log (3x - 1)$

84. $y = \log_3 (2x + 1)$

85. $y = \log_3 (x + 1.2)$

86. $y = \log\left(x - \frac{1}{2}\right)$

87. $k(x) = \log (4 - 2x)$

88. $h(x) = \log (6 - 2x)$

89. $y = \log x^2$

90. $y = \log (x^2 + 1)$

Concept 5: Applications of the Common Logarithmic Function

For Exercises 91–92, use the formula $\text{pH} = -\log[\text{H}^+]$, where $[\text{H}^+]$ represents the concentration of hydrogen ions in moles per liter. Round to two decimal places. **(See Example 8.)**

91. Normally, the level of hydrogen ions in the blood is approximately 4.47×10^{-8} mol/L. Find the pH level of blood.

92. The normal pH level for streams and rivers is between 6.5 and 8.5. A high level of bacteria in a particular stream caused environmentalists to test the water. The level of hydrogen ions was found to be 0.006 mol/L. What is the pH level of the stream?

93. A graduate student in education is doing research to compare the effectiveness of two different teaching techniques designed to teach vocabulary to sixth-graders. The first group of students (group 1) was taught with method I, in which the students worked individually to complete the assignments in a workbook. The second group (group 2) was taught with method II, in which the students worked cooperatively in groups of four to complete the assignments in the same workbook.

None of the students knew any of the vocabulary words before the study began. After completing the assignments in the workbook, the students were then tested on the vocabulary at 1-month intervals to assess how much material they had retained over time. The students' average score t months after completing the assignments are given by the following functions:

Method I: $S_1(t) = 91 - 30 \log (t + 1)$, where t is the time in months and $S_1(t)$ is the average score of students in group 1.

Method II: $S_2(t) = 88 - 15 \log (t + 1)$, where t is the time in months and $S_2(t)$ is the average score of students in group 2.

a. Complete the table to find the average scores for each group of students after the indicated number of months. Round to one decimal place. **(See Example 9.)**

t (months)	0	1	2	6	12	24
$S_1(t)$						
$S_2(t)$						

b. Based on the table of values, what were the average scores for each group immediately after completion of the assigned material ($t = 0$)?

c. Based on the table of values, which teaching method helped students retain the material better for a long time?

94. Generally, the more money a company spends on advertising, the higher the sales. Let a represent the amount of money spent on advertising (in \$100s). Then the amount of money in sales $S(a)$ (in \$1000s) is given by

$$S(a) = 10 + 20 \log (a + 1) \text{ where } a \geq 0.$$

a. The value of $S(1) \approx 16.0$ means that if \$100 is spent on advertising, \$16,000 is returned in sales. Find the values of $S(11)$, $S(21)$, and $S(31)$. Round to one decimal place. Interpret the meaning of each function value in the context of this problem.

b. The graph of $y = S(a)$ is shown here. Use the graph and your answers from part (a) to explain why the money spent in advertising becomes less "efficient" as it is used in larger amounts.

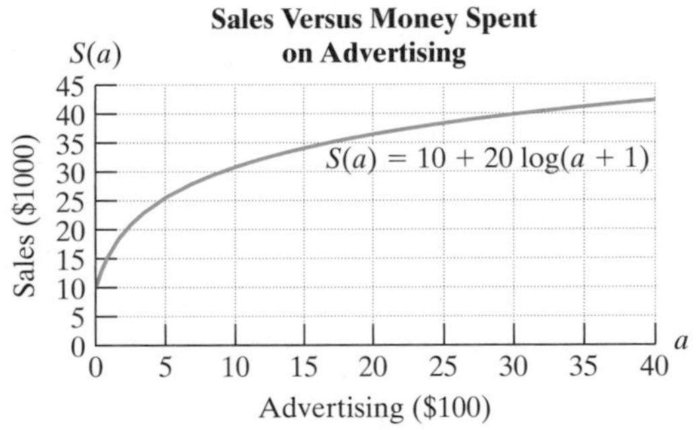

Graphing Calculator Exercises

For Exercises 95–100, graph the function on an appropriate viewing window. From the graph, identify the domain of the function and the location of the vertical asymptote.

95. $y = \log (x + 6)$

96. $y = \log (2x + 4)$

97. $y = \log (0.5x - 1)$

98. $y = \log (x + 8)$

99. $y = \log (2 - x)$

100. $y = \log (3 - x)$

Problem Recognition Exercises

Identifying Graphs of Functions

Match the function with the appropriate graph. Do not use a calculator.

1. $g(x) = 3^x$

2. $f(x) = \log x$

3. $h(x) = x^2$

4. $k(x) = -2x - 3$

5. $L(x) = |x|$

6. $m(x) = \sqrt{x}$

7. $B(x) = 3$

8. $A(x) = -x^2$

9. $n(x) = \sqrt[3]{x}$

10. $p(x) = x^3$

11. $q(x) = \dfrac{1}{x}$

12. $r(x) = x$

a.

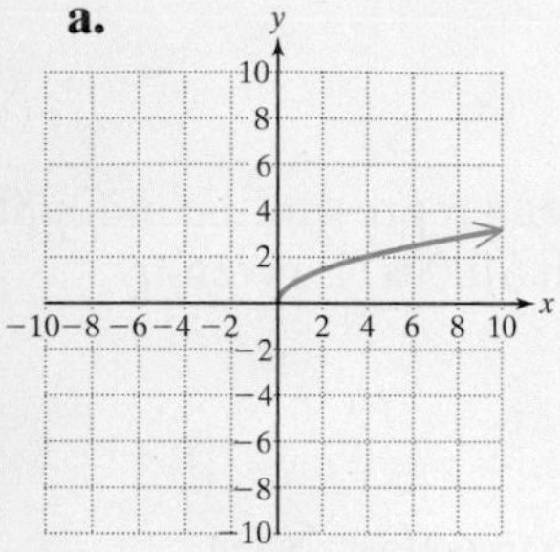

b.

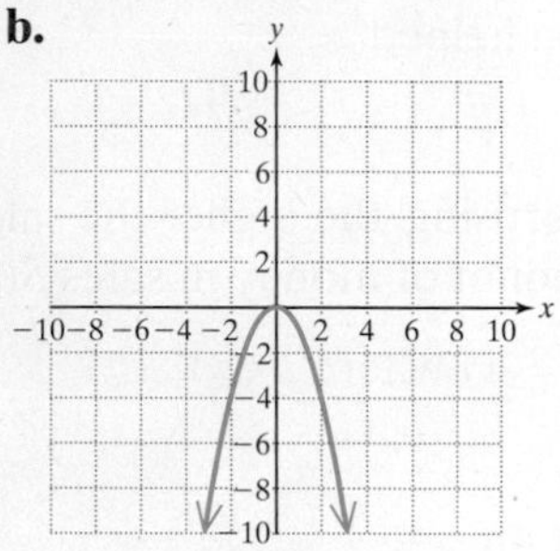

c.

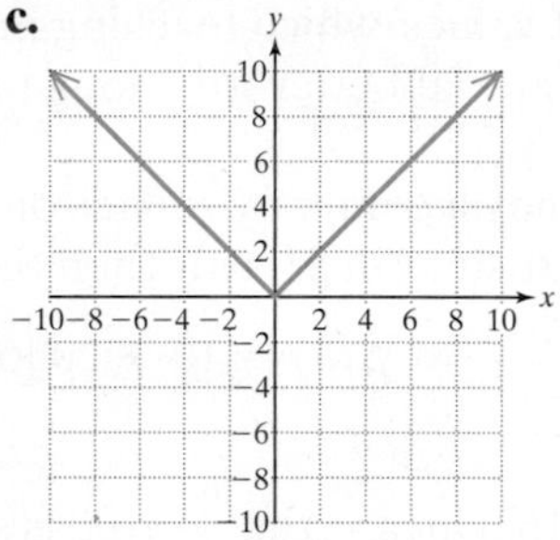

d.

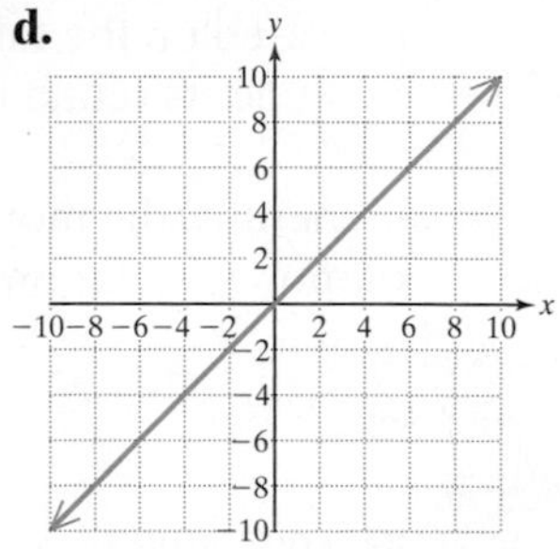

e.

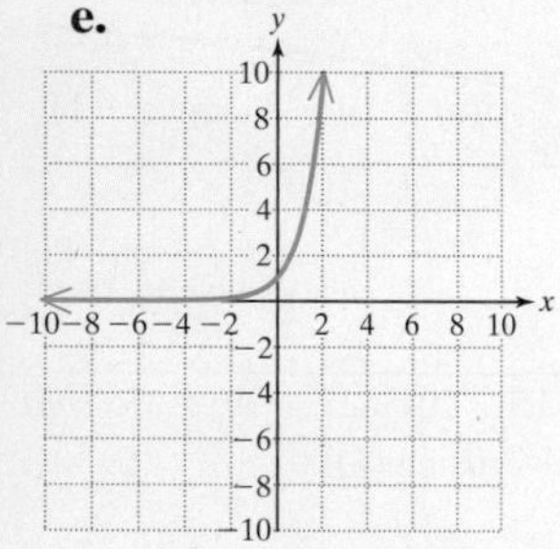

f.

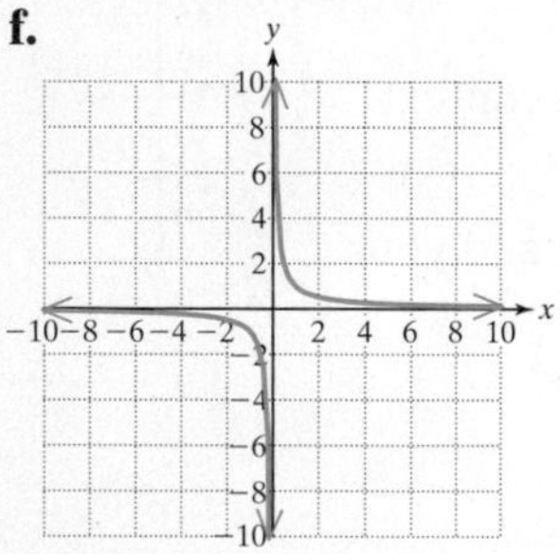

g.

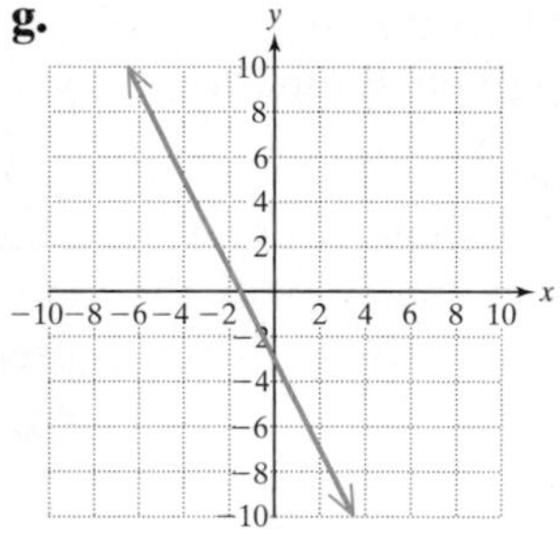

h.

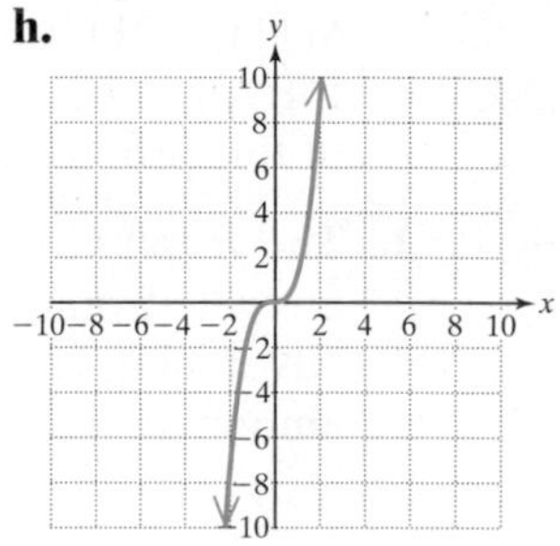

i.

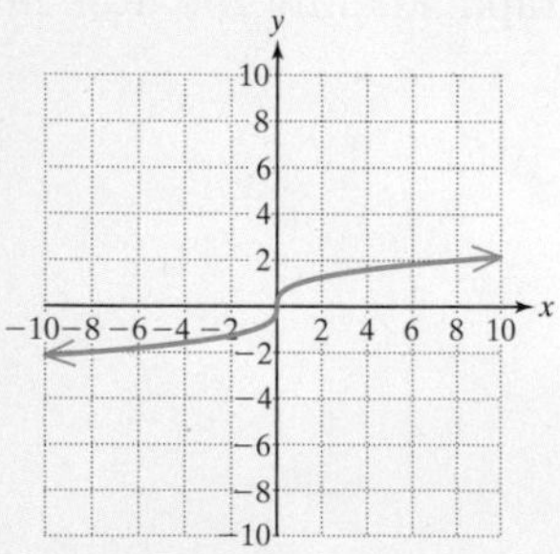

j.

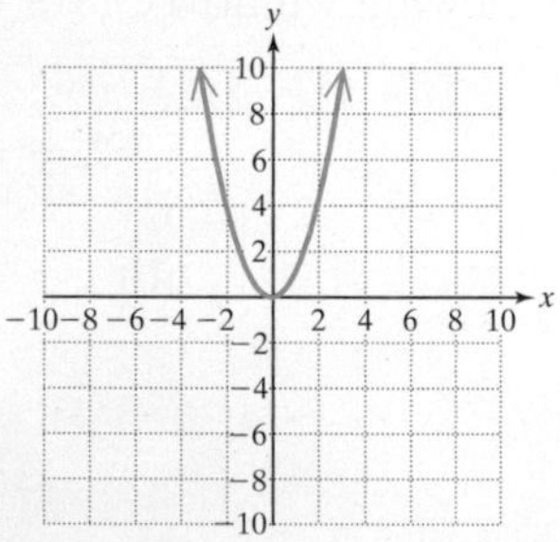

k.

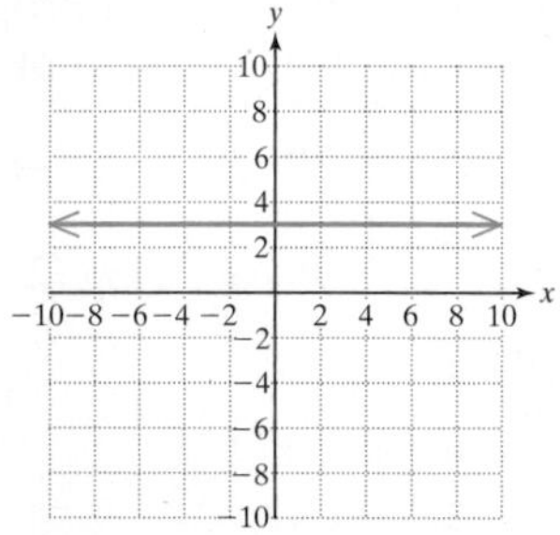

l.

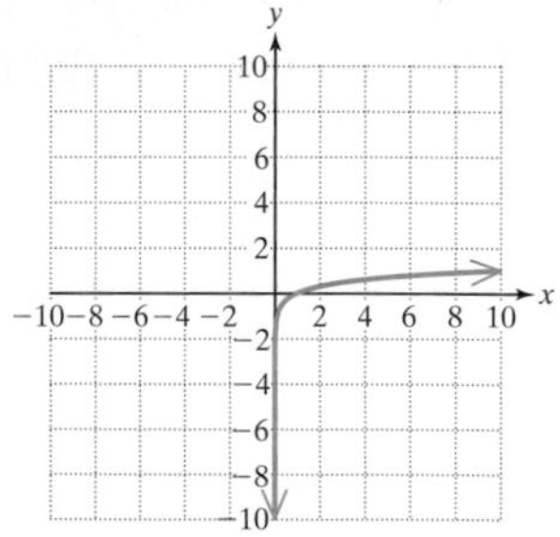

Properties of Logarithms

Section 12.4

Concepts

1. **Properties of Logarithms**
2. **Expanded Logarithmic Expressions**
3. **Single Logarithmic Expressions**

1. Properties of Logarithms

You have already been exposed to certain properties of logarithms that follow directly from the definition. Recall

$$y = \log_b x \qquad \text{is equivalent to} \qquad b^y = x \qquad \text{for } x > 0, b > 0, \text{ and } b \neq 1$$

The following properties follow directly from the definition.

Property	**Explanation**
1. $\log_b 1 = 0$	Exponential form: $b^0 = 1$
2. $\log_b b = 1$	Exponential form: $b^1 = b$
3. $\log_b b^p = p$	Exponential form: $b^p = b^p$
4. $b^{\log_b x} = x$	Logarithmic form: $\log_b x = \log_b x$

Example 1 **Applying the Properties of Logarithms to Simplify Expressions**

Use the properties of logarithms to simplify the expressions. Assume that all variable expressions within the logarithms represent positive real numbers.

a. $\log_8 8 + \log_8 1$ **b.** $10^{\log (x+2)}$ **c.** $\log_{1/2}\left(\frac{1}{2}\right)^x$

Solution:

a. $\log_8 8 + \log_8 1 = 1 + 0 = 1$ Properties 2 and 1

b. $10^{\log (x+2)} = x + 2$ Property 4

c. $\log_{1/2}\left(\frac{1}{2}\right)^x = x$ Property 3

Skill Practice Use the properties of logarithms to simplify the expressions.

1. $\log_5 1 + \log_5 5$ **2.** $15^{\log_{15} 7}$ **3.** $\log_{1/3}\left(\frac{1}{3}\right)^c$

Three additional properties are useful when simplifying logarithmic expressions. The first is the product property for logarithms.

Product Property of Logarithms

Let b, x, and y be positive real numbers where $b \neq 1$. Then

$$\log_b (xy) = \log_b x + \log_b y$$

The logarithm of a product equals the sum of the logarithms of the factors.

Answers

1. 1 **2.** 7 **3.** c

Proof:

Let $M = \log_b x$, which implies $b^M = x$.

Let $N = \log_b y$, which implies $b^N = y$.

Then $xy = b^M b^N = b^{M+N}$.

Writing the expression $xy = b^{M+N}$ in logarithmic form, we have,

$$\log_b (xy) = M + N$$

$$\log_b (xy) = \log_b x + \log_b y \checkmark$$

To demonstrate the product property for logarithms, simplify the following expressions by using the order of operations.

$$\log_3 (3 \cdot 9) \stackrel{?}{=} \log_3 3 + \log_3 9$$

$$\log_3 27 \stackrel{?}{=} 1 + 2$$

$$3 \stackrel{?}{=} 3 \checkmark \text{ True}$$

Quotient Property of Logarithms

Let b, x, and y be positive real numbers where $b \neq 1$. Then

$$\log_b \left(\frac{x}{y}\right) = \log_b x - \log_b y$$

The logarithm of a quotient equals the difference of the logarithms of the numerator and denominator.

The proof of the quotient property for logarithms is similar to the proof of the product property and is omitted here. To demonstrate the quotient property for logarithms, simplify the following expressions by using the order of operations.

$$\log \left(\frac{1{,}000{,}000}{100}\right) \stackrel{?}{=} \log (1{,}000{,}000) - \log (100)$$

$$\log (10{,}000) \stackrel{?}{=} 6 - 2$$

$$4 \stackrel{?}{=} 4 \checkmark \text{ True}$$

Power Property of Logarithms

Let b and x be positive real numbers where $b \neq 1$. Let p be any real number. Then

$$\log_b x^p = p \log_b x$$

To demonstrate the power property for logarithms, simplify the following expressions by using the order of operations.

$$\log_4 4^2 \stackrel{?}{=} 2 \log_4 4$$

$$2 \stackrel{?}{=} 2 \cdot 1$$

$$2 \stackrel{?}{=} 2 \checkmark \text{ True}$$

The properties of logarithms are summarized in the box.

Summary of the Properties of Logarithms

Let b, x, and y be positive real numbers where $b \neq 1$, and let p be a real number. Then the following properties of logarithms are true.

1. $\log_b 1 = 0$

2. $\log_b b = 1$

3. $\log_b b^p = p$

4. $b^{\log_b x} = x$

5. $\log_b (xy) = \log_b x + \log_b y$ — **Product property for logarithms**

6. $\log_b \left(\dfrac{x}{y}\right) = \log_b x - \log_b y$ — **Quotient property for logarithms**

7. $\log_b x^p = p \log_b x$ — **Power property for logarithms**

2. Expanded Logarithmic Expressions

In many applications, it is advantageous to expand a logarithm into a sum or difference of simpler logarithms.

Example 2 Writing a Logarithmic Expression in Expanded Form

Write the expression as the sum or difference of logarithms of x, y, and z. Assume all variables represent positive real numbers.

$$\log_3 \left(\frac{xy^3}{z^2}\right)$$

Solution:

$\log_3 \left(\dfrac{xy^3}{z^2}\right)$

$= \log_3 (xy^3) - \log_3 z^2$ — Quotient property for logarithms (property 6)

$= [\log_3 x + \log_3 y^3] - \log_3 z^2$ — Product property for logarithms (property 5)

$= \log_3 x + 3 \log_3 y - 2 \log_3 z$ — Power property for logarithms (property 7)

Skill Practice Write the expression as the sum or difference of logarithms of a, b, and c. Assume all variables represent positive real numbers.

4. $\log_5 \left(\dfrac{a^2b^3}{c}\right)$

Example 3 Writing a Logarithmic Expression in Expanded Form

Write the expression as the sum or difference of logarithms of x and y. Assume all variables represent positive real numbers.

$$\log \left(\frac{\sqrt{x + y}}{10}\right)$$

Answer

4. $2 \log_5 a + 3 \log_5 b - \log_5 c$

Solution:

$$\log\left(\frac{\sqrt{x+y}}{10}\right)$$

$= \log(\sqrt{x+y}) - \log 10$ — Quotient property for logarithms (property 6)

$= \log(x+y)^{1/2} - 1$ — Write $\sqrt{x+y}$ as $(x+y)^{1/2}$ and simplify $\log 10 = 1$.

$= \frac{1}{2}\log(x+y) - 1$ — Power property for logarithms (property 7)

Skill Practice Write the expression as the sum or difference of logarithms of a and b. Assume $a > b$.

5. $\log \dfrac{(a-b)^2}{\sqrt{10}}$

Example 4 Writing a Logarithmic Expression in Expanded Form

Write the expression as the sum or difference of logarithms of x, y, and z. Assume all variables represent positive real numbers.

$$\log_b \sqrt[5]{\frac{x^4}{yz^3}}$$

Solution:

$$\log_b \sqrt[5]{\frac{x^4}{yz^3}}$$

$= \log_b\left(\frac{x^4}{yz^3}\right)^{1/5}$ — Write $\sqrt[5]{\frac{x^4}{yz^3}}$ as $\left(\frac{x^4}{yz^3}\right)^{1/5}$.

$= \frac{1}{5}\log_b\left(\frac{x^4}{yz^3}\right)$ — Power property for logarithms (property 7)

$= \frac{1}{5}[\log_b x^4 - \log_b (yz^3)]$ — Quotient property for logarithms (property 6)

$= \frac{1}{5}[\log_b x^4 - (\log_b y + \log_b z^3)]$ — Product property for logarithms (property 5)

$= \frac{1}{5}[\log_b x^4 - \log_b y - \log_b z^3]$ — Distributive property

$= \frac{1}{5}[4\log_b x - \log_b y - 3\log_b z]$ — Power property for logarithms (property 7)

or $\frac{4}{5}\log_b x - \frac{1}{5}\log_b y - \frac{3}{5}\log_b z$

Skill Practice Write the expression as the sum or difference of logarithms of a, b, and c. Assume all variables represent positive real numbers.

6. $\log_3 \sqrt[4]{\dfrac{a}{bc^5}}$

Answers

5. $2\log(a-b) - \frac{1}{2}$

6. $\frac{1}{4}\log_3 a - \frac{1}{4}\log_3 b - \frac{5}{4}\log_3 c$

3. Single Logarithmic Expressions

In some applications, it is necessary to write a sum or difference of logarithms as a single logarithm.

Example 5 Writing a Sum or Difference of Logarithms as a Single Logarithm

Rewrite the expression as a single logarithm, and simplify the result, if possible.

$$\log_2 560 - \log_2 7 - \log_2 5$$

Solution:

$\log_2 560 - \log_2 7 - \log_2 5$

$= \log_2 560 - (\log_2 7 + \log_2 5)$	Factor out -1 from the last two terms.
$= \log_2 560 - \log_2 (7 \cdot 5)$	Product property for logarithms (property 5)
$= \log_2\left(\dfrac{560}{7 \cdot 5}\right)$	Quotient property for logarithms (property 6)
$= \log_2 16$	Simplify inside parentheses.
$= \log_2 2^4$	Write 16 in base 2: 2^4
$= 4$	Property 3

Skill Practice Write the expression as a single logarithm, and simplify the result, if possible.

7. $\log_3 54 + \log_3 10 - \log_3 20$

Example 6 Writing a Sum or Difference of Logarithms as a Single Logarithm

Rewrite the expression as a single logarithm, and simplify the result, if possible. Assume all variable expressions within the logarithms represent positive real numbers.

$$2 \log x - \frac{1}{2} \log y + 3 \log z$$

Solution:

$2 \log x - \dfrac{1}{2} \log y + 3 \log z$

$= \log x^2 - \log y^{1/2} + \log z^3$	Power property for logarithms (property 7)
$= \log x^2 + \log z^3 - \log y^{1/2}$	Group terms with positive coefficients.
$= \log (x^2z^3) - \log y^{1/2}$	Product property for logarithms (property 5)
$= \log\left(\dfrac{x^2z^3}{y^{1/2}}\right)$ or $\log\left(\dfrac{x^2z^3}{\sqrt{y}}\right)$	Quotient property for logarithms (property 6)

Skill Practice Write the expression as a single logarithm, and simplify, if possible.

8. $3 \log x + \dfrac{1}{3} \log y - 2 \log z$

Answers

7. 3 **8.** $\log\left(\dfrac{x^3\sqrt[3]{y}}{z^2}\right)$

It is important to note that the properties of logarithms may be used to write a single logarithm as a sum or difference of logarithms. Furthermore, the properties may be used to write a sum or difference of logarithms as a single logarithm. In either case, these operations may change the domain.

For example, consider the function $y = \log_b x^2$. Using the power property for logarithms, we have $y = 2\log_b x$. Consider the domain of each function:

$y = \log_b x^2$ Domain: $(-\infty, 0) \cup (0, \infty)$

$y = 2\log_b x$ Domain: $(0, \infty)$

These two functions are equivalent only for values of x in the intersection of the two domains, that is, for $(0, \infty)$.

Section 12.4 Practice Exercises

Vocabulary and Key Concepts

1. a. Fill in the blanks to complete the basic properties of logarithms.
$\log_b b =$ _______, $\log_b 1 =$ _______, $\log_b b^x =$ _______, and $b^{\log_b x} =$ _______.

b. If b, x, and y are positive real numbers and $b \neq 1$, then $\log_b(xy) =$ _______ and $\log_b\left(\frac{x}{y}\right) =$ _______.

c. If b and x are positive real numbers and $b \neq 1$, then for any real number p, $\log_b x^p$ can be written as _______.

d. Determine if the statement is true or false: $\log_b(xy) = (\log_b x)(\log_b y)$
Use the expression $\log_2 (4 \cdot 8)$ to help you answer.

e. Determine if the statement is true or false: $\log_b\left(\frac{x}{y}\right) = \frac{\log_b x}{\log_b y}$
Use the expression $\log_3\left(\frac{27}{9}\right)$ to help you answer.

f. Determine if the statement is true or false: $\log_b (x)^p = (\log_b x)^p$
Use the expression $\log(1000)^2$ to help you answer.

Review Exercises

For Exercises 2–5, find the values of the logarithmic and exponential expressions without using a calculator.

2. 8^{-2} **3.** $\log 10{,}000$ **4.** $\log_2 32$ **5.** 6^{-1}

For Exercises 6–9, approximate the values of the logarithmic and exponential expressions by using a calculator. Round to four decimal places.

6. $(\sqrt{2})^{\pi}$ **7.** $\log 8$ **8.** $\log 27$ **9.** $\pi^{\sqrt{2}}$

For Exercises 10–13, match the function with the appropriate graph.

10. $f(x) = 4^x$ **11.** $q(x) = \left(\frac{1}{5}\right)^x$ **12.** $h(x) = \log_5 x$ **13.** $k(x) = \log_{1/3} x$

a.

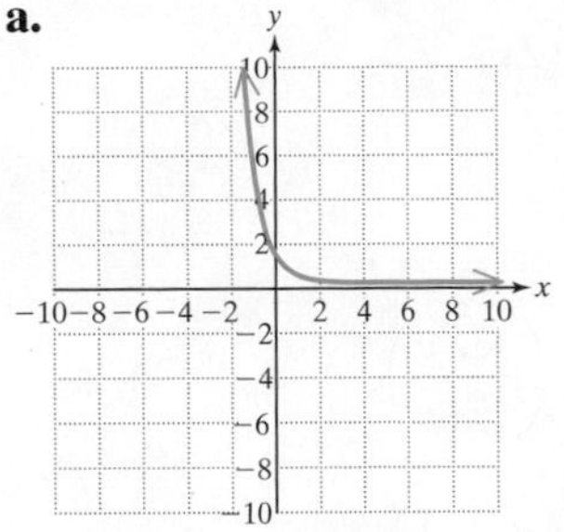

b.

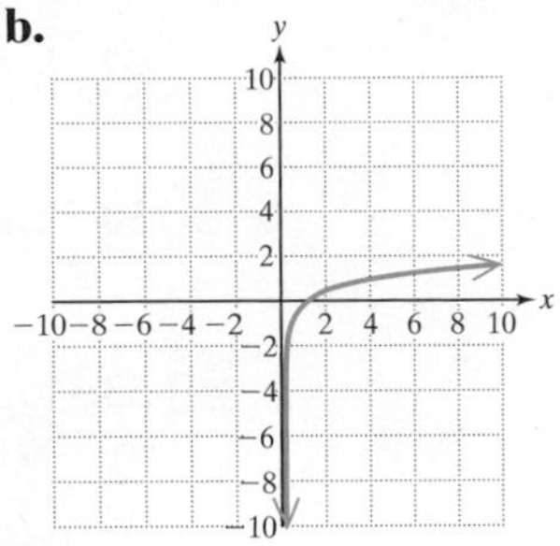

c.

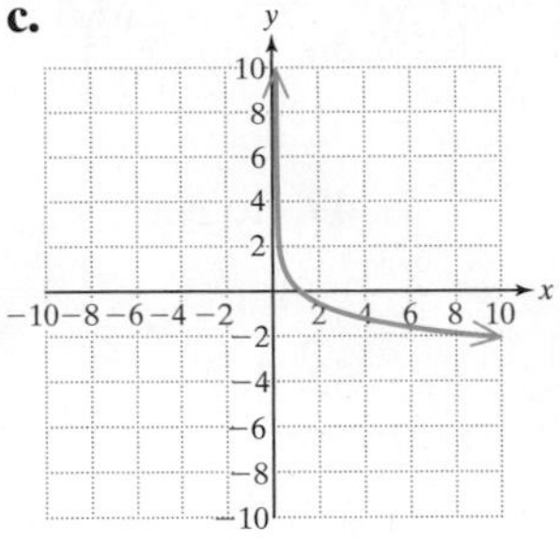

d.

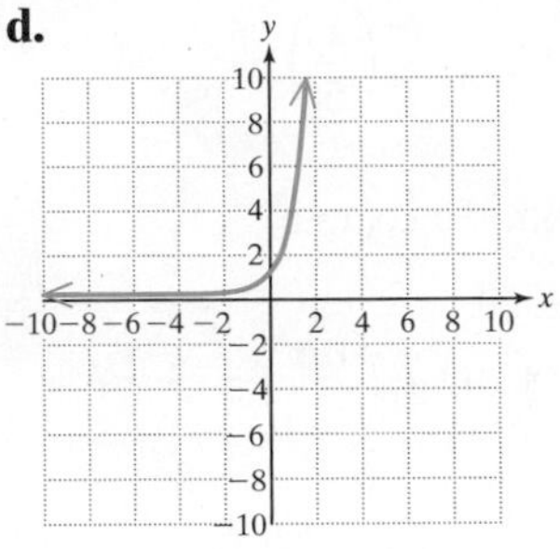

Concept 1: Properties of Logarithms

14. Select the values that are equivalent to $\log_5 5^2$.

a. $\log_5 25$

b. $2 \log_5 5$

c. $\log_5 5 + \log_5 5$

15. Select the values that are equivalent to $\log_2 2^3$.

a. $3 \log_2 2$

b. $\log_2 8$

c. 3

16. Select the values that are equivalent to $\log 10^4$.

a. 4

b. $4 \log 10$

c. $\log 10{,}000$

For Exercises 17–40, evaluate each expression. **(See Example 1.)**

17. $\log_3 3$ **18.** $\log 10$ **19.** $\log_5 5^4$ **20.** $\log_4 4^5$

21. $6^{\log_6 11}$ **22.** $7^{\log_7 2}$ **23.** $\log 10^3$ **24.** $\log_6 6^3$

25. $\log_3 1$ **26.** $\log_8 1$ **27.** $10^{\log 9}$ **28.** $8^{\log_8 5}$

29. $\log_{1/2} 1$ **30.** $\log_{1/3}\left(\frac{1}{3}\right)$ **31.** $\log_2 1 + \log_2 2^3$ **32.** $\log 10^4 + \log 10$

33. $\log_4 4 + \log_2 1$ **34.** $\log_7 7 + \log_4 4^2$ **35.** $\log_{1/4}\left(\frac{1}{4}\right)^{2x}$ **36.** $\log_{2/3}\left(\frac{2}{3}\right)^p$

37. $\log_a a^4$ **38.** $\log_y y^2$ **39.** $\log 10^2 - \log_3 3^2$ **40.** $\log_6 6^4 - \log 10^4$

41. Compare the expressions by approximating their values on a calculator. Which two expressions are equivalent?

a. $\log (3 \cdot 5)$ **b.** $\log 3 \cdot \log 5$ **c.** $\log 3 + \log 5$

42. Compare the expressions by approximating their values on a calculator. Which two expressions are equivalent?

a. $\log\left(\frac{6}{5}\right)$ **b.** $\frac{\log 6}{\log 5}$ **c.** $\log 6 - \log 5$

43. Compare the expressions by approximating their values on a calculator. Which two expressions are equivalent?

a. $\log 20^2$ **b.** $[\log 20]^2$ **c.** $2 \log 20$

44. Compare the expressions by approximating their values on a calculator. Which two expressions are equivalent?

a. $\log \sqrt{4}$ **b.** $\frac{1}{2}\log 4$ **c.** $\sqrt{\log 4}$

Concept 2: Expanded Logarithmic Expressions

For Exercises 45–62, expand into sums and/or differences of logarithms. Assume all variables represent positive real numbers. **(See Examples 2–4.)**

45. $\log_3\left(\frac{x}{5}\right)$

46. $\log_2\left(\frac{y}{z}\right)$

47. $\log(2x)$

48. $\log_6(xyz)$

49. $\log_5 x^4$

50. $\log_7 z^{1/3}$

51. $\log_4\left(\frac{ab}{c}\right)$

52. $\log_2\left(\frac{x}{yz}\right)$

53. $\log_b\left(\frac{\sqrt{xy}}{z^3w}\right)$

54. $\log\left(\frac{a\sqrt[3]{b}}{cd^2}\right)$

55. $\log_2\left(\frac{x+1}{y^2\sqrt{z}}\right)$

56. $\log\left(\frac{a+1}{b\sqrt[3]{c}}\right)$

57. $\log\left(\sqrt[3]{\frac{ab^2}{c}}\right)$

58. $\log_5\left(\sqrt[4]{\frac{w^3z}{x^2}}\right)$

59. $\log\left(\frac{1}{w^5}\right)$

60. $\log_3\left(\frac{1}{z^4}\right)$

61. $\log_b\left(\frac{\sqrt{a}}{b^3c}\right)$

62. $\log_x\left(\frac{x}{y\sqrt{z}}\right)$

Concept 3: Single Logarithmic Expressions

For Exercises 63–78, write the expressions as a single logarithm and simplify if possible. Assume all variable expressions represent positive real numbers. **(See Examples 5–6.)**

63. $\log_3 270 - \log_3 2 - \log_3 5$

64. $\log_5 8 + \log_5 50 - \log_5 16$

65. $\log_7 98 - \log_7 2$

66. $\log_6 24 - \log_6 4$

67. $2\log_3 x - 3\log_3 y + \log_3 z$

68. $\log C + \log A + \log B + \log I + \log N$

69. $2\log_3 a - \frac{1}{4}\log_3 b + \log_3 c$

70. $\log_5 a - \frac{1}{2}\log_5 b - 3\log_5 c$

71. $\log_b x - 3\log_b x + 4\log_b x$

72. $2\log_3 z + \log_3 z - \frac{1}{2}\log_3 z$

73. $5\log_8 a - \log_8 1 + \log_8 8$

74. $\log_2 2 + 2\log_2 b - \log_2 1$

75. $2\log(x+6) + \frac{1}{3}\log y - 5\log z$

76. $\frac{1}{4}\log(a+1) - 2\log b - 4\log c$

77. $\log_b(x+1) - \log_b(x^2-1)$

78. $\log_x(p^2-4) - \log_x(p-2)$

Expanding Your Skills

For Exercises 79–90, find the values of the logarithms given that $\log_b 2 \approx 0.693$, $\log_b 3 \approx 1.099$, and $\log_b 5 \approx 1.609$.

79. $\log_b 6$

80. $\log_b 4$

81. $\log_b 12$

82. $\log_b 25$

83. $\log_b 81$

84. $\log_b 30$

85. $\log_b\left(\frac{5}{2}\right)$

86. $\log_b\left(\frac{25}{3}\right)$

87. $\log_b 10^6$

88. $\log_b 15^3$

89. $\log_b 5^{10}$

90. $\log_b 2^{12}$

91. The intensity of sound waves is measured in decibels and is calculated by the formula

$$B = 10 \log \left(\frac{I}{I_0}\right)$$

where I_0 is the minimum detectable decibel level.

a. Expand this formula by using the properties of logarithms.

b. Let $I_0 = 10^{-16}$ W/cm^2 and simplify.

92. The Richter scale is used to measure the intensity of an earthquake and is calculated by the formula

$$R = \log \left(\frac{I}{I_0}\right)$$

where I_0 is the minimum level detectable by a seismograph.

a. Expand this formula by using the properties of logarithms.

b. Let $I_0 = 1$ and simplify.

Graphing Calculator Exercises

93. a. Graph $Y_1 = \log x^2$ and state its domain.

b. Graph $Y_2 = 2 \log x$ and state its domain.

c. For what values of x are the expressions $\log x^2$ and $2 \log x$ equivalent?

94. a. Graph $Y_1 = \log (x - 1)^2$ and state its domain.

b. Graph $Y_2 = 2 \log (x - 1)$ and state its domain.

c. For what values of x are the expressions $\log (x - 1)^2$ and $2 \log (x - 1)$ equivalent?

The Irrational Number e and Change of Base

Section 12.5

Concepts

1. The Irrational Number *e*
2. Computing Compound Interest
3. The Natural Logarithmic Function
4. Change-of-Base Formula
5. Applications of the Natural Logarithmic Function

1. The Irrational Number e

The exponential function base 10 is particularly easy to work with because integral powers of 10 represent different place positions in the base-10 numbering system. In this section, we introduce another important exponential function whose base is an irrational number called *e*.

Consider the expression $(1 + \frac{1}{x})^x$. The value of the expression for increasingly large values of x approaches a constant (Table 12-5).

Table 12-5

x	$\left(1 + \frac{1}{x}\right)^x$
100	2.70481382942
1000	2.71692393224
10,000	2.71814592683
100,000	2.71826823717
1,000,000	2.71828046932
1,000,000,000	2.71828182710

As x approaches infinity, the expression $(1 + \frac{1}{x})^x$ approaches a constant value that we call ***e***. From Table 12-5, this value is approximately 2.718281828.

$$e \approx 2.718281828$$

The value of e is an irrational number (a nonterminating, nonrepeating decimal) and like the number π, it is a universal constant.

Example 1 Graphing $f(x) = e^x$

Graph the function defined by $f(x) = e^x$.

Solution:

Because the base of the function is greater than 1 ($e \approx 2.718281828$), the graph is an increasing exponential function. We can use a calculator to evaluate $f(x) = e^x$ at several values of x.

TIP: On a scientific calculator, you may need to enter the base and exponent of an exponential expression in reverse order. For example, enter e^2 as:

2 [2nd] [LN]

Calculator Connections

Topic: Evaluating Exponential Expressions Base *e*

Practice using your calculator by evaluating e^x for $x = 1, x = 2$, and $x = -1$.

```
e^(1)
          2.718281828
e^(2)
          7.389056099
e^(-1)
          .3678794412
```

If you are using your calculator correctly, your answers should match those found in Table 12-6. Values are rounded to three decimal places. The corresponding graph of $f(x) = e^x$ is shown in Figure 12-14.

Table 12-6

x	$f(x) = e^x$
−3	0.050
−2	0.135
−1	0.368
0	1.000
1	2.718
2	7.389
3	20.086

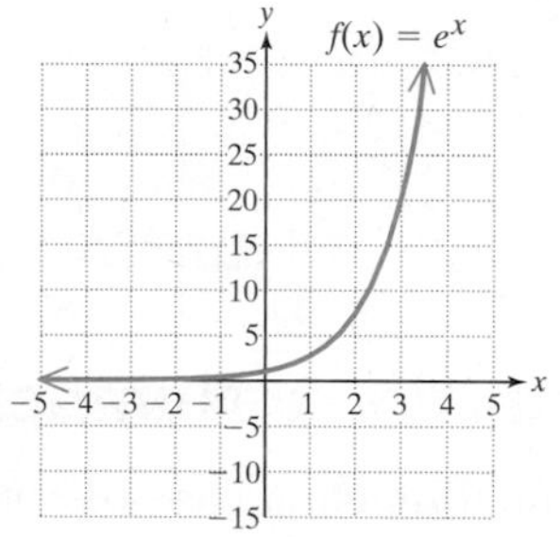

Figure 12-14

Skill Practice

1. Graph $f(x) = e^x + 1$.

2. Computing Compound Interest

One particularly interesting application of exponential functions is in computing compound interest.

1. If the number of compounding periods per year is finite, then the amount in an account is given by

$$A(t) = P\left(1 + \frac{r}{n}\right)^{nt}$$

where P is the initial principal, r is the annual interest rate, n is the number of times compounded per year, and t is the time in years that the money is invested.

Answer

1.

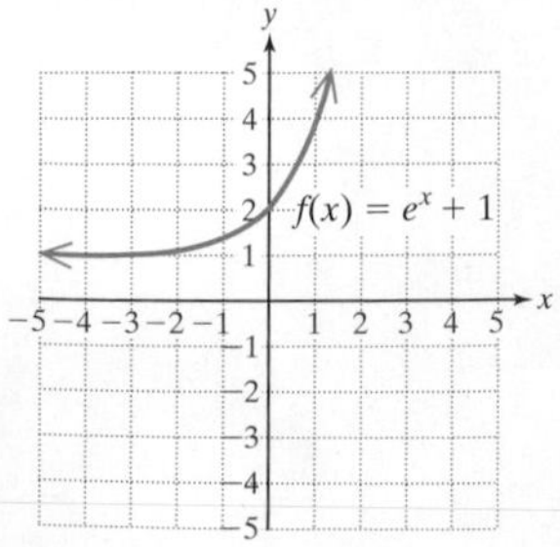

2. If the number of compound periods per year is infinite, then interest is said to be **compounded continuously**. In such a case, the amount in an account is given by

$$A(t) = Pe^{rt}$$

where P is the initial principal, r is the annual interest rate, and t is the time in years that the money is invested.

Example 2 Computing the Balance on an Account

Suppose \$5000 is invested in an account earning 6.5% interest. Find the balance in the account after 10 yr under the following compounding options.

a. Compounded annually **b.** Compounded quarterly

c. Compounded monthly **d.** Compounded daily

e. Compounded continuously

Solution:

Compounding Option	n Value	Formula	Result
Annually	$n = 1$	$A(10) = 5000\left(1 + \frac{0.065}{1}\right)^{(1)(10)}$	\$9385.69
Quarterly	$n = 4$	$A(10) = 5000\left(1 + \frac{0.065}{4}\right)^{(4)(10)}$	\$9527.79
Monthly	$n = 12$	$A(10) = 5000\left(1 + \frac{0.065}{12}\right)^{(12)(10)}$	\$9560.92
Daily	$n = 365$	$A(10) = 5000\left(1 + \frac{0.065}{365}\right)^{(365)(10)}$	\$9577.15
Continuously	Not applicable	$A(10) = 5000e^{(0.065)(10)}$	\$9577.70

Notice that there is a \$191.46 difference in the account balance between annual compounding and daily compounding. However, the difference between compounding daily and compounding continuously is small—\$0.55. As n gets infinitely large, the function defined by

$$A(t) = P\left(1 + \frac{r}{n}\right)^{nt} \quad \text{converges to } A(t) = Pe^{rt}.$$

Skill Practice

2. Suppose \$1000 is invested at 5%. Find the balance after 8 yr under the following options.

a. Compounded annually **b.** Compounded quarterly

c. Compounded monthly **d.** Compounded daily

e. Compounded continuously

3. The Natural Logarithmic Function

Recall that the common logarithmic function $y = \log x$ has a base of 10. Another important logarithmic function is called the **natural logarithmic function**. The natural logarithmic function has a base of e and is written as $y = \ln x$. That is,

$$y = \ln x = \log_e x$$

Answer

2. a. \$1477.46 **b.** \$1488.13
c. \$1490.59 **d.** \$1491.78
e. \$1491.82

TIP: On a scientific calculator, you may need to enter a logarithm and argument in reverse order. For example, enter ln 2 as

2 [LN]

Calculator Connections

Topic: Evaluating Natural Logarithms

```
ln(1)
                0
ln(2)
     .6931471806
ln(3)
     1.098612289
```

Example 3 Graphing $y = \ln x$

Graph $y = \ln x$.

Solution:

Because the base of the function $y = \ln x$ is e and $e > 1$, the graph is an increasing logarithmic function. We can use a calculator to find specific points on the graph of $y = \ln x$ by pressing the [LN] key.

Practice using your calculator by evaluating $\ln x$ for the following values of x. If you are using your calculator correctly, your answers should match those found in Table 12-7. Values are rounded to three decimal places. The corresponding graph of $y = \ln x$ is shown in Figure 12-15.

Table 12-7

x	$\ln x$
0.25	−1.386
0.5	−0.693
1	0.000
2	0.693
3	1.099
4	1.386
5	1.609
6	1.792
7	1.946

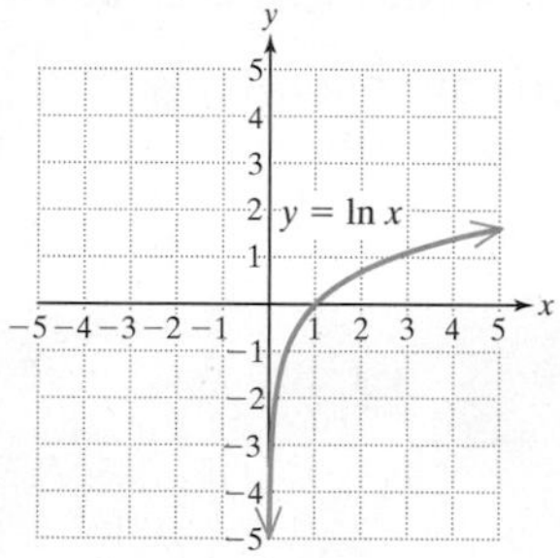

Figure 12-15

Skill Practice

3. Graph $y = \ln x + 1$.

The properties of logarithms stated in Section 12.4 are also true for natural logarithms.

Properties of the Natural Logarithmic Function

Let x and y be positive real numbers, and let p be a real number. Then the following properties are true.

1. $\ln 1 = 0$
2. $\ln e = 1$
3. $\ln e^p = p$
4. $e^{\ln x} = x$
5. $\ln(xy) = \ln x + \ln y$ **Product property for logarithms**
6. $\ln\left(\frac{x}{y}\right) = \ln x - \ln y$ **Quotient property for logarithms**
7. $\ln x^p = p \ln x$ **Power property for logarithms**

Answer

3.

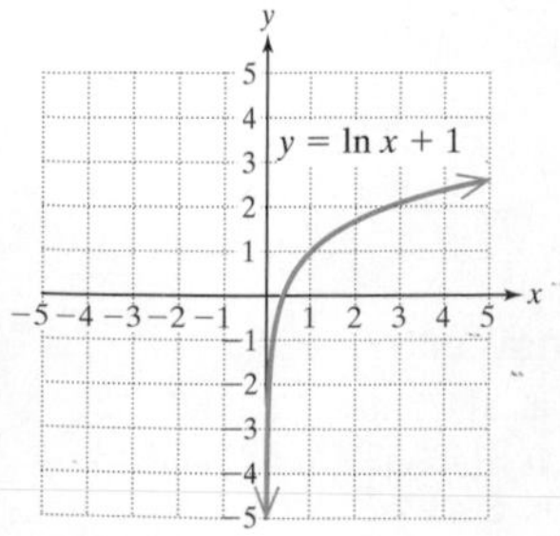

Example 4 **Simplifying Expressions with Natural Logarithms**

Simplify the expressions. Assume that all variable expressions within the logarithms represent positive real numbers.

a. $\ln e$ **b.** $\ln 1$ **c.** $\ln (e^{x+1})$ **d.** $e^{\ln (x+1)}$

Solution:

a. $\ln e = 1$ Property 2

b. $\ln 1 = 0$ Property 1

c. $\ln (e^{x+1}) = x + 1$ Property 3

d. $e^{\ln (x+1)} = x + 1$ Property 4

Skill Practice Simplify.

4. $\ln e^2$ **5.** $-3 \ln 1$ **6.** $\ln e^{(x+y)}$ **7.** $e^{\ln (3x)}$

Example 5 **Writing a Sum or Difference of Natural Logarithms as a Single Logarithm**

Write the expression as a single logarithm. Assume that all variable expressions within the logarithms represent positive real numbers.

$$\ln x - \frac{1}{3}\ln y - \ln z$$

Solution:

$\ln x - \frac{1}{3}\ln y - \ln z$

$= \ln x - \ln y^{1/3} - \ln z$ Power property for logarithms (property 7)

$= \ln x - (\ln y^{1/3} + \ln z)$ Factor out -1 from the last two terms.

$= \ln x - \ln (y^{1/3} \cdot z)$ Product property for logarithms (property 5)

$= \ln\left(\frac{x}{y^{1/3}z}\right)$ Quotient property for logarithms (property 6)

$= \ln\left(\frac{x}{\sqrt[3]{y}\, z}\right)$ Write the rational exponent as a radical.

Skill Practice Write as a single logarithm.

8. $\frac{1}{4}\ln a - \ln b + \ln c$

Answers

4. 2 **5.** 0 **6.** $x + y$

7. $3x$ **8.** $\ln\left(\frac{\sqrt[4]{a}\, c}{b}\right)$

Example 6 **Writing a Logarithmic Expression in Expanded Form**

Write the expression as a sum or difference of logarithms of x and y. Assume all variable expressions within the logarithm represent positive real numbers.

$$\ln\left(\frac{e}{x^2\sqrt{y}}\right)$$

Solution:

$\ln\left(\dfrac{e}{x^2\sqrt{y}}\right)$

$= \ln e - \ln (x^2\sqrt{y})$	Quotient property for logarithms (property 6)
$= \ln e - (\ln x^2 + \ln \sqrt{y})$	Product property for logarithms (property 5)
$= 1 - \ln x^2 - \ln y^{1/2}$	Distributive property. Also simplify $\ln e = 1$ (property 2).
$= 1 - 2\ln x - \dfrac{1}{2}\ln y$	Power property for logarithms (property 7)

Skill Practice Write as a sum or difference of logarithms of x and y.

9. $\ln\left(\dfrac{x^3\sqrt{y}}{e^2}\right)$

4. Change-of-Base Formula

A calculator can be used to approximate the value of a logarithm with a base of 10 or a base of e by using the LOG key or the LN key, respectively. However, to use a calculator to evaluate a logarithmic expression with a base other than 10 or e, we must use the **change-of-base formula**.

Change-of-Base Formula

Let a and b be positive real numbers such that $a \neq 1$ and $b \neq 1$. Then for any positive real number x,

$$\log_b x = \frac{\log_a x}{\log_a b}$$

Proof:

Let $M = \log_b x$, which implies that $b^M = x$.

Take the logarithm, base a, on both sides:	$\log_a b^M = \log_a x$
Apply the power property for logarithms:	$M \cdot \log_a b = \log_a x$
Divide both sides by $\log_a b$:	$\dfrac{M \cdot \cancel{\log_a b}}{\cancel{\log_a b}} = \dfrac{\log_a x}{\log_a b}$
	$M = \dfrac{\log_a x}{\log_a b}$
Because $M = \log_b x$, we have	$\log_b x = \dfrac{\log_a x}{\log_a b}$ ✔

Answer

9. $3\ln x + \dfrac{1}{2}\ln y - 2$

The change-of-base formula converts a logarithm of one base to a ratio of logarithms of a different base. For the sake of using a calculator, we often apply the change-of-base formula with base 10 or base e.

Example 7 Using the Change-of-Base Formula

a. Use the change-of-base formula to evaluate $\log_4 80$ by using base 10. (Round to three decimal places.)

b. Use the change-of-base formula to evaluate $\log_4 80$ by using base e. (Round to three decimal places.)

Solution:

a. $\log_4 80 = \dfrac{\log_{10} 80}{\log_{10} 4} = \dfrac{\log 80}{\log 4} \approx \dfrac{1.903089987}{0.6020599913} \approx 3.161$

b. $\log_4 80 = \dfrac{\log_e 80}{\log_e 4} = \dfrac{\ln 80}{\ln 4} \approx \dfrac{4.382026635}{1.386294361} \approx 3.161$

To check the result, we see that $4^{3.161} \approx 80$.

Skill Practice

10. Use the change-of-base formula to evaluate $\log_5 95$ by using base 10. Round to three decimal places.

11. Use the change-of-base formula to evaluate $\log_5 95$ by using base e. Round to three decimal places.

Calculator Connections

Topic: Applying the Change-of-Base Formula

Use the change-of-base formula to evaluate $\log_4 80$.

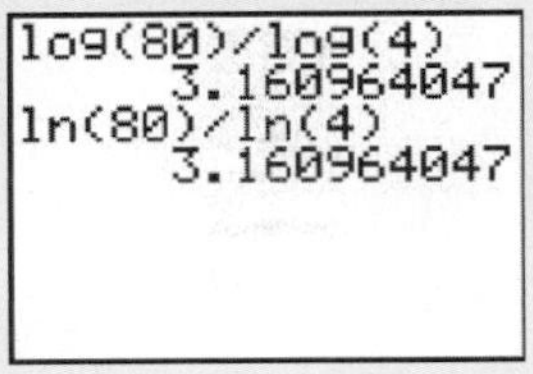

Calculator Connections

Topic: Using the Change-of-Base Formula to Graph Logarithmic Functions

The change-of-base formula can be used to graph logarithmic functions with bases other than 10 or e. For example, to graph $Y_1 = \log_2 x$, we can enter the function as either

$$Y_1 = (\log x)/(\log 2) \quad \text{or} \quad Y_1 = (\ln x)/(\ln 2)$$

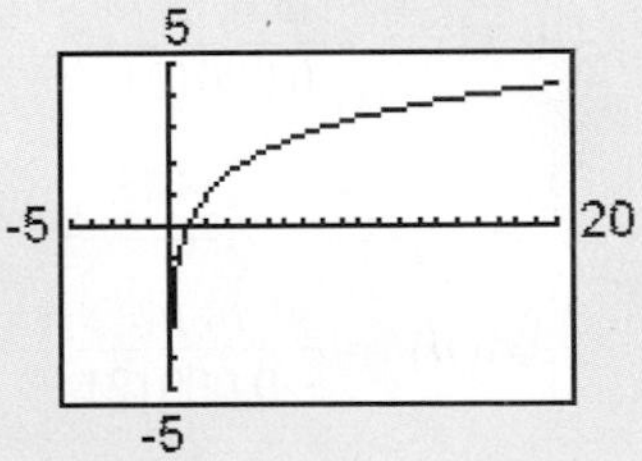

5. Applications of the Natural Logarithmic Function

Plant and animal tissue contains both carbon 12 and carbon 14. Carbon 12 is a stable form of carbon, whereas carbon 14 is a radioactive isotope with a half-life of approximately 5730 years. While a plant or animal is living, it takes in carbon from the atmosphere either through photosynthesis or through its food. The ratio of carbon 14 to carbon 12 in a living organism is constant and is the same as the ratio found in the atmosphere.

Answers

10. 2.829 **11.** 2.829

When a plant or animal dies, it no longer ingests carbon from the atmosphere. The amount of stable carbon 12 remains unchanged from the time of death, but the carbon 14 begins to decay. Because the rate of decay is constant, a tissue sample can be dated by comparing the percent of carbon 14 still present to the percentage of carbon 14 assumed to be in its original living state.

The age of a tissue sample is a function of the percent of carbon 14 still present in the organism according to the following model:

$$A(p) = \frac{\ln p}{-0.000121}$$

where $A(p)$ is the age in years and p is the percentage (in decimal form) of carbon 14 still present.

Example 8 Applying the Natural Logarithmic Function to Radioactive Decay

Using the formula

$$A(p) = \frac{\ln p}{-0.000121}$$

a. Find the age of a bone that has 72% of its initial carbon 14.

b. Find the age of the Iceman, a body uncovered in the mountains of northern Italy in 1991. Samples of his hair revealed that 52.7% of the original carbon 14 was present after his death.

Solution:

a. $A(p) = \dfrac{\ln p}{-0.000121}$

$A(0.72) = \dfrac{\ln 0.72}{-0.000121}$ Substitute 0.72 for p.

≈ 2715 years

b. $A(p) = \dfrac{\ln p}{-0.000121}$

$A(0.527) = \dfrac{\ln 0.527}{-0.000121}$ Substitute 0.527 for p.

≈ 5300 years The body of the Iceman is approximately 5300 yr old.

Skill Practice

12. Use the formula

$$A(p) = \frac{\ln p}{-0.000121}$$

(where $A(p)$ is the age in years and p is the percent of carbon 14 still present) to determine the age of a human skull that has 90% of its initial carbon 14.

Answer

12. ≈ 871 yr

Section 12.5 Practice Exercises

Vocabulary and Key Concepts

1. a. As x becomes increasingly large, the value of $(1 + \frac{1}{x})^x$ approaches ____________ ≈ 2.71828.

b. The function $f(x) = e^x$ is the exponential function base ____________.

c. The logarithmic function base e is called the __________ logarithmic function and is denoted by $y =$ ________.

d. If x is a positive real number, then $\ln 1 =$ ______, $\ln e =$ ______, $\ln e^p =$ ______, and $e^{\ln x} =$ ______.

e. If x and y are positive real numbers, then $\ln(xy) =$ __________ and $\ln\left(\frac{x}{y}\right) =$ __________.

f. If x is a positive real number, then for any real number p, $\ln x^p$ can be written as ____________.

g. The change-of-base formula states that $\log_b x = \frac{\log_a x}{\square}$, where a is a positive real number and $a \neq 1$.

Review Exercises

For Exercises 2–3, write the expression as a single logarithm. Assume that all variables represent positive real numbers.

2. $\log_5 x + 3 \log_5 y - \log_5 z$

3. $\log_3 a - 5 \log_3 c + \frac{1}{2} \log_3 d$

For Exercises 4–5, write the expression as the sum or difference of logarithms of x, y, and z. Assume that all variables represent positive real numbers.

4. $\log\left(\frac{\sqrt{x}}{yz^4}\right)$

5. $\log_6 \sqrt[4]{\frac{xy^2}{z^3}}$

Concept 1: The Irrational Number *e*

6. From memory, write a decimal approximation of the number e, correct to three decimal places.

For Exercises 7–10, graph the equation by completing the table and plotting points. Identify the domain. Round to two decimal places when necessary. **(See Example 1.)**

7. $y = e^{x+1}$

x	y
−4	
−3	
−2	
−1	
0	
1	

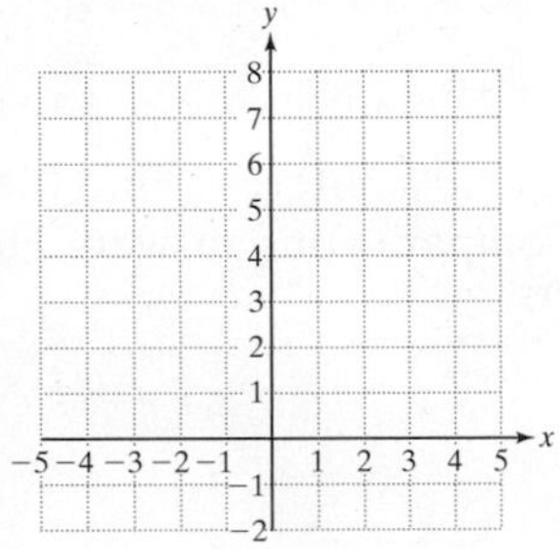

8. $y = e^{x+2}$

x	y
−5	
−4	
−3	
−2	
−1	
0	

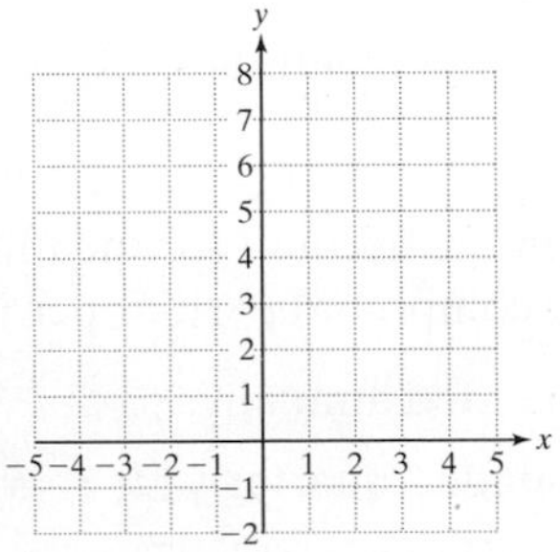

9. $y = e^x + 2$

x	y
−2	
−1	
0	
1	
2	
3	

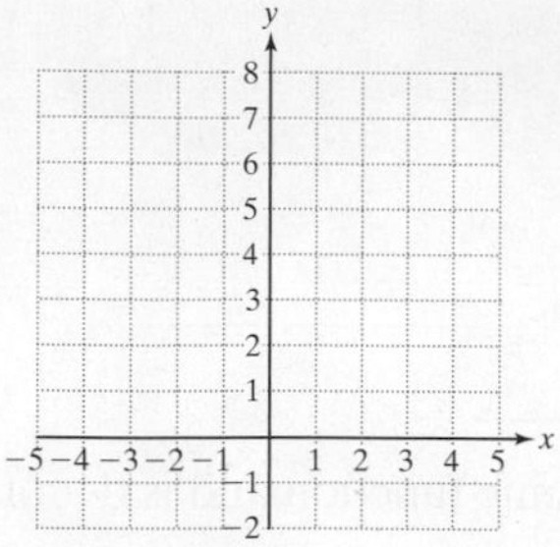

10. $y = e^x - 1$

x	y
−4	
−3	
−2	
−1	
0	
1	

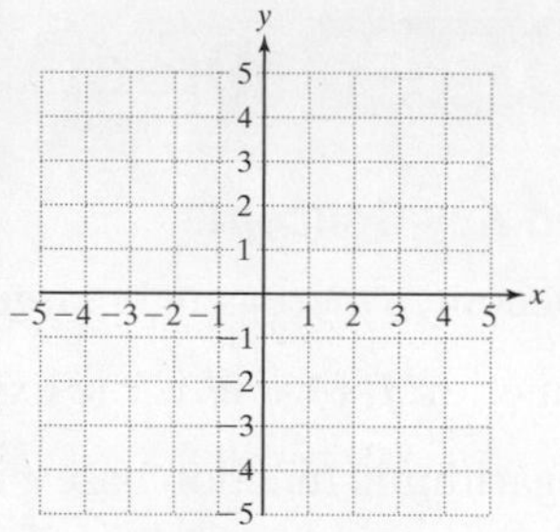

Concept 2: Computing Compound Interest

In Exercises 11–16, use the model

$$A(t) = P\left(1 + \frac{r}{n}\right)^{nt}$$

for interest compounded n times per year. Use the model $A(t) = Pe^{rt}$ for interest compounded continuously.

11. Suppose an investor deposits \$10,000 in a certificate of deposit for 5 yr for which the interest is compounded monthly. Find the total amount of money in the account for the following interest rates. Compare your answers and comment on the effect of interest rate on an investment. **(See Example 2.)**

a. $r = 4.0\%$ **b.** $r = 6.0\%$ **c.** $r = 8.0\%$ **d.** $r = 9.5\%$

12. Suppose an investor deposits \$5000 in a certificate of deposit for 8 yr for which the interest is compounded quarterly. Find the total amount of money in the account for the following interest rates. Compare your answers and comment on the effect of interest rate on an investment.

a. $r = 4.5\%$ **b.** $r = 5.5\%$ **c.** $r = 7.0\%$ **d.** $r = 9.0\%$

13. Suppose an investor deposits \$8000 in a savings account for 10 yr at 4.5% interest. Find the total amount of money in the account for the following compounding options. Compare your answers. How does the number of compound periods per year affect the total investment?

a. Compounded annually
b. Compounded quarterly
c. Compounded monthly
d. Compounded daily
e. Compounded continuously

14. Suppose an investor deposits \$15,000 in a savings account for 8 yr at 5.0% interest. Find the total amount of money in the account for the following compounding options. Compare your answers. How does the number of compound periods per year affect the total investment?

a. Compounded annually
b. Compounded quarterly
c. Compounded monthly
d. Compounded daily
e. Compounded continuously

15. Suppose an investor deposits \$5000 in an account earning 6.5% interest compounded continuously. Find the total amount in the account for the following time periods. How does the length of time affect the amount of interest earned?

a. 5 yr **b.** 10 yr **c.** 15 yr **d.** 20 yr **e.** 30 yr

16. Suppose an investor deposits \$10,000 in an account earning 6.0% interest compounded continuously. Find the total amount in the account for the following time periods. How does the length of time affect the amount of interest earned?

a. 5 yr **b.** 10 yr **c.** 15 yr **d.** 20 yr **e.** 30 yr

Concept 3: The Natural Logarithmic Function

For Exercises 17–20, graph the equation by completing the table and plotting the points. Identify the domain. Round to two decimal places when necessary. **(See Example 3.)**

17. $y = \ln(x - 2)$

x	y
2.25	
2.50	
2.75	
3	
4	
5	
6	

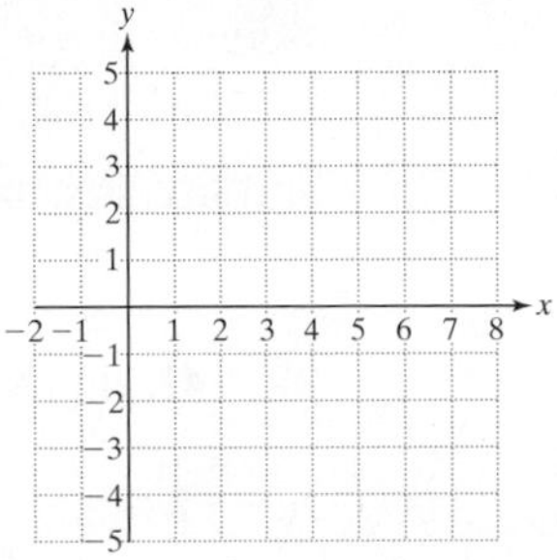

18. $y = \ln(x - 1)$

x	y
1.25	
1.50	
1.75	
2	
3	
4	
5	

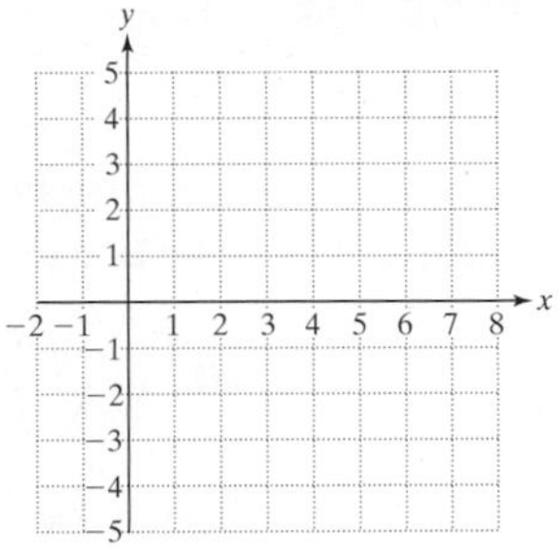

19. $y = \ln x - 1$

x	y
0.25	
0.5	
0.75	
1	
2	
3	
4	

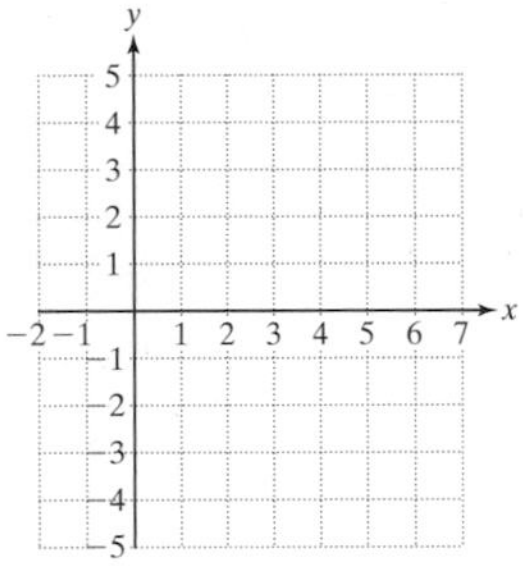

20. $y = \ln x + 2$

x	y
0.25	
0.5	
0.75	
1	
2	
3	
4	

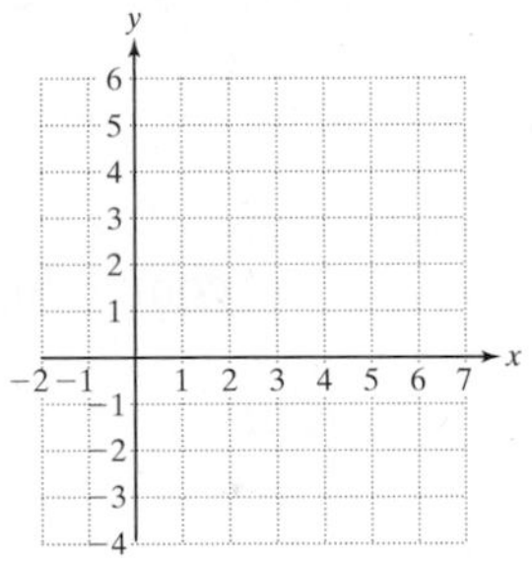

21. a. Graph $f(x) = 10^x$ and $g(x) = \log x$.

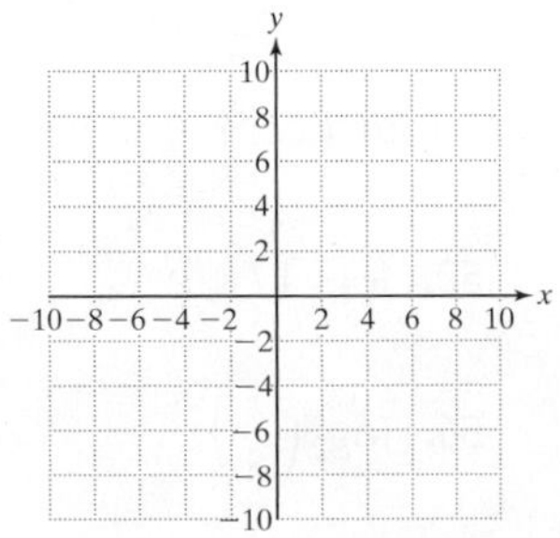

b. Identify the domain and range of *f*.

c. Identify the domain and range of *g*.

22. a. Graph $f(x) = e^x$ and $g(x) = \ln x$.

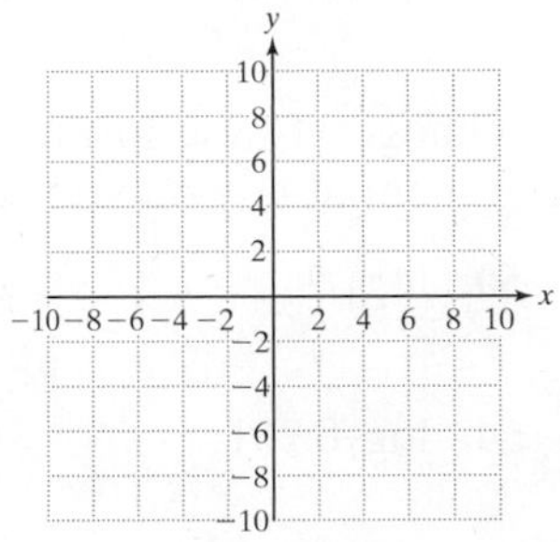

b. Identify the domain and range of *f*.

c. Identify the domain and range of *g*.

For Exercises 23–30, simplify the expressions. Assume all variables represent positive real numbers. **(See Example 4.)**

23. $\ln e$ **24.** $\ln e^2$ **25.** $\ln 1$ **26.** $e^{\ln x}$

27. $\ln e^{-6}$ **28.** $\ln e^{(5-3x)}$ **29.** $e^{\ln(2x+3)}$ **30.** $e^{\ln 4}$

For Exercises 31–38, write the expression as a single logarithm. Assume all variables represent positive real numbers. **(See Example 5.)**

31. $6 \ln p + \frac{1}{3} \ln q$

32. $2 \ln w + \ln z$

33. $\frac{1}{2}(\ln x - 3 \ln y)$

34. $\frac{1}{3}(4 \ln a - \ln b)$

35. $2 \ln a - \ln b - \frac{1}{3} \ln c$

36. $-\ln x + 3 \ln y - \ln z$

37. $4 \ln x - 3 \ln y - \ln z$

38. $\frac{1}{2} \ln c + \ln a - 2 \ln b$

For Exercises 39–46, write the expression as a sum and/or difference of ln a, ln b, and ln c. Assume all variables represent positive real numbers. **(See Example 6.)**

39. $\ln\left(\frac{a}{b}\right)^2$

40. $\ln \sqrt[3]{\frac{a}{b}}$

41. $\ln(b^2 \cdot e)$

42. $\ln(\sqrt{c} \cdot e)$

43. $\ln\left(\frac{a^4\sqrt{b}}{c}\right)$

44. $\ln\left(\frac{\sqrt{ab}}{c^3}\right)$

45. $\ln\left(\frac{ab}{c^2}\right)^{1/5}$

46. $\ln \sqrt{2ab}$

Concept 4: Change-of-Base Formula

47. **a.** Evaluate $\log_6 200$ by computing $\frac{\log 200}{\log 6}$ to four decimal places.

b. Evaluate $\log_6 200$ by computing $\frac{\ln 200}{\ln 6}$ to four decimal places.

c. How do your answers to parts (a) and (b) compare?

48. **a.** Evaluate $\log_8 120$ by computing $\frac{\log 120}{\log 8}$ to four decimal places.

b. Evaluate $\log_8 120$ by computing $\frac{\ln 120}{\ln 8}$ to four decimal places.

c. How do your answers to parts (a) and (b) compare?

For Exercises 49–60, use the change-of-base formula to approximate the logarithms to four decimal places. Check your answers by using the exponential key on your calculator. **(See Example 7.)**

49. $\log_2 7$

50. $\log_3 5$

51. $\log_8 24$

52. $\log_4 17$

53. $\log_8 0.012$

54. $\log_7 0.251$

55. $\log_9 1$

56. $\log_2\left(\frac{1}{5}\right)$

57. $\log_4\left(\frac{1}{100}\right)$

58. $\log_5 0.0025$

59. $\log_7 0.0006$

60. $\log_2 0.24$

Concept 5: Applications of the Natural Logarithmic Function

Under continuous compounding, the amount of time t in years required for an investment to double is a function of the interest rate r according to the formula:

$$t = \frac{\ln 2}{r}$$

Use the formula for Exercises 61–63. **(See Example 8.)**

61. **a.** If you invest \$5000, how long will it take the investment to reach \$10,000 if the interest rate is 4.5%? Round to one decimal place.

b. If you invest \$5000, how long will it take the investment to reach \$10,000 if the interest rate is 10%? Round to one decimal place.

c. Using the doubling time found in part (b), how long would it take a \$5000 investment to reach \$20,000 if the interest rate is 10%?

62. **a.** If you invest \$3000, how long will it take the investment to reach \$6000 if the interest rate is 5.5%? Round to one decimal place.

b. If you invest \$3000, how long will it take the investment to reach \$6000 if the interest rate is 8%? Round to one decimal place.

c. Using the doubling time found in part (b), how long would it take a \$3000 investment to reach \$12,000 if the interest rate is 8%?

63. **a.** If you invest \$4000, how long will it take the investment to reach \$8000 if the interest rate is 3.5%? Round to one decimal place.

b. If you invest \$4000, how long will it take the investment to reach \$8000 if the interest rate is 5%? Round to one decimal place.

c. Using the doubling time found in part (b), how long would it take a \$4000 investment to reach \$16,000 if the interest rate is 5%?

64. On August 31, 1854, an epidemic of cholera was discovered in London, England, resulting from a contaminated community water pump at Broad Street. By the end of September more than 600 citizens who drank water from the pump had died.

The cumulative number of deaths from cholera in the 1854 London epidemic can be approximated by

$$D(t) = 91 + 160 \ln(t + 1)$$

where t is the number of days after the start of the epidemic ($t = 0$ corresponds to September 1, 1854).

a. Approximate the total number of deaths as of September 1 ($t = 0$).

b. Approximate the total number of deaths as of September 5, September 10, and September 20.

Graphing Calculator Exercises

65. **a.** Graph the function defined by $f(x) = \log_3 x$ by graphing $Y_1 = \frac{\log x}{\log 3}$.

b. Graph the function defined by $f(x) = \log_3 x$ by graphing $Y_2 = \frac{\ln x}{\ln 3}$.

c. Does it appear that $Y_1 = Y_2$ on the standard viewing window?

Example 2 **Solving a Logarithmic Equation**

Solve the equation. $\log_4 x = 1 - \log_4(x - 3)$

Solution:

$$\log_4 x = 1 - \log_4(x - 3)$$

$\log_4 x + \log_4(x - 3) = 1$ — Isolate the logarithms on one side of the equation.

$\log_4[x(x - 3)] = 1$ — Write as a single logarithm.

$\log_4(x^2 - 3x) = 1$ — Simplify inside the parentheses.

$x^2 - 3x = 4^1$ — Write the equation in exponential form.

$x^2 - 3x - 4 = 0$ — The resulting equation is quadratic.

$(x - 4)(x + 1) = 0$ — Factor.

$x = 4$ or $x = -1$ — Apply the zero product rule.

Notice that -1 is *not* a solution because $\log_4 x$ is not defined at $x = -1$. However, $x = 4$ *is* defined in both expressions $\log_4 x$ and $\log_4(x - 3)$. We can substitute $x = 4$ into the original equation to show that it checks.

Check: $x = 4$

$$\log_4 x = 1 - \log_4(x - 3)$$

$$\log_4 4 \stackrel{?}{=} 1 - \log_4(4 - 3)$$

$$1 \stackrel{?}{=} 1 - \log_4 1$$

$$1 \stackrel{?}{=} 1 - 0 \checkmark \text{ True}$$

The solution set is {4}. (The value -1 does not check.)

Skill Practice Solve the equation.

2. $\log_3(x - 8) = 2 - \log_3 x$

Example 3 **Solving a Logarithmic Equation**

Solve the equation. $\log(x + 300) = 3.7$

Solution:

$\log(x + 300) = 3.7$ — The equation has a single logarithm that is already isolated.

$10^{3.7} = x + 300$ — Write the equation in exponential form.

$10^{3.7} - 300 = x$ — Solve for x.

$$x = 10^{3.7} - 300$$

$$\approx 4711.87$$

Answer

2. {9} (The value -1 does not check.)

Check: $x = 10^{3.7} - 300$ — Check the exact value of x in the original equation.

$$\log(x + 300) = 3.7$$
$$\log[(10^{3.7} - 300) + 300] \stackrel{?}{=} 3.7$$
$$\log(10^{3.7} - 300 + 300) \stackrel{?}{=} 3.7$$
$$\log 10^{3.7} \stackrel{?}{=} 3.7$$ Property 3 of logarithms: $\log_b b^p = p$
$$3.7 \stackrel{?}{=} 3.7 \checkmark \text{ True}$$

The solution $10^{3.7} - 300$ checks.

The solution set is $\{10^{3.7} - 300\}$.

Skill Practice Solve the equation.

3. $\log(p + 6) = 1.3$

The following property is another useful tool to solve a logarithmic equation. This is demonstrated in Example 4.

Equivalence of Logarithmic Expressions

Let x, y, and b represent real numbers such that $x > 0$, $y > 0$, $b > 0$, and $b \neq 1$. Then

$$\log_b x = \log_b y \quad \text{implies} \quad x = y$$

Example 4 Solving a Logarithmic Equation

Solve the equation.

$$\ln(x + 2) + \ln(x - 1) = \ln(9x - 17)$$

Solution:

$$\ln(x + 2) + \ln(x - 1) = \ln(9x - 17)$$

$$\ln[(x + 2)(x - 1)] = \ln(9x - 17)$$ Write the logarithms on the left-hand side as a single logarithm.

$$\ln(x^2 + x - 2) = \ln(9x - 17)$$ Simplify.

$$x^2 + x - 2 = 9x - 17$$ Use the equivalence property of logarithms. That is, equate the arguments of each log.

$$x^2 - 8x + 15 = 0$$ Solve the resulting quadratic equation.

$$(x - 5)(x - 3) = 0$$

$$x = 5 \quad \text{or} \quad x = 3$$

Answer

3. $\{10^{1.3} - 6\}$

TIP: The equation from Example 7 is written in the form b^x = constant. In this special case, we also have the option of rewriting the equation in its corresponding logarithmic form to solve for x.

$$4^x = 25$$
$$x = \log_4 25$$
$$= \frac{\ln 25}{\ln 4} \quad \text{(Change-of-base formula)}$$

Solving Exponential Equations

Step 1 Isolate one of the exponential expressions in the equation.

Step 2 Take a logarithm on both sides of the equation. (The natural logarithmic function or the common logarithmic function is often used so that the final answer can be approximated with a calculator.)

Step 3 Use the power property of logarithms (property 7) to write exponents as factors. Recall: $\log_b M^p = p \log_b M$.

Step 4 Solve the resulting equation from step 3.

Example 8 Solving an Exponential Equation by Taking a Logarithm on Both Sides

Solve the equation. $e^{-3.6x} - 2 = 7.74$

Solution:

$e^{-3.6x} = 9.74$ — Add 2 to both sides to isolate the exponential expression.

$\ln e^{-3.6x} = \ln 9.74$ — The exponential expression has a base of e, so it is convenient to take the natural logarithm of both sides.

$(-3.6x) \ln e = \ln 9.74$ — Use the power property of logarithms.

$-3.6x = \ln 9.74$ — Simplify (recall that $\ln e = 1$).

$$x = \frac{\ln 9.74}{-3.6} \approx -0.632$$

The solution set is $\left\{-\frac{\ln 9.74}{3.6}\right\}$.

Skill Practice Solve the equation.

8. $e^{-0.2t} + 1 = 8.52$

Answer

8. $\left\{\frac{\ln 7.52}{-0.2}\right\}$

Example 9 Solving an Exponential Equation by Taking a Logarithm on Both Sides

Solve the equation. $2^{x+3} = 7^x$

Solution:

$$2^{x+3} = 7^x$$

$$\ln 2^{(x+3)} = \ln 7^x$$ Take the natural logarithm of both sides.

$$(x + 3) \ln 2 = x \ln 7$$ Use the power property of logarithms.

$$x(\ln 2) + 3(\ln 2) = x \ln 7$$ Apply the distributive property.

$$x(\ln 2) - x(\ln 7) = -3 \ln 2$$ Collect x-terms on one side.

$$x(\ln 2 - \ln 7) = -3 \ln 2$$ Factor out x.

$$\frac{x\cancel{(\ln 2 - \ln 7)}}{\cancel{(\ln 2 - \ln 7)}} = \frac{-3 \ln 2}{\ln 2 - \ln 7}$$ Solve for x.

$$x = \frac{-3 \ln 2}{\ln 2 - \ln 7} \approx 1.66$$

The solution set is $\left\{-\frac{3 \ln 2}{\ln 2 - \ln 7}\right\}$.

TIP: The exponential equation $2^{x+3} = 7^x$ could have been solved by taking a logarithm of *any* base on both sides of the equation.

Skill Practice Solve the equation.

9. $3^x = 8^{x+2}$

3. Applications

Example 10 Applying an Exponential Function to World Population

The population of the world was estimated to have reached 6.5 billion in April 2006. The population growth rate for the world is estimated to be 1.4%. (*Source:* U.S. Census Bureau)

$$P(t) = 6.5(1.014)^t$$

represents the world population in billions as a function of the number of years after April 2006 ($t = 0$ represents April 2006).

a. Use the function to estimate the world population in April 2010.

b. Use the function to estimate the amount of time after April 2006 required for the world population to reach 13 billion.

Solution:

a. $P(t) = 6.5(1.014)^t$

$P(4) = 6.5(1.014)^4$ The year 2010 corresponds to $t = 4$.

≈ 6.87 In 2010, the world's population was approximately 6.87 billion.

Answer

9. $\left\{\frac{2 \ln 8}{\ln 3 - \ln 8}\right\}$

b. $P(t) = 6.5(1.014)^t$

$13 = 6.5(1.014)^t$ Substitute $P(t) = 13$ and solve for t.

$\frac{13}{6.5} = \frac{6.5(1.014)^t}{6.5}$ Isolate the exponential expression on one side of the equation.

$2 = 1.014^t$

$\ln 2 = \ln 1.014^t$ Take the natural logarithm of both sides.

$\ln 2 = t \ln 1.014$ Use the power property of logarithms.

$\frac{\ln 2}{\ln 1.014} = \frac{t \ln 1.014}{\ln 1.014}$ Solve for t.

$t = \frac{\ln 2}{\ln 1.014} \approx 50$ The population will reach 13 billion (double the April 2006 value) approximately 50 yr after 2006.

Note: It has taken thousands of years for the world's population to reach 6.5 billion. However, with a growth rate of 1.4%, it will take only 50 years to gain an additional 6.5 billion, if this trend continues.

Skill Practice Use the population function from Example 10.

10. Estimate the world population in April 2020.

11. Estimate the year in which the world population will reach 9 billion.

On Friday, April 25, 1986, a nuclear accident occurred at the Chernobyl nuclear reactor, resulting in radioactive contaminates being released into the atmosphere. The most hazardous isotopes released in this accident were ^{137}Cs (cesium 137), ^{131}I (iodine 131), and ^{90}Sr (strontium 90). People living close to Chernobyl (in Ukraine) were at risk of radiation exposure from inhalation, from absorption through the skin, and from food contamination. Years after the incident, scientists have seen an increase in the incidence of thyroid disease among children living in the contaminated areas. Because iodine is readily absorbed in the thyroid gland, scientists suspect that radiation from iodine 131 is the cause.

Example 11 Applying an Exponential Equation to Radioactive Decay

The half-life of radioactive iodine, ^{131}I, is 8.04 days. If 10 g of iodine 131 is initially present, then the amount of radioactive iodine still present after t days is approximated by

$$A(t) = 10e^{-0.0862t}$$

where t is the time in days.

a. Use the model to approximate the amount of ^{131}I still present after 2 weeks. Round to the nearest 0.1 g.

b. How long will it take for the amount of ^{131}I to decay to 0.5 g? Round to the nearest 0.1 day.

Answers

10. Approximately 7.9 billion

11. The year 2029

Solution:

a. $A(t) = 10e^{-0.0862t}$

$A(14) = 10e^{-0.0862(14)}$ Substitute $t = 14$ (2 weeks).

≈ 3.0 g There was 3.0 g still present after 2 weeks.

b. $A(t) = 10e^{-0.0862t}$

$0.5 = 10e^{-0.0862t}$ Substitute $A = 0.5$.

$\dfrac{0.5}{10} = \dfrac{10e^{-0.0862t}}{10}$ Isolate the exponential expression.

$0.05 = e^{-0.0862t}$

$\ln 0.05 = \ln e^{-0.0862t}$ Take the natural logarithm of both sides.

$\ln 0.05 = -0.0862t$ The resulting equation is linear.

$\dfrac{\ln 0.05}{-0.0862} = \dfrac{-0.0862t}{-0.0862}$ Solve for t.

$t = \dfrac{\ln 0.05}{-0.0862} \approx 34.8$ days It will take 34.8 days for 10 g of ^{131}I to decay to 0.5 g.

Skill Practice Radioactive strontium 90 (^{90}Sr) has a half-life of 28 yr. If 100 g of strontium 90 is initially present, the amount left after t years is approximated by

$$A(t) = 100e^{-0.0248t}$$

12. Find the amount of ^{90}Sr present after 85 yr.

13. How long will it take for the amount of ^{90}Sr to decay to 40 g?

Answers

12. 12.1 g **13.** 36.9 years

Section 12.6 Practice Exercises

Vocabulary and Key Concepts

1. a. The equivalence property of logarithmic expressions states that if $\log_b x = \log_b y$, then __________.

b. The equivalence property of exponential expressions states that if $b^x = b^y$, then __________.

Review Exercises

For Exercises 2–6, write the expression as a single logarithm. Assume all variables represent positive real numbers.

2. $\log_b (x - 1) + \log_b (x + 2)$

3. $\log_b x + \log_b (2x + 3)$

4. $\log_b x - \log_b (1 - x)$

5. $\log_b (x + 2) - \log_b (3x - 5)$

6. $2 \log_b x - \log_b (x + 1)$

Concept 1: Solving Logarithmic Equations

For Exercises 7–38, solve the logarithmic equations. **(See Examples 1–4.)**

7. $\log_3 x = 2$

8. $\log_4 x = 9$

9. $\log p = 42$

10. $\log q = \frac{1}{2}$

11. $\ln x = 0.08$

12. $\ln x = 19$

13. $\log (x + 40) = -9.2$

14. $\log (z - 3) = -6.7$

15. $\log_x 25 = 2 \quad (x > 0)$

16. $\log_x 100 = 2 \quad (x > 0)$

17. $\log_b 10{,}000 = 4 \quad (b > 0)$

18. $\log_b e^3 = 3 \quad (b > 0)$

19. $\log_y 5 = \frac{1}{2} \quad (y > 0)$

20. $\log_b 8 = \frac{1}{2} \quad (b > 0)$

21. $\log_4 (c + 5) = 3$

22. $\log_5 (a - 4) = 2$

23. $\log_5 (4y + 1) = 1$

24. $\log_6 (5t - 2) = 1$

25. $\ln (1 - x) = 0$

26. $\log_4 (2 - x) = 1$

27. $\log_3 8 - \log_3 (x + 5) = 2$

28. $\log_2 (x + 3) - \log_2 (x + 2) = 1$

29. $\log_2 (h - 1) + \log_2 (h + 1) = 3$

30. $\log_3 k + \log_3 (2k + 3) = 2$

31. $\log (x + 2) = \log (3x - 6)$

32. $\log x = \log (1 - x)$

33. $\ln x - \ln (4x - 9) = 0$

34. $\ln (x + 5) - \ln x = \ln (4x)$

35. $\log_5 (3t + 2) - \log_5 t = \log_5 4$

36. $\log (6y - 7) + \log y = \log 5$

37. $\log (4m) = \log 2 + \log (m - 3)$

38. $\log (-h) + \log 3 = \log (2h - 15)$

Concept 2: Solving Exponential Equations

For Exercises 39–54, solve the exponential equation by using the property that $b^x = b^y$ implies $x = y$, for $b > 0$ and $b \neq 1$. **(See Examples 5–6.)**

39. $5^x = 625$

40. $3^x = 81$

41. $2^{-x} = 64$

42. $6^{-x} = 216$

43. $36^x = 6$

44. $343^x = 7$

45. $4^{2x-1} = 64$

46. $5^{3x-1} = 125$

47. $81^{3x-4} = \frac{1}{243}$

48. $4^{2x-7} = \frac{1}{128}$

49. $\left(\frac{2}{3}\right)^{-x+4} = \frac{8}{27}$

50. $\left(\frac{1}{4}\right)^{3x+2} = \frac{1}{64}$

51. $16^{-x+1} = 8^{5x}$

52. $27^{(1/3)x} = \left(\frac{1}{9}\right)^{2x-1}$

53. $(4^x)^{x+1} = 16$

54. $(3^x)^{x+2} = \frac{1}{3}$

For Exercises 55–74, solve the exponential equation by taking the logarithm of both sides. **(See Examples 7–9.)**

55. $8^a = 21$

56. $6^y = 39$

57. $e^x = 8.1254$

58. $e^x = 0.3151$

59. $10^t = 0.0138$

60. $10^p = 16.8125$

61. $e^{0.07h} - 6 = 9$

62. $e^{0.03k} + 7 = 11$

63. $e^{1.2t} = 3$

64. $e^{1.5t} = 7$

65. $3^{x+1} = 5^x$

66. $2^{x-1} = 7^x$

67. $2^{x+2} = 6^x$

68. $5^{x-2} = 3^x$

69. $32e^{0.04m} = 128$

70. $8e^{0.05n} = 160$

71. $6e^{x/3} = 125$

72. $8e^{x/5} = 155$

73. $5^{x-2} - 4 = 16$

74. $2^{x+4} + 17 = 50$

Concept 3: Applications

75. The population of China can be modeled by the function

$$P(t) = 1237(1.0095)^t$$

where $P(t)$ is in millions and t is the number of years since 1998. **(See Example 10.)**

a. Using this model, what was the population in the year 2002?

b. Predict the population in the year 2016.

c. If this growth rate continues, in what year will the population reach 2 billion people (2 billion is 2000 million)?

76. The population of Delhi, India, can be modeled by the function

$$P(t) = 9817(1.031)^t$$

where $P(t)$ is in thousands and t is the number of years since 2001.

a. Using this model, predict the population in the year 2018.

b. If this growth rate continues, in what year will the population reach 15 million (15 million is 15,000 thousand)?

77. The growth of a certain bacteria in a culture is given by the model

$$A(t) = 500e^{0.0277t}$$

where $A(t)$ is the number of bacteria and t is time in minutes.

a. What is the initial number of bacteria?

b. What is the population after 10 min?

c. How long will it take for the population to double (that is, reach 1000)?

78. The population of the bacteria *Salmonella typhimurium* is given by the model

$$A(t) = 300e^{0.01733t}$$

where $A(t)$ is the number of bacteria and t is time in minutes.

a. What is the initial number of bacteria?

b. What is the population after 10 min?

c. How long will it take for the population to double?

79. Suppose \$5000 is invested at 7% interest compounded continuously. How long will it take for the investment to grow to \$10,000? Use the model $A(t) = Pe^{rt}$ and round to the nearest tenth of a year.

80. Suppose \$2000 is invested at 10% interest compounded continuously. How long will it take for the investment to triple? Use the model $A(t) = Pe^{rt}$ and round to the nearest year.

81. Suppose that \$8000 is invested at 4.5% interest compounded monthly. How long will it take the investment to reach \$10,000? Use the model $A(t) = P\left(1 + \frac{r}{n}\right)^{nt}$ and round to the nearest year.

82. Suppose that a couple invests \$30,000 in a bond fund that pays 6.5% interest compounded quarterly. How long will it take the investment to reach \$250,000? Use the model $A(t) = P\left(1 + \frac{r}{n}\right)^{nt}$ and round to the nearest year.

Section 12.5 The Irrational Number *e* and Change of Base

Key Concepts

The function $y = e^x$ is the exponential function with base e.

The **natural logarithm function** $y = \ln x$ is the logarithm function with base e.

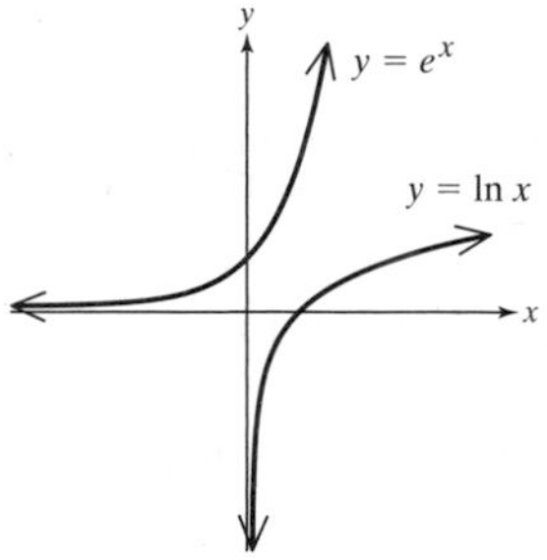

Change-of-Base Formula

$$\log_b x = \frac{\log_a x}{\log_a b} \qquad a > 0, a \neq 1, b > 0, b \neq 1$$

Examples

Example 1

Use a calculator to approximate the value of the expressions.

$e^{7.5} \approx 1808.0424$

$e^{-\pi} \approx 0.0432$

$\ln 107 \approx 4.6728$

$\ln\left(\frac{1}{\sqrt{2}}\right) \approx -0.3466$

Example 2

$\log_3 59 = \frac{\log 59}{\log 3} \approx 3.7115$

Section 12.6 Logarithmic and Exponential Equations and Applications

Key Concepts

Guidelines to Solve Logarithmic Equations

1. Isolate the logarithms on one side of the equation.
2. Write a sum or difference of logarithms as a single logarithm.
3. Rewrite the equation in step 2 in exponential form.
4. Solve the resulting equation from step 3.
5. Check all solutions to verify that they are within the domain of the logarithmic expressions in the equation.

Examples

Example 1

$\log(3x - 1) + 1 = \log(2x + 1)$

Step 1: $\log(3x - 1) - \log(2x + 1) = -1$

Step 2: $\log\left(\frac{3x - 1}{2x + 1}\right) = -1$

Step 3: $10^{-1} = \frac{3x - 1}{2x + 1}$

Step 4: $\frac{1}{10} = \frac{3x - 1}{2x + 1}$

$2x + 1 = 10(3x - 1)$

$2x + 1 = 30x - 10$

$-28x = -11$

$x = \frac{11}{28}$ The solution checks.

Step 5: The solution set is $\left\{\frac{11}{28}\right\}$.

The equivalence of exponential expressions can be used to solve **exponential equations.**

If $b^x = b^y$, then $x = y$.

Example 2

$5^{2x} = 125$

$5^{2x} = 5^3$ implies that $2x = 3$

$x = \frac{3}{2}$

The solution set is $\left\{\frac{3}{2}\right\}$.

Guidelines to Solve Exponential Equations

1. Isolate one of the exponential expressions in the equation.
2. Take a logarithm of both sides of the equation.
3. Use the power property of logarithms to write exponents as factors.
4. Solve the resulting equation from step 3.

Example 3

$4^{x+1} - 2 = 1055$

Step 1: $4^{x+1} = 1057$

Step 2: $\ln 4^{x+1} = \ln 1057$

Step 3: $(x + 1) \ln 4 = \ln 1057$

Step 4: $x + 1 = \dfrac{\ln 1057}{\ln 4}$

$x = \dfrac{\ln 1057}{\ln 4} - 1 \approx 4.023$

The solution set is $\left\{\dfrac{\ln 1057}{\ln 4} - 1\right\}$.

Chapter 12 Review Exercises

Section 12.1

For Exercises 1–2, determine if the function is one-to-one by using the horizontal line test.

1.

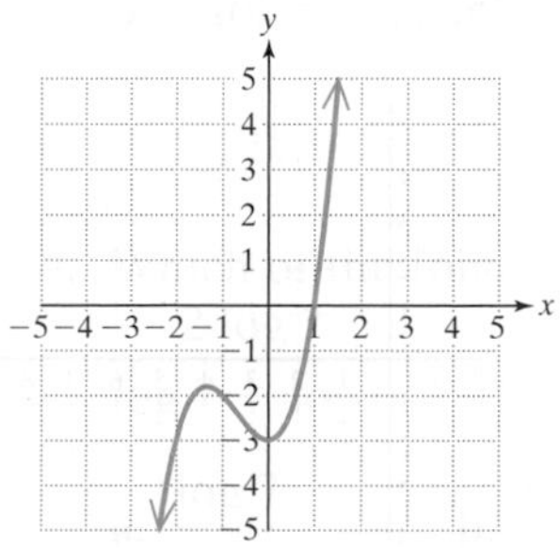

2.

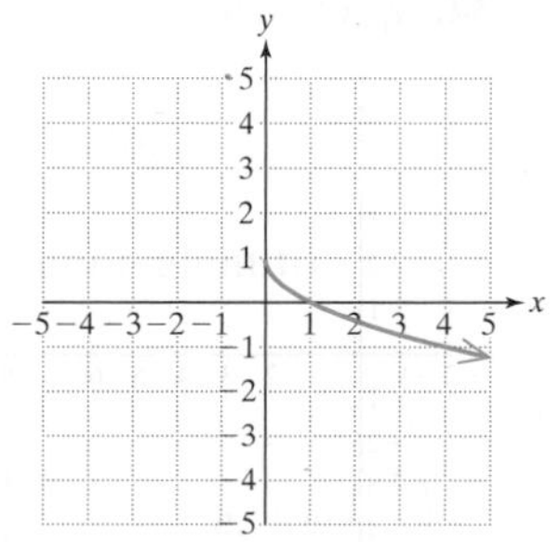

For Exercises 3–7, write the inverse for each one-to-one function.

3. $\{(3, 5), (2, 9), (0, -1), (4, 1)\}$

4. $q(x) = \frac{3}{4}x - 2$

5. $g(x) = \sqrt[5]{x} + 3$

6. $f(x) = (x - 1)^3$

7. $n(x) = \dfrac{4}{x - 2}$

8. Verify that the functions defined by $f(x) = 5x - 2$ and $g(x) = \frac{1}{5}x + \frac{2}{5}$ are inverses by showing that $(f \circ g)(x) = x$ and $(g \circ f)(x) = x$.

9. Graph the functions q and q^{-1} from Exercise 4 on the same grid. What can you say about the relationship between these two graphs?

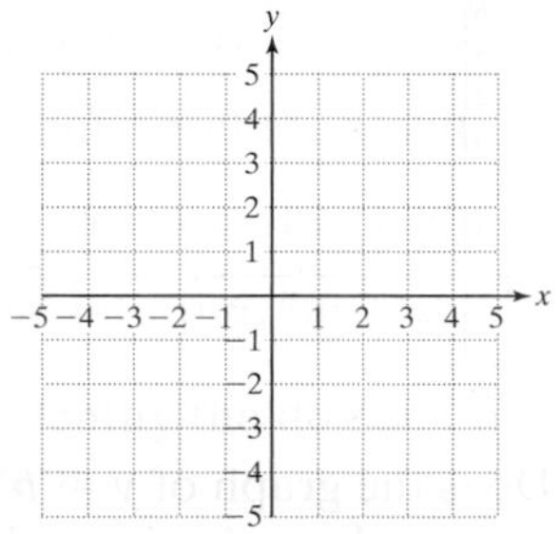

67. $q(x) = \ln(x + 5)$

68. $p(x) = \ln(x - 7)$

69. $r(x) = \ln(3x - 4)$

70. $w(x) = \ln(5 - x)$

Section 12.6

For Exercises 71–88, solve the equations.

71. $\log_5 x = 3$

72. $\log_7 x = -2$

73. $\log_6 y = 3$

74. $\log_3 y = \frac{1}{12}$

75. $\log(2w - 1) = 3$

76. $\log_2(3w + 5) = 5$

77. $-1 + \log p = -\log(p - 3)$

78. $\log_4(2 + t) - 3 = \log_4(3 - 5t)$

79. $4^{3x+5} = 16$

80. $5^{7x} = 625$

81. $4^a = 21$

82. $5^a = 18$

83. $e^{-x} = 0.1$

84. $e^{-2x} = 0.06$

85. $10^{2n} = 1512$

86. $10^{-3m} = \frac{1}{821}$

87. $2^{x+3} = 7^x$

88. $14^{x-5} = 6^x$

89. Radioactive iodine (^{131}I) is used to treat patients with a hyperactive (overactive) thyroid. The half-life of radioactive iodine is 8.04 days. If a patient is given an initial dose of 2 μg, then the amount of iodine in the body after t days is approximated by

$$A(t) = 2e^{-0.0862t}$$

where t is the time in days and $A(t)$ is the amount (in micrograms) of ^{131}I remaining.

a. How much radioactive iodine is present after a week? Round to two decimal places.

b. How much radioactive iodine is present after 30 days? Round to two decimal places.

c. How long will it take for the level of radioactive iodine to reach 0.5 μg?

90. The growth of a certain bacteria in a culture is given by the model $A(t) = 150e^{0.007t}$, where $A(t)$ is the number of bacteria and t is time in minutes.

a. What is the initial number of bacteria?

b. What is the population after $\frac{1}{2}$ hr?

c. How long will it take for the population to double?

91. The value of a car is depreciated with time according to

$$V(t) = 15{,}000e^{-0.15t}$$

where $V(t)$ is the value in dollars and t is the time in years.

a. Find $V(0)$ and interpret the result in the context of this problem.

b. Find $V(10)$ and interpret the result in the context of this problem. Round to the nearest dollar.

c. Find the time required for the value of the car to drop to \$5000. Round to the nearest tenth of a year.

Chapter 12 Test

1. Explain how to determine graphically if a function is one-to-one.

2. Which of the functions is one-to-one?

a.

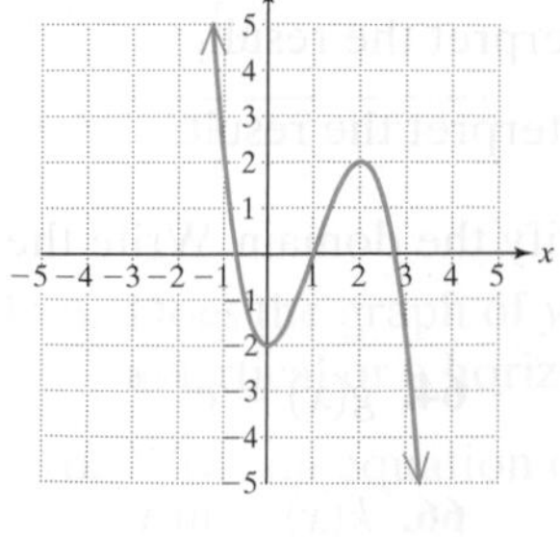

b.

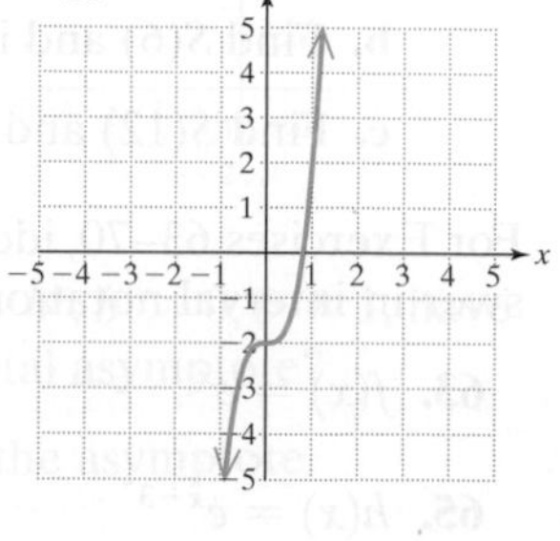

3. Write an equation of the inverse of the one-to-one function defined by $f(x) = \frac{1}{4}x + 3$.

4. Write an equation of the inverse of the function defined by $g(x) = (x - 1)^2, \quad x \geq 1$.

5. Given the graph of the function $y = p(x)$, graph its inverse $p^{-1}(x)$.

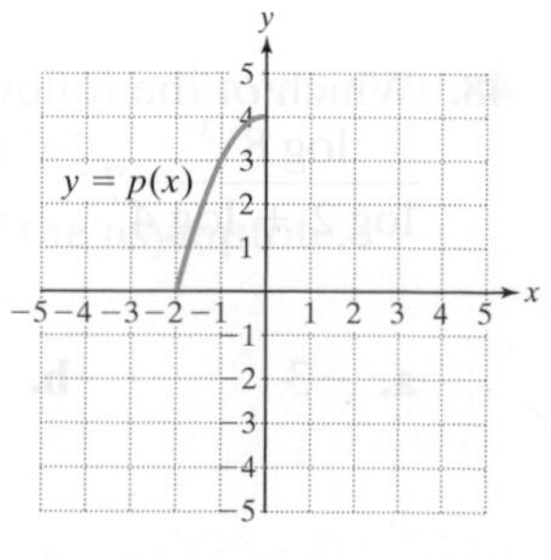

6. Use a calculator to approximate the expression to four decimal places.

a. $10^{2/3}$ **b.** $3^{\sqrt{10}}$ **c.** 8^{π}

7. Graph $f(x) = 4^{x-1}$.

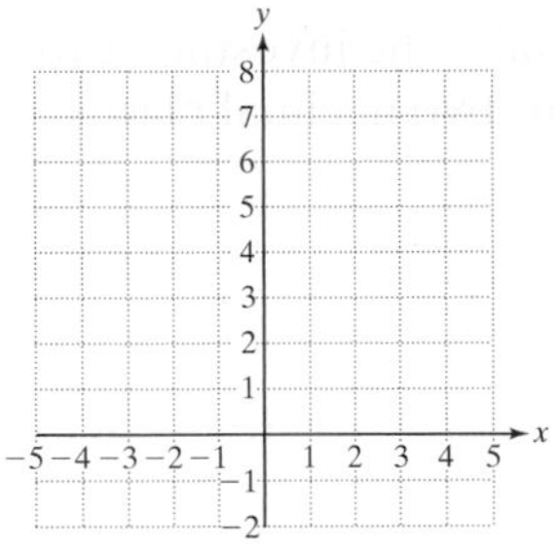

8. **a.** Write in logarithmic form. $16^{3/4} = 8$

b. Write in exponential form. $\log_x 31 = 5$

9. Graph $g(x) = \log_3 x$.

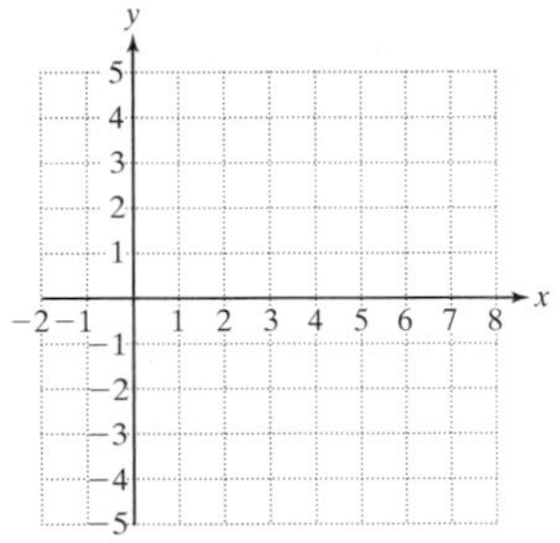

10. Complete the change-of-base formula: $\log_b n =$ _____

11. Use a calculator to approximate the expression to four decimal places:

a. $\log 21$ **b.** $\log_4 13$ **c.** $\log_{1/2} 6$

12. Using the properties of logarithms, expand and simplify. Assume all variables represent positive real numbers.

a. $-\log_3\left(\dfrac{3}{9x}\right)$ **b.** $\log\left(\dfrac{1}{10^5}\right)$

13. Write as a single logarithm. Assume all variables represent positive real numbers.

a. $\dfrac{1}{2}\log_b x + 3\log_b y$ **b.** $\log a - 4\log a$

14. Use a calculator to approximate the expression to four decimal places, if necessary.

a. $e^{1/2}$ **b.** e^{-3}

c. $\ln\left(\dfrac{1}{3}\right)$ **d.** $\ln e$

15. Identify the graphs as $y = e^x$ or $y = \ln x$.

a.

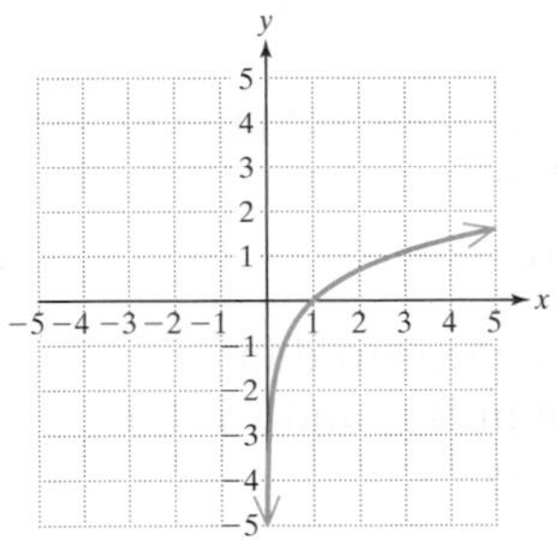

b.

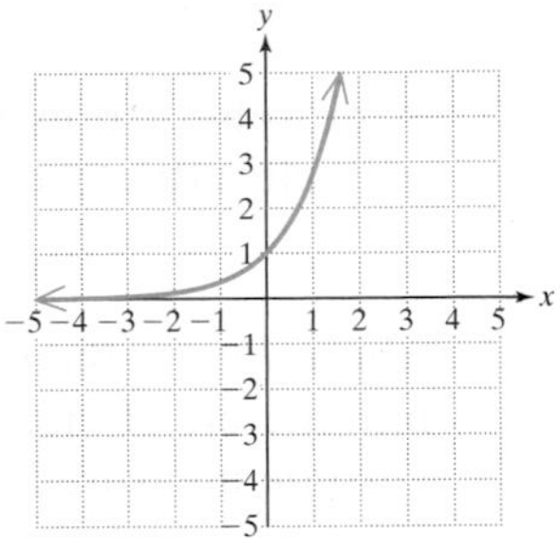

16. Researchers found that t months after taking a course, students remembered $p\%$ of the material according to

$$p(t) = 92 - 20\ln(t + 1)$$

where $0 \le t \le 24$ is the time in months.

a. Find $p(4)$ and interpret the results.

b. Find $p(12)$ and interpret the results.

c. Find $p(0)$ and interpret the results.

17. The population of New York City has a 2% growth rate and can be modeled by the function $P(t) = 8008(1.02)^t$, where $P(t)$ is in thousands and t is in years ($t = 0$ corresponds to the year 2000).

a. Using this model, predict the population in the year 2010.

b. If this growth rate continues, in what year will the population reach 12 million (12 million is 12,000 thousand)?

18. A certain bacterial culture grows according to

$$P(t) = \frac{1{,}500{,}000}{1 + 5000e^{-0.8t}}$$

where P is the population of the bacteria and t is the time in hours.

a. Find $P(0)$ and interpret the result. Round to the nearest whole number.

b. How many bacteria will be present after 6 hr?

c. How many bacteria will be present after 12 hr?

d. How many bacteria will be present after 18 hr?

For Exercises 19–26, solve the exponential and logarithmic equations.

19. $\log x + \log(x - 21) = 2$

20. $\log_{1/2} x = -5$

21. $\ln(x + 7) = 2.4$

22. $3^{x+4} = \dfrac{1}{27}$

Calculator Connections

Topic: Graphing a Circle

Graphing calculators are designed to graph *functions*, in which y is written in terms of x. A circle is not a function. However, it can be graphed as the union of two functions—one representing the top semicircle and the other representing the bottom semicircle.

Solving for y in Example 2, we have

$$(x - 3)^2 + (y + 4)^2 = 36$$

$$(y + 4)^2 = 36 - (x - 3)^2$$

$$y + 4 = \pm\sqrt{36 - (x - 3)^2}$$

$$y = -4 \pm \sqrt{36 - (x - 3)^2}$$

Graph these functions as Y_1 and Y_2, using a square viewing window.

$$Y_1 = -4 + \sqrt{36 - (x - 3)^2}$$

$$Y_2 = -4 - \sqrt{36 - (x - 3)^2}$$

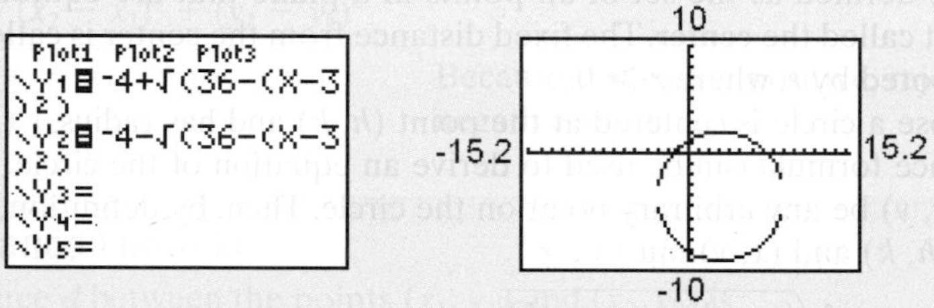

Notice that the image from the calculator does not show the upper and lower semicircles connecting at their endpoints, when in fact the semicircles should "hook up." This is due to the calculator's limited resolution.

Example 3 Graphing a Circle

Find the center and radius of each circle. Then graph the circle.

a. $x^2 + \left(y - \frac{10}{3}\right)^2 = \frac{25}{9}$ **b.** $x^2 + y^2 = 10$

Solution:

a. $x^2 + \left(y - \frac{10}{3}\right)^2 = \frac{25}{9}$

$$(x - 0)^2 + \left(y - \frac{10}{3}\right)^2 = \left(\frac{5}{3}\right)^2$$

The equation is now in standard form $(x - h)^2 + (y - k)^2 = r^2$. The center is $\left(0, \frac{10}{3}\right)$ and the radius is $\frac{5}{3}$ (Figure 13-5).

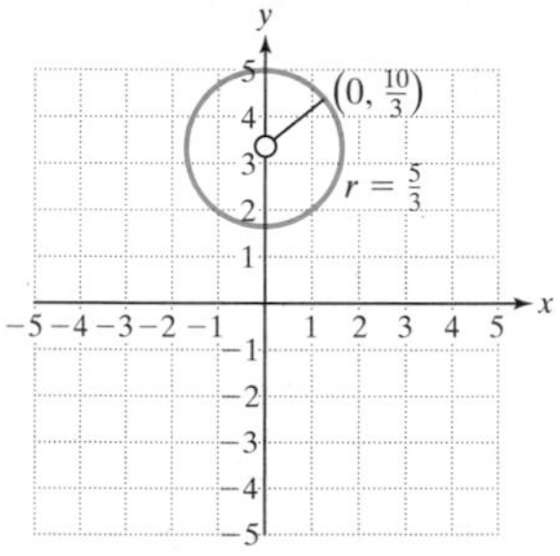

Figure 13-5

b. $x^2 + y^2 = 10$

$(x - 0)^2 + (y - 0)^2 = (\sqrt{10})^2$

$(x - h)^2 + (y - k)^2 = r^2$

The center is (0, 0) and the radius is $\sqrt{10} \approx 3.16$ (Figure 13-6).

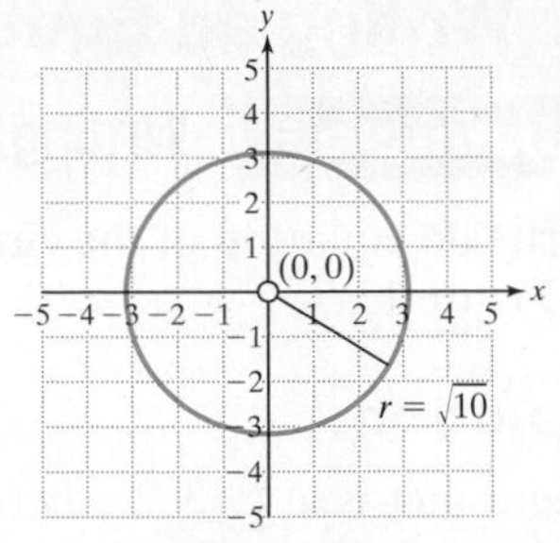

Figure 13-6

Skill Practice Find the center and radius of the circle. Then graph the circle.

3. $\left(x + \frac{7}{2}\right)^2 + y^2 = \frac{9}{4}$

Sometimes it is necessary to complete the square to write an equation of a circle in standard form.

Example 4 Writing the Equation of a Circle in the Form $(x - h)^2 + (y - k)^2 = r^2$

Identify the center and radius of the circle given by the equation $x^2 + y^2 + 2x - 16y + 61 = 0$.

Solution:

$x^2 + y^2 + 2x - 16y + 61 = 0$ — To identify the center and radius, write the equation in the form $(x - h)^2 + (y - k)^2 = r^2$.

$(x^2 + 2x \quad) + (y^2 - 16y \quad) = -61$ — Group the x terms and group the y terms. Move the constant to the right-hand side.

$(x^2 + 2x + 1) + (y^2 - 16y + 64) = -61 + 1 + 64$

- Complete the square on x. Add $[\frac{1}{2}(2)]^2 = 1$ to both sides of the equation.
- Complete the square on y. Add $[\frac{1}{2}(-16)]^2 = 64$ to both sides of the equation.

$(x + 1)^2 + (y - 8)^2 = 4$ — Factor and simplify.

$[x - (-1)]^2 + (y - 8)^2 = 2^2$ — Standard form: $(x - h)^2 + (y - k)^2 = r^2$.

The center is $(-1, 8)$ and the radius is 2.

Skill Practice

4. Identify the center and radius of the circle given by the equation

$$x^2 + y^2 - 10x + 4y - 7 = 0$$

Answers

3. Center: $\left(-\frac{7}{2}, 0\right)$; radius: $\frac{3}{2}$

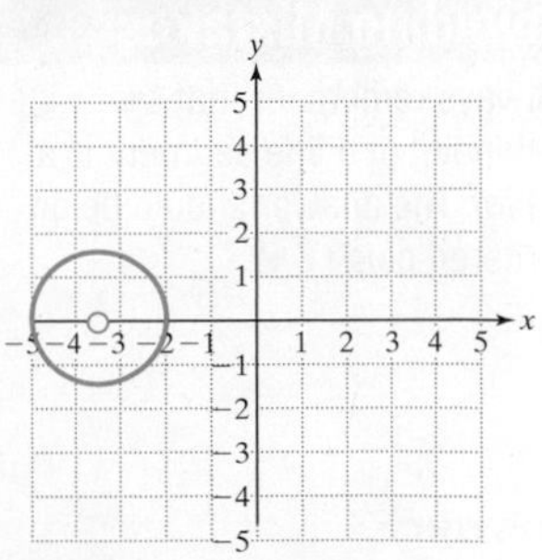

4. Center: $(5, -2)$; radius: 6

3. Writing an Equation of a Circle

Example 5 Writing an Equation of a Circle

Write an equation of the circle shown in Figure 13-7.

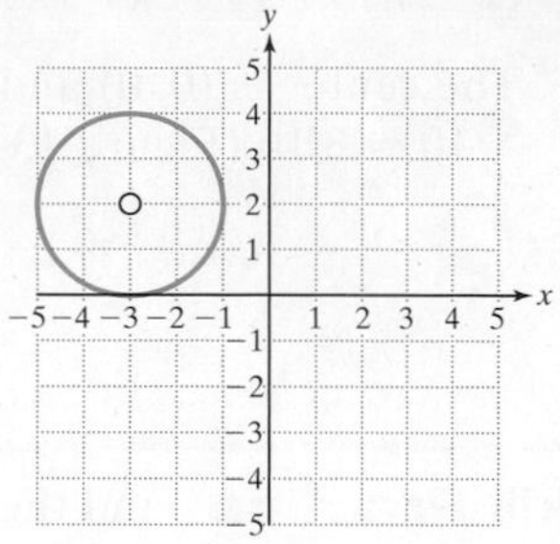

Figure 13-7

Solution:

The center is at $(-3, 2)$; therefore, $h = -3$ and $k = 2$. From the graph, $r = 2$.

$$(x - h)^2 + (y - k)^2 = r^2$$
$$[x - (-3)]^2 + (y - 2)^2 = (2)^2$$
$$(x + 3)^2 + (y - 2)^2 = 4$$

Avoiding Mistakes

Be sure that you *subtract* both coordinates of the center, when substituting the coordinates into the standard form of a circle.

Skill Practice

5. Write an equation for a circle whose center is $(6, -1)$ and whose radius is 8.

4. The Midpoint Formula

Consider two points in the coordinate plane and the line segment determined by the points. It is sometimes necessary to determine the point that is halfway between the endpoints of the segment. This point is called the *midpoint*. If the coordinates of the endpoints are represented by (x_1, y_1) and (x_2, y_2), then the midpoint of the segment is given by the following formula.

Midpoint formula: $\left(\dfrac{x_1 + x_2}{2}, \dfrac{y_1 + y_2}{2}\right)$

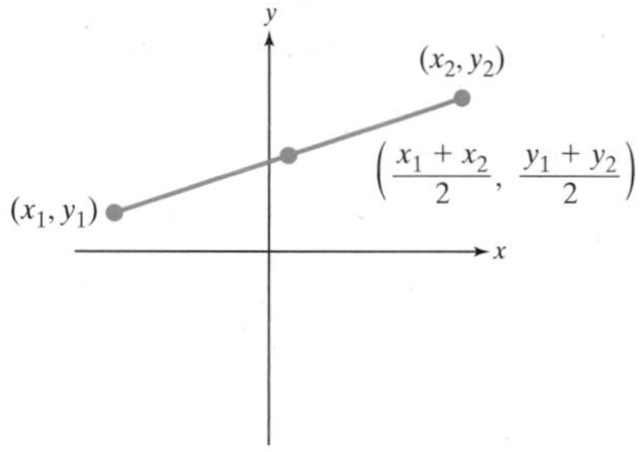

TIP: The midpoint of a line segment is found by taking the *average* of the *x*-coordinates and the *average* of the *y*-coordinates of the endpoints.

Example 6 Finding the Midpoint of a Segment

Find the midpoint of the line segment with the given endpoints.

a. $(-4, 6)$ and $(8, 1)$ **b.** $(-1.2, -3.1)$ and $(-6.6, 1.2)$

Solution:

a. $(-4, 6)$ and $(8, 1)$
(x_1, y_1) (x_2, y_2)

$\left(\dfrac{-4 + 8}{2}, \dfrac{6 + 1}{2}\right)$ Apply the midpoint formula: $\left(\dfrac{x_1 + x_2}{2}, \dfrac{y_1 + y_2}{2}\right)$.

$\left(2, \dfrac{7}{2}\right)$ Simplify.

The midpoint of the segment is $\left(2, \frac{7}{2}\right)$.

Avoiding Mistakes

Always remember that the midpoint of a line segment is a *point*. The answer should be an ordered pair, (x, y).

Answer

5. $(x - 6)^2 + (y + 1)^2 = 64$

b. $(-1.2, -3.1)$ and $(-6.6, 1.2)$
(x_1, y_1) (x_2, y_2)

$\left(\frac{-1.2 + (-6.6)}{2}, \frac{-3.1 + 1.2}{2}\right)$ Apply the midpoint formula.

$(-3.9, -0.95)$ Simplify.

Skill Practice Find the midpoint of the line segment with the given endpoints.

6. $(5, 6)$ and $(-10, 4)$ **7.** $(-2.6, -6.3)$ and $(1.2, 4.1)$

Example 7 Applying the Midpoint Formula

Suppose that $(-2, 3)$ and $(4, 1)$ are endpoints of a diameter of a circle.

a. Find the center of the circle. **b.** Write an equation of the circle.

Solution:

a. Because the midpoint of a diameter of a circle is the center of the circle, apply the midpoint formula. See Figure 13-8.

$(-2, 3)$ and $(4, 1)$
(x_1, y_1) (x_2, y_2)

$\left(\frac{x_1 + x_2}{2}, \frac{y_1 + y_2}{2}\right)$

$\left(\frac{-2 + 4}{2}, \frac{3 + 1}{2}\right)$ Apply the midpoint formula.

$(1, 2)$ Simplify.

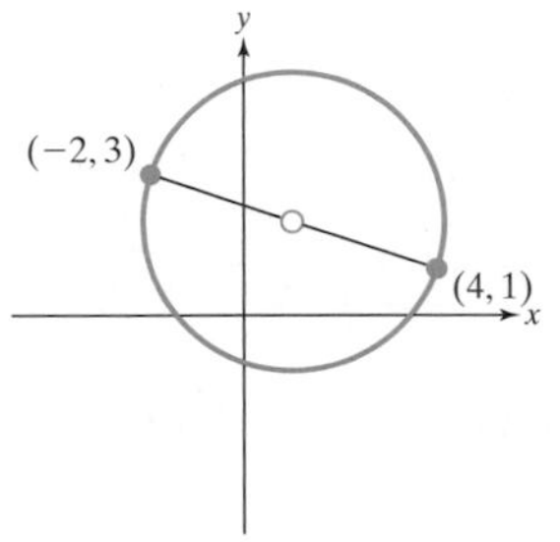

Figure 13-8

The center of the circle is $(1, 2)$.

b. The radius can be determined by finding the distance between the center and either endpoint of the diameter.

$(1, 2)$ and $(4, 1)$
(x_1, y_1) (x_2, y_2)

$d = \sqrt{(x_2 - x_1)^2 + (y_2 - y_1)^2}$ Apply the distance formula.

$d = \sqrt{(4 - 1)^2 + (1 - 2)^2}$ Substitute $(1, 2)$ and $(4, 1)$ for (x_1, y_1) and (x_2, y_2).

$= \sqrt{(3)^2 + (-1)^2}$ Simplify.

$= \sqrt{10}$

The circle is represented by $(x - 1)^2 + (y - 2)^2 = (\sqrt{10})^2$
or $(x - 1)^2 + (y - 2)^2 = 10$.

Skill Practice

8. Suppose that $(3, 2)$ and $(7, 10)$ are endpoints of a diameter of a circle.
a. Find the center of the circle.
b. Write an equation of the circle.

Answers

6. $\left(-\frac{5}{2}, 5\right)$ **7.** $(-0.7, -1.1)$
8. a. $(5, 6)$
b. $(x - 5)^2 + (y - 6)^2 = 20$

Section 13.1 Practice Exercises

Vocabulary and Key Concepts

1. a. The distance between two distinct points (x_1, y_1) and (x_2, y_2) is given by $d =$ ________________.
   b. A __________ is the set of all points equidistant from a fixed point called the __________.
   c. The distance from the center of a circle to any point on the circle is called the __________ and is often denoted by r.
   d. The standard equation of a circle with center (h, k) and radius r is given by ________________.
   e. The midpoint of the line segment with endpoints (x_1, y_1) and (x_2, y_2) is given by __________.

Concept 1: Distance Formula

For Exercises 2–16, use the distance formula to find the distance between the two points. **(See Example 1.)**

2. $(-2, 7)$ and $(4, -5)$
3. $(1, 10)$ and $(-2, 4)$
4. $(0, 5)$ and $(-3, 8)$
5. $(6, 7)$ and $(3, 2)$
6. $\left(\frac{2}{3}, \frac{1}{5}\right)$ and $\left(-\frac{5}{6}, \frac{3}{10}\right)$
7. $\left(-\frac{1}{2}, \frac{5}{8}\right)$ and $\left(-\frac{3}{2}, \frac{1}{4}\right)$
8. $(4, 13)$ and $(4, -6)$
9. $(-2, 5)$ and $(-2, 9)$
10. $(8, -6)$ and $(-2, -6)$
11. $(7, 2)$ and $(15, 2)$
12. $(-6, -2)$ and $(-3, -5)$
13. $(-1, -5)$ and $(-5, -9)$
14. $(3\sqrt{5}, 2\sqrt{7})$ and $(-\sqrt{5}, -3\sqrt{7})$
15. $(4\sqrt{6}, -2\sqrt{2})$ and $(2\sqrt{6}, \sqrt{2})$
16. $(6, 0)$ and $(0, -1)$
17. Explain how to find the distance between 5 and -7 on the y-axis.
18. Explain how to find the distance between 15 and -37 on the x-axis.
19. Find the values of y such that the distance between the points $(4, 7)$ and $(-4, y)$ is 10 units.
20. Find the values of x such that the distance between the points $(-4, -2)$ and $(x, 3)$ is 13 units.
21. Find the values of x such that the distance between the points $(x, 2)$ and $(4, -1)$ is 5 units.
22. Find the values of y such that the distance between the points $(-5, 2)$ and $(3, y)$ is 10 units.

For Exercises 23–26, determine if the three points define the vertices of a right triangle.

23. $(-3, 2), (-2, -4)$, and $(3, 3)$
24. $(1, -2), (-2, 4)$, and $(7, 1)$
25. $(-3, -2), (4, -3)$, and $(1, 5)$
26. $(1, 4), (5, 3)$, and $(2, 0)$

Concept 2: Circles

For Exercises 27–47, identify the center and radius of the circle and then graph the circle. Complete the square, if necessary. **(See Examples 2–4.)**

27. $(x - 4)^2 + (y + 2)^2 = 9$

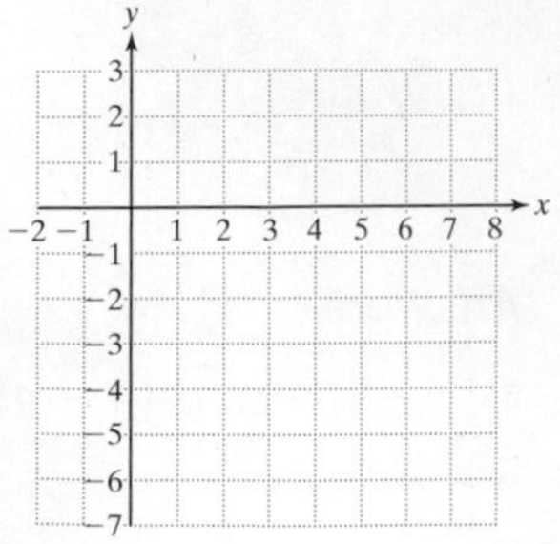

28. $(x - 3)^2 + (y + 1)^2 = 16$

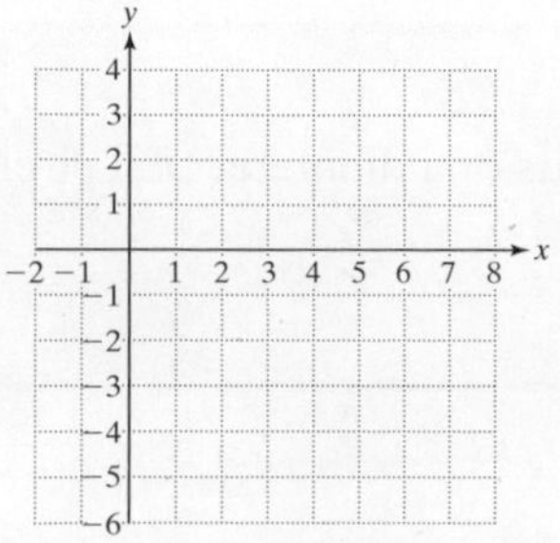

29. $(x + 1)^2 + (y + 1)^2 = 1$

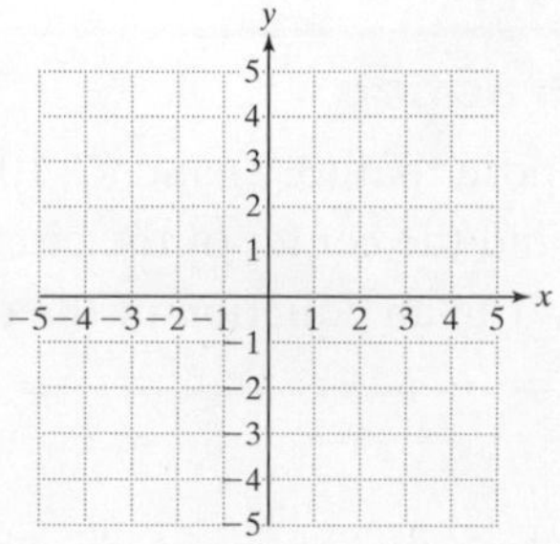

30. $(x - 4)^2 + (y - 4)^2 = 4$

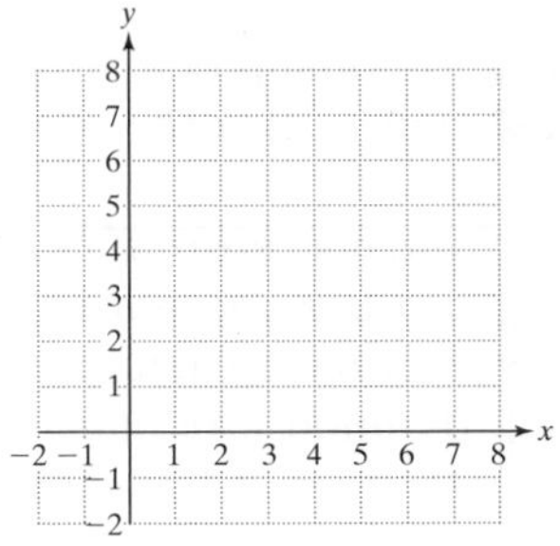

31. $x^2 + (y - 2)^2 = 4$

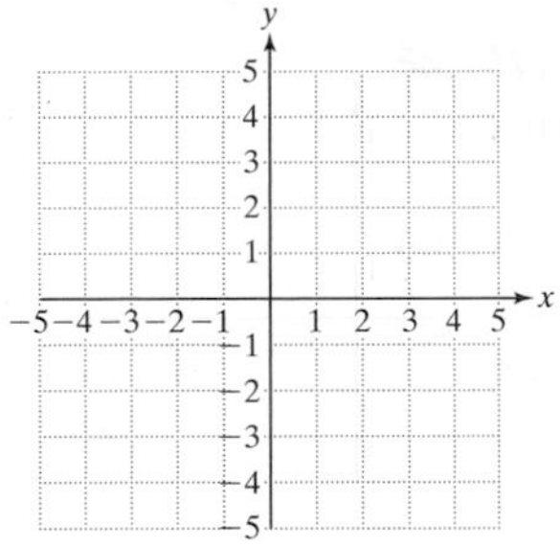

32. $(x + 1)^2 + y^2 = 1$

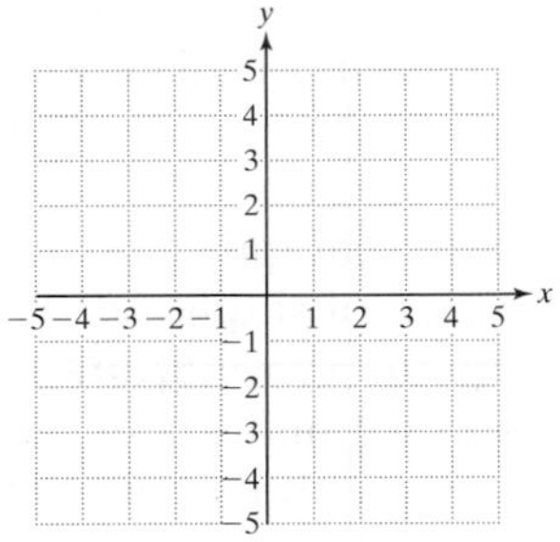

33. $(x - 3)^2 + y^2 = 8$

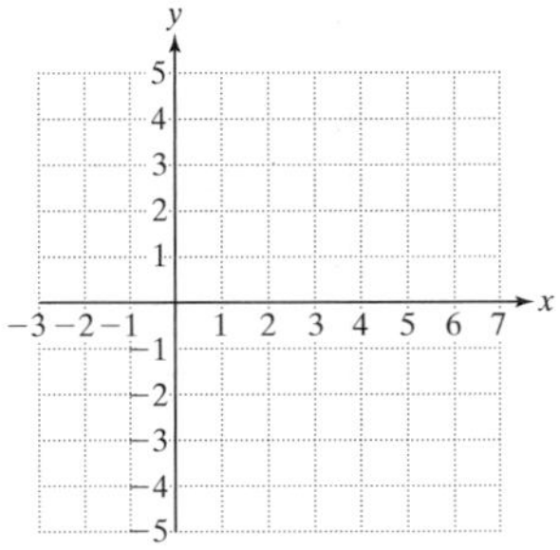

34. $x^2 + (y + 2)^2 = 20$

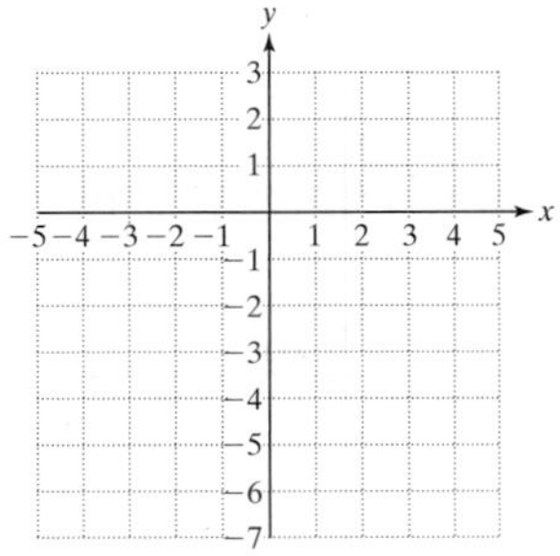

35. $x^2 + y^2 = 6$

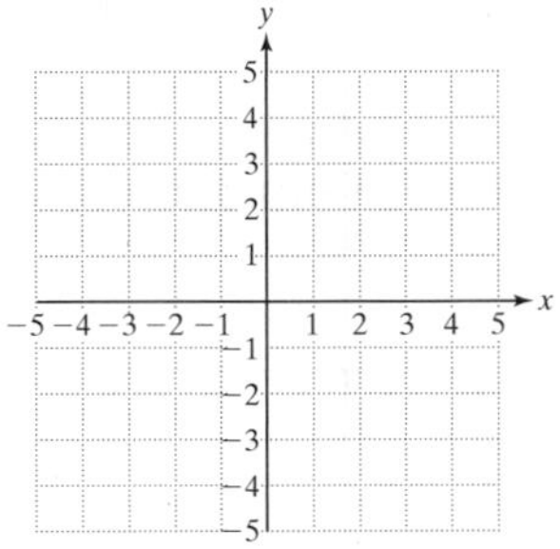

36. $x^2 + y^2 = 15$

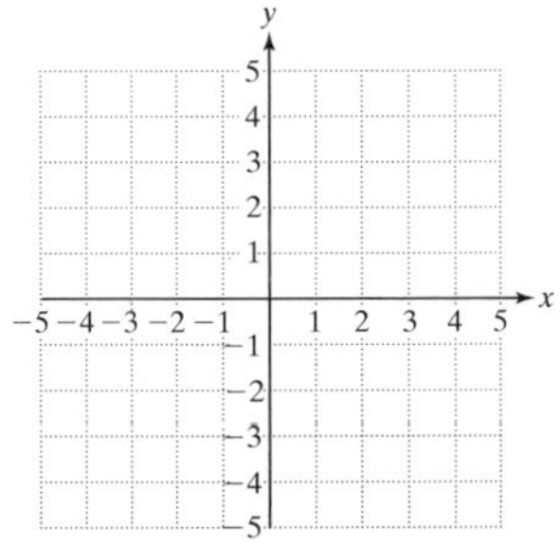

37. $\left(x + \frac{4}{5}\right)^2 + y^2 = \frac{64}{25}$

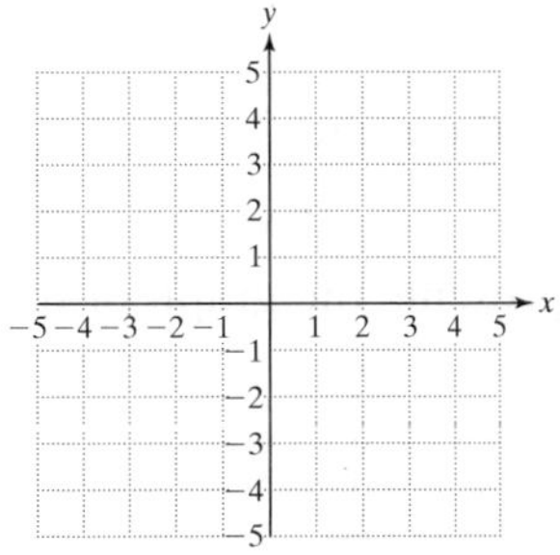

38. $x^2 + \left(y - \frac{5}{2}\right)^2 = \frac{9}{4}$

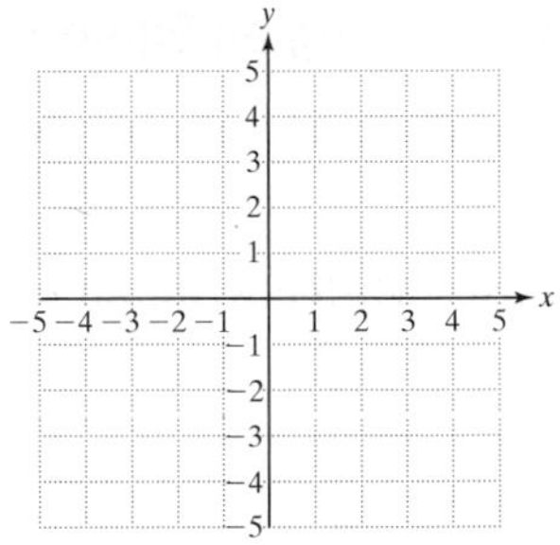

39. $x^2 + y^2 - 2x - 6y - 26 = 0$

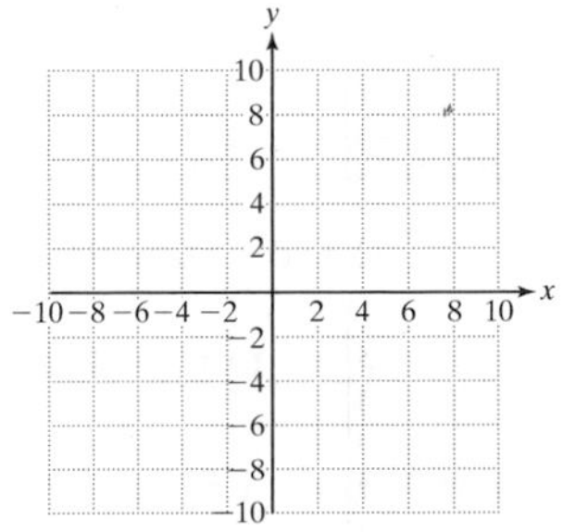

40. $x^2 + y^2 + 4x - 8y + 16 = 0$

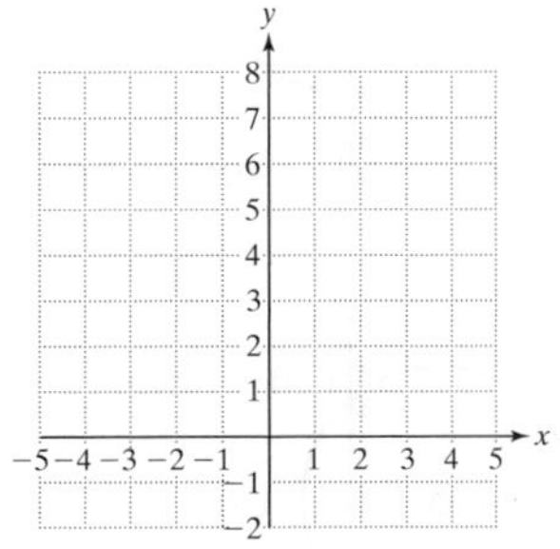

41. $x^2 + y^2 - 6y + 5 = 0$

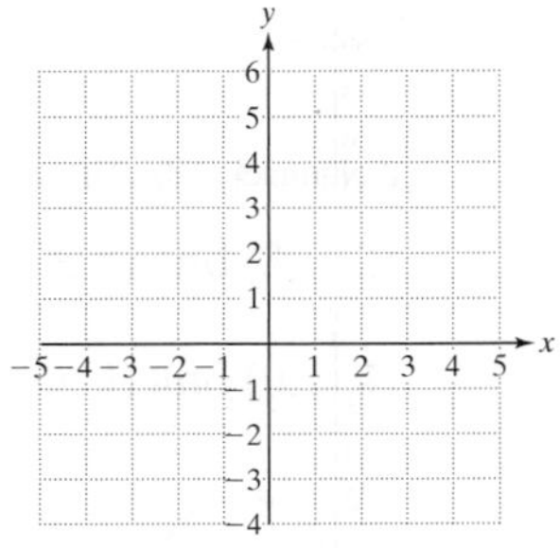

73. Two courier trucks leave the warehouse to make deliveries. One travels 20 mi north and 30 mi east. The other truck travels 5 mi south and 50 mi east. If the two drivers want to meet for lunch at a restaurant at a point halfway between them, where should they meet relative to the warehouse? (*Hint:* Label the warehouse as the origin, and find the coordinates of the restaurant. See the figure.)

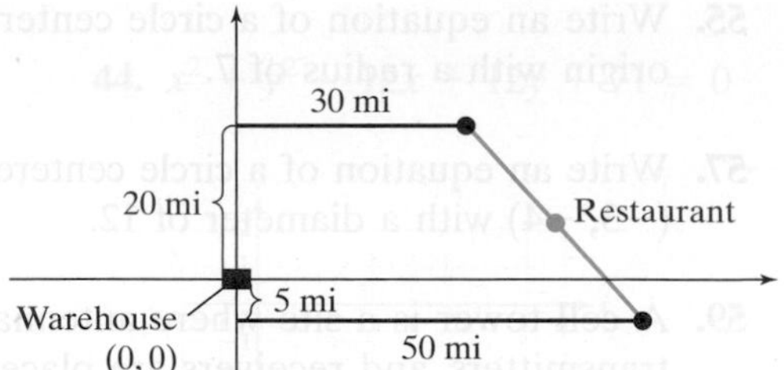

74. A map of a hiking area is drawn so that the Visitor Center is at the origin of a rectangular grid. Two hikers are located at positions $(-1, 1)$ and $(-3, -2)$ with respect to the Visitor Center where all units are in miles. A campground is located exactly halfway between the hikers. What are the coordinates of the campground?

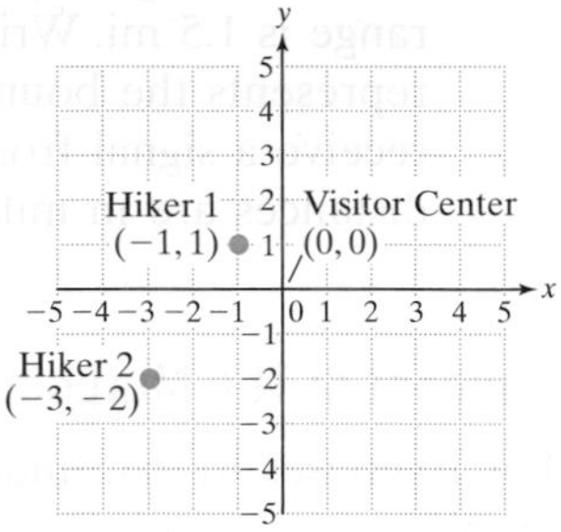

For Exercises 75–78, the two given points are endpoints of a diameter of a circle.

a. Find the center of the circle.

b. Write an equation of the circle. **(See Example 7.)**

75. $(-1, 2)$ and $(3, 4)$ **76.** $(-3, 3)$ and $(7, -1)$ **77.** $(-2, 3)$ and $(2, 3)$ **78.** $(-1, 3)$ and $(-1, -3)$

Expanding Your Skills

79. Write an equation of a circle whose center is (4, 4) and is tangent to the x- and y-axes. (*Hint:* Sketch the circle first.)

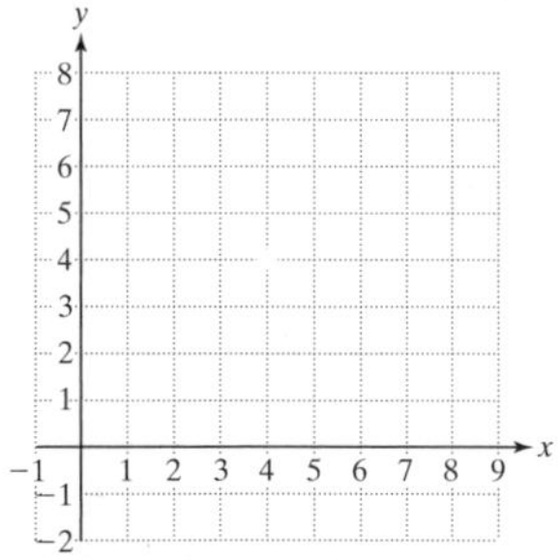

80. Write an equation of a circle whose center is $(-3, 3)$ and is tangent to the x- and y-axes. (*Hint:* Sketch the circle first.)

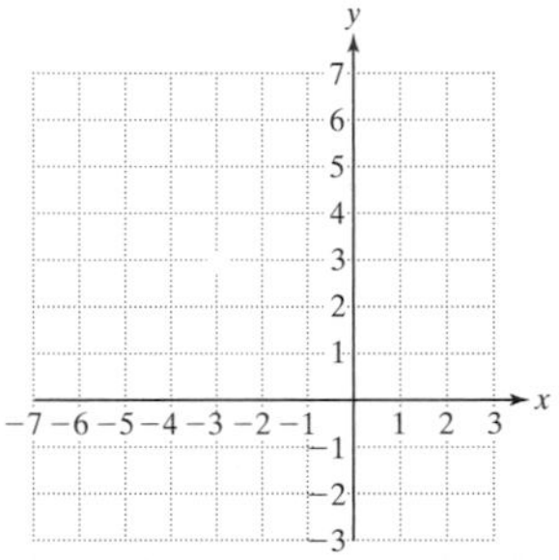

81. Write an equation of a circle whose center is (1, 1) and that passes through the point $(-4, 3)$.

82. Write an equation of a circle whose center is $(-3, -1)$ and that passes through the point $(5, -2)$.

Graphing Calculator Exercises

For Exercises 83–88, graph the circles from the indicated exercise on a square viewing window, and approximate the center and the radius from the graph.

83. $(x - 4)^2 + (y + 2)^2 = 9$ (Exercise 27)

84. $(x - 3)^2 + (y + 1)^2 = 16$ (Exercise 28)

85. $x^2 + (y - 2)^2 = 4$ (Exercise 31)

86. $(x + 1)^2 + y^2 = 1$ (Exercise 32)

87. $x^2 + y^2 = 6$ (Exercise 35)

88. $x^2 + y^2 = 15$ (Exercise 36)

More on the Parabola

Section 13.2

Concepts

1. Introduction to Conic Sections
2. Parabola—Vertical Axis of Symmetry
3. Parabola—Horizontal Axis of Symmetry
4. Vertex Formula

1. Introduction to Conic Sections

Recall that the graph of a second-degree equation of the form $y = ax^2 + bx + c$ $(a \neq 0)$ is a parabola. In Section 13.1 we learned that the graph of $(x - h)^2 + (y - k)^2 = r^2$ is a circle. These and two other types of figures called ellipses and hyperbolas are called **conic sections**. Conic sections derive their names because each is the intersection of a plane and a double-napped cone.

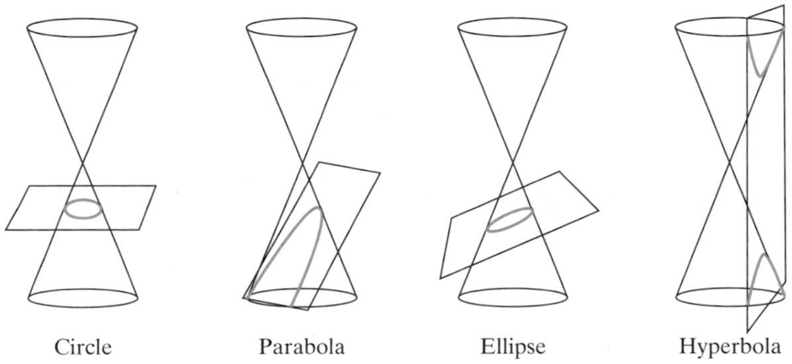

2. Parabola—Vertical Axis of Symmetry

A **parabola** is defined by a set of points in a plane that are equidistant from a fixed line (called the directrix) and a fixed point (called the focus) not on the directrix (Figure 13-9). Parabolas have numerous real-world applications. For example, a flashlight has a mirror with the cross section in the shape of a parabola. The bulb is located at the focus. The light hits the mirror and is reflected outward parallel to the sides of the cylinder. This forms a beam of light (Figure 13-10).

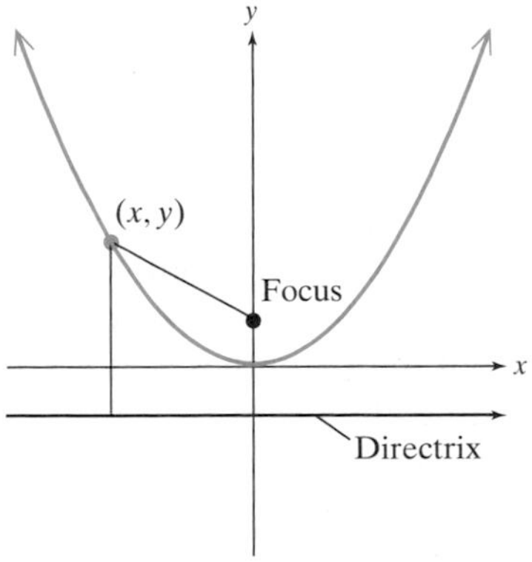

Figure 13-9

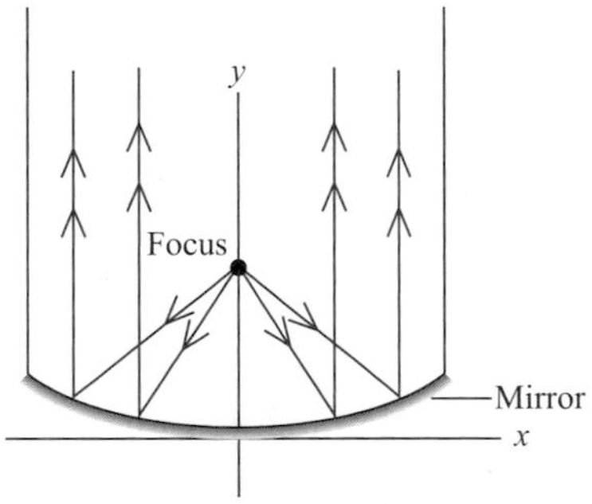

Figure 13-10

The graph of the solutions to the quadratic equation $y = ax^2 + bx + c$ is a parabola. We graphed parabolas of this type in Section 11.4. Recall that the **vertex** is the highest or the lowest point of a parabola. The **axis of symmetry** of the parabola is a line that passes through the vertex and is perpendicular to the directrix (Figure 13-11).

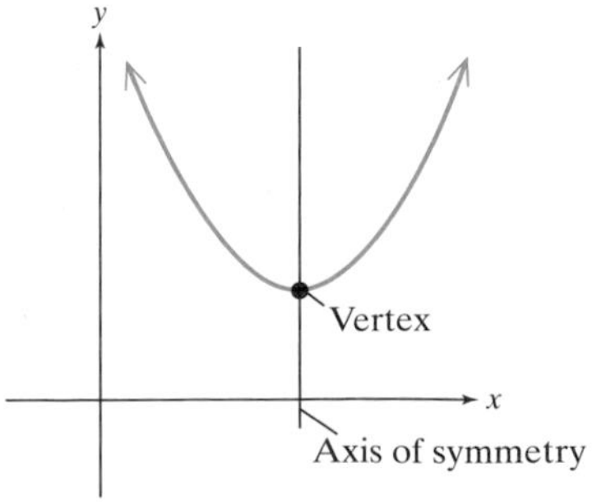

Figure 13-11

For Exercises 5–6, identify the center and radius of the circle and then graph the circle.

5. $x^2 + (y + 1)^2 = 16$

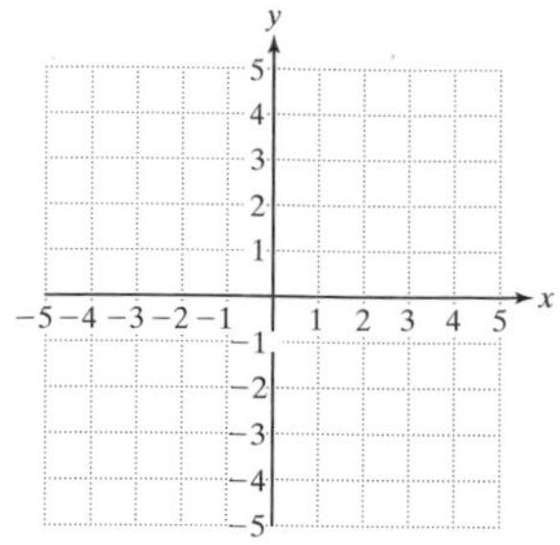

6. $(x - 3)^2 + y^2 = 4$

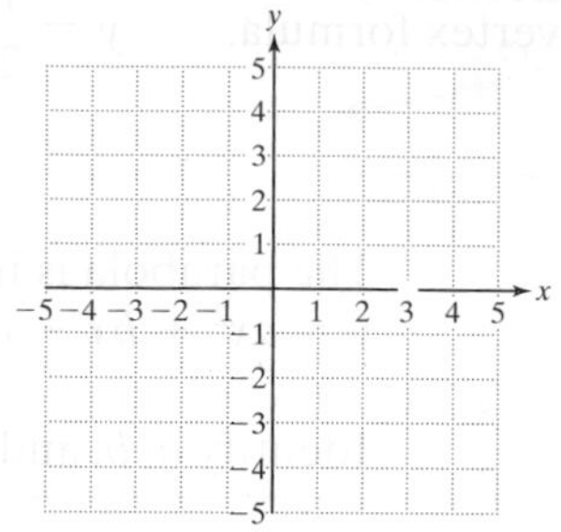

7. Find the midpoint of the line segment between the points $(7, -3)$ and $(4, 5)$.

8. Find the midpoint of the line segment between the points $(-3, 0)$ and $(-1, 9)$.

Concept 2: Parabola—Vertical Axis of Symmetry

For Exercises 9–16, use the equation of the parabola in standard form $y = a(x - h)^2 + k$ to determine the coordinates of the vertex and the equation of the axis of symmetry (complete the square if necessary). Then graph the parabola. **(See Example 1.)**

9. $y = (x + 2)^2 + 1$

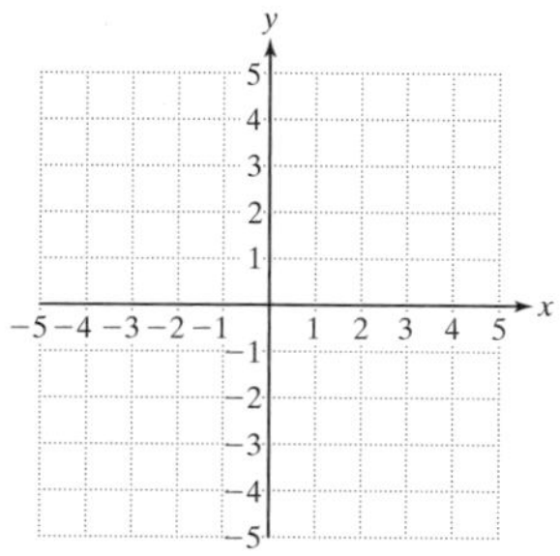

10. $y = (x - 1)^2 + 1$

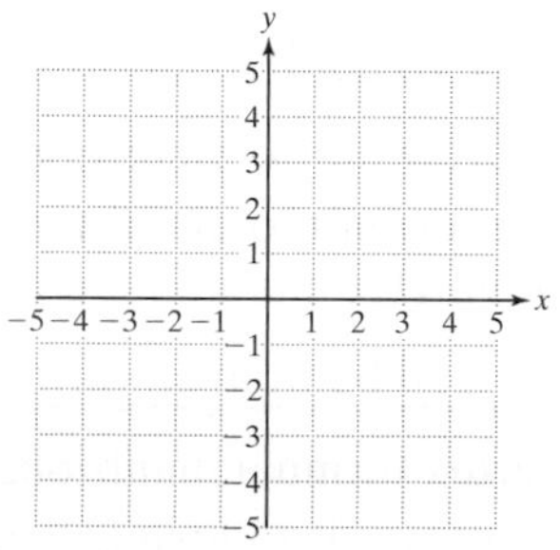

11. $y = x^2 - 4x + 3$

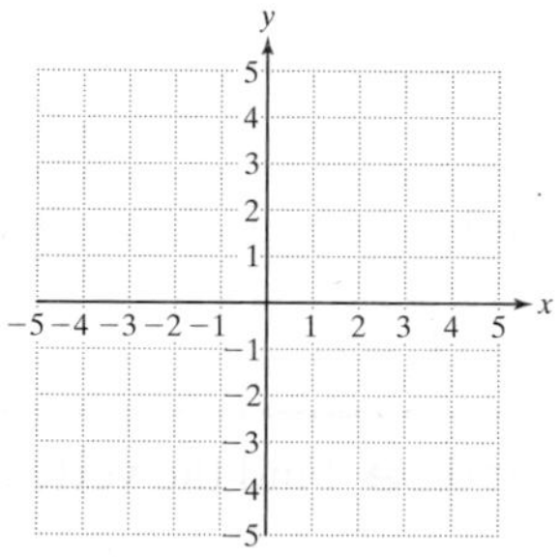

12. $y = x^2 + 6x + 5$

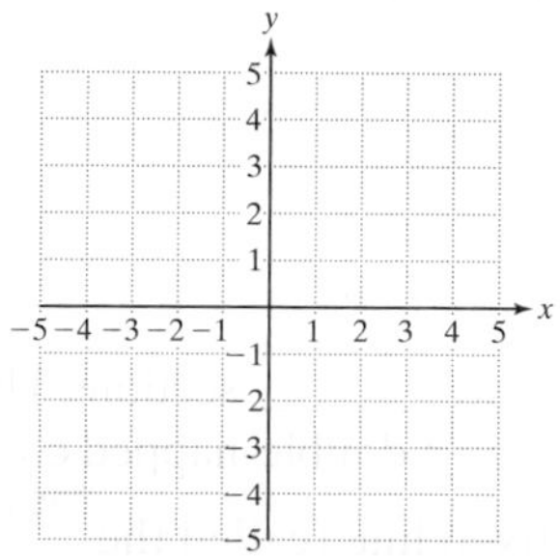

13. $y = -2x^2 + 8x$

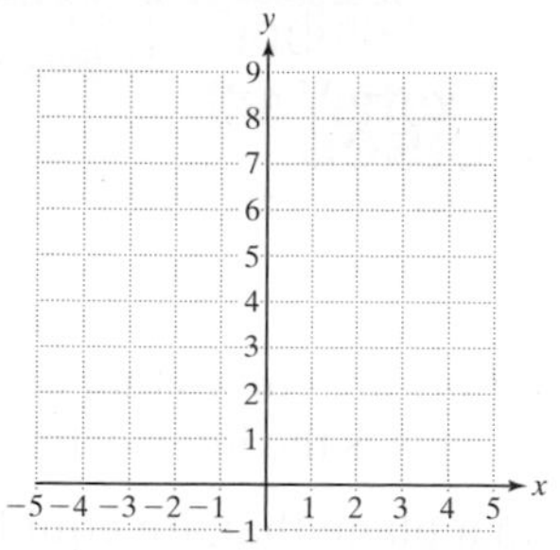

14. $y = -3x^2 - 6x$

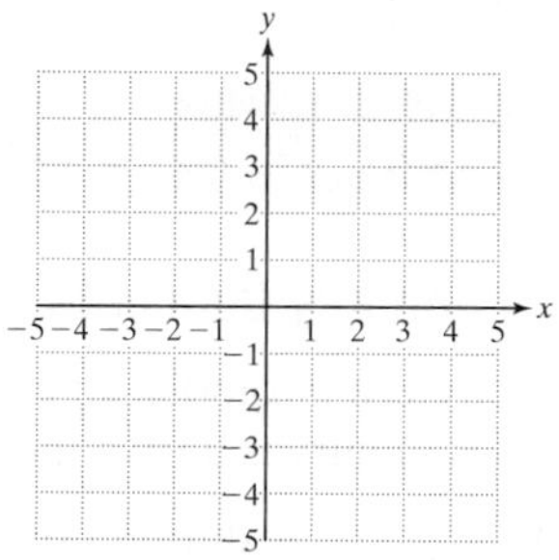

15. $y = -x^2 - 3x + 2$

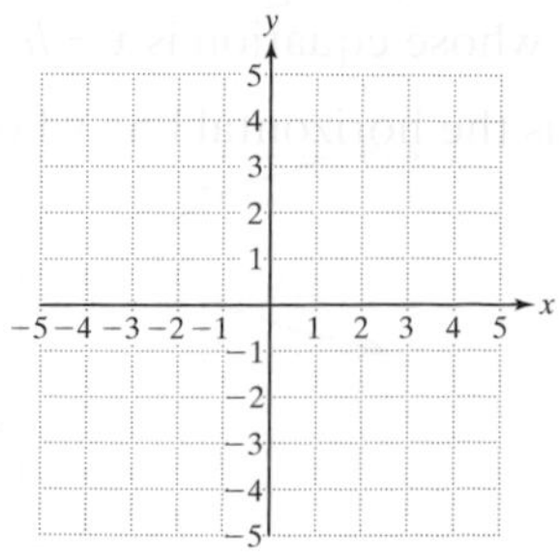

16. $y = -x^2 + x - 4$

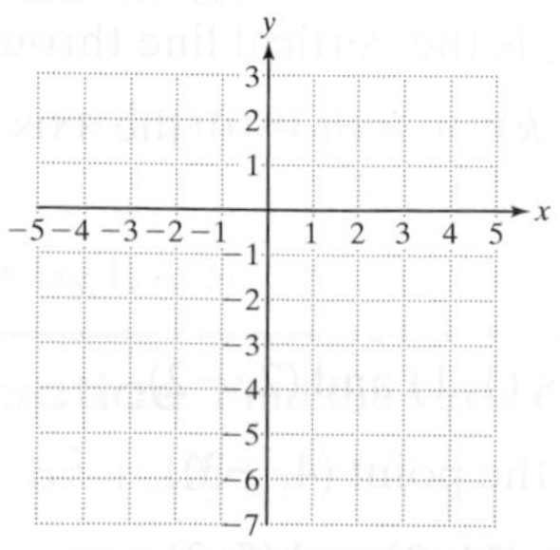

Concept 3: Parabola—Horizontal Axis of Symmetry

For Exercises 17–24, use the equation of the parabola in standard form $x = a(y - k)^2 + h$ to determine the coordinates of the vertex and the axis of symmetry (complete the square if necessary). Then graph the parabola. **(See Examples 2–3.)**

17. $x = y^2 - 3$

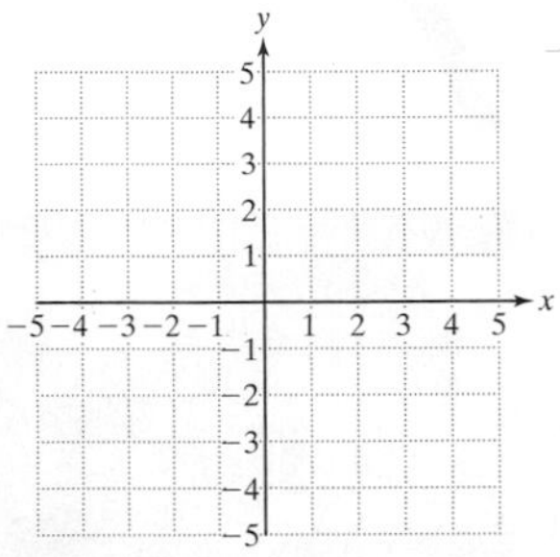

18. $x = y^2 + 1$

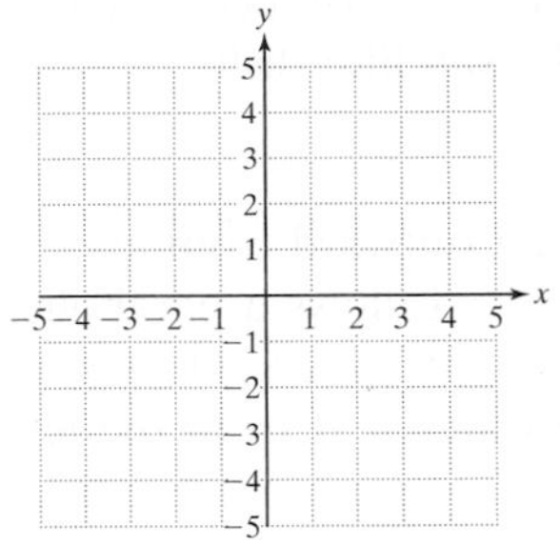

19. $x = -(y - 3)^2 - 3$

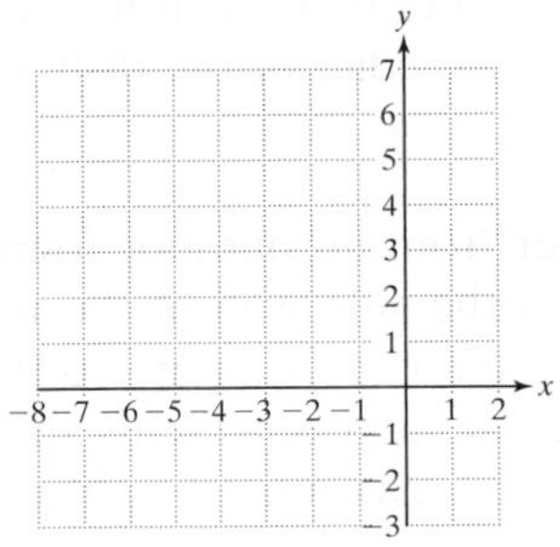

20. $x = -2(y + 2)^2 + 1$

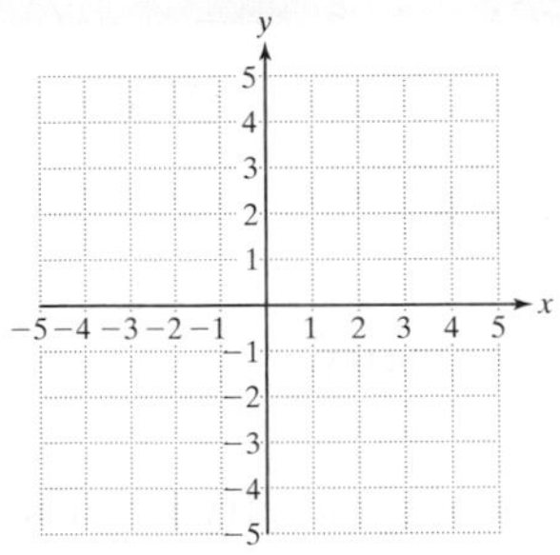

21. $x = -y^2 + 4y - 4$

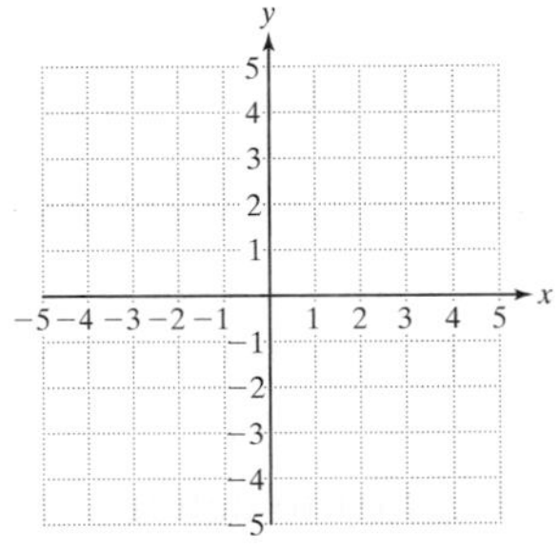

22. $x = -4y^2 - 4y - 2$

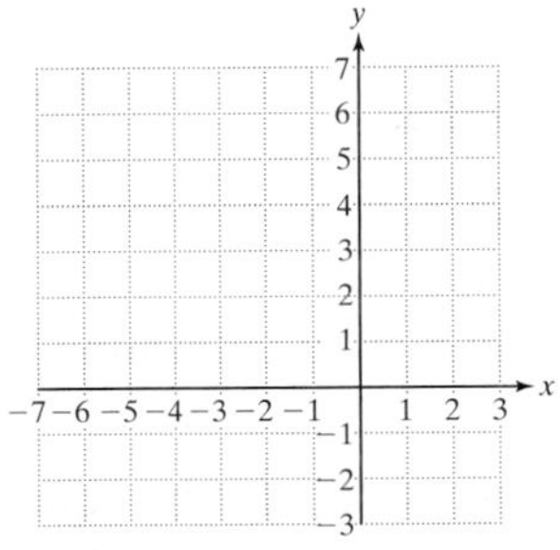

23. $x = y^2 - 2y + 2$

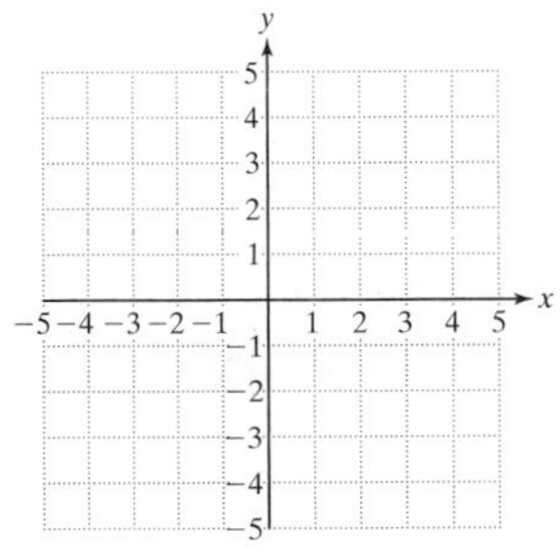

24. $x = y^2 + 4y + 1$

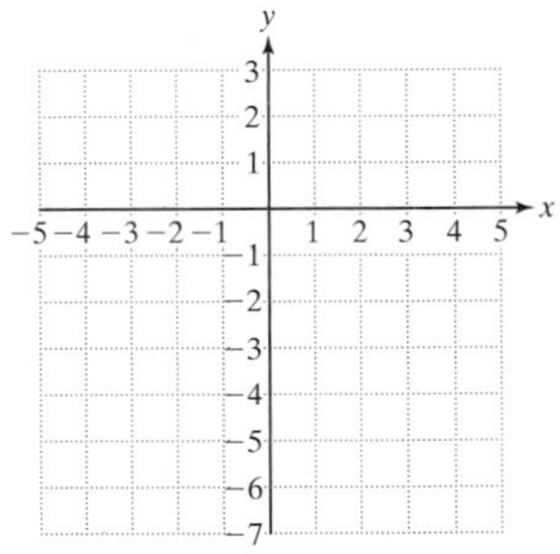

Concept 4: Vertex Formula

For Exercises 25–33, determine the vertex by using the vertex formula. **(See Examples 4–5.)**

25. $y = x^2 - 4x + 3$

26. $y = x^2 + 6x - 2$

27. $x = y^2 + 2y + 6$

28. $x = y^2 - 8y + 3$

29. $y = -\frac{1}{4}x^2 + x + \frac{3}{4}$

30. $y = -\frac{1}{2}x^2 - x + \frac{1}{2}$

31. $y = x^2 - 3x + 2$

32. $x = -2y^2 + 16y + 1$

33. $x = -3y^2 - 6y + 7$

Example 2 Graphing an Ellipse

Graph the ellipse given by the equation. $25x^2 + y^2 = 25$

Solution:

$25x^2 + y^2 = 25$ Divide both sides by 25.

$$\frac{25x^2}{25} + \frac{y^2}{25} = \frac{25}{25}$$

$$x^2 + \frac{y^2}{25} = 1$$

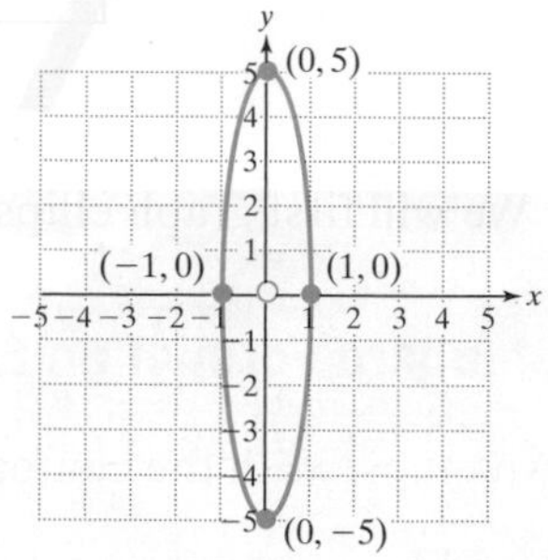

The equation can then be written as $\frac{x^2}{1^2} + \frac{y^2}{5^2} = 1.$

The equation is in standard form $\frac{x^2}{a^2} + \frac{y^2}{b^2} = 1,$

therefore, $a = 1$ and $b = 5$.

Graph the intercepts $(1, 0), (-1, 0), (0, 5)$, and $(0, -5)$ and sketch the ellipse.

Skill Practice

2. Graph the ellipse given by the equation $x^2 + 9y^2 = 9$.

A circle is a special case of an ellipse where $a = b$. Therefore, it is not surprising that we graph an ellipse centered at the point (h, k) in much the same way we graph a circle.

Example 3 Graphing an Ellipse Whose Center Is Not at the Origin

Graph the ellipse given by the equation. $\frac{(x-1)^2}{16} + \frac{(y+3)^2}{4} = 1$

Solution:

Animation

Just as we would find the center of a circle, we see that the center of the ellipse is $(1, -3)$. Now we can use the values of a and b to help us plot four strategic points to define the curve.

The equation can be written as
$$\frac{(x-1)^2}{(4)^2} + \frac{(y+3)^2}{(2)^2} = 1.$$

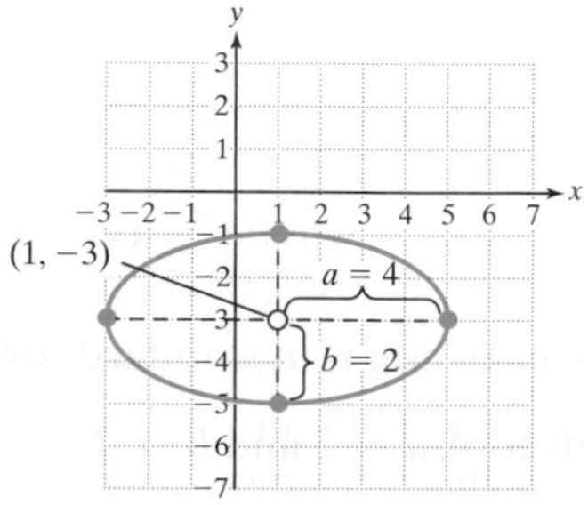

From this, we have $a = 4$ and $b = 2$. To sketch the curve, locate the center at $(1, -3)$. Then move $a = 4$ units to the left and right of the center and plot two points. Similarly, move $b = 2$ units up and down from the center and plot two points.

Skill Practice

3. Graph the ellipse $\frac{(x+1)^2}{4} + \frac{(y-4)^2}{9} = 1.$

Answers

2.

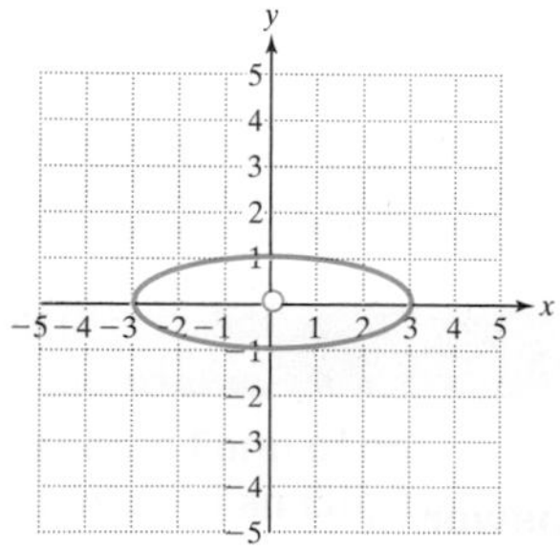

3.

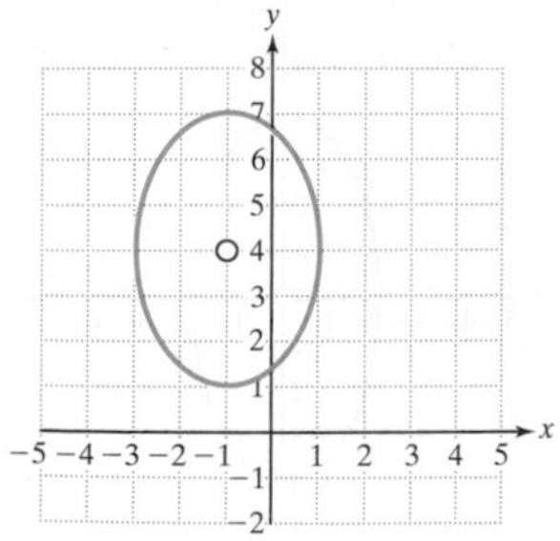

2. Standard Form of an Equation of a Hyperbola

A **hyperbola** is the set of all points (x, y) such that the absolute value of the *difference* of the distances between (x, y) and two distinct points is a constant. The fixed points are called the foci of the hyperbola. The graph of a hyperbola has two parts, called branches. A hyperbola has two vertices that lie on an axis of symmetry called the **transverse axis**. For the hyperbolas studied here, the transverse axis is either horizontal or vertical.

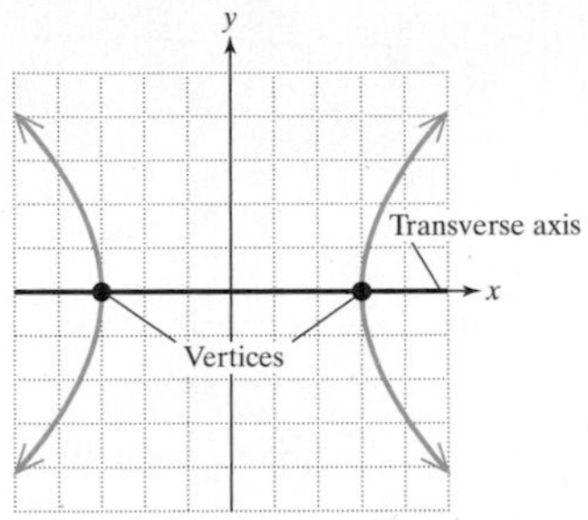

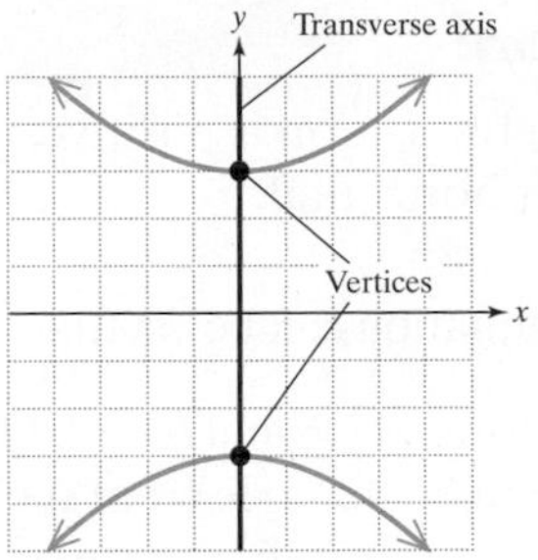

Standard Forms of an Equation of a Hyperbola with Center at the Origin

Let a and b represent positive real numbers.

Horizontal transverse axis:

The standard form of an equation of a hyperbola with a *horizontal transverse axis* and center at the origin is given by $\frac{x^2}{a^2} - \frac{y^2}{b^2} = 1$.

Note: The x term is positive. The branches of the hyperbola open left and right.

Vertical transverse axis:

The standard form of an equation of a hyperbola with a *vertical transverse axis* and center at the origin is given by $\frac{y^2}{b^2} - \frac{x^2}{a^2} = 1$.

Note: The y term is positive. The branches of the hyperbola open up and down.

In the standard forms of an equation of a hyperbola, the right side must equal 1.

To graph a hyperbola centered at the origin, first construct a reference rectangle. Draw this rectangle by using the points (a, b), $(-a, b)$, $(a, -b)$, and $(-a, -b)$. Asymptotes lie on the diagonals of the rectangle. The branches of the hyperbola are drawn to approach the asymptotes.

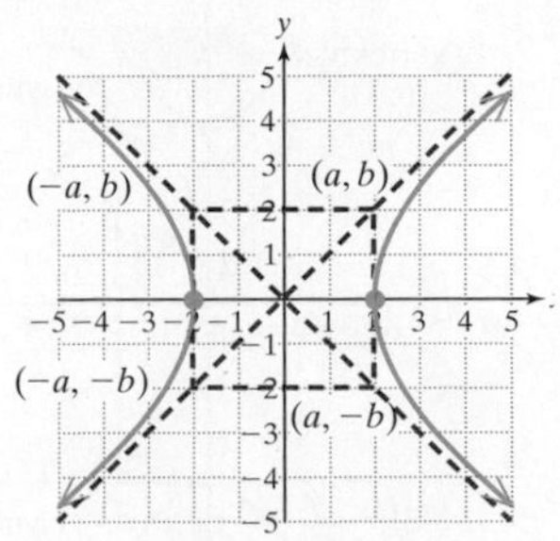

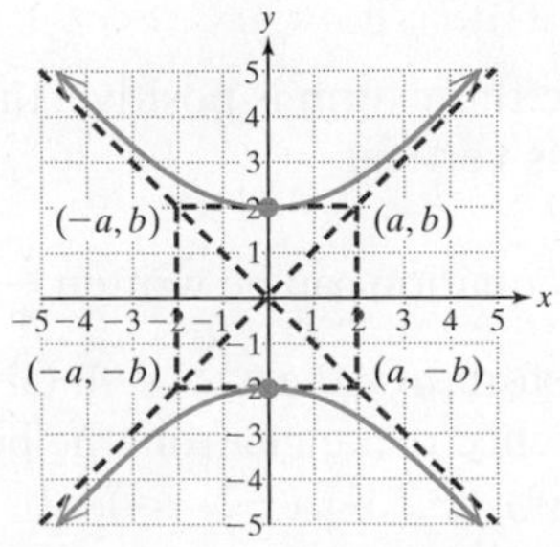

Example 4 Graphing a Hyperbola

Graph the hyperbola given by the equation. $\dfrac{x^2}{36} - \dfrac{y^2}{9} = 1$

a. Determine whether the transverse axis is horizontal or vertical.

b. Draw the reference rectangle and asymptotes.

c. Graph the hyperbola and label the vertices.

Solution:

a. Since the x-term is positive, the transverse axis is horizontal.

b. The equation can be written $\dfrac{x^2}{6^2} - \dfrac{y^2}{3^2} = 1$; therefore, $a = 6$ and $b = 3$. Graph the reference rectangle from the points $(6, 3), (6, -3), (-6, 3), (-6, -3)$.

c. The vertices are $(-6, 0)$ and $(6, 0)$.

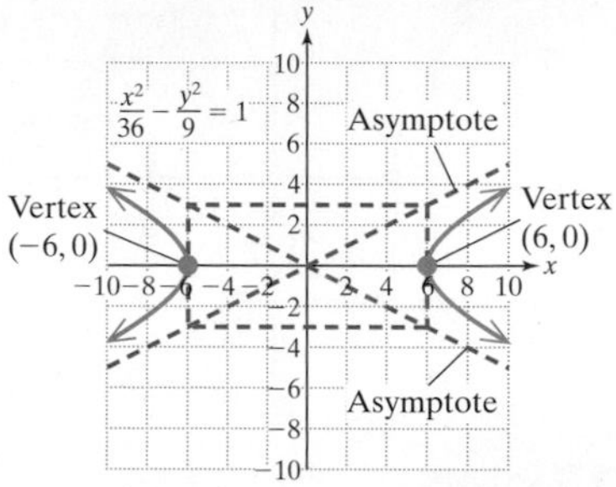

Skill Practice

4. Graph the hyperbola $x^2 - \dfrac{y^2}{9} = 1$.

Example 5 Graphing a Hyperbola

Graph the hyperbola given by the equation. $y^2 - 4x^2 - 16 = 0$

a. Write the equation in standard form to determine whether the transverse axis is horizontal or vertical.

b. Draw the reference rectangle and asymptotes.

c. Graph the hyperbola and label the vertices.

Solution:

a. $y^2 - 4x^2 - 16 = 0$

$y^2 - 4x^2 = 16$ Isolate the constant term on the right.

$\dfrac{y^2}{16} - \dfrac{4x^2}{16} = \dfrac{16}{16}$ Divide by 16 to make the constant term 1.

$\dfrac{y^2}{16} - \dfrac{x^2}{4} = 1$

Since the y term is positive, the transverse axis is vertical.

b. The equation can be written $\dfrac{y^2}{4^2} - \dfrac{x^2}{2^2} = 1$; therefore, $a = 2$ and $b = 4$. Graph the reference rectangle from the points $(2, 4)$, $(2, -4), (-2, 4), (-2, -4)$.

c. The vertices are $(0, 4)$ and $(0, -4)$.

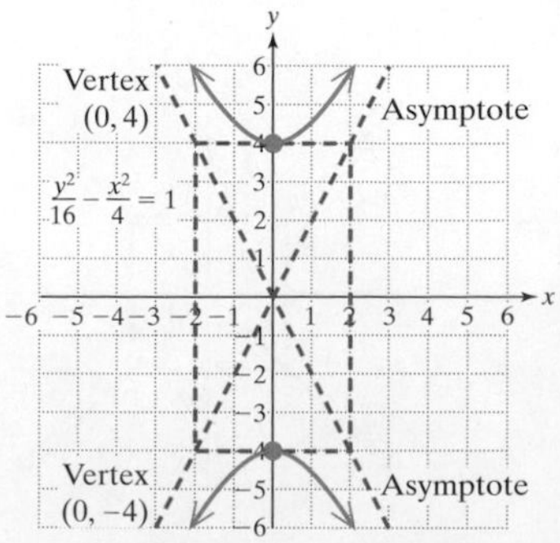

Skill Practice

5. Graph the hyperbola $9y^2 - 4x^2 = 36$.

Answers

4.

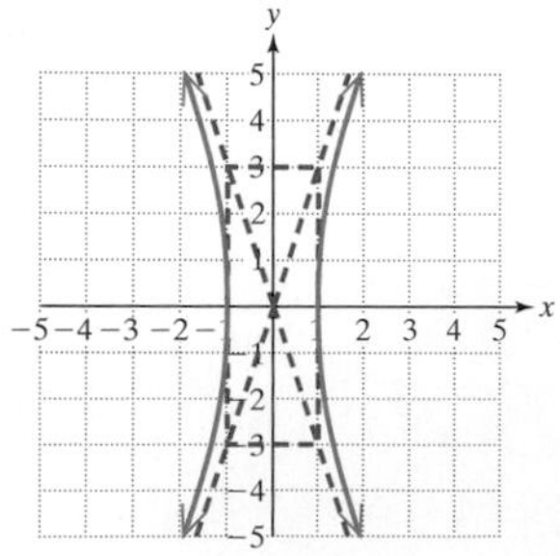

5.

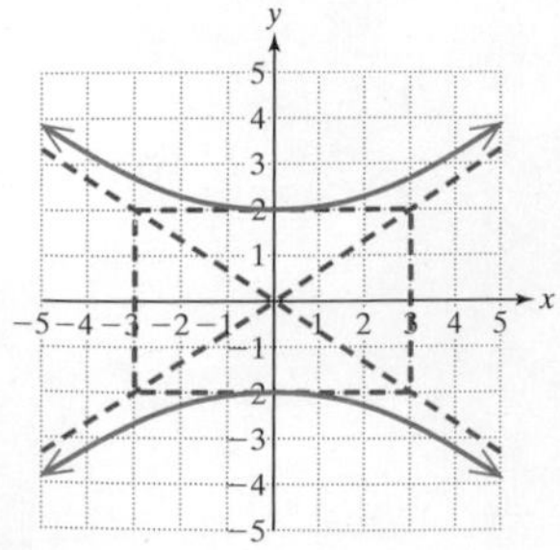

The following summarizes the steps for graphing ellipses and hyperbolas.

Graphing an Ellipse with Center at the Origin	Graphing a Hyperbola with Center at the Origin
1. Write the equation in standard form: $\frac{x^2}{a^2} + \frac{y^2}{b^2} = 1$ **2.** Plot the intercepts. x-intercepts: $(a, 0)$ and $(-a, 0)$ y-intercepts: $(0, b)$ and $(0, -b)$ **3.** Sketch the ellipse through the intercepts.	**1.** Write the equation in standard form: • Horizontal transverse axis: $\frac{x^2}{a^2} - \frac{y^2}{b^2} = 1$ • Vertical transverse axis: $\frac{y^2}{b^2} - \frac{x^2}{a^2} = 1$ **2.** Draw the reference rectangle through the points (a, b), $(a, -b)$, $(-a, b)$, and $(-a, -b)$. **3.** Draw the asymptotes. **4.** Plot the vertices and sketch the hyperbola.

Section 13.3 Practice Exercises

Vocabulary and Key Concepts

1. a. A(n) __________ is the set of all points (x, y) such that the sum of the distances between (x, y) and two distinct points (called __________) is constant.

b. The standard form of an equation of an __________ with center at the origin is $\frac{x^2}{a^2} + \frac{y^2}{b^2} = 1$.

c. A(n) __________ is the set of all points (x, y) such that the absolute value of the difference in distances between (x, y) and two distinct points (called __________) is a constant.

d. A hyperbola has two vertices that lie on an axis of symmetry called the __________ axis.

e. The standard form of an equation of a hyperbola with a *horizontal* transverse axis and center at $(0, 0)$, is given by __________.

f. The standard form of an equation of a hyperbola with a *vertical* transverse axis and center at $(0, 0)$, is given by __________.

Review Exercises

2. Write the standard form of a circle with center at (h, k) and radius, r.

For Exercises 3–4, identify the center and radius of the circle.

3. $x^2 + y^2 - 16x + 12y = 0$

4. $x^2 + y^2 + 4x + 4y - 1 = 0$

For Exercises 5–6, identify the vertex and the axis of symmetry.

5. $y = 3(x + 3)^2 - 1$

6. $x = -\frac{1}{4}(y - 1)^2 - 6$

7. Write an equation for a circle whose center has coordinates $\left(\frac{1}{2}, \frac{5}{2}\right)$ with radius equal to $\frac{1}{2}$.

8. Write the equation for the circle centered at the origin and with radius equal to $\frac{1}{8}$.

Concept 1: Standard Form of an Equation of an Ellipse

For Exercises 9–16, find the *x*- and *y*-intercepts and graph the ellipse. **(See Examples 1–2.)**

9. $\frac{x^2}{4} + \frac{y^2}{9} = 1$

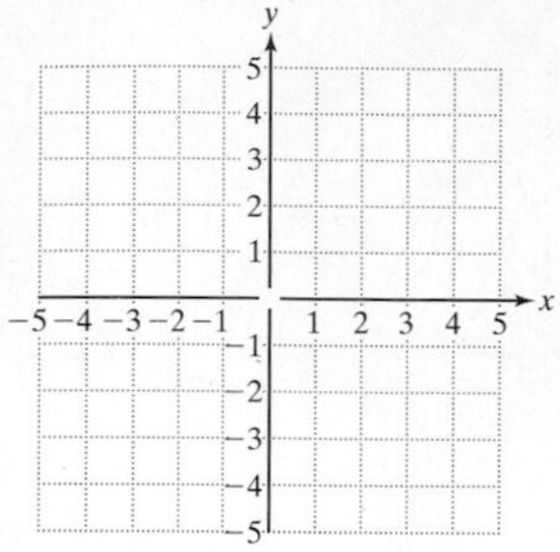

10. $\frac{x^2}{16} + \frac{y^2}{25} = 1$

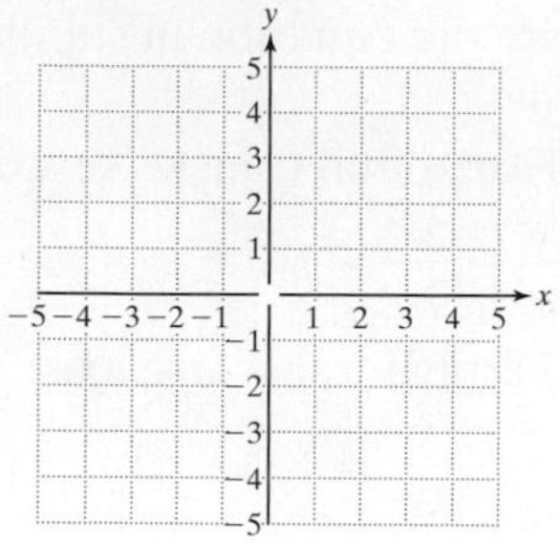

11. $\frac{x^2}{16} + \frac{y^2}{9} = 1$

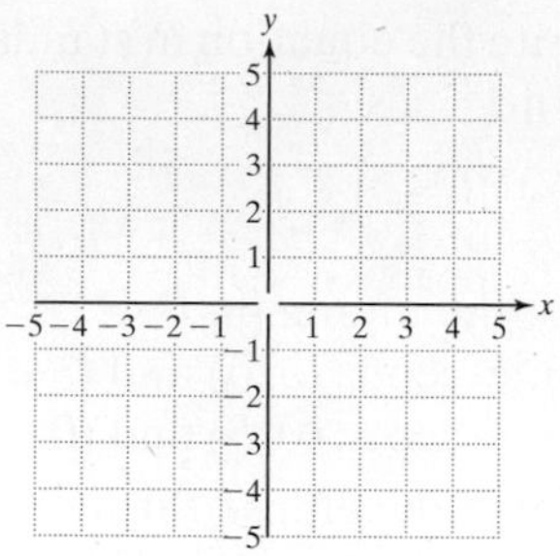

12. $\frac{x^2}{36} + \frac{y^2}{4} = 1$

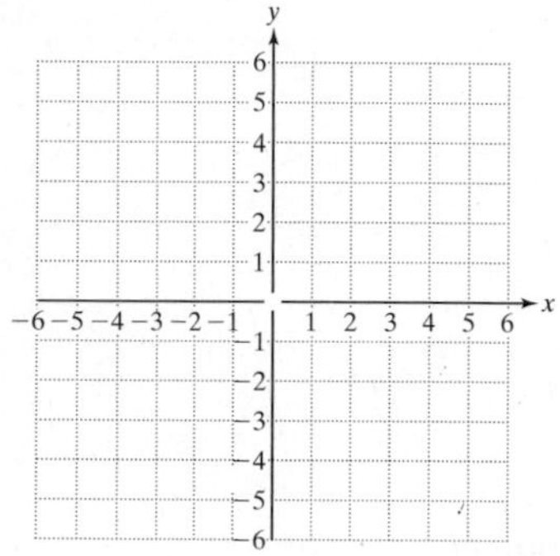

13. $4x^2 + y^2 = 4$

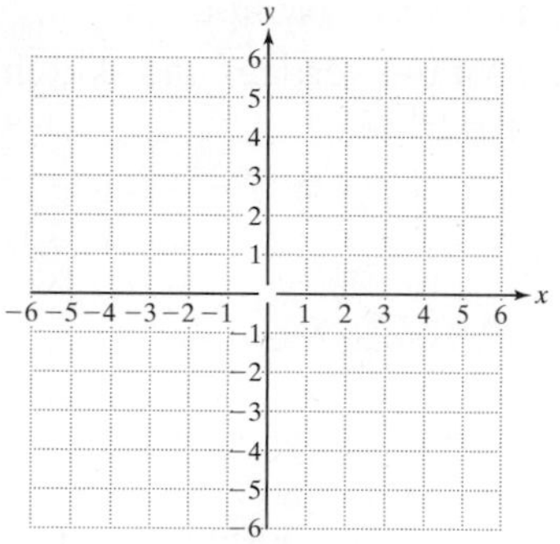

14. $9x^2 + y^2 = 36$

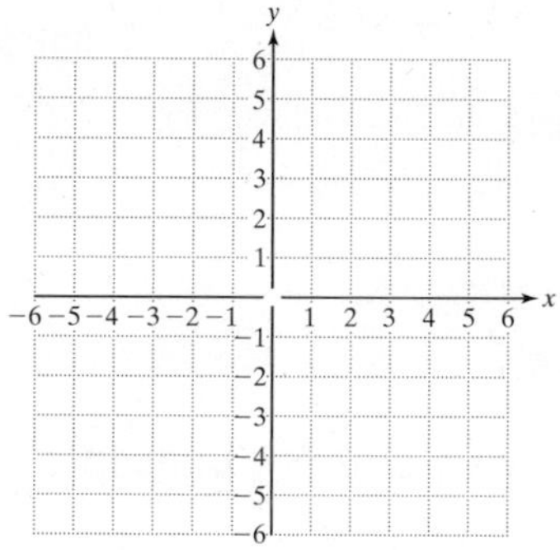

15. $x^2 + 25y^2 - 25 = 0$

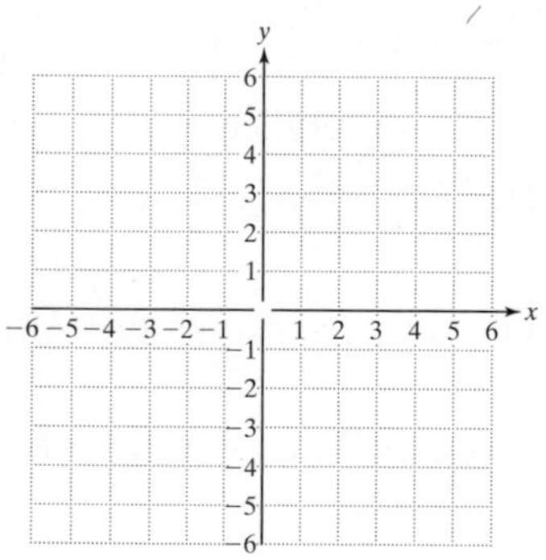

16. $4x^2 + 9y^2 = 144$

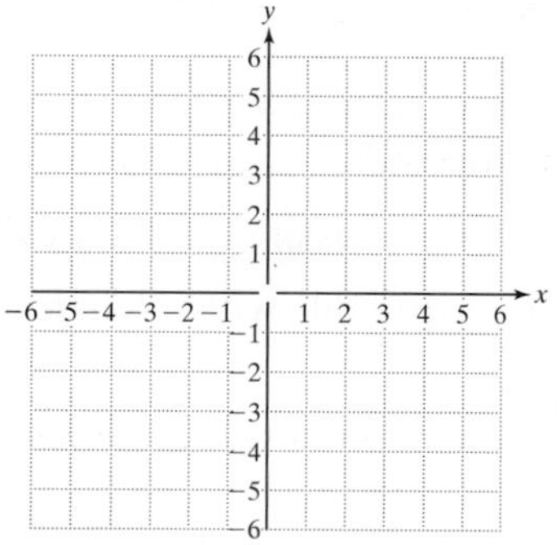

For Exercises 17–24, identify the center (h, k) of the ellipse. Then graph the ellipse. **(See Example 3.)**

17. $\frac{(x-4)^2}{4} + \frac{(y-5)^2}{9} = 1$

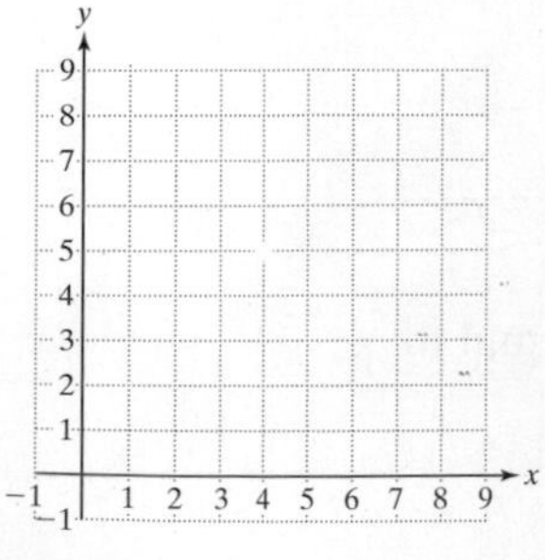

18. $\frac{(x+2)^2}{9} + \frac{(y-1)^2}{16} = 1$

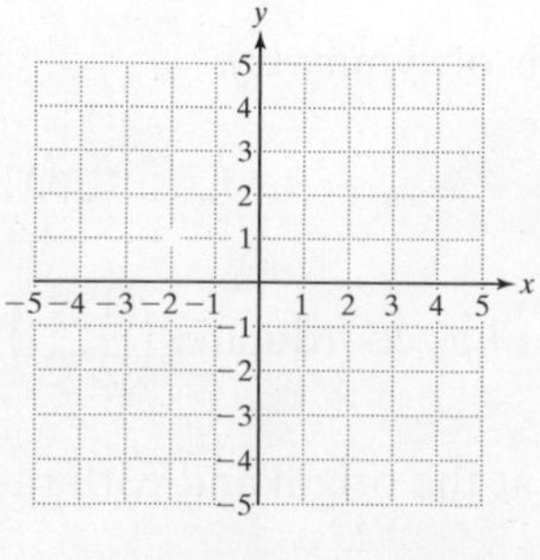

19. $\frac{(x+1)^2}{25} + \frac{(y-2)^2}{9} = 1$

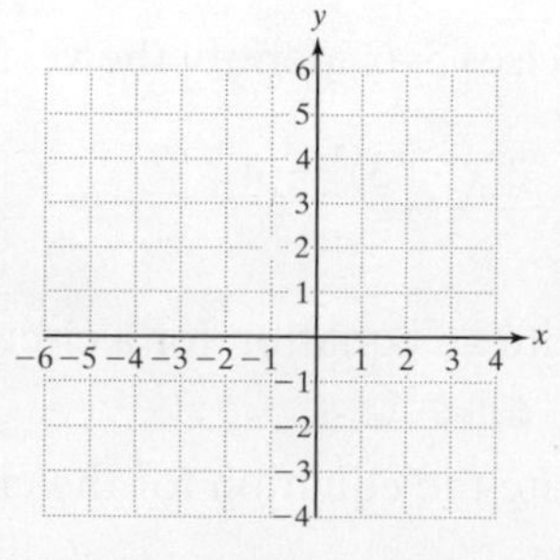

20. $\dfrac{(x-4)^2}{25}+\dfrac{(y+1)^2}{16}=1$

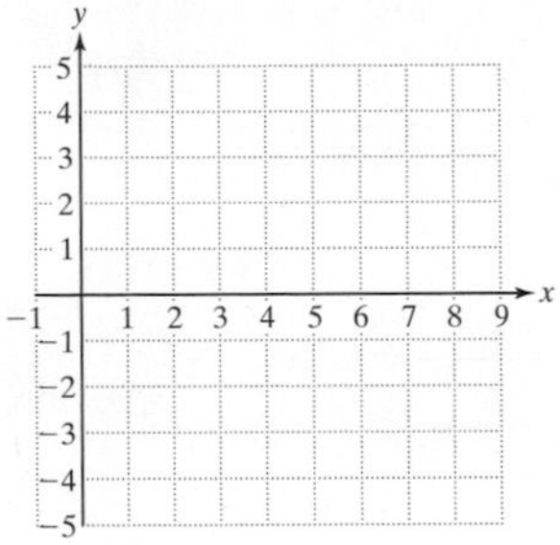

21. $\dfrac{(x-2)^2}{9}+(y+3)^2=1$

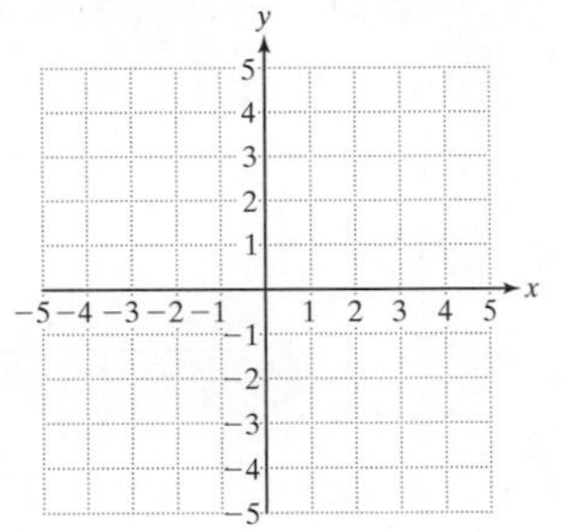

22. $(x-5)^2+\dfrac{(y-3)^2}{4}=1$

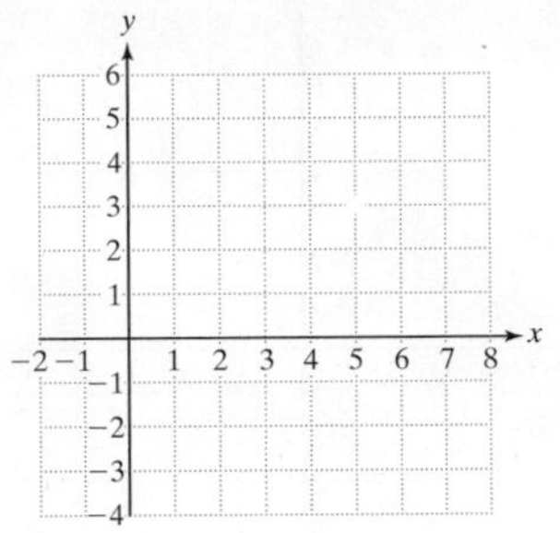

23. $\dfrac{x^2}{36}+\dfrac{(y-1)^2}{25}=1$

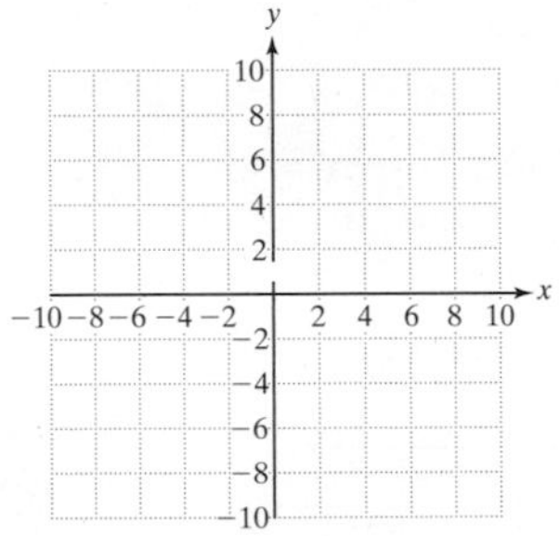

24. $\dfrac{(x+5)^2}{4}+\dfrac{y^2}{16}=1$

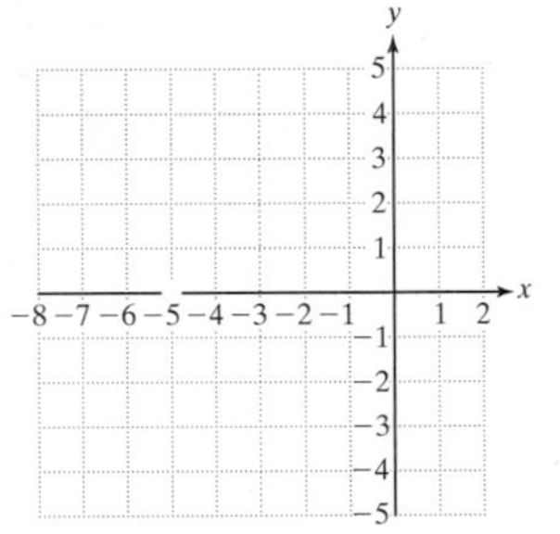

Concept 2: Standard Form of an Equation of a Hyperbola

For Exercises 25–32, determine whether the transverse axis is horizontal or vertical.

25. $\dfrac{y^2}{6}-\dfrac{x^2}{18}=1$

26. $\dfrac{y^2}{10}-\dfrac{x^2}{4}=1$

27. $\dfrac{x^2}{20}-\dfrac{y^2}{15}=1$

28. $\dfrac{x^2}{12}-\dfrac{y^2}{9}=1$

29. $x^2-y^2=12$

30. $x^2-y^2=15$

31. $x^2-3y^2=-9$

32. $2x^2-y^2=-10$

For Exercises 33–40, use the equation in standard form to graph the hyperbola. Label the vertices of the hyperbola. **(See Examples 4–5.)**

33. $\dfrac{x^2}{25}-\dfrac{y^2}{16}=1$

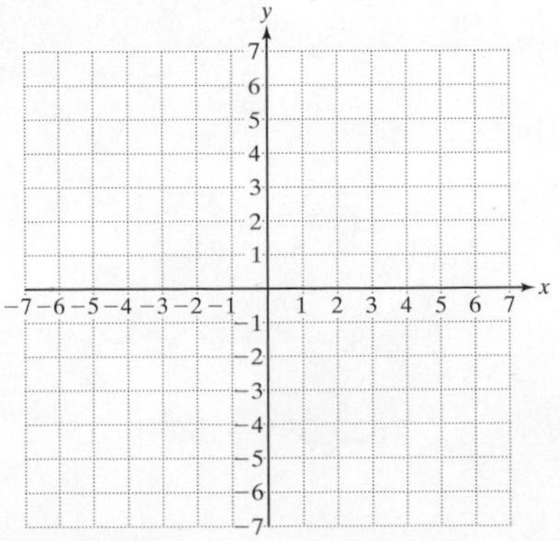

34. $\dfrac{x^2}{9}-\dfrac{y^2}{36}=1$

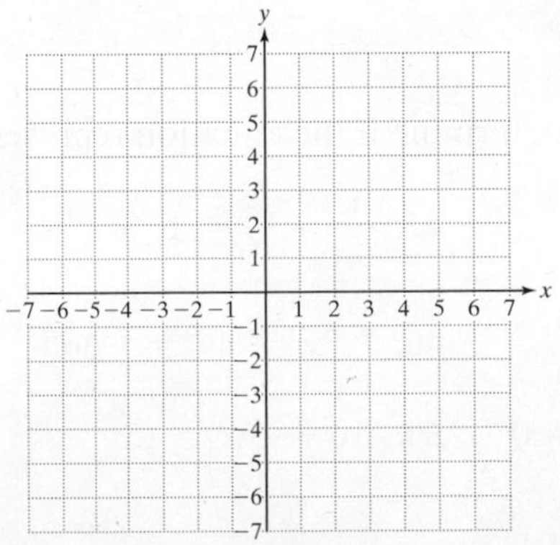

35. $\dfrac{y^2}{4} - \dfrac{x^2}{4} = 1$

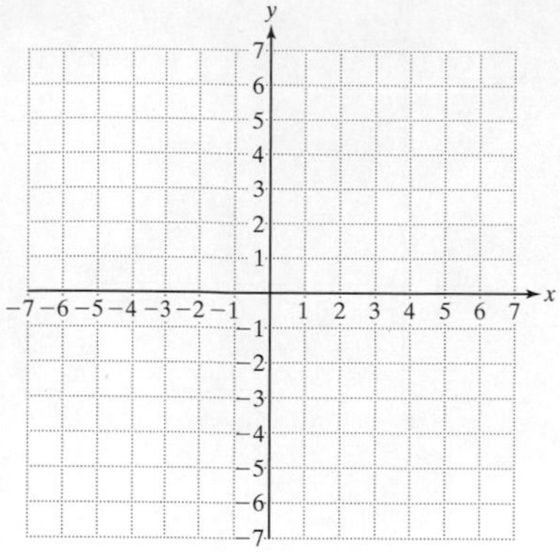

36. $\dfrac{y^2}{9} - \dfrac{x^2}{9} = 1$

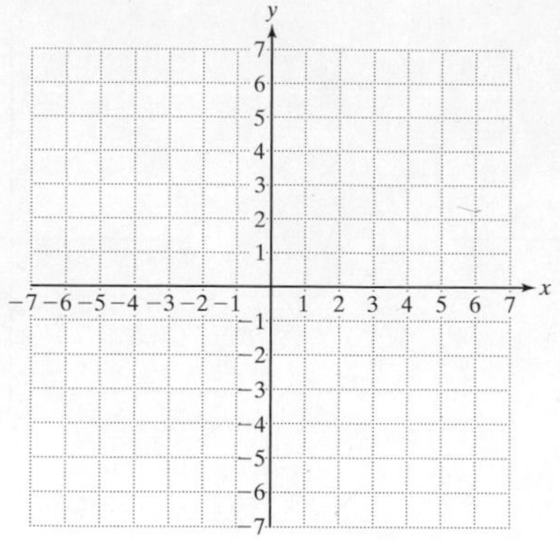

37. $36x^2 - y^2 = 36$

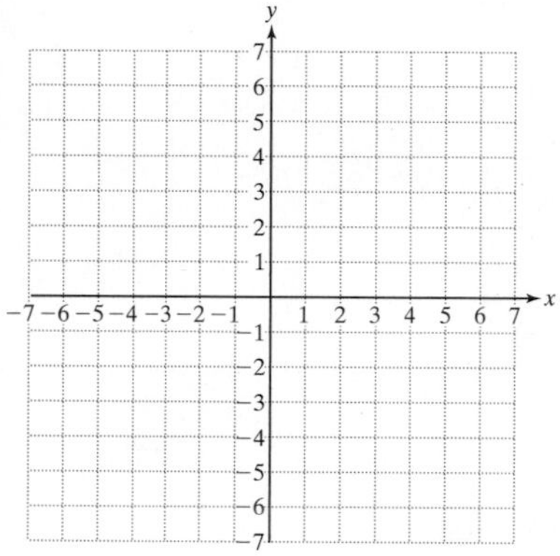

38. $x^2 - 25y^2 = 25$

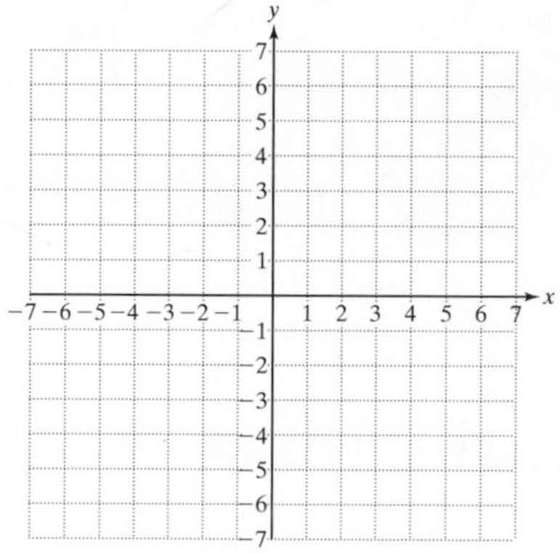

39. $y^2 - 4x^2 - 16 = 0$

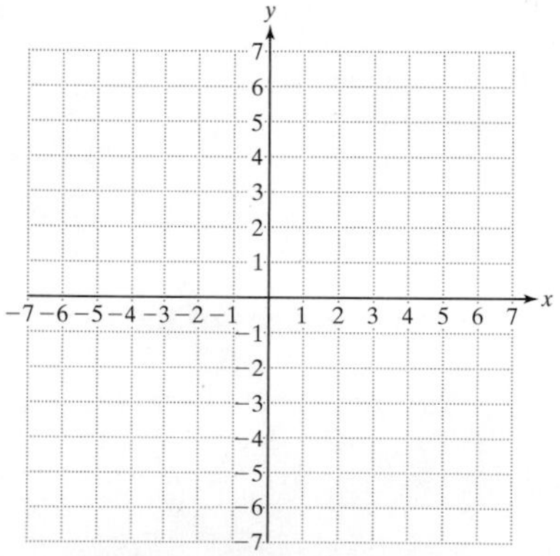

40. $y^2 - 4x^2 - 36 = 0$

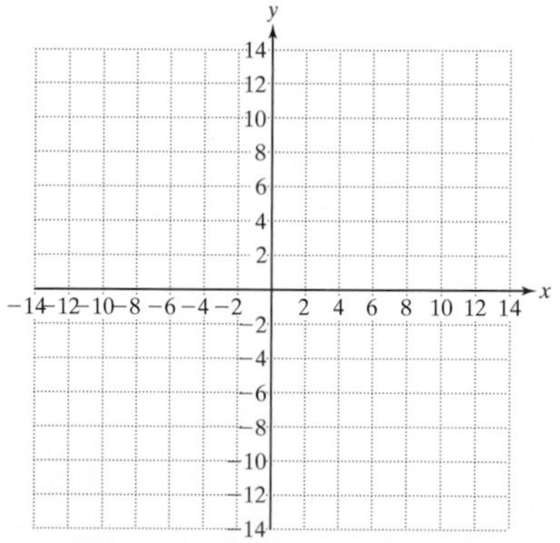

Mixed Exercises

For Exercises 41–52, determine if the equation represents an ellipse or a hyperbola.

41. $\dfrac{x^2}{6} - \dfrac{y^2}{10} = 1$

42. $\dfrac{x^2}{14} + \dfrac{y^2}{2} = 1$

43. $\dfrac{y^2}{4} + \dfrac{x^2}{16} = 1$

44. $\dfrac{x^2}{5} + \dfrac{y^2}{10} = 1$

45. $4x^2 + y^2 = 16$

46. $-3x^2 - 4y^2 = -36$

47. $-y^2 + 2x^2 = -10$

48. $x^2 - y^2 = -1$

49. $5x^2 + y^2 - 10 = 0$

50. $5x^2 - 3y^2 = 15$

51. $y^2 - 6x^2 = 6$

52. $3x^2 + 5y^2 = 15$

Expanding Your Skills

53. An arch for a tunnel is in the shape of a semiellipse. The distance between vertices is 120 ft, and the height to the top of the arch is 50 ft. Find the height of the arch 10 ft from the center. Round to the nearest foot.

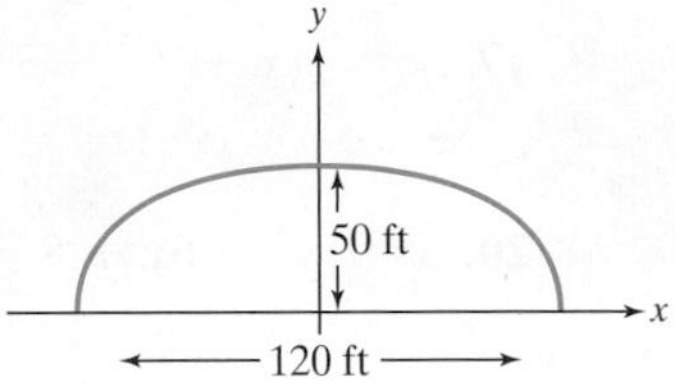

54. A bridge over a gorge is supported by an arch in the shape of a semiellipse. The length of the bridge is 400 ft, and the height is 100 ft. Find the height of the arch 50 ft from the center. Round to the nearest foot.

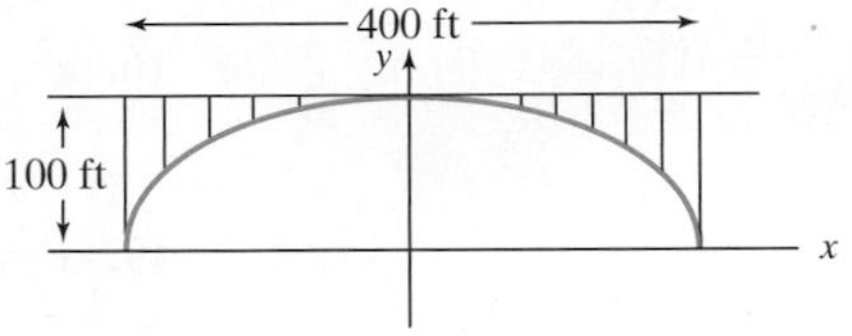

In Exercises 55–58, graph the hyperbola centered at (h, k) by following these guidelines. First locate the center. Then draw the reference rectangle relative to the center (h, k). Using the reference rectangle as a guide, sketch the hyperbola. Label the center and vertices.

55. $\dfrac{(x-1)^2}{9} - \dfrac{(y+2)^2}{4} = 1$

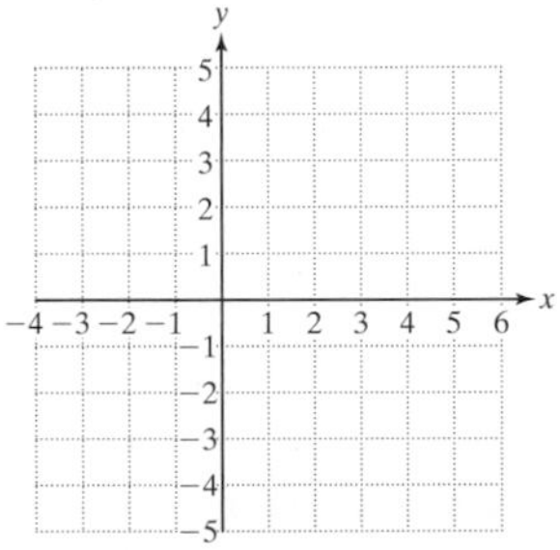

56. $\dfrac{(x+2)^2}{16} - \dfrac{(y-3)^2}{4} = 1$

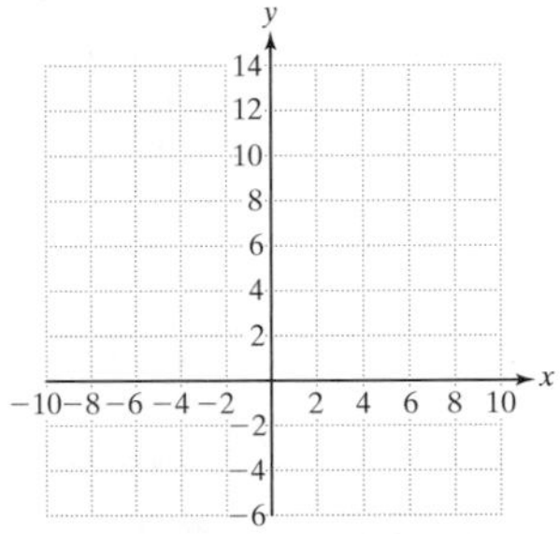

57. $\dfrac{(y-1)^2}{4} - (x+3)^2 = 1$

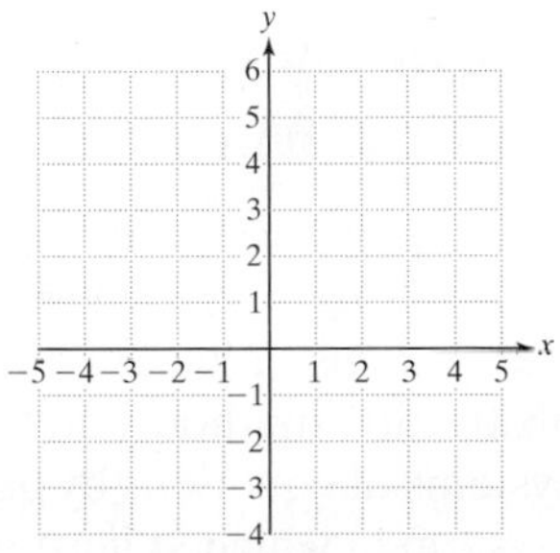

58. $(y+2)^2 - \dfrac{(x+3)^2}{4} = 1$

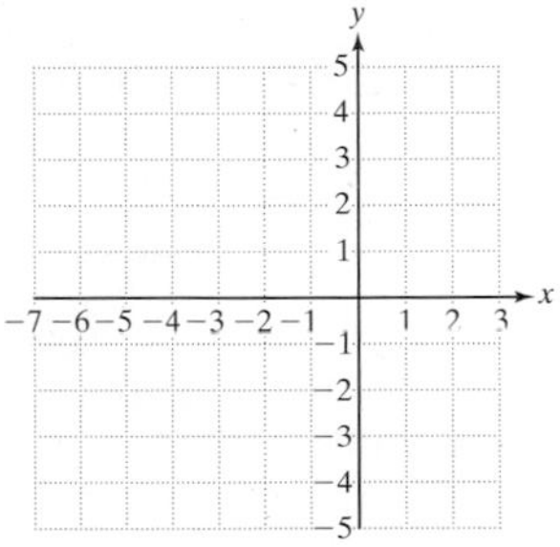

Problem Recognition Exercises

Formulas and Conic Sections

For Exercises 1–8, identify the formula.

1. $(x-h)^2 + (y-k)^2 = r^2$

2. $\dfrac{x^2}{a^2} + \dfrac{y^2}{b^2} = 1$

3. $\sqrt{(x_2 - x_1)^2 + (y_2 - y_1)^2}$

4. $\left(\dfrac{x_1 + x_2}{2}, \dfrac{y_1 + y_2}{2}\right)$

5. $y = a(x-h)^2 + k$

6. $\dfrac{x^2}{a^2} - \dfrac{y^2}{b^2} = 1$

7. $\dfrac{y^2}{b^2} - \dfrac{x^2}{a^2} = 1$

8. $x = a(y-k)^2 + h$

For Exercises 9–30, identify the equation as representing a circle, parabola, ellipse, hyperbola, or none of the above.

9. $y = -2(x - 3)^2 + 4$

10. $\dfrac{x^2}{4} - \dfrac{y^2}{1} = 1$

11. $(x + 3)^2 + (y + 2)^2 = 4$

12. $(x - 2)^2 + (y - 4)^2 = 9$

13. $\dfrac{x^2}{9} - \dfrac{y^2}{9} = 1$

14. $\dfrac{x^2}{9} + \dfrac{y^2}{16} = 1$

15. $\dfrac{x^2}{16} + \dfrac{y^2}{4} = 0$

16. $x^2 + y^2 - 2x + 4y - 4 = 0$

17. $y = \dfrac{1}{2}(x + 2)^2 - 3$

18. $\dfrac{x^2}{4} - \dfrac{y^2}{2} = 1$

19. $x = (y + 2)^2 - 4$

20. $x^2 + y^2 + 6x + 8 = 0$

21. $(x - 1)^2 + (y + 1)^2 = 0$

22. $x = -(y - 2)^2 - 1$

23. $\dfrac{x^2}{25} + \dfrac{y^2}{4} = 1$

24. $x^2 + y^2 = 15$

25. $y = (x - 6)^2 + 4$

26. $\dfrac{(x + 1)^2}{2} + \dfrac{(y + 1)^2}{5} = 1$

27. $\dfrac{y^2}{3} - \dfrac{x^2}{3} = 1$

28. $3x^2 + 3y^2 = 1$

29. $\dfrac{x^2}{9} + \dfrac{y^2}{12} = 1$

30. $x = (y + 2)^2 - 5$

Section 13.4 Nonlinear Systems of Equations in Two Variables

Concepts

1. **Solving Nonlinear Systems of Equations by the Substitution Method**
2. **Solving Nonlinear Systems of Equations by the Addition Method**

1. Solving Nonlinear Systems of Equations by the Substitution Method

Recall that a linear equation in two variables x and y is an equation that can be written in the form $Ax + By = C$, where A and B are not both zero. In Sections 4.1–4.3, we solved systems of linear equations in two variables by using the graphing method, the substitution method, and the addition method. In this section, we will solve *nonlinear* systems of equations by using the same methods. A **nonlinear system of equations** is a system in which at least one of the equations is nonlinear.

Graphing the equations in a nonlinear system helps to determine the number of solutions and to approximate the coordinates of the solutions. The substitution method is used most often to solve a nonlinear system of equations analytically.

Example 1 Solving a Nonlinear System of Equations

Given the system
$$x - 7y = -25$$
$$x^2 + y^2 = 25$$

a. Solve the system by graphing.

b. Solve the system by the substitution method.

Solution:

a. $x - 7y = -25$ is a line (the slope-intercept form is $y = \frac{1}{7}x + \frac{25}{7}$).

$x^2 + y^2 = 25$ is a circle centered at the origin with radius 5.

From Figure 13-16, we appear to have two solutions $(-4, 3)$ and $(3, 4)$.

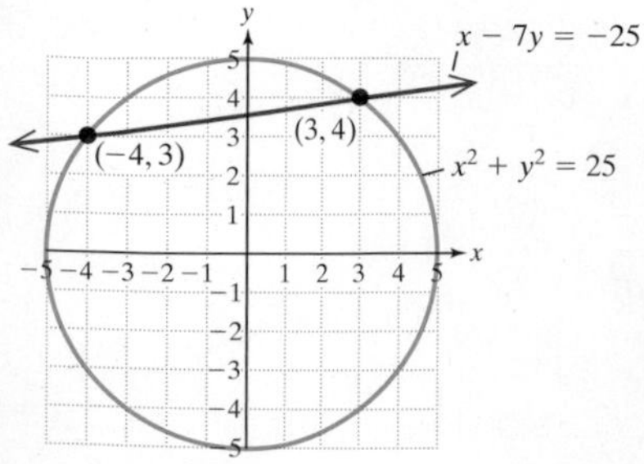

Figure 13-16

b. To use the substitution method, isolate one of the variables from one of the equations. We will solve for x in the first equation.

$\boxed{A}$ $x - 7y = -25 \xrightarrow{\text{Solve for } x.} x = 7y - 25$

$\boxed{B}$ $x^2 + y^2 = 25$

$\boxed{B}$ $(7y - 25)^2 + y^2 = 25$ Substitute $(7y - 25)$ for x in the second equation.

$49y^2 - 350y + 625 + y^2 = 25$ The resulting equation is quadratic in y.

$50y^2 - 350y + 600 = 0$ Set the equation equal to zero.

$50(y^2 - 7y + 12) = 0$ Factor.

$50(y - 3)(y - 4) = 0$

$y = 3$ or $y = 4$

For each value of y, find the corresponding x value from the equation $x = 7y - 25$.

$y = 3$: $x = 7(3) - 25 = -4$ The solution point is $(-4, 3)$.

$y = 4$: $x = 7(4) - 25 = 3$ The solution point is $(3, 4)$. (See Figure 13-16.)

The solution set is $\{(-4, 3), (3, 4)\}$.

Skill Practice Given the system

$$2x + y = 5$$
$$x^2 + y^2 = 50$$

1. Solve the system by graphing.
2. Solve the system by the substitution method.

Example 2 Solving a Nonlinear System by the Substitution Method

Given the system $y = \sqrt{x}$
$x^2 + y^2 = 20$

a. Sketch the graphs.
b. Solve the system by the substitution method.

Solution:

a. $y = \sqrt{x}$ is one of the six basic functions graphed in Section 8.3.

$x^2 + y^2 = 20$ is a circle centered at the origin with radius $\sqrt{20} \approx 4.5$.

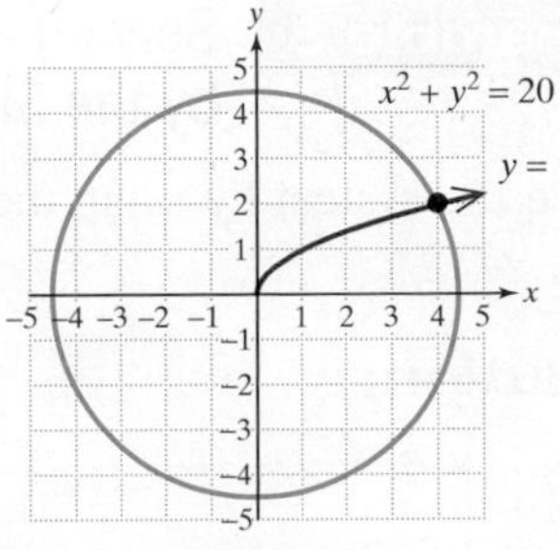

Figure 13-17

From Figure 13-17, we see that there is one solution.

Answers

1.

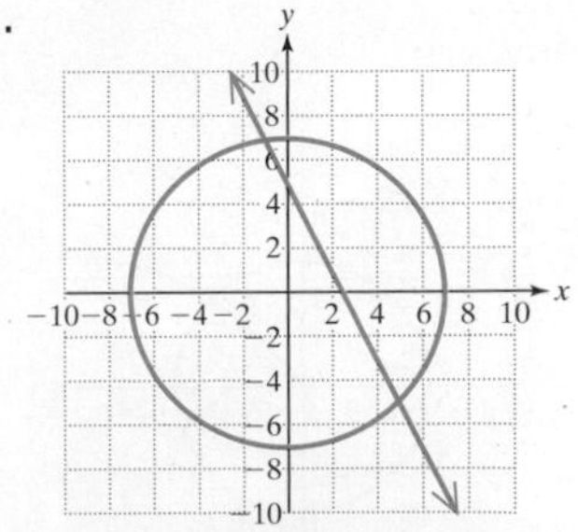

The solutions appear to be $(-1, 7)$ and $(5, -5)$.

2. $\{(-1, 7), (5, -5)\}$

b. To use the substitution method, we will substitute $y = \sqrt{x}$ into equation B.

A $\quad y = \sqrt{x} \quad$ Substitute $y = \sqrt{x}$ into the second equation.

B $\quad x^2 + y^2 = 20$

B $\quad x^2 + (\sqrt{x})^2 = 20$

$x^2 + x = 20$

$x^2 + x - 20 = 0 \quad$ Set the second equation equal to zero.

$(x + 5)(x - 4) = 0 \quad$ Factor.

~~$x = -5$~~ or $x = 4 \quad$ Reject $x = -5$ because it is not in the domain of $y = \sqrt{x}$.

Substitute $x = 4$ into the equation $y = \sqrt{x}$.

If $x = 4$, then $y = \sqrt{4} = 2$. The solution set is $\{(4, 2)\}$.

Skill Practice Given the system

$$y = \sqrt{2x}$$
$$x^2 + y^2 = 8$$

3. Sketch the graphs.

4. Solve the system by using the substitution method.

Calculator Connections

Topic: Graphing a Nonlinear System of Equations

Graph the equations from Example 2 to confirm your solution to the system of equations. Use an *Intersect* feature to approximate the point of intersection. Recall that the circle must be entered into the calculator as two functions:

$$Y_1 = \sqrt{20 - x^2}$$
$$Y_2 = -\sqrt{20 - x^2}$$
$$Y_3 = \sqrt{x}$$

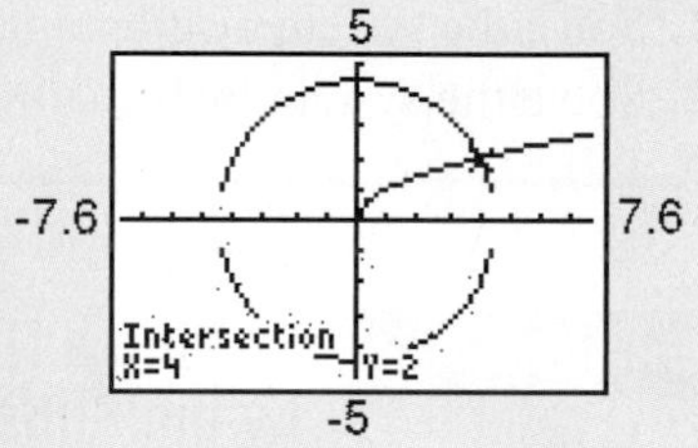

Example 3 **Solving a Nonlinear System by the Substitution Method**

Solve the system by using the substitution method. $\quad y = \sqrt[3]{x}$

$y = x$

Solution:

A $\quad y = \sqrt[3]{x}$

B $\quad y = x$

$\sqrt[3]{x} = x \quad$ Because y is isolated in both equations, we can equate the expressions for y.

$(\sqrt[3]{x})^3 = (x)^3 \quad$ To solve the radical equation, raise both sides to the third power.

Answers

3.

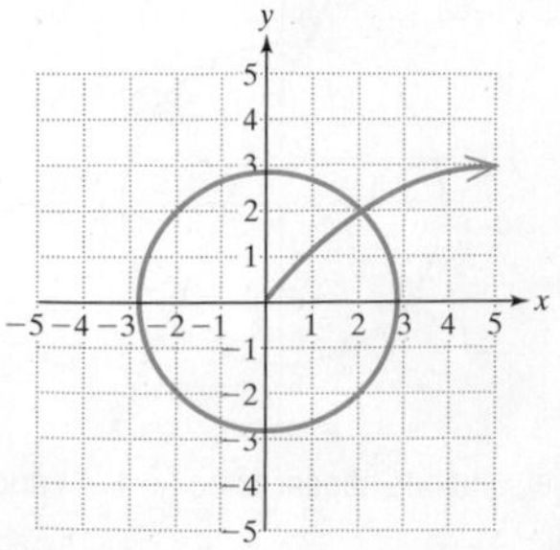

4. $\{(2, 2)\}$

$x = x^3$	This is a third-degree polynomial equation.
$0 = x^3 - x$	Set the equation equal to zero.
$0 = x(x^2 - 1)$	Factor out the GCF.
$0 = x(x + 1)(x - 1)$	Factor completely.

$x = 0 \quad \text{or} \quad x = -1 \quad \text{or} \quad x = 1$

For each value of x, find the corresponding y-value from either original equation. We will use equation $\boxed{B}$: $y = x$.

If $x = 0$, then $y = 0$.	The solution point is $(0, 0)$.
If $x = -1$, then $y = -1$.	The solution point is $(-1, -1)$.
If $x = 1$, then $y = 1$.	The solution point is $(1, 1)$.

The solution set is $\{(0, 0), (-1, -1), (1, 1)\}$. See Figure 13-18.

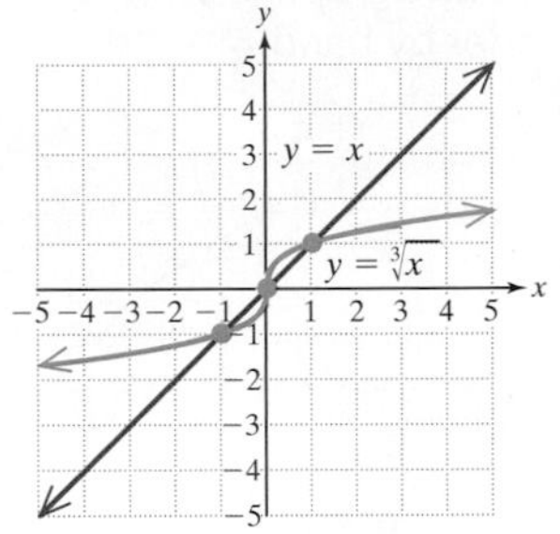

Figure 13-18

Skill Practice Solve the system by using the substitution method.

5. $y = \sqrt[3]{9x}$
$y = x$

2. Solving Nonlinear Systems of Equations by the Addition Method

The substitution method is used most often to solve a system of nonlinear equations. In some situations, however, the addition method offers an efficient means of finding a solution. Example 4 demonstrates that we can eliminate a variable from both equations provided the terms containing the corresponding variables are *like* terms.

Example 4 **Solving a Nonlinear System of Equations by the Addition Method**

Solve the system.
$$2x^2 + y^2 = 17$$
$$x^2 + 2y^2 = 22$$

Solution:

$\boxed{A}$ $2x^2 + y^2 = 17$ Notice that the y^2 terms are *like* in each equation.

$\boxed{B}$ $x^2 + 2y^2 = 22$ To eliminate the y^2 terms, multiply the first equation by -2.

$\boxed{A}$ $2x^2 + y^2 = 17 \xrightarrow{\text{Multiply by } -2.} -4x^2 - 2y^2 = -34$

$\boxed{B}$ $x^2 + 2y^2 = 22 \longrightarrow x^2 + 2y^2 = 22$

$-3x^2 = -12$ Eliminate the y^2 term.

$$\frac{-3x^2}{-3} = \frac{-12}{-3}$$

$$x^2 = 4$$

$x = \pm 2$ Use the square root property.

TIP: In Example 4, the x^2 terms are also *like* in both equations. We could have eliminated the x^2 terms by multiplying equation $\boxed{B}$ by -2.

Answer

5. $\{(0, 0), (3, 3), (-3, -3)\}$

Substitute each value of x into one of the original equations to solve for y. We will use equation $\boxed{A}$: $2x^2 + y^2 = 17$.

$x = 2$: $\boxed{A}$
$$2(2)^2 + y^2 = 17$$
$$8 + y^2 = 17$$
$$y^2 = 9$$
$$y = \pm 3$$ The solution points are (2, 3) and (2, −3).

$x = -2$: $\boxed{A}$
$$2(-2)^2 + y^2 = 17$$
$$8 + y^2 = 17$$
$$y^2 = 9$$
$$y = \pm 3$$ The solution points are (−2, 3) and (−2, −3).

The solution set is $\{(2, 3), (2, -3), (-2, 3), (-2, -3)\}$.

TIP: The two equations in Example 4 are ellipses but an exact graph is difficult to render by hand.

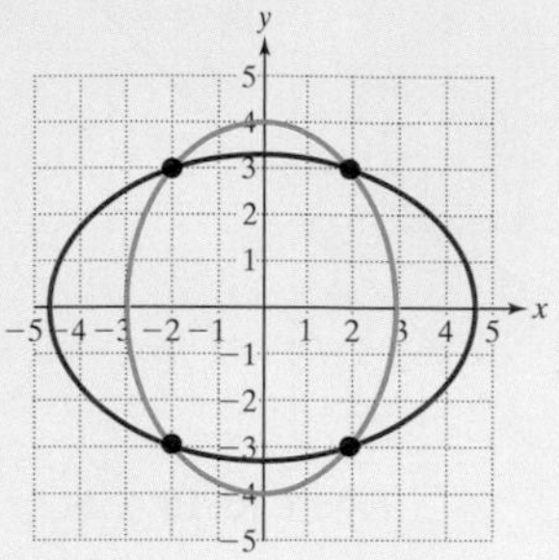

To check the solutions to the system, verify that each ordered pair satisfies both equations.

Skill Practice Solve the system by using the addition method.

6. $x^2 - y^2 = 24$
$3x^2 + y^2 = 76$

Answer

6. $\{(5, 1), (5, -1), (-5, 1), (-5, -1)\}$

TIP: It is important to note that the addition method can be used only if two equations share a pair of *like* terms. The substitution method is effective in solving a wider range of systems of equations. The system in Example 4 could also have been solved by using substitution.

$\boxed{A}$ $2x^2 + y^2 = 17 \xrightarrow{\text{Solve for } y^2.} y^2 = 17 - 2x^2$

$\boxed{B}$ $x^2 + 2y^2 = 22$

$\boxed{B}$ $x^2 + 2(17 - 2x^2) = 22$
$$x^2 + 34 - 4x^2 = 22$$
$$-3x^2 = -12$$
$$x^2 = 4$$
$$x = \pm 2$$

$x = 2$: $y^2 = 17 - 2(2)^2$
$$y^2 = 9$$
$$y = \pm 3$$ The solutions are (2, 3) and (2, −3).

$x = -2$: $y^2 = 17 - 2(-2)^2$
$$y^2 = 9$$
$$y = \pm 3$$ The solutions are (−2, 3) and (−2, −3).

Section 13.4 Practice Exercises

Vocabulary and Key Concepts

1. a. A __________ system of equations in two variables is a system in which at least one of the equations is nonlinear.

b. Graphically, the solution set to a nonlinear system of equations is the set of ordered pairs representing the points of __________ of the graphs of the two equations.

Review Exercises

2. Write the distance formula between two points (x_1, y_1) and (x_2, y_2) from memory.

3. Find the distance between the two points $(8, -1)$ and $(1, -8)$.

4. Write an equation representing the set of all points 2 units from the point $(-1, 1)$.

5. Write an equation representing the set of all points 8 units from the point $(-5, 3)$.

6. Write the formula for the midpoint between the points (x_1, y_1) and (x_2, y_2).

7. Find the midpoint of the segment with the endpoints $(3, -9)$ and $(-4, 2)$.

8. Find the midpoint of the segment with the endpoints $(2.4, 1.8)$ and $(-1.6, -5.2)$.

Concept 1: Solving Nonlinear Systems of Equations by the Substitution Method

For Exercises 9–16, use sketches to explain.

9. How many points of intersection are possible between a line and a parabola?

10. How many points of intersection are possible between a line and a circle?

11. How many points of intersection are possible between two distinct circles?

12. How many points of intersection are possible between two distinct parabolas of the form $y = ax^2 + bx + c$, $a \neq 0$?

13. How many points of intersection are possible between a circle and a parabola?

14. How many points of intersection are possible between two distinct lines?

15. How many points of intersection are possible with an ellipse and a hyperbola?

16. How many points of intersection are possible with an ellipse and a parabola?

For Exercises 17–22, sketch each system of equations. Then solve the system by the substitution method. **(See Example 1.)**

17. $y = x + 3$

$x^2 + y = 9$

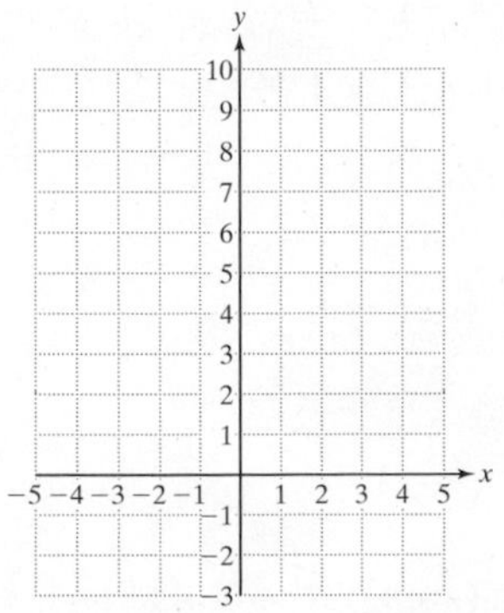

18. $y = x - 2$

$x^2 + y = 4$

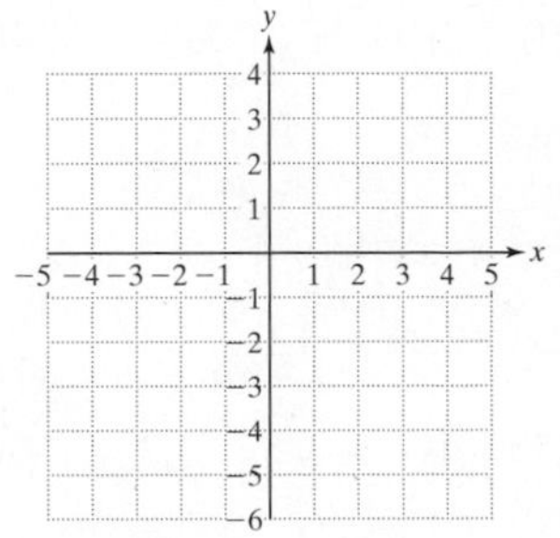

19. $x^2 + y^2 = 1$

$y = x + 1$

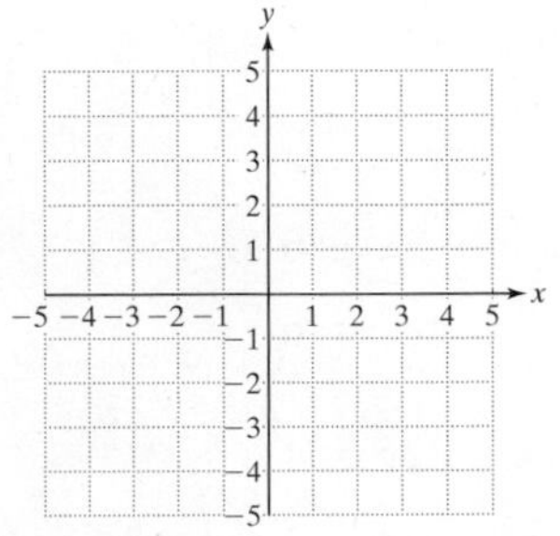

20. $x^2 + y^2 = 25$

$y = 2x$

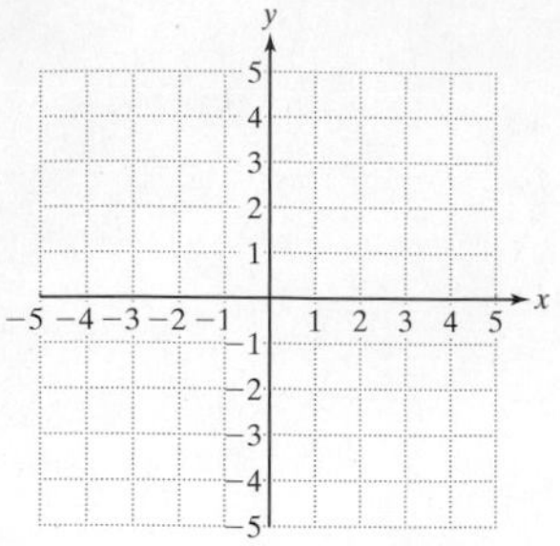

21. $x^2 + y^2 = 6$

$y = x^2$

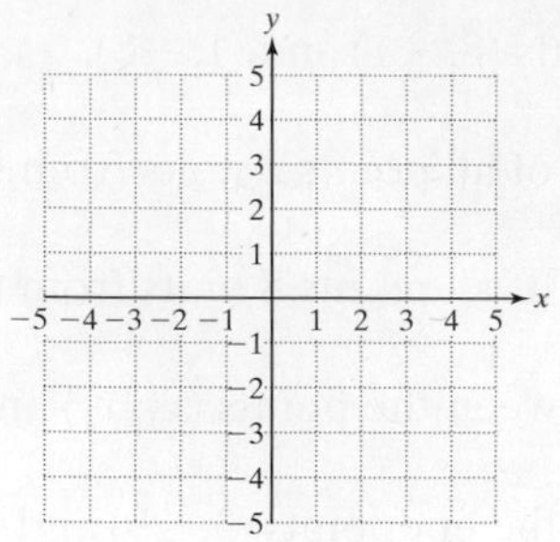

22. $x^2 + y^2 = 12$

$y = x^2$

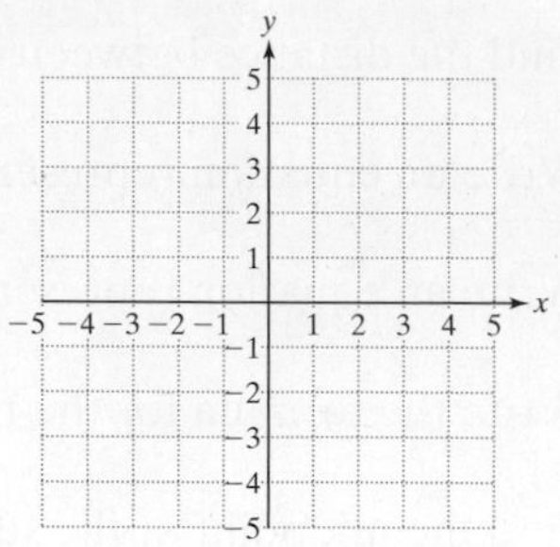

For Exercises 23–31, solve the system by the substitution method. **(See Examples 2–3.)**

23. $y = \sqrt{x}$

$2x^2 - y^2 = 1$

24. $x^2 + y^2 = 30$

$y = \sqrt{x}$

25. $y = x^2$

$y = -\sqrt{x}$

26. $y = -x^2$

$y = -\sqrt{x}$

27. $y = x^2$

$y = (x - 3)^2$

28. $y = (x + 4)^2$

$y = x^2$

29. $y = x^2 + 6x$

$y = 4x$

30. $y = 3x^2 - 6x$

$y = 3x$

31. $x^2 - 5x + y = 0$

$y = 3x + 1$

Concept 2: Solving Nonlinear Systems of Equations by the Addition Method

For Exercises 32–48, solve the system of nonlinear equations by the addition method if appropriate. **(See Example 4.)**

32. $x^2 + y^2 = 13$

$x^2 - y^2 = 5$

33. $4x^2 - y^2 = 4$

$4x^2 + y^2 = 4$

34. $9x^2 + 4y^2 = 36$

$x^2 + y^2 = 9$

35. $x^2 + y^2 = 4$

$2x^2 + y^2 = 8$

36. $3x^2 + 4y^2 = 16$

$2x^2 - 3y^2 = 5$

37. $2x^2 - 5y^2 = -2$

$3x^2 + 2y^2 = 35$

38. $x^2 + y^2 = 169$

$12x - 5y = 0$

39. $x^2 + y^2 = 100$

$4y - 3x = 0$

40. $\dfrac{x^2}{4} + \dfrac{y^2}{9} = 1$

$x^2 + y^2 = 4$

41. $\dfrac{x^2}{16} + \dfrac{y^2}{4} = 1$

$x^2 + y^2 = 4$

42. $\dfrac{x^2}{10} + \dfrac{y^2}{10} = 1$

$2x^2 + y^2 = 11$

43. $2y = -x + 2$

$x^2 + 4y^2 = 4$

44. $2y = -3x - 6$

$9x^2 + 4y^2 = 36$

45. $x^2 - xy = -4$

$2x^2 - xy = 12$

46. $x^2 - xy = 3$

$2x^2 + xy = 6$

47. $3x^2 + 2xy = 4$

$x^2 - xy = 3$

48. $x^2 - 3xy = 8$

$x^2 + xy = 4$

Expanding Your Skills

49. The sum of two numbers is 7. The sum of the squares of the numbers is 25. Find the numbers.

50. The sum of the squares of two numbers is 100. The sum of the numbers is 2. Find the numbers.

51. The sum of the squares of two numbers is 32. The difference of the squares of the numbers is 18. Find the numbers.

52. The sum of the squares of two numbers is 24. The difference of the squares of the numbers is 8. Find the numbers.

Graphing Calculator Exercises

For Exercises 53–56, use the *Intersect* feature to approximate the solutions to the system.

53. $y = x + 3$ (Exercise 17)
$x^2 + y = 9$

54. $y = x - 2$ (Exercise 18)
$x^2 + y = 4$

55. $y = x^2$ (Exercise 25)
$y = -\sqrt{x}$

56. $y = -x^2$ (Exercise 26)
$y = -\sqrt{x}$

For Exercises 57–58, graph the system on a square viewing window. What can be said about the solution to the system?

57. $x^2 + y^2 = 4$
$y = x^2 + 3$

58. $x^2 + y^2 = 16$
$y = -x^2 - 5$

Nonlinear Inequalities and Systems of Inequalities

Section 13.5

1. Nonlinear Inequalities in Two Variables

Concepts

1. **Nonlinear Inequalities in Two Variables**
2. **Systems of Nonlinear Inequalities in Two Variables**

In Section 9.5 we graphed the solution sets to linear inequalities in two variables. For example, to graph the solution set to $y \le 2x + 1$, first graph the related equation $y = 2x + 1$. This is the line shown in Figure 13-19. Then using test points, we see that points on and below the line make up the solution set to the inequality.

Test Point Above: (−2, 2)	**Test Point Below: (0, 0)**
$y \le 2x + 1$	$y \le 2x + 1$
$2 \overset{?}{\le} 2(-2) + 1$	$0 \overset{?}{\le} 2(0) + 1$
$2 \overset{?}{\le} -3$ False	$0 \overset{?}{\le} 1$ ✓True

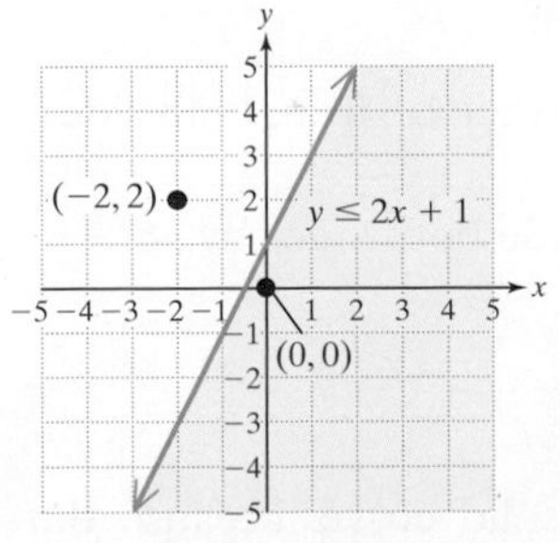

Figure 13-19

Example 1 Graphing a Nonlinear Inequality in Two Variables

Graph the solution set of the inequality $x^2 + y^2 < 16$.

Avoiding Mistakes

The first step in solving an inequality in two variables is to graph the related equation.

Solution:

The related equation $x^2 + y^2 = 16$ is a circle of radius 4, centered at the origin. Graph the related equation by using a dashed curve because the points satisfying the equation $x^2 + y^2 = 16$ are not part of the solution to the strict inequality $x^2 + y^2 < 16$. See Figure 13-20.

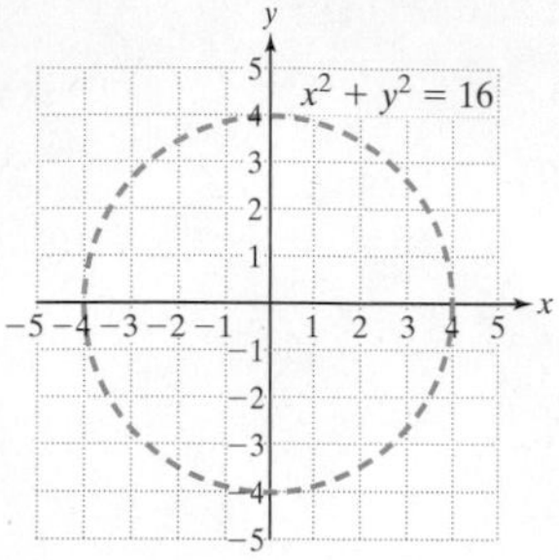

Figure 13-20

Notice that the dashed curve separates the xy-plane into two regions, one "inside" the circle, the other "outside" the circle. Select a test point from each region and test the point in the original inequality.

Test Point "Inside": (0, 0)	**Test Point "Outside": (4, 4)**
$x^2 + y^2 < 16$	$x^2 + y^2 < 16$
$(0)^2 + (0)^2 \overset{?}{<} 16$	$(4)^2 + (4)^2 \overset{?}{<} 16$
$0 \overset{?}{<} 16$ True	$32 \overset{?}{<} 16$ False

The inequality $x^2 + y^2 < 16$ is true at the test point $(0, 0)$. Therefore, the solution set is the region "inside" the circle. See Figure 13-21.

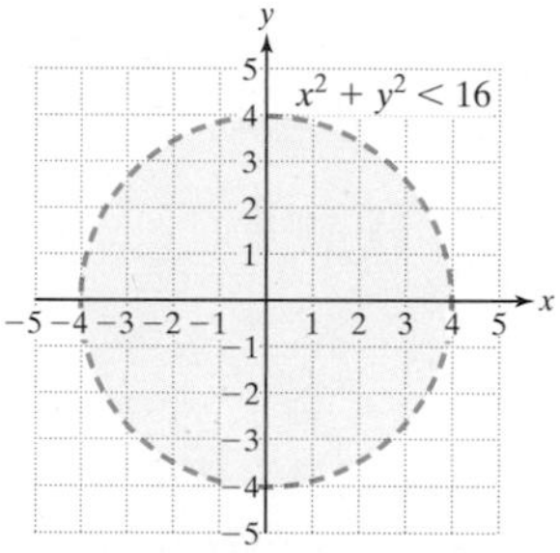

Figure 13-21

Skill Practice

1. Graph the solution set of the inequality $x^2 + y^2 \geq 9$.

Example 2 Graphing a Nonlinear Inequality in Two Variables

Graph the solution set of the inequality $9y^2 \geq 36 + 4x^2$.

Solution:

First graph the related equation $9y^2 = 36 + 4x^2$. Notice that the equation can be written in the standard form of a hyperbola.

$$9y^2 = 36 + 4x^2$$

$$9y^2 - 4x^2 = 36 \quad \text{Subtract } 4x^2 \text{ from both sides.}$$

$$\frac{9y^2}{36} - \frac{4x^2}{36} = \frac{36}{36} \quad \text{Divide both sides by 36.}$$

$$\frac{y^2}{4} - \frac{x^2}{9} = 1$$

Graph the hyperbola as a solid curve, because the original inequality includes equality. See Figure 13-22.

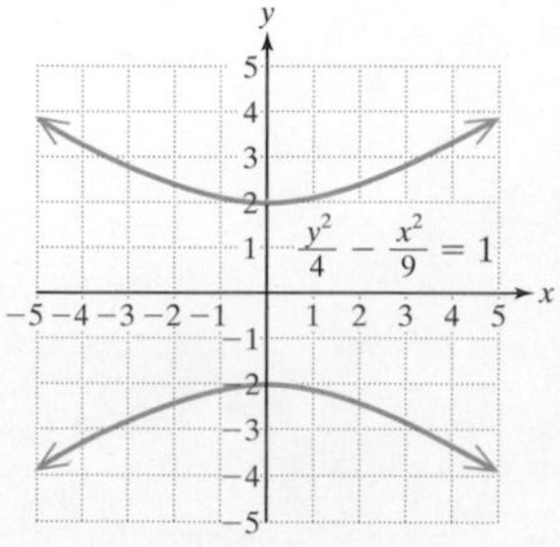

Figure 13-22

Answer

1.

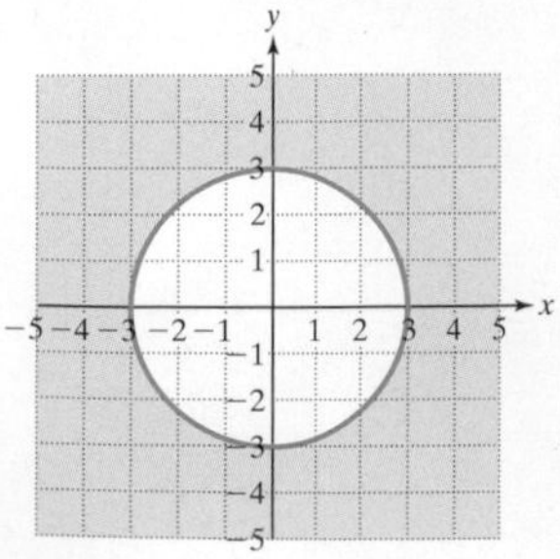

The hyperbola divides the xy-plane into three regions: a region above the upper branch, a region between the branches, and a region below the lower branch. Select a test point from each region.

$$9y^2 \geq 36 + 4x^2$$

Test: (0, 3)	**Test: (0, 0)**	**Test: (0, −3)**
$9(3)^2 \stackrel{?}{\geq} 36 + 4(0)^2$	$9(0)^2 \stackrel{?}{\geq} 36 + 4(0)^2$	$9(-3)^2 \stackrel{?}{\geq} 36 + 4(0)^2$
$81 \stackrel{?}{\geq} 36$ True	$0 \stackrel{?}{\geq} 36$ False	$81 \stackrel{?}{\geq} 36$ True

Shade the regions above the top branch and below the bottom branch of the hyperbola. See Figure 13-23.

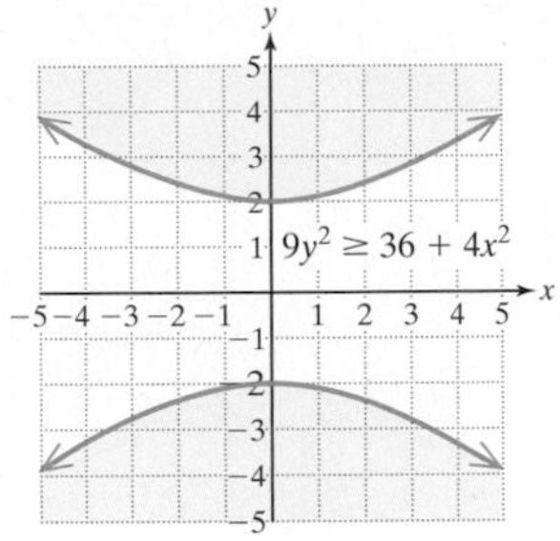

Figure 13-23

Skill Practice

2. Graph the solution set of the inequality $9x^2 < 144 - 16y^2$.

2. Systems of Nonlinear Inequalities in Two Variables

In Section 13.4 we solved systems of nonlinear equations in two variables. The solution set for such a system is the set of ordered pairs that satisfy both equations simultaneously. We will now solve systems of nonlinear inequalities in two variables. Similarly, the solution set is the set of all ordered pairs that simultaneously satisfy each inequality. To solve a system of inequalities, we will graph the solution to each individual inequality and then take the intersection of the solution sets.

Example 3 Graphing a System of Nonlinear Inequalities in Two Variables

Graph the solution set.

$$y > \frac{1}{3}x^2$$

$$y < -x^2 + 2$$

Solution:

The solution to $y > \frac{1}{3}x^2$ is the set of points above the parabola $y = \frac{1}{3}x^2$. See Figure 13-24. The solution to $y < -x^2 + 2$ is the set of points below the parabola $y = -x^2 + 2$. See Figure 13-25.

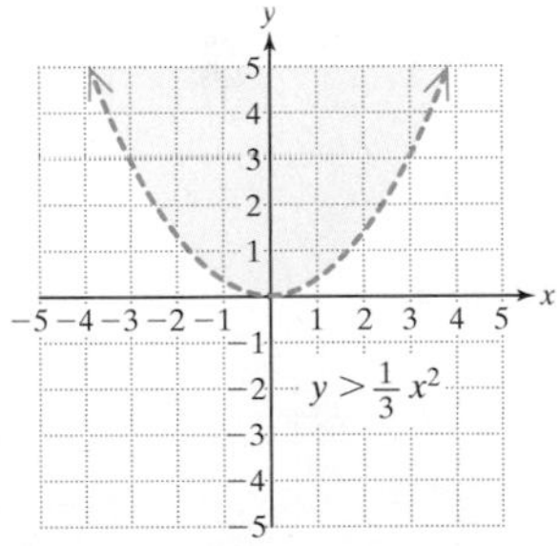

Figure 13-24

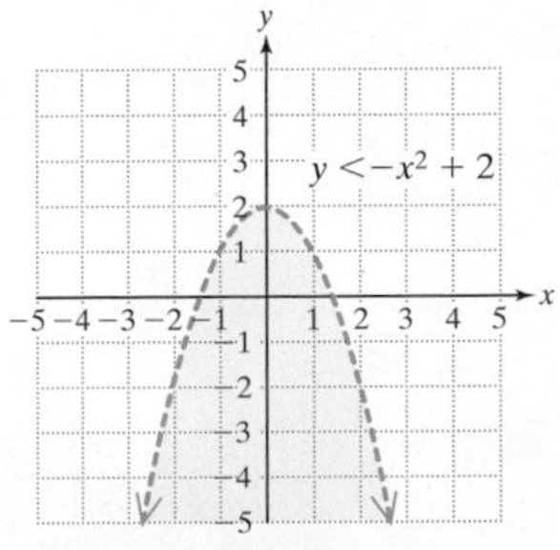

Figure 13-25

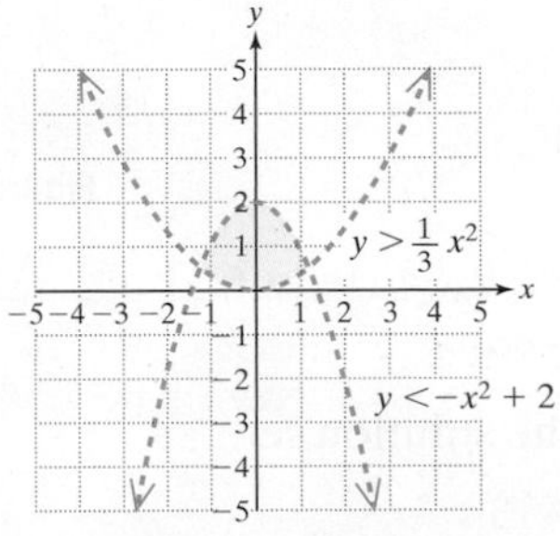

Figure 13-26

The solution to the system of inequalities is the intersection of the solution sets of the individual inequalities. See Figure 13-26.

Answer

2.

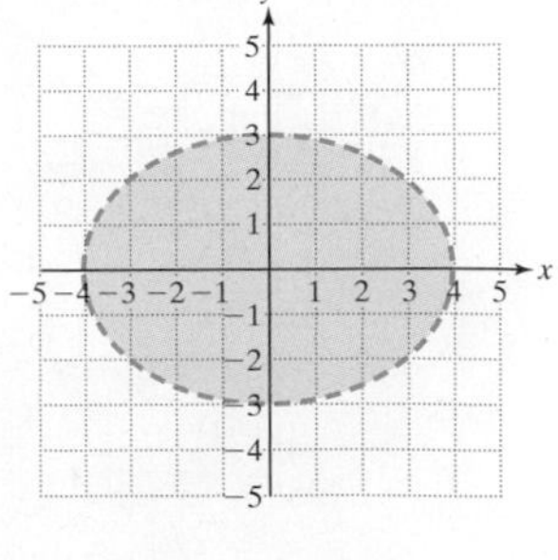

Skill Practice

3. Graph the solution set.

$$\frac{x^2}{4} + \frac{y^2}{9} < 1$$
$$x > y^2$$

Example 4 Graphing a System of Nonlinear Inequalities in Two Variables

Graph the solution set.
$$y > e^x$$
$$y < -x^2 + 4$$

Solution:

The solution to $y > e^x$ is the set of points above the curve $y = e^x$. See Figure 13-27. The solution to $y < -x^2 + 4$ is the set of points below the parabola $y = -x^2 + 4$. See Figure 13-28.

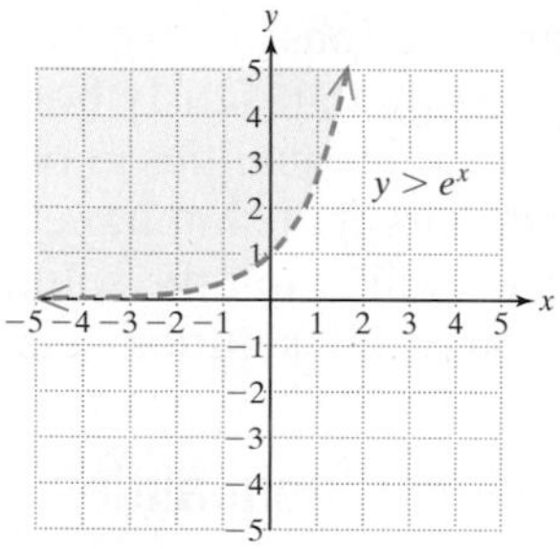

Figure 13-27

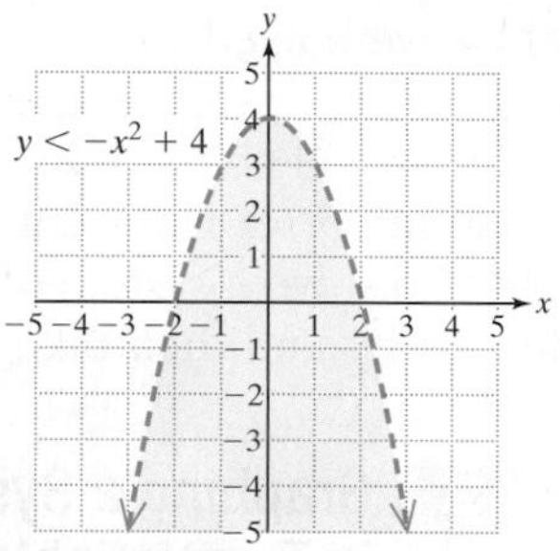

Figure 13-28

The solution to the system of inequalities is the intersection of the solution sets of the individual inequalities. See Figure 13-29.

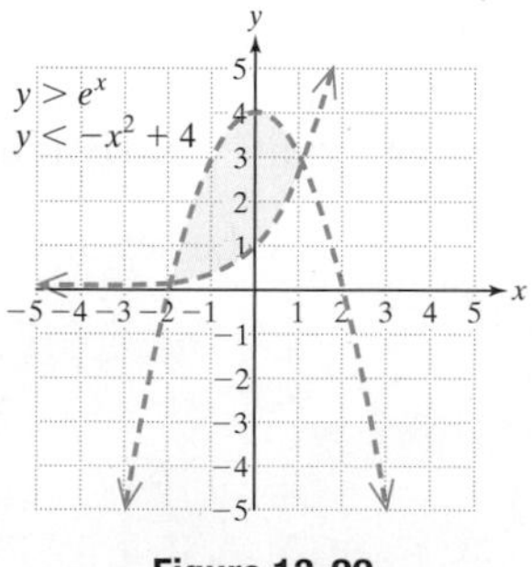

Figure 13-29

Skill Practice

4. Graph the solution set.

$$y > \frac{1}{2}x^2$$
$$x > y^2$$

Answers

3.

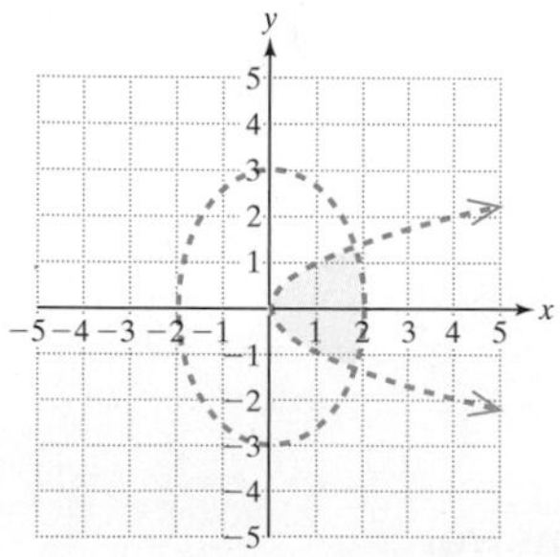

4.

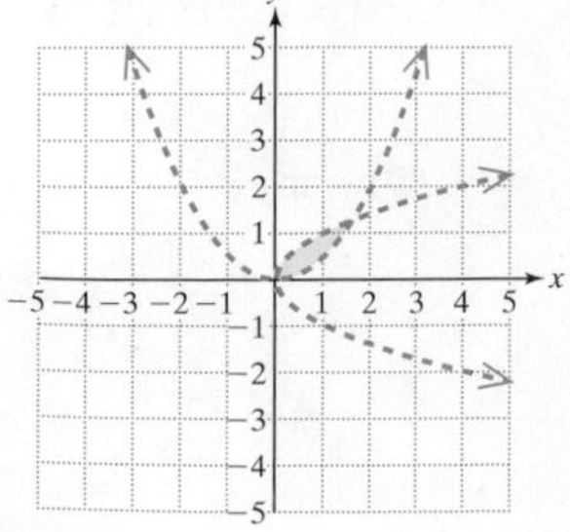

Section 13.5 Practice Exercises

Review Exercises

For Exercises 1–12, match the equation with its graph.

1. $y = \left(\frac{1}{3}\right)^x$

2. $y = 4x - 1$

3. $y = -4x^2$

4. $y = e^x$

5. $y = x^3$

6. $\frac{x^2}{4} + \frac{y^2}{9} = 1$

7. $\frac{x^2}{4} - \frac{y^2}{9} = 1$

8. $y = \frac{1}{x}$

9. $y = \log_2(x)$

10. $y = \sqrt{x}$

11. $(x + 2)^2 + (y - 1)^2 = 4$

12. $x = -y^2$

a.
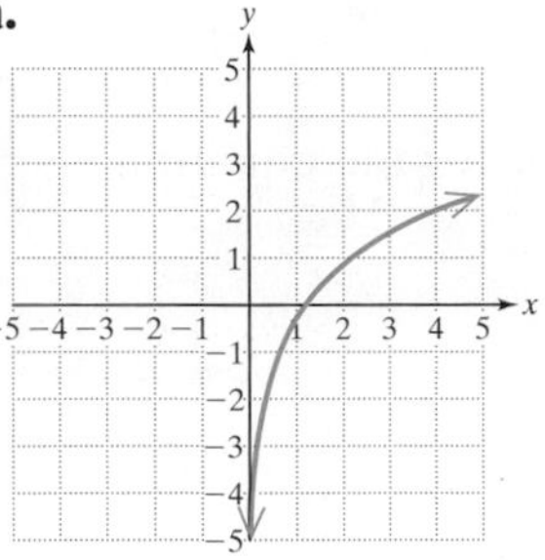

b.
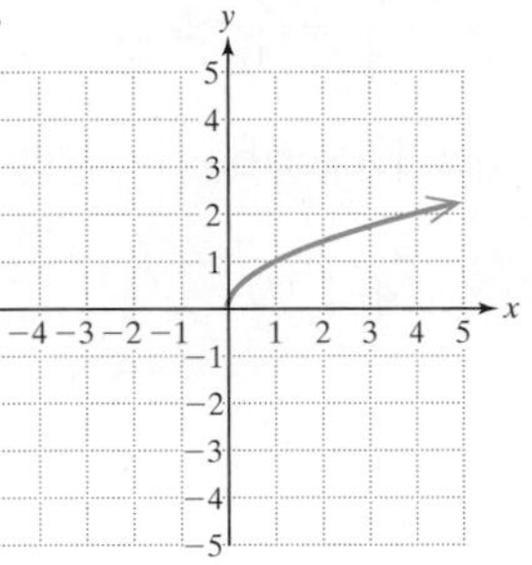

c.
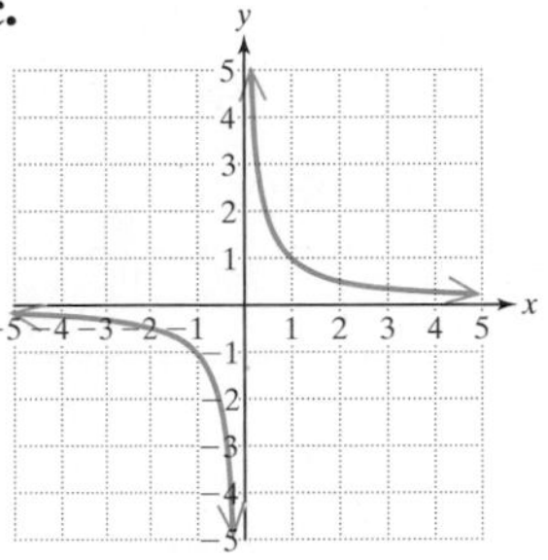

d.
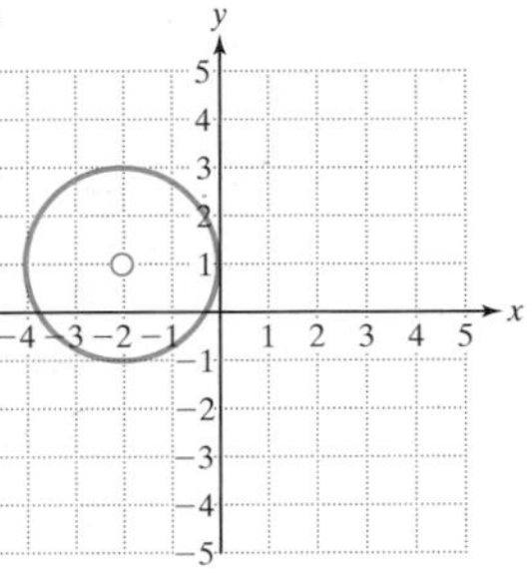

e.
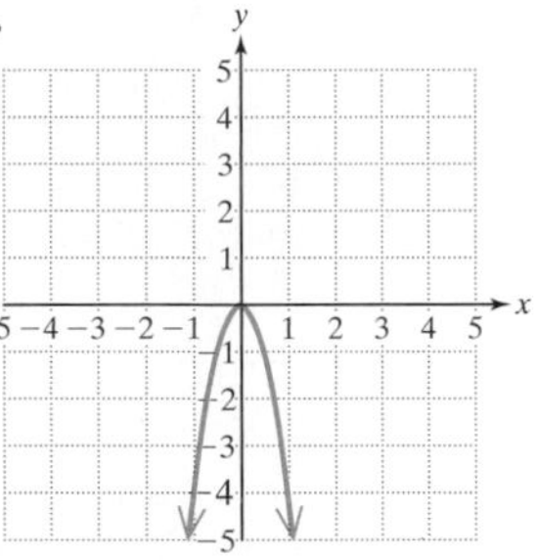

f.
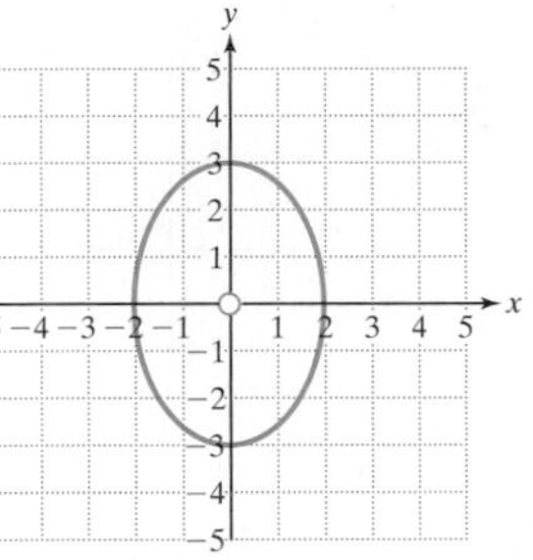

g.
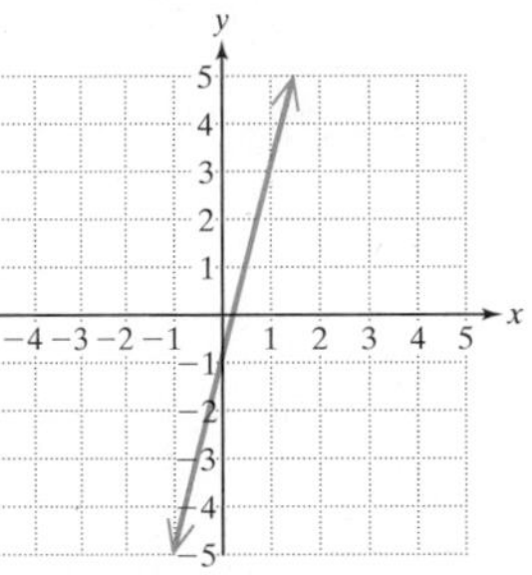

h.
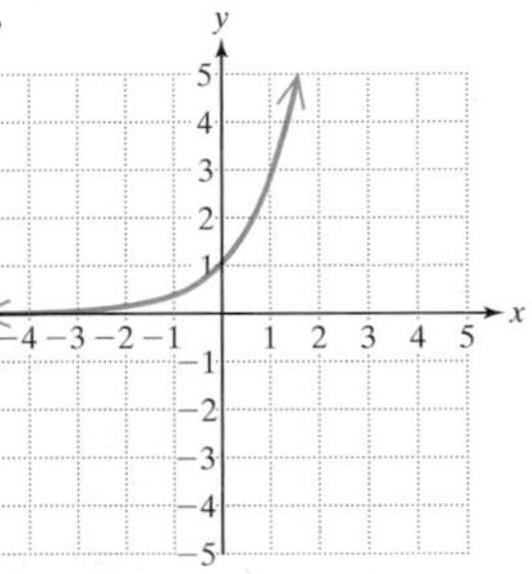

i.
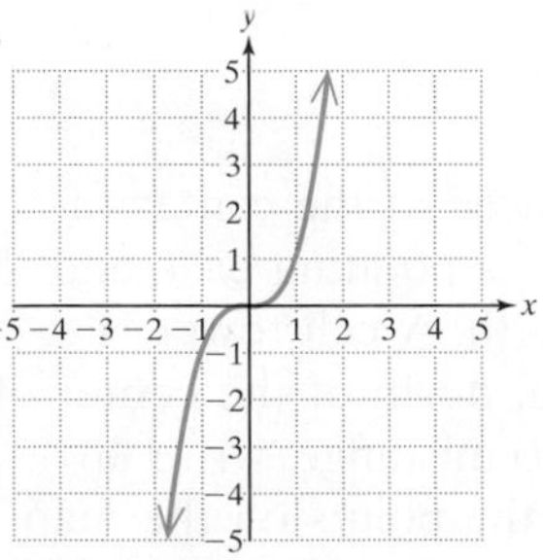

j.
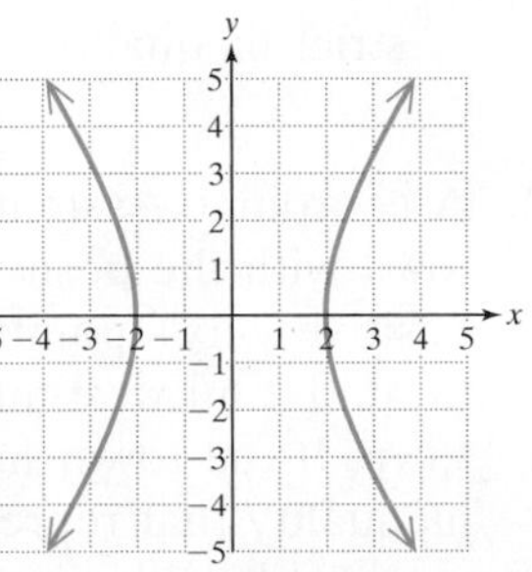

k.
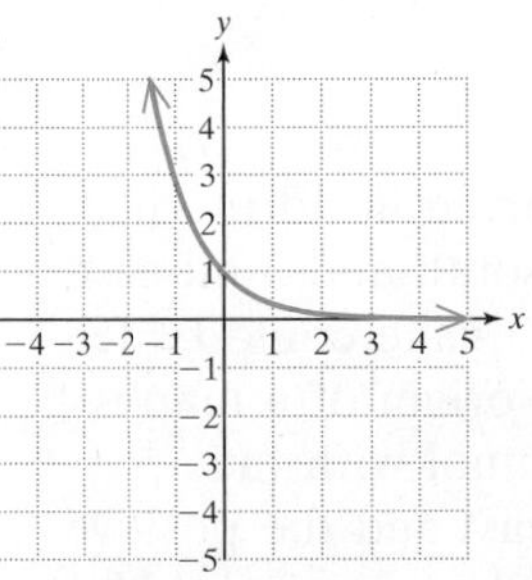

l.
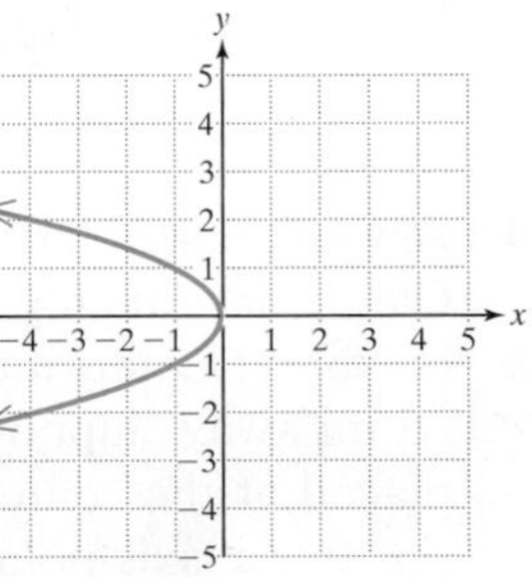

Concept 1: Nonlinear Inequalities in Two Variables

13. True or false? The point (2, 3) satisfies the inequality $-x^2 + y^3 > 1$.

14. True or false? The point (4, −2) satisfies the inequality $4x^2 - 2x + 1 + y^2 < 3$.

15. True or false? The point (5, 4) satisfies the system of inequalities.

$$\frac{x^2}{36} + \frac{y^2}{25} < 1$$
$$x^2 + y^2 \geq 4$$

16. True or false? The point (1, −2) satisfies the system of inequalities.

$$y < x^2$$
$$y > x^2 - 4$$

17. a. Graph the solution set for $x^2 + y^2 \le 9$.

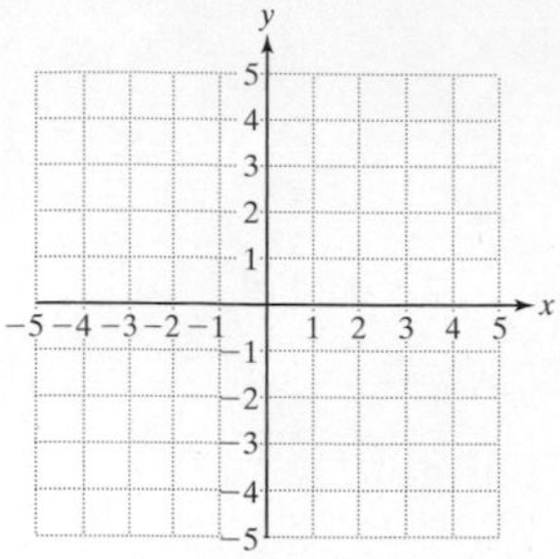

b. Describe the solution set for the inequality $x^2 + y^2 \ge 9$.

c. Describe the solution set for the equation $x^2 + y^2 = 9$

18. a. Graph the solution set for $\frac{x^2}{4} + \frac{y^2}{9} \ge 1$.

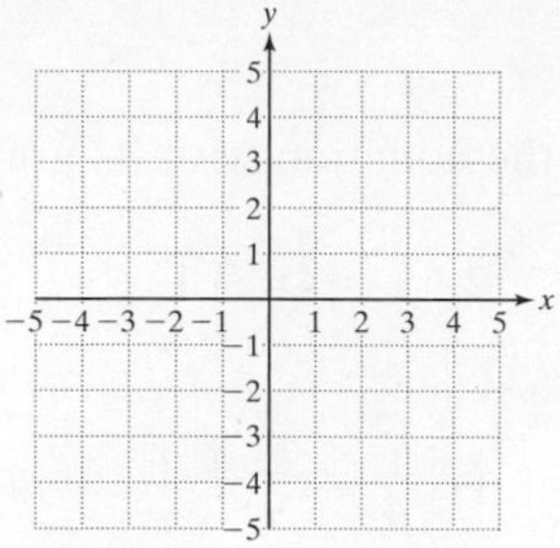

b. Describe the solution set for the inequality $\frac{x^2}{4} + \frac{y^2}{9} \le 1$.

c. Describe the solution set for the equation $\frac{x^2}{4} + \frac{y^2}{9} = 1$

19. a. Graph the solution set for $y \ge x^2 + 1$.

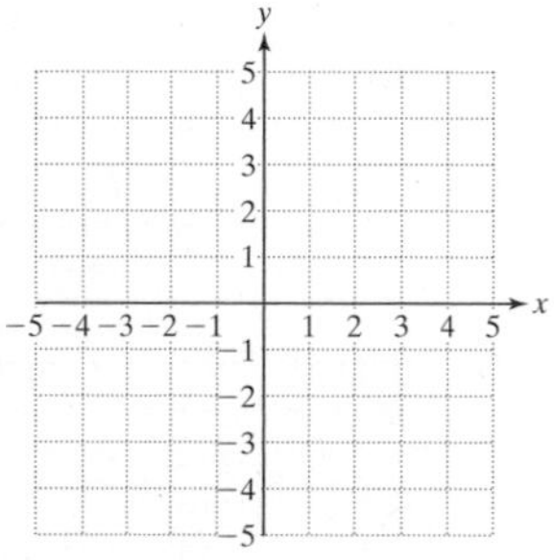

b. How would the solution change for the strict inequality $y > x^2 + 1$?

20. a. Graph the solution set for $\frac{x^2}{4} - \frac{y^2}{9} \le 1$.

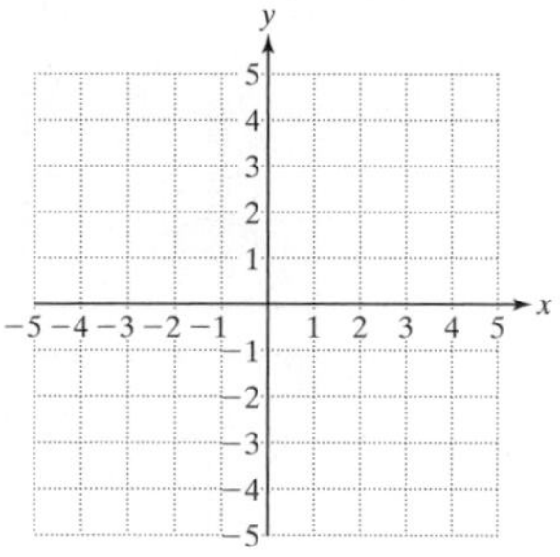

b. How would the solution change for the strict inequality $\frac{x^2}{4} - \frac{y^2}{9} < 1$?

21. A weak earthquake occurred in northern California roughly 4 mi south and 3 mi east of Sunol, California. The quake could be felt 25 mi away. Suppose the origin of a map is placed at the center of Sunol with the positive x-axis pointing east and the positive y-axis pointing north. Find an inequality that describes the points on the map for which the earthquake could be felt.

22. A coordinate system is placed at the center of a town with the positive x-axis pointing east, and the positive y-axis pointing north. A cell tower is located 2 mi west and 4 mi north of the center of town. If the tower has a 30-mi range, write an inequality that represents the points on the map serviced by this tower.

For Exercises 23–37, graph the solution set. **(See Examples 1–2.)**

23. $2x + y \geq 1$

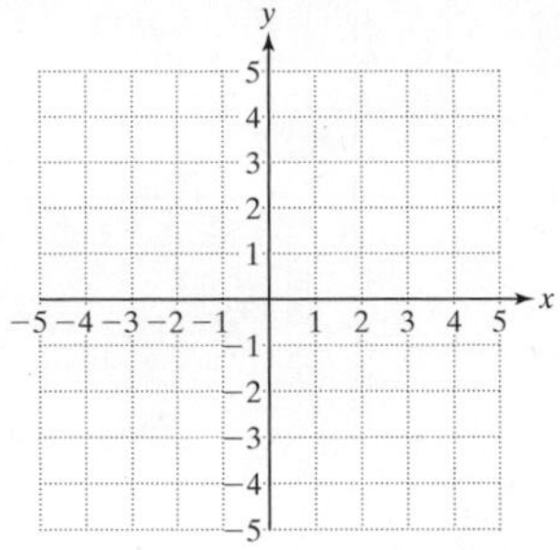

24. $3x + 2y \geq 6$

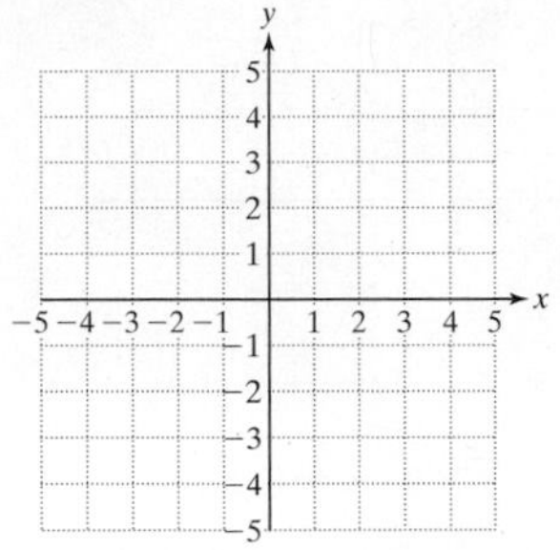

25. $x \leq y^2$

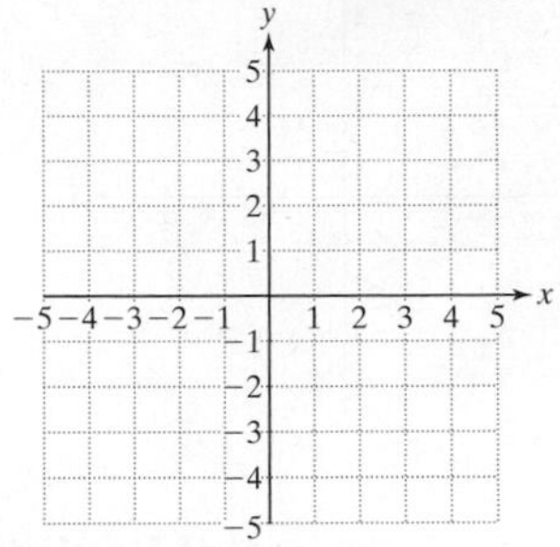

26. $y \leq -x^2$

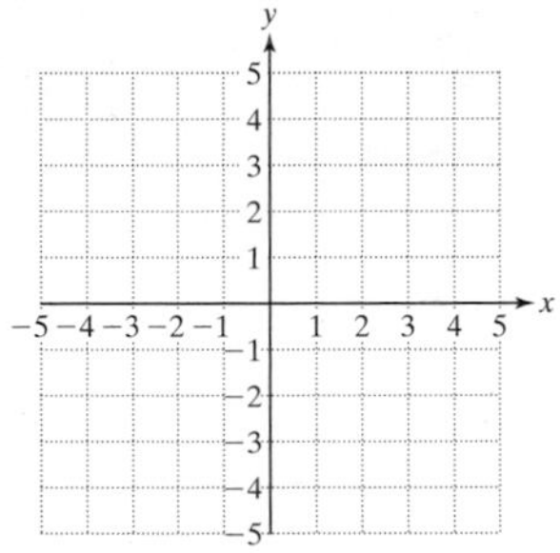

27. $(x - 1)^2 + (y + 2)^2 > 9$

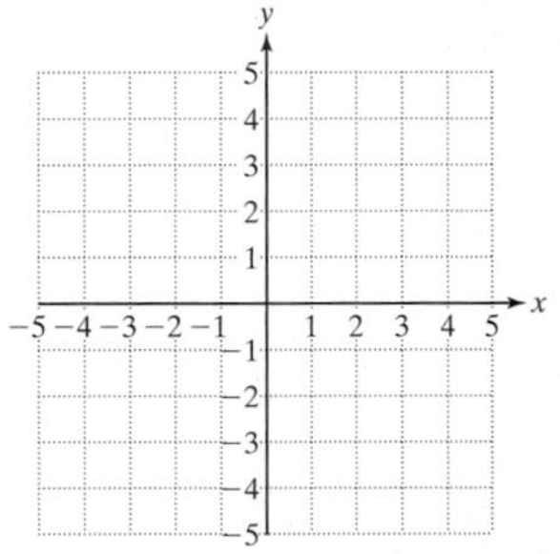

28. $(x + 1)^2 + (y - 4)^2 > 1$

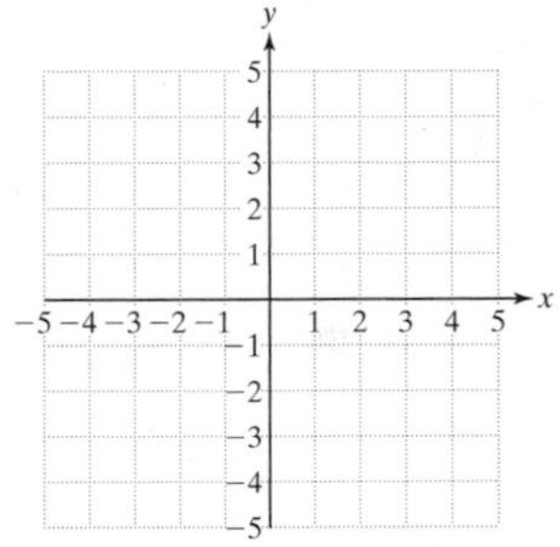

29. $x + y^2 \geq 4$

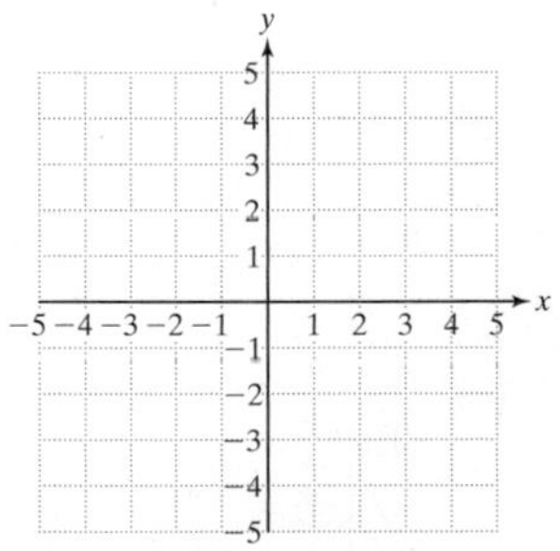

30. $x^2 + 2x + y - 1 \leq 0$

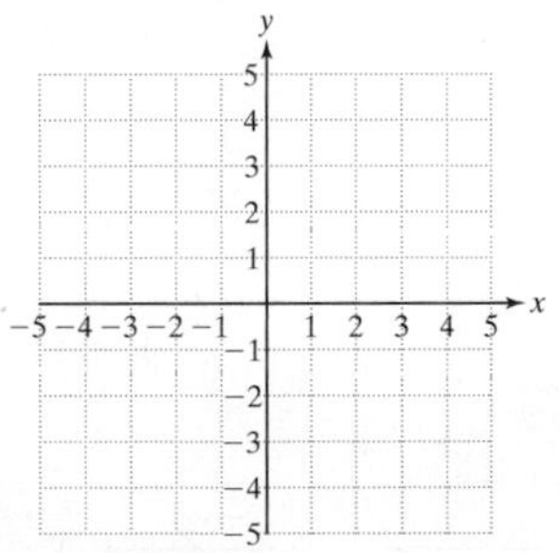

31. $9x^2 - y^2 > 9$

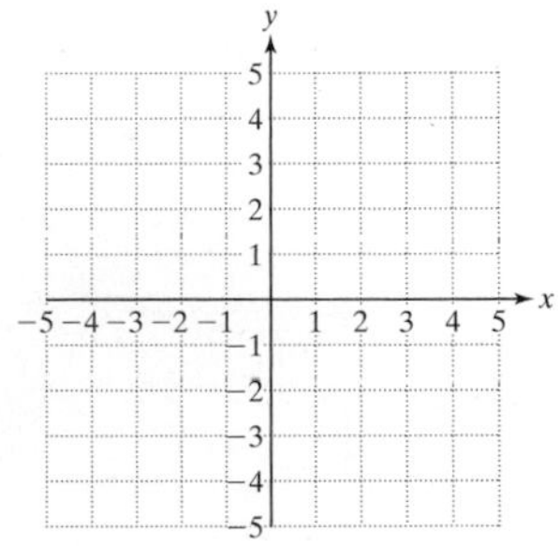

32. $y^2 - 4x^2 \leq 4$

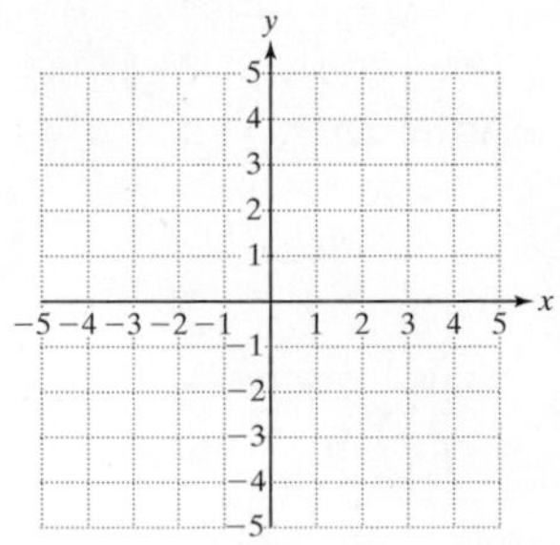

33. $x^2 + 16y^2 \leq 16$

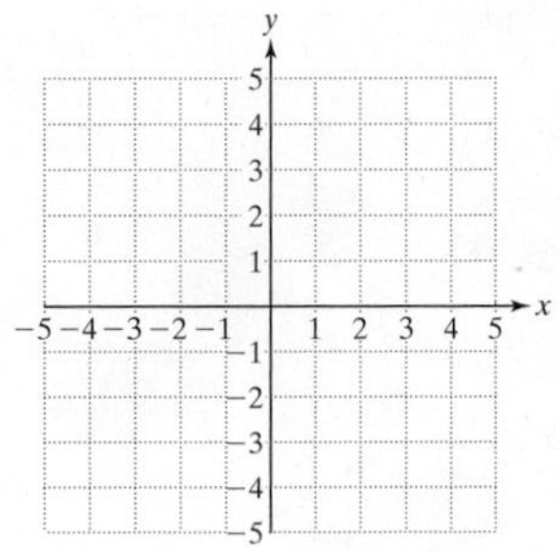

34. $4x^2 + y^2 \leq 4$

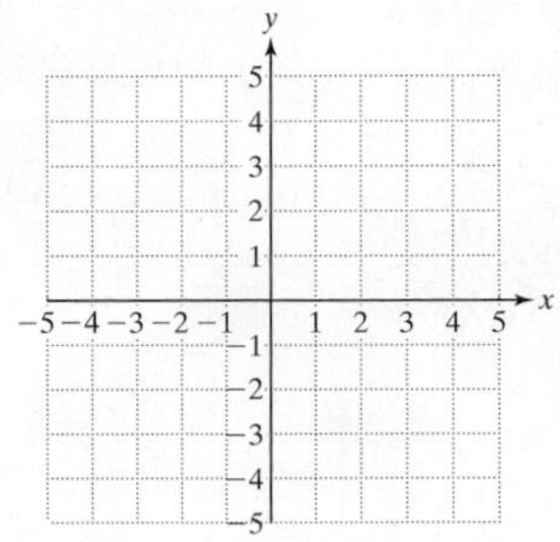

35. $y \leq \ln x$

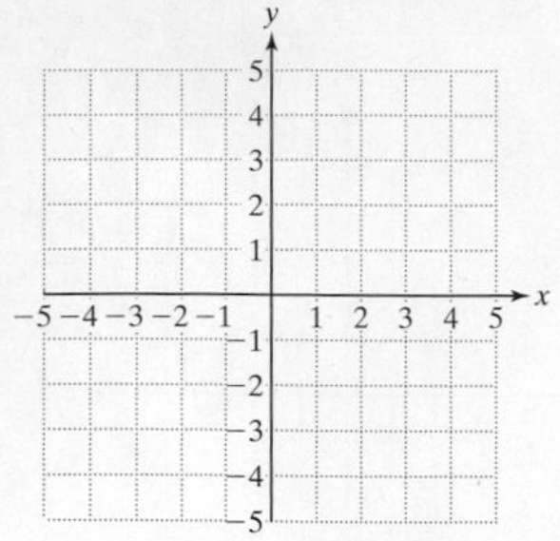

36. $y \leq \log x$

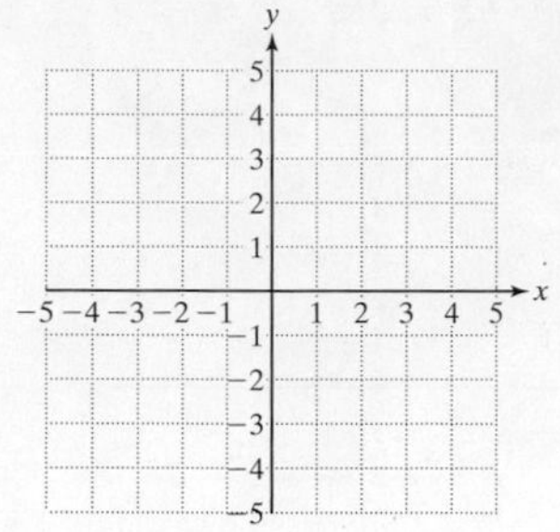

37. $y > 5^x$

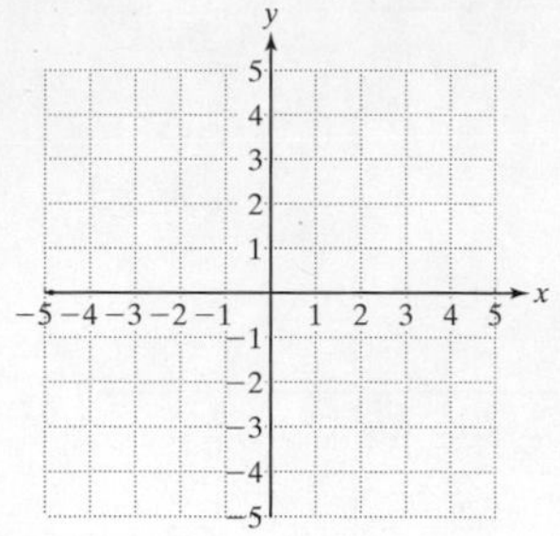

Concept 2: Systems of Nonlinear Inequalities in Two Variables

For Exercises 38–51, graph the solution set to the system of inequalities. **(See Examples 3–4.)**

38. $y < \sqrt{x}$
$x > 1$

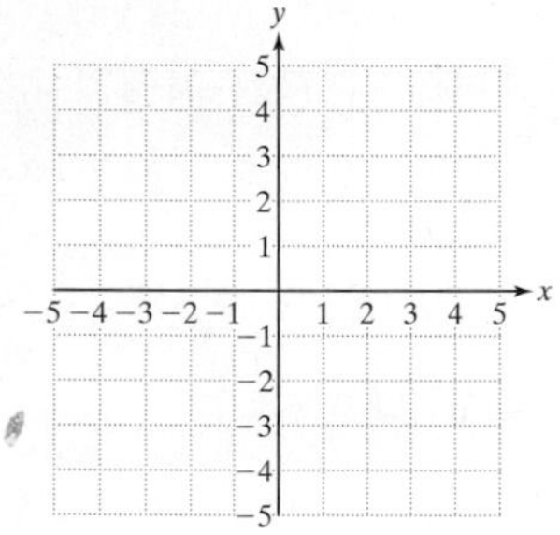

39. $y \geq \sqrt{x}$
$x \geq 0$

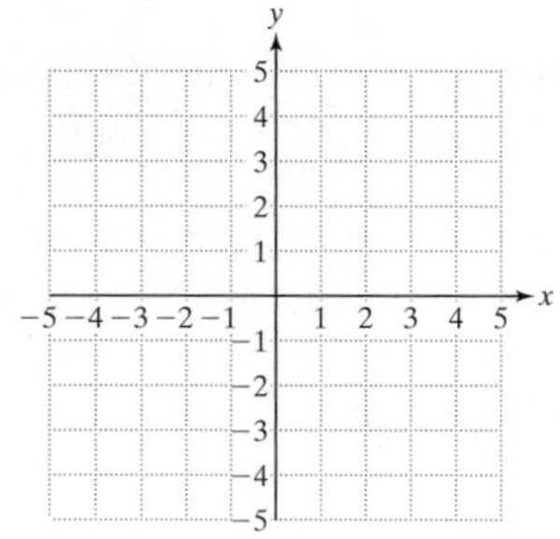

40. $\dfrac{x^2}{36} + \dfrac{y^2}{25} < 1$
$x^2 + y^2 \geq 4$

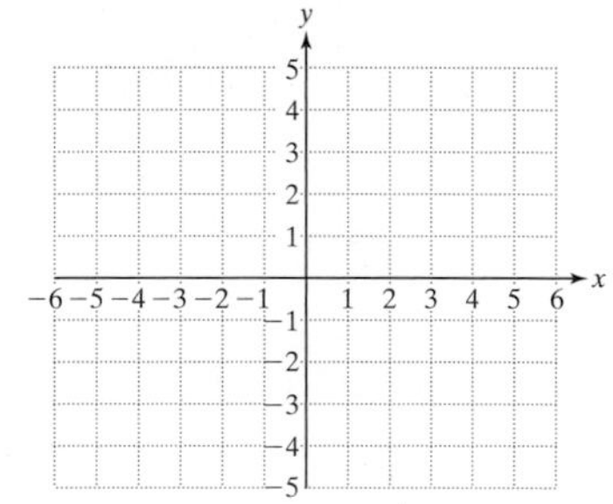

41. $x^2 - y^2 \geq 1$
$x \leq 0$

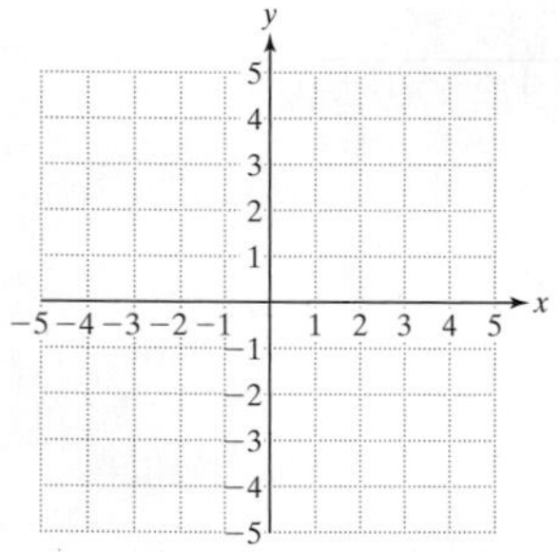

42. $y < x^2$
$y > x^2 - 4$

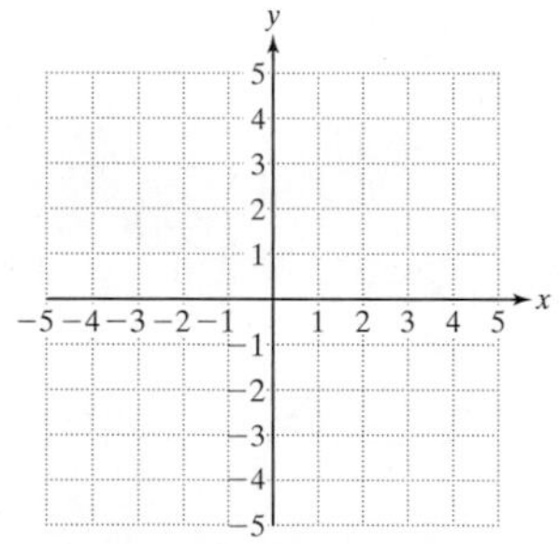

43. $y^2 - x^2 \geq 1$
$y \geq 0$

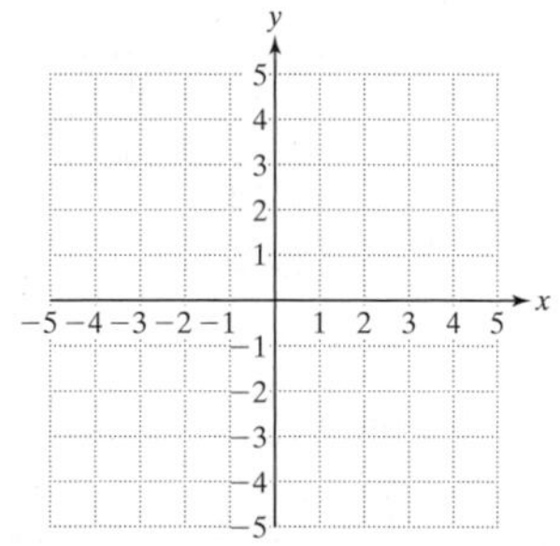

44. $y < \dfrac{1}{x}$
$y > 0$
$y < x$

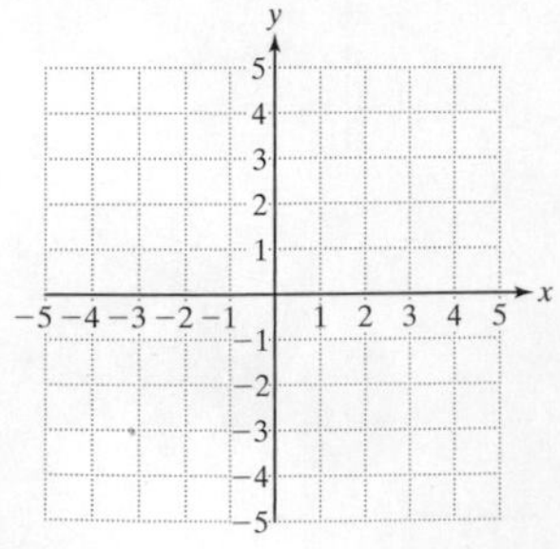

45. $y > x^3$
$y < 8$
$x > 0$

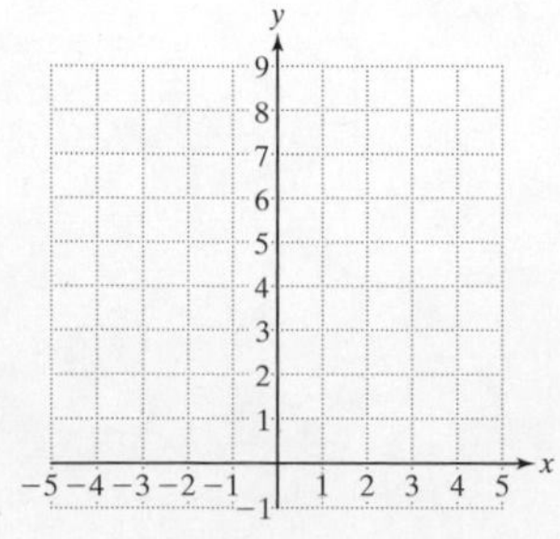

46. $x^2 + y^2 \geq 25$
$x^2 + y^2 \leq 9$

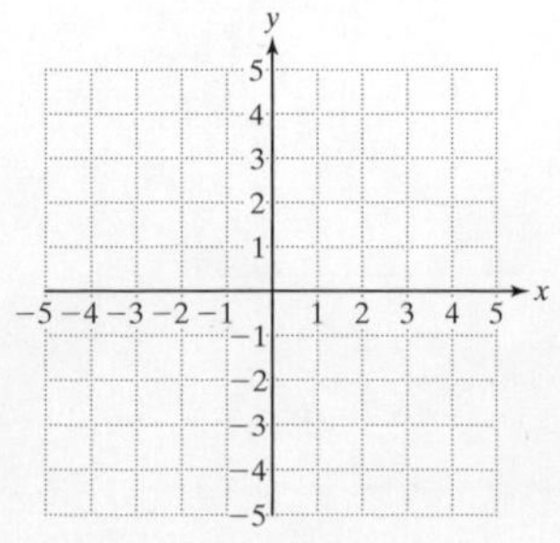

47. $\dfrac{x^2}{4} + \dfrac{y^2}{25} \geq 1$

$x^2 + \dfrac{y^2}{4} \leq 1$

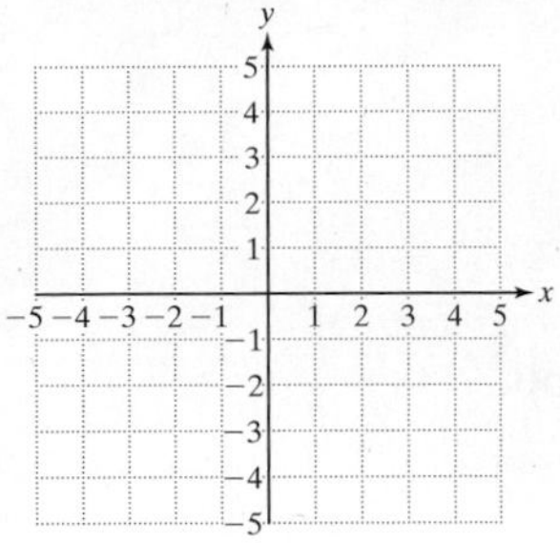

48. $x < -(y - 1)^2 + 3$

$x + y > 2$

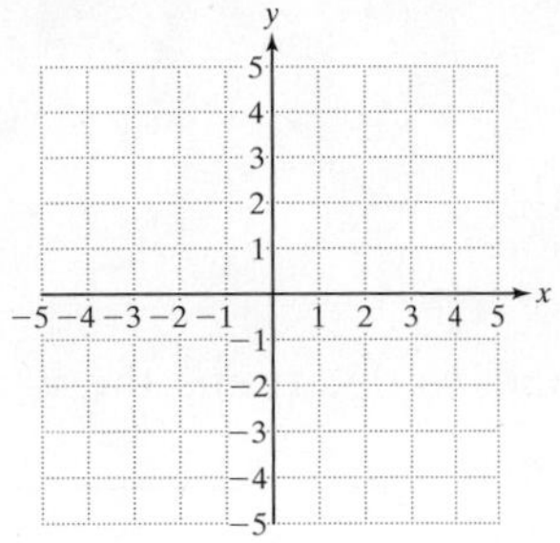

49. $x > (y - 2)^2 + 1$

$x - y < 1$

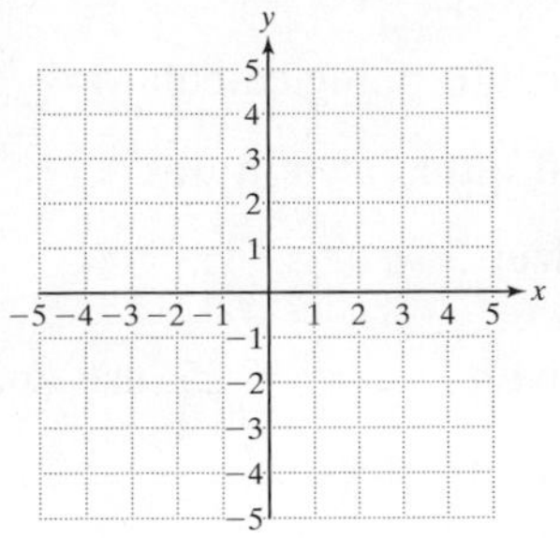

50. $x^2 + y^2 < 25$

$y < \dfrac{4}{3}x$

$y > -\dfrac{4}{3}x$

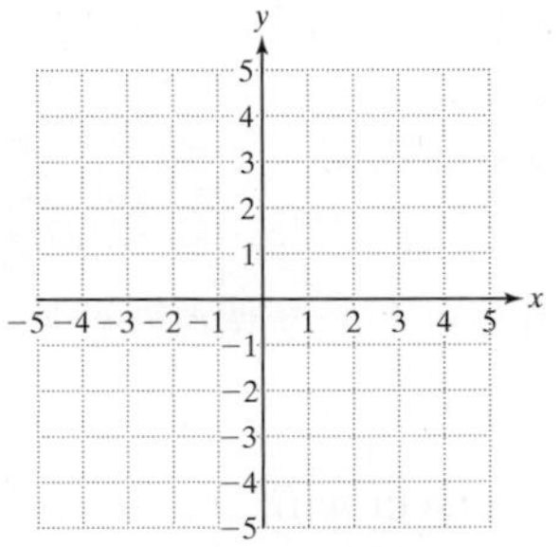

51. $y < e^x$

$y > 1$

$x < 2$

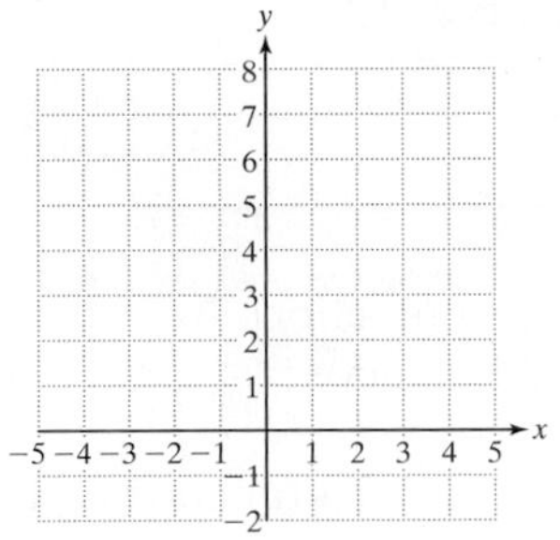

Expanding Your Skills

For Exercises 52–55, graph the compound inequalities.

52. $x^2 + y^2 \leq 36$ or $x + y \geq 0$

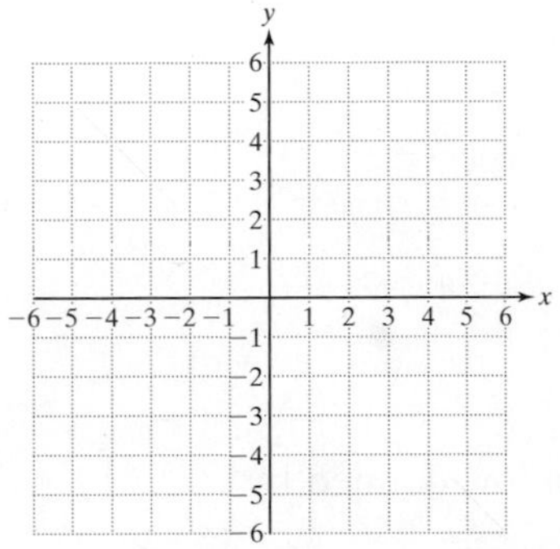

53. $y \leq -x^2 + 4$ or $y \geq x^2 - 4$

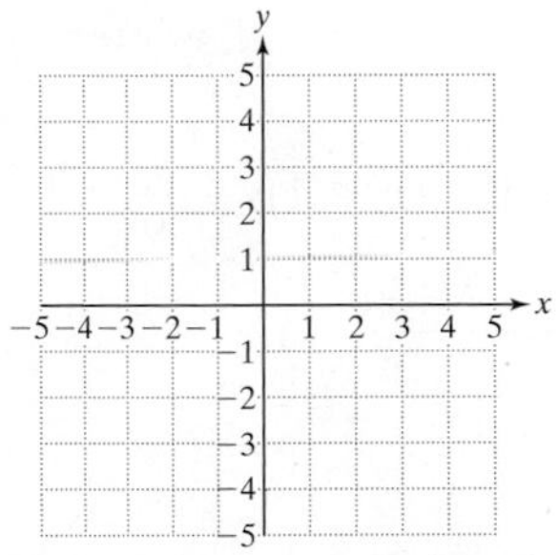

54. $y + 1 \geq x^2$ or $y + 1 \leq -x^2$

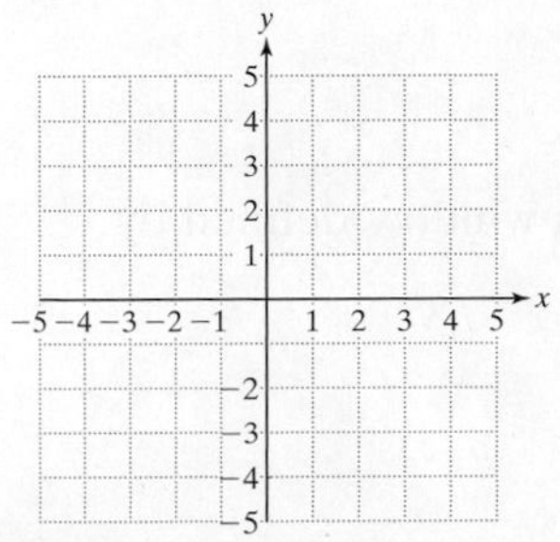

55. $(x + 2)^2 + (y + 3)^2 \leq 4$ or $x \geq y^2$

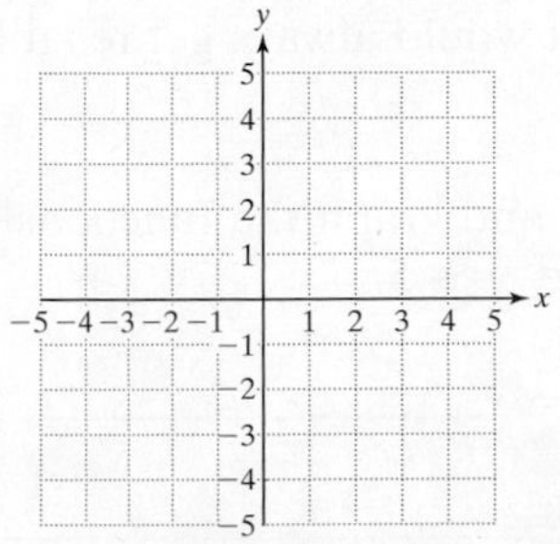

Group Activity

Investigating the Graphs of Conic Sections on a Calculator

Materials: Graphing calculator

Estimated time: 15 minutes

Group Size: 3

1. a. Given $x^2 + y^2 = 25$, use analytical methods to determine the x- and y-intercepts.

x-intercepts: __________ y-intercepts: __________

b. Solve the equation for y: $x^2 + y^2 = 25$. (*Hint:* When taking the square root of both sides of the equation, don't forget the $\pm$.)

$Y_1 =$ _______________

$Y_2 =$ _______________

c. Graph the two functions from part (b) on a graphing calculator. Use a window defined by $-7.6 \le x \le 7.6$ and $-5 \le y \le 5$.

d. Does it look like the functions graphed on the calculator intersect with the x-axis? Why do the x-intercepts not show up in the graph? If you relied solely on your calculator to find the x-intercepts, do you think that you would always get reliable results?

2. a. Given $(x + 1)^2 - \frac{y^2}{9} = 1$, use analytical methods to find the x- and y-intercepts.

x-intercepts: __________ y-intercepts: __________

b. Solve the equation for y. $(x + 1)^2 - \frac{y^2}{9} = 1$

$Y_1 =$ _______________

$Y_2 =$ _______________

c. Graph the two functions from part (b) on a graphing calculator. Use a window defined by $-7.6 \le x \le 7.6$ and $-5 \le y \le 5$.

d. Does it look like the functions graphed on the calculator intersect with the x-axis? Why do the x-intercepts not show up in the graph? If you relied solely on your calculator to find the x-intercepts, do you think that you would always get reliable results?

3. Solve the equation for y and graph the functions on a graphing calculator. Use a window defined by $-7.6 \le x \le 7.6$ and $-5 \le y \le 5$.

a. $\frac{x^2}{4} + \frac{y^2}{16} = 1$ $Y_1 =$ _______________

$Y_2 =$ _______________

b. What are the x-intercepts for the equation $\frac{x^2}{4} + \frac{y^2}{16} = 1$?

x-intercepts: _______________

Chapter 13 Summary

Section 13.1 Distance Formula, Midpoint Formula, and Circles

Key Concepts

The distance between two points (x_1, y_1) and (x_2, y_2) is

$d = \sqrt{(x_2 - x_1)^2 + (y_2 - y_1)^2}$

The standard equation of a **circle** with center (h, k) and radius r is

$(x - h)^2 + (y - k)^2 = r^2$

The midpoint between two points is found by using the formula:

$\left(\frac{x_1 + x_2}{2}, \frac{y_1 + y_2}{2}\right)$

Examples

Example 1

Find the distance between two points.

$(5, -2)$ and $(-1, -6)$

$$\begin{aligned} d &= \sqrt{(-1 - 5)^2 + [-6 - (-2)]^2} \\ &= \sqrt{(-6)^2 + (-4)^2} \\ &= \sqrt{36 + 16} \\ &= \sqrt{52} = 2\sqrt{13} \end{aligned}$$

Example 2

Find the center and radius of the circle.

$$x^2 + y^2 - 8x + 6y = 0$$
$$(x^2 - 8x + 16) + (y^2 + 6y + 9) = 16 + 9$$
$$(x - 4)^2 + (y + 3)^2 = 25$$

The center is $(4, -3)$ and the radius is 5.

Example 3

Find the midpoint between $(-3, 1)$ and $(5, 7)$.

$\left(\frac{-3 + 5}{2}, \frac{1 + 7}{2}\right) = (1, 4)$

Section 13.2 More on the Parabola

Key Concepts

A **parabola** is the set of points in a plane that are equidistant from a fixed line (called the directrix) and a fixed point (called the focus) not on the directrix.

The standard form of an equation of a parabola with **vertex** (h, k) and vertical **axis of symmetry** is

$$y = a(x - h)^2 + k \qquad \text{where } a \neq 0$$

- The equation of the axis of symmetry is $x = h$.
- If $a > 0$, the parabola opens upward.
- If $a < 0$, the parabola opens downward.

The standard form of an equation of a parabola with vertex (h, k) and horizontal axis of symmetry is

$$x = a(y - k)^2 + h \qquad \text{where } a \neq 0$$

- The equation of the axis of symmetry is $y = k$.
- If $a > 0$, the parabola opens to the right.
- If $a < 0$, the parabola opens to the left.

Examples

Example 1

Given the parabola $y = (x - 2)^2 + 1$:

The vertex is $(2, 1)$.

The axis of symmetry is $x = 2$.

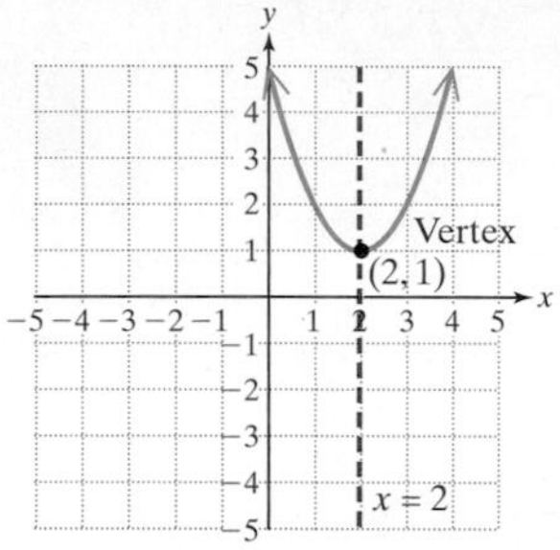

Example 2

Given the parabola $x = -\frac{1}{4}y^2 + 1$,

determine the coordinates of the vertex and the equation of the axis of symmetry.

$$x = -\frac{1}{4}(y - 0)^2 + 1$$

The vertex is $(1, 0)$.

The axis of symmetry is $y = 0$.

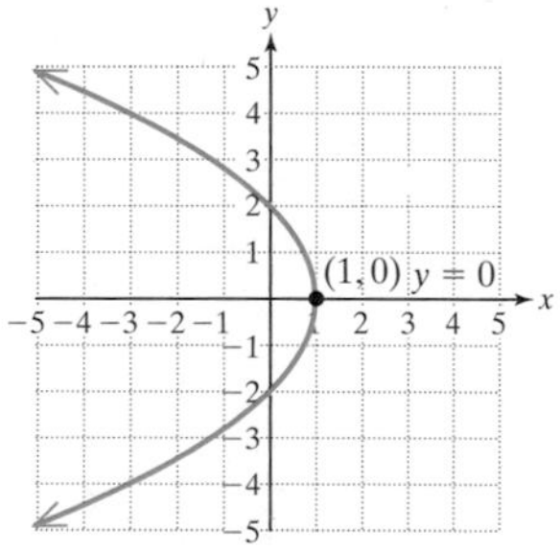

Section 13.3 The Ellipse and Hyperbola

Key Concepts

An **ellipse** is the set of all points (x, y) such that the sum of the distances between (x, y) and two distinct points (called foci) is constant.

Standard Form of an Ellipse with Center at the Origin

An ellipse with the center at the origin has the equation

$$\frac{x^2}{a^2} + \frac{y^2}{b^2} = 1$$

where a and b are positive real numbers.

For an ellipse centered at the origin, the x-intercepts are given by $(a, 0)$ and $(-a, 0)$, and the y-intercepts are given by $(0, b)$ and $(0, -b)$.

A **hyperbola** is the set of all points (x, y) such that the absolute value of the difference of the distances between (x, y) and two distinct points is a constant. The fixed points are called the foci of the hyperbola.

Standard Forms of an Equation of a Hyperbola

Let a and b represent positive real numbers.

Horizontal Transverse Axis. The standard form of an equation of a hyperbola with a horizontal transverse axis and center at the origin is given by

$$\frac{x^2}{a^2} - \frac{y^2}{b^2} = 1$$

Vertical Transverse Axis. The standard form of an equation of a hyperbola with a vertical transverse axis and center at the origin is given by

$$\frac{y^2}{b^2} - \frac{x^2}{a^2} = 1$$

Examples

Example 1

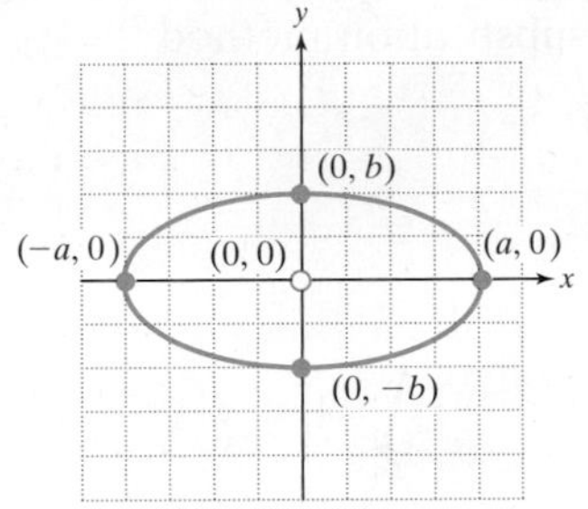

Example 2

$$\frac{x^2}{25} + \frac{y^2}{9} = 1$$

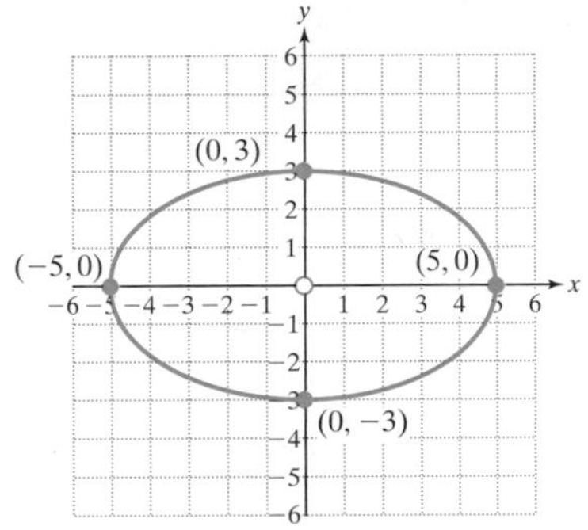

Example 3

$$\frac{x^2}{4} - \frac{y^2}{16} = 1$$

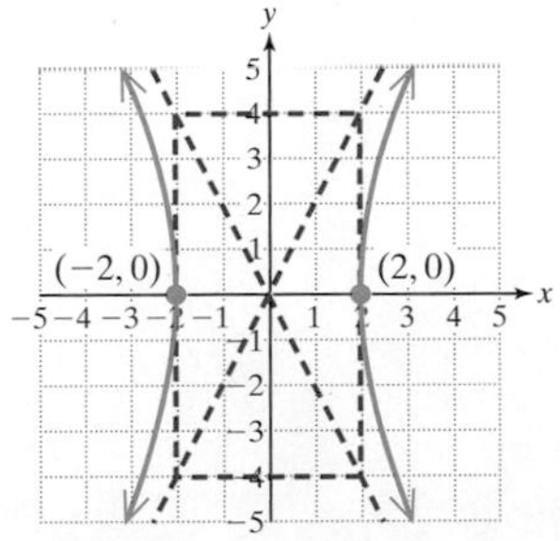

Example 4

$$\frac{y^2}{4} - \frac{x^2}{16} = 1$$

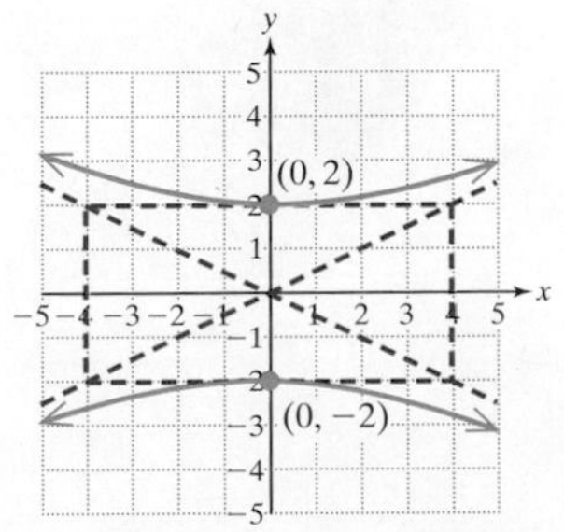

Section 13.4 Nonlinear Systems of Equations in Two Variables

Key Concepts

A **nonlinear system of equations** can be solved by graphing or by the substitution method.

$2x^2 + y^2 = 15$

$x^2 - y = 0$

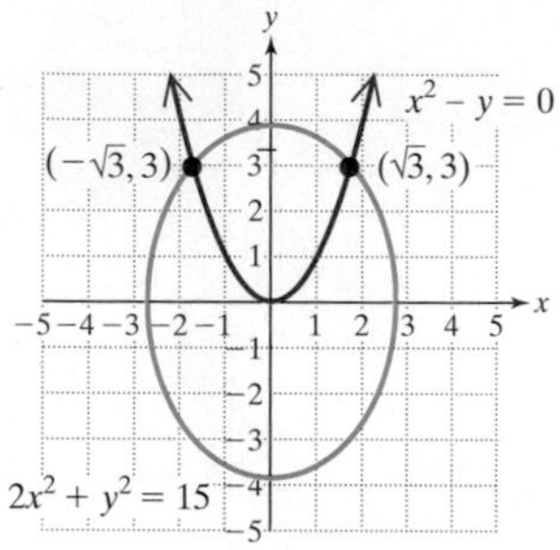

Examples

Example 1

A $\quad 2x^2 + y^2 = 15$

B $\quad x^2 - y = 0 \quad$ Solve for y: $y = x^2$

A $\quad 2x^2 + (x^2)^2 = 15 \quad$ Substitute in first equation.

$2x^2 + x^4 = 15$

$x^4 + 2x^2 - 15 = 0$

$(x^2 + 5)(x^2 - 3) = 0$

$x^2 + 5 = 0$ or $x^2 - 3 = 0$

~~$x^2 = -5$~~ or $x^2 = 3$

$x = \pm\sqrt{3}$

If $x = \sqrt{3}$ then $y = (\sqrt{3})^2 = 3$.

If $x = -\sqrt{3}$ then $y = (-\sqrt{3})^2 = 3$.

Points of intersection are $(\sqrt{3}, 3)$ and $(-\sqrt{3}, 3)$.

The solution set is $\{(\sqrt{3}, 3), (-\sqrt{3}, 3)\}$.

Section 13.5 Nonlinear Inequalities and Systems of Inequalities

Key Concepts

Graph a nonlinear inequality by using the test point method. That is, graph the related equation. Then choose test points in each region to determine where the inequality is true.

Example 1

$y \geq x^2$

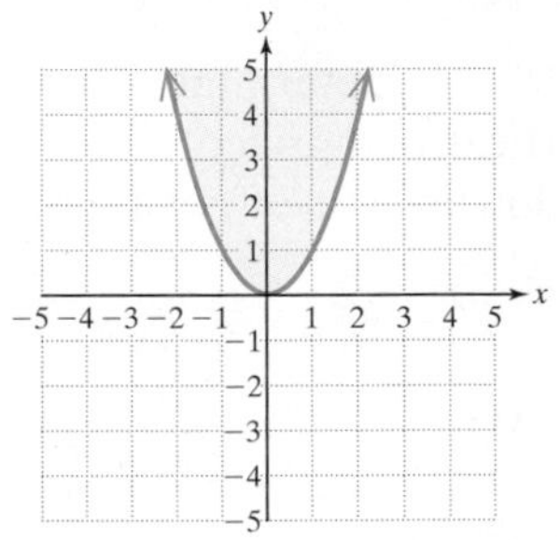

Graph a system of nonlinear inequalities by finding the intersection of the solution sets. That is, graph the solution set for each individual inequality, then take the intersection.

Examples

Example 2

$x^2 + y^2 < 4$

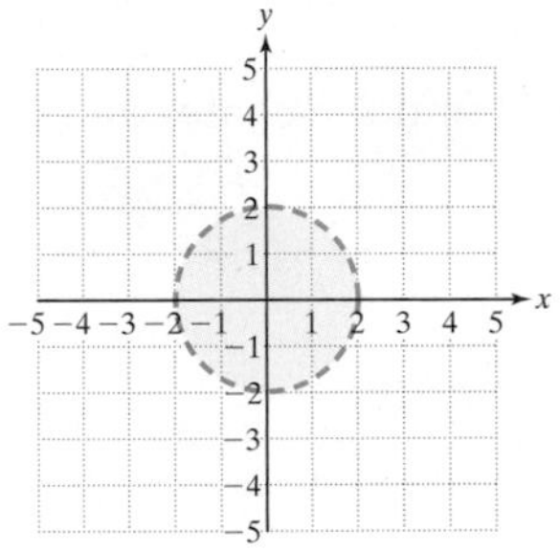

Example 3

$x \geq 0, \quad y > x^2, \quad \text{and} \quad x^2 + y^2 < 4$

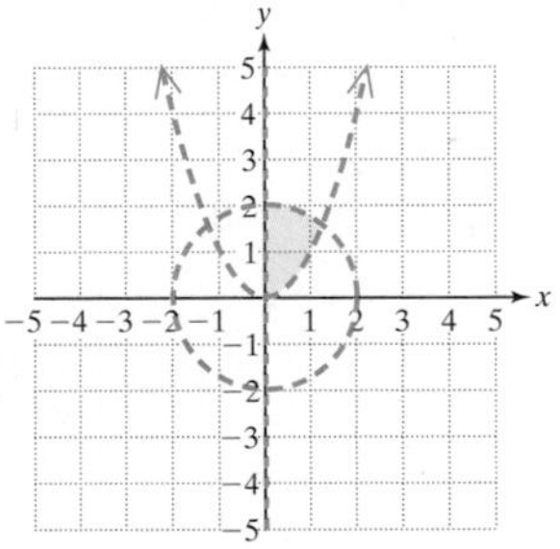

Chapter 13 Review Exercises

Section 13.1

For Exercises 1–4, find the distance between the two points by using the distance formula.

1. $(-6, 3)$ and $(0, 1)$ **2.** $(4, 13)$ and $(-1, 5)$

3. Find x such that $(x, 5)$ is 5 units from $(2, 9)$.

4. Find x such that $(-3, 4)$ is 3 units from $(x, 1)$.

For Exercises 5–8, find the center and the radius of the circle.

5. $(x - 12)^2 + (y - 3)^2 = 16$

6. $(x + 7)^2 + (y - 5)^2 = 81$

7. $(x + 3)^2 + (y + 8)^2 = 20$

8. $(x - 1)^2 + (y + 6)^2 = 32$

9. A stained glass window is in the shape of a circle with a 16-in. diameter. Find an equation of the circle relative to the origin for each of the following graphs.

a.

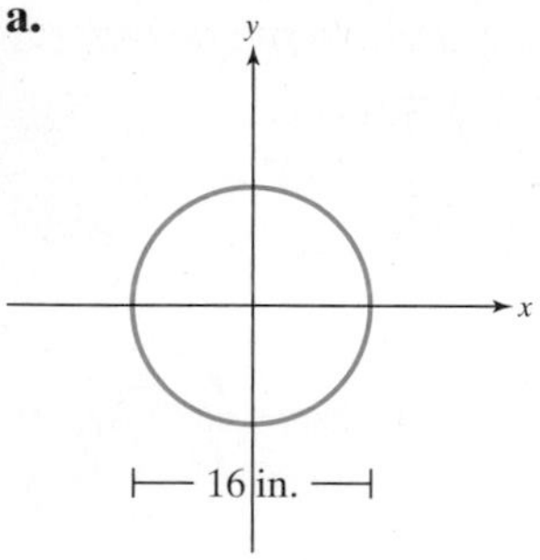

b.

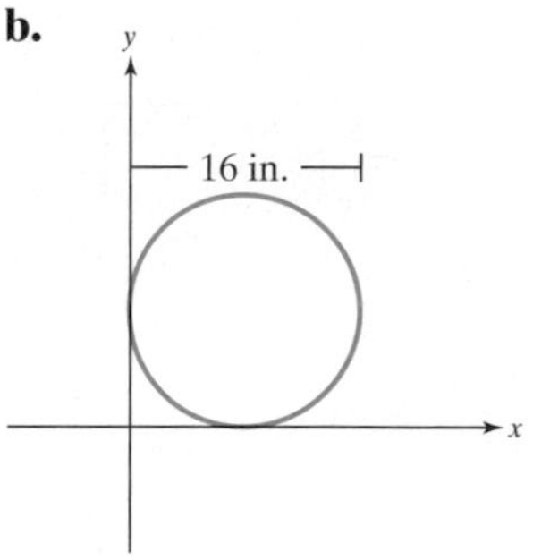

For Exercises 10–13, write the equation of the circle in standard form by completing the square.

10. $x^2 + y^2 + 12x - 10y + 51 = 0$

11. $x^2 + y^2 + 4x + 16y + 60 = 0$

12. $x^2 + y^2 - x - 4y + \frac{1}{4} = 0$

13. $x^2 + y^2 - 6x - \frac{2}{3}y + \frac{1}{9} = 0$

14. Write an equation of a circle with center at the origin and a diameter of 7 m.

15. Write an equation of a circle with center $(0, 2)$ and radius 3 m.

For Exercises 16–17, find the midpoint of the segment with the given endpoints.

16. $(-3, 1)$ and $(-5, -5)$ **17.** $(0, 9)$ and $(-2, 7)$

Section 13.2

For Exercises 18–21, determine whether the axis of symmetry is vertical or horizontal and if the parabola opens upward, downward, left, or right.

18. $y = -2(x - 3)^2 + 2$

19. $x = 3(y - 9)^2 + 1$

20. $x = -(y + 4)^2 - 8$

21. $y = (x + 3)^2 - 10$

For Exercises 22–25, determine the coordinates of the vertex and the equation of the axis of symmetry. Then use this information to graph the parabola.

22. $x = -(y - 1)^2$

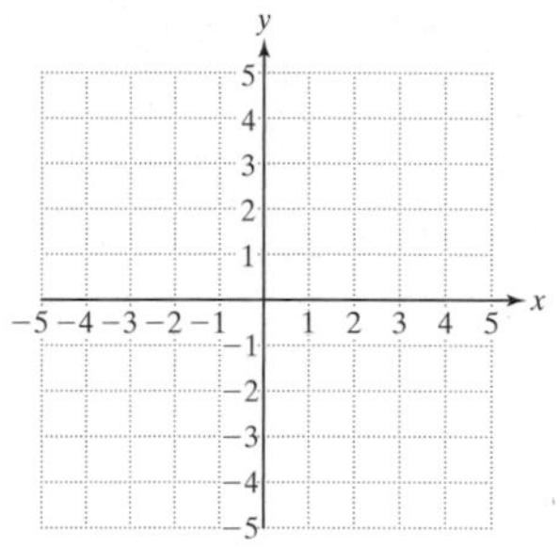

23. $y = (x + 2)^2$

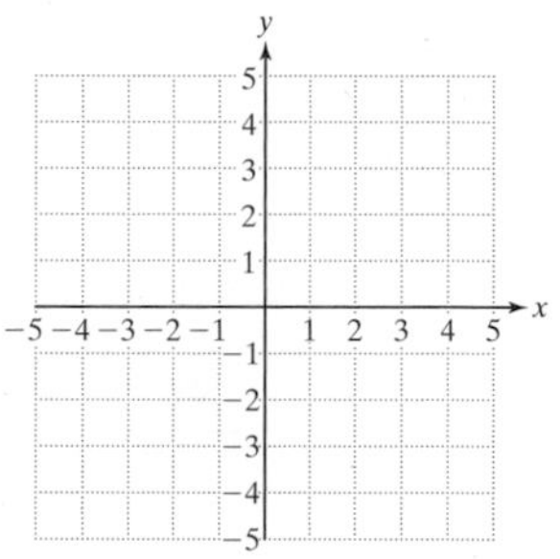

24. $y = -\frac{1}{4}x^2$

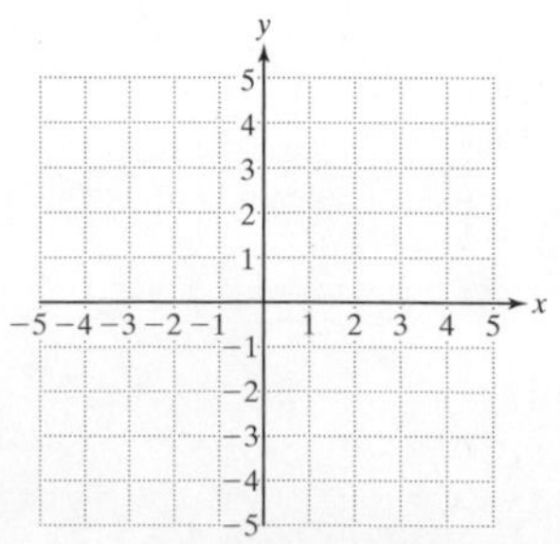

25. $x = 2y^2 - 1$

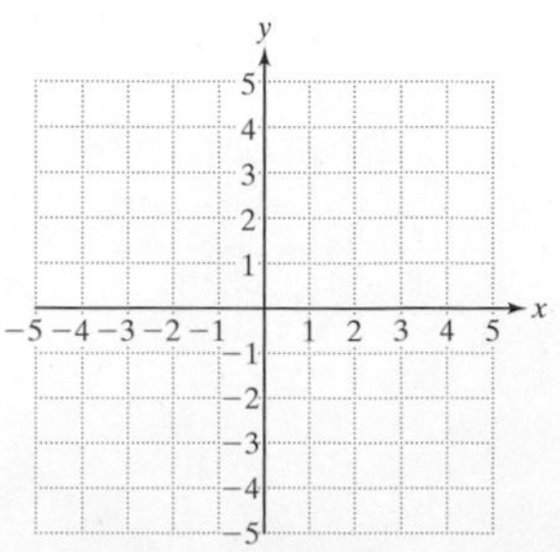

For Exercises 26–29, write the equation in standard form $y = a(x - h)^2 + k$ or $x = a(y - k)^2 + h$. Then identify the vertex and axis of symmetry.

26. $y = x^2 - 6x + 5$

27. $x = y^2 + 4y + 2$

28. $x = -4y^2 + 4y$

29. $y = -2x^2 - 2x$

Section 13.3

For Exercises 30–31, identify the x- and y-intercepts. Then graph the ellipse.

30. $\dfrac{x^2}{9} + \dfrac{y^2}{25} = 1$

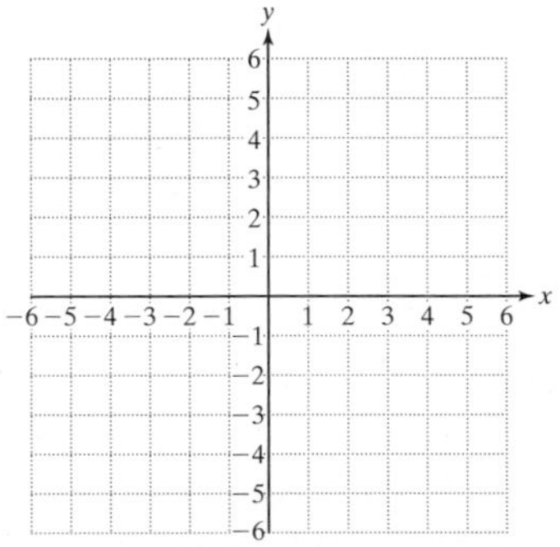

31. $x^2 + 4y^2 = 36$

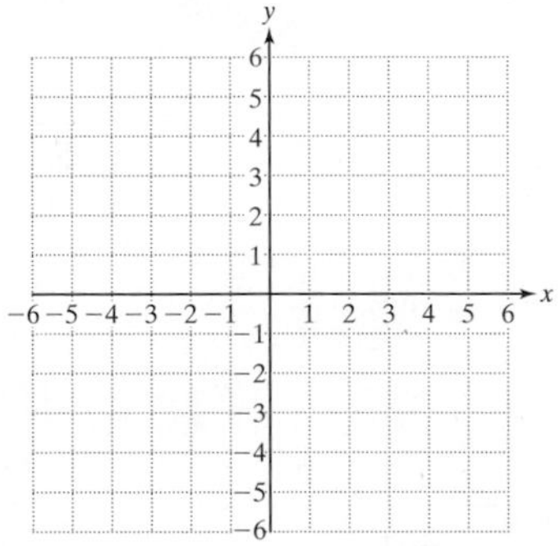

For Exercises 32–33, identify the center of the ellipse and graph the ellipse.

32. $\dfrac{(x - 5)^2}{4} + \dfrac{(y + 3)^2}{16} = 1$

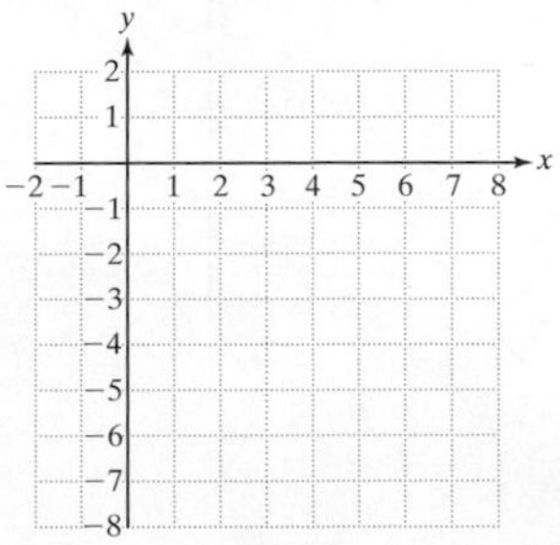

33. $\dfrac{x^2}{25} + \dfrac{(y - 2)^2}{9} = 1$

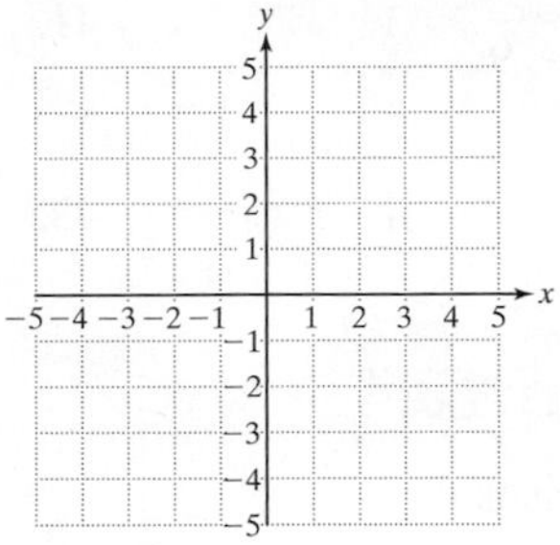

For Exercises 34–37, determine whether the transverse axis is horizontal or vertical.

34. $\dfrac{x^2}{12} - \dfrac{y^2}{16} = 1$

35. $\dfrac{y^2}{9} - \dfrac{x^2}{9} = 1$

36. $y^2 - 8x^2 = 16$

37. $3x^2 - y^2 = 18$

For Exercises 38–39, graph the hyperbola by first drawing the reference rectangle and the asymptotes. Label the vertices.

38. $\dfrac{x^2}{4} - y^2 = 1$

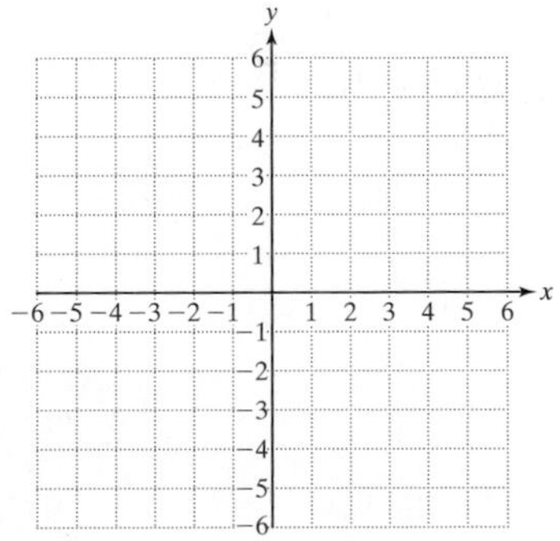

39. $y^2 - x^2 = 16$

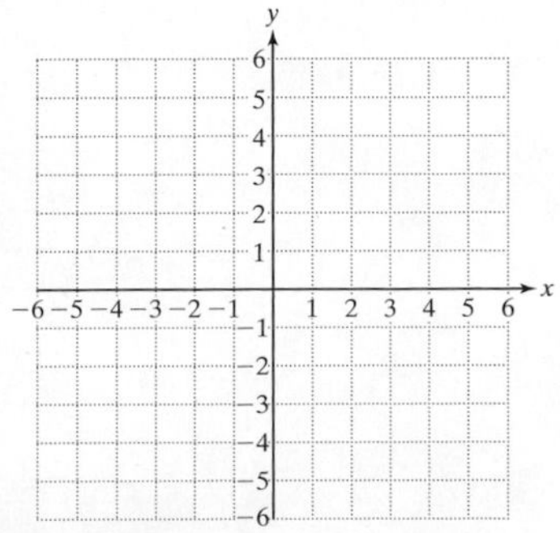

For Exercises 40–43, identify the equations as representing an ellipse or a hyperbola.

40. $\dfrac{x^2}{4} - \dfrac{y^2}{9} = 1$

41. $\dfrac{x^2}{16} + \dfrac{y^2}{9} = 1$

42. $\dfrac{x^2}{4} + \dfrac{y^2}{1} = 1$

43. $\dfrac{y^2}{1} - \dfrac{x^2}{16} = 1$

Section 13.4

For Exercises 44–47,

a. Identify each equation as representing a line, a parabola, a circle, an ellipse, or a hyperbola.

b. Graph both equations on the same coordinate system.

c. Solve the system analytically and verify the answers from the graph.

44. $3x + 2y = 10$

$y = x^2 - 5$

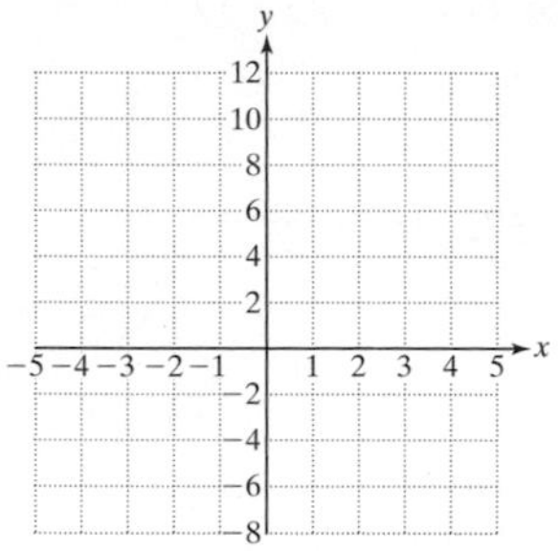

45. $4x + 2y = 10$

$y = x^2 - 10$

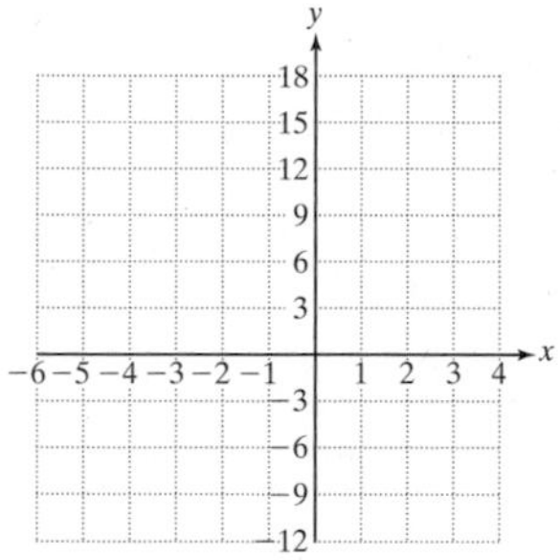

46. $x^2 + y^2 = 9$

$2x + y = 3$

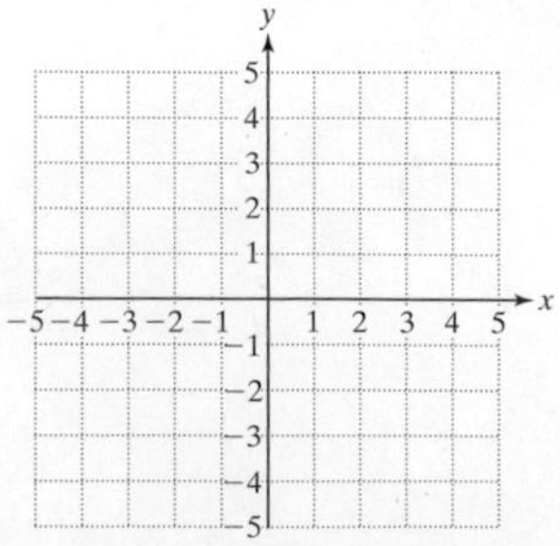

47. $x^2 + y^2 = 16$

$x - 2y = 8$

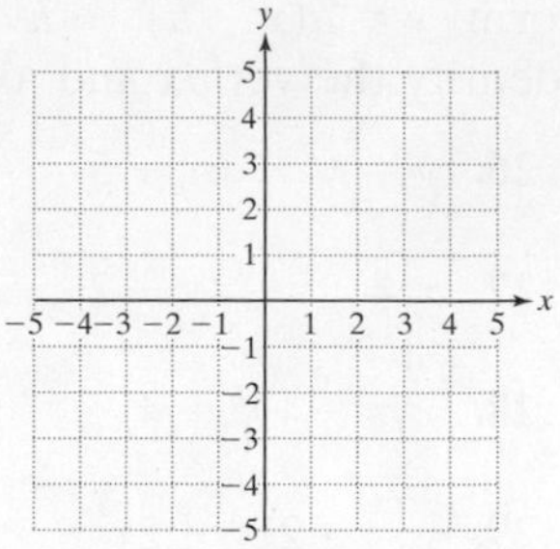

For Exercises 48–53, solve the system of nonlinear equations by using either the substitution method or the addition method.

48. $x^2 + 2y^2 = 8$

$2x - y = 2$

49. $x^2 + 4y^2 = 29$

$x - y = -4$

50. $x - y = 4$

$y^2 = 2x$

51. $y = x^2$

$6x^2 - y^2 = 8$

52. $x^2 + y^2 = 10$

$x^2 + 9y^2 = 18$

53. $x^2 + y^2 = 61$

$x^2 - y^2 = 11$

Section 13.5

For Exercises 54–59, graph the solution set to the inequality.

54. $\dfrac{x^2}{16} + \dfrac{y^2}{81} < 1$

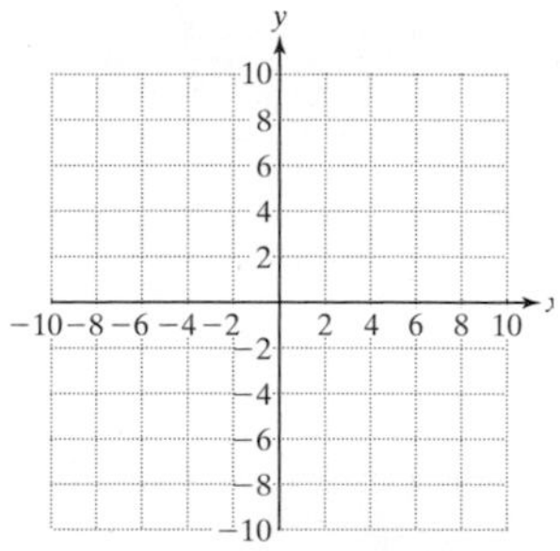

55. $\dfrac{x^2}{25} + \dfrac{y^2}{4} > 1$

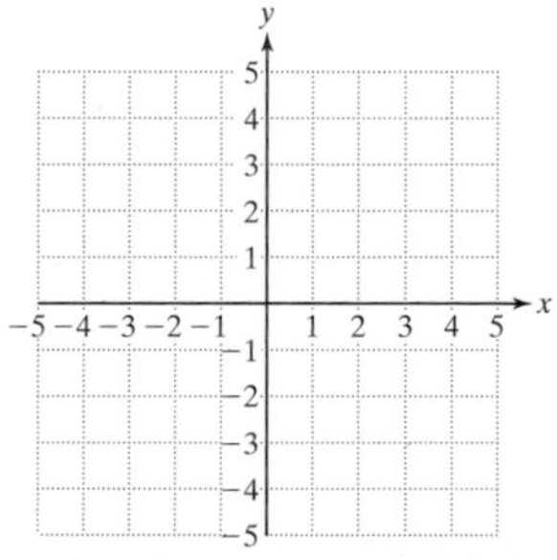

56. $(x - 3)^2 + (y + 1)^2 \geq 9$

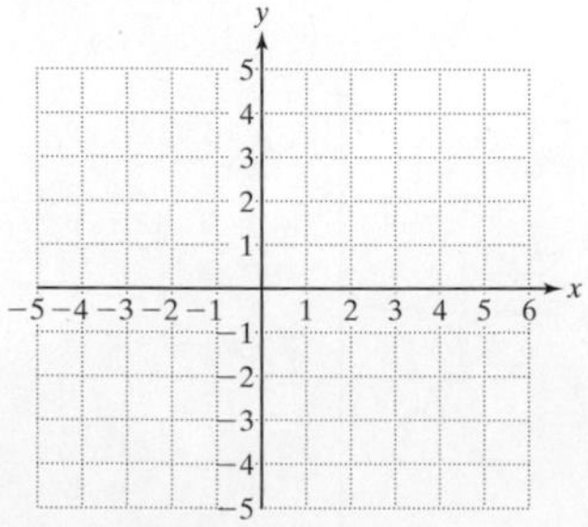

57. $(x + 2)^2 + (y + 1)^2 \le 4$

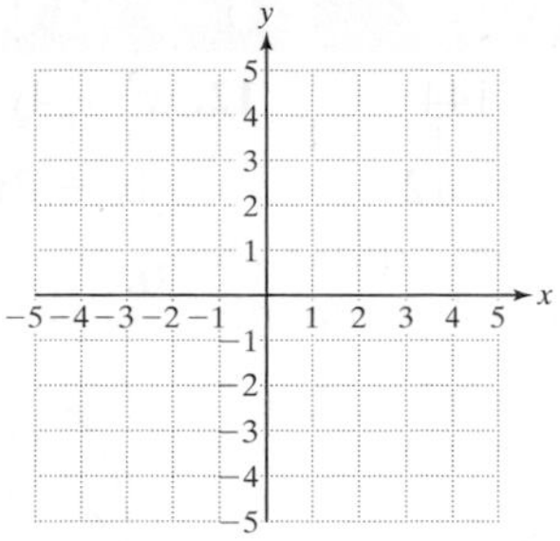

58. $y > (x - 1)^2$

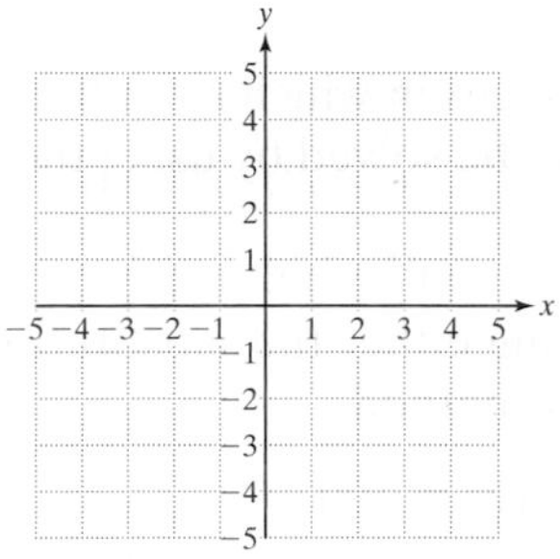

59. $x^2 - \dfrac{y^2}{4} \le 1$

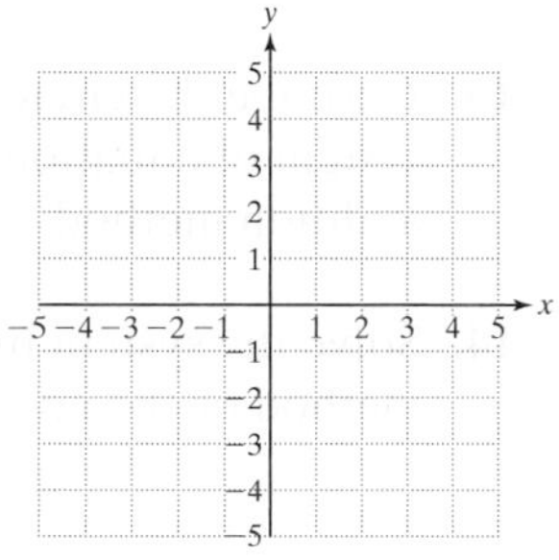

For Exercises 60–61, graph the solution set to the system of nonlinear inequalities.

60. $y > 2^x$
$x^2 + y^2 < 4$

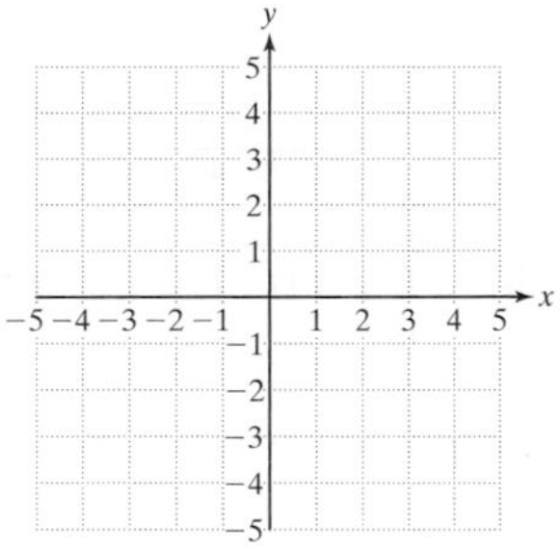

61. $y < x^2$
$x^2 + y^2 < 9$

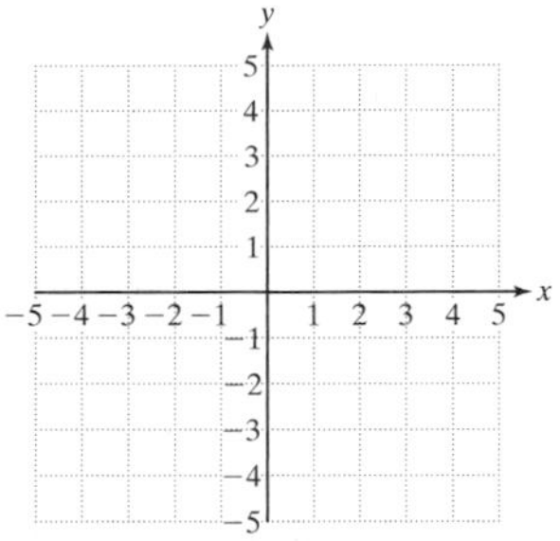

Chapter 13 Test

1. Use the distance formula to find the distance between the two points $(-5, 2)$ and $(-1, 6)$.

2. Determine the center and radius of the circle.

$$\left(x - \frac{5}{6}\right)^2 + \left(y + \frac{1}{3}\right)^2 = \frac{25}{49}$$

3. Determine the center and radius of the circle.

$$x^2 + y^2 - 4y - 5 = 0$$

4. Let $(0, 4)$ be the center of a circle that passes through the point $(-2, 5)$.

a. What is the radius of the circle?

b. Write the equation of the circle in standard form.

5. Find the center of the circle that has a diameter with endpoints $(7.3, -1.2)$ and $(0.3, 5.1)$.

6. Determine the vertex and the equation of the axis of symmetry. Then graph the parabola.

$$x = -(y - 2)^2 + 3$$

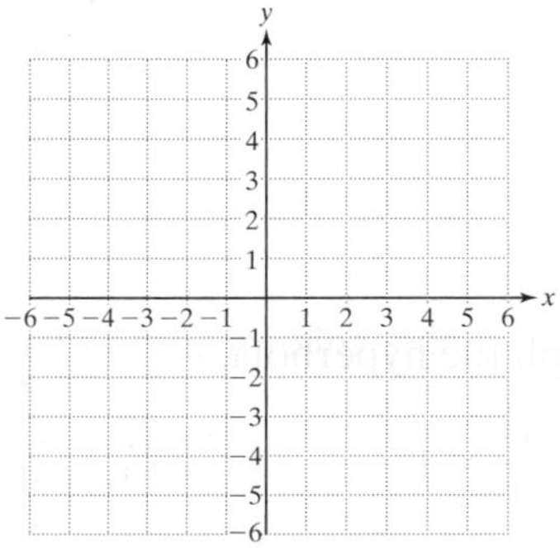

25. An automobile starts from rest and accelerates at a constant rate for 10 sec. The distance, $d(t)$, in feet traveled by the car is given by

$$d(t) = 4.4t^2$$

where $0 \le t \le 10$ is the time in seconds.

a. How far has the car traveled after 2, 3, and 4 sec, respectively?

b. How long will it take for the car to travel 281.6 ft?

26. Solve the equation $125w^3 + 1 = 0$ by factoring and using the quadratic formula. (*Hint:* You will find one real solution and two imaginary solutions.)

27. Solve. $\dfrac{x}{x+2} - \dfrac{3}{x-1} = \dfrac{1}{x^2 + x - 2}$

28. Find the coordinates of the vertex of the parabola defined by $f(x) = x^2 + 10x - 11$ by completing the square.

29. Graph the quadratic function defined by $g(x) = -x^2 - 2x + 3$.

a. Label the x-intercepts.

b. Label the y-intercept.

c. Label the vertex.

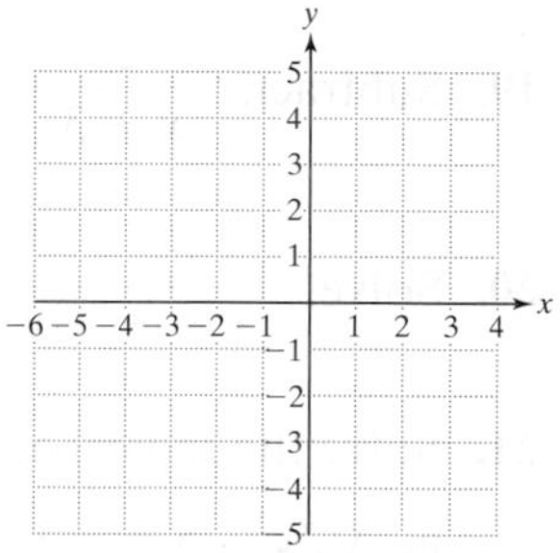

30. Solve the inequality and write the answer in interval notation.

$$|x - 9| - 3 < 7$$

31. Solve the inequality: $|2x - 5| \ge 4$

32. Write the expression in logarithmic form. $8^{5/3} = 32$

33. Solve. $5^2 = 125^x$

34. For $h(x) = x^3 - 1$, find $h^{-1}(x)$.

35. Write an equation representing the set of all points 4 units from the point $(0, 5)$.

36. Graph the ellipse. $\dfrac{x^2}{4} + \dfrac{y^2}{25} = 1$

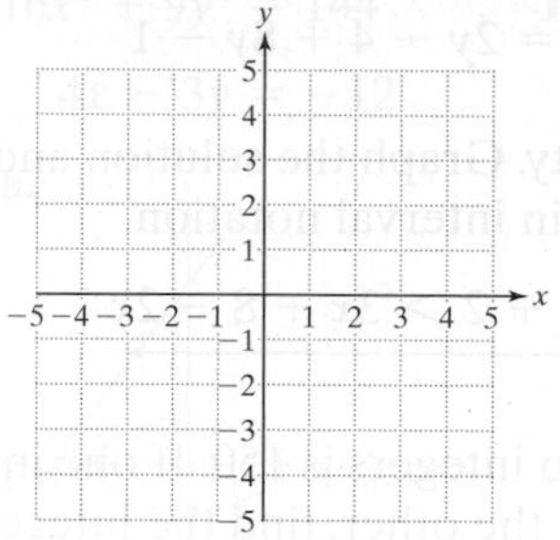

37. Determine the center of the circle, given the endpoints of a diameter.

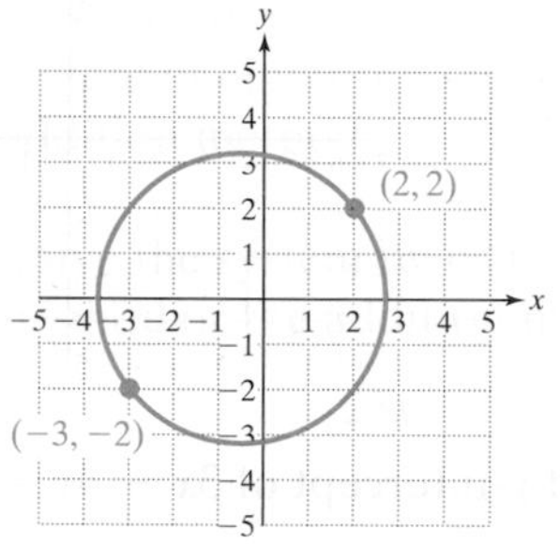

38. Solve the system of nonlinear equations.

$$x^2 + y^2 = 16$$
$$y = -x^2 - 4$$

39. Graph the solution set.

$$y^2 - x^2 < 1$$

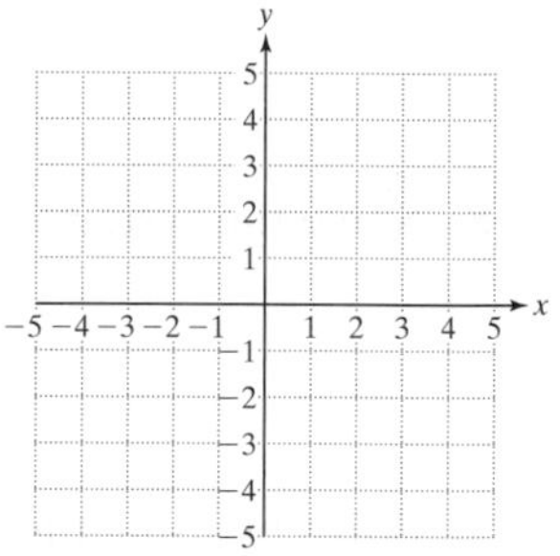

40. Graph the solution set to this system.

$$y > \left(\frac{1}{2}\right)^x$$
$$x < 0$$

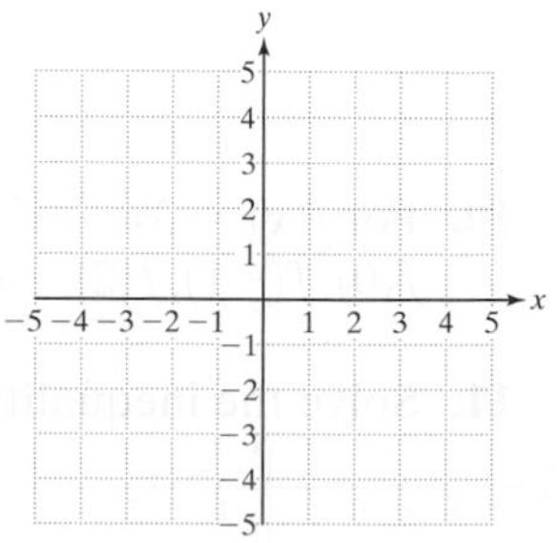

Binomial Expansions, Sequences, and Series

14

CHAPTER OUTLINE

14.1 Binomial Expansions 990

14.2 Sequences and Series 996

14.3 Arithmetic Sequences and Series 1005

14.4 Geometric Sequences and Series 1011

Problem Recognition Exercises: Identifying Arithmetic and Geometric Sequences 1019

Group Activity: Investigating Mean and Standard Deviation 1020

Chapter 14

We begin this chapter by learning how to expand expressions of the form $(a + b)^n$. Then we study a new type of function called a sequence. A sequence is a progression of terms, and the sum of the terms in a sequence is called a series. We will study arithmetic and geometric sequences. These are sequences in which successive terms differ by a fixed constant or by a fixed ratio.

Are You Prepared?

To practice working with sequences, try Exercises 1–8. In each case, fill in the blanks with the next three terms that follow the given pattern.

1. 1, 4, 7, 10, ______, ______, ______
2. 6, −2, −10, −18, ______, ______, ______
3. 3, 6, 12, 24, ______, ______, ______
4. 9, 3, 1, $\frac{1}{3}$, ______, ______, ______
5. 1, 4, 9, 16, ______, ______, ______
6. −4, 12, −36, 108, ______, ______, ______
7. $x^7, x^6y, x^5y^2, x^4y^3$, ______, ______, ______
8. $a^6b^3, a^5b^4, a^4b^5, a^3b^6$, ______, ______, ______
9. Expand the expression. $(a + b)^2 =$ ____________
10. Expand the expression. $(a + b)^3 =$ ____________
11. Based on your answers to Exercises 9 and 10, how many terms are in the expansion of $(a + b)^n$? ______

Section 14.1 Binomial Expansions

Concepts

1. **Binomial Expansions and Pascal's Triangle**
2. **Factorial Notation**
3. **The Binomial Theorem**

1. Binomial Expansions and Pascal's Triangle

In Section 5.6 we learned how to square a binomial.

$$(a + b)^2 = a^2 + 2ab + b^2$$

The expression $a^2 + 2ab + b^2$ is called the **binomial expansion** of $(a + b)^2$. To expand $(a + b)^3$, we can find the product $(a + b)(a + b)^2$.

$$\begin{aligned}(a + b)(a + b)^2 &= (a + b)(a^2 + 2ab + b^2)\\ &= a^3 + 2a^2b + ab^2 + a^2b + 2ab^2 + b^3\\ &= a^3 + 3a^2b + 3ab^2 + b^3\end{aligned}$$

Similarly, to expand $(a + b)^4$, we can multiply $(a + b)$ by $(a + b)^3$. Using this method, we can expand several powers of $(a + b)$ to find the following pattern:

$$\begin{aligned}(a + b)^0 &= 1\\ (a + b)^1 &= a + b\\ (a + b)^2 &= a^2 + 2ab + b^2\\ (a + b)^3 &= a^3 + 3a^2b + 3ab^2 + b^3\\ (a + b)^4 &= a^4 + 4a^3b + 6a^2b^2 + 4ab^3 + b^4\\ (a + b)^5 &= a^5 + 5a^4b + 10a^3b^2 + 10a^2b^3 + 5ab^4 + b^5\end{aligned}$$

Notice that the exponents on a decrease from left to right, while the exponents on b increase from left to right. Also observe that for each term, the sum of the exponents is equal to the exponent to which $(a + b)$ is raised. Finally, notice that the number of terms in the expansion is exactly 1 more than the power to which $(a + b)$ is raised. For example, the expansion of $(a + b)^4$ has five terms, and the expansion of $(a + b)^5$ has six terms.

With these guidelines in mind, we know that $(a + b)^6$ will contain seven terms involving

$$a^6 \qquad a^5b \qquad a^4b^2 \qquad a^3b^3 \qquad a^2b^4 \qquad ab^5 \qquad b^6$$

We can complete the expansion of $(a + b)^6$ if we can determine the correct coefficients of each term.

If we write the coefficients for several expansions of $(a + b)^n$, where $n \geq 0$, we have a triangular array of numbers.

$(a + b)^0 = 1$	1
$(a + b)^1 = 1a + 1b$	1 1
$(a + b)^2 = 1a^2 + 2ab + 1b^2$	1 2 1
$(a + b)^3 = 1a^3 + 3a^2b + 3ab^2 + 1b^3$	1 3 3 1
$(a + b)^4 = 1a^4 + 4a^3b + 6a^2b^2 + 4ab^3 + 1b^4$	1 4 6 4 1
$(a + b)^5 = 1a^5 + 5a^4b + 10a^3b^2 + 10a^2b^3 + 5ab^4 + 1b^5$	1 5 10 10 5 1

Each row begins and ends with a 1, and each entry in between is the sum of the two entries from the line above. For example, in the last row, $5 = 1 + 4$, $10 = 4 + 6$, and so on. This triangular array of coefficients for a binomial expansion is called **Pascal's triangle**, named after French mathematician Blaise Pascal (1623–1662).

1
1 1
1 2 1
1 3 3 1
1 4 6 4 1
1 5 10 10 5 1
1 6 15 20 15 6 1

By using the pattern shown in Pascal's triangle, the coefficients corresponding to $(a + b)^6$ would be 1, 6, 15, 20, 15, 6, 1. By inserting the coefficients, the sum becomes

$$(a + b)^6 = 1a^6 + 6a^5b + 15a^4b^2 + 20a^3b^3 + 15a^2b^4 + 6ab^5 + 1b^6$$

2. Factorial Notation

Although Pascal's triangle provides an easy method to find the coefficients of $(a + b)^n$, it is impractical for large values of n. A more efficient method to find the coefficients of a binomial expansion involves **factorial notation**.

Definition of $n!$

Let n be a positive integer. Then $n!$ (read as "n factorial") is defined as the product of integers from 1 through n. That is,

$$n! = n(n - 1)(n - 2) \cdot \cdot \cdot (2)(1)$$

Note: We define $0! = 1$.

Example 1 Evaluating Factorial Notation

Evaluate the expressions.

a. $4!$ **b.** $10!$ **c.** $0!$

Solution:

a. $4! = 4 \cdot 3 \cdot 2 \cdot 1 = 24$

b. $10! = 10 \cdot 9 \cdot 8 \cdot 7 \cdot 6 \cdot 5 \cdot 4 \cdot 3 \cdot 2 \cdot 1 = 3{,}628{,}800$

c. $0! = 1$ by definition

Skill Practice Evaluate the expressions.

1. $3!$ **2.** $8!$ **3.** $1!$

Calculator Connections

Topic: Evaluating Expressions with Factorial Notation

Most calculators have a [!] function. Try evaluating the expressions from Example 1 on a calculator:

Answers

1. 6 **2.** 40,320 **3.** 1

Sometimes factorial notation is used with other operations such as multiplication and division.

Example 2 Evaluating Expressions with Factorials

Evaluate the expressions.

a. $\dfrac{4!}{4! \cdot 0!}$ **b.** $\dfrac{4!}{3! \cdot 1!}$ **c.** $\dfrac{4!}{2! \cdot 2!}$ **d.** $\dfrac{4!}{1! \cdot 3!}$ **e.** $\dfrac{4!}{0! \cdot 4!}$

Solution:

a. $\dfrac{4!}{4! \cdot 0!} = \dfrac{\cancel{4!}}{\cancel{4!} \cdot 1} = 1$

b. $\dfrac{4!}{3! \cdot 1!} = \dfrac{4 \cdot \cancel{3!}}{\cancel{3!} \cdot 1} = 4$

c. $\dfrac{4!}{2! \cdot 2!} = \dfrac{4 \cdot 3 \cdot \cancel{2!}}{\cancel{2!} \cdot 2 \cdot 1} = \dfrac{12}{2} = 6$

d. $\dfrac{4!}{1! \cdot 3!} = \dfrac{4 \cdot \cancel{3!}}{1 \cdot \cancel{3!}} = 4$

e. $\dfrac{4!}{0! \cdot 4!} = \dfrac{\cancel{4!}}{1 \cdot \cancel{4!}} = 1$

Calculator Connections

Topic: Multiplying and Dividing Factorial Expressions

To evaluate the expressions from Example 2 on a calculator, use parentheses around the factors in the denominator.

```
4!/(4!*0!)
                1
4!/(3!*1!)
                4
4!/(2!*2!)
                6
```

Skill Practice Evaluate.

4. $\dfrac{5!}{5!0!}$ **5.** $\dfrac{5!}{4!1!}$ **6.** $\dfrac{5!}{3!2!}$

3. The Binomial Theorem

Notice from Example 2 that the values of

$$\frac{4!}{4! \cdot 0!} \quad \frac{4!}{3! \cdot 1!} \quad \frac{4!}{2! \cdot 2!} \quad \frac{4!}{1! \cdot 3!} \quad \text{and} \quad \frac{4!}{0! \cdot 4!}$$

correspond to the values 1, 4, 6, 4, 1, which are the coefficients for the expansion of $(a + b)^4$. Generalizing this pattern, we see the coefficients for the terms in the expansion of $(a + b)^n$ are given by

$$\frac{n!}{r! \cdot (n - r)!}$$

where r corresponds to the exponent on the factor of a and $(n - r)$ corresponds to the exponent on the factor of b. Using this formula for the coefficients in a binomial expansion results in the **binomial theorem**.

Answers

4. 1 **5.** 5 **6.** 10

The Binomial Theorem

For any positive integer n,

$$(a+b)^n = \frac{n!}{n!\cdot 0!}a^n + \frac{n!}{(n-1)!\cdot 1!}a^{(n-1)}b + \frac{n!}{(n-2)!\cdot 2!}a^{(n-2)}b^2 + \cdots + \frac{n!}{0!\cdot n!}b^n$$

Example 3 Applying the Binomial Theorem

Write out the first three terms of the expansion of $(a+b)^{10}$.

Solution:

The first three terms of $(a+b)^{10}$ are

$$\frac{10!}{10!\cdot 0!}a^{10} + \frac{10!}{9!\cdot 1!}a^9b + \frac{10!}{8!\cdot 2!}a^8b^2$$

$$= \frac{\cancel{10!}}{\cancel{10!}\cdot 1}a^{10} + \frac{10\cdot\cancel{9!}}{\cancel{9!}\cdot 1!}a^9b + \frac{10\cdot 9\cdot\cancel{8!}}{\cancel{8!}\cdot 2\cdot 1}a^8b^2$$

$$= a^{10} + 10a^9b + 45a^8b^2$$

TIP: When applying the binomial theorem, exponents on a and b must add up to n.

Skill Practice

7. Write out the first three terms of $(x+y)^5$.

Example 4 Applying the Binomial Theorem

Use the binomial theorem to expand $(2m+7)^3$.

Solution:

This expression is of the form $(a+b)^3$, where $a = 2m$ and $b = 7$. Applying the binomial theorem we have

$$(a+b)^3 = \frac{3!}{3!\cdot 0!}a^3 + \frac{3!}{2!\cdot 1!}a^2b + \frac{3!}{1!\cdot 2!}ab^2 + \frac{3!}{0!\cdot 3!}b^3$$

$$= \frac{3!}{3!\cdot 0!}(2m)^3 + \frac{3!}{2!\cdot 1!}(2m)^2(7) + \frac{3!}{1!\cdot 2!}(2m)(7)^2 + \frac{3!}{0!\cdot 3!}(7)^3$$

$$= 1\cdot(8m^3) + 3\cdot(4m^2)(7) + 3\cdot(2m)(49) + 1\cdot(343)$$

$$= 8m^3 + 84m^2 + 294m + 343$$

TIP: The values of $\frac{n!}{r!\cdot(n-r)!}$ can also be found by using Pascal's triangle.

1
1 1
1 2 1
1 3 3 1

Skill Practice

8. Use the binomial theorem to expand $(3y+4)^3$.

Answers

7. $x^5 + 5x^4y + 10x^3y^2$
8. $27y^3 + 108y^2 + 144y + 64$

Example 5 Applying the Binomial Theorem

Use the binomial theorem to expand $(3x^2 - 5y)^4$.

Solution:

Write $(3x^2 - 5y)^4$ as $[(3x^2) + (-5y)]^4$. In this case, the expressions $3x^2$ and $-5y$ may be substituted for a and b in the expansion of $(a + b)^4$.

$$(a+b)^4 = \frac{4!}{4!\cdot 0!}a^4 + \frac{4!}{3!\cdot 1!}a^3b + \frac{4!}{2!\cdot 2!}a^2b^2 + \frac{4!}{1!\cdot 3!}ab^3 + \frac{4!}{0!\cdot 4!}b^4$$

$$= \frac{4!}{4!\cdot 0!}(3x^2)^4 + \frac{4!}{3!\cdot 1!}(3x^2)^3(-5y) + \frac{4!}{2!\cdot 2!}(3x^2)^2(-5y)^2 + \frac{4!}{1!\cdot 3!}(3x^2)(-5y)^3 + \frac{4!}{0!\cdot 4!}(-5y)^4$$

$$= 1\cdot(81x^8) + 4\cdot(27x^6)(-5y) + 6\cdot(9x^4)(25y^2) + 4\cdot(3x^2)(-125y^3) + 1\cdot(625y^4)$$

$$= 81x^8 - 540x^6y + 1350x^4y^2 - 1500x^2y^3 + 625y^4$$

TIP: The values of $\frac{n!}{r!\cdot(n-r)!}$ can also be found by using Pascal's triangle.

```
      1
     1 1
    1 2 1
   1 3 3 1
  1 4 6 4 1
```

Skill Practice

9. Use the binomial theorem to expand $(2a - 3b^2)^4$.

The binomial theorem may also be used to find a specific term in a binomial expansion.

Example 6 Finding a Specific Term in a Binomial Expansion

Find the fourth term of the expansion $(a + b)^{13}$.

Solution:

There are 14 terms in the expansion of $(a + b)^{13}$. The first term will have variable factors $a^{13}b^0$. The second term will have variable factors $a^{12}b^1$. The third term will have $a^{11}b^2$, and the fourth term will have $a^{10}b^3$. Hence, the fourth term is

$$\frac{13!}{10!\cdot 3!}a^{10}b^3 = 286a^{10}b^3$$

Skill Practice

10. Find the fourth term of $(x + y)^8$.

From Example 6, we see that for the kth term in the expansion $(a + b)^n$, where k is an integer greater than zero, the variable factors are $a^{n-(k-1)}$ and b^{k-1}. Therefore, to find the kth term of $(a + b)^n$, we can make the following generalization.

Finding a Specific Term in a Binomial Expansion

Let n and k be positive integers such that $k \le n$. Then the kth term in the expansion of $(a + b)^n$ is given by

$$\frac{n!}{[n-(k-1)]!\cdot(k-1)!}\cdot a^{n-(k-1)}\cdot b^{k-1}$$

Answers

9. $16a^4 - 96a^3b^2 + 216a^2b^4 - 216ab^6 + 81b^8$

10. $56x^5y^3$

Example 7 Finding a Specific Term in a Binomial Expansion

Find the sixth term of $(p^3 + 2w)^8$.

Solution:

Apply the formula.

$$\frac{n!}{[n-(k-1)]! \cdot (k-1)!} \cdot a^{n-(k-1)} \cdot b^{k-1} \quad \text{with } n = 8, k = 6, a = p^3, \text{and } b = 2w$$

$$\frac{8!}{[8-(6-1)]! \cdot (6-1)!} \cdot (p^3)^{8-(6-1)} \cdot (2w)^{6-1}$$

$$= \frac{8!}{(3)! \cdot (5)!} \cdot (p^3)^3 \cdot (2w)^5$$

$$= 56 \cdot (p^9) \cdot (32w^5)$$

$$= 1792p^9w^5$$

Skill Practice

11. Find the fifth term of $(t - m^2)^8$.

Answer

11. $70t^4m^8$

Section 14.1 Practice Exercises

Vocabulary and Key Concepts

1. a. The expanded form of $(a + b)^2$ = ___________. The expanded form of $(a + b)^3$ = _______________.
These are both called ___________ expansions.

b. Given a positive integer n, the value of $n!$ is _______________. Furthermore, $n!$ is read as "n ___________."

c. $3! =$ ___________, $2! =$ ___________, $1! =$ ___________, and $0! =$ ___________.

d. The ___________ theorem states that for any positive integer n,

$$(a+b)^n = \frac{n!}{n! \cdot 0!}a^n + \frac{n!}{(n-1)! \cdot 1!}a^{(n-1)}b + \frac{n!}{(n-2)! \cdot 2!}a^{(n-2)}b^2 + \cdots + \frac{n!}{0! \cdot n!}b^n.$$

e. The coefficients of the binomial expansion of $(a + b)^n$ can also be found by using ___________ triangle.

Concept 1: Binomial Expansions and Pascal's Triangle

For Exercises 2–7, expand the binomials. Use Pascal's triangle to find the coefficients.

2. $(x + y)^4$ **3.** $(a + b)^3$ **4.** $(4 + p)^3$

5. $(1 + g)^4$ **6.** $(a^2 + b)^6$ **7.** $(p + q^2)^7$

For Exercises 8–13, rewrite each binomial of the form $(a - b)^n$ as $[a + (-b)]^n$. Then expand the binomials. Use Pascal's triangle to find the coefficients.

8. $(t - 2)^5$ **9.** $(s - t)^5$

10. $(p^2 - w)^3$ **11.** $(5 - u^3)^4$

12. $(a - b^2)^4$ **13.** $(x^2 - 4)^3$

14. For $a > 0$ and $b > 0$, what happens to the signs of the terms when expanding the binomial $(a - b)^n$ compared with $(a + b)^n$?

Concept 2: Factorial Notation

For Exercises 15–18, evaluate the expression. **(See Example 1.)**

15. $5!$ **16.** $3!$ **17.** $0!$ **18.** $1!$

19. True or false: $0! \neq 1!$

20. True or false: $n!$ is defined for negative integers.

21. True or false: $n! = n$ for $n = 1$ and 2.

22. Show that $9! = 9 \cdot 8!$

23. Show that $6! = 6 \cdot 5!$

24. Show that $8! = 8 \cdot 7!$

For Exercises 25–32, evaluate the expression. **(See Example 2.)**

25. $\frac{8!}{4!}$ **26.** $\frac{7!}{5!}$ **27.** $\frac{3!}{0!}$ **28.** $\frac{4!}{0!}$

29. $\frac{8!}{3! \cdot 5!}$ **30.** $\frac{6!}{2! \cdot 4!}$ **31.** $\frac{4!}{0! \cdot 4!}$ **32.** $\frac{6!}{0! \cdot 6!}$

Concept 3: The Binomial Theorem

For Exercises 33–36, find the first three terms of the expansion. **(See Example 3.)**

33. $(m + n)^{11}$ **34.** $(p + q)^9$ **35.** $(u^2 - v)^{12}$ **36.** $(r - s^2)^8$

37. How many terms are in the expansion of $(a + b)^8$?

38. How many terms are in the expansion of $(x + y)^{13}$?

For Exercises 39–50, use the binomial theorem to expand the binomials. **(See Examples 4–5.)**

39. $(s + t)^6$ **40.** $(h + k)^4$ **41.** $(b - 3)^3$ **42.** $(c - 2)^5$

43. $(2x + y)^4$ **44.** $(p + 3q)^3$ **45.** $(c^2 - d)^7$ **46.** $(u - v^3)^6$

47. $\left(\frac{a}{2} - b\right)^5$ **48.** $\left(\frac{s}{3} + t\right)^5$ **49.** $(x + 4y)^4$ **50.** $(3y - w)^3$

For Exercises 51–56, find the indicated term of the binomial expansion. **(See Examples 6–7.)**

51. $(m - n)^{11}$; sixth term **52.** $(p - q)^9$; fourth term **53.** $(u^2 - v)^{12}$; fifth term

54. $(2r - s^2)^8$; sixth term **55.** $(5f + g)^9$; 10th term **56.** $(4m + n)^{10}$; 11th term

Section 14.2 Sequences and Series

Concepts

1. Finite and Infinite Sequences
2. Series

1. Finite and Infinite Sequences

In day-to-day life, we think of a sequence as a set of items with some order or pattern. In mathematics, a sequence is a list of terms that correspond to the set of positive integers.

For example, suppose Justine is allowed to choose between two salary plans. Plan A offers \$48,000 as a starting salary with a 5% raise each year. Plan B offers

$50,000 with a $2000 raise each year. Then the following sequences represent the salaries for each plan for the first 5 yr:

Plan A:	$48,000	$50,400	$52,920	$55,566	$58,344.30
Plan B:	$50,000	$52,000	$54,000	$56,000	$58,000

By studying sequences we can see that Plan A yields a better salary if Justine plans to stay in the job for at least 5 yr.

These sequences are called *finite sequences* because they have a finite number of terms. The sequence 1, 4, 9, 16, 25, . . . is called an *infinite sequence* because it continues indefinitely.

Because the terms in a sequence are related to the set of positive integers, we give a formal definition of finite and infinite sequences, using the language of functions.

Definition of Finite and Infinite Sequences

An **infinite sequence** is a function whose domain is the set of positive integers. A **finite sequence** is a function whose domain is the set of the first n positive integers.

For any positive integer n, the value of the sequence is denoted by a_n (read as "a sub n"). The values $a_1, a_2, a_3, \ldots$ are called the **terms of the sequence**. The expression a_n defines the ***n*th term** (or general term) **of the sequence**.

Example 1 Listing the Terms of a Sequence

List the terms of the following sequences.

a. $a_n = 3n^2 - 4, \quad 1 \le n \le 4$ **b.** $a_n = 3 \cdot 2^n$

Solution:

a. The domain is restricted to the first four positive integers, indicating that the sequence is finite.

n	a_n
1	$3(1)^2 - 4 = -1$
2	$3(2)^2 - 4 = 8$
3	$3(3)^2 - 4 = 23$
4	$3(4)^2 - 4 = 44$

The sequence is $-1, 8, 23, 44$.

b. The sequence $a_n = 3 \cdot 2^n$ has no restrictions on its domain; therefore, it is an infinite sequence.

n	a_n
1	$3 \cdot 2^1 = 6$
2	$3 \cdot 2^2 = 12$
3	$3 \cdot 2^3 = 24$
4	$3 \cdot 2^4 = 48$
. . .	

The sequence is $6, 12, 24, 48, \ldots$

Skill Practice List the terms of the sequences.

1. $a_n = n^3 - 2, \quad 1 \le n \le 3$ **2.** $a_n = \left(\frac{2}{3}\right)^n$

Answers

1. $-1, 6, 25$ **2.** $\frac{2}{3}, \frac{4}{9}, \frac{8}{27}, \ldots$

Calculator Connections

Topic: Displaying Terms of a Sequence

If the nth term of a sequence is known, a seq(function on a graphing utility can display a list of terms. Finding the first four terms of the sequence from Example 1(b) is outlined here: $a_n = 3 \cdot 2^n$.

- Select the MODE key and highlight SEQ.
- Then access the seq(function from the LIST menu and enter the parameters as prompted.
- Paste the seq(command on the home screen and select ENTER.

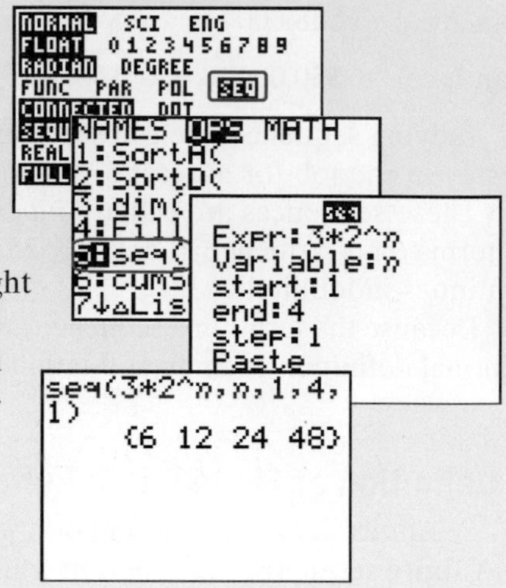

Sometimes the terms of a sequence may have alternating signs. Such a sequence is called an **alternating sequence**.

Example 2 Listing the Terms of an Alternating Sequence

List the first four terms of each alternating sequence.

a. $a_n = (-1)^n \cdot \dfrac{1}{n}$ **b.** $a_n = (-1)^{n+1} \cdot \left(\dfrac{2}{3}\right)^n$

Solution:

a.

n	a_n
1	$(-1)^1 \cdot \dfrac{1}{1} = -1$
2	$(-1)^2 \cdot \dfrac{1}{2} = \dfrac{1}{2}$
3	$(-1)^3 \cdot \dfrac{1}{3} = -\dfrac{1}{3}$
4	$(-1)^4 \cdot \dfrac{1}{4} = \dfrac{1}{4}$

The first four terms are $-1, \frac{1}{2}, -\frac{1}{3}, \frac{1}{4}$.

TIP: Notice that the factor $(-1)^n$ makes the even-numbered terms positive and the odd-numbered terms negative.

b.

n	a_n
1	$(-1)^{1+1} \cdot \left(\dfrac{2}{3}\right)^1 = (-1)^2 \cdot \left(\dfrac{2}{3}\right) = \dfrac{2}{3}$
2	$(-1)^{2+1} \cdot \left(\dfrac{2}{3}\right)^2 = (-1)^3 \cdot \left(\dfrac{4}{9}\right) = -\dfrac{4}{9}$
3	$(-1)^{3+1} \cdot \left(\dfrac{2}{3}\right)^3 = (-1)^4 \cdot \left(\dfrac{8}{27}\right) = \dfrac{8}{27}$
4	$(-1)^{4+1} \cdot \left(\dfrac{2}{3}\right)^4 = (-1)^5 \cdot \left(\dfrac{16}{81}\right) = -\dfrac{16}{81}$

TIP: Notice that the factor $(-1)^{n+1}$ makes the odd-numbered terms positive and the even-numbered terms negative.

The first four terms are $\frac{2}{3}, -\frac{4}{9}, \frac{8}{27}, -\frac{16}{81}$.

Skill Practice List the first four terms of each alternating sequence.

3. $a_n = (-1)^n\left(\frac{1}{2}\right)^n$ **4.** $a_n = (-1)^{n+1}\left(\frac{2}{n}\right)$

In Examples 1 and 2, we were given the formula for the nth term of a sequence and asked to list several terms of the sequence. We now consider the reverse process. Given several terms of the sequence, we will find a formula for the nth term. To do so, look for a pattern that establishes each term as a function of the term number.

Example 3 Finding the *n*th Term of a Sequence

Find a formula for the nth term of the sequence.

a. $\frac{1}{2}, \frac{2}{3}, \frac{3}{4}, \frac{4}{5}, \ldots$ **b.** $-2, 4, -6, 8, -10, \ldots$ **c.** $\frac{1}{2}, \frac{1}{4}, \frac{1}{8}, \frac{1}{16}, \ldots$

Solution:

a. For each term in the sequence, the numerator is equal to the term number, and the denominator is equal to 1 more than the term number. Therefore, the nth term may be given by

$$a_n = \frac{n}{n+1}$$

b. The odd-numbered terms are negative, and the even-numbered terms are positive. The factor $(-1)^n$ will produce the required alternation of signs. The numbers 2, 4, 6, 8, 10, . . . are equal to 2(1), 2(2), 2(3), 2(4), 2(5), ... Therefore, the nth term may be given by

$$a_n = (-1)^n \cdot 2n$$

c. The denominators are consecutive powers of 2. The sequence can be written as

$$\frac{1}{2^1}, \frac{1}{2^2}, \frac{1}{2^3}, \frac{1}{2^4}, \ldots$$

Therefore, the nth term may be given by

$$a_n = \frac{1}{2^n}$$

Skill Practice Find a formula for the nth term of the sequence.

5. $\frac{1}{3}, \frac{1}{9}, \frac{1}{27}, \frac{1}{81}, \ldots$ **6.** $-1, 4, -9, 16, -25, \ldots$ **7.** $\frac{3}{2}, \frac{4}{3}, \frac{5}{4}, \frac{6}{5}, \frac{7}{6}, \ldots$

Answers

3. $-\frac{1}{2}, \frac{1}{4}, -\frac{1}{8}, \frac{1}{16}$

4. $2, -1, \frac{2}{3}, -\frac{1}{2}$

5. $a_n = \frac{1}{3^n}$ **6.** $a_n = (-1)^n n^2$

7. $a_n = \frac{n+2}{n+1}$

TIP: The first few terms of a sequence are not sufficient to define the sequence uniquely. For example, consider the sequence

$$\frac{1}{2}, \frac{1}{4}, \frac{1}{8}, \ldots$$

The following formulas both produce the first three terms, but differ at the fourth term:

$$a_n = \frac{1}{2^n} \quad \text{and} \quad b_n = \frac{1}{n^2 - n + 2}$$

$$a_4 = \frac{1}{16} \quad \text{whereas} \quad b_4 = \frac{1}{14}$$

To define a sequence uniquely, the nth term must be provided.

Example 4 Using a Sequence in an Application

A child drops a ball from a height of 4 ft. With each bounce, the ball rebounds to 50% of its height. Write a sequence whose terms represent the heights from which the ball falls (begin with the initial height from which the ball was dropped).

Solution:

The ball first drops 4 ft and then rebounds to a new height of 0.50(4 ft) = 2 ft. Similarly, it falls from 2 ft and rebounds 0.50(2 ft) = 1 ft. Repeating this process, we have

$$4, 2, 1, \frac{1}{2}, \frac{1}{4}, \frac{1}{8}, \ldots$$

The nth term can be represented by $a_n = 4 \cdot (0.50)^{n-1}$.

Skill Practice

8. The first swing of a pendulum measures 30°. If each swing that follows is 25% less, list the first three terms of this sequence.

2. Series

In many mathematical applications it is important to find the sum of the terms of a sequence. For example, suppose that the yearly interest earned in an account over a 4-yr period is given by the sequence

$$\$250, \quad \$265, \quad \$278.25, \quad \$292.16$$

The sum of the terms gives the total interest earned

$$\$250 + \$265 + \$278.25 + \$292.16 = \$1085.41$$

By adding the terms of a sequence, we obtain a series.

Definition of a Series

The indicated sum of the terms of a sequence is called a **series**.

Answer

8. 30°, 22.5°, 16.875°

As with a sequence, a series may be a finite or an infinite sum of terms.

A convenient notation used to denote the sum of a set of terms is called **summation notation**, or sigma notation. The Greek letter Σ (sigma) is used to indicate sums. For example, the sum of the first four terms of the sequence defined by $a_n = n^3$ are denoted by

$$\sum_{n=1}^{4} n^3$$

This is read as "the sum from n equals 1 to 4 of n^3" and is simplified as

$$\begin{aligned}\sum_{n=1}^{4} n^3 &= (1)^3 + (2)^3 + (3)^3 + (4)^3\\ &= 1 + 8 + 27 + 64\\ &= 100\end{aligned}$$

In this example, the letter n is called the **index of summation**. Many times, the letters i, j, and k are also used for the index of summation.

Calculator Connections

Topic: Finding the Sum of a Finite Sequence of Terms

The sum of a finite series may be found on a graphing calculator if the nth term of the corresponding sequence is known. The calculator takes the sum of a sequence by using the Sum and Seq functions.

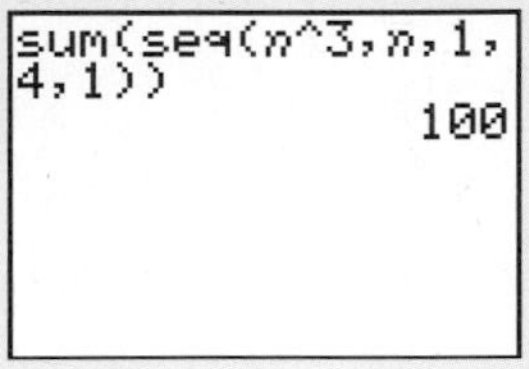

Example 5 Finding a Sum from Summation Notation

Find the sum. $\displaystyle\sum_{i=1}^{4} 2^i$

Solution:

$$\begin{aligned}\sum_{i=1}^{4} 2^i &= 2^1 + 2^2 + 2^3 + 2^4\\ &= 2 + 4 + 8 + 16\\ &= 30\end{aligned}$$

Skill Practice Find the sum.

9. $\displaystyle\sum_{i=1}^{4} i(i + 4)$

Example 6 Finding a Sum from Summation Notation

Find the sum. $\displaystyle\sum_{i=1}^{3} (-1)^{i+1} \cdot (3i + 4)$

Solution:

$$\begin{aligned}\sum_{i=1}^{3} (-1)^{i+1} \cdot (3i + 4) &= (-1)^{1+1} \cdot [3(1) + 4] + (-1)^{2+1} \cdot [3(2) + 4]\\ &\quad + (-1)^{3+1} \cdot [3(3) + 4]\\ &= (-1)^2 \cdot (7) + (-1)^3 \cdot (10) + (-1)^4 \cdot (13)\\ &= 7 - 10 + 13\\ &= 10\end{aligned}$$

Avoiding Mistakes

The letter i is used as a variable for the index of summation. In this context, it does not represent an imaginary number.

Skill Practice Find the sum.

10. $\displaystyle\sum_{i=1}^{4} (-1)^i(4i - 3)$

Answers

9. 70 **10.** 8

Example 7 Converting to Summation Notation

Write the series in summation notation.

a. $\frac{2}{3} + \frac{4}{9} + \frac{8}{27} + \frac{16}{81}$ Use n as the index of summation.

b. $1 - \frac{1}{2} + \frac{1}{3} - \frac{1}{4} + \frac{1}{5} - \frac{1}{6}$ Use j as the index of summation.

Solution:

a. The sum can be written as

$$\left(\frac{2}{3}\right)^1 + \left(\frac{2}{3}\right)^2 + \left(\frac{2}{3}\right)^3 + \left(\frac{2}{3}\right)^4$$

Taking n from 1 to 4, we have

$$\sum_{n=1}^{4} \left(\frac{2}{3}\right)^n$$

b. The even-numbered terms are negative. The factor $(-1)^{j+1}$ is negative for even values of j. Therefore, the series can be written as

$$\sum_{j=1}^{6} (-1)^{j+1} \cdot \frac{1}{j}$$

Skill Practice Write the series in summation notation.

11. $\frac{1}{4} + \frac{1}{16} + \frac{1}{64} + \frac{1}{256}$

12. $\frac{1}{2} - \frac{1}{4} + \frac{1}{6} - \frac{1}{8} + \frac{1}{10}$

Answers

11. $\sum_{i=1}^{4} \frac{1}{4^i}$

12. $\sum_{i=1}^{5} (-1)^{i+1} \frac{1}{2i}$

Section 14.2 Practice Exercises

Vocabulary and Key Concepts

1. a. A(n) (finite/infinite) sequence is a function whose domain is the set of positive integers. A(n) (finite/infinite) sequence is a function whose domain is the set of the first n positive integers.

b. Given a sequence, the values a_1, a_2, a_3, and so on are called the _______ of the sequence. The expression a_n defines the _______ term (or general term) of the sequence.

c. In an _______________ sequence, consecutive terms alternate in sign.

d. A sum of a sequence is called a _______.

e. To represent a sum of terms, ________ notation is often used and is represented by the Greek letter $\sum$.

f. Given the sum $\sum_{n=1}^{5} n^2$, the letter n is called the _______ of summation. In expanded form, this series is $(1)^2 + (2)^2 +$ _______ $= 55$.

Review Exercises

For Exercises 2–4, evaluate the expression.

2. $9!$

3. $\frac{8!}{2! \cdot 6!}$

4. $\frac{7!}{7! \cdot 0!}$

For Exercises 5–6, expand the binomial.

5. $(2x + z)^4$

6. $(4m - 3t)^3$

Concept 1: Finite and Infinite Sequences

For Exercises 7–18, list the terms of each sequence. **(See Examples 1–2.)**

7. $a_n = 3n + 1, \quad 1 \le n \le 5$

8. $a_n = -2n + 3, \quad 1 \le n \le 5$

9. $a_n = \sqrt{n + 2}, \quad 1 \le n \le 4$

10. $a_n = \sqrt{n - 1}, \quad 1 \le n \le 4$

11. $a_n = (-1)^n \dfrac{n + 1}{n + 2}, \quad 1 \le n \le 4$

12. $a_n = (-1)^n \dfrac{n - 1}{n + 2}, \quad 1 \le n \le 4$

13. $a_n = (-1)^{n+1}(n^2 - 1), \quad 1 \le n \le 3$

14. $a_n = (-1)^{n+1}(n^2), \quad 1 \le n \le 3$

15. $a_n = n^2 - n, \quad 1 \le n \le 6$

16. $a_n = n(n^2 - 1), \quad 1 \le n \le 6$

17. $a_n = (-1)^n 3^n, \quad 1 \le n \le 4$

18. $a_n = (-1)^n n, \quad 1 \le n \le 4$

19. If the nth term of a sequence is $a_n = (-1)^n \cdot n^2$, which terms are positive and which are negative?

20. If the nth term of a sequence is $a_n = (-1)^{n-1} \cdot \frac{1}{n}$, which terms are positive and which are negative?

For Exercises 21–32, find a formula for the nth term of the sequence. Answers may vary. **(See Example 3.)**

21. $2, 4, 6, 8, \ldots$

22. $3, 6, 9, 12, \ldots$

23. $1, 3, 5, 7, \ldots$

24. $3, 5, 7, 9, \ldots$

25. $1, \frac{1}{4}, \frac{1}{9}, \frac{1}{16}, \ldots$

26. $\frac{1}{2}, \frac{2}{3}, \frac{3}{4}, \frac{4}{5}, \ldots$

27. $1, -1, 1, -1, \ldots$

28. $-1, 1 -1, 1, \ldots$

29. $-2, 4, -8, 16, \ldots$

30. $3, -9, 27, -81, \ldots$

31. $\frac{3}{5}, \frac{3}{25}, \frac{3}{125}, \frac{3}{625}, \ldots$

32. $\frac{1}{4}, \frac{1}{16}, \frac{1}{64}, \frac{1}{256}, \ldots$

33. Edmond borrowed \$500. To pay off the loan, he agreed to pay 2% of the balance plus \$50 each month. Write a sequence representing the amount Edmond will pay each month for the next 4 months. Round each term to the nearest cent.

34. Janice deposited \$1000 in a savings account that pays 3% interest compounded annually. Write a sequence representing the amount Janice receives in interest each year for the first 4 yr. Round each term to the nearest cent.

35. A certain bacteria culture doubles its size each day. If there are 25,000 bacteria on the first day, write a sequence representing the population each day for the first week (7 days). **(See Example 4.)**

36. A radioactive chemical decays by one-half of its amount each week. If there is 16 g of the chemical in week 1, write a sequence representing the amount present each week for 2 months (8 weeks).

Concept 2: Series

37. What is the difference between a sequence and a series?

38. **a.** Identify the index of summation for the series. $\displaystyle\sum_{k=1}^{7} (k^2 + 1)$

b. How many terms does this series have?

For Exercises 39–54, find the sums. **(See Examples 5–6.)**

39. $\sum_{i=1}^{4}(3i^2)$

40. $\sum_{i=1}^{4}(2i^2)$

41. $\sum_{j=0}^{4}\left(\frac{1}{2}\right)^j$

42. $\sum_{j=0}^{4}\left(\frac{1}{3}\right)^j$

43. $\sum_{i=1}^{6}5$

44. $\sum_{i=1}^{7}3$

45. $\sum_{j=1}^{4}(-1)^j(5j)$

46. $\sum_{j=1}^{4}(-1)^j(4j)$

47. $\sum_{i=1}^{4}\frac{i+1}{i}$

48. $\sum_{i=2}^{5}\frac{i-1}{i}$

49. $\sum_{j=1}^{3}(j+1)(j+2)$

50. $\sum_{j=1}^{3}j(j+2)$

51. $\sum_{k=1}^{7}(-1)^k$

52. $\sum_{k=0}^{5}(-1)^{k+1}$

53. $\sum_{k=1}^{5}k^2$

54. $\sum_{k=1}^{5}2^k$

For Exercises 55–66, write the series in summation notation. **(See Example 7.)**

55. $1 + 2 + 3 + 4 + 5 + 6$

56. $1 - 2 + 3 - 4 + 5 - 6$

57. $4 + 4 + 4 + 4 + 4$

58. $8 + 8 + 8 + 8 + 8$

59. $4 + 8 + 12 + 16 + 20$

60. $3 + 6 + 9 + 12 + 15$

61. $\frac{1}{3} - \frac{1}{9} + \frac{1}{27} - \frac{1}{81}$

62. $\frac{1}{2} - \frac{1}{4} + \frac{1}{8} - \frac{1}{16}$

63. $\frac{5}{11} + \frac{6}{22} + \frac{7}{33} + \frac{8}{44} + \frac{9}{55} + \frac{10}{66}$

64. $-\frac{5}{7} - \frac{10}{8} - \frac{15}{9} - \frac{20}{10} - \frac{25}{11} - \frac{30}{12} - \frac{35}{13}$

65. $x + x^2 + x^3 + x^4 + x^5$

66. $y^2 + y^4 + y^6 + y^8 + y^{10}$

Expanding Your Skills

Some sequences are defined by a recursion formula, which defines each term of a sequence in terms of one or more of its preceding terms. For example, if $a_1 = 5$ and $a_n = 2a_{n-1} + 1$ for $n > 1$, then the terms of the sequence are 5, 11, 23, 47, ... In this case, each term after the first is one more than twice the term before it.

For Exercises 67–70, list the first five terms of the sequence.

67. $a_1 = -3, a_n = a_{n-1} + 5 \quad \text{for } n > 1$

68. $a_1 = 10, a_n = a_{n-1} - 3 \quad \text{for } n > 1$

69. $a_1 = 5, a_n = 4a_{n-1} + 1 \quad \text{for } n > 1$

70. $a_1 = -2, a_n = -3a_{n-1} + 4 \quad \text{for } n > 1$

71. A famous sequence in mathematics is called the Fibonacci sequence, named after the Italian mathematician Leonardo Fibonacci of the thirteenth century. The Fibonacci sequence is defined by

$$a_1 = 1$$

$$a_2 = 1$$

$$a_n = a_{n-1} + a_{n-2} \quad \text{for } n > 2$$

This definition implies that beginning with the third term, each term is the sum of the preceding two terms. Write out the first 10 terms of the Fibonacci sequence.

Arithmetic Sequences and Series

Section 14.3

Concepts

1. Arithmetic Sequences
2. Arithmetic Series

1. Arithmetic Sequences

In this section and the next, we will study two special types of sequences and series. The first is called an arithmetic sequence, for example:

$$4, 7, 10, 13, 16, \ldots$$

This sequence is an arithmetic sequence. Note the characteristic that each successive term after the first is a fixed value more than the previous term (in this case the terms differ by 3).

Definition of an Arithmetic Sequence

An **arithmetic sequence** is a sequence in which the difference between consecutive terms is constant.

The fixed difference between a term and its predecessor is called the **common difference** and is denoted by the letter d. The common difference is the difference between a term and its predecessor. That is,

$$d = a_{n+1} - a_n$$

Furthermore, if a_1 is the first term, then

$a_1 = a_1 + 0d$

$a_2 = a_1 + 1d$ is the second term,

$a_3 = a_1 + 2d$ is the third term,

$a_4 = a_1 + 3d$ is the fourth term, and so on.

$\ldots$

In general, $a_n = a_1 + (n - 1)d$.

***n*th Term of an Arithmetic Sequence**

The nth term of an arithmetic sequence is given by

$$a_n = a_1 + (n - 1)d$$

where a_1 is the first term of the sequence and d is the common difference.

Example 1 Writing the *n*th Term of an Arithmetic Sequence

Write the nth term of the sequence. $9, 2, -5, -12, \ldots$

Solution:

$9, \quad 2, \quad -5, \quad -12, \ldots$

$-7 \quad -7 \quad -7$

The common difference can be found by subtracting a term from its predecessor: $2 - 9 = -7$

TIP: Notice that the terms of an arithmetic sequence increase or decrease linearly. In Example 1, the terms decrease by 7 for each subsequent term. This is similar to a line with a slope of -7.

With $a_1 = 9$ and $d = -7$, we have

$$a_n = 9 + (n - 1)(-7)$$
$$= 9 - 7n + 7$$
$$= -7n + 16$$

Skill Practice Write the nth term of the sequence.

1. $-3, -1, 1, 3, 5, \ldots$

In Example 1, the common difference between terms is -7. Accordingly, each term of the sequence *decreases* by 7.

The formula $a_n = a_1 + (n - 1)d$ contains four variables: a_n, a_1, n, and d. Consequently, if we know the value of three of the four variables, we can solve for the fourth.

Example 2 Finding a Specified Term of an Arithmetic Sequence

Find the ninth term of the arithmetic sequence in which $a_1 = -4$ and $a_{22} = 164$.

Solution:

To find the value of the ninth term a_9, we need to determine the value of d. To find d, substitute $a_1 = -4$, $n = 22$, and $a_{22} = 164$ into the formula $a_n = a_1 + (n - 1)d$.

$$a_n = a_1 + (n - 1)d$$
$$164 = -4 + (22 - 1)d$$
$$164 = -4 + 21d$$
$$168 = 21d$$
$$d = 8$$

Therefore, $a_n = -4 + (n - 1)(8)$

$$a_9 = -4 + (9 - 1)(8)$$
$$= -4 + (8)(8)$$
$$= 60$$

Skill Practice

2. Find the tenth term of the arithmetic sequence in which $a_1 = 14$ and $a_{15} = -28$. (*Hint:* First find d.)

Example 3 Finding the Number of Terms in an Arithmetic Sequence

Find the number of terms of the sequence $7, 3, -1, -5, \ldots, -113$.

Answers

1. $2n - 5$ **2.** $d = -3$, $a_{10} = -13$

Solution:

To find the number of terms n, we can substitute $a_1 = 7, d = -4$, and $a_n = -113$ into the formula for the nth term.

$$a_n = a_1 + (n - 1)d$$
$$-113 = 7 + (n - 1)(-4)$$
$$-113 = 7 - 4n + 4$$
$$-113 = 11 - 4n$$
$$-124 = -4n$$
$$n = 31$$

Skill Practice Find the number of terms of the sequence.

3. $-15, -11, -7, -3, \ldots, 81$

2. Arithmetic Series

The indicated sum of an arithmetic sequence is called an **arithmetic series**. For example, the series

$$3 + 7 + 11 + 15 + 19 + 23$$

is an arithmetic series because the common difference between terms is constant (4). Adding the terms in a lengthy sum is cumbersome, so we offer the following "shortcut," which is developed here. Let S represent the sum of the terms in the series.

$S = 3 + 7 + 11 + 15 + 19 + 23$ Add the terms in ascending order.

$S = 23 + 19 + 15 + 11 + 7 + 3$ Add the terms in descending order.

$2S = 26 + 26 + 26 + 26 + 26 + 26$ Adding the two series produces six terms of 26.

$$2S = 6 \cdot 26$$
$$S = \frac{6 \cdot 26}{2}$$
$$= 78$$

By adding the terms in ascending and descending order, we double the sum but create a pattern that is easily added. This is true in general. To find the sum, S_n, of the first n terms of the arithmetic series $a_1 + a_2 + a_3 + \cdots + a_n$, we have

$S_n = a_1 + (a_1 + d) + (a_1 + 2d) + \cdots + a_n$ Ascending order

$S_n = a_n + (a_n - d) + (a_n - 2d) + \cdots + a_1$ Descending order

$$2S_n = (a_1 + a_n) + (a_1 + a_n) + (a_1 + a_n) + \cdots + (a_1 + a_n)$$
$$2S_n = n(a_1 + a_n)$$
$$S_n = \frac{n}{2}(a_1 + a_n)$$

Answer

3. 25

Sum of an Arithmetic Series

The sum, S_n, of the first n terms of an arithmetic series is given by

$$S_n = \frac{n}{2}(a_1 + a_n)$$

where a_1 is the first term of the series and a_n is the nth term of the series.

Example 4 Finding the Sum of an Arithmetic Series

Find the sum of the series. $\sum_{i=1}^{25}(2i + 3)$

Avoiding Mistakes

When we apply the sum formula $S_n = \frac{n}{2}(a_1 + a_n)$ to find the sum $\sum_{i=1}^{n} a_n$, the index of summation, i, must begin at 1.

Solution:

In this series, $n = 25$. Furthermore, $a_1 = 2(1) + 3 = 5$ and $a_{25} = 2(25) + 3 = 53$. Therefore,

$$S_{25} = \frac{25}{2}(5 + 53) \quad \text{Apply the formula } S_n = \frac{n}{2}(a_1 + a_n).$$

$$= \frac{25}{2}(58) \quad \text{Simplify.}$$

$$= 725$$

Skill Practice Find the sum of the series.

4. $\sum_{i=1}^{20}(3i - 2)$

Example 5 Finding the Sum of an Arithmetic Series

Find the sum of the series.

$$-3 + (-5) + (-7) + \cdots + (-127)$$

Solution:

For this series, $a_1 = -3$ and $a_n = -127$. However, to determine the sum, we also need to find the value of n. The difference between the second term and its predecessor is $-5 - (-3) = -2$. Thus, $d = -2$. We have

$$-127 = -3 + (n - 1)(-2) \quad \text{Apply the formula } a_n = a_1 + (n - 1)d.$$

$$-127 = -3 - 2n + 2 \quad \text{Apply the distributive property.}$$

$$-127 = -1 - 2n \quad \text{Combine } \textit{like} \text{ terms.}$$

$$-126 = -2n \quad \text{Solve for } n.$$

$$n = 63$$

Using $n = 63$, $a_1 = -3$, and $a_{63} = -127$, we have

$$S_n = \frac{n}{2}(a_1 + a_n) = \frac{63}{2}[-3 + (-127)] = \frac{63}{2}(-130) = -4095$$

Skill Practice Find the sum of the series.

5. $8 + 3 + (-2) + \cdots + (-137)$

Answers

4. 590 **5.** −1935

Section 14.3 Practice Exercises

Vocabulary and Key Concepts

1. a. An ____________ sequence is a sequence in which the difference between consecutive terms is constant.

b. The common ____________ between a term and its predecessor in an arithmetic sequence is often denoted by the letter d.

c. The nth term of an arithmetic sequence is given by $a_n =$ ____________, where a_n is the nth term, a_1 is the first term, n is the number of terms, and ____________ is the common difference between terms.

d. An indicated sum of an arithmetic sequence is called an arithmetic ____________.

e. The sum S_n of the first n terms of an arithmetic series is given by $S_n =$ ____________, where a_1 is the first term and a_n is the nth term.

Review Exercises

2. Write the first four terms of the sequence. $c_n = \dfrac{n^2}{n+1}$

3. Write the first four terms of the sequence. $d_n = (-1)^n$

4. Find the sum. $\displaystyle\sum_{n=1}^{10} (-1)^{n+1}$

5. Find the sum. $\displaystyle\sum_{n=1}^{5} (1 - 4n)$

Concept 1: Arithmetic Sequences

6. Explain how to determine if a sequence is arithmetic.

For Exercises 7–12, the first term of an arithmetic sequence is given along with its common difference. Write the first five terms of the sequence.

7. $a_1 = 3, d = 8$

8. $a_1 = -5, d = 2$

9. $a_1 = 80, d = -20$

10. $a_1 = -4, d = -5$

11. $a_1 = 3, d = \dfrac{3}{4}$

12. $a_1 = 1, d = \dfrac{2}{3}$

For Exercises 13–18, find the common difference d for each arithmetic sequence.

13. $1, 3, 5, 7, 9, \ldots$

14. $2, 8, 14, 20, 26, \ldots$

15. $6, 3, 0, -3, -6, \ldots$

16. $8, 3, -2, -7, -12, \ldots$

17. $-7, -9, -11, -13, -15, \ldots$

18. $-15, -11, -7, -3, 1, \ldots$

For Exercises 19–24, write the first five terms of the arithmetic sequence.

19. $a_1 = 3, d = 5$

20. $a_1 = -3, d = 2$

21. $a_1 = 2, d = \dfrac{1}{2}$

22. $a_1 = 0, d = \dfrac{1}{3}$

23. $a_1 = 2, d = -4$

24. $a_1 = 10, d = -6$

For Exercises 25–33, write the nth term of the sequence. **(See Example 1.)**

25. 0, 5, 10, 15, 20, . . .

26. 7, 12, 17, 22, 27, . . .

27. −2, −4, −6, −8, −10, . . .

28. 1, −3, −7, −11, −15, . . .

29. $2, \frac{5}{2}, 3, \frac{7}{2}, 4, \ldots$

30. $1, \frac{4}{3}, \frac{5}{3}, 2, \frac{7}{3}, \ldots$

31. 21, 17, 13, 9, 5, . . .

32. 9, 6, 3, 0, −3, . . .

33. −8, −2, 4, 10, 16, . . .

For Exercises 34–41, find the indicated term of each arithmetic sequence. **(See Example 2.)**

34. Find the eighth term given $a_1 = -6$ and $d = -3$.

35. Find the sixth term given $a_1 = -3$ and $d = 4$.

36. Find the 12th term given $a_1 = -8$ and $d = -2$.

37. Find the ninth term given $a_1 = -1$ and $d = 6$.

38. Find the tenth term given $a_1 = 1$ and $a_7 = 31$.

39. Find the seventh term given $a_1 = 0$ and $a_{10} = -45$.

40. Find the sixth term given $a_1 = 3$ and $a_{13} = 39$.

41. Find the 11th term given $a_1 = 12$ and $a_6 = -18$.

For Exercises 42–49, find the number of terms, n, of each arithmetic sequence. **(See Example 3.)**

42. 2, 0, −2, . . . , −56

43. 8, 13, 18, . . . , 98

44. 1, −3, −7, . . . , −67

45. 1, 5, 9, . . . , 85

46. $1, \frac{3}{4}, \frac{1}{2}, \ldots, -4$

47. $2, \frac{5}{2}, 3, \ldots, 13$

48. $-\frac{5}{3}, -1, -\frac{1}{3}, \ldots, \frac{37}{3}$

49. $\frac{13}{3}, \frac{19}{3}, \frac{25}{3}, \ldots, \frac{73}{3}$

50. If the third and fourth terms of an arithmetic sequence are 18 and 21, what are the first and second terms?

51. If the third and fourth terms of an arithmetic sequence are −8 and −11, what are the first and second terms?

Concept 2: Arithmetic Series

52. Explain the difference between an arithmetic sequence and an arithmetic series.

For Exercises 53–66, find the sum of the arithmetic series. **(See Examples 4–5.)**

53. $\sum_{i=1}^{20} (3i + 2)$

54. $\sum_{i=1}^{15} (2i - 3)$

55. $\sum_{i=1}^{20} (i + 4)$

56. $\sum_{i=1}^{25} (i - 3)$

57. $\sum_{j=1}^{10} (4 - j)$

58. $\sum_{j=1}^{10} (6 - j)$

59. $\sum_{j=1}^{15} \left(\frac{2}{3}j + 1\right)$

60. $\sum_{j=1}^{15} \left(\frac{1}{2}j - 2\right)$

61. 4 + 8 + 12 + · · · + 84

62. 4 + 9 + 14 + · · · + 49

63. 6 + 8 + 10 + · · · + 34

64. −4 + (−3) + (−2) + · · · + 12

65. −3 + (−7) + (−11) + · · · + (−39)

66. 2 + 5 + 8 + · · · + 53

67. Find the sum of the first 100 positive integers.

68. Find the sum of the first 50 positive even integers.

69. The seating in a certain theater is arranged so that there are 30 seats in row 1, 32 in row 2, 34 in row 3, and so on. If there are 20 rows, how many total seats are there? What is the total revenue if the average ticket price is \$15 per seat and the theater is sold out?

70. A triangular array of dominoes has one domino in the first row, two dominoes in the second row, three dominoes in the third row, and so on. If there are 15 rows, how many dominoes are in the array?

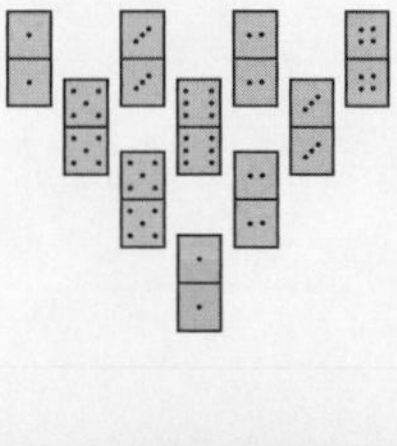

Geometric Sequences and Series

Section 14.4

Concepts

1. Geometric Sequences
2. Geometric Series

1. Geometric Sequences

The sequence 2, 4, 8, 16, 32, . . . is not an arithmetic sequence because the difference between terms is not constant. However, a different pattern exists. Notice that each term after the first is 2 times the preceding term. This sequence is called a geometric sequence.

Definition of a Geometric Sequence

A **geometric sequence** is a sequence in which the ratio between each term and its predecessor is constant.

The constant quotient of a term and its predecessor is called the **common ratio** and is denoted by r. The common ratio is found by dividing a term by the preceding term. That is,

$$r = \frac{a_{n+1}}{a_n}$$

For the sequence 2, 4, 8, 16, 32, . . . we have $r = \frac{4}{2} = \frac{8}{4} = \frac{16}{8} = \frac{32}{16} = 2$.

If a_1 denotes the first term of a geometric sequence, then

$a_2 = a_1 r$ is the second term,

$a_3 = a_1 r^2$ is the third term,

$a_4 = a_1 r^3$ is the fourth term, and so on.

. . .

This pattern gives $a_n = a_1 r^{n-1}$.

*n*th Term of a Geometric Sequence

The nth term of a geometric sequence is given by

$$a_n = a_1 r^{n-1}$$

where a_1 is the first term and r is the common ratio.

Example 1 Finding the *n*th Term of a Geometric Sequence

Find the nth term of the sequence. **a.** $-1, 4, -16, 64, \ldots$ **b.** $12, 8, \frac{16}{3}, \frac{32}{9}, \ldots$

Solution:

a. The common ratio is found by dividing any term (after the first) by its predecessor.

$$r = \frac{4}{-1} = -4$$

With $r = -4$ and $a_1 = -1$, we have $a_n = -1(-4)^{n-1}$.

b. The common ratio is $r = \frac{8}{12} = \frac{2}{3}$. With $a_1 = 12$ and $r = \frac{2}{3}$, we have

$$a_n = 12\left(\frac{2}{3}\right)^{n-1}$$

Skill Practice Find the nth term of the geometric sequence.

1. 6, 12, 24, 48, . . . **2.** $6, 2, \frac{2}{3}, \frac{2}{9}, \ldots$

The formula $a_n = a_1 r^{n-1}$ contains the variables a_n, a_1, n, and r. If we know the value of three of the four variables, we can find the fourth.

Example 2 **Finding a Specified Term of a Geometric Sequence**

Given $a_n = 6\left(\frac{1}{2}\right)^{n-1}$, find a_5.

Solution:

$$a_n = 6\left(\frac{1}{2}\right)^{n-1}$$

$$a_5 = 6\left(\frac{1}{2}\right)^{5-1} = 6\left(\frac{1}{2}\right)^{4} = 6\left(\frac{1}{16}\right) = \frac{3}{8}$$

Skill Practice

3. Given $a_n = 3(-2)^{n-1}$, find a_6.

Example 3 **Finding a Specified Term of a Geometric Sequence**

Find the first term of the geometric sequence where $a_5 = -162$ and $r = 3$.

Solution:

$-162 = a_1(3)^{5-1}$ Substitute $a_5 = -162$, $n = 5$, and $r = 3$ into the formula $a_n = a_1 r^{n-1}$.

$-162 = a_1(3)^4$ Simplify and solve for a_1.

$-162 = a_1(81)$

$a_1 = -2$

Skill Practice

4. Find the first term of the geometric sequence where $a_4 = \frac{25}{32}$ and $r = \frac{1}{4}$.

2. Geometric Series

The indicated sum of a geometric sequence is called a **geometric series**. For example,

$$1 + 3 + 9 + 27 + 81 + 243$$

is a geometric series. To find the sum, consider the following procedure. Let S represent the sum

$$S = 1 + 3 + 9 + 27 + 81 + 243$$

Answers

1. $a_n = 6(2)^{n-1}$ **2.** $a_n = 6\left(\frac{1}{3}\right)^{n-1}$

3. -96 **4.** 50

Now multiply S by the common ratio, which in this case is 3.

$$3S = 3 + 9 + 27 + 81 + 243 + 729$$

Then

$$\begin{aligned} 3S - S &= (3 + 9 + 27 + 81 + 243 + 729) - (1 + 3 + 9 + 27 + 81 + 243) \\ 2S &= 3 + 9 + 27 + 81 + 243 + 729 - 1 - 3 - 9 - 27 - 81 - 243 \\ 2S &= 729 - 1 \qquad \text{The terms in red form a sum of zero.} \\ 2S &= 728 \\ S &= 364 \end{aligned}$$

A similar procedure can be used to find the sum S_n of the first n terms of any geometric series. Subtract rS_n from S_n.

$$\begin{aligned} S_n &= a_1 + a_1r + a_1r^2 + \cdots + a_1r^{n-1} \\ rS_n &= a_1r + a_1r^2 + a_1r^3 + \cdots + a_1r^n \end{aligned}$$

$$S_n - rS_n = (a_1 - a_1r) + (a_1r - a_1r^2) + (a_1r^2 - a_1r^3) + \cdots + (a_1r^{n-1} - a_1r^n)$$

$$\begin{aligned} S_n - rS_n &= a_1 - a_1r^n && \text{The terms in red form a sum of zero.} \\ S_n(1 - r) &= a_1(1 - r^n) && \text{Factor each side of the equation.} \\ S_n &= \frac{a_1(1 - r^n)}{1 - r} && \text{Divide by } (1 - r). \end{aligned}$$

Sum of a Geometric Series

The sum, S_n, of the first n terms of a geometric series $\sum_{i=1}^{n} a_1r^{i-1}$ is given by

$$S_n = \frac{a_1(1 - r^n)}{1 - r}$$

where a_1 is the first term of the series, r is the common ratio, and $r \neq 1$.

Example 4 Finding the Sum of a Geometric Series

Find the sum of the series. $\sum_{i=1}^{6} 4\left(\frac{1}{2}\right)^{i-1}$

Solution:

By expanding the terms of this series, we see that the series is geometric.

$$\sum_{i=1}^{6} 4\left(\frac{1}{2}\right)^{i-1} = 4 + 2 + 1 + \frac{1}{2} + \frac{1}{4} + \frac{1}{8}$$

We have: $a_1 = 4$, $r = \frac{1}{2}$, and $n = 6$,

$$S_n = \frac{a_1(1 - r^n)}{1 - r} = \frac{4[1 - (\frac{1}{2})^6]}{1 - \frac{1}{2}} = \frac{4(1 - \frac{1}{64})}{\frac{1}{2}} = 8\left(\frac{63}{64}\right) = \frac{63}{8}$$

Skill Practice Find the sum of the geometric series.

5. $\frac{1}{9} + \frac{1}{3} + 1 + 3 + 9 + 27$

Answer

5. $\frac{364}{9}$

Example 5 Finding the Sum of a Geometric Series

Find the sum of the series $5 + 10 + 20 + \cdots + 5120$.

Solution:

The common ratio is 2 and $a_1 = 5$. The nth term of the sequence can be written as $a_n = 5(2)^{n-1}$. To find the value of n, substitute 5120 for a_n.

$5120 = 5(2)^{n-1}$

$\frac{5120}{5} = \frac{5(2)^{n-1}}{5}$ Divide both sides by 5.

$1024 = 2^{n-1}$ To solve the exponential equation, write each side as a power of 2.

$2^{10} = 2^{n-1}$

$10 = n - 1$ From Section 12.6, we know that if $b^x = b^y$, then $x = y$.

$n = 11$

With $a_1 = 5$, $r = 2$, and $n = 11$, we have

$$S_n = \frac{a_1(1 - r^n)}{1 - r} = \frac{5(1 - 2^{11})}{1 - 2} = \frac{5(1 - 2048)}{-1} = \frac{5(-2047)}{-1} = 10{,}235$$

Skill Practice Find the sum of the geometric series.

6. $3 + 6 + 12 + \cdots + 768$

Consider a geometric series where $|r| < 1$. For increasing values of n, r^n decreases. For example,

$$\left(\frac{1}{2}\right)^5 = 0.03125 \qquad \left(\frac{1}{2}\right)^{10} \approx 0.00097656 \qquad \left(\frac{1}{2}\right)^{15} \approx 0.00003052$$

For $|r| < 1$, r^n approaches 0 as n gets larger and larger. As n approaches infinity, the sum

$$S = \frac{a_1(1 - r^n)}{1 - r} \quad \text{approaches} \quad \frac{a_1(1 - 0)}{1 - r} = \frac{a_1}{1 - r}$$

Sum of an Infinite Geometric Series

Given an infinite geometric series $a_1 + a_1r + a_1r^2 + \cdots$, with $|r| < 1$, the sum S of all terms in the series is given by

$$S = \frac{a_1}{1 - r}$$

Note: If $|r| \geq 1$, then the sum does not exist.

Example 6 Finding the Sum of an Infinite Geometric Series

Find the sum of the series. $\sum_{i=1}^{\infty} \left(\frac{1}{3}\right)^{i-1}$

Solution:

In this example, the upper limit of summation is ∞. This indicates that we have an infinite series where the pattern for the sum of terms continues indefinitely.

$$\sum_{i=1}^{\infty} \left(\frac{1}{3}\right)^{i-1} = 1 + \frac{1}{3} + \frac{1}{9} + \frac{1}{27} + \frac{1}{81} + \cdots$$

Answer

6. 1533

The series is geometric with $a_1 = 1$ and $r = \frac{1}{3}$. Because $|r| = |\frac{1}{3}| < 1$, we have

$$S = \frac{a_1}{1 - r} = \frac{1}{1 - \frac{1}{3}} = \frac{1}{\frac{2}{3}} = \frac{3}{2}$$

The sum is $\frac{3}{2}$.

Skill Practice Find the sum of the series.

7. $\sum_{i=1}^{\infty} 4\left(\frac{3}{4}\right)^{i-1}$

Example 7 Using a Geometric Series in a Physics Application

A child drops a ball from a height of 4 ft. With each bounce, the ball rebounds to 50% of its original height. Determine the total distance traveled by the ball.

Solution:

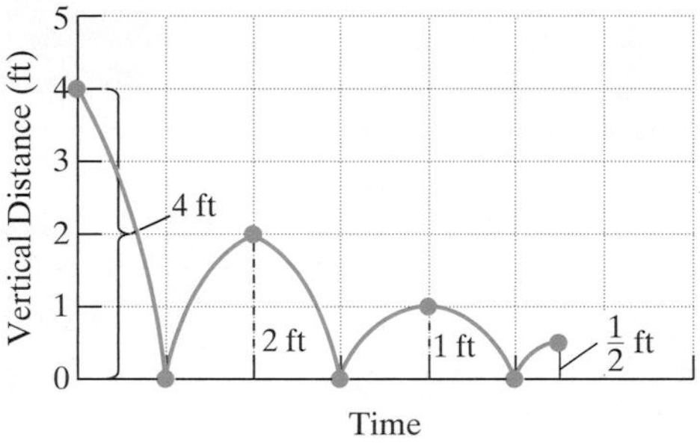

The heights (in ft) from which the ball drops are given by the sequence

$$4, 2, 1, \frac{1}{2}, \frac{1}{4}, \ldots$$

After the ball falls from its initial height of 4 ft, the distance traveled for every bounce thereafter is doubled (the ball travels up and down). Therefore, the total distance traveled is given by the series

$$4 + 2 \cdot 2 + 2 \cdot 1 + 2 \cdot \frac{1}{2} + 2 \cdot \frac{1}{4} + \cdots$$

or equivalently $$4 + 4 + 2 + 1 + \frac{1}{2} + \cdots$$

The series $4 + 2 + 1 + \frac{1}{2} + \cdots$ is an infinite geometric series with $a_1 = 4$ and $r = \frac{1}{2}$.

Initial height from which the ball was dropped ↓ Infinite geometric series ↓

$$4 \quad + \quad \underbrace{4 + 2 + 1 + \frac{1}{2} + \cdots}$$

$$= 4 + \frac{4}{1 - \frac{1}{2}}$$

$$= 4 + \frac{4}{\frac{1}{2}}$$

$$= 4 + 8 = 12$$

The ball traveled a total of 12 ft.

Skill Practice

8. A child drops a ball from a height of 3 ft. With each bounce, the ball rebounds to $\frac{1}{3}$ of its original height. Determine the total distance traveled by the ball.

Answers

7. 16 **8.** 6 ft

Section 14.4 Practice Exercises

Vocabulary and Key Concepts

1. **a.** A ________ sequence is a sequence in which the ratio between each term and its predecessor is constant.

   b. The common ________ between a term and its predecessor in a geometric sequence is often denoted by r.

   c. The nth term of a geometric sequence is given by $a_n =$ ________, where a_n is the nth term in the sequence, a_1 is the first term, and r is the common ratio.

   d. The sum S_n of the first n terms of a geometric series $\sum_{i=1}^{n} a_1 r^{i-1}$ is given by $S_n =$ ________, where a_1 is the first term and r is the common ratio.

   e. Given an infinite geometric series $a_1 + a_2 r + a_1 r^2 + \cdots$ with $|r| < 1$, the sum of all terms in the sequence is given by $S =$ ________. If $|r| \geq$ ________, then the sum does not exist.

Review Exercises

2. Determine the common difference. $7, 1, -5, -11, \ldots$

3. Write an expression for the nth term of the sequence. $-4, 0, 4, 8, 12, \ldots$

4. Find the sum of the series. $\sum_{i=1}^{6} (3i^2 - 4)$

5. Find the fifth term of the arithmetic sequence with $a_1 = -15$ and $d = 10$.

Concept 1: Geometric Sequences

6. Explain how to determine if a sequence is geometric.

For Exercises 7–12, the first term of a geometric sequence is given along with the common ratio. Write the first four terms of the sequence.

7. $a_n = 1; r = 10$
8. $a_n = 2; r = 5$
9. $a_n = 64; r = \frac{1}{2}$
10. $a_n = 3; r = \frac{2}{3}$
11. $a_n = 8; r = -\frac{1}{4}$
12. $a_n = 9; r = -\frac{1}{3}$

For Exercises 13–18, determine the common ratio, r, for the geometric sequence.

13. $5, 10, 20, 40, \ldots$
14. $-2, -1, -\frac{1}{2}, -\frac{1}{4}, \ldots$
15. $8, -2, \frac{1}{2}, -\frac{1}{8}, \ldots$
16. $4, -12, 36, -108, \ldots$
17. $3, -6, 12, -24, \ldots$
18. $1, 4, 16, 64, \ldots$

For Exercises 19–24, write the first five terms of the geometric sequence.

19. $a_1 = -3, r = -2$
20. $a_1 = -4, r = -1$
21. $a_1 = 6, r = \frac{1}{2}$
22. $a_1 = 8, r = \frac{1}{4}$
23. $a_1 = -1, r = 6$
24. $a_1 = 2, r = -3$

For Exercises 25–30, find the nth term of each geometric sequence. **(See Example 1.)**

25. 3, 12, 48, 192, . . .

26. 2, 6, 18, 54, . . .

27. −5, 15, −45, 135, . . .

28. −6, 12, −24, 48, . . .

29. $\frac{1}{2}, 2, 8, 32, \ldots$

30. $\frac{16}{3}, 4, 3, \frac{9}{4}, \ldots$

For Exercises 31–40, find the indicated term of each geometric sequence. **(See Examples 2–3.)**

31. Given $a_n = 2\left(\frac{1}{2}\right)^{n-1}$, find a_8.

32. Given $a_n = -3\left(\frac{1}{2}\right)^{n-1}$, find a_8.

33. Given $a_n = 4\left(-\frac{3}{2}\right)^{n-1}$, find a_6.

34. Given $a_n = 6\left(-\frac{1}{3}\right)^{n-1}$, find a_6.

35. Given $a_n = -3(2)^{n-1}$, find a_5.

36. Given $a_n = 5(3)^{n-1}$, find a_4.

37. Given $a_5 = -\frac{16}{9}$ and $r = -\frac{2}{3}$, find a_1.

38. Given $a_6 = \frac{5}{16}$ and $r = -\frac{1}{2}$, find a_1.

39. Given $a_7 = 8$ and $r = 2$, find a_1.

40. Given $a_6 = 27$ and $r = 3$, find a_1.

41. If the second and third terms of a geometric sequence are 16 and 64, what is the first term?

42. If the second and third terms of a geometric sequence are $\frac{1}{3}$ and $\frac{1}{9}$, what is the first term?

Concept 2: Geometric Series

43. Explain the difference between a geometric sequence and a geometric series.

44. **a.** Write the series in expanded form. $\sum_{i=1}^{5} 4(2)^{i-1}$

b. Find the sum. $\sum_{i=1}^{5} 4(2)^{i-1}$

45. **a.** Write the series in expanded form. $\sum_{i=1}^{4} 3(4)^{i-1}$

b. Find the sum. $\sum_{i=1}^{4} 3(4)^{i-1}$

46. **a.** Write the series in expanded form. $\sum_{i=1}^{4} 6\left(\frac{1}{2}\right)^{i-1}$

b. Find the sum. $\sum_{i=1}^{4} 6\left(\frac{1}{2}\right)^{i-1}$

For Exercises 47–56, find the sum of the geometric series. **(See Examples 4–5.)**

47. $10 + 2 + \frac{2}{5} + \frac{2}{25} + \frac{2}{125}$

48. $1 + 3 + 9 + 27 + 81 + 243$

49. $-2 + 1 + \left(-\frac{1}{2}\right) + \frac{1}{4} + \left(-\frac{1}{8}\right)$

50. $\frac{1}{4} + (-1) + 4 + (-16) + 64$

51. $12 + 16 + \frac{64}{3} + \frac{256}{9} + \frac{1024}{27}$

52. $9 + 6 + 4 + \frac{8}{3} + \frac{16}{9}$

53. $1 + \frac{2}{3} + \frac{4}{9} + \cdots + \frac{32}{243}$

54. $\frac{8}{3} + 2 + \frac{3}{2} + \cdots + \frac{243}{512}$

55. $-4 + 8 + (-16) + \cdots + (-256)$

56. $-\frac{7}{3} + 7 + (-21) + \cdots + 5103$

57. A deposit of \$1000 is made in an account that earns 5% interest compounded annually. The balance in the account after n years is given by

$$a_n = 1000(1.05)^n \quad \text{for } n \geq 1$$

a. List the first four terms of the sequence. Round to the nearest cent.

b. Find the balance after 10 yr, 20 yr, and 40 yr by computing a_{10}, a_{20}, and a_{40}. Round to the nearest cent.

58. A home purchased for \$125,000 increases by 4% of its value each year. The value of the home after n years is given by

$$a_n = 125{,}000(1.04)^n \quad \text{for } n \geq 1$$

a. List the first four terms of the sequence. Round to the nearest dollar.

b. Find the value of the home after 5 yr, 10 yr, and 20 yr by computing a_5, a_{10}, and a_{20}. Round to the nearest dollar.

For Exercises 59–64, first find the common ratio r. Then determine the sum of the infinite series, if it exists. **(See Example 6.)**

59. $1 + \frac{1}{6} + \frac{1}{36} + \frac{1}{216} + \cdots$

60. $-2 + \left(-\frac{1}{2}\right) + \left(-\frac{1}{8}\right) + \left(-\frac{1}{32}\right) + \cdots$

61. $\sum_{i=1}^{\infty} \left(-\frac{1}{4}\right)^{i-1}$

62. $\sum_{i=1}^{\infty} \left(-\frac{1}{5}\right)^{i-1}$

63. $\frac{2}{3} + (-1) + \frac{3}{2} + \left(-\frac{9}{4}\right) + \cdots$

64. $3 + 5 + \frac{25}{3} + \frac{125}{9} + \cdots$

65. Suppose \$200 million is spent by tourists at a certain resort town. Further suppose that 75% of the revenue is respent in the community and then respent over and over, each time at a rate of 75%. The series

$$200 + 200(0.75) + 200(0.75)^2 + 200(0.75)^3 + \cdots$$

gives the total amount spent (and respent) in the community. Find the sum of the infinite series. **(See Example 7.)**

66. A bungee jumper jumps off a platform and stretches the cord 80 ft before rebounding upward. Each successive bounce stretches the cord 60% of its previous length. The total vertical distance traveled is given by

$$80 + 2(0.60)(80) + 2(0.60)^2(80) + 2(0.60)^3(80) + \cdots$$

After the first term, the series is an infinite geometric series. Compute the total vertical distance traveled.

67. A ball drops from a height of 4 ft. With each bounce, the ball rebounds to $\frac{3}{4}$ of its height. The total vertical distance traveled is given by

$$4 + 2\left(\frac{3}{4}\right)(4) + 2\left(\frac{3}{4}\right)^2(4) + 2\left(\frac{3}{4}\right)^3(4) + \cdots$$

After the first term, the series is an infinite geometric series. Compute the total vertical distance traveled.

68. The repeating decimal number $0.\overline{2}$ can be written as an infinite geometric series by

$$\frac{2}{10} + \frac{2}{100} + \frac{2}{1000} + \cdots$$

a. What is a_1? **b.** What is r? **c.** Find the sum of the series.

69. The repeating decimal number $0.\overline{7}$ can be written as an infinite geometric series by

$$\frac{7}{10} + \frac{7}{100} + \frac{7}{1000} + \cdots$$

a. What is a_1? **b.** What is r? **c.** Find the sum of the series.

Expanding Your Skills

70. The yearly salary for job A is \$40,000 initially with an annual raise of \$3000 per year. The yearly salary for job B is \$38,000 initially with an annual raise of 6% per year.

a. Find the total earnings for job A over 20 yr. Is this an arithmetic or geometric series?

b. For job B, what is the amount of the raise after 1 yr?

c. Find the total earnings for job B over 20 yr. Round to the nearest dollar. Is this an arithmetic or geometric series?

d. What is the difference in total salary earned over 20 yr between job A and job B?

71. a. Brook has a job that pays \$48,000 the first year. She receives a 4% raise each year. Find the sum of her yearly salaries over a 20-yr period. Round to the nearest dollar.

b. Chamille has a job that pays \$48,000 the first year. She receives a 4.5% raise each year. Find the sum of her yearly salaries over a 20-yr period. Round to the nearest dollar.

c. Chamille's raise each year was 0.5% higher than Brook's raise. How much more total income did Chamille receive than Brook over 20 yr?

Problem Recognition Exercises

Identifying Arithmetic and Geometric Sequences

For Exercises 1–18, determine if the sequence is arithmetic, geometric, or neither. If the sequence is arithmetic, find *d*. If the sequence is geometric, find *r*.

1. $5, -\frac{5}{2}, \frac{5}{4}, -\frac{5}{8}, \ldots$

2. $\frac{1}{2}, 1, \frac{3}{2}, 2, \frac{5}{2}, \ldots$

3. $-2, -4, -8, -16, -32, \ldots$

4. $-2, -4, -7, -11, -16, \ldots$

5. $-\frac{1}{3}, \frac{1}{3}, 1, \frac{5}{3}, \ldots$

6. $1, -\frac{3}{2}, \frac{9}{4}, -\frac{27}{8}, \ldots$

7. $2, 6, 11, 17, 24, \ldots$

8. $2, -2, 2, -2, 2, \ldots$

9. $-2, -4, -6, -8, -10, \ldots$

10. $1, 3, 1, 3, 1, \ldots$

11. $0, 1, 0, 1, 0, 1, \ldots$

12. $2, 6, 10, 14, 18, 22, \ldots$

13. $\frac{1}{4}\pi, \frac{1}{2}\pi, \frac{3}{4}\pi, \pi, \frac{5}{4}\pi, \cdots$

14. $-1, 1, -1, 1, -1, \ldots$

15. $1, 4, 9, 16, 25, \ldots$

16. $\frac{1}{3}e, \frac{2}{3}e, e, \frac{4}{3}e, \frac{5}{3}e, \cdots$

17. $\frac{\pi}{2}, \frac{\pi}{3}, \frac{\pi}{4}, \frac{\pi}{5}, \frac{\pi}{6}, \cdots$

18. $2, 6, 18, 54, 162, \ldots$

Group Activity

Investigating Mean and Standard Deviation

Materials: A computer with Internet access and a calculator

Estimated time: 15–20 minutes

Group Size: 2

To study the characteristics of a population, statisticians often use a sample or part of the population. A sample of data values is smaller and less cumbersome than data from the entire population. Furthermore, if the sample is taken randomly, the sample is generally a good representation of the population as a whole.

Once a collection of data is obtained, statisticians may compute the mean and standard deviation of the sample. The mean is the average of the data values. The standard deviation is a measure of variability and is based on finding the deviation between the given data values and the mean.

The formulas to compute sample mean (denoted by $\bar{x}$) and sample standard deviation (denoted by s) are as follows. In each case, the sample size is n, and the individual data values are denoted by $x_1, x_2, x_3, \ldots, x_n$. Notice that sometimes the summations are given without the index of summation. This is common practice in statistics. The index of summation is understood to be from 1 to n.

$$\bar{x} = \frac{\sum_{i=1}^{n} x_i}{n}$$

- Take the sum of the data values $(x_1 + x_2 + x_3 + \cdots + x_n)$ and divide by n.

$$s = \sqrt{\frac{n \cdot \Sigma(x^2) - (\Sigma x)^2}{n(n-1)}}$$

- For the first term in the numerator, square each value of x first, then take the sum and multiply by the sample size, n.
- For the second term in the numerator, add the values of x first and then square the result.

1. The following data represent a sample of eight breakfast cereals and the corresponding number of calories for a 1-cup serving. Find the mean number of calories. Round to one decimal place.

160 120 140 240 180 210 380 320

2. Use the data from Question 1 to compute the standard deviation. Use the given chart to help you organize the calculations. Round to one decimal place.

Brand	x	x^2
1	160	
2	120	
3	140	
4	240	
5	180	
6	210	
7	380	
8	320	
Sum:		

3. Select two cities in different parts of the country that have roughly the same latitude (same distance north from the equator) such as Phoenix, Arizona, and Charleston, South Carolina. Visit a website that gives the average monthly temperatures for each city for a 1-yr period. Record the data here.

	Jan.	Feb.	Mar.	Apr.	May	June	July	Aug.	Sept.	Oct.	Nov.	Dec.
City 1 temp.												
City 2 temp.												

4. Compute the mean and standard deviation for the average monthly temperature for each city.

5. Based on the mean and standard deviation, what conclusions can you make about the differences between the monthly temperatures of each city?

Chapter 14 Summary

Section 14.1 Binomial Expansions

Key Concepts

For a whole number, n, the expression $\boldsymbol{n!}$ (read as "n factorial") is defined as the product of integers from 1 to n, for $n \geq 1$.

$n! = n(n-1)(n-2)\ldots(2)(1)$

$0! = 1$ by definition

For a positive integer, n, the expression $(a+b)^n$ can be expanded using the **binomial theorem**:

$$(a+b)^n = \frac{n!}{n!\cdot 0!}a^n + \frac{n!}{(n-1)!\cdot 1!}a^{(n-1)}b + \frac{n!}{(n-2)!\cdot 2!}a^{(n-2)}b^2 + \cdots + \frac{n!}{0!\cdot n!}b^n$$

The coefficients of the expansion may also be found by using **Pascal's triangle**.

$$\begin{array}{ccccccccc} & & & & 1 & & & & \\ & & & 1 & & 1 & & & \\ & & 1 & & 2 & & 1 & & \\ & 1 & & 3 & & 3 & & 1 & \\ 1 & & 4 & & 6 & & 4 & & 1 \end{array}$$

Let n and k be positive integers such that $k \leq n$. Then the kth term in the expansion of $(a+b)^n$ is

$$\frac{n!}{[n-(k-1)]!\cdot(k-1)!}\cdot a^{n-(k-1)}\cdot b^{k-1}$$

Examples

Example 1

$6! = (6)(5)(4)(3)(2)(1) = 720$

Example 2

$$\frac{7!}{2!\cdot 5!} = \frac{7\cdot \overset{3}{\cancel{6}}\cdot \cancel{5\cdot 4\cdot 3\cdot 2\cdot 1}}{(2\cdot 1)(\cancel{5\cdot 4\cdot 3\cdot 2\cdot 1})} = 21$$

Example 3

$$(2x-4y)^4 = [2x+(-4y)]^4$$

$$= \frac{4!}{4!\cdot 0!}(2x)^4 + \frac{4!}{3!\cdot 1!}(2x)^3(-4y) + \frac{4!}{2!\cdot 2!}(2x)^2(-4y)^2 + \frac{4!}{1!\cdot 3!}(2x)(-4y)^3 + \frac{4!}{0!\cdot 4!}(-4y)^4$$

$$= 1(2x)^4 + 4(2x)^3(-4y) + 6(2x)^2(-4y)^2 + 4(2x)(-4y)^3 + 1(-4y)^4$$

$$= 16x^4 - 128x^3y + 384x^2y^2 - 512xy^3 + 256y^4$$

Example 4

The third term of $(3x+y^2)^7$ is

$$\frac{7!}{[7-(3-1)]!\cdot(3-1)!}\cdot(3x)^{7-(3-1)}\cdot(y^2)^{3-1}$$

$$= \frac{7!}{5!\cdot 2!}(3x)^5(y^2)^2$$

$$= 5103x^5y^4$$

Section 14.2 Sequences and Series

Key Concepts

An **infinite sequence** is a function whose domain is the set of positive integers.

A **finite sequence** is a function whose domain is the set of the first n positive integers.

The expression a_n defines the nth term (or general term) of a sequence.

A **series** is the sum of a sequence.

Examples

Example 1

$$a_n = 8 - 3n$$
$$= 5, 2, -1, -4, -7, -10, \ldots$$

Example 2

$$a_n = (-1)^n \frac{n}{n+1} \qquad \text{for } 1 \le n \le 5$$
$$= -\frac{1}{2}, \frac{2}{3}, -\frac{3}{4}, \frac{4}{5}, -\frac{5}{6}$$

Example 3

$$\sum_{i=1}^{4} 5i = 5 + 10 + 15 + 20 = 50$$

Section 14.3 Arithmetic Sequences and Series

Key Concepts

An **arithmetic sequence** is a sequence in which the **common difference**, d, between two consecutive terms is a constant.

The nth term of an arithmetic sequence is given by

$$a_n = a_1 + (n - 1)d$$

This formula has four variables, a_n, a_1, n, and d. Sometimes it is necessary to solve for one or more of the variables before the nth term can be identified.

Examples

Example 1

Write the nth term of the sequence: 10, 8, 6, 4, . . .

$a_1 = 10$ (the first term)

$d = -2$ (the common difference)

$a_n = 10 + (n - 1) \cdot (-2)$

$a_n = -2n + 12$

Example 2

Find the 12th term of the arithmetic sequence in which $a_1 = -6$ and $a_{20} = 51$.

$a_n = a_1 + (n - 1)d$ Find d first.

$51 = -6 + (20 - 1)d$ Substitute known values for a_1 and a_{20}.

$57 = 19d$

$3 = d$

$a_n = -6 + (n - 1) \cdot 3 \longrightarrow a_{12} = -6 + (12 - 1) \cdot 3$

$a_{12} = 27$

The sum of an arithmetic sequence is an **arithmetic series.** The sum of the first n terms of an arithmetic series is given by

$$S_n = \frac{n}{2}(a_1 + a_n)$$

Example 3

Find the sum. $\sum_{i=1}^{50}(3i - 1)$

$n = 50, a_1 = 2, a_{50} = 149$

$$S_n = \frac{n}{2}(a_1 + a_n) = \frac{50}{2}(2 + 149)$$

$$= 3775$$

Section 14.4 Geometric Sequences and Series

Key Concepts

A **geometric sequence** is a sequence in which the ratio between each term and its predecessor is constant. This constant is called the **common ratio**, ***r***.

The nth term of a geometric sequence is given by

$$a_n = a_1r^{n-1}$$

The sum of a geometric sequence is called a **geometric series.** The sum of the first n terms of a geometric series is given by

$$S_n = \frac{a_1(1 - r^n)}{1 - r}$$

The sum of an infinite geometric series is given by

$$S_n = \frac{a_1}{1 - r} \quad \text{provided } |r| < 1$$

Examples

Example 1

Find the common ratio: $\frac{8}{5}, \frac{6}{5}, \frac{9}{10}, \frac{27}{40}, \ldots$

$$r = \frac{6}{5} \div \frac{8}{5} = \frac{6}{5} \cdot \frac{5}{8} = \frac{30}{40} = \frac{3}{4}$$

Example 2

Find the fourth term.

$$a_n = 3\left(\frac{2}{3}\right)^{n-1} \longrightarrow a_4 = 3\left(\frac{2}{3}\right)^{4-1} = 3\left(\frac{2}{3}\right)^3 = \frac{8}{9}$$

Example 3

Find the sum. $48, 24, 12, 6, 3, \frac{3}{2}$

$a_1 = 48, r = \frac{1}{2}, n = 6$

$$S_n = \frac{a_1(1 - r^n)}{1 - r} = \frac{48[1 - (\frac{1}{2})^6]}{1 - \frac{1}{2}} = \frac{189}{2}$$

Example 4

Find the sum of the series: $4 - 2 + 1 - \frac{1}{2} + \cdots$

$a_1 = 4$ and the common ratio is $-2 \div 4 = -\frac{1}{2}$.

Since $|-\frac{1}{2}| < 1$,

$$S_n = \frac{a_1}{1 - r} = \frac{4}{1 - \left(-\frac{1}{2}\right)} = \frac{4}{\frac{3}{2}} = \frac{8}{3}$$

Chapter 14 Review Exercises

Section 14.1

For Exercises 1–4, simplify the expression.

1. $8!$ **2.** $5!$ **3.** $\dfrac{12!}{10! \cdot 2!}$ **4.** $\dfrac{9!}{6! \cdot 3!}$

For Exercises 5–6, expand the binomial.

5. $(x^2 + 4)^5$

6. $(c - 3d)^4$

7. Find the first three terms of the binomial expansion. $(a - 2b)^{11}$

8. Find the fourth term of the binomial expansion. $(x^2 + 3y)^8$

9. Find the eighth term of the binomial expansion. $(5x - y^3)^{10}$

10. Find the middle term of the binomial expansion. $(a + 2b)^6$

Section 14.2

For Exercises 11–14, write the terms of the sequence.

11. $a_n = -3n + 4;\ 1 \le n \le 5$

12. $a_n = -2n^3;\ 1 \le n \le 3$

13. $a_n = (-1)^{n+1} \cdot \dfrac{n}{n + 2};\ 1 \le n \le 4$

14. $a_n = \left(-\dfrac{2}{3}\right)^n;\ 1 \le n \le 4$

For Exercises 15–16, write a formula for the nth term of the sequence.

15. $\dfrac{1}{2}, \dfrac{2}{3}, \dfrac{3}{4}, \dfrac{4}{5}, \ldots$

16. $-\dfrac{3}{2}, \dfrac{3}{4}, -\dfrac{3}{8}, \dfrac{3}{16}, \ldots$

17. What is the index of summation for the series?

$$\sum_{k=1}^{7} (2n + 3)$$

18. How many terms are in the series? $\displaystyle\sum_{j=1}^{5} j^3$

For Exercises 19–20, find the sum of the series.

19. $\displaystyle\sum_{i=1}^{7} 5(-1)^{i-1}$ **20.** $\displaystyle\sum_{n=1}^{5} (-2)^n$

21. Write the sum in summation notation.

$$\frac{4}{1} + \frac{5}{2} + \frac{6}{3} + \frac{7}{4} + \frac{8}{5} + \frac{9}{6} + \frac{10}{7}$$

22. Study the figures and the corresponding expression for the area of each region. Write the nth term of a sequence representing the area of a region with base n.

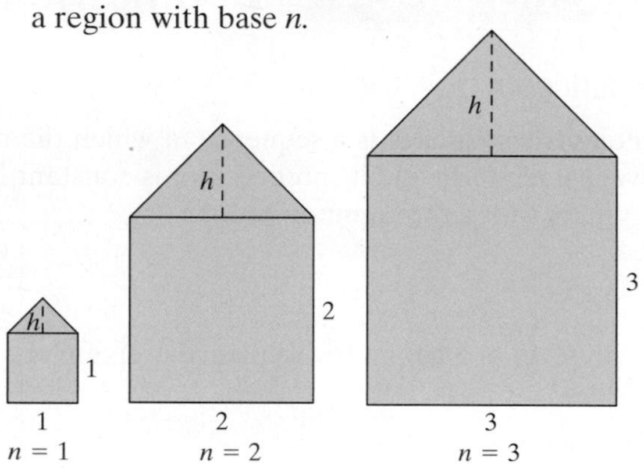

$A = 1 + \frac{1}{2}h$ $A = 4 + h$ $A = 9 + \frac{3}{2}h$

Section 14.3

For Exercises 23–24, write the first five terms of the arithmetic sequence.

23. $a_1 = -12,\ d = 1.5$ **24.** $a_1 = \dfrac{2}{3},\ d = \dfrac{1}{3}$

For Exercises 25–26, write an expression for the nth term of the sequence.

25. $1, 11, 21, 31, \ldots$ **26.** $6, -8, -22, -36, \ldots$

For Exercises 27–28, find the indicated term of the arithmetic sequence.

27. $a_n = \dfrac{1}{2} + (n - 1) \cdot \dfrac{1}{4}$; 17th term

28. $a_1 = -11, d = -6$; 25th term

For Exercises 29–30, find the number of terms.

29. $3, 8, 13, 18, \ldots, 118$

30. $4, 1, -2, -5, \ldots, -50$

31. Find the common difference for an arithmetic sequence, given $a_1 = -40$ and $a_{19} = 140$.

32. Write an expression for the nth term of the arithmetic sequence, $14, 9, 4, -1, -6, \ldots$.

For Exercises 33–36, find the sum of the arithmetic series.

33. $\sum_{k=1}^{40} (5 - k)$

34. $\sum_{i=1}^{20} (0.25i + 2)$

35. $-6 + (-4) + (-2) + \cdots + 34$

36. $4 + 5 + 6 + \cdots + 109$

Section 14.4

For Exercises 37–38, find the common ratio.

37. $5, 15, 45, 135, \ldots$

38. $2, 2.4, 2.88, 3.456$

For Exercises 39–40, write the first four terms of the geometric series.

39. $a_1 = -1$ and $r = -\frac{1}{4}$

40. $a_n = 10(2)^{n-1}$

For Exercises 41–42, write an expression for the nth term of the geometric series.

41. $-4, -8, -16, -32, \ldots$

42. $6, -2, \frac{2}{3}, -\frac{2}{9}, \ldots$

43. Given $a_n = 4\left(\frac{2}{3}\right)^{n-1}$, find a_6.

44. Given $a_n = 10(3)^{n-1}$, find a_4.

45. Given $a_7 = \frac{1}{16}$ and $r = \frac{1}{2}$, find a_1.

46. Given $a_5 = 81$ and $r = 3$, find a_1.

47. Find the sum of the series. $\sum_{n=1}^{8} 5(2)^{n-1}$

48. Find the sum of the series.
$\frac{1}{3} + (-1) + 3 + (-9) + \cdots + (-81)$

49. Find the sum of the series.
$6 + 4 + \frac{8}{3} + \frac{16}{9} + \cdots$

50. Find the sum of the series.
$10 + 2 + \frac{2}{5} + \frac{2}{25} + \cdots$

51. An investment of $10,000 is originally invested in a mutual fund. After 10 yr, the yearly return averaged approximately 7%. The balance on the account is given by $b_n = 10{,}000(1.07)^n$.

a. Find the first three terms of the sequence.

b. Interpret the value of b_3.

c. Find the amount in the account after 10 yr.

Chapter 14 Test

For Exercises 1–2, simplify.

1. $0!$

2. $\frac{10!}{6! \cdot 4!}$

3. Write the expansion of $(a + b)^4$. Use Pascal's triangle to determine the coefficients of the expansion.

4. Expand. $(3y - 2x^2)^4$

5. Find the sixth term. $(a - c^3)^8$

6. Write the terms of the sequence.
$a_n = -\frac{3}{n + 2}; 1 \le n \le 4$

7. Find the sum. $\sum_{i=1}^{5} i^2 + 2$

8. **a.** An 8-in. tomato seedling is planted on Sunday. Each day, it grows an average of 1.5 in. Write five terms representing the height of the plant each day, beginning with Sunday.

b. Write the nth term of the sequence.

9. Write the series in summation notation.
$x^3 + x^6 + x^9 + x^{12}$

10. Find the common difference. $3, \frac{13}{4}, \frac{7}{2}, \frac{15}{4}, \ldots$

11. Find the common ratio. $9, 3, 1, \frac{1}{3}, \ldots$

12. Given an arithmetic sequence with $a_1 = -15$ and $d = -3$,

a. Write the first four terms of the sequence.

b. Write an expression for the nth term of the sequence.

c. Find the 40th term of the sequence.

13. Given a geometric sequence with $a_1 = 4$ and $r = -2$,

a. Write the first four terms of the sequence.

b. Write an expression for the nth term of the sequence.

c. Find the 10th term of the sequence.

14. Write an expression for the nth term of the sequence. $\frac{3}{5}, \frac{3}{10}, \frac{3}{20}, \frac{3}{40}, \ldots$

15. Write an expression for the nth term of the sequence. $20, 18, 16, 14, \ldots$

16. Find the number of terms in the sequence.
$3, 10, 17, 24, \ldots, 213$

17. Find the number of terms in the sequence.
$1, \frac{2}{3}, \frac{4}{9}, \ldots, \frac{64}{729}$

18. Find the sum of the arithmetic series.
$$\sum_{i=1}^{100} (8 + 2i)$$

19. Find the sum of the geometric series.
$$\sum_{n=1}^{10} 8\left(\frac{1}{2}\right)^{n-1}$$

20. Find the sum of the infinite geometric series.
$4 + 2 + 1 + \frac{1}{2} + \cdots$

21. Given a geometric series with $a_6 = 9$ and $r = 3$, find a_1.

22. Find the 18th term of the arithmetic sequence in which $a_1 = -66$ and $a_{40} = -378$.

23. Suppose a student smokes one pack of cigarettes per day at a cost of \$3.00 per pack.

a. If the student quits smoking and puts the \$3.00 saved per day in a jar, how much money will the student have saved at the end of 1 yr?

b. If the student takes the savings from part (a) and invests the money in a bond fund paying 6% annual interest, how much will this money be worth a year later?

c. Suppose that the student reinvests the principal and interest each year so that the money is compounded annually. The student will have:

end of 1 yr \$1095
end of 2 yr (\$1095)(1.06) = \$1160.70
end of 3 yr $(\$1095)(1.06)^2 = \$1230.34$
...

The sequence $a_n = 1095(1.06)^{n-1}$ represents the value of the investment at the end of n years. Find the value of the investment after 30 yr. (Round to two decimal places.)

d. Now suppose that the student saves \$1095 per year each year for 30 yr. Further suppose that the student invests each year's savings at 6% interest compounded annually. The following series represents the total savings plus interest over 30 yr. Find the sum.

$$\sum_{n=1}^{30} 1095(1.06)^{n-1}$$

Chapters 1–14 Cumulative Review Exercises

For Exercises 1–8, simplify the expressions.

1. $(2x - 3)(x - 4) - (x - 5)^2$

2. $\dfrac{5a^2b^{-3}}{25a^{-4}b} \cdot \left(\dfrac{10c^0}{b^3}\right)^2$

3. $64^{-2/3}$

4. $\dfrac{5}{\sqrt{10}}$

5. $\dfrac{2c^2 - 3c - 20}{2c^2 - 32}$

6. $\dfrac{x^{-1} - y^{-1}}{y^{-2} - x^{-2}}$

7. $\log_3 81$

8. $\sqrt[3]{54x^5y^{12}z^2}$

For Exercises 9–12, perform the indicated operations.

9. $\dfrac{a^3 + 64}{16 - a^2} \div \dfrac{a^3 - 4a^2 + 16a}{a^2 - 3a - 4}$

10. $\dfrac{1}{x^2 - 7x + 10} + \dfrac{1}{x^2 + 8x - 20}$

11. $\sqrt{50x^5} + 4x\sqrt{2x^3} - x^2\sqrt{8x}$

12. $(\sqrt{x} + 3\sqrt{y})(\sqrt{x} - 3\sqrt{y})$

13. Divide using long division or synthetic division.
$\dfrac{2x^4 - x^3 + 5x - 7}{x - 2}$

For Exercises 14–17, factor completely.

14. $6a^2 - 17a - 14$

15. $75c^3 - 12c$

16. $27x^3 + 64y^6$

17. $w^3 + 9w^2 - 4w - 36$

For Exercises 18–25, solve the equation.

18. $\dfrac{1}{2}t - \dfrac{3}{5} = \dfrac{1}{10}t + 1$

19. $\dfrac{9}{x - 4} + \dfrac{3}{x + 2} = \dfrac{6}{x^2 - 2x - 8}$

20. $\sqrt[3]{4x + 3} - 9 = -7$

21. $(5y - 2)^2 + 7 = 4$

22. $c^4 - 17c^2 + 16 = 0$

23. $|x + 5| = |3x - 2|$

24. $5^{2x+1} = 125$

25. $\log x + \log(x + 3) = 1$

26. Write the expression as a single logarithm.

$\ln x - 5 \ln y + \dfrac{1}{2} \ln z$

27. Use a calculator to approximate the value of the expression. Round to four decimal places.

$\log_7 895$

For Exercises 28–32, solve the inequality. Write the answer in interval notation if possible.

28. $2x - 4 < 6$ and $-3x \le 6$

29. $3x(x + 5)(x - 1) \ge 0$

30. $x^2 - 10x \le -25$

31. $\dfrac{3}{x + 4} \le 1$

32. $|2x - 4| + 5 > 7$

For Exercises 33–35, graph the equation.

33. $3x - 2y = 6$

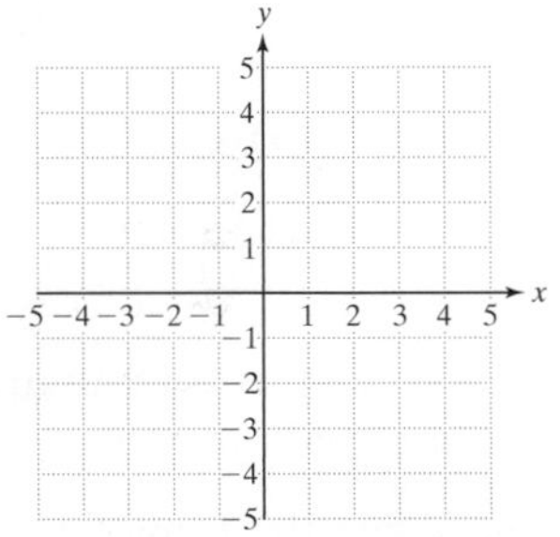

34. $(x - 2)^2 + y^2 = 9$

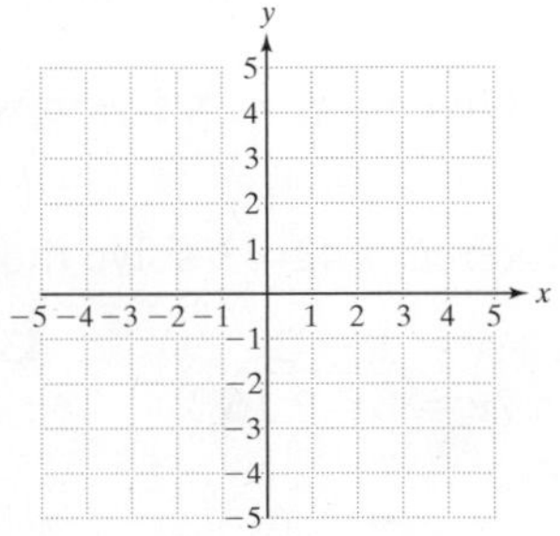

35. $y = 2^x$

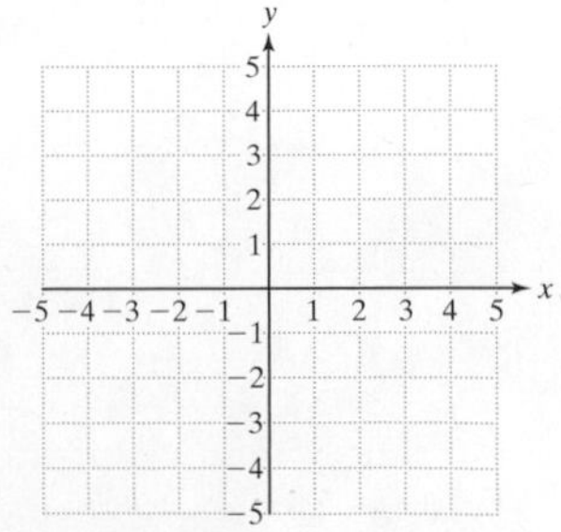

36. Graph the solution set. $\frac{x^2}{9} + \frac{y^2}{25} \leq 1$

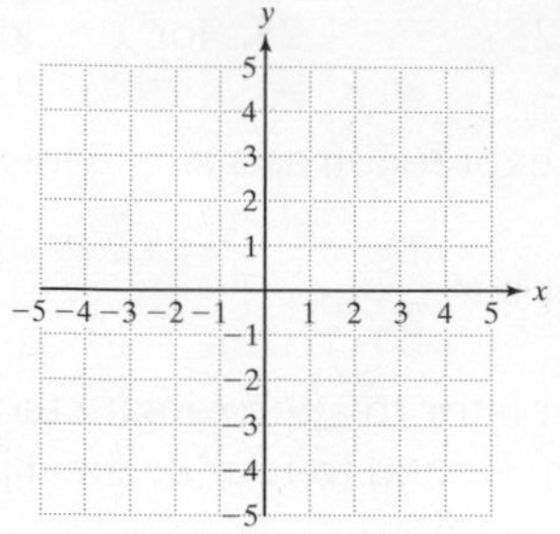

37. Given $f(x) = x^2 + 6x + 5$,

a. Determine the x-intercepts.

b. Determine the y-intercept.

c. Determine the vertex of the parabola.

38. Determine the slope and y-intercept of the line defined by $4x + y = 6$

39. Write an equation of the line passing through the point $(4, -2)$ and perpendicular to the line defined by $x - 5y = 2$.

40. Refer to the graph of $y = f(x)$.

a. Find $f(-1)$.

b. Find $f(4)$.

c. For what value(s) of x is $f(x) = 3$?

d. Write the domain in interval notation.

e. Write the range in interval notation.

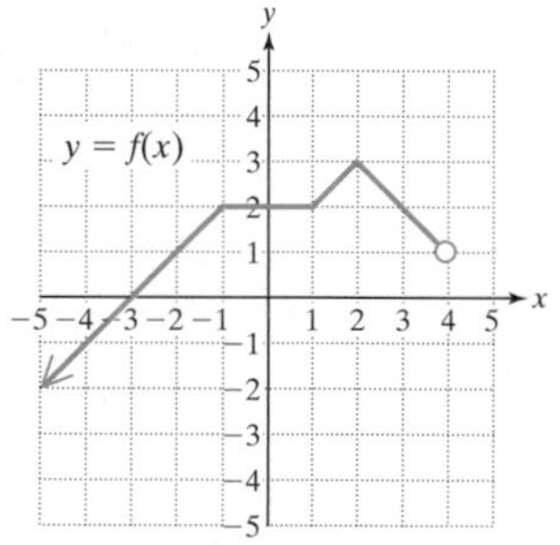

41. Given $f(x) = \sqrt{5 - x}$, write the domain of f.

For Exercises 42–43, solve the system.

42.
$$\begin{aligned} x &= 1 - 2y \\ 7y &= 3x - 16 \end{aligned}$$

43.
$$\begin{aligned} x \quad\quad\;\; + 2z &= 7 \\ 2x + 4y \quad\quad\;\; &= 10 \\ -3y + 5z &= 9 \end{aligned}$$

44. Given the points $(9, -4)$ and $(3, 0)$:

a. Find the distance between the points.

b. Find the midpoint of the line segment between the two points.

45. Given $A = \frac{1}{2}(b_1 + b_2)h$, solve for b_1.

46. The time, $t(n)$(in minutes), required for a rat to run through a maze depends on the number of trials, n, that the rat has practiced. Find $t(9)$ and interpret its meaning in the context of this problem.

$$t(n) = \frac{3n + 15}{n + 1} \quad \text{for } n \geq 1$$

47. The speed of a car varies inversely as the time to travel a fixed distance. A car traveling the speed limit of 60 mph travels between two points in 10 sec. How fast is a car moving if it takes only 8 sec to cover the same distance?

48. Two angles are supplementary. One angle measures 9° more than twice the other angle. Find the measures of the angles.

49. Chemique invests \$3000 less in an account earning 5% simple interest than she does in an account earning 6.5% simple interest. At the end of 1 yr, she earns a total of \$770 in interest. Find the amount invested in each account.

50. Against a headwind, a plane can travel 4950 mi in 11 hr. On the return trip flying with the same wind, the plane can fly the same distance in 9 hr. Find the wind speed and the speed of the plane in still air.

Additional Topics Appendix

Additional Factoring

Section A.1

Concepts

1. **Factoring by Using Substitution**
2. **Factoring 1 Term with 3 Terms**
3. **Additional Factoring Strategies**

1. Factoring by Using Substitution

The trinomial $u^2 + 4u - 21$ has a leading coefficient 1 and factors as $(u + 7)(u - 3)$. Now compare the following polynomials to $u^2 + 4u - 21$. In each case, the variable expressions in the first and second terms are the same. Furthermore, the coefficients are 1, 4, and -21. By letting the single variable u represent the variable expression in parentheses, the polynomial is a quadratic trinomial in u.

Polynomial	Substitution	New form
$u^2 + 4u - 21$		
$(a + b)^2 + 4(a + b) - 21$ $\longrightarrow$	Let $u = a + b$ $\longrightarrow$	$u^2 + 4u - 21$
$(y - 3)^2 + 4(y - 3) - 21$ $\longrightarrow$	Let $u = y - 3$ $\longrightarrow$	$u^2 + 4u - 21$

With an appropriate substitution, the polynomials on the left are easier to factor.

Example 1 **Factoring by Using Substitution**

Factor completely. $(a + b)^2 + 4(a + b) - 21$

Solution:

$(a + b)^2 + 4(a + b) - 21$ — The polynomial is a quadratic trinomial with variable $(a + b)$.

$= u^2 + 4u - 21$ — Let $u = a + b$.

$= (u + 7)(u - 3)$ — Factor the trinomial.

$= [(a + b) + 7][(a + b) - 3]$ — Back substitute.

$= (a + b + 7)(a + b - 3)$ — Simplify.

Skill Practice Factor completely.

1. $(w - 6)^2 - 3(w - 6) - 10$

In Examples 2 and 3, we use substitution to factor a difference of squares and a sum of cubes.

Answer

1. $(w - 11)(w - 4)$

Example 2 **Factoring by Using Substitution**

Factor completely. $9(4x - 1)^2 - 25$

Solution:

$9(4x - 1)^2 - 25$	The polynomial is a difference of squares.
$= 9u^2 - 25$	Let $u = 4x - 1$.
$= (3u - 5)(3u + 5)$	Factor as $a^2 - b^2 = (a - b)(a + b)$.
$= [3(4x - 1) - 5][3(4x - 1) + 5]$	Back substitute.
$= (12x - 3 - 5)(12x - 3 + 5)$	Apply the distributive property and simplify.
$= (12x - 8)(12x + 2)$	The remaining factors each have a common factor.
$= 4(3x - 2)2(6x + 1)$	Factor out 4 from the first binomial and 2 from the second binomial.
$= 8(3x - 2)(6x + 1)$	Simplify.

Skill Practice Factor completely.

2. $(2x + 1)^2 - 9$

Example 3 **Factoring by Using Substitution**

Factor completely. $(x + 1)^3 + 8$

Solution:

$(x + 1)^3 + 8$	The polynomial is a sum of cubes.
$= u^3 + 8$	Let $u = x + 1$.
$= (u + 2)(u^2 - 2u + 4)$	Factor as $a^3 + b^3 = (a + b)(a^2 - ab + b^2)$.
$= [(x + 1) + 2][(x + 1)^2 - 2(x + 1) + 4]$	Back substitute.
$= (x + 3)[(x^2 + 2x + 1) - 2x - 2 + 4]$	Apply the distributive property.
$= (x + 3)(x^2 + 3)$	Simplify.

Skill Practice Factor completely.

3. $(y + 3)^3 + 64$

2. Factoring 1 Term with 3 Terms

When confronted by a 4-term polynomial, sometimes the standard method of grouping does not apply. For example, consider the polynomial $x^2 - y^2 - 6y - 9$. Notice that grouping 2 terms with 2 terms does not result in common binomial factors.

$$x^2 - y^2 \,\vdots\, - 6y - 9$$
$$= 1(\underbrace{x^2 - y^2}) - 3(\underbrace{2x - 3})$$

Binomial factors do not match.

Answers

2. $4(x - 1)(x + 2)$
3. $(y + 7)(y^2 + 2y + 13)$

However, if a factor of -1 is removed from the last three terms, the last three terms result in a perfect square trinomial. This is called grouping 1 term with 3 terms.

Example 4 Factoring by Grouping 1 Term with 3 Terms

Factor completely. $x^2 - y^2 - 6y - 9$

Solution:

This polynomial has 4 terms. However, the standard grouping method does not work even if we try rearranging terms.

$x^2 - y^2 - 6y - 9$	We might try grouping one term with three terms. The reason is that after factoring out -1 from the last three terms we have a perfect square trinomial.
$= x^2 - 1(y^2 + 6y + 9)$	
$= x^2 - (y + 3)^2$ ← difference of squares	The resulting expression is a difference of squares $a^2 - b^2$ where $a = x$ and $b = (y + 3)$.
$= x^2 - u^2$	The difference of squares can be factored by using substitution. Let $u = y + 3$.
$= (x + u)(x - u)$	Factor as $a^2 - b^2 = (a + b)(a - b)$.
$= [x + (y + 3)][x - (y + 3)]$	Back substitute.
$= (x + y + 3)(x - y - 3)$	Simplify.

Skill Practice Factor completely.

4. $n^2 - m^2 - 8m - 16$

The difference of squares $(x)^2 - (y + 3)^2$ can also be factored without using a substitution.

$$(x)^2 - (y + 3)^2$$
$$= [x + (y + 3)][x - (y + 3)]$$
$$= (x + y + 3)(x - y - 3)$$

3. Additional Factoring Strategies

Thus far, we have learned how to factor polynomials that fit the following patterns.

- Difference of squares
- Difference of cubes
- Sum of cubes
- Perfect square trinomials
- Nonperfect square trinomials
- Grouping 2 terms by 2 terms
- Grouping 3 terms by 1 term

Answer

4. $(n + m + 4)(n - m - 4)$

Many polynomials do not fit any of these patterns, and many polynomials do not factor using these techniques. However, sometimes a combination of patterns exists and we can find the factored form. In Example 5, the polynomial has 6 terms. We might try grouping 3 terms with 3 terms or 4 terms with 2 terms, or even 2 terms, 2 terms and 2 terms. In any case, we should expect to try a variety of approaches before a workable strategy is identified.

Example 5 Factoring a Polynomial

Factor completely. $2ac + 2a - bc - b - c - 1$

Solution:

$2ac + 2a - bc - b - c - 1$ — The polynomial has 6 terms. After considerable trial and error, we might try grouping the first 2 terms, the second 2 terms, and the last 2 terms.

$= 2ac + 2a \,\vdots - bc - b \,\vdots - c - 1$

$= 2a(c + 1) - b(c + 1) - 1(c + 1)$ — Factor out the GCF from each pair of terms.

$= (c + 1)(2a - b - 1)$ — Factor out the common factor of $c + 1$.

Skill Practice Factor completely.

5. $xy + 2y + 3xz + 6z - x - 2$

Answer

5. $(x + 2)(y + 3z - 1)$

Section A.1 Practice Exercises

Vocabulary and Key Concepts

1. Given the expression $(3x - 2)^2 - (3x - 2) - 12$, what substitution could be used for u to make this a simpler quadratic trinomial in terms of u?
2. Given the expression $49(p - 3)^2 - 36$, what substitution could be used for u to make this a simpler difference of squares in terms of u?
3. What would be the first step to factor $x^2 - 4x + 4 - y^2$ by grouping 3 terms with 1 term?
4. What would be the first two steps to factor $9a^2 - 4b^2 - 20b - 25$ by grouping 1 term with 3 terms?

Concept 1: Factoring by Using Substitution

For Exercises 5–20, factor completely. **(See Examples 1–3.)**

5. $(4t - 1)^2 + 3(4t - 1) - 4$
6. $(2p + 5)^2 - 4(2p + 5) - 12$
7. $2(w - 2)^2 - 5(w - 2) - 3$
8. $3(y + 4)^2 + 11(y + 4) - 4$
9. $25(x + 4)^2 - y^2$
10. $36(y - 5)^2 - z^2$
11. $9(5a - 3)^2 - 4$
12. $25(3b + 7)^2 - 16$
13. $(t - 2)^2 - (2t + 1)^2$
14. $(w + 3)^2 - (3w - 5)^2$
15. $(a + b)^3 + c^3$
16. $(x + 4)^3 - y^3$

17. $27c^3 - (d + 2)^3$

18. $125v^3 + (w - 1)^3$

19. $4x^2 + 28x(2y + 1) + 49(2y + 1)^2$

20. $9a^2 - 12a(b + 1) + 4(b + 1)^2$

Concept 2: Factoring 1 Term with 3 Terms

For Exercises 21–28, factor completely. **(See Example 4.)**

21. $x^2 - 10x + 25 - y^2$

22. $m^2 - 22m + 121 - n^2$

23. $a^2 - x^2 - 18xy - 81y^2$

24. $c^2 - a^2 + 16ab - 64b^2$

25. $25a^2 + 20ab + 4b^2 - 100c^2$

26. $36x^2 + 60xy + 25y^2 - 121z^2$

27. $64w^2 - 9t^2 + 24tp - 16p^2$

28. $49k^2 - 25m^2 + 30mn - 9n^2$

Concept 3: Additional Strategies and Mixed Exercises

For Exercises 29–68, factor completely. **(See Example 5.)**

29. $x^2 - 4y^2 - x - 2y$

30. $9v^2 - w^2 - 3v + w$

31. $w^7 + 8w^4 - w^3 - 8$

32. $t^5 - 125t^2 - 4t^3 + 500$

33. $xy - 4x + 2yz - 8z - 2y + 8$

34. $ax + 4a + 2bx + 8b - cx - 4c$

35. $x^2 + xy - 2y^2 + x - y$

36. $a^2 + 2ab - 3b^2 - b + a$

37. $n^6 - 63n^3 - 64$

38. $m^6 + 7m^3 - 8$

39. $(a + b)^2 - 6(a + b)(c - d) + 9(c - d)^2$

40. $(x + 1)^2 - 4(x + 1)(x - 2) + 4(x - 2)^2$

41. $4x^4 - 10x^3 - 36x^2 + 90x$

42. $15x^4 - 5x^3 - 60x^2 + 20x$

43. $a^2 + 2ab + b^2 - a - b$

44. $v^2 + 6vw + 9w^2 - v - 3w$

45. $x^2(x + y) - y^2(x + y)$

46. $u^2(u - v) - v^2(u - v)$

47. $(a + 3)^4 + 6(a + 3)^3$

48. $(4 - b)^4 - 2(4 - b)^3$

49. $24(3x + 5)^3 - 30(3x + 5)^2$

50. $10(2y + 3)^2 + 15(2y + 3)$

51. $\frac{1}{100}x^2 + \frac{1}{35}x + \frac{1}{49}$

52. $\frac{1}{25}a^2 + \frac{1}{15}a + \frac{1}{36}$

53. $(5x^2 - 1)^2 - 4(5x^2 - 1) - 5$

54. $(x^3 + 4)^2 - 10(x^3 + 4) + 24$

55. $16p^4 - q^4$

56. $s^4t^4 - 81$

57. $y^3 + \frac{1}{64}$

58. $z^3 + \frac{1}{125}$

59. $6a^3 + a^2b - 6ab^2 - b^3$

60. $4p^3 + 12p^2q - pq^2 - 3q^3$

61. $\frac{1}{9}t^2 + \frac{1}{6}t + \frac{1}{16}$

62. $\frac{1}{25}y^2 + \frac{1}{5}y + \frac{1}{4}$

63. $6ax + 2bx - by - 3ay$

64. $5pq - 4q - 12 + 15p$

65. $x^8 - 1$

66. $y^8 - 256$

67. $25c^2 - 9d^2 + 5c - 3d$

68. $5wx^3 + 5wy^3 - 2zx^3 - 2zy^3$

Section A.2 Mean, Median, and Mode

Concepts

1. Mean
2. Median
3. Mode
4. Weighted Mean

1. Mean

When given a list of numerical data, it is often desirable to obtain a single number that represents the central value of the data. In this section, we discuss three such values called the mean, median, and mode.

Definition of a Mean

The mean (or average) of a set of numbers is the sum of the values divided by the number of values. We can write this as a formula.

$$\text{Mean} = \frac{\text{sum of the values}}{\text{number of values}}$$

Example 1 Finding the Mean of a Data Set

A small business employs five workers. Their yearly salaries are

\$42,000 \$36,000 \$45,000 \$35,000 \$38,000

a. Find the mean yearly salary for the five employees.

b. Suppose the owner of the business makes \$218,000 per year. Find the mean salary for all six individuals (that is, include the owner's salary).

Solution:

a. Mean salary of five employees

$$= \frac{42{,}000 + 36{,}000 + 45{,}000 + 35{,}000 + 38{,}000}{5}$$

$$= \frac{196{,}000}{5} \quad \text{Add the data values.}$$

$$= 39{,}200 \quad \text{Divide.}$$

Avoiding Mistakes

When computing a mean remember to add the data first before dividing.

The mean salary for employees is \$39,200.

b. Mean of all six individuals

$$= \frac{42{,}000 + 36{,}000 + 45{,}000 + 35{,}000 + 38{,}000 + 218{,}000}{6}$$

$$= \frac{414{,}000}{6}$$

$$= 69{,}000$$

The mean salary with the owner's salary included is \$69,000.

Skill Practice Housing prices for five homes in one neighborhood are given.

$108,000 $149,000 $164,000 $118,000 $144,000

1. Find the mean of these five prices.
2. Suppose a new home is built in the neighborhood for $1.3 million ($1,300,000). Find the mean price of all six homes.

2. Median

In Example 1, you may have noticed that the mean salary was greatly affected by the unusually high value of $218,000. For this reason, you may want to use a different measure of "center" called the median. The median is the "middle" number in an ordered list of numbers.

Finding the Median

To compute the median of a list of numbers, first arrange the numbers in order from least to greatest.

- If the number of data values in the list is *odd*, then the median is the middle number in the list.
- If the number of data values is *even*, there is no single middle number. Therefore, the median is the mean (average) of the two middle numbers in the list.

Example 2 Finding the Median of a Data Set

Consider the salaries of the five workers from Example 1.

$42,000 $36,000 $45,000 $35,000 $38,000

a. Find the median salary for the five workers.

b. Find the median salary including the owner's salary of $218,000.

Solution:

a. 35,000 36,000 38,000 42,000 45,000 Arrange the data in order.

Because there are five data values (an *odd* number), the median is the middle number.

The median is $38,000.

b. Now consider the scores of all six individuals (including the owner). Arrange the data in order.

35,000 36,000 38,000 42,000 45,000 218,000

$\dfrac{38,000 + 42,000}{2}$ There are six data values (an *even* number). The median is the average of the two middle numbers.

$= \dfrac{80,000}{2}$ Add the two middle numbers.

$= 40,000$ Divide.

The median of all six salaries is $40,000.

Answers

1. $136,600 **2.** $330,500

Skill Practice Housing prices for five homes in one neighborhood are given.

$108,000 $149,000 $164,000 $118,000 $144,000

3. Find the median price of these five houses.
4. Suppose a new home is built in the neighborhood for $1,300,000. Find the median price of all six homes. Compare this price with the mean in Skill Practice Exercise 2.

In Examples 1 and 2, the mean of all six salaries is $69,000, whereas the median is $40,000. These examples show that the median is a better representation for a central value when the data list has an unusually high (or low) value.

Example 3 Determining the Median of a Data Set

The average monthly temperatures (in °C) for the South Pole are given in the table. Find the median temperature. (*Source:* NOAA)

Jan.	Feb.	March	April	May	June	July	Aug.	Sept.	Oct.	Nov.	Dec.
−2.9	−9.5	−19.2	−20.7	−21.7	−23.0	−25.7	−26.1	−24.6	−18.9	−9.7	−3.4

Solution:

First arrange the numbers in order from least to greatest.

$-26.1 \quad -25.7 \quad -24.6 \quad -23.0 \quad -21.7 \quad -20.7 \quad -19.2 \quad -18.9 \quad -9.7 \quad -9.5 \quad -3.4 \quad -2.9$

$$\text{Median} = \frac{-20.7 + (-19.2)}{2} = -19.95$$

TIP: Note that the median may not be one of the original data values.

There are 12 data values (an *even* number). Therefore, the median is the average of the two middle numbers. The median temperature at the South Pole is −19.95°C.

Skill Practice The gain or loss for a stock is given for an 8-day period. Find the median gain or loss.

5. −2.4   −2.0   1.25   0.6
   −1.8   −0.4   0.6   −0.9

3. Mode

A third representative value for a list of data is called the mode.

Definition of a Mode

The mode of a set of data is the value or values that occur most often.

- If two values occur most often we say the data are bimodal.
- If more than two values occur most often, we say there is no mode.

Answers

3. $144,000   4. $146,500
5. −0.65

Example 4 Finding the Mode of a Data Set

The student-to-teacher ratio is given for elementary schools for ten selected states. For example, California has a student-to-teacher ratio of 20.6. This means that there are approximately 20.6 students per teacher in California elementary schools. (*Source:* National Center for Education Statistics)

ME	ND	WI	NH	RI	IL	IN	MS	CA	UT
12.5	13.4	14.1	14.5	14.8	16.1	16.1	16.1	20.6	21.9

Find the mode of the student-to-teacher ratio for these states.

Solution:

The data value 16.1 appears most often. Therefore, the mode is 16.1 students per teacher.

Skill Practice The monthly rainfall amounts (in inches) for Houston, Texas, are given. Find the mode. (*Source:* NOAA)

6. 4.5 3.0 3.2 3.5 5.1 6.8
4.3 4.5 5.6 5.3 4.5 3.8

Example 5 Finding the Mode of a Data Set

Find the mode of the list of average monthly temperatures for Albany, New York. Values are in °F.

Jan.	Feb.	March	April	May	June	July	Aug.	Sept.	Oct.	Nov.	Dec.
22	25	35	47	58	66	71	69	61	49	39	26

Solution:

No data value occurs most often. There is no mode for this set of data.

Skill Practice

7. Find the mode of the weights in pounds of babies born one day at Brackenridge Hospital in Austin, Texas.
7.2 8.1 6.9 9.3 8.3 7.7 7.9 6.4 7.5

Example 6 Finding the Mode of a Data Set

The grades for a quiz in college algebra are as follows. The scores are out of a possible 10 points.

9	4	6	9	9	8	2	1	4	9
5	10	10	5	7	7	9	8	7	3
9	7	10	7	10	1	7	4	5	6

Answers

6. 4.5 in. **7.** There is no mode.

Solution:

Sometimes arranging the data in order makes it easier to find the repeated values.

1	1	2	3	4	4	4	5	5	5
6	6	7	7	7	7	7	7	8	8
9	9	9	9	9	9	10	10	10	10

The score of 7 occurs 6 times. The score of 9 occurs 6 times. There are two modes, 7 and 9, because these scores both occur more than any other score. We say that these data are *bimodal.*

TIP: To remember the difference between median and mode, think of the *median* of a highway that goes down the *middle*. Think of the word *mode* as sounding similar to the word *most*.

Skill Practice

8. The ages of children participating in an after-school sports program are given. Find the mode(s).

13	15	17	15	14	15	16	16
15	16	12	13	15	14	16	15
15	16	16	13	16	13	14	18

4. Weighted Mean

Sometimes data values in a list appear multiple times. In such a case, we can compute a weighted mean. In Example 7, we demonstrate how to use a weighted mean to compute a grade point average (GPA). To compute GPA, each grade is assigned a numerical value. For example, an "A" is worth 4 points, a "B" is worth 3 points, and so on. Then each grade for a course is "weighted" by the number of credit-hours that the course is worth.

Example 7 Using a Weighted Mean to Compute GPA

At a certain college, the grades A–F are assigned numerical values as follows.

A = 4.0 B+ = 3.5 B = 3.0 C+ = 2.5

C = 2.0 D+ = 1.5 D = 1.0 F = 0.0

Elmer takes the following classes with the grades as shown. Determine Elmer's GPA.

Course	Grade	Number of Credit-Hours
Prealgebra	A = 4 pts	3
Study Skills	C = 2 pts	1
First Aid	B+ = 3.5 pts	2
English I	D = 1.0 pt	4

Solution:

The data in the table can be visualized as follows.

4 pts	4 pts	4 pts	2 pts	3.5 pts	3.5 pts	1 pt	1 pt	1 pt	1pt
A	A	A	C	B+	B+	D	D	D	D
3 of these			1 of these	2 of these		4 of these			

Answer

8. There are two modes, 15 and 16.

The number of grade points earned for each course is the product of the grade for the course and the number of credit-hours for the course. For example:

Grade points for Prealgebra: (4 pts)(3 credit-hours) = 12 points

Course	Grade	Number of Credit-Hours (Weights)	Product Number of Grade Points
Prealgebra	A = 4 pts	3	(4 pts)(3 credit-hours) = 12 pts
Study Skills	C = 2 pts	1	(2 pts)(1 credit-hour) = 2 pts
First Aid	B+ = 3.5 pts	2	(3.5 pts)(2 credit-hours) = 7 pts
English I	D = 1.0 pt	4	(1 pt)(4 credit-hours) = 4 pts
		Total hours: 10	Total grade points: 25 pts

To determine GPA, we will add the number of grade points earned for each course and then divide by the total number of credit-hours taken.

$\text{Mean} = \frac{25}{10} = 2.5$ Elmer's GPA for this term is 2.5.

Skill Practice

9. Clyde received the following grades for the semester. Use the numerical values assigned to grades from Example 7 to find Clyde's GPA.

Course	Grade	Credit-Hours
Math	B+	4
Science	C	3
Speech	A	3

In Example 7, notice that the value of each grade is "weighted" by the number of credit-hours. The grade of "A" for Prealgebra is weighted three times. The grade of "C" for the study skills course is weighted one time. The grade that hurt Elmer's GPA was the "D" in English. Not only did he receive a low grade, but the course was weighted heavily (4 credit-hours). In Exercise 47, we recompute Elmer's GPA with a "B" in English to see how this grade affects his GPA.

Answer

9. 3.2

Section A.2 Practice Exercises

Concept 1: Mean

For Exercises 1–7, find the mean of each set of numbers. **(See Example 1.)**

1. 93, 96, 88, 72, 91

2. 4, 6, 5, 10, 4, 5, 8

3. 3, 8, 5, 7, 4, 2, 7, 4

4. 0, 5, 7, 4, 7, 2, 4, 3

5. 7, 6, 5, 10, 8, 4, 8, 6, 0

6. −10, −13, −18, −20, −15

7. −22, −14, −12, −16, −15

8. Compute the mean of your test scores for this class up to this point.

9. The flight times in hours for six flights between New York and Los Angeles are given. Find the mean flight time. Round to the nearest tenth of an hour.

5.5, 6.0, 5.8, 5.8, 6.0, 5.6

10. A nurse takes the temperature of a patient every 10 min and records the temperatures as follows: 98°F, 98.4°F, 98.9°F, 100.1°F, and 99.2°F. Find the patient's mean temperature.

11. The number of Calories for six different chicken sandwiches and chicken salads is given in the table.

a. What is the mean number of Calories for a chicken sandwich? Round to the nearest whole unit.

b. What is the mean number of Calories for a salad with chicken? Round to the nearest whole unit.

c. What is the difference in the means?

Chicken Sandwiches	Salads with Chicken
360	310
370	325
380	350
400	390
400	440
470	500

12. The heights of the players from two NBA teams are given in the table. All heights are in inches.

a. Find the mean height for the players on the Philadelphia 76ers.

b. Find the mean height for the players on the Milwaukee Bucks.

c. What is the difference in the mean heights?

Philadelphia 76ers' Height (in.)	Milwaukee Bucks' Height (in.)
83	70
83	83
72	82
79	72
77	82
84	85
75	75
76	75
82	78
79	77

13. Zach received the following scores for his first four tests: 98%, 80%, 78%, 90%.

a. Find Zach's mean test score.

b. Zach got a 59% on his fifth test. Find the mean of all five tests.

c. How did the low score of 59% affect the overall mean of five tests?

14. The prices of four steam irons are \$50, \$30, \$25, and \$45.

a. Find the mean of these prices.

b. An iron that costs \$140 is added to the list. What is the mean of all five irons?

c. How does the expensive iron affect the mean?

Concept 2: Median

For Exercises 15–20, find the median for each set of numbers. **(See Examples 2–3.)**

15. 16, 14, 22, 13, 20, 19, 17

16. 32, 35, 22, 36, 30, 31, 38

17. 109, 118, 111, 110, 123, 100

18. 134, 132, 120, 135, 140, 118

19. $-58, -55, -50, -40, -40, -55$

20. $-82, -90, -99, -82, -88, -87$

21. The infant mortality rates for five countries are given in the table. Find the median.

Country	Infant Mortality Rate (Deaths per 1000)
Sweden	3.93
Japan	4.10
Finland	3.82
Andorra	4.09
Singapore	3.87

22. The snowfall amounts for five winter months in Burlington, Vermont, are given in the table. Find the median.

Month	Snowfall (in.)
November	6.6
December	18.1
January	18.8
February	16.8
March	12.4

23. Jonas Slackman played 8 golf tournaments, each with 72-holes of golf. His scores for the tournaments are given. Find the median score.

$-3, -5, 1, 4, -8, 2, 8, -1$

24. Andrew Strauss recorded the daily low temperature (in °C) at his home in Virginia for 8 days in January. Find the median temperature.

$5, 6, -5, 1, -4, -11, -8, -5$

25. The number of passengers (in millions) on 9 leading airlines for a recent year is listed. Find the median number of passengers. (*Source:* International Airline Transport Association)

48.3, 42.4, 91.6, 86.8, 46.5, 71.2, 45.4, 56.4, 51.7

26. For a recent year the number of albums sold (in millions) is listed for the 10 best sellers. Find the median number of albums sold.

2.7, 3.0, 4.8, 7.4, 3.4, 2.6, 3.0, 3.0, 3.9, 3.2

Concept 3: Mode

For Exercises 27–32, find the mode(s) for each set of numbers. **(See Examples 4–5.)**

27. 4, 5, 3, 8, 4, 9, 4, 2, 1, 4

28. 12, 14, 13, 17, 19, 18, 19, 17, 17

29. $-28, -21, -24, -23, -24, -30, -21$

30. $-45, -42, -40, -41, -49, -49, -42$

31. 90, 89, 91, 77, 88

32. 132, 253, 553, 255, 552, 234

33. The table gives the price of seven "smart" cell phones. Find the mode.

Brand and Model	Price ($)
Samsung	600
Kyocera	400
Sony Ericsson	800
PalmOne	450
Motorola	300
Siemens	600

34. The table gives the number of hazardous waste sites for selected states. Find the mode.

State	Number of Sites
Florida	51
New Jersey	112
Michigan	67
Wisconsin	39
California	96
Pennsylvania	94
Illinois	39
New York	90

35. The unemployment rates in percent for nine countries are given. Find the mode. **(See Example 6.)**

6.3%, 7.0%, 5.8%, 9.1%, 5.2%, 8.8%, 8.4%, 5.8%, 5.2%

36. The list gives the number of children who were absent from class for an 11-day period. Find the mode.

4, 1, 6, 2, 4, 4, 4, 2, 2, 3, 2

Mixed Exercises

37. Six test scores for Jonathan's history class are listed. Find the mean and median. Round to the nearest tenth if necessary. Did the mean or median give a better overall score for Jonathan's performance?

92%, 98%, 43%, 98%, 97%, 85%

38. Nora's math test results are listed. Find the mean and median. Round to the nearest tenth if necessary. Did the mean or median give a better overall score for Nora's performance?

52%, 85%, 89%, 90%, 83%, 89%

(a closed figure constructed from line segments), the perimeter is the sum of the lengths of the sides. For a circle, the distance around the outside is called the circumference.

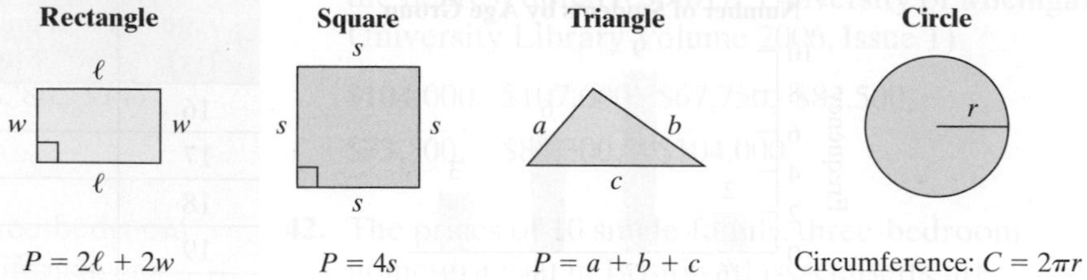

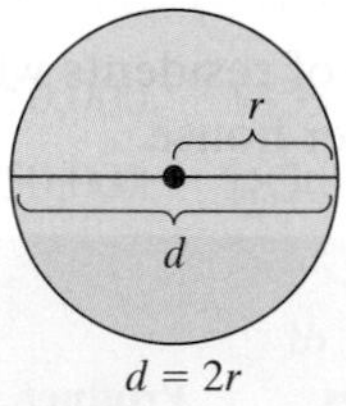

For a circle, r represents the length of a radius—the distance from the center to any point on the circle. The length of a diameter, d, of a circle is twice that of a radius. Thus, $d = 2r$. The number π is a constant equal to the circumference of a circle divided by the length of a diameter. That is, $\pi = \frac{C}{d}$. The value of π is often approximated by 3.14 or $\frac{22}{7}$.

Example 1 Finding Perimeter and Circumference

Find the perimeter or circumference as indicated. Use 3.14 for π.

a. Perimeter of the rectangle

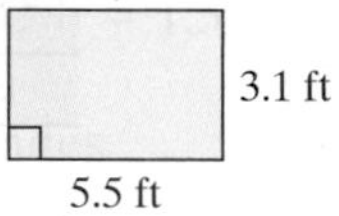

b. Circumference of the circle

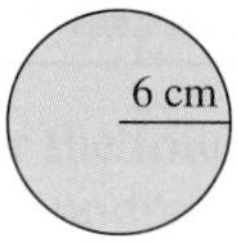

Solution:

a. $P = 2\ell + 2w$

$= 2(5.5\text{ ft}) + 2(3.1\text{ ft})$ Substitute $\ell = 5.5$ ft and $w = 3.1$ *ft*.

$= 11\text{ ft} + 6.2\text{ ft}$

$= 17.2\text{ ft}$ The perimeter is 17.2 ft.

b. $C = 2\pi r$

$\approx 2(3.14)(6\text{ cm})$ Substitute 3.14 for π and $r = 6$ cm.

$= 6.28(6\text{ cm})$

$= 37.68\text{ cm}$ The circumference is 37.68 cm.

TIP: If a calculator is used to find the circumference of a circle, use the π key to get a more accurate answer.

Skill Practice

1. Find the perimeter of the square.

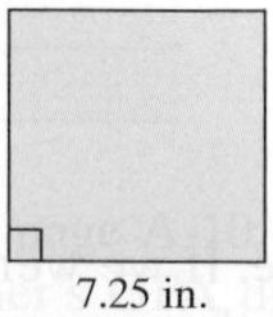

2. Find the circumference. Use 3.14 for π.

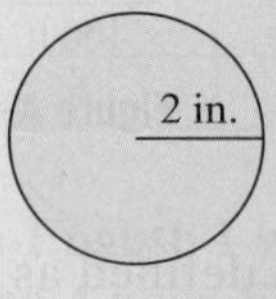

Answers

1. 29 in. **2.** 12.56 in.

2. Area

The area of a geometric figure is the number of square units that can be enclosed within the figure. In applications, we would find the area of a region if we were laying carpet or putting down sod for a lawn. For example, the rectangle shown in Figure A-2 encloses 6 square inches (6 in.^{2}).

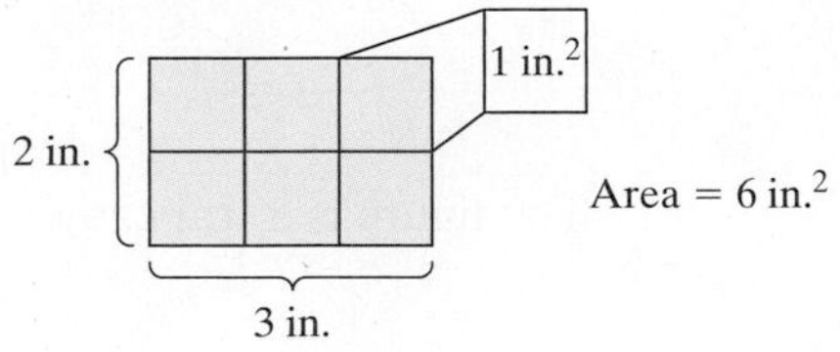

Figure A-2

The formulas used to compute the area for several common geometric shapes are given here:

Rectangle **Square** **Parallelogram** **Triangle** **Trapezoid** **Circle**

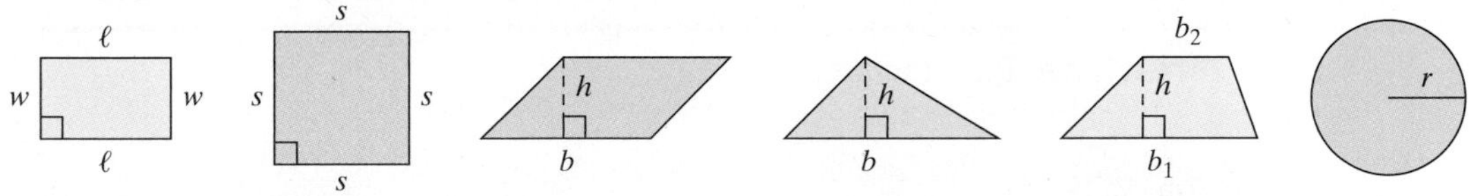

Rectangle	Square	Parallelogram	Triangle	Trapezoid	Circle
$A = \ell w$	$A = s^2$	$A = bh$	$A = \frac{1}{2}bh$	$A = \frac{1}{2}(b_1 + b_2)h$	$A = \pi r^2$

Example 2 **Finding Area**

Find the area.

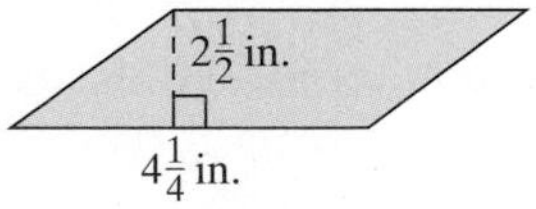

Solution:

$A = bh$ The figure is a parallelogram.

$= (4\frac{1}{4}\text{ in.})(2\frac{1}{2}\text{ in.})$ Substitute $b = 4\frac{1}{4}$ in. and $h = 2\frac{1}{2}$ in.

$= \left(\frac{17}{4}\text{ in.}\right)\left(\frac{5}{2}\text{ in.}\right)$

$= \frac{85}{8}\text{ in.}^2 \text{ or } 10\frac{5}{8}\text{ in.}^2$

Skill Practice Find the area.

3.

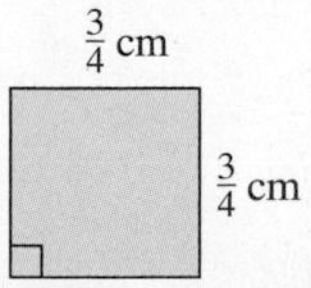

TIP: The units of area are given in square units such as square inches (in.^{2}), square feet (ft^2), square yards (yd^2), square centimeters (cm^2), and so on.

Answer

3. $\frac{9}{16}$ cm^2

Example 3 **Finding Area**

Find the area.

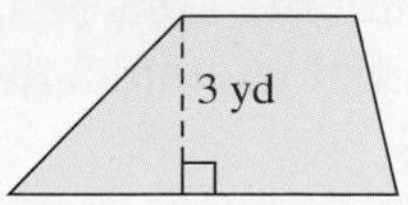

Solution:

$$A = \frac{1}{2}(b_1 + b_2)h$$ The figure is a trapezoid.

$$= \frac{1}{2}(16 \text{ yd} + 10 \text{ yd})(3 \text{ yd})$$ Substitute $b_1 = 16$ yd, $b_2 = 10$ yd, and $h = 3$ yd.

$$= \frac{1}{2}(26 \text{ yd})(3 \text{ yd})$$

$$= (13 \text{ yd})(3 \text{ yd})$$

$$= 39 \text{ yd}^2$$ The area is 39 yd^2.

Skill Practice Find the area.

4.

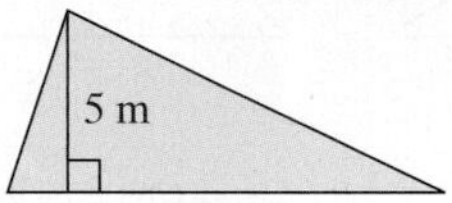

Example 4 **Finding the Area of a Circle**

Find the area of a circular fountain if the diameter is 50 ft. Use 3.14 for π.

Solution:

$$A = \pi r^2$$ We need the radius, which is $\frac{1}{2}$ the diameter. $r = \frac{1}{2}(50) = 25$ ft

$$\approx (3.14)(25 \text{ ft})^2$$ Substitute 3.14 for π and $r = 25$ ft.

$$= (3.14)(625 \text{ ft}^2)$$

$$= 1962.5 \text{ ft}^2$$ The area of the fountain is 1962.5 ft^2.

Skill Practice Find the area of the circular region. Use 3.14 for π.

5.

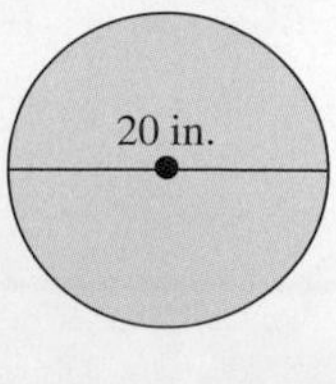

Answers

4. 30 m^2 **5.** 314 in.^2

3. Volume

The volume of a solid is the number of cubic units that can be enclosed within a solid. The solid shown in Figure A-3 contains 18 cubic inches (18 in.^{3}). In applications, volume might refer to the amount of water in a swimming pool.

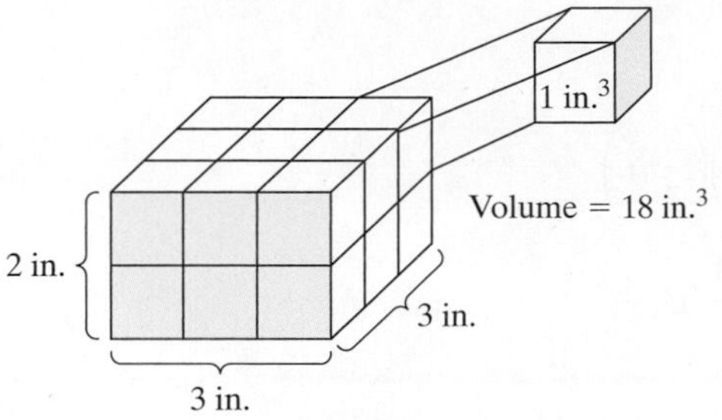

Figure A-3

The formulas used to compute the volume of several common solids are given here:

Rectangular Solid	**Cube**	**Right Circular Cylinder**

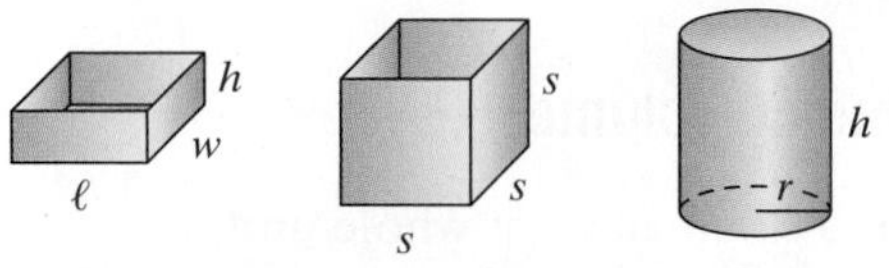

$V = \ell wh$	$V = s^3$	$V = \pi r^2 h$

TIP: Notice that the volume formulas for the three figures just shown are given by the product of the area of the base and the height of the figure:

$V = \ell wh$	$V = s \cdot s \cdot s$	$V = \pi r^2 h$
↑ Area of Rectangular Base	↑ Area of Square Base	↑ Area of Circular Base

Right Circular Cone	**Sphere**

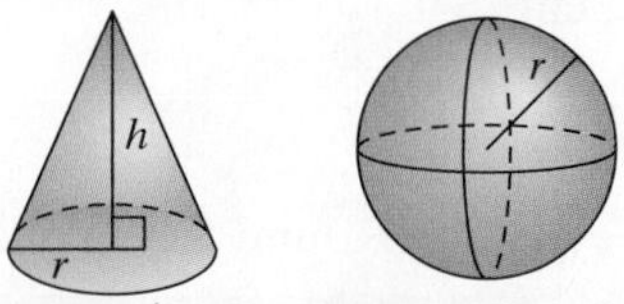

$V = \frac{1}{3}\pi r^2 h$	$V = \frac{4}{3}\pi r^3$

Example 5 Finding Volume

Find the volume.

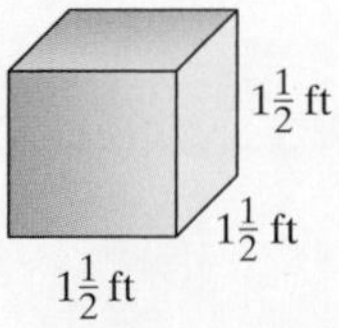

Solution:

$V = s^3$ The object is a cube.

$= (1\tfrac{1}{2}\text{ ft})^3$ Substitute $s = 1\tfrac{1}{2}$ ft.

$= \left(\frac{3}{2}\text{ ft}\right)^3$

$= \left(\frac{3}{2}\text{ ft}\right)\left(\frac{3}{2}\text{ ft}\right)\left(\frac{3}{2}\text{ ft}\right)$

$= \frac{27}{8}\text{ ft}^3$, or $3\frac{3}{8}\text{ ft}^3$

TIP: The units of volume are cubic units such as cubic inches (in.^3), cubic feet (ft^3), cubic yards (yd^3), cubic centimeters (cm^3), and so on.

Skill Practice Find the volume.

6.

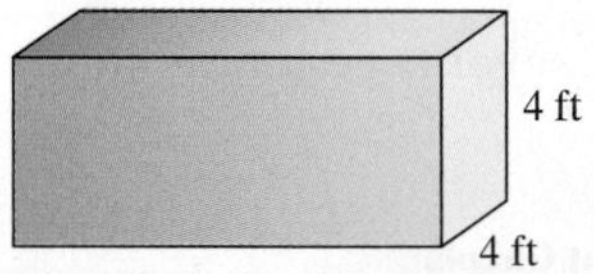

Example 6 Finding Volume

Find the volume. Round to the nearest whole unit.

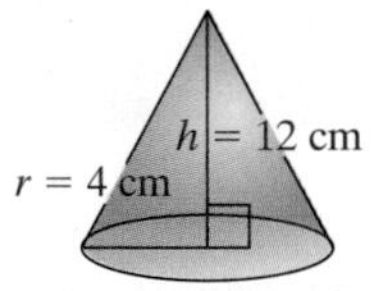

Solution:

$V = \frac{1}{3}\pi r^2 h$ The object is a right circular cone.

$\approx \frac{1}{3}(3.14)(4\text{ cm})^2(12\text{ cm})$ Substitute 3.14 for π, $r = 4$ cm, and $h = 12$ cm.

$= \frac{1}{3}(3.14)(16\text{ cm}^2)(12\text{ cm})$

$= 200.96\text{ cm}^3$

$\approx 201\text{ cm}^3$ Round to the nearest whole unit.

Skill Practice Find the volume. Use 3.14 for π. Round to the nearest whole unit.

7.

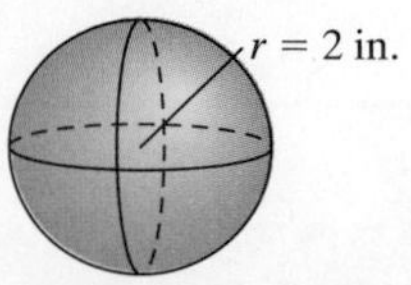

Answers

6. 128 ft^3 **7.** 33 in.^3

Example 7 **Finding Volume in an Application**

An underground gas tank is in the shape of a right circular cylinder. Find the volume of the tank. Use 3.14 for π.

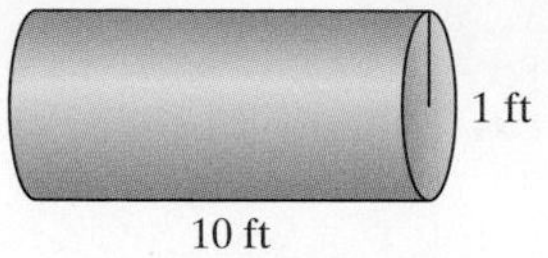

Solution:

$V = \pi r^2 h$

$\approx (3.14)(1\text{ ft})^2(10\text{ ft})$ Substitute 3.14 for π, $r = 1$ ft, and $h = 10$ ft.

$= (3.14)(1\text{ ft}^2)(10\text{ ft})$

$= 31.4\text{ ft}^3$ The tank holds 31.4 ft^3 of gasoline.

Skill Practice

8. Find the volume of soda in the can. Use 3.14 for π. Round to the nearest whole unit.

4. Angles

Applications involving angles and their measure come up often in the study of algebra, trigonometry, calculus, and applied sciences. The most common unit to measure an angle is the degree (°). Several angles and their corresponding degree measure are shown in Figure A-4.

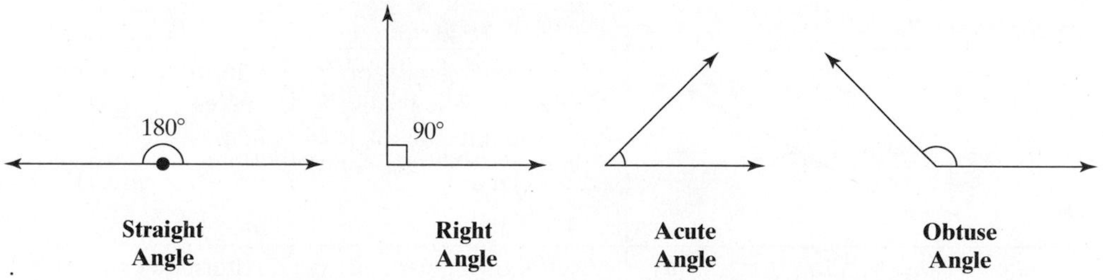

Figure A-4

- An angle that measures 90° is a right angle (right angles are often marked with a square or corner symbol, □).
- An angle that measures 180° is called a straight angle.
- An angle that measures between 0° and 90° is called an acute angle.
- An angle that measures between 90° and 180° is called an obtuse angle.
- Two angles with the same measure are congruent angles.

The measure of an angle will be denoted by the symbol m written in front of the angle. Therefore, the measure of $\angle A$ is denoted $m(\angle A)$.

Answer

8. 339 cm^3

- Two angles are complementary if the sum of their measures is 90°.

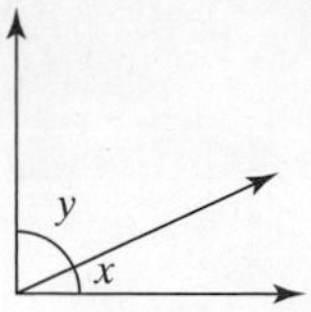

$m(\angle x) + m(\angle y) = 90°$

- Two angles are supplementary if the sum of their measures is 180°.

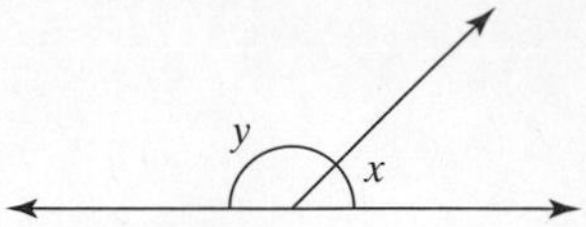

$m(\angle x) + m(\angle y) = 180°$

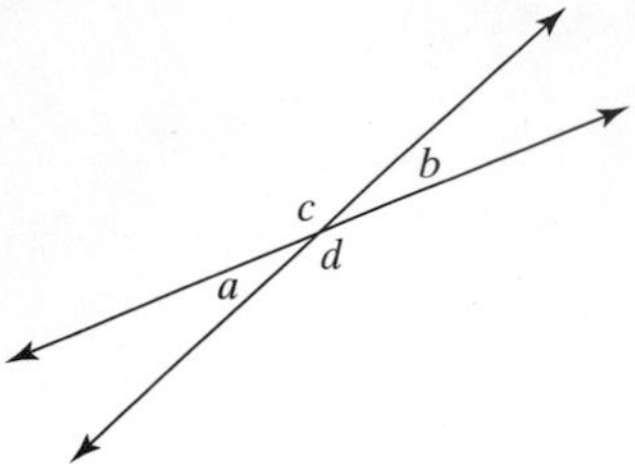

Figure A-5

When two lines intersect, four angles are formed (Figure A-5). In Figure A-6, $\angle a$ and $\angle b$ are a pair of vertical angles. Another set of vertical angles is the pair $\angle c$ and $\angle d$. An important property of vertical angles is that the measures of two vertical angles are *equal*. In the figure, $m(\angle a) = m(\angle b)$ and $m(\angle c) = m(\angle d)$.

Parallel lines are lines that lie in the same plane and do not intersect. In Figure A-6, the lines L_1 and L_2 are parallel lines. If a line intersects two parallel lines, the line forms eight angles with the parallel lines.

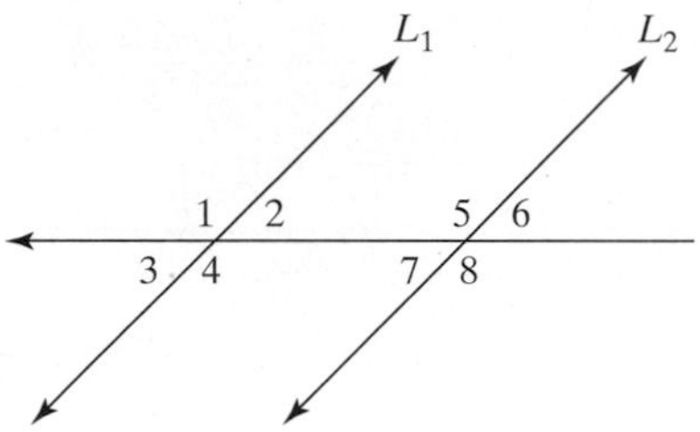

Figure A-6

The measures of angles 1–8 in Figure A-6 have the following special properties.

L_1 and L_2 are Parallel	Name of Angles	Property
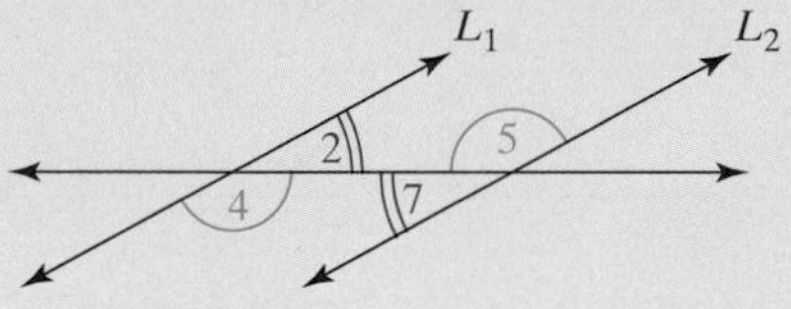	The following pairs of angles are called alternate interior angles: $\angle 2$ and $\angle 7$ $\angle 4$ and $\angle 5$	Alternate interior angles are equal in measure. $m(\angle 2) = m(\angle 7)$ $m(\angle 4) = m(\angle 5)$
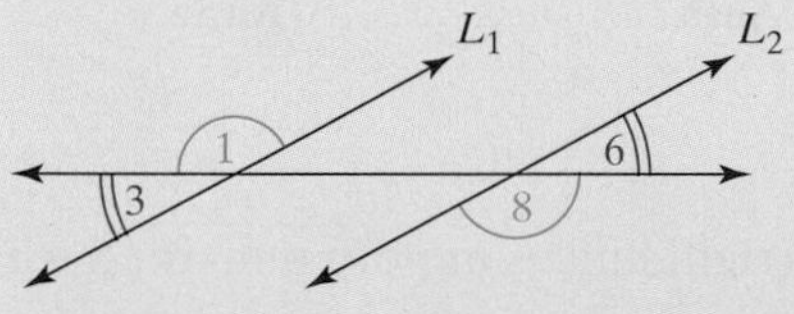	The following pairs of angles are called alternate exterior angles: $\angle 1$ and $\angle 8$ $\angle 3$ and $\angle 6$	Alternate exterior angles are equal in measure. $m(\angle 1) = m(\angle 8)$ $m(\angle 3) = m(\angle 6)$
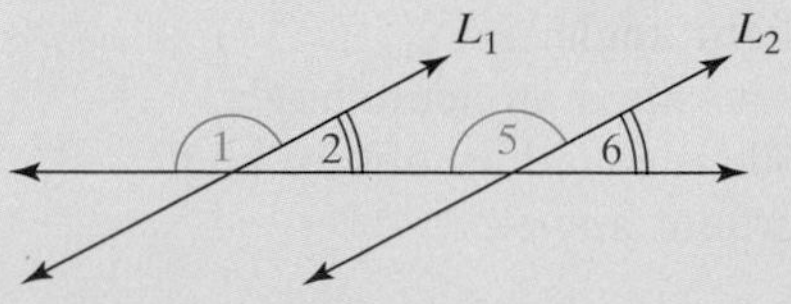 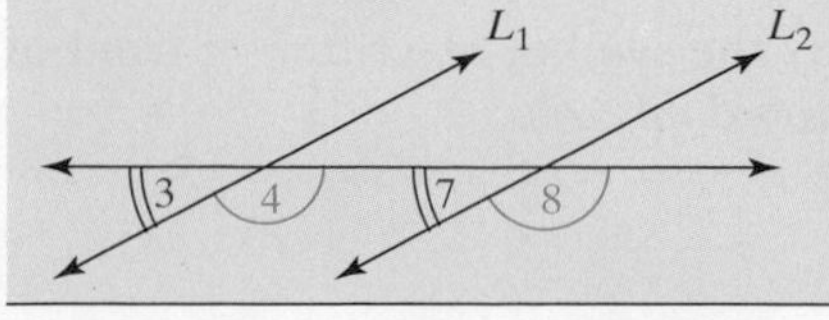	The following pairs of angles are called corresponding angles: $\angle 1$ and $\angle 5$ $\angle 2$ and $\angle 6$ $\angle 3$ and $\angle 7$ $\angle 4$ and $\angle 8$	Corresponding angles are equal in measure. $m(\angle 1) = m(\angle 5)$ $m(\angle 2) = m(\angle 6)$ $m(\angle 3) = m(\angle 7)$ $m(\angle 4) = m(\angle 8)$

Example 8 Finding the Measures of Angles in a Diagram

Find the measure of each angle and explain how the angle is related to the given angle of 70°.

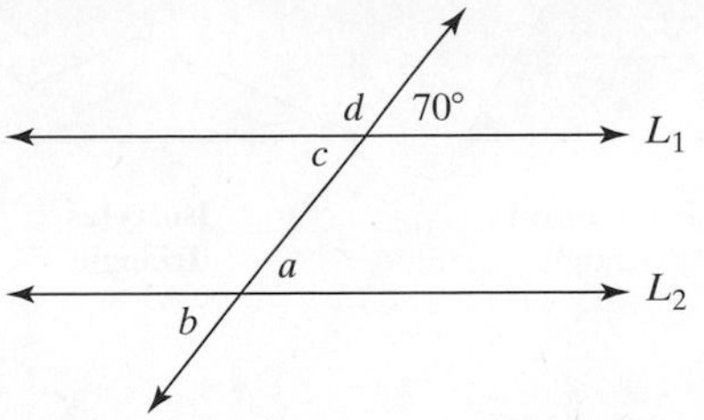

a. $\angle a$ **b.** $\angle b$

c. $\angle c$ **d.** $\angle d$

Solution:

a. $m(\angle a) = 70°$ $\angle a$ is a corresponding angle to the given angle of 70°.

b. $m(\angle b) = 70°$ $\angle b$ and the given angle of 70° are alternate exterior angles.

c. $m(\angle c) = 70°$ $\angle c$ and the given angle of 70° are vertical angles.

d. $m(\angle d) = 110°$ $\angle d$ is the supplement of the given angle of 70°.

Skill Practice Refer to the figure. Assume that lines L_1 and L_2 are parallel.

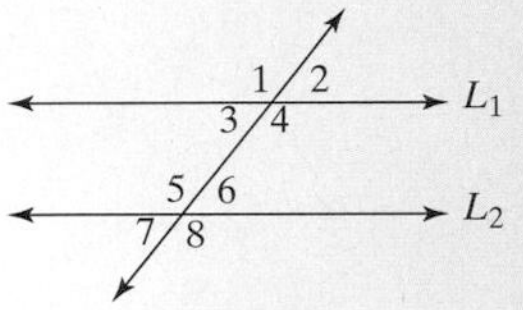

9. Given that $m(\angle 3) = 23°$, find $m(\angle 2)$, $m(\angle 4)$, $m(\angle 7)$, and $m(\angle 8)$.

5. Triangles

Triangles are categorized by the measures of the angles (Figure A-7) and by the number of equal sides or angles (Figure A-8).

- An acute triangle is a triangle in which all three angles are acute.
- A right triangle is a triangle in which one angle is a right angle.
- An obtuse triangle is a triangle in which one angle is obtuse.

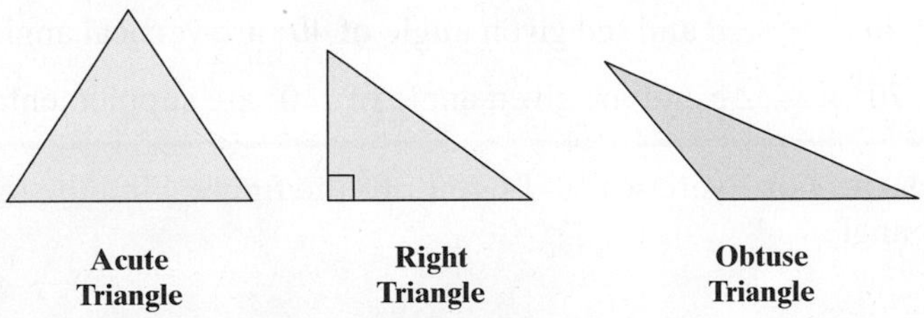

Figure A-7

- An equilateral triangle is a triangle in which all three sides (and all three angles) are equal in measure.
- An isosceles triangle is a triangle in which two sides are equal in measure (the angles opposite the equal sides are also equal in measure).
- A scalene triangle is a triangle in which no sides (or angles) are equal in measure.

Answer

9. $m(\angle 2) = 23°$; $m(\angle 4) = 157°$; $m(\angle 7) = 23°$; $m(\angle 8) = 157°$

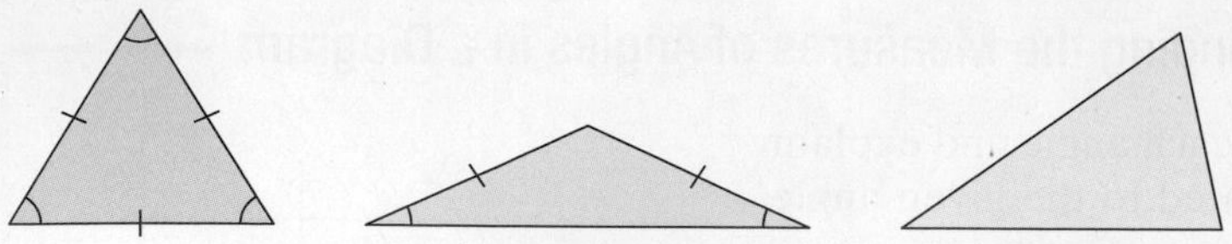

Equilateral Triangle	Isosceles Triangle	Scalene Triangle

Figure A-8

The following important property is true for all triangles.

Sum of the Angles in a Triangle

The sum of the measures of the angles of a triangle is 180°.

Example 9 **Finding the Measures of Angles in a Diagram**

Find the measure of each angle in the figure.

a. $\angle a$

b. $\angle b$

c. $\angle c$

d. $\angle d$

e. $\angle e$

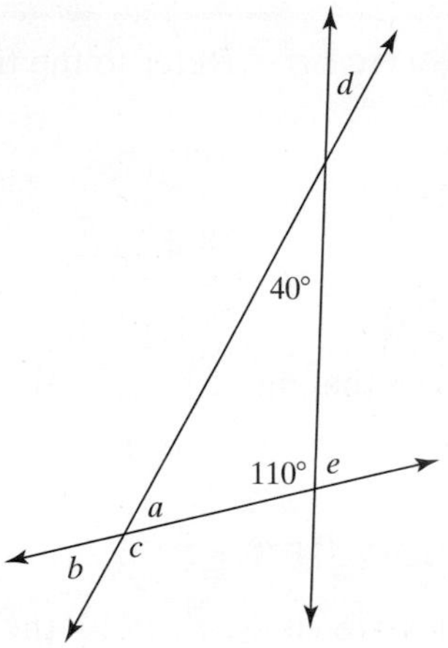

Solution:

a. $m(\angle a) = 30°$	The sum of the angles in a triangle is 180°.
b. $m(\angle b) = 30°$	$\angle a$ and $\angle b$ are vertical angles and have equal measures.
c. $m(\angle c) = 150°$	$\angle c$ and $\angle a$ are supplementary angles ($\angle c$ and $\angle b$ are also supplementary).
d. $m(\angle d) = 40°$	$\angle d$ and the given angle of 40° are vertical angles.
e. $m(\angle e) = 70°$	$\angle e$ and the given angle of 110° are supplementary angles.

Skill Practice For Exercises 10–14, refer to the figure. Find the measure of the indicated angle.

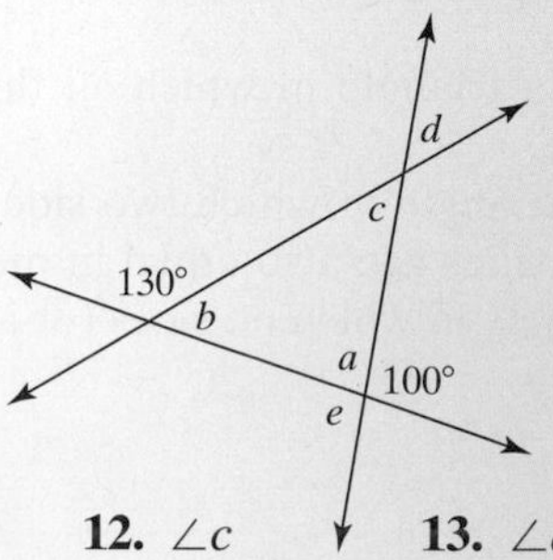

10. $\angle a$ **11.** $\angle b$ **12.** $\angle c$ **13.** $\angle d$ **14.** $\angle e$

Answers

10. 80° **11.** 50° **12.** 50°
13. 50° **14.** 100°

Section A.3 Practice Exercises

Concept 1: Perimeter

1. Would you measure area or perimeter to determine the amount of decorative fence needed to enclose a garden?

2. Identify which of the following units could be measures of perimeter.

a. Square inches ($in.^2$) **b.** Meters (m) **c.** Cubic feet (ft^3)
d. Cubic meters (m^3) **e.** Miles (mi) **f.** Square centimeters (cm^2)
g. Square yards (yd^2) **h.** Cubic inches ($in.^3$) **i.** Kilometers (km)

For Exercises 3–10, find the perimeter or circumference of each figure. Use 3.14 for π. **(See Example 1.)**

3.
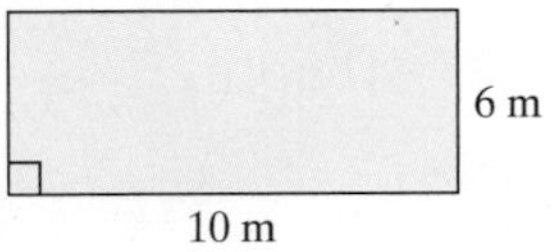

4.
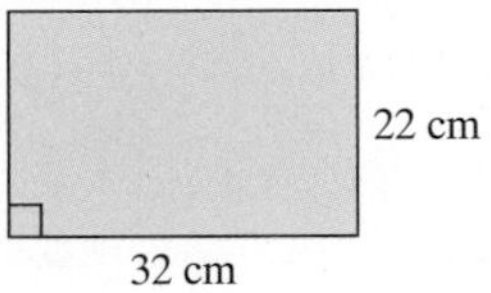

5.
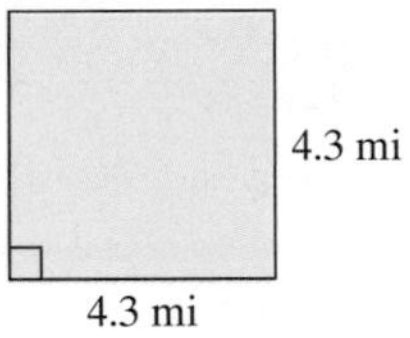

6.
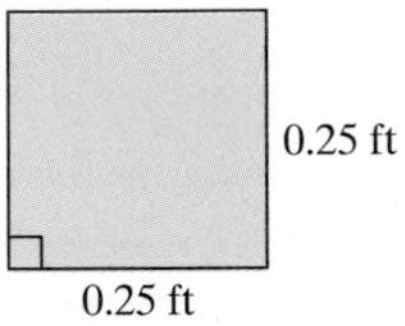

7.
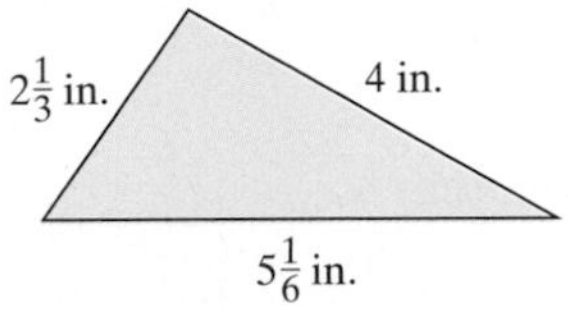

8.
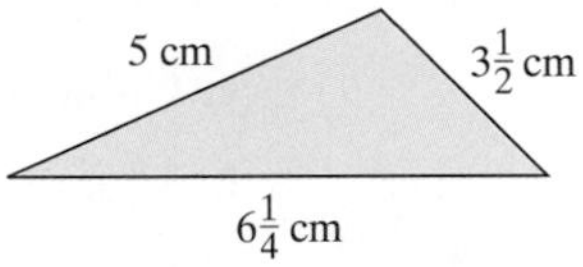

9.
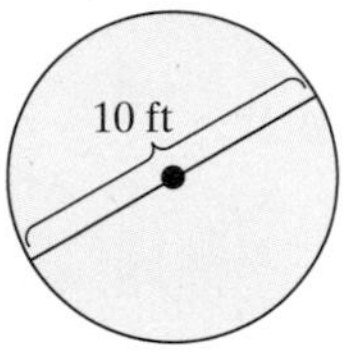

10.
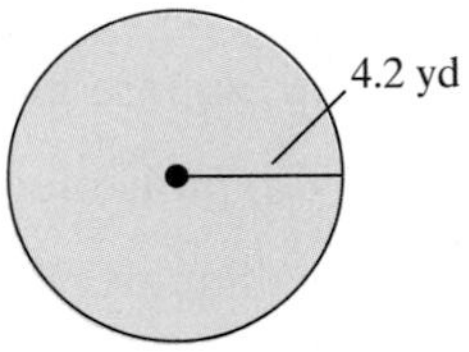

Concept 2: Area

11. Identify which of the following units could be measures of area.

a. Square inches ($in.^2$) **b.** Meters (m) **c.** Cubic feet (ft^3)
d. Cubic meters (m^3) **e.** Miles (mi) **f.** Square centimeters (cm^2)
g. Square yards (yd^2) **h.** Cubic inches ($in.^3$) **i.** Kilometers (km)

12. Would you measure area or perimeter to determine the amount of carpeting needed for a room?

For Exercises 13–26, find the area. Use 3.14 for π. **(See Examples 2–4.)**

13.
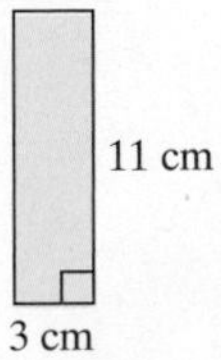

14.
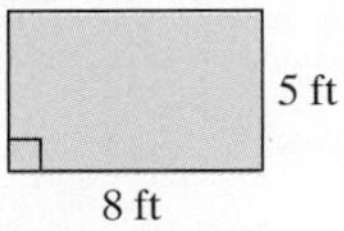

15.
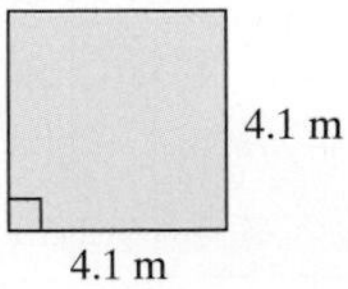

16.
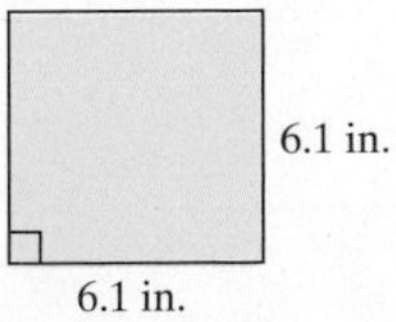

17.
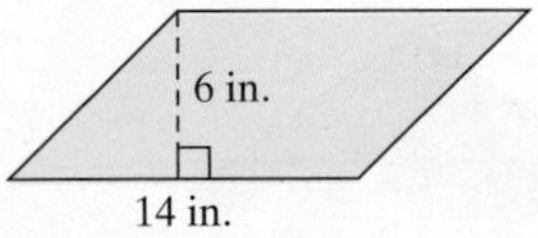

18.
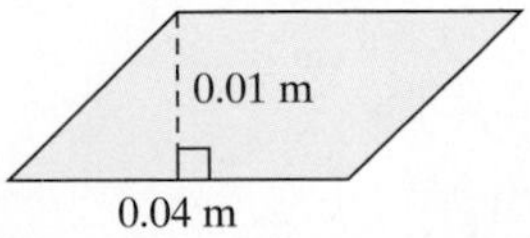

19.

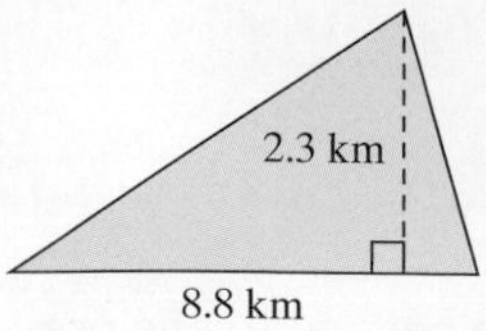

20.

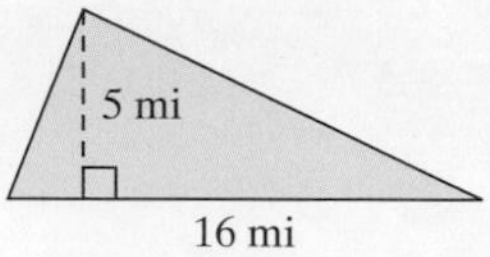

21.

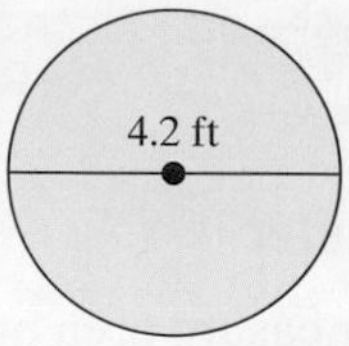

22.

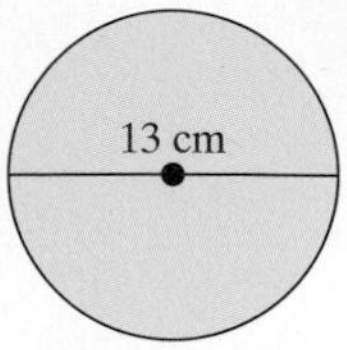

23.

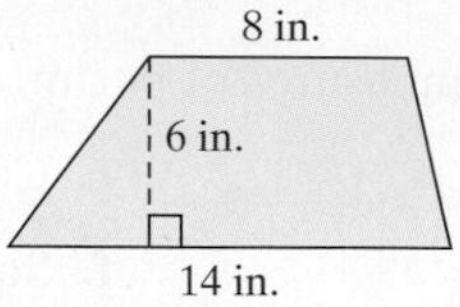

24.

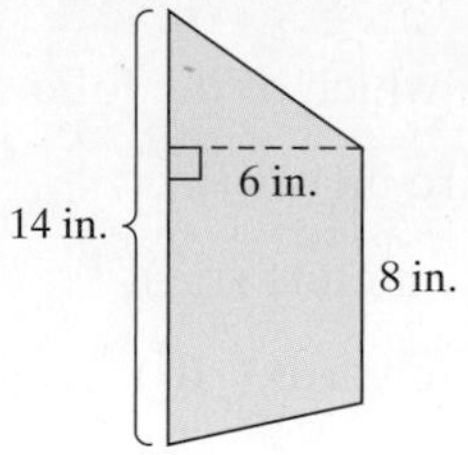

25.

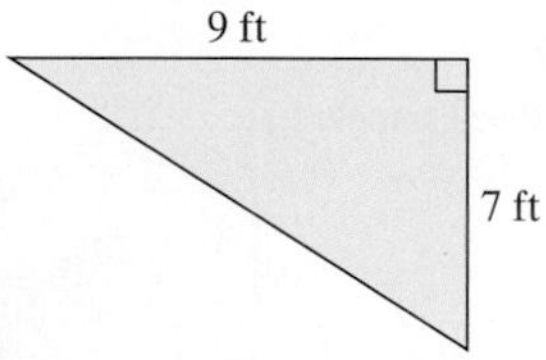

26.

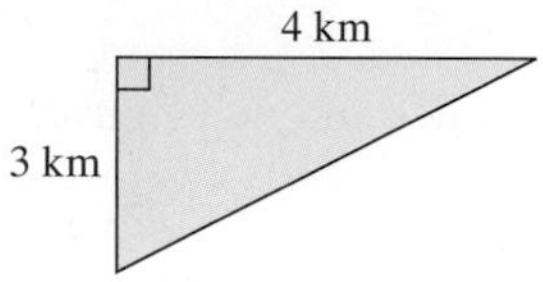

Concept 3: Volume

27. Identify which of the following units could be measures of volume.

a. Square inches ($in.^2$) **b.** Meters (m) **c.** Cubic feet (ft^3)

d. Cubic meters (m^3) **e.** Miles (mi) **f.** Square centimeters (cm^2)

g. Square yards (yd^2) **h.** Cubic inches ($in.^3$) **i.** Kilometers (km)

28. Would you measure perimeter, area, or volume to determine the amount of water needed to fill a swimming pool?

For Exercises 29–36, find the volume of each figure. Use 3.14 for π. **(See Examples 5–7.)**

29.

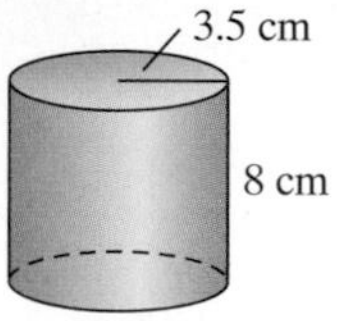

30.

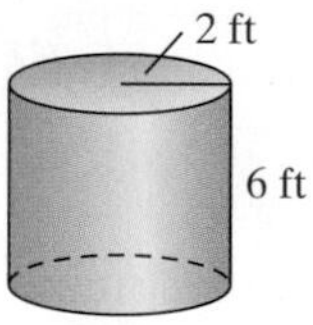

31.

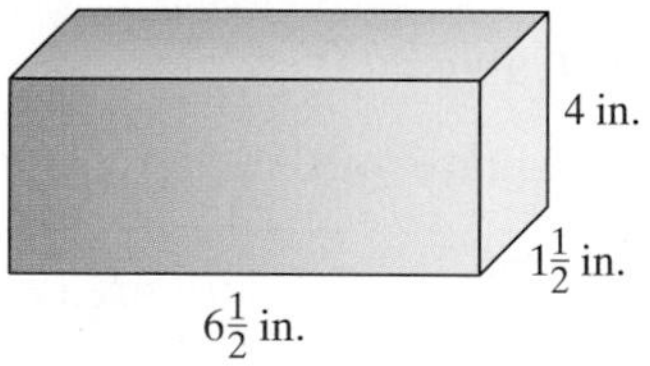

32.

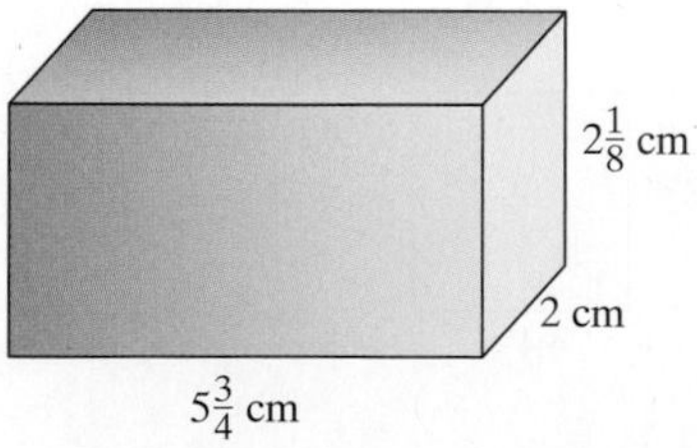

33.

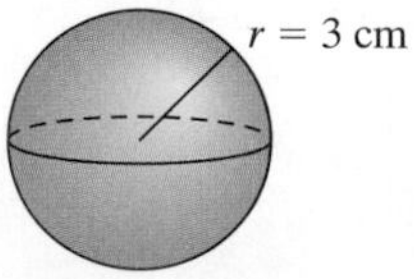

34.

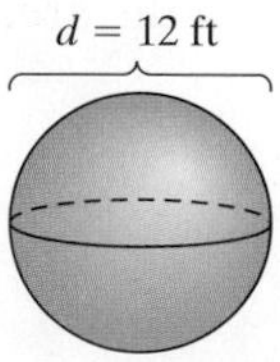

35.

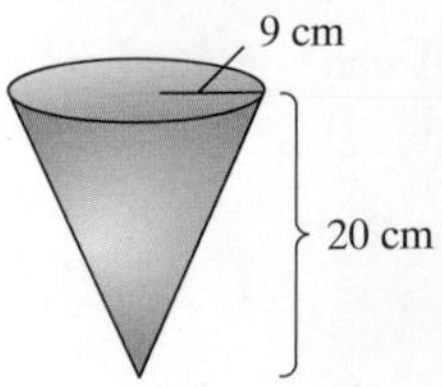

36.

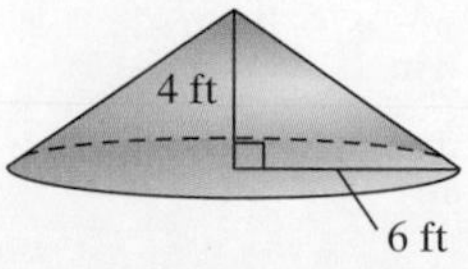

37. A florist sells balloons and needs to know how much helium to order. Each balloon is approximately spherical with a radius of 9 in. How much helium is needed to fill one balloon?

38. Find the volume of a spherical ball whose radius is 2 in. Use 3.14 for π. Round to the nearest whole unit.

39. Find the volume of a snow cone in the shape of a right circular cone whose radius is 3 cm and whose height is 12 cm. Use 3.14 for π.

40. A landscaping supply company has a pile of gravel in the shape of a right circular cone whose radius is 10 yd and whose height is 18 yd. Find the volume of the gravel. Use 3.14 for π.

Mixed Exercises: Perimeter, Area, and Volume

41. A wall measuring 20 ft by 8 ft can be painted for $40.

   a. What is the price per square foot?

   b. At this rate, how much would it cost to paint the remaining three walls that measure 20 ft by 8 ft, 16 ft by 8 ft, and 16 ft by 8 ft?

42. Suppose it costs $336 to carpet a 16 ft by 12 ft room.

   a. What is the price per square foot?

   b. At this rate, how much would it cost to carpet a room that is 20 ft by 32 ft?

43. If you were to purchase fencing for a garden, would you measure the perimeter or area of the garden?

44. If you were to purchase sod (grass) for your front yard, would you measure the perimeter or area of the yard?

45. How much fencing is needed to enclose a triangularly shaped garden whose sides measure 12 ft, 22 ft, and 20 ft?

46. A regulation soccer field is 100 yd long by 60 yd wide. Find the perimeter of the field.

47. a. An American football field is 360 ft long by 160 ft wide. What is the area of the field?

   b. How many pieces of sod, each 1 ft wide and 3 ft long, are needed to sod an entire field? (*Hint:* First find the area of a piece of sod.)

48. The Transamerica Tower in San Francisco is a pyramid with triangular sides (excluding the "wings"). Each side measures 145 ft wide with a height of 853 ft. What is the area of each side?

49. a. Find the area of a circular pizza that is 8 in. in diameter (the radius is 4 in.). Use 3.14 for π.

   b. Find the area of a circular pizza that is 12 in. in diameter (the radius is 6 in.).

   c. Assume that the 8-in. diameter and 12-in. diameter pizzas are both the same thickness. Which would provide more pizza, two 8-in. pizzas or one 12-in. pizza?

50. a. Find the area of a rectangular pizza that is 12 in. by 8 in.

   b. Find the area of a circular pizza that has a 16-in. diameter. Use 3.14 for π.

   c. Assume that the two pizzas have the same thickness. Which would provide more pizza? Two rectangular pizzas or one circular pizza?

51. Find the volume of a soup can in the shape of a right circular cylinder if its radius is 3.2 cm and its height is 9 cm. Use 3.14 for π.

52. Find the volume of a coffee mug whose radius is 2.5 in. and whose height is 6 in. Use 3.14 for π.

Concept 4: Angles

For Exercises 53–58, answer true or false. If an answer is false, explain why.

53. The sum of the measures of two right angles equals the measure of a straight angle.

54. Two right angles are complementary.

55. Two right angles are supplementary.

56. Two acute angles cannot be supplementary.

57. Two obtuse angles cannot be supplementary.

58. An obtuse angle and an acute angle can be supplementary.

59. If possible, find two acute angles that are supplementary.

60. If possible, find two acute angles that are complementary. Answers may vary.

61. If possible, find an obtuse angle and an acute angle that are supplementary. Answers may vary.

62. If possible, find two obtuse angles that are supplementary.

63. What angle is its own complement?

64. What angle is its own supplement?

65. Refer to the figure.

a. State all the pairs of vertical angles.

b. State all the pairs of supplementary angles.

c. If the measure of $\angle 4$ is 80°, find the measures of $\angle 1$, $\angle 2$, and $\angle 3$.

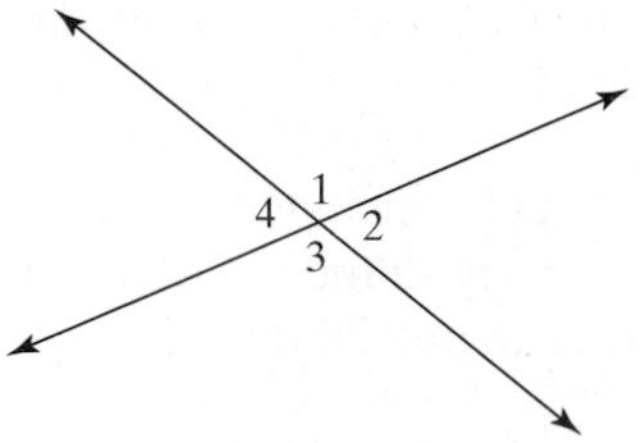

66. Refer to the figure.

a. State all the pairs of vertical angles.

b. State all the pairs of supplementary angles.

c. If the measure of $\angle a$ is 25°, find the measures of $\angle b$, $\angle c$, and $\angle d$.

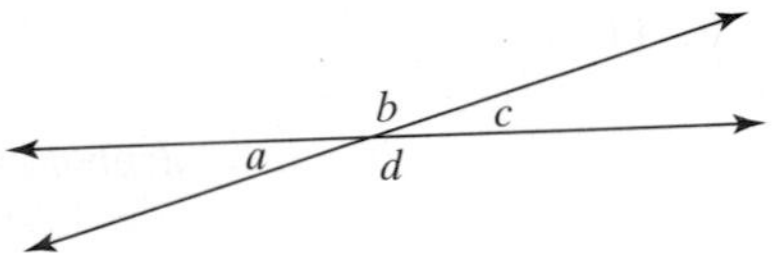

For Exercises 67–70, the measure of an angle is given. Find the measure of its complement.

67. 33° **68.** 87° **69.** 12° **70.** 45°

For Exercises 71–74, the measure of an angle is given. Find the measure of its supplement.

71. 33° **72.** 87° **73.** 122° **74.** 90°

For Exercises 75–82, refer to the figure. Assume that L_1 and L_2 are parallel lines. **(See Example 8.)**

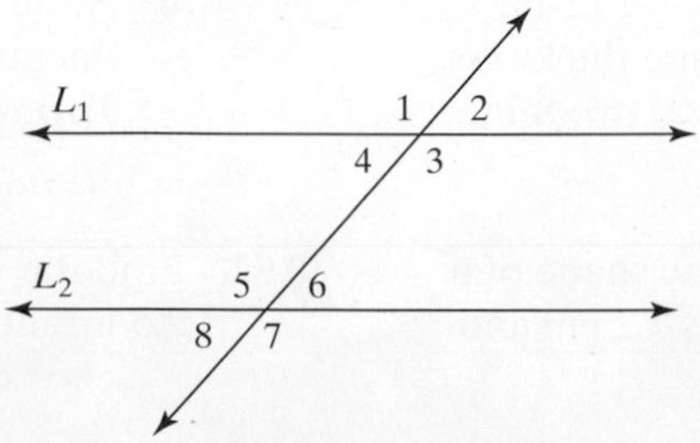

75. $m(\angle 5) = m(\angle\_\_\_\_\_)$ Reason: Vertical angles have equal measures.

76. $m(\angle 5) = m(\angle\_\_\_\_\_)$ Reason: Alternate interior angles have equal measures.

77. $m(\angle 5) = m(\angle\_\_\_\_\_)$ Reason: Corresponding angles have equal measures.

78. $m(\angle 7) = m(\angle\_\_\_\_\_)$ Reason: Corresponding angles have equal measures.

79. $m(\angle 7) = m(\angle\_\_\_\_\_)$ Reason: Alternate exterior angles have equal measures.

80. $m(\angle 7) = m(\angle\_\_\_\_\_)$ Reason: Vertical angles have equal measures.

81. $m(\angle 3) = m(\angle\_\_\_\_\_)$ Reason: Alternate interior angles have equal measures.

82. $m(\angle 3) = m(\angle\_\_\_\_\_)$ Reason: Vertical angles have equal measures.

83. Find the measure of angles *a*–*g* in the figure. Assume that L_1 and L_2 are parallel.

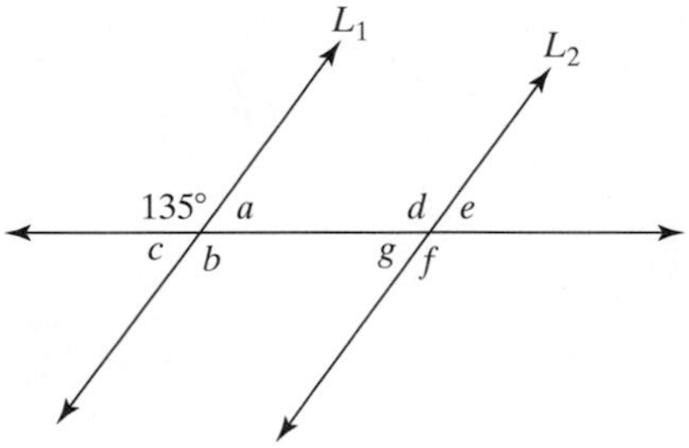

84. Find the measure of angles *a*–*g* in the figure. Assume that L_1 and L_2 are parallel.

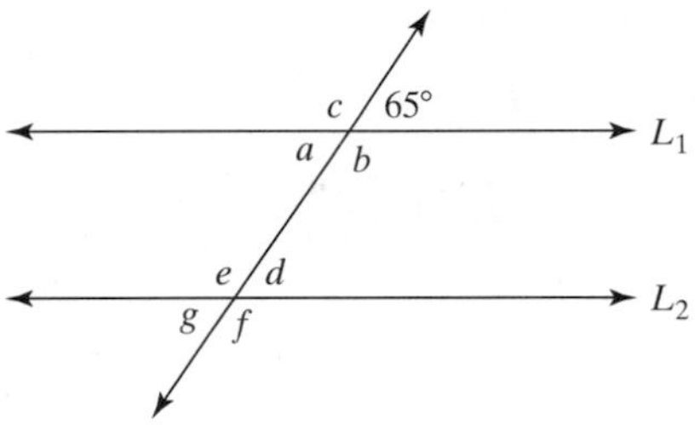

Concept 5: Triangles

For Exercises 85–88, identify the triangle as equilateral, isosceles, or scalene.

85.

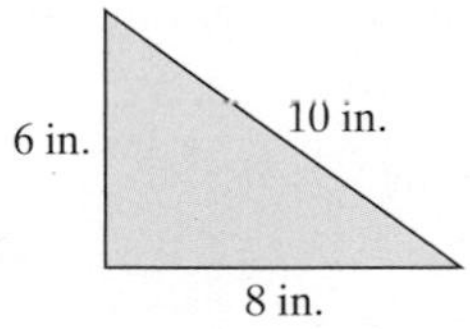

86.

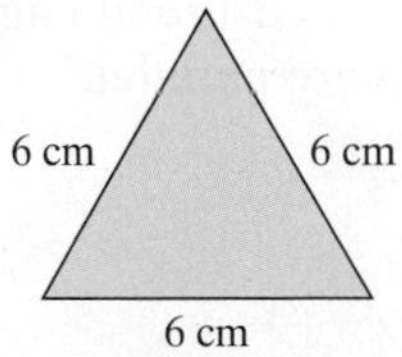

87.

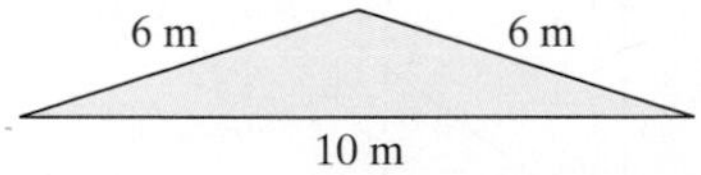

88.

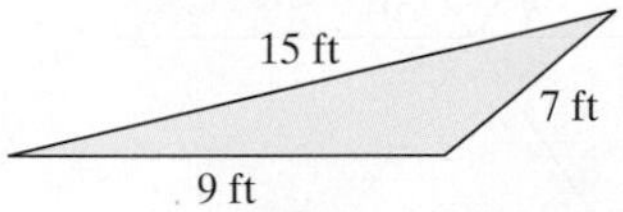

89. True or False? If a triangle is equilateral, then it is not scalene.

90. True or False? If a triangle is isosceles, then it is also scalene.

91. Can a triangle be both a right triangle and an obtuse triangle? Explain.

92. Can a triangle be both a right triangle and an isosceles triangle? Explain.

For Exercises 93–96, find the measure of each missing angle.

93.

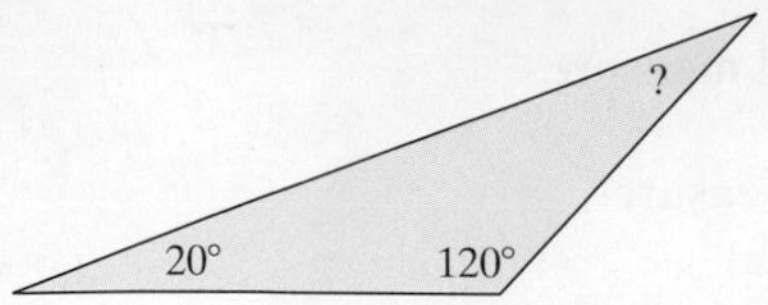

94.

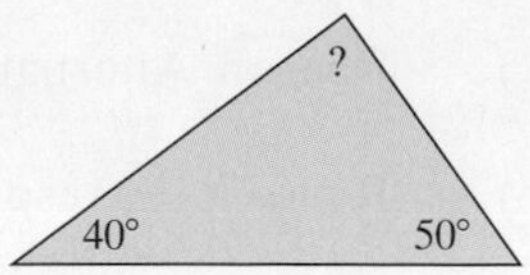

95.

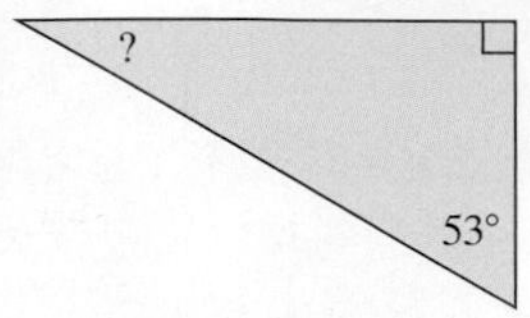

96.

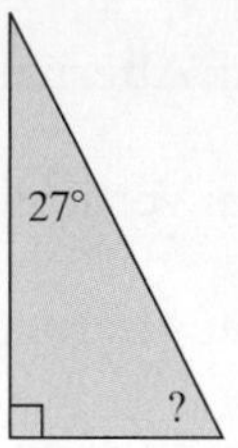

97. Refer to the figure. Find the measure of angles *a*–*j*. **(See Example 9.)**

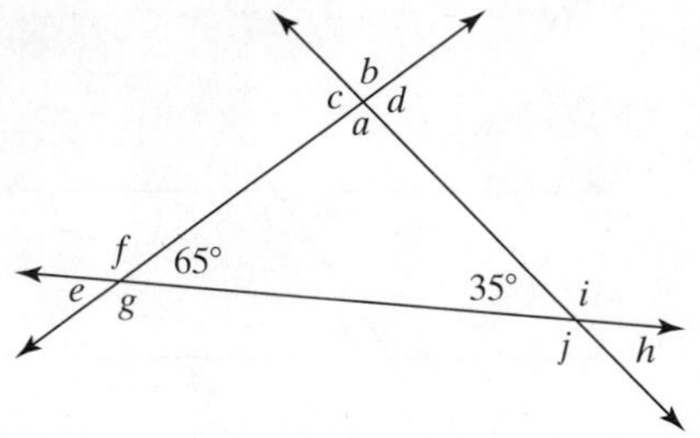

98. Refer to the figure. Find the measure of angles *a*–*j*.

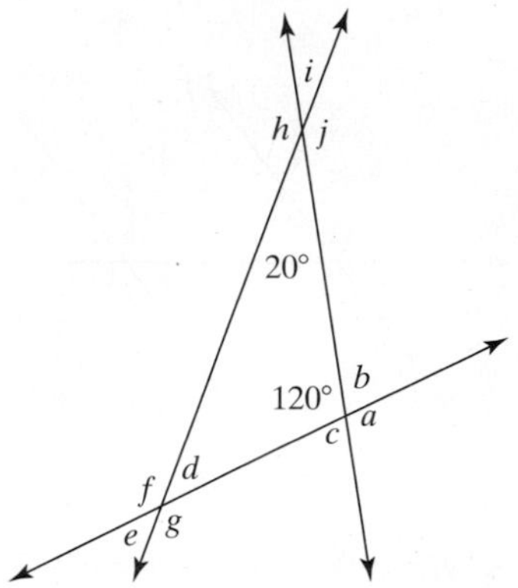

99. Refer to the figure. Find the measure of angles *a*–*k*. Assume that L_1 and L_2 are parallel.

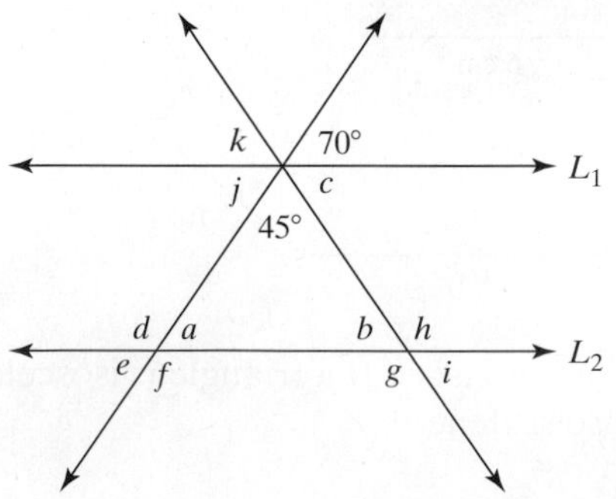

100. Refer to the figure. Find the measure of angles *a*–*k*. Assume that L_1 and L_2 are parallel.

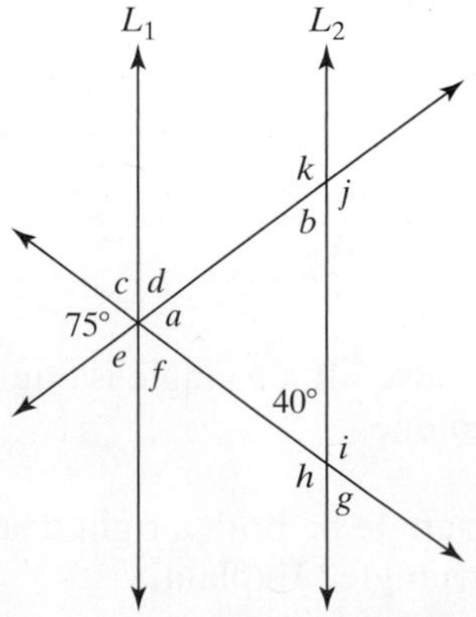

Expanding Your Skills

For Exercises 101–102, find the perimeter.

101.

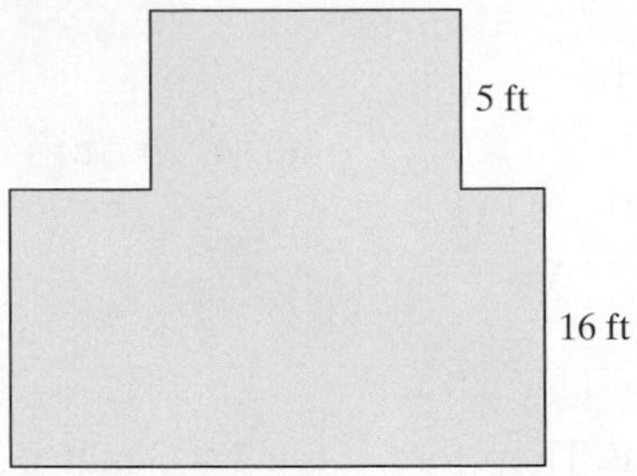

102.

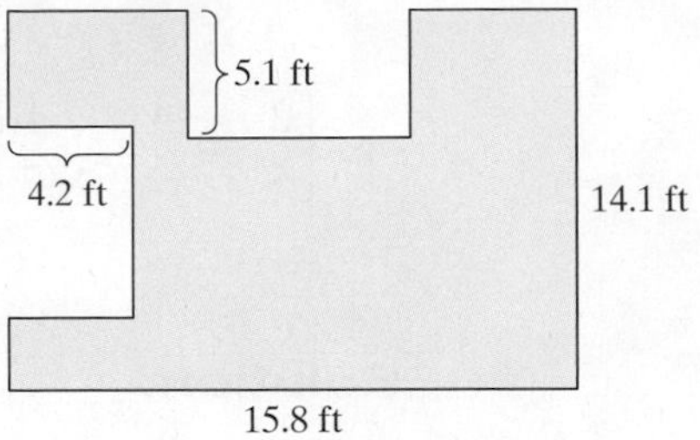

For Exercises 103–106, find the area of the shaded region. Use 3.14 for π.

103.

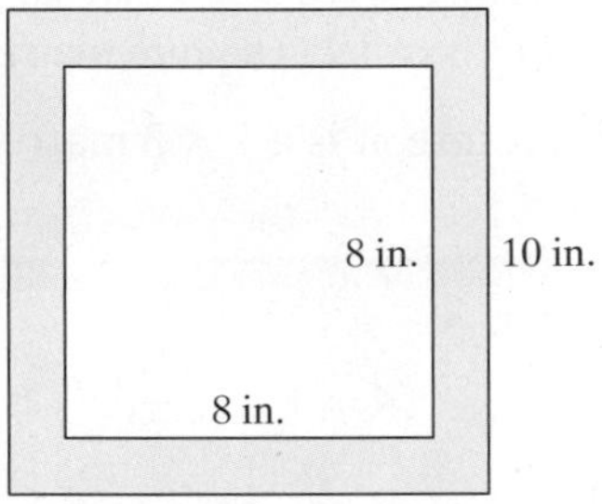

104.

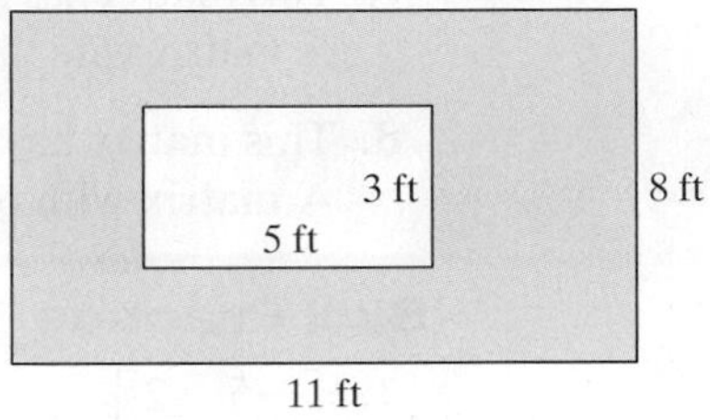

105.

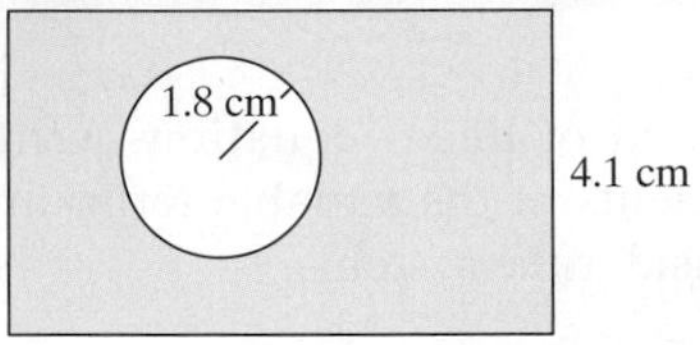

106.

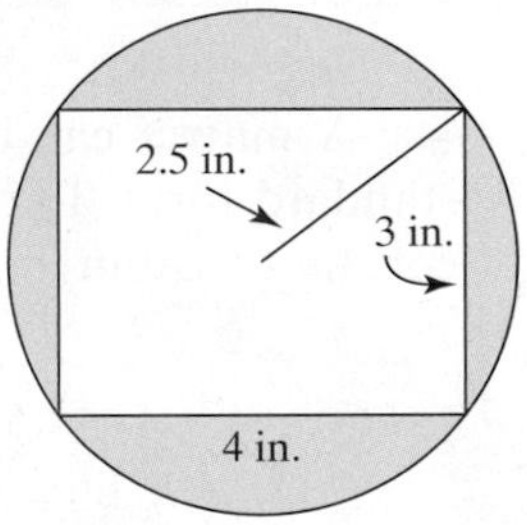

Solving Systems of Linear Equations by Using Matrices

Section A.4

Concepts

1. **Introduction to Matrices**
2. **Solving Systems of Linear Equations by Using the Gauss-Jordan Method**

1. Introduction to Matrices

In Sections 4.2, 4.3, and 4.5, we solved systems of linear equations by using the substitution method and the addition method. We now present a third method called the Gauss-Jordan method that uses matrices to solve a linear system.

A **matrix** is a rectangular array of numbers (the plural of *matrix* is *matrices*). The rows of a matrix are read horizontally, and the columns of a matrix are read vertically. Every number or entry within a matrix is called an element of the matrix.

The **order of a matrix** is determined by the number of rows and number of columns. A matrix with m rows and n columns is an $m \times n$ (read as "m by n") matrix. Notice that with the order of a matrix, the number of rows is given first, followed by the number of columns.

Example 1 Determining the Order of a Matrix

Determine the order of each matrix.

a. $\begin{bmatrix} 2 & -4 & 1 \\ 5 & \pi & \sqrt{7} \end{bmatrix}$ **b.** $\begin{bmatrix} 1.9 \\ 0 \\ 7.2 \\ -6.1 \end{bmatrix}$ **c.** $\begin{bmatrix} 1 & 0 & 0 \\ 0 & 1 & 0 \\ 0 & 0 & 1 \end{bmatrix}$ **d.** $[a \quad b \quad c]$

Solution:

a. This matrix has two rows and three columns. Therefore, it is a 2×3 matrix.

b. This matrix has four rows and one column. Therefore, it is a 4×1 matrix. A matrix with one column is called a **column matrix**.

c. This matrix has three rows and three columns. Therefore, it is a 3×3 matrix. A matrix with the same number of rows and columns is called a **square matrix**.

d. This matrix has one row and three columns. Therefore, it is a 1×3 matrix. A matrix with one row is called a **row matrix**.

Skill Practice Determine the order of the matrix.

1. $\begin{bmatrix} -5 & 2 \\ 1 & 3 \\ 8 & 9 \end{bmatrix}$ **2.** $[4 \quad -8]$ **3.** $\begin{bmatrix} 5 \\ 10 \\ 15 \end{bmatrix}$ **4.** $\begin{bmatrix} 2 & -0.5 \\ -1 & 6 \end{bmatrix}$

A matrix can be used to represent a system of linear equations written in standard form. To do so, we extract the coefficients of the variable terms and the constants within the equation. For example, consider the system

$$\begin{aligned} 2x - y &= 5 \\ x + 2y &= -5 \end{aligned}$$

The matrix **A** is called the **coefficient matrix**.

$$\mathbf{A} = \begin{bmatrix} 2 & -1 \\ 1 & 2 \end{bmatrix}$$

If we extract both the coefficients and the constants from the equations, we can construct the **augmented matrix** of the system:

$$\left[\begin{array}{cc|c} 2 & -1 & 5 \\ 1 & 2 & -5 \end{array}\right]$$

A vertical bar is inserted into an augmented matrix to designate the position of the equal signs.

Example 2 Writing an Augmented Matrix for a System of Linear Equations

Write the augmented matrix for each linear system.

a. $\begin{aligned} -3x - 4y &= 3 \\ 2x + 4y &= 2 \end{aligned}$ **b.** $\begin{aligned} 2x \quad\quad - 3z &= 14 \\ 2y + z &= 2 \\ x + y \quad\quad &= 4 \end{aligned}$

Answers

1. 3×2 2. 1×2
3. 3×1 4. 2×2

Solution:

a. $\left[\begin{array}{cc|c} -3 & -4 & 3 \\ 2 & 4 & 2 \end{array}\right]$ **b.** $\left[\begin{array}{ccc|c} 2 & 0 & -3 & 14 \\ 0 & 2 & 1 & 2 \\ 1 & 1 & 0 & 4 \end{array}\right]$

TIP: Notice that zeros are inserted to denote the coefficient of each missing term.

Skill Practice Write the augmented matrix for each system.

5. $\begin{aligned} -x + y &= 4 \\ 2x - y &= 1 \end{aligned}$ **6.** $\begin{aligned} 2x - y + z &= 14 \\ -3x + 4y \quad &= 8 \\ x - y + 5z &= 0 \end{aligned}$

Example 3 Writing a Linear System from an Augmented Matrix

Write a system of linear equations represented by each augmented matrix.

a. $\left[\begin{array}{cc|c} 2 & -5 & -8 \\ 4 & 1 & 6 \end{array}\right]$ **b.** $\left[\begin{array}{ccc|c} 2 & -1 & 3 & 14 \\ 1 & 1 & -2 & -5 \\ 3 & 1 & -1 & 2 \end{array}\right]$ **c.** $\left[\begin{array}{ccc|c} 1 & 0 & 0 & 4 \\ 0 & 1 & 0 & -1 \\ 0 & 0 & 1 & 0 \end{array}\right]$

Solution:

a. $\begin{aligned} 2x - 5y &= -8 \\ 4x + y &= 6 \end{aligned}$ **b.** $\begin{aligned} 2x - y + 3z &= 14 \\ x + y - 2z &= -5 \\ 3x + y - z &= 2 \end{aligned}$

c. $\begin{aligned} x + 0y + 0z &= 4 \\ 0x + y + 0z &= -1 \\ 0x + 0y + z &= 0 \end{aligned}$ or $\begin{aligned} x &= 4 \\ y &= -1 \\ z &= 0 \end{aligned}$

Skill Practice Write a system of linear equations represented by each augmented matrix.

7. $\left[\begin{array}{cc|c} 2 & 3 & 5 \\ -1 & 8 & 1 \end{array}\right]$ **8.** $\left[\begin{array}{ccc|c} -3 & 2 & 1 & 4 \\ 14 & 1 & 0 & 20 \\ -8 & 3 & 5 & 6 \end{array}\right]$ **9.** $\left[\begin{array}{ccc|c} 1 & 0 & 0 & -8 \\ 0 & 1 & 0 & 2 \\ 0 & 0 & 1 & 15 \end{array}\right]$

2. Solving Systems of Linear Equations by Using the Gauss-Jordan Method

We know that interchanging two equations results in an equivalent system of linear equations. Interchanging two rows in an augmented matrix results in an equivalent augmented matrix. Similarly, because each row in an augmented matrix represents a linear equation, we can perform the following elementary row operations that result in an equivalent augmented matrix.

Elementary Row Operations

The following *elementary row operations* performed on an augmented matrix produce an equivalent augmented matrix:

- Interchange two rows.
- Multiply every element in a row by a nonzero real number.
- Add a multiple of one row to another row.

Answers

5. $\left[\begin{array}{cc|c} -1 & 1 & 4 \\ 2 & -1 & 1 \end{array}\right]$

6. $\left[\begin{array}{ccc|c} 2 & -1 & 1 & 14 \\ -3 & 4 & 0 & 8 \\ 1 & -1 & 5 & 0 \end{array}\right]$

7. $\begin{aligned} 2x + 3y &= 5 \\ -x + 8y &= 1 \end{aligned}$

8. $\begin{aligned} -3x + 2y + z &= 4 \\ 14x + y \quad &= 20 \\ -8x + 3y + 5z &= 6 \end{aligned}$

9. $x = -8$, $y = 2$, $z = 15$

$$2R_3 + R_1 \Rightarrow R_1 \quad -2R_3 + R_2 \Rightarrow R_2 \longrightarrow \left[\begin{array}{ccc|c} 1 & 0 & 0 & 3 \\ 0 & 1 & 0 & 2 \\ 0 & 0 & 1 & -1 \end{array}\right]$$

Multiply row 3 by 2 and add the result to row 1. Multiply row 3 by −2 and add the result to row 2.

From the reduced row echelon form of the matrix, we have $x = 3$, $y = 2$, and $z = -1$. The solution set is $\{(3, 2, -1)\}$.

Skill Practice Solve by using the Gauss-Jordan method.

11.
$$\begin{aligned} x + y + z &= 2 \\ x - y + z &= 4 \\ x + 4y + 2z &= 1 \end{aligned}$$

It is particularly easy to recognize a system of dependent equations or an inconsistent system of equations from the reduced row echelon form of an augmented matrix. This is demonstrated in Examples 6 and 7.

Example 6 Solving a System of Dependent Equations by Using the Gauss-Jordan Method

Solve by using the Gauss-Jordan method.

$$\begin{aligned} x - 3y &= 4 \\ \frac{1}{2}x - \frac{3}{2}y &= 2 \end{aligned}$$

Solution:

$$\left[\begin{array}{cc|c} 1 & -3 & 4 \\ \frac{1}{2} & -\frac{3}{2} & 2 \end{array}\right]$$

Set up the augmented matrix.

$$-\tfrac{1}{2}R_1 + R_2 \Rightarrow R_2 \longrightarrow \left[\begin{array}{cc|c} 1 & -3 & 4 \\ 0 & 0 & 0 \end{array}\right]$$

Multiply row 1 by $-\frac{1}{2}$ and add the result to row 2.

The second row of the augmented matrix represents the equation $0 = 0$. The equations are dependent. The solution set is $\{(x, y) \mid x - 3y = 4\}$.

Skill Practice Solve by using the Gauss-Jordan method.

12.
$$\begin{aligned} 4x - 6y &= 16 \\ 6x - 9y &= 24 \end{aligned}$$

Answers

11. $\{(1, -1, 2)\}$

12. Infinitely many solutions; $\{(x, y) \mid 4x - 6y = 16\}$; dependent equations

Example 7 Solving an Inconsistent System by Using the Gauss-Jordan Method

Solve by using the Gauss-Jordan method.

$$x + 3y = 2$$
$$-3x - 9y = 1$$

Solution:

$$\left[\begin{array}{rr|r} 1 & 3 & 2 \\ -3 & -9 & 1 \end{array}\right]$$ Set up the augmented matrix.

$$\xrightarrow{3R_1 + R_2 \Rightarrow R_2} \left[\begin{array}{rr|r} 1 & 3 & 2 \\ 0 & 0 & 7 \end{array}\right]$$ Multiply row 1 by 3 and add the result to row 2.

The second row of the augmented matrix represents the contradiction $0 = 7$. The system is inconsistent. There is no solution, { }.

Skill Practice Solve by using the Gauss-Jordan method.

13. $6x + 10y = 1$
$15x + 25y = 3$

Calculator Connections

Topic: Entering a Matrix into a Calculator

Many graphing calculators have a matrix editor in which the user defines the order of the matrix and then enters the elements of the matrix. For example, the 2×3 matrix

$$\mathbf{D} = \left[\begin{array}{rr|r} 2 & -3 & -13 \\ 3 & 1 & 8 \end{array}\right]$$

is entered as shown.

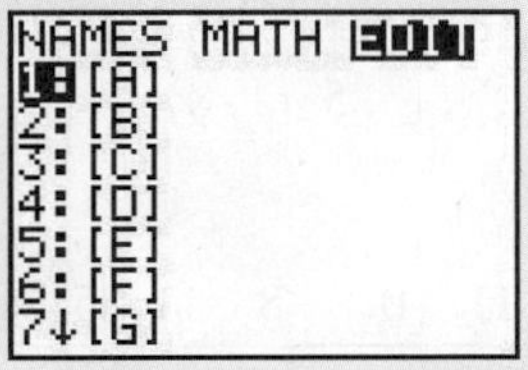

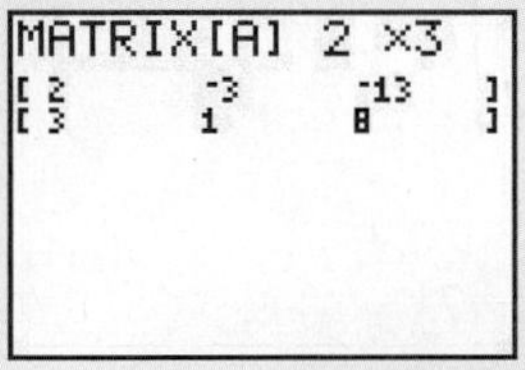

Once an augmented matrix has been entered into a graphing calculator, a *rref* function can be used to transform the matrix into reduced row echelon form.

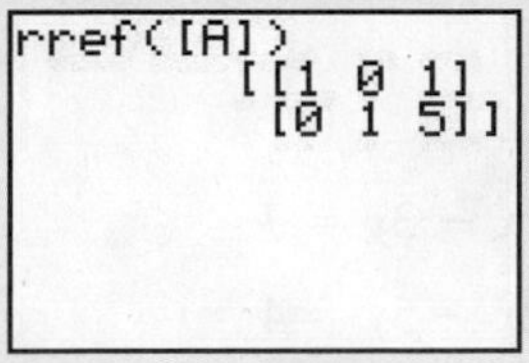

Answer

13. No solution; { }; inconsistent system

Section A.4 Practice Exercises

Vocabulary and Key Concepts

1. **a.** A _______ is a rectangular array of numbers. The order of a matrix is $m \times n$ where m is the number of _______ and n is the number of _______.

   b. A matrix that has exactly one column is called a _______ matrix. A matrix that has exactly _______ row is called a row matrix, and a matrix with the same number of rows and columns is called a _______ matrix.

   c. Given the system of equations shown, matrix **A** is called the _______ matrix. The matrix **B** is called the _______ matrix.

$$\begin{aligned} 3x - 2y &= 6 \\ 4x + 5y &= 9 \end{aligned} \qquad \mathbf{A} = \begin{bmatrix} 3 & -2 \\ 4 & 5 \end{bmatrix} \qquad \mathbf{B} = \left[\begin{array}{cc|c} 3 & -2 & 6 \\ 4 & 5 & 9 \end{array}\right]$$

   d. The matrix **A** is said to be written in reduced _______ form.

$$\mathbf{A} = \left[\begin{array}{cc|c} 1 & 0 & 8 \\ 0 & 1 & 2 \end{array}\right]$$

Review Exercises

2. How much 50% acid solution should be mixed with pure acid to obtain 20 L of a mixture that is 70% acid?

For Exercises 3–5, solve the system by using any method.

3. $\begin{aligned} x - 6y &= 9 \\ x + 2y &= 13 \end{aligned}$

4. $\begin{aligned} x + y - z &= 8 \\ x - 2y + z &= 3 \\ x + 3y + 2z &= 7 \end{aligned}$

5. $\begin{aligned} 2x - y + z &= -4 \\ -x + y + 3z &= -7 \\ x + 3y - 4z &= 22 \end{aligned}$

Concept 1: Introduction to Matrices

For Exercises 6–14, **(a)** determine the order of each matrix and **(b)** determine if the matrix is a row matrix, a column matrix, a square matrix, or none of these. **(See Example 1.)**

6. $\begin{bmatrix} 4 \\ 5 \\ -3 \\ 0 \end{bmatrix}$

7. $\begin{bmatrix} 5 \\ -1 \\ 2 \end{bmatrix}$

8. $\begin{bmatrix} -9 & 4 & 3 \\ -1 & -8 & 4 \\ 5 & 8 & 7 \end{bmatrix}$

9. $\begin{bmatrix} 3 & -9 \\ -1 & -3 \end{bmatrix}$

10. $\begin{bmatrix} 4 & -7 \end{bmatrix}$

11. $\begin{bmatrix} 0 & -8 & 11 & 5 \end{bmatrix}$

12. $\begin{bmatrix} 5 & -8.1 & 4.2 & 0 \\ 4.3 & -9 & 18 & 3 \end{bmatrix}$

13. $\begin{bmatrix} \frac{1}{3} & \frac{3}{4} & 6 \\ -2 & 1 & -\frac{7}{8} \end{bmatrix}$

14. $\begin{bmatrix} 5 & 1 \\ -1 & 2 \\ 0 & 7 \end{bmatrix}$

For Exercises 15–18, set up the augmented matrix. **(See Example 2.)**

15. $\begin{aligned} x - 2y &= -1 \\ 2x + y &= -7 \end{aligned}$

16. $\begin{aligned} x - 3y &= 3 \\ 2x - 5y &= 4 \end{aligned}$

17. $\begin{aligned} x - 2y &= 5 - z \\ 2x + 6y + 3z &= -2 \\ 3x - y - 2z &= 1 \end{aligned}$

18. $\begin{aligned} 5x - 17 &= -2z \\ 8x + 6z &= 26 + y \\ 8x + 3y - 12z &= 24 \end{aligned}$

For Exercises 19–22, write a system of linear equations represented by the augmented matrix. **(See Example 3.)**

19. $\left[\begin{array}{rr|r} 4 & 3 & 6 \\ 12 & 5 & -6 \end{array}\right]$

20. $\left[\begin{array}{rr|r} -2 & 5 & -15 \\ -7 & 15 & -45 \end{array}\right]$

21. $\left[\begin{array}{rrr|r} 1 & 0 & 0 & 4 \\ 0 & 1 & 0 & -1 \\ 0 & 0 & 1 & 7 \end{array}\right]$

22. $\left[\begin{array}{rrr|r} 1 & 0 & 0 & 0.5 \\ 0 & 1 & 0 & 6.1 \\ 0 & 0 & 1 & 3.9 \end{array}\right]$

Concept 2: Solving Systems of Linear Equations by Using the Gauss-Jordan Method

23. Given the matrix **E**

$$\mathbf{E} = \left[\begin{array}{rr|r} 3 & -2 & 8 \\ 9 & -1 & 7 \end{array}\right]$$

a. What is the element in the second row and third column?

b. What is the element in the first row and second column?

24. Given the matrix **F**

$$\mathbf{F} = \left[\begin{array}{rr|r} 1 & 8 & 0 \\ 12 & -13 & -2 \end{array}\right]$$

a. What is the element in the second row and second column?

b. What is the element in the first row and third column?

25. Given the matrix **Z**

$$\mathbf{Z} = \left[\begin{array}{rr|r} 2 & 1 & 11 \\ 2 & -1 & 1 \end{array}\right]$$

write the matrix obtained by multiplying the elements in the first row by $\frac{1}{2}$.

26. Given the matrix **J**

$$\mathbf{J} = \left[\begin{array}{rr|r} 1 & 1 & 7 \\ 0 & 3 & -6 \end{array}\right]$$

write the matrix obtained by multiplying the elements in the second row by $\frac{1}{3}$.

27. Given the matrix **K**

$$\mathbf{K} = \left[\begin{array}{rr|r} 5 & 2 & 1 \\ 1 & -4 & 3 \end{array}\right]$$

write the matrix obtained by interchanging rows 1 and 2.

28. Given the matrix **L**

$$\mathbf{L} = \left[\begin{array}{rr|r} 9 & 6 & 13 \\ -7 & 2 & 19 \end{array}\right]$$

write the matrix obtained by interchanging rows 1 and 2.

29. Given the matrix **M**

$$\mathbf{M} = \left[\begin{array}{rr|r} 1 & 5 & 2 \\ -3 & -4 & -1 \end{array}\right]$$

write the matrix obtained by multiplying the first row by 3 and adding the result to row 2.

30. Given the matrix **N**

$$\mathbf{N} = \left[\begin{array}{rr|r} 1 & 3 & -5 \\ -2 & 2 & 12 \end{array}\right]$$

write the matrix obtained by multiplying the first row by 2 and adding the result to row 2.

31. Given the matrix **R**

$$\mathbf{R} = \left[\begin{array}{rrr|r} 1 & 3 & 0 & -1 \\ 4 & 1 & -5 & 6 \\ -2 & 0 & -3 & 10 \end{array}\right]$$

a. Write the matrix obtained by multiplying the first row by -4 and adding the result to row 2.

b. Using the matrix obtained from part (a), write the matrix obtained by multiplying the first row by 2 and adding the result to row 3.

32. Given the matrix **S**

$$\mathbf{S} = \left[\begin{array}{rrr|r} 1 & 2 & 0 & 10 \\ 5 & 1 & -4 & 3 \\ -3 & 4 & 5 & 2 \end{array}\right]$$

a. Write the matrix obtained by multiplying the first row by -5 and adding the result to row 2.

b. Using the matrix obtained from part (a), write the matrix obtained by multiplying the first row by 3 and adding the result to row 3.

For Exercises 33–36, use the augmented matrices **A**, **B**, **C**, and **D** to answer true or false.

$$\mathbf{A} = \left[\begin{array}{cc|c} 6 & -4 & 2 \\ 5 & -2 & 7 \end{array}\right] \quad \mathbf{B} = \left[\begin{array}{cc|c} 5 & -2 & 7 \\ 6 & -4 & 2 \end{array}\right] \quad \mathbf{C} = \left[\begin{array}{cc|c} 1 & -\frac{2}{3} & \frac{1}{3} \\ 5 & -2 & 7 \end{array}\right] \quad \mathbf{D} = \left[\begin{array}{cc|c} 5 & -2 & 7 \\ -12 & 8 & -4 \end{array}\right]$$

33. The matrix **A** is a 2×3 matrix.

34. Matrix **B** is equivalent to matrix **A**.

35. Matrix **A** is equivalent to matrix **C**.

36. Matrix **B** is equivalent to matrix **D**.

37. What does the notation $R_2 \Leftrightarrow R_1$ mean when one is performing the Gauss-Jordan method?

38. What does the notation $2R_3 \Rightarrow R_3$ mean when one is performing the Gauss-Jordan method?

39. What does the notation $-3R_1 + R_2 \Rightarrow R_2$ mean when one is performing the Gauss-Jordan method?

40. What does the notation $4R_2 + R_3 \Rightarrow R_3$ mean when one is performing the Gauss-Jordan method?

For Exercises 41–56, solve the system by using the Gauss-Jordan method. For systems that do not have one unique solution, also state the number of solutions and whether the system is inconsistent or the equations are dependent. **(See Example 4–7.)**

41. $x - 2y = -1$
$2x + y = -7$

42. $x - 3y = 3$
$2x - 5y = 4$

43. $x + 3y = 6$
$-4x - 9y = 3$

44. $2x - 3y = -2$
$x + 2y = 13$

45. $x + 3y = 3$
$4x + 12y = 12$

46. $2x + 5y = 1$
$-4x - 10y = -2$

47. $x - y = 4$
$2x + y = 5$

48. $2x - y = 0$
$x + y = 3$

49. $x + 3y = -1$
$-3x - 6y = 12$

50. $x + y = 4$
$2x - 4y = -4$

51. $3x + y = -4$
$-6x - 2y = 3$

52. $2x + y = 4$
$6x + 3y = -1$

53. $x + y + z = 6$
$x - y + z = 2$
$x + y - z = 0$

54. $2x - 3y - 2z = 11$
$x + 3y + 8z = 1$
$3x - y + 14z = -2$

55. $x - 2y = 5 - z$
$2x + 6y + 3z = -10$
$3x - y - 2z = 5$

56. $5x = 10z + 15$
$x - y + 6z = 23$
$x + 3y - 12z = 13$

Graphing Calculator Exercises

For Exercises 57–62, use the matrix features on a graphing calculator to express each augmented matrix in reduced row echelon form. Compare your results to the solution you obtained in the indicated exercise.

57. $\left[\begin{array}{cc|c} 1 & -2 & -1 \\ 2 & 1 & -7 \end{array}\right]$

Compare with Exercise 41.

58. $\left[\begin{array}{cc|c} 1 & -3 & 3 \\ 2 & -5 & 4 \end{array}\right]$

Compare with Exercise 42.

59. $\left[\begin{array}{cc|c} 1 & 3 & 6 \\ -4 & -9 & 3 \end{array}\right]$

Compare with Exercise 43.

60. $\left[\begin{array}{cc|c} 2 & -3 & -2 \\ 1 & 2 & 13 \end{array}\right]$

Compare with Exercise 44.

61. $\left[\begin{array}{ccc|c} 1 & 1 & 1 & 6 \\ 1 & -1 & 1 & 2 \\ 1 & 1 & -1 & 0 \end{array}\right]$

Compare with Exercise 53.

62. $\left[\begin{array}{ccc|c} 2 & -3 & -2 & 11 \\ 1 & 3 & 8 & 1 \\ 3 & -1 & 14 & -2 \end{array}\right]$

Compare with Exercise 54.

Determinants and Cramer's Rule

Section A.5

Concepts

1. Introduction to Determinants
2. Determinant of a 3 × 3 Matrix
3. Cramer's Rule

1. Introduction to Determinants

Associated with every square matrix is a real number called the **determinant** of the matrix. A determinant of a square matrix **A**, denoted det **A**, is written by enclosing the elements of the matrix within two vertical bars. For example,

$$\text{If } \mathbf{A} = \begin{bmatrix} 2 & -1 \\ 6 & 0 \end{bmatrix} \quad \text{then } \det \mathbf{A} = \begin{vmatrix} 2 & -1 \\ 6 & 0 \end{vmatrix}$$

$$\text{If } \mathbf{B} = \begin{bmatrix} 0 & -5 & 1 \\ 4 & 0 & \frac{1}{2} \\ -2 & 10 & 1 \end{bmatrix} \quad \text{then } \det \mathbf{B} = \begin{vmatrix} 0 & -5 & 1 \\ 4 & 0 & \frac{1}{2} \\ -2 & 10 & 1 \end{vmatrix}$$

Determinants have many applications in mathematics, including solving systems of linear equations, finding the area of a triangle, determining whether three points are collinear, and finding an equation of a line between two points.

The determinant of a 2 × 2 matrix is defined as follows:

Definition of a Determinant of a 2 × 2 Matrix

The determinant of the matrix $\begin{bmatrix} a & b \\ c & d \end{bmatrix}$ is the real number $ad - bc$. It is written as

$$\begin{vmatrix} a & b \\ c & d \end{vmatrix} = ad - bc$$

Example 1 Evaluating a 2 × 2 Determinant

Evaluate the determinants.

a. $\begin{vmatrix} 6 & -2 \\ 5 & \frac{1}{3} \end{vmatrix}$ **b.** $\begin{vmatrix} 2 & -11 \\ 0 & 0 \end{vmatrix}$

Solution:

a. $\begin{vmatrix} 6 & -2 \\ 5 & \frac{1}{3} \end{vmatrix}$ For this determinant, $a = 6, b = -2, c = 5$, and $d = \frac{1}{3}$.

$$\begin{aligned} ad - bc &= (6)\left(\frac{1}{3}\right) - (-2)(5) \\ &= 2 + 10 \\ &= 12 \end{aligned}$$

b. $\begin{vmatrix} 2 & -11 \\ 0 & 0 \end{vmatrix}$ For this determinant, $a = 2, b = -11, c = 0, d = 0$.

$$\begin{aligned} ad - bc &= (2)(0) - (-11)(0) \\ &= 0 - 0 \\ &= 0 \end{aligned}$$

TIP: Example 1(b) illustrates that the value of a determinant having a row of all zeros is 0. The same is true for a determinant having a column of all zeros.

Skill Practice Evaluate the determinants.

1. $\begin{vmatrix} 2 & 8 \\ -1 & 5 \end{vmatrix}$ **2.** $\begin{vmatrix} -6 & 0 \\ 4 & 0 \end{vmatrix}$

Answers

1. 18 2. 0

2. Determinant of a 3 × 3 Matrix

To find the determinant of a 3 × 3 matrix, we first need to define the **minor** of an element of the matrix. For any element of a 3 × 3 matrix, the minor of that element is the determinant of the 2 × 2 matrix obtained by deleting the row and column in which the element resides. For example, consider the matrix

$$\begin{bmatrix} 5 & -1 & 6 \\ 0 & -7 & 1 \\ 4 & 2 & 6 \end{bmatrix}$$

The minor of the element 5 is found by deleting the first row and first column and then evaluating the determinant of the remaining 2 × 2 matrix:

$$\begin{bmatrix} 5 & -1 & 6 \\ 0 & -7 & 1 \\ 4 & 2 & 6 \end{bmatrix}$$ Now evaluate the determinant: $$\begin{vmatrix} -7 & 1 \\ 2 & 6 \end{vmatrix} = (-7)(6) - (1)(2) = -44$$

For this matrix, the minor for the element 5 is −44.

To find the minor of the element −7, delete the second row and second column, and then evaluate the determinant of the remaining 2 × 2 matrix.

$$\begin{bmatrix} 5 & -1 & 6 \\ 0 & -7 & 1 \\ 4 & 2 & 6 \end{bmatrix}$$ Now evaluate the determinant: $$\begin{vmatrix} 5 & 6 \\ 4 & 6 \end{vmatrix} = (5)(6) - (6)(4) = 6$$

For this matrix, the minor for the element −7 is 6.

Example 2 **Determining the Minor for Elements in a 3 × 3 Matrix**

Find the minor for each element in the first column of the matrix.

$$\begin{bmatrix} 3 & 4 & -1 \\ 2 & -4 & 5 \\ 0 & 1 & -6 \end{bmatrix}$$

Solution:

For 3: $\begin{bmatrix} 3 & 4 & -1 \\ 2 & -4 & 5 \\ 0 & 1 & -6 \end{bmatrix}$ The minor is: $\begin{vmatrix} -4 & 5 \\ 1 & -6 \end{vmatrix} = (-4)(-6) - (5)(1) = 19$

For 2: $\begin{bmatrix} 3 & 4 & -1 \\ 2 & -4 & 5 \\ 0 & 1 & -6 \end{bmatrix}$ The minor is: $\begin{vmatrix} 4 & -1 \\ 1 & -6 \end{vmatrix} = (4)(-6) - (-1)(1) = -23$

For 0: $\begin{bmatrix} 3 & 4 & -1 \\ 2 & -4 & 5 \\ 0 & 1 & -6 \end{bmatrix}$ The minor is: $\begin{vmatrix} 4 & -1 \\ -4 & 5 \end{vmatrix} = (4)(5) - (-1)(-4) = 16$

Skill Practice Find the minor for the element 3.

3. $\begin{bmatrix} -1 & 8 & -6 \\ \frac{1}{2} & 3 & 2 \\ 5 & 7 & 4 \end{bmatrix}$

Answer

3. $\begin{vmatrix} -1 & -6 \\ 5 & 4 \end{vmatrix} = 26$

The determinant of a 3×3 matrix is defined as follows.

Definition of a Determinant of a 3 × 3 Matrix

$$\begin{vmatrix} a_1 & b_1 & c_1 \\ a_2 & b_2 & c_2 \\ a_3 & b_3 & c_3 \end{vmatrix} = a_1 \cdot \begin{vmatrix} b_2 & c_2 \\ b_3 & c_3 \end{vmatrix} - a_2 \cdot \begin{vmatrix} b_1 & c_1 \\ b_3 & c_3 \end{vmatrix} + a_3 \cdot \begin{vmatrix} b_1 & c_1 \\ b_2 & c_2 \end{vmatrix}$$

From this definition, we see that the determinant of a 3×3 matrix can be written as

$$a_1 \cdot (\text{minor of } a_1) - a_2 \cdot (\text{minor of } a_2) + a_3 \cdot (\text{minor of } a_3)$$

Evaluating determinants in this way is called *expanding minors*.

Example 3 Evaluating a 3 × 3 Determinant

Evaluate the determinant. $\begin{vmatrix} 2 & 4 & 2 \\ 1 & -3 & 0 \\ -5 & 5 & -1 \end{vmatrix}$

Solution:

$$\begin{vmatrix} 2 & 4 & 2 \\ 1 & -3 & 0 \\ -5 & 5 & -1 \end{vmatrix} = 2 \cdot \begin{vmatrix} -3 & 0 \\ 5 & -1 \end{vmatrix} - (1) \cdot \begin{vmatrix} 4 & 2 \\ 5 & -1 \end{vmatrix} + (-5) \cdot \begin{vmatrix} 4 & 2 \\ -3 & 0 \end{vmatrix}$$

$$= 2[(-3)(-1) - (0)(5)] - 1[(4)(-1) - (2)(5)] - 5[(4)(0) - (2)(-3)]$$

$$= 2(3) - 1(-14) - 5(6)$$

$$= 6 + 14 - 30$$

$$= -10$$

Skill Practice Evaluate the determinant.

4. $\begin{vmatrix} -2 & 4 & 9 \\ 5 & -1 & 2 \\ 1 & 1 & 6 \end{vmatrix}$

Although we defined the determinant of a matrix by expanding the minors of the elements in the first column, *any row or column can be used.* However, we must choose the correct sign to apply to each term in the expansion. The following array of signs is helpful.

$$\begin{matrix} + & - & + \\ - & + & - \\ + & - & + \end{matrix}$$

The signs alternate for each row and column, beginning with + in the first row, first column.

TIP: There is another method to determine the signs for each term of the expansion. For the a_{ij} element, multiply the term by $(-1)^{i+j}$.

Answer

4. -42

Example 4 Evaluating a 3 × 3 Determinant

Evaluate the determinant by expanding minors about the elements in the second row.

$$\begin{vmatrix} 2 & 4 & 2 \\ 1 & -3 & 0 \\ -5 & 5 & -1 \end{vmatrix}$$

Solution:

Signs obtained from the array of signs

$$\begin{vmatrix} 2 & 4 & 2 \\ 1 & -3 & 0 \\ -5 & 5 & -1 \end{vmatrix} = -(1) \cdot \begin{vmatrix} 4 & 2 \\ 5 & -1 \end{vmatrix} + (-3) \cdot \begin{vmatrix} 2 & 2 \\ -5 & -1 \end{vmatrix} - (0) \cdot \begin{vmatrix} 2 & 4 \\ -5 & 5 \end{vmatrix}$$

$$= -1[(4)(-1) - (2)(5)] - 3[(2)(-1) - (2)(-5)] - 0$$

$$= -1(-14) - 3(8)$$

$$= 14 - 24$$

$$= -10$$

Skill Practice Evaluate the determinant.

5. $\begin{vmatrix} 4 & -1 & 2 \\ 3 & 6 & -8 \\ 0 & \frac{1}{2} & 5 \end{vmatrix}$

Notice that the value of the determinant obtained in Examples 3 and 4 is the same.

Calculator Connections

Topic: Evaluating a Determinant

The determinant of a matrix can be evaluated on a graphing calculator. First use the matrix editor to enter the elements of the matrix. Then use a *det* function to evaluate the determinant. The determinant from Examples 3 and 4 is evaluated below.

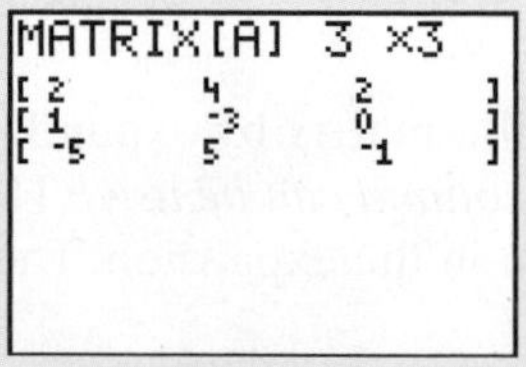

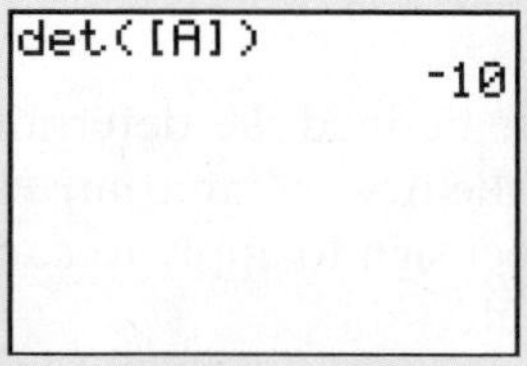

In Example 4, the third term in the expansion of minors was zero because the element 0 when multiplied by its minor is zero. To simplify the arithmetic in evaluating a determinant of a 3 × 3 matrix, expand about the row or column that has the most 0 elements.

Answer

5. 154

3. Cramer's Rule

In Sections 4.2, 4.3, and A.4, we learned three methods to solve a system of linear equations: the substitution method, the addition method, and the Gauss-Jordan method. In this section, we will learn another method called **Cramer's rule** to solve a system of linear equations.

Cramer's Rule for a 2 × 2 System of Linear Equations

The solution to the system

$$a_1x + b_1y = c_1$$
$$a_2x + b_2y = c_2$$

is given by $x = \dfrac{\mathbf{D}_x}{\mathbf{D}}$ and $y = \dfrac{\mathbf{D}_y}{\mathbf{D}}$

where $\mathbf{D} = \begin{vmatrix} a_1 & b_1 \\ a_2 & b_2 \end{vmatrix}$ (and $\mathbf{D} \neq 0$) $\quad \mathbf{D}_x = \begin{vmatrix} c_1 & b_1 \\ c_2 & b_2 \end{vmatrix} \quad \mathbf{D}_y = \begin{vmatrix} a_1 & c_1 \\ a_2 & c_2 \end{vmatrix}$

Example 5 Using Cramer's Rule to Solve a 2 × 2 System of Linear Equations

Solve the system by using Cramer's rule.

$$3x - 5y = 11$$
$$-x + 3y = -5$$

Solution:

For this system: $a_1 = 3 \quad b_1 = -5 \quad c_1 = 11$

$a_2 = -1 \quad b_2 = 3 \quad c_2 = -5$

$$\mathbf{D} = \begin{vmatrix} 3 & -5 \\ -1 & 3 \end{vmatrix} = (3)(3) - (-5)(-1) = 9 - 5 = 4$$

$$\mathbf{D}_x = \begin{vmatrix} 11 & -5 \\ -5 & 3 \end{vmatrix} = (11)(3) - (-5)(-5) = 33 - 25 = 8$$

$$\mathbf{D}_y = \begin{vmatrix} 3 & 11 \\ -1 & -5 \end{vmatrix} = (3)(-5) - (11)(-1) = -15 + 11 = -4$$

Therefore, $x = \dfrac{\mathbf{D}_x}{\mathbf{D}} = \dfrac{8}{4} = 2 \qquad y = \dfrac{\mathbf{D}_y}{\mathbf{D}} = \dfrac{-4}{4} = -1$

Check the ordered pair $(2, -1)$ in both original equations.

Check: $3x - 5y = 11 \longrightarrow 3(2) - 5(-1) \stackrel{?}{=} 11$ ✔

$-x + 3y = -5 \longrightarrow -(2) + 3(-1) \stackrel{?}{=} -5$ ✔

The solution set is $\{(2, -1)\}$.

Skill Practice Solve using Cramer's rule.

6. $2x + y = 5$
$-x - 3y = 5$

Answer

6. $\{(4, -3)\}$

TIP: Here are some memory tips to help you remember Cramer's rule.

1. The determinant **D** is the determinant of the coefficients of x and y.

Coefficients of x-terms, y-terms:

$$\mathbf{D} = \begin{vmatrix} a_1 & b_1 \\ a_2 & b_2 \end{vmatrix}$$

2. The determinant $\mathbf{D}_x$ has the column of x-term coefficients replaced by c_1 and c_2.

x-coefficients replaced by c_1 and c_2:

$$\mathbf{D}_x = \begin{vmatrix} c_1 & b_1 \\ c_2 & b_2 \end{vmatrix}$$

3. The determinant $\mathbf{D}_y$ has the column of y-term coefficients replaced by c_1 and c_2.

y-coefficients replaced by c_1 and c_2:

$$\mathbf{D}_y = \begin{vmatrix} a_1 & c_1 \\ a_2 & c_2 \end{vmatrix}$$

It is important to note that the linear equations must be written in standard form to apply Cramer's rule.

Example 6 Using Cramer's Rule to Solve a 2 × 2 System of Linear Equations

Solve the system by using Cramer's rule.

$$-16y = -40x - 7$$
$$40y = 24x + 27$$

Solution:

$$\begin{aligned} -16y &= -40x - 7 &\longrightarrow\quad 40x - 16y &= -7 \\ 40y &= 24x + 27 &\longrightarrow\quad -24x + 40y &= 27 \end{aligned}$$

Rewrite each equation in standard form.

For this system: $a_1 = 40$ $b_1 = -16$ $c_1 = -7$

$a_2 = -24$ $b_2 = 40$ $c_2 = 27$

$$\mathbf{D} = \begin{vmatrix} 40 & -16 \\ -24 & 40 \end{vmatrix} = (40)(40) - (-16)(-24) = 1216$$

$$\mathbf{D}_x = \begin{vmatrix} -7 & -16 \\ 27 & 40 \end{vmatrix} = (-7)(40) - (-16)(27) = 152$$

$$\mathbf{D}_y = \begin{vmatrix} 40 & -7 \\ -24 & 27 \end{vmatrix} = (40)(27) - (-7)(-24) = 912$$

Therefore, $x = \dfrac{\mathbf{D}_x}{\mathbf{D}} = \dfrac{152}{1216} = \dfrac{1}{8}$ $\quad y = \dfrac{\mathbf{D}_y}{\mathbf{D}} = \dfrac{912}{1216} = \dfrac{3}{4}$

The ordered pair $\left(\frac{1}{8}, \frac{3}{4}\right)$ checks in both original equations.

The solution set is $\left\{\left(\frac{1}{8}, \frac{3}{4}\right)\right\}$.

Skill Practice Solve by using Cramer's rule.

7. $9x = 12y - 8$
$30y = -18x - 7$

Answer

7. $\left\{\left(-\frac{2}{3}, \frac{1}{6}\right)\right\}$

Cramer's rule can be used to solve a 3×3 system of linear equations by using a similar pattern of determinants.

Cramer's Rule for a 3 × 3 System of Linear Equations

The solution to the system

$$\begin{aligned} a_1x + b_1y + c_1z &= d_1 \\ a_2x + b_2y + c_2z &= d_2 \\ a_3x + b_3y + c_3z &= d_3 \end{aligned}$$

is given by $x = \dfrac{\mathbf{D}_x}{\mathbf{D}}$ $\quad y = \dfrac{\mathbf{D}_y}{\mathbf{D}}$ and $\quad z = \dfrac{\mathbf{D}_z}{\mathbf{D}}$

where $\mathbf{D} = \begin{vmatrix} a_1 & b_1 & c_1 \\ a_2 & b_2 & c_2 \\ a_3 & b_3 & c_3 \end{vmatrix}$ (and $\mathbf{D} \neq 0$) $\quad \mathbf{D}_x = \begin{vmatrix} d_1 & b_1 & c_1 \\ d_2 & b_2 & c_2 \\ d_3 & b_3 & c_3 \end{vmatrix}$

$\mathbf{D}_y = \begin{vmatrix} a_1 & d_1 & c_1 \\ a_2 & d_2 & c_2 \\ a_3 & d_3 & c_3 \end{vmatrix}$ $\quad \mathbf{D}_z = \begin{vmatrix} a_1 & b_1 & d_1 \\ a_2 & b_2 & d_2 \\ a_3 & b_3 & d_3 \end{vmatrix}$

Example 7 Using Cramer's Rule to Solve a 3 × 3 System of Linear Equations

Solve the system by using Cramer's rule.

$$\begin{aligned} 2x - 3y + 5z &= 11 \\ -5x + 7y - 2z &= -6 \\ 9x - 2y + 3z &= 4 \end{aligned}$$

Solution:

$$\mathbf{D} = \begin{vmatrix} 2 & -3 & 5 \\ -5 & 7 & -2 \\ 9 & -2 & 3 \end{vmatrix} = 2 \cdot \begin{vmatrix} 7 & -2 \\ -2 & 3 \end{vmatrix} - (-5) \cdot \begin{vmatrix} -3 & 5 \\ -2 & 3 \end{vmatrix} + 9 \cdot \begin{vmatrix} -3 & 5 \\ 7 & -2 \end{vmatrix}$$

$$= 2(17) + 5(1) + 9(-29)$$

$$= -222$$

$$\mathbf{D}_x = \begin{vmatrix} 11 & -3 & 5 \\ -6 & 7 & -2 \\ 4 & -2 & 3 \end{vmatrix} = 11 \cdot \begin{vmatrix} 7 & -2 \\ -2 & 3 \end{vmatrix} - (-6) \cdot \begin{vmatrix} -3 & 5 \\ -2 & 3 \end{vmatrix} + 4 \cdot \begin{vmatrix} -3 & 5 \\ 7 & -2 \end{vmatrix}$$

$$= 11(17) + 6(1) + 4(-29)$$

$$= 77$$

$$\mathbf{D}_y = \begin{vmatrix} 2 & 11 & 5 \\ -5 & -6 & -2 \\ 9 & 4 & 3 \end{vmatrix} = 2 \cdot \begin{vmatrix} -6 & -2 \\ 4 & 3 \end{vmatrix} - (-5) \cdot \begin{vmatrix} 11 & 5 \\ 4 & 3 \end{vmatrix} + 9 \cdot \begin{vmatrix} 11 & 5 \\ -6 & -2 \end{vmatrix}$$

$$= 2(-10) + 5(13) + 9(8)$$

$$= 117$$

TIP: In Example 7, we expanded the determinants about the first column.

$$\mathbf{D}_z = \begin{vmatrix} 2 & -3 & 11 \\ -5 & 7 & -6 \\ 9 & -2 & 4 \end{vmatrix} = 2 \cdot \begin{vmatrix} 7 & -6 \\ -2 & 4 \end{vmatrix} - (-5) \cdot \begin{vmatrix} -3 & 11 \\ -2 & 4 \end{vmatrix} + 9 \cdot \begin{vmatrix} -3 & 11 \\ 7 & -6 \end{vmatrix}$$

$$= 2(16) + 5(10) + 9(-59)$$

$$= -449$$

$$x = \frac{\mathbf{D}_x}{\mathbf{D}} = \frac{77}{-222} = -\frac{77}{222}$$

$$y = \frac{\mathbf{D}_y}{\mathbf{D}} = \frac{117}{-222} = -\frac{39}{74}$$

$$z = \frac{\mathbf{D}_z}{\mathbf{D}} = \frac{-449}{-222} = \frac{449}{222}$$

The solution $\left(-\frac{77}{222}, -\frac{39}{74}, \frac{449}{222}\right)$ checks in each of the original equations.

The solution set is $\left\{\left(-\frac{77}{222}, -\frac{39}{74}, \frac{449}{222}\right)\right\}$.

Skill Practice Solve by using Cramer's rule.

8. $x + 3y - 3z = -14$
$x - 4y + z = 2$
$x + y + 2z = 6$

Cramer's rule may seem cumbersome for solving a 3×3 system of linear equations. However, it provides convenient formulas that can be programmed into a computer or calculator to solve for x, y, and z. Cramer's rule can also be extended to solve a 4×4 system of linear equations, a 5×5 system of linear equations, and in general an $n \times n$ system of linear equations.

It is important to remember that Cramer's rule does not apply if $\mathbf{D} = 0$. In such a case, either the equations are dependent or the system is inconsistent, and another method may be needed to analyze the system.

Example 8 Analyzing a Dependent System of Equations

Solve the system. Use Cramer's rule if possible.

$$2x - 3y = 6$$
$$-6x + 9y = -18$$

Solution:

$$\mathbf{D} = \begin{vmatrix} 2 & -3 \\ -6 & 9 \end{vmatrix} = (2)(9) - (-3)(-6) = 18 - 18 = 0$$

Because $\mathbf{D} = 0$, Cramer's rule does not apply. Using the addition method to solve the system, we have

$$\begin{aligned} 2x - 3y &= 6 \xrightarrow{\text{Multiply by 3.}} & 6x - 9y &= 18 \\ -6x + 9y &= -18 \longrightarrow & -6x + 9y &= -18 \\ & & 0 &= 0 \end{aligned}$$

The equations are dependent.

The solution set is $\{(x, y) \mid 2x - 3y = 6\}$.

TIP: When Cramer's rule does not apply, that is, when $\mathbf{D} = 0$, you may also use the substitution method or the Gauss-Jordan method to get a solution.

Answer

8. $\{(-2, 0, 4)\}$

Skill Practice Solve. Use Cramer's rule if possible.

9. $x - 6y = 2$
$2x - 12y = -2$

TIP: In a 2×2 system of equations, if $\mathbf{D} = 0$, then the equations are dependent or the system is inconsistent.

- If $\mathbf{D} = 0$ and both $\mathbf{D}_x = 0$ and $\mathbf{D}_y = 0$, then the equations are dependent and the system has infinitely many solutions.
- If $\mathbf{D} = 0$ and either $\mathbf{D}_x \neq 0$ or $\mathbf{D}_y \neq 0$, then the system is inconsistent and has no solution.

Answer
9. { }; inconsistent system

Section A.5 Practice Exercises

Vocabulary and Key Concepts

1. **a.** Given the matrix $\mathbf{A} = \begin{bmatrix} a & b \\ c & d \end{bmatrix}$, the ________ of $\mathbf{A}$ is denoted det $\mathbf{A}$ and is written as $\begin{vmatrix} a & b \\ c & d \end{vmatrix}$. The value of det $\mathbf{A}$ is the real number equal to ________.

   b. Given a 3×3 matrix, the ________ of an element in the matrix is the determinant of the 2×2 matrix formed by deleting the row and column in which the element resides.

   c. Complete the expression on the right to represent the value of the 3×3 determinant shown here.

$$\begin{vmatrix} a_1 & b_1 & c_1 \\ a_2 & b_2 & c_2 \\ a_3 & b_3 & c_3 \end{vmatrix} = a_1\begin{vmatrix} b_2 & c_2 \\ b_3 & c_3 \end{vmatrix} - \square\begin{vmatrix} b_1 & c_1 \\ b_3 & c_3 \end{vmatrix} + a_3\begin{vmatrix} \square & \square \\ \square & \square \end{vmatrix}$$

Concept 1: Introduction to Determinants

For Exercises 2–7, evaluate the determinant of the 2×2 matrix. **(See Example 1.)**

2. $\begin{vmatrix} -3 & 1 \\ 5 & 2 \end{vmatrix}$

3. $\begin{vmatrix} 5 & 6 \\ 4 & 8 \end{vmatrix}$

4. $\begin{vmatrix} -2 & 2 \\ -3 & -5 \end{vmatrix}$

5. $\begin{vmatrix} 5 & -1 \\ 1 & 0 \end{vmatrix}$

6. $\begin{vmatrix} \frac{1}{2} & 3 \\ -2 & 4 \end{vmatrix}$

7. $\begin{vmatrix} -3 & \frac{1}{4} \\ 8 & -2 \end{vmatrix}$

Concept 2: Determinant of a 3 × 3 Matrix

For Exercises 8–11, evaluate the minor corresponding to the given element from matrix $\mathbf{A}$. **(See Example 2.)**

$$\mathbf{A} = \begin{bmatrix} 4 & -1 & 8 \\ 2 & 6 & 0 \\ -7 & 5 & 3 \end{bmatrix}$$

8. 4

9. -1

10. 2

11. 3

For Exercises 65–66, refer to the following system of four variables.

$$\begin{aligned} x + y + z + w &= 0 \\ 2x \quad\quad - z + w &= 5 \\ 2x + y \quad\quad - w &= 0 \\ y + z \quad\quad &= -1 \end{aligned}$$

65. **a.** Evaluate the determinant $\mathbf{D}$.

b. Evaluate the determinant $\mathbf{D}_x$.

c. Solve for x by computing $\dfrac{\mathbf{D}_x}{\mathbf{D}}$.

66. **a.** Evaluate the determinant $\mathbf{D}_y$.

b. Solve for y by computing $\dfrac{\mathbf{D}_y}{\mathbf{D}}$.

67. Two angles are complementary. The measure of one angle is $\frac{5}{7}$ the measure of the other. Find the measures of the two angles.

68. Two angles are supplementary. The measure of the larger angle is 61° more than $\frac{3}{4}$ the measure of the smaller angle. Find the measures of the angles.

69. An electronics store sells iPods, iPads, and iPhones. In a recent month, twice as many iPods as iPhones were sold. The number of iPods sold was five more than the sum of iPads and iPhones. The total number of devices sold was 75. Find the number iPods, iPads, and iPhones sold.

70. A group was surveyed regarding e-readers. The group represented a total of 100 e-reader users. The number of Kindles used was 44 more than the sum of the number Kobos and iPads. The number of Kobos was 50 less than the number of Kindles. Find the number of each type of e-reader.

71. Suppose 1000 people were surveyed in southern California, and 445 said that they worked-out at least three times a week. If $\frac{1}{2}$ of the women and $\frac{3}{8}$ of the men said that they worked-out at least three times a week, how many men and how many women were in the survey?

72. During a 1-hr television program, there were 22 commercials. Some commercials were 15 sec and some were 30 sec long. Find the number of 15-sec commercials and the number of 30-sec commercials if the total playing time for commercials was 9.5 min.

Student Answer Appendix

Chapter 1

Chapter Opener Puzzle

18	+	2	+	10	=	30
÷		+		−		÷
3	×	4	−	7	=	5
−		+		+		÷
2	×	0	+	6	=	6
=		=		=		=
4	+	6	−	9	=	1

Section 1.1 Practice Exercises, pp. 17–21

1. a. product **b.** factors **c.** numerator; b **d.** lowest **e.** 1; 4 **f.** reciprocals **g.** multiple **h.** least
3. Numerator: 2; denominator: 3; proper
5. Numerator: 5; denominator: 2; improper
7. Numerator: 4; denominator: 4; improper
9. Numerator: 5; denominator: 1; improper
11. $\frac{3}{4}$ **13.** $\frac{4}{3}$ **15.** $\frac{1}{6}$ **17.** $\frac{2}{2}$ **19.** $\frac{5}{2}$ or $2\frac{1}{2}$ **21.** $\frac{6}{2}$ or 3
23. The set of whole numbers includes the number 0 and the set of natural numbers does not.
25. For example: $\frac{2}{4}$ **27.** Prime **29.** Composite
31. Composite **33.** Prime **35.** $2 \times 2 \times 3 \times 3$
37. $2 \times 3 \times 7$ **39.** $2 \times 5 \times 11$ **41.** $3 \times 3 \times 3 \times 5$
43. $\frac{1}{5}$ **45.** $\frac{8}{3}$ or $2\frac{2}{3}$ **47.** $\frac{7}{8}$ **49.** $\frac{3}{4}$ **51.** $\frac{5}{8}$ **53.** $\frac{4}{3}$ or $1\frac{1}{3}$
55. False: When adding or subtracting fractions, it is necessary to have a common denominator.
57. $\frac{4}{3}$ or $1\frac{1}{3}$ **59.** $\frac{2}{3}$ **61.** $\frac{9}{2}$ or $4\frac{1}{2}$ **63.** $\frac{3}{5}$ **65.** $\frac{5}{3}$ or $1\frac{2}{3}$
67. $\frac{90}{13}$ or $6\frac{12}{13}$ **69.** \$704 **71.** 35 students **73.** 8 pieces
75. 8 jars **77.** $\frac{3}{7}$ **79.** $\frac{1}{2}$ **81.** 30 **83.** 40 **85.** $\frac{7}{8}$
87. $\frac{43}{40}$ or $1\frac{3}{40}$ **89.** $\frac{3}{26}$ **91.** $\frac{29}{36}$ **93.** $\frac{6}{5}$ or $1\frac{1}{5}$ **95.** $\frac{35}{48}$
97. $\frac{7}{24}$ **99.** $\frac{51}{28}$ or $1\frac{23}{28}$ **101.** $\frac{11}{12}$ cup sugar **103.** $\frac{7}{50}$ in.
105. $\frac{46}{5}$ or $9\frac{1}{5}$ **107.** $\frac{1}{6}$ **109.** $\frac{11}{54}$ **111.** $\frac{7}{2}$ or $3\frac{1}{2}$
113. $\frac{13}{8}$ or $1\frac{5}{8}$ **115.** $\frac{59}{12}$ or $4\frac{11}{12}$ **117.** $\frac{1}{8}$ **119.** $8\frac{19}{24}$ in.
121. $1\frac{7}{12}$ hr **123.** $2\frac{1}{4}$ lb **125.** 25 in.

Section 1.2 Calculator Connections, pp. 30–31

1. ≈ 3.464101615 **2.** ≈ 9.949874371
3. ≈ 12.56637061 **4.** ≈ 1.772453851

Section 1.2 Practice Exercises, pp. 31–34

1. a. variable **b.** constants **c.** set **d.** inequalities **e.** a is less than b **f.** c is greater than or equal to d **g.** 5 is not equal to 6 **h.** opposites **i.** $|a|$; 0 **3.** $8\frac{1}{4}$ or $\frac{33}{4}$ **5.** 15 **7.** 3
9. 4 **11.** 5.3 **13.** $\frac{1}{80}$ **15. a.** \$3.87 **b.** \$10.32 **c.** \$12.90 **17. a.** 375 calories **b.** 630 calories **c.** 270 calories
19.

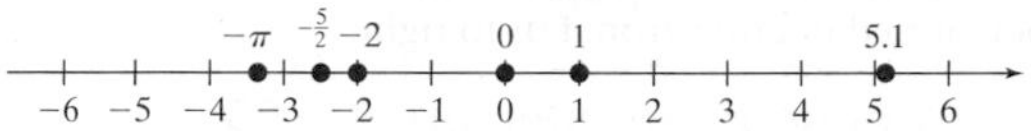

21. a; rational **23.** b; rational **25.** a; rational
27. c; irrational **29.** a; rational **31.** a; rational
33. b; rational **35.** c; irrational **37.** For example: $\pi, -\sqrt{2}, \sqrt{3}$
39. For example: $-4, -1, 0$ **41.** For example: $-\frac{3}{4}, \frac{1}{2}, 0.206$
43. $-\frac{3}{2}, -4, 0.\overline{6}, 0, 1$ **45.** 1 **47.** $-4, 0, 1$ **49. a.** $>$ **b.** $>$ **c.** $<$ **d.** $>$ **51.** -18 **53.** 6.1 **55.** $\frac{5}{8}$ **57.** $-\frac{7}{3}$
59. 3 **61.** $-\frac{7}{3}$ **63.** 8 **65.** -72.1 **67.** 2 **69.** 1.5
71. -1.5 **73.** $\frac{3}{2}$ **75.** -10 **77.** $-\frac{1}{2}$
79. False, $|n|$ is never negative. **81.** True **83.** False
85. True **87.** False **89.** False **91.** False
93. True **95.** True **97.** False **99.** True
101. True **103.** True **105.** For all $a < 0$

Section 1.3 Calculator Connections, pp. 41–42

1. 2 **2.** 91 **3.** 84 **4.** 12 **5.** 49 **6.** 18

1–3.

```
(4+6)/(8-3)
                 2
110-5*(2+1)-4
                91
100-2*(5-3)^3
                84
```

4–6.

```
3+(4-1)²
                12
(12-6+1)²
                49
3*8-√(32+2²)
                18
```

7. 4 **8.** 27 **9.** 0.5

7–9.

```
√(18-2)
                 4
(4*3-3*3)^3
                27
(20-3²)/(26-2²)
                .5
```

Section 1.3 Practice Exercises, pp. 42–45

1. a. quotient; product; sum; difference **b.** base; exponent; power **c.** 8^2 **d.** p^4 **e.** radical; square **f.** order of operations
3. 56 **5.** -19 **7.** $\left(\frac{1}{6}\right)^4$ **9.** a^3b^2 **11.** $(5c)^5$
13. a. x **b.** Yes, 1 **15.** $x \cdot x \cdot x$ **17.** $2b \cdot 2b \cdot 2b$
19. $10 \cdot y \cdot y \cdot y \cdot y$ **21.** $2 \cdot w \cdot z \cdot z$ **23.** 36 **25.** $\frac{1}{49}$
27. 0.008 **29.** 64 **31.** 9 **33.** 2 **35.** 12 **37.** 4
39. $\frac{1}{3}$ **41.** $\frac{5}{9}$ **43.** 20 **45.** 60 **47.** 8 **49.** 78 **51.** 0
53. $\frac{7}{6}$ **55.** 45 **57.** 16 **59.** 15 **61.** 19 **63.** 75 **65.** 3
67. 39 **69.** 26 **71.** $\frac{5}{12}$ **73.** $\frac{5}{2}$ **75. a.** 0.12 **b.** Yes. $0.12 < 0.20$ **77.** 57,600 ft^2 **79.** 21 ft^2 **81.** $3x$

Chapter 2

Chapter Opener Puzzle

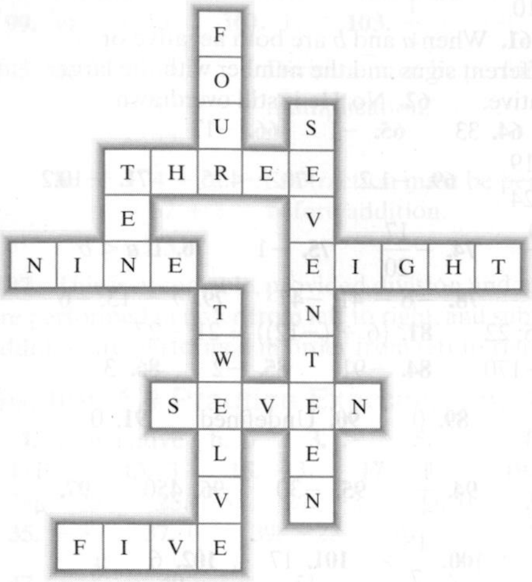

$8 \cdot \left(\frac{3}{8}\right) = \underline{\text{three}}$ $6 \cdot \left(\frac{2}{3}\right) = \underline{\text{four}}$

$100(0.17) = \underline{\text{seventeen}}$ $100(0.09) = \underline{\text{nine}}$

$\underline{\text{five}} \cdot \left(\frac{2}{5}\right) = 2$ $\underline{\text{seven}} \cdot \left(\frac{6}{7}\right) = 6$

$\underline{\text{eight}} \cdot \left(\frac{3}{4}\right) = 6$ $\underline{\text{twelve}} \cdot \left(\frac{5}{6}\right) = 10$

$\underline{\text{ten}} \cdot (0.4) = 4$

Section 2.1 Practice Exercises, pp. 109–111

1. a. equation **b.** solution **c.** linear **d.** solution set **3.** Expression **5.** Equation **7.** Substitute the value into the equation and determine if the right-hand side is equal to the left-hand side. **9.** No **11.** Yes **13.** Yes **15.** $\{-1\}$ **17.** $\{20\}$ **19.** $\{-17\}$ **21.** $\{-16\}$ **23.** $\{0\}$ **25.** $\{1.3\}$ **27.** $\left\{\frac{11}{2}\right\}$ or $\left\{5\frac{1}{2}\right\}$ **29.** $\{-2\}$ **31.** $\{-2.13\}$ **33.** $\{-3.2675\}$ **35.** $\{9\}$ **37.** $\{-4\}$ **39.** $\{0\}$ **41.** $\{-15\}$ **43.** $\left\{-\frac{4}{5}\right\}$ **45.** $\{-10\}$ **47.** $\{4\}$ **49.** $\{41\}$ **51.** $\{-127\}$ **53.** $\{-2.6\}$ **55.** $-8 + x = 42$; The number is 50. **57.** $x - (-6) = 18$; The number is 12. **59.** $x \cdot 7 = -63$ or $7x = -63$; The number is -9. **61.** $x - 3.2 = 2.1$; The number is 5.3. **63.** $\frac{x}{12} = \frac{1}{3}$; The number is 4. **65.** $x + \frac{5}{8} = \frac{13}{8}$; The number is 1. **67. a.** $\{10\}$ **b.** $\left\{-\frac{1}{9}\right\}$ **69. a.** $\{-12\}$ **b.** $\left\{\frac{22}{3}\right\}$ **71.** $\{-36\}$ **73.** $\{16\}$ **75.** $\{2\}$ **77.** $\left\{-\frac{7}{4}\right\}$ **79.** $\{11\}$ **81.** $\{-36\}$ **83.** $\left\{\frac{7}{2}\right\}$ **85.** $\{4\}$ **87.** $\{3.6\}$ **89.** $\{0.4084\}$ **91.** Yes **93.** No **95.** Yes **97.** Yes **99.** For example: $y + 9 = 15$ **101.** For example: $2p = -8$ **103.** For example: $5a + 5 = 5$ **105.** $\{-1\}$ **107.** $\{7\}$

Section 2.2 Practice Exercises, pp. 118–120

1. a. conditional **b.** contradiction **c.** empty or null **d.** identity **3.** $4w + 8$ **5.** $6y - 22$ **7.** $\{19\}$ **9.** $\{-3\}$ **11.** $\{-5\}$ **13.** $\{2\}$ **15.** $\{6\}$ **17.** $\left\{\frac{5}{2}\right\}$ **19.** $\{-42\}$ **21.** $\left\{-\frac{3}{4}\right\}$ **23.** $\{5\}$ **25.** $\{-4\}$ **27.** $\{-26\}$ **29.** $\{10\}$ **31.** $\{-8\}$ **33.** $\left\{-\frac{7}{3}\right\}$ **35.** $\{0\}$ **37.** $\{-3\}$ **39.** $\{-2\}$ **41.** $\left\{\frac{9}{2}\right\}$ **43.** $\left\{-\frac{1}{3}\right\}$ **45.** $\{10\}$ **47.** $\{-6\}$ **49.** $\{0\}$ **51.** $\{-2\}$ **53.** $\left\{-\frac{25}{4}\right\}$ **55.** $\left\{\frac{10}{3}\right\}$ **57.** $\{-0.25\}$ **59.** { }; contradiction **61.** $\{-15\}$; conditional equation **63.** The set of real numbers; identity **65.** One solution **67.** Infinitely many solutions **69.** $\{7\}$ **71.** $\left\{\frac{1}{2}\right\}$ **73.** $\{0\}$ **75.** The set of real numbers **77.** $\{-46\}$ **79.** $\{2\}$ **81.** $\left\{\frac{13}{2}\right\}$ **83.** $\{-5\}$ **85.** { } **87.** $\{2.205\}$ **89.** $\{10\}$ **91.** $\{-1\}$ **93.** $a = 15$ **95.** $a = 4$ **97.** For example: $5x + 2 = 2 + 5x$

Section 2.3 Practice Exercises, pp. 126–127

1. a. clearing fractions **b.** clearing decimals **3.** $\{-2\}$ **5.** $\{-5\}$ **7.** { } **9.** 18, 36 **11.** 100; 1000; 10,000 **13.** 30, 60 **15.** $\{4\}$ **17.** $\{-12\}$ **19.** $\left\{-\frac{15}{4}\right\}$ **21.** $\{8\}$ **23.** $\{3\}$ **25.** $\{15\}$ **27.** { } **29.** The set of real numbers **31.** $\{5\}$ **33.** $\{2\}$ **35.** $\{-15\}$ **37.** $\{6\}$ **39.** $\{107\}$ **41.** The set of real numbers **43.** $\{67\}$ **45.** $\{90\}$ **47.** $\{4\}$ **49.** $\{4\}$ **51.** { } **53.** $\{-0.25\}$ **55.** $\{-6\}$ **57.** $\left\{\frac{8}{3}\right\}$ or $\left\{2\frac{2}{3}\right\}$ **59.** $\{-11\}$ **61.** $\left\{\frac{1}{10}\right\}$ **63.** $\{-2\}$ **65.** $\{-1\}$ **67.** $\{2\}$

Chapter 2 Problem Recognition Exercises, p. 128

1. Expression; $-4b + 18$ **2.** Expression; $20p - 30$ **3.** Equation; $\{-8\}$ **4.** Equation; $\{-14\}$ **5.** Equation; $\left\{\frac{1}{3}\right\}$ **6.** Equation; $\left\{-\frac{4}{3}\right\}$ **7.** Expression; $6z - 23$ **8.** Expression; $-x - 9$ **9.** Equation; $\left\{\frac{7}{9}\right\}$ **10.** Equation; $\left\{-\frac{13}{10}\right\}$ **11.** Equation; $\{20\}$ **12.** Equation; $\{-3\}$ **13.** Equation; $\left\{\frac{1}{2}\right\}$ **14.** Equation; $\{-6\}$ **15.** Expression; $\frac{5}{8}x + \frac{7}{4}$ **16.** Expression; $-26t + 18$ **17.** Equation; { } **18.** Equation; { } **19.** Equation; $\left\{\frac{23}{12}\right\}$ **20.** Equation; $\left\{\frac{5}{8}\right\}$ **21.** Equation; The set of real numbers **22.** Equation; The set of real numbers **23.** Equation; $\left\{\frac{1}{2}\right\}$ **24.** Equation; $\{0\}$ **25.** Expression; 0 **26.** Expression; -1 **27.** Expression; $2a + 13$ **28.** Expression; $8q + 3$ **29.** Equation; $\{10\}$ **30.** Equation; $\left\{-\frac{1}{20}\right\}$ **31.** Expression; $-\frac{1}{6}y + \frac{1}{3}$ **32.** Expression; $\frac{7}{10}x + \frac{2}{5}$

Section 2.4 Practice Exercises, pp. 135–138

1. a. consecutive **b.** even **c.** odd **d.** 1 **e.** 2 **f.** 2 **3.** $x - 5{,}682{,}080$ **5.** $10x$ **7.** $3x - 20$ **9.** The number is -4. **11.** The number is -3. **13.** The number is 5. **15.** The number is -5. **17.** The number is 3. **19. a.** $x + 1, x + 2$ **b.** $x - 1, x - 2$ **21.** The integers are -34 and -33.

23. The integers are 13 and 15. **25.** The sides are 14 in., 15 in., 16 in., 17 in., and 18 in. **27.** The integers are −54, −52, and −50. **29.** The integers are 13, 15, and 17. **31.** The lengths of the pieces are 33 cm and 53 cm. **33.** Karen's iPod has 23 playlists and Clarann's iPod has 35 playlists. **35.** There were 201 Republicans and 232 Democrats. **37.** *CSI* had 13.17 million viewers and *Criminal Minds* had 14.23 million viewers. **39.** The Congo River is 4370 km long, and the Nile River is 6825 km. **41.** The area of Africa is 30,065,000 km². The area of Asia is 44,579,000 km². **43.** They walked 12.3 mi on the first day and 8.2 mi on the second. **45.** The pieces are 9 in., 17 in., and 22 in. **47.** The integers are 42, 43, and 44. **49.** Carrie Underwood earned $14 million and Jennifer Hudson earned $5 million. **51.** The number is 11. **53.** The page numbers are 470 and 471. **55.** The number is 10. **57.** The deepest point in the Arctic Ocean is 5122 m. **59.** The number is $\frac{7}{16}$. **61.** The number is 2.5.

Section 2.5 Practice Exercises, pp. 143–146

1. a. simple **b.** 100 **3.** The numbers are 21 and 22. **5.** 12.5% **7.** 85% **9.** 0.75 **11.** 1050.8 **13.** 885 **15.** 2200 **17.** Molly will have to pay $106.99. **19.** Approximately 231,000 cases **21.** 2% **23.** Javon's taxable income was $84,000. **25.** Aidan would earn $27 more in the CD. **27.** Bob borrowed $1200. **29.** The rate is 6%. **31.** Perry needs to invest $3302. **33. a.** $20.40 **b.** $149.60 **35.** The original price was $470.59. **37.** The discount rate is 12%. **39.** The original dosage was 15 cc. **41.** The tax rate is 5%. **43.** The original cost was $5.20 per pack. **45.** The original price was $210,000. **47.** Alina made $4600 that month. **49.** Diane sold $645 over $200 worth of merchandise.

Section 2.6 Calculator Connections, p. 152

1. 140.056 **2.** 31.831 **3.** 1.273 **4.** 0.455

1–2.

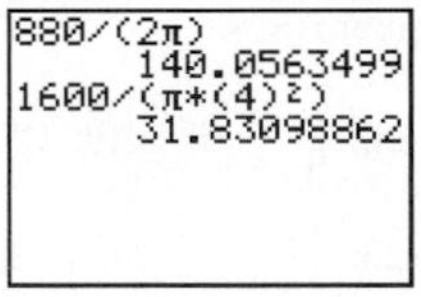

3–4.

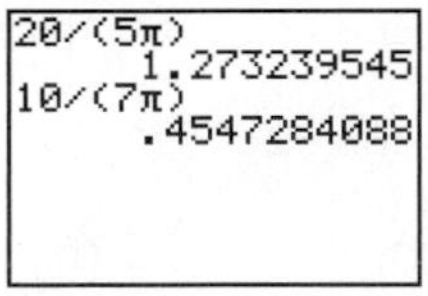

Section 2.6 Practice Exercises, pp. 152–156

1. $\{-5\}$ **3.** $\{0\}$ **5.** $\{-2\}$ **7.** $\{\ \}$ **9.** $a = P - b - c$ **11.** $y = x + z$ **13.** $q = p - 250$ **15.** $b = \frac{A}{h}$ **17.** $t = \frac{PV}{nr}$ **19.** $x = 5 + y$ **21.** $y = -3x - 19$

23. $y = \frac{-2x + 6}{3}$ or $y = -\frac{2}{3}x + 2$

25. $x = \frac{y + 9}{-2}$ or $x = -\frac{1}{2}y - \frac{9}{2}$

27. $y = \frac{-4x + 12}{-3}$ or $y = \frac{4}{3}x - 4$

29. $y = \frac{-ax + c}{b}$ or $y = -\frac{a}{b}x + \frac{c}{b}$

31. $t = \frac{A - P}{Pr}$ or $t = \frac{A}{Pr} - \frac{1}{r}$

33. $c = \frac{a - 2b}{2}$ or $c = \frac{a}{2} - b$ **35.** $y = 2Q - x$

37. $a = MS$ **39.** $R = \frac{P}{I^2}$

41. The length is 7 ft, and the width is 5 ft. **43.** The length is 120 yd and the width is 30 yd. **45.** The length is 195 m, and the width is 100 m. **47.** The sides are 22 m, 22 m, and 27 m. **49.** "Adjacent supplementary angles form a straight angle." The words *Supplementary* and *Straight* both begin with the same letter. **51.** The angles are 23.5° and 66.5°. **53.** The angles are 34.8° and 145.2°. **55.** $x = 20$; the vertical angles measure 37°. **57.** The measures of the angles are 30°, 60°, and 90°. **59.** The measures of the angles are 42°, 54°, and 84°. **61.** $x = 17$; the measures of the angles are 34° and 56°.

63. a. $A = lw$ **b.** $w = \frac{A}{l}$ **c.** The width is 29.5 ft.

65. a. $P = 2l + 2w$ **b.** $l = \frac{P - 2w}{2}$ **c.** The length is 103 m.

67. a. $C = 2\pi r$ **b.** $r = \frac{C}{2\pi}$ **c.** The radius is approximately 140 ft.

69. a. 415.48 m² **b.** 10,386.89 m³

Section 2.7 Practice Exercises, pp. 161–165

1. a. $x = \frac{c + by}{a}$ **3.** $y = \frac{18 - 7x}{x}$ **5.** $\{4\}$ **7.** $200 - t$ **9.** $100 - x$ **11.** $3000 - y$ **13.** 53 tickets were sold at $3 and 28 tickets were sold at $2. **15.** Josh downloaded 17 songs for $0.90 and 8 songs for $1.50. **17.** Christopher has 5 Wii games and 15 DS games. **19.** $x + 7$ **21.** $d + 2000$ **23.** Mix 500 gal of 5% ethanol fuel mixture. **25.** The pharmacist needs to use 21 mL of the 1% saline solution. **27.** The contractor needs to mix 6.75 oz of 50% acid solution. **29. a.** 300 mi **b.** $5x$ **c.** $5(x + 12)$ or $5x + 60$ **31.** She walks 4 mph to the lake. **33.** Bryan hiked 6 mi up the canyon. **35.** The plane travels 600 mph in still air. **37.** The slower car travels 48 mph and the faster car travels 52 mph. **39.** The speeds of the vehicles are 40 mph and 50 mph. **41.** Sarah walks 3.5 mph and Jeanette runs 7 mph. **43. a.** 2 lb **b.** $0.10x$ **c.** $0.10(x + 3) = 0.10x + 0.30$ **45.** Mix 10 lb of coffee sold at $12 per pound and 40 lb of coffee sold at $8 per pound. **47.** The boats will meet in $\frac{3}{4}$ hr (45 min). **49.** Sam purchased 16 packages of wax and 5 bottles of sunscreen. **51.** 2.5 quarts of 85% chlorine solution **53.** 20 L of water must be added. **55.** The Japanese bullet train travels 300 km/hr and the Acela Express travels 240 km/hr.

Section 2.8 Practice Exercises, pp. 176–180

1. a. linear inequality **b.** inequality **c.** set-builder; interval **3.** $\{-3\}$ **5.**

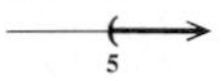

7.

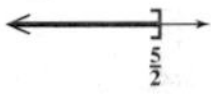

9.

11.

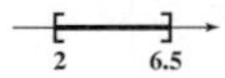

13.

15.

Set-Builder Notation	Graph	Interval Notation
17. $\{x \mid x \geq 6\}$	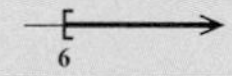	$[6, \infty)$
19. $\{x \mid x \leq 2.1\}$	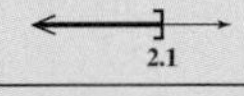	$(-\infty, 2.1]$
21. $\{x \mid -2 < x \leq 7\}$		$(-2, 7]$

Set-Builder Notation	Graph	Interval Notation
23. $\left\{x \mid x > \frac{3}{4}\right\}$	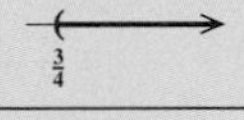	$\left(\frac{3}{4}, \infty\right)$
25. $\{x \mid -1 < x < 8\}$	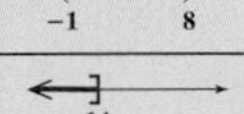	$(-1, 8)$
27. $\{x \mid x \leq -14\}$	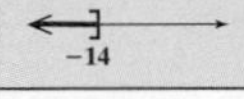	$(-\infty, -14]$

Set-Builder Notation	Graph	Interval Notation
29. $\{x\|x \geq 18\}$	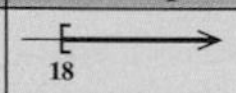	$[18, \infty)$
31. $\{x\|x < -0.6\}$	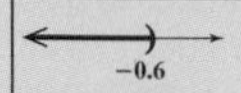	$(-\infty, -0.6)$
33. $\{x\|-3.5 \leq x < 7.1\}$	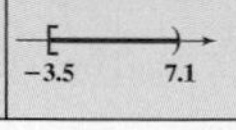	$[-3.5, 7.1)$

35. a. $\{3\}$
b. $\{x|x > 3\}; (3, \infty)$

37. a. $\{13\}$
b. $\{p|p \leq 13\}; (-\infty, 13]$

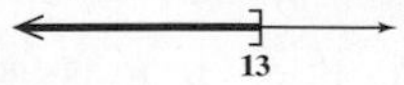

39. a. $\{-3\}$
b. $\{c|c < -3\}; (-\infty, -3)$

41. a. $\left\{-\frac{3}{2}\right\}$
b. $\left\{z|z \geq -\frac{3}{2}\right\}; \left[-\frac{3}{2}, \infty\right)$

43. $(-1, 4]$

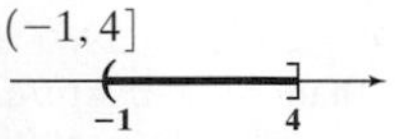

45. $(-3, 5)$

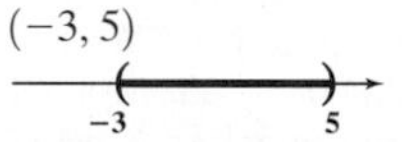

47. $[2, 6]$

49. a. $\{x|x \leq 1\}$ **b.** $(-\infty, 1]$

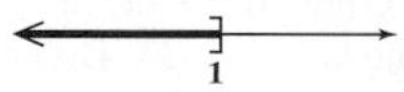

51. a. $\{q|q > 10\}$
b. $(10, \infty)$

53. a. $\{x|x > 3\}$
b. $(3, \infty)$

55. a. $\{c|c > 2\}$
b. $(2, \infty)$

57. a. $\{c|c < -2\}$
b. $(-\infty, -2)$

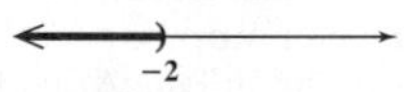

59. a. $\{h|h \geq 14\}$
b. $[14, \infty)$

61. a. $\{x|x \geq -24\}$
b. $[-24, \infty)$

63. a. $\{p|-3 \leq p < 3\}$
b. $[-3, 3)$

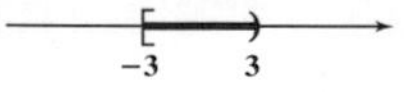

65. a. $\left\{h|0 < h < \frac{5}{2}\right\}$
b. $\left(0, \frac{5}{2}\right)$

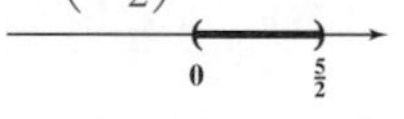

67. a. $\{x|10 < x < 12\}$
b. $(10, 12)$

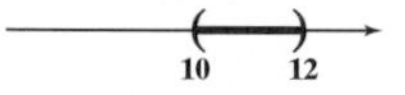

69. a. $\{x|-8 \leq x < 24\}$
b. $[-8, 24)$

71. a. $\{y|y > -9\}$
b. $(-9, \infty)$

73. a. $\left\{x|x \geq -\frac{15}{2}\right\}$
b. $\left[-\frac{15}{2}, \infty\right)$

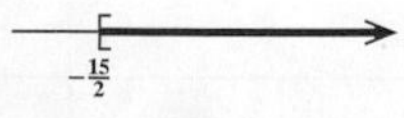

75. a. $\{x|x < -3\}$
b. $(-\infty, -3)$

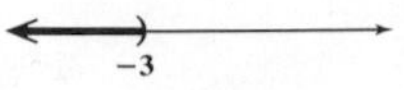

77. a. $\left\{b|b \geq -\frac{1}{3}\right\}$
b. $\left[-\frac{1}{3}, \infty\right)$

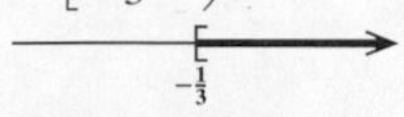

79. a. $\{n|n > -3\}$
b. $(-3, \infty)$

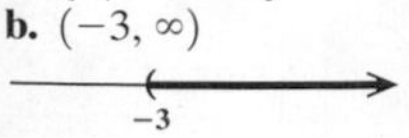

81. a. $\{x|x < 7\}$
b. $(-\infty, 7)$

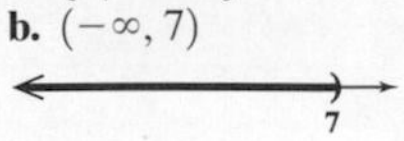

83. a. $\{x|x \leq -5\}$
b. $(-\infty, -5]$

85. a. $\{z|z \leq -2\}$
b. $(-\infty, -2]$

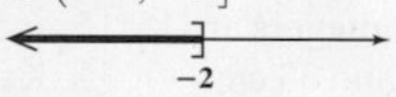

87. a. $\left\{a|a > -\frac{2}{3}\right\}$
b. $\left(-\frac{2}{3}, \infty\right)$

89. a. $\left\{p|p \leq \frac{15}{4}\right\}$
b. $\left(-\infty, \frac{15}{4}\right]$

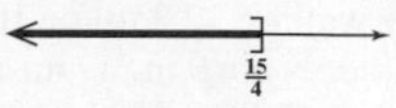

91. a. $\{y|y < -9\}$
b. $(-\infty, -9)$

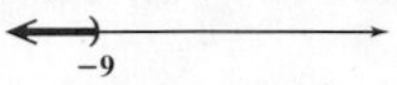

93. a. $\{a|a > -3\}$
b. $(-3, \infty)$

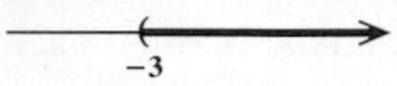

95. a. $\{x|x \leq 0\}$ **b.** $(-\infty, 0]$

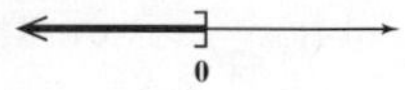

97. No **99.** Yes **101.** $L \geq 10$ **103.** $w > 75$
105. $t \leq 72$ **107.** $L \geq 8$ **109.** $2 < h < 5$
111. More than 10.2 in. of rain is needed. **113.** Trevor needs at least 86 to get a B in the course. **115. a.** \$1539
b. 200 birdhouses cost \$1440. It is cheaper to purchase 200 birdhouses because the discount is greater. **117.** If there were more than 145 text messages, the unlimited option would be a better deal.
119. Madison needs to babysit a minimum of 39.5 hr.

Chapter 2 Review Exercises, pp. 187–190

1. a. Equation **b.** Expression **c.** Equation **d.** Equation
2. A linear equation can be written in the form $ax + b = c, a \neq 0$.
3. a. No **b.** Yes **c.** No **d.** Yes **4. a.** No **b.** Yes
5. $\{-8\}$ **6.** $\{15\}$ **7.** $\left\{\frac{21}{4}\right\}$ **8.** $\{70\}$ **9.** $\left\{-\frac{21}{5}\right\}$
10. $\{-60\}$ **11.** $\left\{-\frac{10}{7}\right\}$ **12.** $\{27\}$ **13.** The number is 60.
14. The number is $\frac{7}{24}$. **15.** The number is -8.
16. The number is -2. **17.** $\{1\}$ **18.** $\left\{-\frac{3}{5}\right\}$ **19.** $\{2\}$
20. $\{-6\}$ **21.** $\{-3\}$ **22.** $\{18\}$ **23.** $\left\{\frac{3}{4}\right\}$ **24.** $\{-3\}$
25. $\{0\}$ **26.** $\left\{\frac{1}{8}\right\}$ **27.** $\{2\}$ **28.** $\{6\}$ **29.** A contradiction has no solution and an identity is true for all real numbers.
30. Identity **31.** Conditional equation **32.** Contradiction
33. Identity **34.** Contradiction **35.** Conditional equation
36. $\{6\}$ **37.** $\{22\}$ **38.** $\{13\}$ **39.** $\{-27\}$ **40.** $\{-10\}$
41. $\{-7\}$ **42.** $\left\{\frac{5}{3}\right\}$ **43.** $\left\{-\frac{9}{4}\right\}$ **44.** $\{2.5\}$ **45.** $\{-4\}$
46. $\{-4.2\}$ **47.** $\{2.5\}$ **48.** $\{-312\}$ **49.** $\{200\}$ **50.** $\{\ \}$
51. $\{\ \}$ **52.** The set of real numbers **53.** The set of real numbers **54.** The number is 30. **55.** The number is 11.
56. The number is -7. **57.** The number is -10.
58. The integers are 66, 68, and 70. **59.** The integers are 27, 28, and 29. **60.** The sides are 25 in., 26 in., and 27 in.
61. The sides are 36 cm, 37 cm, 38 cm, 39 cm, and 40 cm.
62. In 1975 the minimum salary was \$16,000.
63. Indiana has 6.2 million people and Kentucky has 4.1 million.
64. 23.8 **65.** 28.8 **66.** 12.5% **67.** 95% **68.** 160
69. 1750 **70.** The dinner was \$40 before tax and tip.
71. a. \$840 **b.** \$3840 **72.** He invested \$12,000.
73. The novel originally cost \$29.50. **74.** $K = C + 273$
75. $C = K - 273$ **76.** $s = \frac{P}{4}$ **77.** $s = \frac{P}{3}$
78. $x = \frac{y - b}{m}$ **79.** $x = \frac{c - a}{b}$ **80.** $y = \frac{-2x - 2}{5}$
81. $b = \frac{Q - 4a}{4}$ or $b = \frac{Q}{4} - a$ **82.** The height is 7 m.

83. a. $h = \frac{3V}{\pi r^2}$ **b.** The height is 5.1 in. **84.** The angles are 22°, 78°, and 80°. **85.** The angles are 50° and 40°.
86. The length is 5 ft, and the width is 4 ft. **87.** $x = 20$. The angle measure is 65°. **88.** The measure of angle y is 53°.
89. The truck travels 45 km/hr in bad weather and 60 km/hr in good weather. **90.** Gus rides 15 mph and Winston rides 18 mph.
91. The cars will be 327.6 mi apart after 2.8 hr (2 hr and 48 min).
92. They meet in 2.25 hr (2 hr and 15 min). **93.** 2 lb of 24% fat content beef is needed. **94.** 20 lb of the 40% solder should be used.
95. $(-2, \infty)$ 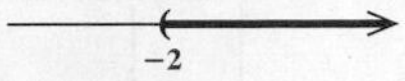

96. $\left(-\infty, \frac{1}{2}\right]$ 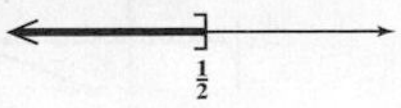

97. $(-1, 4]$ 

98. a. \$637 **b.** 300 plants cost \$1410, and 295 plants cost \$1416. 295 plants cost more.
99. $\{c \mid c < 17\}; (-\infty, 17)$ 

100. $\left\{w \mid w > -\frac{1}{3}\right\}; \left(-\frac{1}{3}, \infty\right)$ 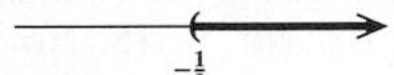

101. $\{x \mid x \le -6\}; (-\infty, -6]$ 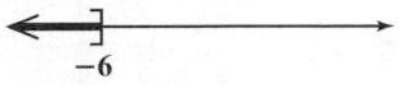

102. $\left\{y \mid y \le -\frac{14}{5}\right\}; \left(-\infty, -\frac{14}{5}\right]$ 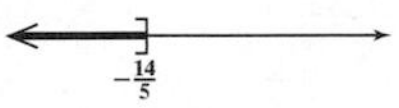

103. $\{a \mid a \ge 49\}; [49, \infty)$ 

104. $\{t \mid t < 34.5\}; (-\infty, 34.5)$ 

105. $\{k \mid k > 18\}; (18, \infty)$ 

106. $\left\{h \mid h \le \frac{5}{2}\right\}; \left(-\infty, \frac{5}{2}\right]$ 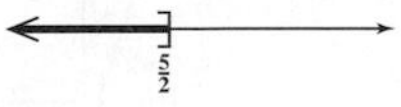

107. $\{x \mid x < -1\}; (-\infty, -1)$ 

108. $\{b \mid -3 < b \le 7\}; (-3, 7]$ 

109. $\{z \mid -6 \le z \le 5\}; [-6, 5]$ 

110. More than 2.5 in. is required.
111. Collette can have at most 18 wings.

Chapter 2 Test, pp. 190–191

1. b, d **2. a.** $5x + 7$ **b.** $\{9\}$ **3.** $\left\{\frac{7}{3}\right\}$ **4.** { }
5. $\{-16\}$ **6.** $\left\{\frac{13}{4}\right\}$ **7.** $\{12\}$ **8.** $\left\{\frac{20}{21}\right\}$ **9.** $\left\{-\frac{16}{9}\right\}$
10. $\{15\}$ **11.** The set of real numbers **12.** $\{-3\}$
13. $\{-47\}$ **14.** $y = -3x - 4$ **15.** $r = \frac{C}{2\pi}$ **16.** 90
17. a. $(-\infty, 0)$ **b.** $[-2, 5)$

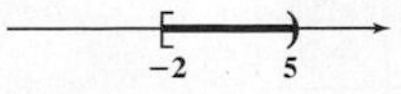

18. $\{x \mid x > -2\}; (-2, \infty)$ **19.** $\{x \mid x \le -4\}; (-\infty, -4]$
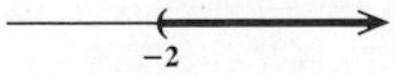

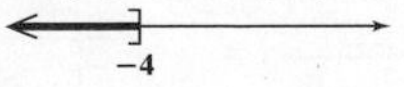

20. $\left\{y \mid y > - > \frac{3}{2}\right\}; \left(-\frac{3}{2}, \infty\right)$ 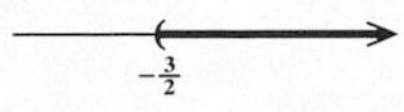

21. $\{p \mid -5 \le p \le 1\}; [-5, 1]$
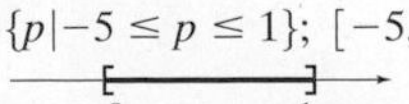

22. The cost was \$82.00. **23.** Clarita originally borrowed \$5000.
24. The numbers are 18 and 13. **25.** One family travels 55 mph and the other travels 50 mph. **26.** More than 26.5 in. is required.
27. The sides are 61 in., 62 in., 63 in., 64 in., and 65 in.
28. Matthew needs 30 lb of macadamia nuts.
29. Each basketball ticket was \$36.32, and each hockey ticket was \$40.64. **30.** The measures of the angles are 32° and 58°.
31. The field is 110 m long and 75 m wide. **32.** $y = 30$; The measures of the angles are 30°, 39°, and 111°.

Chapters 1–2 Cumulative Review Exercises, pp. 191–192

1. $\frac{1}{2}$ **2.** -7 **3.** $-\frac{5}{12}$ **4.** 16 **5.** 4
6. $\sqrt{5^2 - 9}; 4$ **7.** $-14 + 12; -2$ **8.** $-7x^2y, 4xy, -6$
9. $9x + 13$ **10.** $\{4\}$ **11.** $\{-7.2\}$
12. The set of real numbers **13.** $\{-8\}$ **14.** $\left\{-\frac{4}{7}\right\}$
15. $\{-80\}$ **16.** The numbers are 77 and 79. **17.** The cost before tax was \$350.00. **18.** The height is $\frac{41}{6}$ cm or $6\frac{5}{6}$ cm.
19. $\{x \mid x > -2\}; (-2, \infty)$ **20.** $\{x \mid -1 \le x \le 9\}; [-1, 9]$
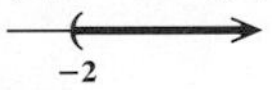

Chapter 3

Chapter Opener Puzzle

THE	EQUATION	$y = mx + b$
1	2	
IS	WRITTEN	IN
3	4	5
SLOPE-INTERCEPT		FORM
6 7		8

Section 3.1 Practice Exercises, pp. 198–203

1. a. x; y-axis **b.** ordered **c.** origin; (0, 0) **d.** quadrants **e.** negative **f.** III **3. a.** Month 10 **b.** 30 **c.** Between months 3 and 5 and between months 10 and 12 **d.** Months 8 and 9 **e.** Month 3 **f.** 80 **5. a.** On day 1 the price per share was \$89.25. **b.** \$1.75 **c.** $-\$2.75$

7.
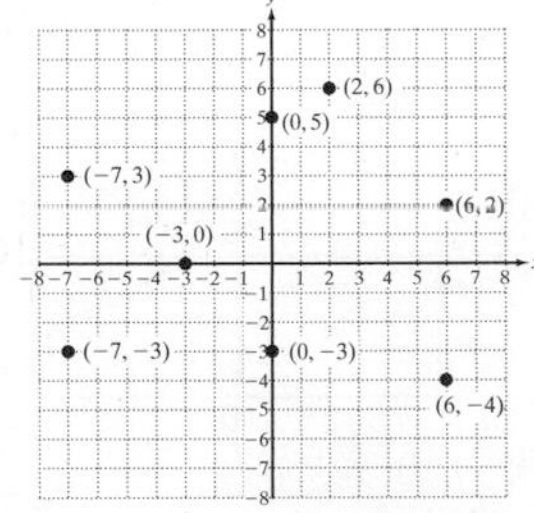

9.
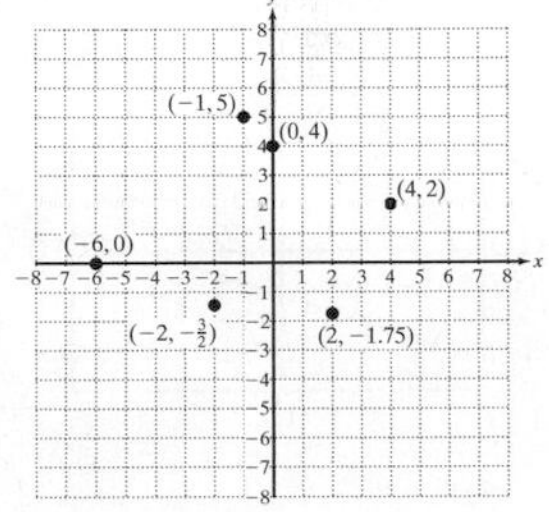

11. IV **13.** II **15.** III **17.** I
19. $(0, -5)$ lies on the y-axis. **21.** $(\frac{7}{8}, 0)$ is located on the x-axis.
23. $A(-4, 2), B(\frac{1}{2}, 4), C(3, -4), D(-3, -4), E(0, -3), F(5, 0)$
25. a. $A(400, 200), B(200, -150), C(-300, -200), D(-300, 250), E(0, 450)$ **b.** 450 m **27. a.** (250, 225), (175, 193), (315, 330), (220, 209), (450, 570), (400, 480), (190, 185); the ordered pair (250, 225) means that 250 people produce \$225 in popcorn sales.
b.
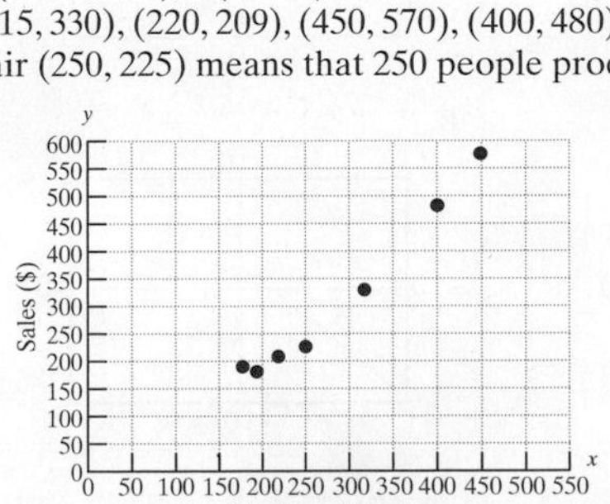

29. a. $(1, -10.2), (2, -9.0), (3, -2.5), (4, 5.7), (5, 13.0), (6, 18.3), (7, 20.9), (8, 19.6), (9, 14.8), (10, 8.7), (11, 2.0), (12, -6.9)$.

b.

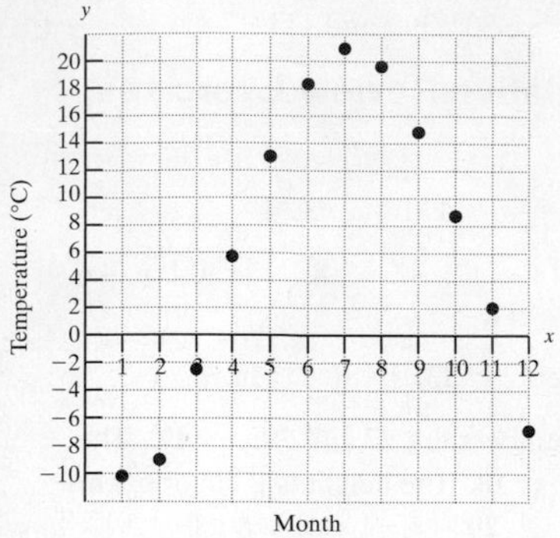

31. a.

Percent of Males/Females with 4 or More Years of College, United States

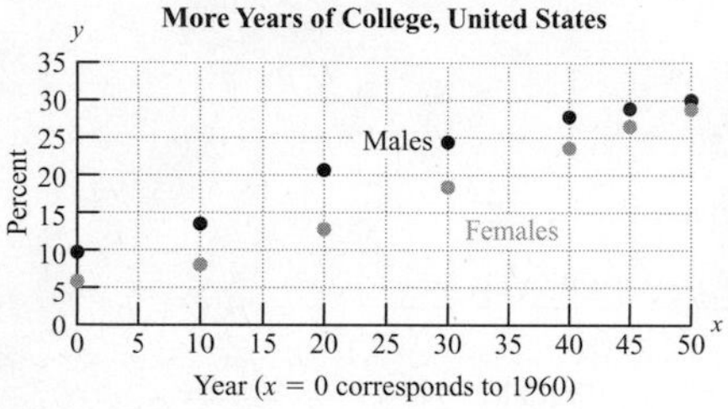

b. Increasing **c.** Increasing

Section 3.2 Calculator Connections, pp. 211–212

1.

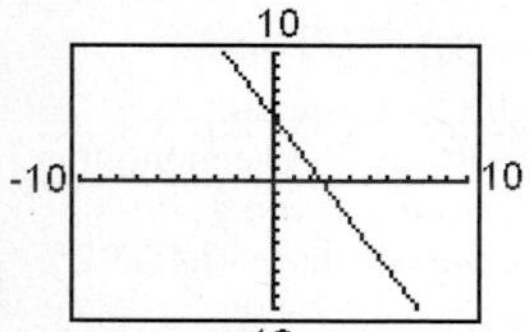

2.

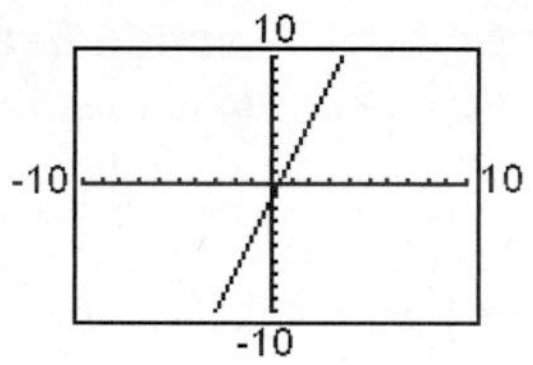

3.

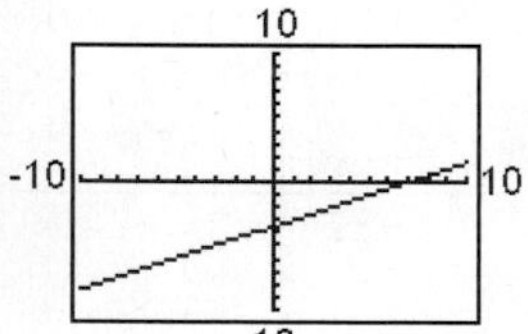

4.

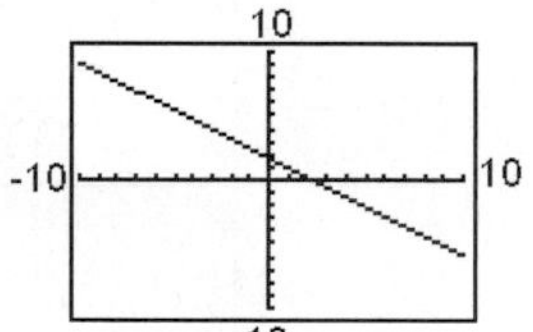

5.

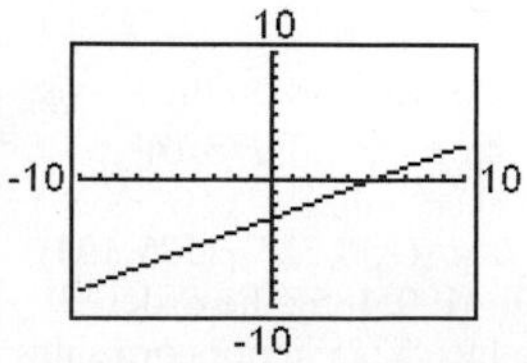

6.

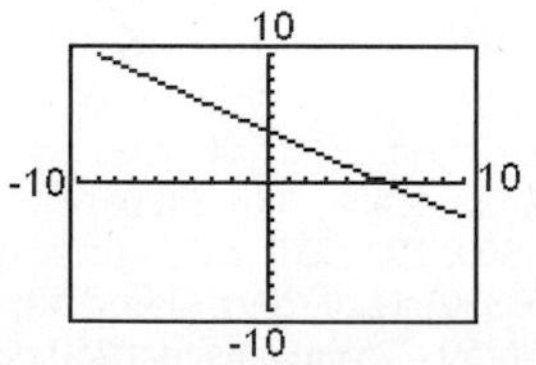

7.

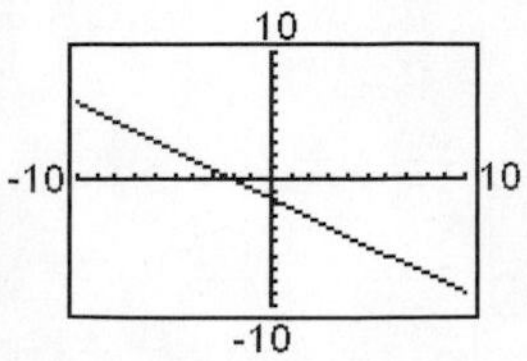

8.

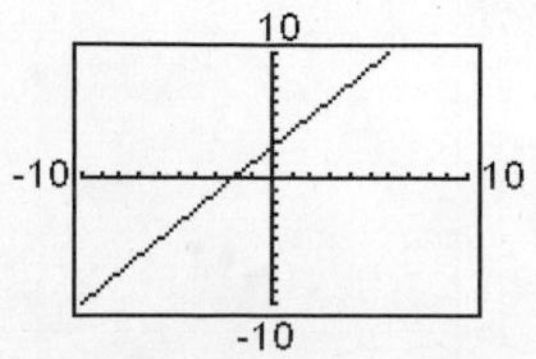

9.

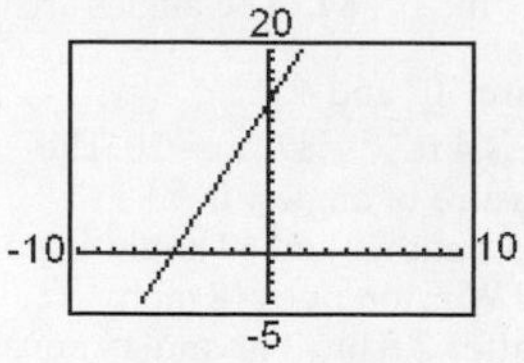

10.

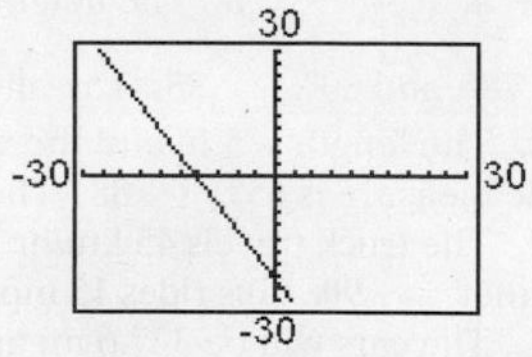

11.

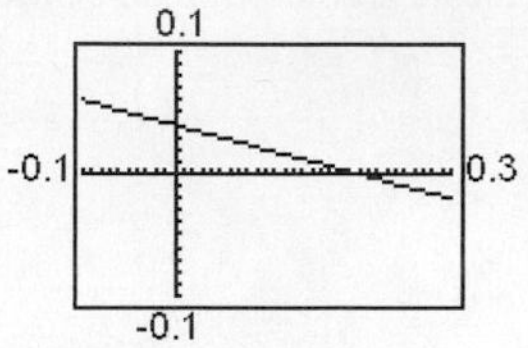

12.

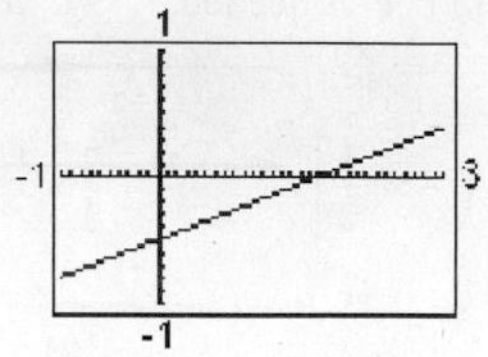

Section 3.2 Practice Exercises, pp. 212–218

1. a. $Ax + By = C$ **b.** x-intercept **c.** y-intercept **d.** vertical **e.** horizontal **3.** $(-2, -2)$; quadrant III **5.** $(-5, 0)$; x-axis **7.** $(-3, 2)$; quadrant II **9.** Yes **11.** Yes **13.** No **15.** No **17.** Yes

19.

x	y
1	−3
−2	0
−3	1
−4	2

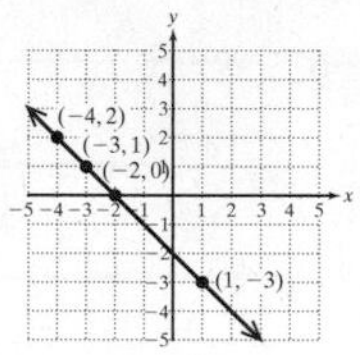

21.

x	y
−2	3
−1	0
−4	9

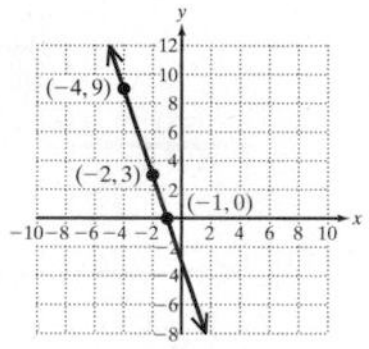

23.

x	y
0	4
2	0
3	−2

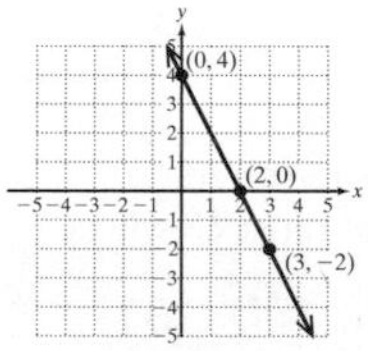

25.

x	y
0	−2
5	−5
10	−8

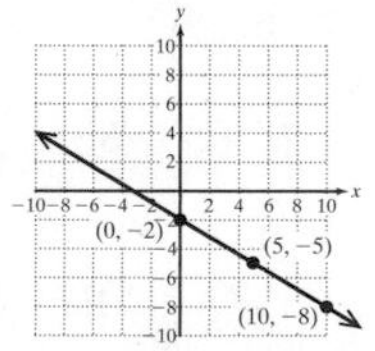

27.

x	y
0	−2
−3	−2
5	−2

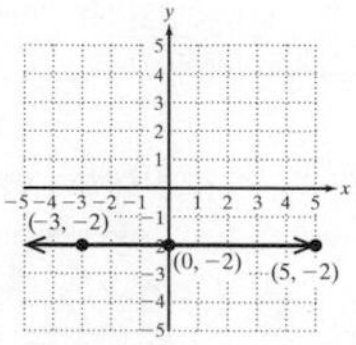

29.

x	y
3/2	−1
3/2	2
3/2	−3

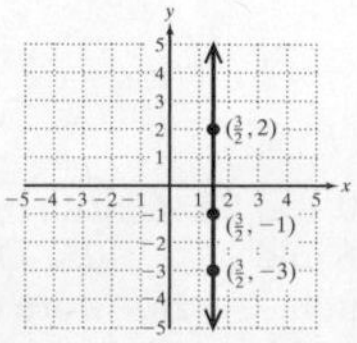

31.

x	y
0	4.6
1	3.4
2	2.2

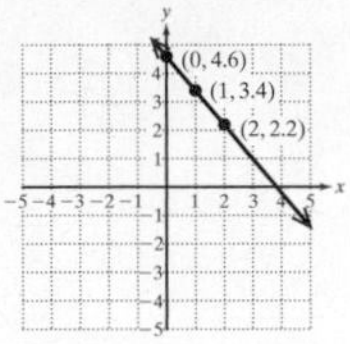

33.

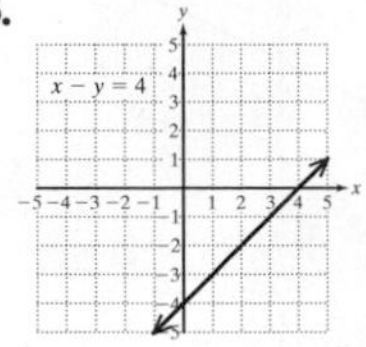

35.

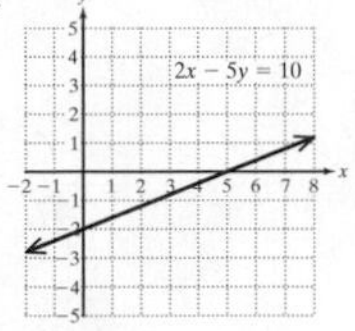

37.

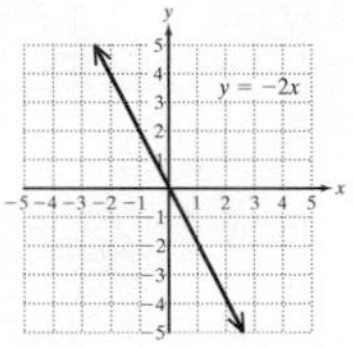

39.

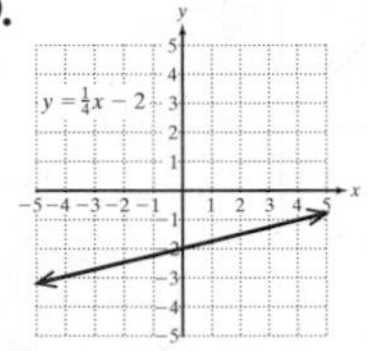

41.

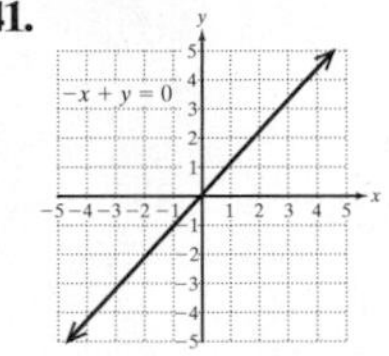

43.

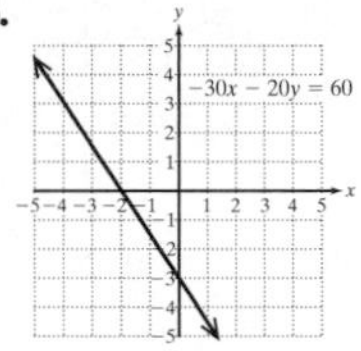

45. y-axis **47.** x-intercept: $(-1, 0)$; y-intercept: $(0, -3)$
49. x-intercept: $(-4, 0)$; y-intercept: $(0, 1)$

51. x-intercept: $\left(-\dfrac{9}{4}, 0\right)$; y-intercept: $(0, 3)$

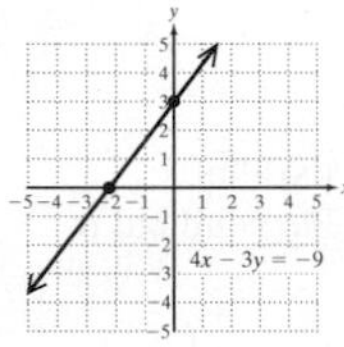

53. x-intercept: $\left(\dfrac{8}{3}, 0\right)$; y-intercept: $(0, 2)$

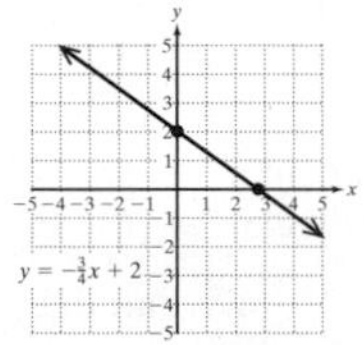

55. x-intercept: $(-4, 0)$; y-intercept: $(0, 8)$

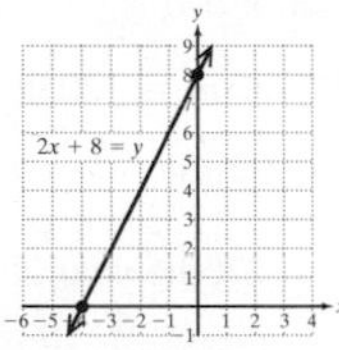

57. x-intercept: $(0, 0)$; y-intercept: $(0, 0)$

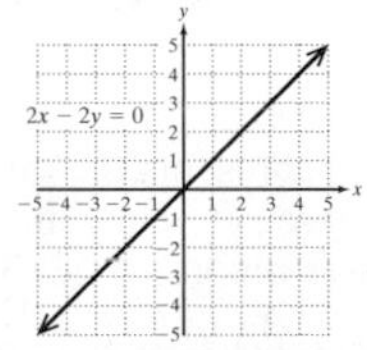

59. x-intercept: $(10, 0)$; y-intercept: $(0, 5)$

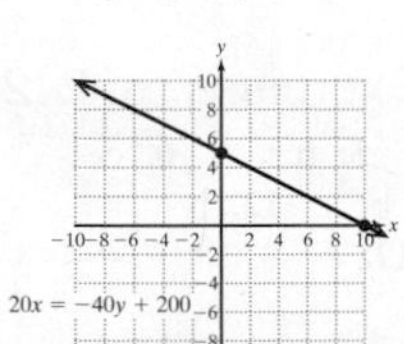

61. x-intercept: $(0, 0)$; y-intercept: $(0, 0)$

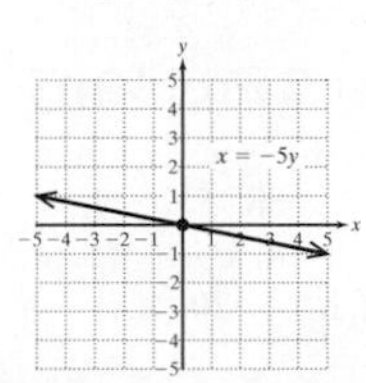

63. True **65.** True

67. a. Horizontal line **c.** no x-intercept; y-intercept: $(0, -1)$

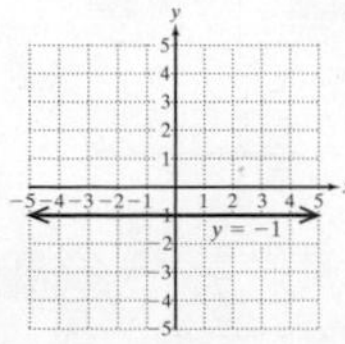

69. a. Vertical line **c.** x-intercept: $(4, 0)$; no y-intercept

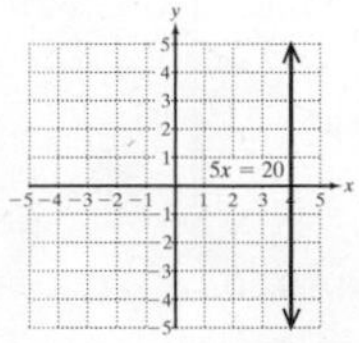

71. a. Horizontal line **c.** no x-intercept; y-intercept $(0, 3)$

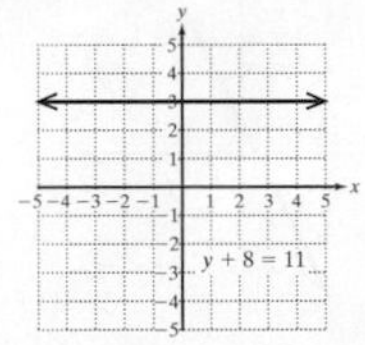

73. a. Vertical line **c.** All points on the y-axis are y-intercepts; x-intercept: $(0, 0)$

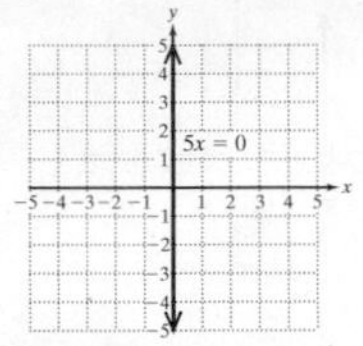

75. A horizontal line may not have an x-intercept. A vertical line may not have a y-intercept. **77.** a, b, d **79. a.** $y = 11{,}190$ **b.** $x = 3$ **c.** $(1, 11190)$ One year after purchase the value of the car is \$11,190. $(3, 9140)$ Three years after purchase the value of the car is \$9140.

Section 3.3 Practice Exercises, pp. 225–231

1. a. slope; $\dfrac{y_2 - y_1}{x_2 - x_1}$ **b.** parallel **c.** right **d.** -1 **e.** undefined; horizontal

3. x-intercept: $(6, 0)$; y-intercept: $(0, -2)$

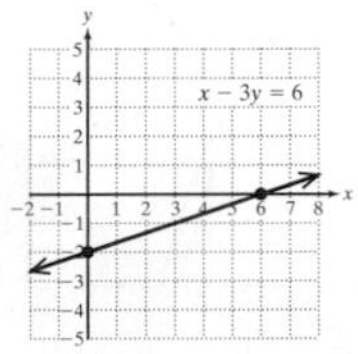

5. x-intercept: none; y-intercept: $\left(0, \dfrac{3}{2}\right)$

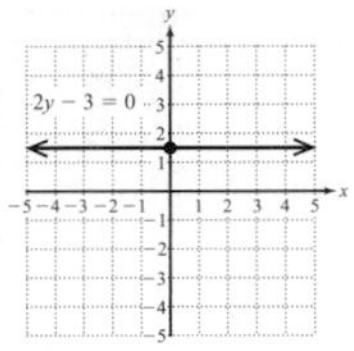

7. $m = \dfrac{1}{3}$ **9.** $m = \dfrac{6}{11}$ **11.** undefined **13.** positive
15. Negative **17.** Zero **19.** Undefined **21.** Positive
23. Negative **25.** $m = \dfrac{1}{2}$ **27.** $m = -3$ **29.** $m = 0$
31. The slope is undefined. **33.** $\dfrac{1}{3}$ **35.** -3 **37.** $\dfrac{3}{5}$
39. Zero **41.** Undefined **43.** $\dfrac{28}{5}$ **45.** $-\dfrac{7}{8}$
47. -0.45 or $-\dfrac{9}{20}$ **49.** -0.15 or $-\dfrac{3}{20}$ **51. a.** -2 **b.** $\dfrac{1}{2}$
53. a. 0 **b.** undefined **55. a.** $\dfrac{4}{5}$ **b.** $-\dfrac{5}{4}$ **57.** Perpendicular
59. Parallel **61.** Neither **63.** l_1: $m = 2$, l_2: $m = 2$; parallel
65. l_1: $m = 5$, l_2: $m = -\dfrac{1}{5}$; perpendicular
67. l_1: $m = \dfrac{1}{4}$, l_2: $m = 4$; neither **69.** The average rate of change is $-\$160$ per year. **71. a.** $m = 47$ **b.** The number of male prisoners increased at a rate of 47 thousand per year during this time period. **73. a.** 1 mi **b.** 2 mi **c.** 3 mi **d.** $m = 0.2$; The distance between a lightning strike and an observer increases by 0.2 mi for every additional second between seeing lightning and hearing thunder.

75. $m = \dfrac{3}{4}$ **77.** $m = 0$

79. For example: $(4, -4)$ and $(-2, 0)$

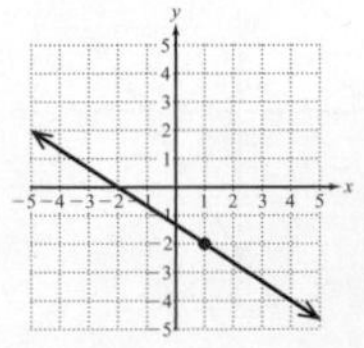

81. For example: $(3, 5)$ and $(1, -1)$

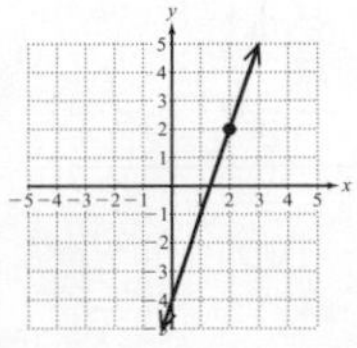

83. For example: $(-3, 1)$ and $(-3, 4)$

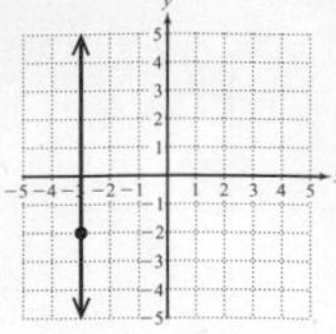

85.

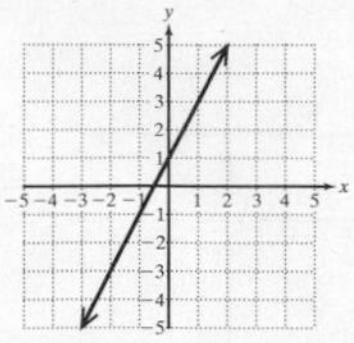

87.

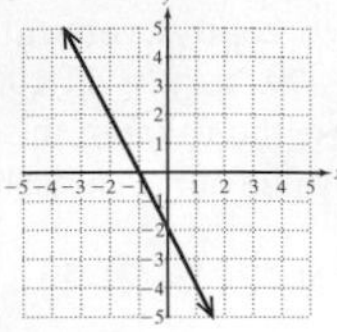

89.

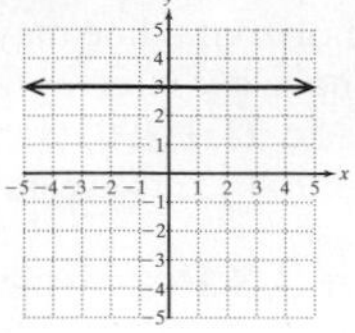

91. $\dfrac{3m - 3n}{2b}$ or $\dfrac{-3m + 3n}{-2b}$ **93.** $\left(\dfrac{c}{a}, 0\right)$

95. For example: $(7, 1)$

Section 3.4 Calculator Connections, p. 237

1. Perpendicular

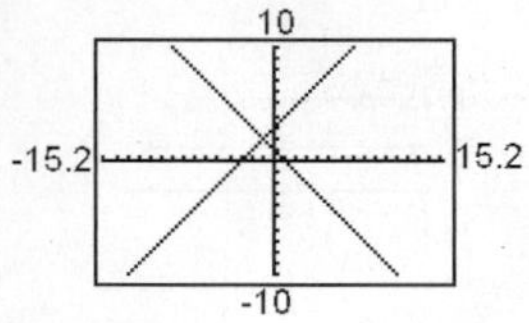

2. Parallel

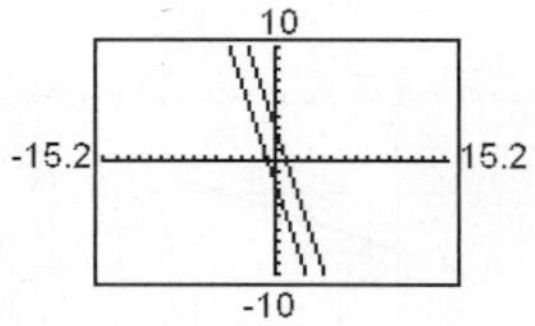

3. Neither

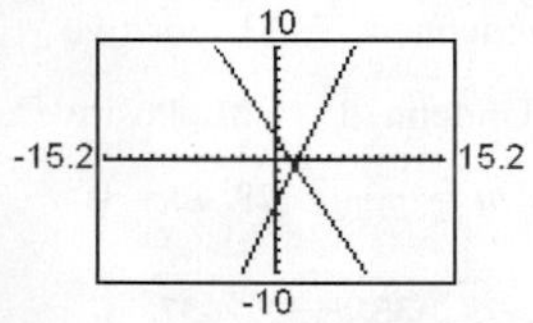

4. The lines may appear parallel; however, they are not parallel because the slopes are different. **5.** The lines may appear to coincide on a graph; however, they are not the same line because the y-intercepts are different. **6.** The line may appear to be horizontal, but it is not. The slope is 0.001 rather than 0.

Section 3.4 Practice Exercises, pp. 238–242

1. a. $y = mx + b$ **b.** standard **3.** x-intercept: $(10, 0)$; y-intercept: $(0, -2)$ **5.** x-intercept: none; y-intercept: $(0, -3)$ **7.** x-intercept: $(0, 0)$; y-intercept: $(0, 0)$ **9.** x-intercept: $(4, 0)$; y-intercept: none **11.** $m = -2$; y-intercept: $(0, 3)$ **13.** $m = 1$; y-intercept: $(0, -2)$ **15.** $m = -1$; y-intercept: $(0, 0)$

17. $m = \dfrac{3}{4}$; y-intercept: $(0, -1)$ **19.** $m = \dfrac{2}{5}$; y-intercept: $\left(0, -\dfrac{4}{5}\right)$ **21.** $m = 3$; y-intercept: $(0, -5)$

23. $m = -1$; y-intercept: $(0, 6)$ **25.** Undefined slope; no y-intercept **27.** $m = 0$; y-intercept: $\left(0, -\dfrac{1}{4}\right)$

29. $m = \dfrac{2}{3}$; y-intercept: $(0, 0)$

31.

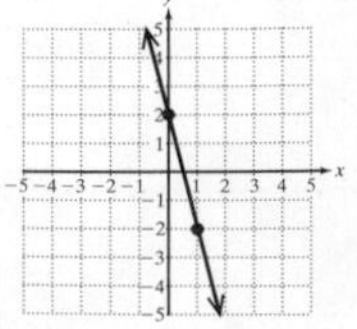

33.

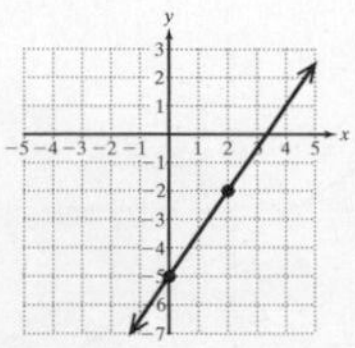

35. b **37.** e **39.** c

41. $y = -2x + 9$

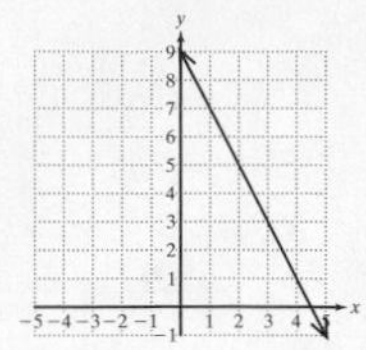

43. $y = \dfrac{1}{2}x - 3$

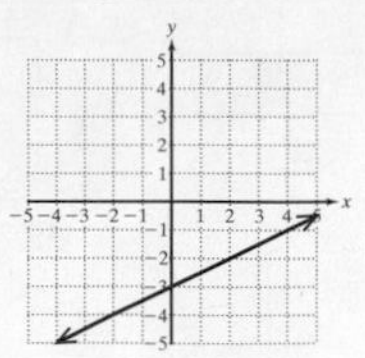

45. $y = -\dfrac{1}{2}x + \dfrac{3}{2}$

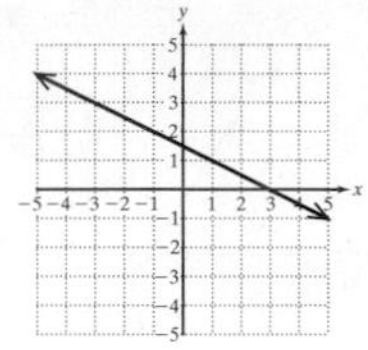

47. $y = -x$

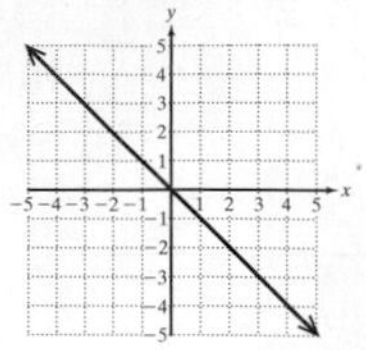

49. $y = \dfrac{4}{5}x$

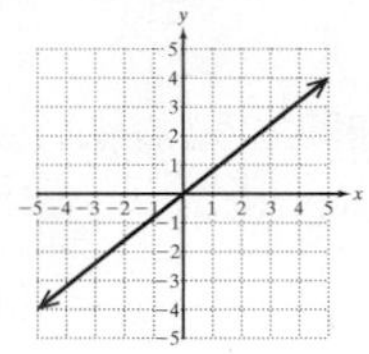

51. $y = -\dfrac{2}{3}$

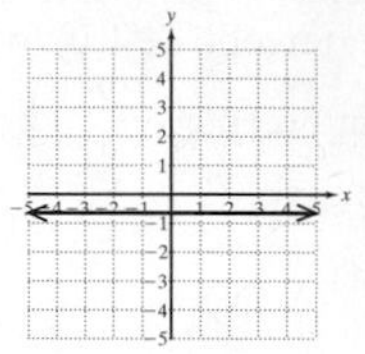

53. Perpendicular **55.** Neither **57.** Parallel **59.** Perpendicular **61.** Parallel **63.** Perpendicular **65.** Neither **67.** Parallel **69.** $y = -\dfrac{1}{3}x + 2$

71. $y = 10x - 19$ **73.** $y = 6x - 8$ **75.** $y = \dfrac{1}{2}x - 3$

77. $y = -11$ **79.** $y = 5x$ **81.** $y = -2x + 3$

83. $y = -\dfrac{1}{3}x + 2$ **85.** $y = 4x - 1$ **87. a.** $m = 1203$; The slope represents the rate of increase in the number of cases of Lyme disease per year. **b.** $(0, 10006)$; In the year 1993 there were 10,006 cases reported. **c.** 30,457 cases **d.** $x = 22$; the year 2015

89. $y = -\dfrac{A}{B}x + \dfrac{C}{B}$; the slope is $-\dfrac{A}{B}$.

91. $m = -\dfrac{6}{7}$ **93.** $m = \dfrac{11}{8}$

Chapter 3 Problem Recognition Exercises, p. 242

1. a, c, d **2.** b, f, h **3.** a **4.** f **5.** b, f **6.** c **7.** c, d **8.** f **9.** e **10.** g **11.** b **12.** h **13.** g **14.** e **15.** c **16.** b, h **17.** e **18.** e **19.** b, f, h **20.** c, d

Section 3.5 Practice Exercises, pp. 247–251

1. a. $Ax + By = C$ **b.** horizontal **c.** vertical **d.** slope; y-intercept **e.** $y - y_1 = m(x - x_1)$

3.

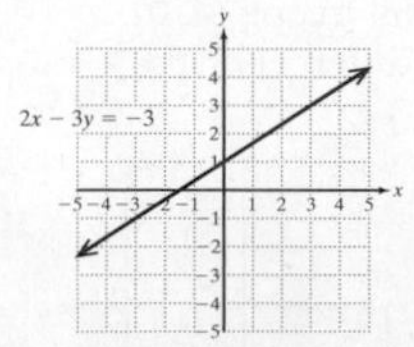

5.

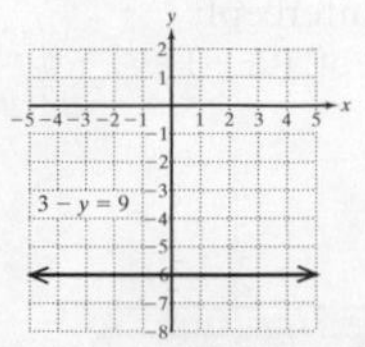

7. 9 **9.** 0 **11.** $y = 3x + 7$ or $3x - y = -7$

13. $y = -4x - 14$ or $4x + y = -14$ **15.** $y = -\dfrac{1}{2}x - \dfrac{1}{2}$ or $x + 2y = -1$ **17.** $y = 2x - 2$ or $2x - y = 2$

19. $y = -x - 4$ or $x + y = -4$
21. $y = -0.2x - 2.86$ or $20x + 100y = -286$
23. $y = -2x + 1$ **25.** $y = 2x + 4$ **27.** $y = \frac{1}{2}x - 1$
29. $y = 4x + 13$ or $4x - y = -13$
31. $y = -\frac{3}{2}x + 6$ or $3x + 2y = 12$
33. $y = -2x - 8$ or $2x + y = -8$ **35.** $y = -\frac{1}{5}x - 6$ or $x + 5y = -30$ **37.** iv **39.** vi **41.** iii **43.** $y = 1$
45. $x = 2$ **47.** $y = 2$ **49.** $y = \frac{1}{4}x + 8$ or $x - 4y = -32$
51. $y = 3x - 8$ or $3x - y = 8$ **53.** $y = 4.5x - 25.6$ or $45x - 10y = 256$ **55.** $x = -6$ **57.** $y = -2$
59. $x = -4$ **61.** $y = 2x - 4$ **63.** $y = -\frac{1}{2}x + 1$

Section 3.6 Calculator Connections, p. 255

1. 13.3

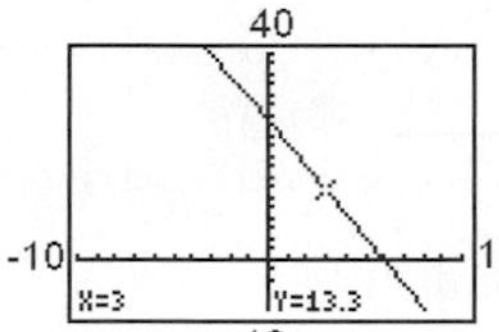

2. −42.3

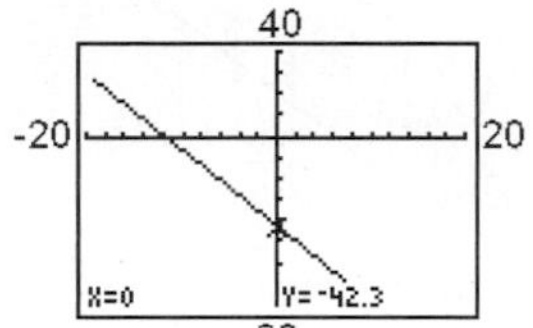

3. 345

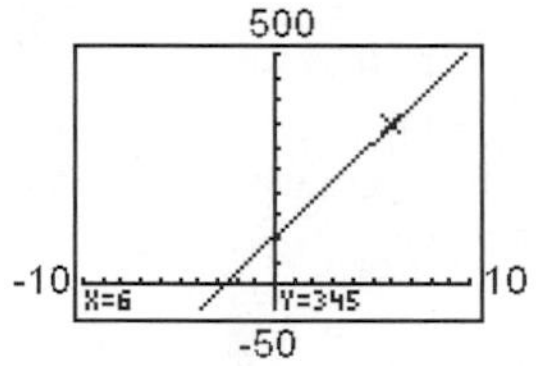

4. 95

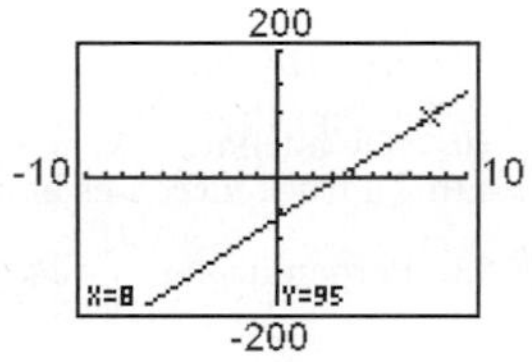

Section 3.6 Practice Exercises, pp. 255–259

1. $m = -\frac{5}{2}$ **3.** x-intercept: (6, 0); y-intercept: (0, 5)
5. x-intercept: (−2, 0); y-intercept: (0, −4) **7.** x-intercept: none; y-intercept: (0, −9) **9. a.** \$3.00 **b.** \$7.90 **c.** The y-intercept is (0, 1.6). This indicates that the minimum wage was \$1.60 per hour in the year 1970. **d.** The slope is 0.14. This indicates that the minimum wage has risen approximately \$0.14 per year during this period.
11. a. $m = \frac{2}{7}$ **b.** $m = \frac{4}{7}$ **c.** $m = \frac{2}{7}$ means that Grindel's weight increased at a rate of 2 oz in 7 days. $m = \frac{4}{7}$ means that Frisco's weight increased at a rate of 4 oz in 7 days. **d.** Frisco gained weight more rapidly. **13. a.** \$106.95 **b.** \$201.95 **c.** (0, 11.95). For 0 kilowatt-hours used, the cost consists of only the fixed monthly tax of \$11.95. **d.** $m = 0.095$. The cost increases by \$0.095 for each kilowatt-hour used. **15. a.** $m = -1.0$ **b.** $y = -x + 1051$ **c.** The minimum pressure was approximately 921 mb.
17. a. $m = 21.5$ **b.** The slope means that the consumption of wind energy in the United States increased by 21.5 trillion Btu per year. **c.** $y = 21.5x + 57$ **d.** 272 trillion Btu **19. a.** $y = 0.20x + 39.99$ **b.** \$47.99 **21. a.** $y = 90x + 105$ **b.** \$1185.00
23. a. $y = 0.8x + 100$ **b.** \$260.00

Chapter 3 Review Exercises, pp. 265–269

1.

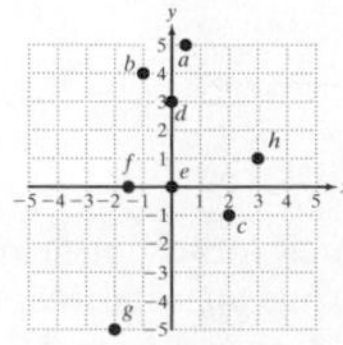

2. $A(4, -3)$; $B(-3, -2)$; $C(\frac{5}{2}, 5)$; $D(-4, 1)$; $E(-\frac{1}{2}, 0)$; $F(0, -5)$
3. III **4.** II **5.** IV **6.** I **7.** IV **8.** III **9.** x-axis **10.** y-axis **11. a.** On day 1, the price was \$26.25. **b.** Day 2 **c.** \$2.25 **12. a.** In 2003 (8 years after 1995), there was only one space shuttle launch. (This was the year that the Columbia and its crew were lost.)
b.

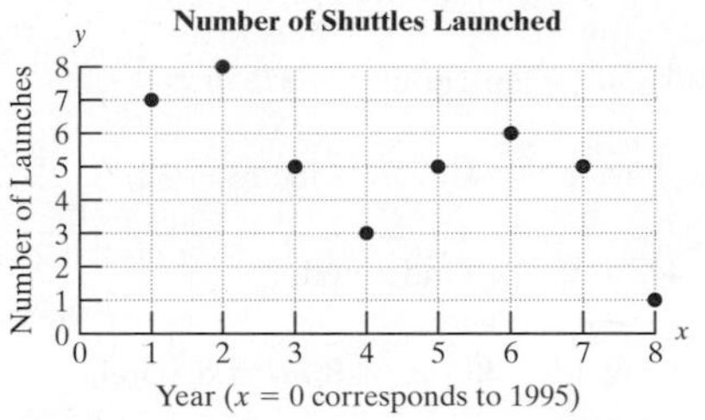

13. No **14.** No **15.** Yes **16.** Yes

17.

x	y
2	1
3	4
1	−2

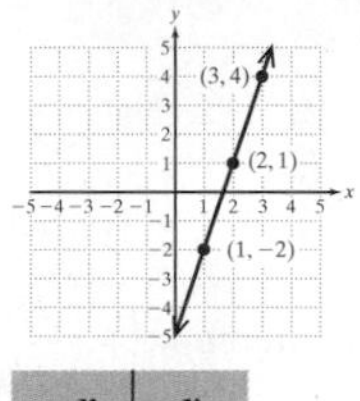

18.

x	y
0	2
−2	7/3
−6	3

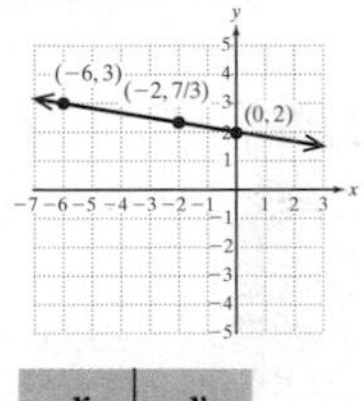

19.

x	y
0	−1
3	1
−6	−5

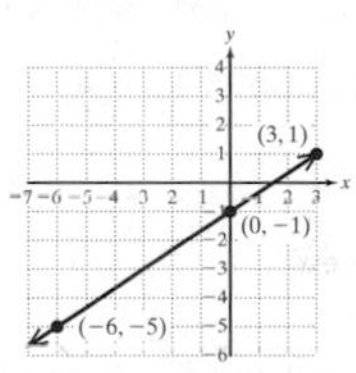

20.

x	y
0	−3
−3	3
1	−5

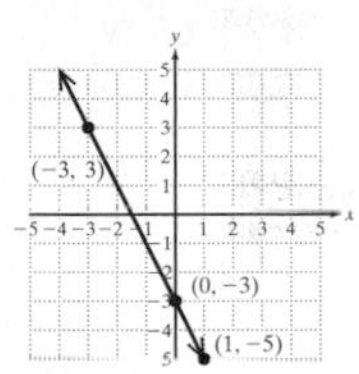

21.

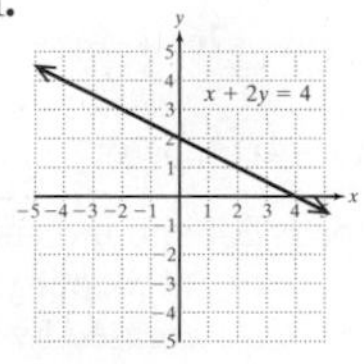

22.

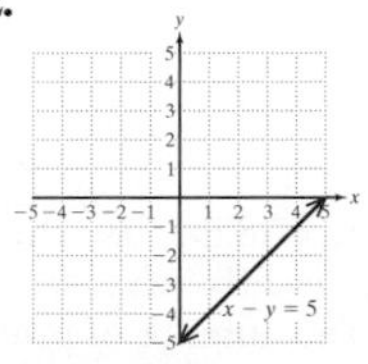

23.

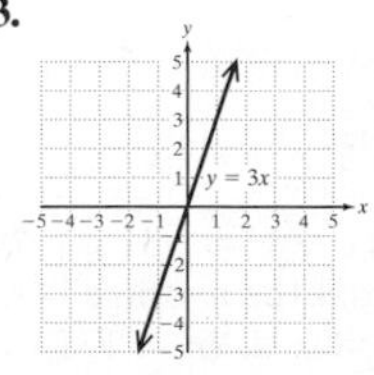

24.

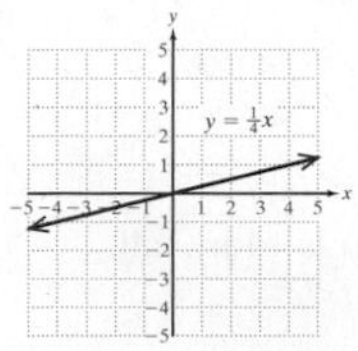

25. Vertical

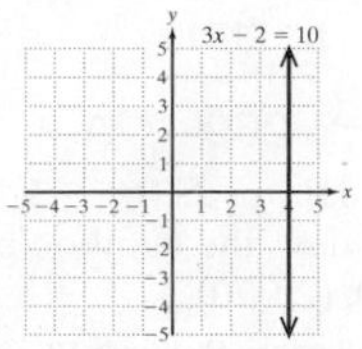

26. Vertical

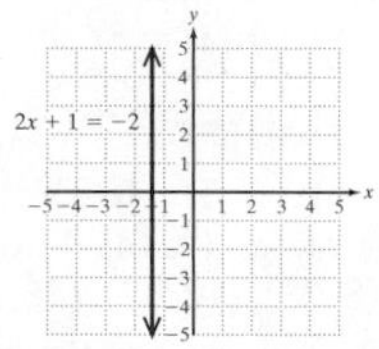

27. Horizontal

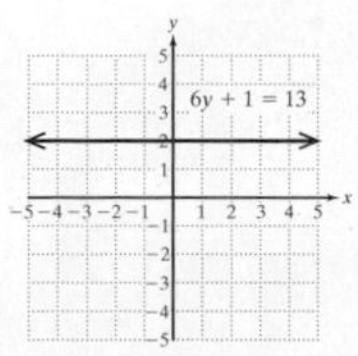

28. Horizontal

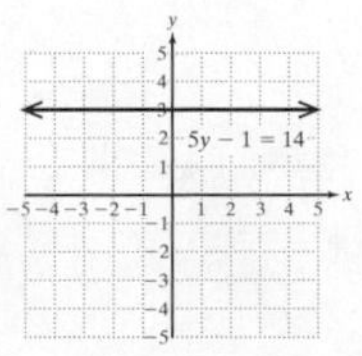

29. x-intercept: $(-3, 0)$; y-intercept: $\left(0, \frac{3}{2}\right)$
30. x-intercept: $(3, 0)$; y-intercept: $(0, 6)$ **31.** x-intercept: $(0, 0)$; y-intercept: $(0, 0)$ **32.** x-intercept: $(0, 0)$; y-intercept: $(0, 0)$
33. x-intercept: none; y-intercept: $(0, -4)$ **34.** x-intercept: none; y-intercept: $(0, 2)$ **35.** x-intercept: $\left(-\frac{5}{2}, 0\right)$; y-intercept: none
36. x-intercept: $\left(\frac{1}{3}, 0\right)$; y-intercept: none **37.** $m = \frac{12}{5}$
38. -2 **39.** $-\frac{2}{3}$ **40.** 8 **41.** Undefined **42.** 0
43. a. -5 **b.** $\frac{1}{5}$ **44. a.** 0 **b.** Undefined
45. $m_1 = \frac{2}{3}$; $m_2 = \frac{2}{3}$; parallel **46.** $m_1 = 8$; $m_2 = 8$; parallel
47. $m_1 = -\frac{5}{12}$; $m_2 = \frac{12}{5}$; perpendicular **48.** $m_1 =$ undefined; $m_2 = 0$; perpendicular **49. a.** $m = 35$ **b.** The number of kilowatt-hours increased at a rate of 35 kilowatt-hours per day.
50. a. $m = -994$ **b.** The number of new cars sold in Maryland decreased at a rate of 994 cars per year.
51. $y = \frac{5}{2}x - 5$; $m = \frac{5}{2}$; y-intercept: $(0, -5)$
52. $y = -\frac{3}{4}x + 3$; $m = -\frac{3}{4}$; y-intercept: $(0, 3)$
53. $y = \frac{1}{3}x$; $m = \frac{1}{3}$; y-intercept: $(0, 0)$ **54.** $y = \frac{12}{5}$; $m = 0$; y-intercept: $\left(0, \frac{12}{5}\right)$ **55.** $y = -\frac{5}{2}$; $m = 0$; y-intercept: $\left(0, -\frac{5}{2}\right)$
56. $y = x$; $m = 1$; y-intercept: $(0, 0)$ **57.** Neither
58. Perpendicular **59.** Parallel **60.** Parallel
61. Perpendicular **62.** Neither **63.** $y = -\frac{4}{3}x - 1$ or $4x + 3y = -3$ **64.** $y = 5x$ or $5x - y = 0$ **65.** $y = -\frac{4}{3}x - 6$ or $4x + 3y = -18$ **66.** $y = 5x - 3$ or $5x - y = 3$
67. For example: $y = 3x + 2$ **68.** For example: $5x + 2y = -4$
69. $m = \frac{y_2 - y_1}{x_2 - x_1}$ **70.** $y - y_1 = m(x - x_1)$
71. For example: $x = 6$ **72.** For example: $y = -5$
73. $y = -6x + 2$ or $6x + y = 2$ **74.** $y = \frac{2}{3}x + \frac{5}{3}$ or $2x - 3y = -5$ **75.** $y = \frac{1}{4}x - 4$ or $x - 4y = 16$ **76.** $y = -5$
77. $y = \frac{6}{5}x + 6$ or $6x - 5y = -30$ **78.** $y = 4x + 31$ or $4x - y = -31$ **79. a.** 47.8 in. **b.** The slope is 2.4 and indicates that the average height for girls increases at a rate of 2.4 in. per year.
80. a. $m = 137$ **b.** The number of prescriptions increased by 137 million per year during this time period. **c.** $y = 137x + 2825$ **d.** 4880 million **81. a.** $y = 20x + 55$ **b.** \$235
82. a. $y = 8x + 700$ **b.** \$1340

Chapter 3 Test, pp. 269–271

1. a. II **b.** IV **c.** III **2.** 0 **3.** 0
4. a. (4, 14) After 4 days the bamboo plant is 14 in. tall. (8, 28), (12, 42), (16, 56), (20, 70)
b.

Height of Bamboo Plant per Day

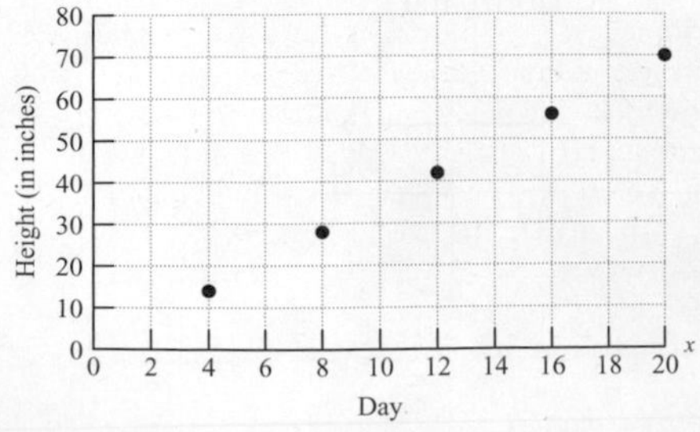

c. Approximately 35 in.
5. a. No **b.** Yes **c.** Yes **d.** Yes
6.

x	y
0	-2
4	-1
6	$-\frac{1}{2}$

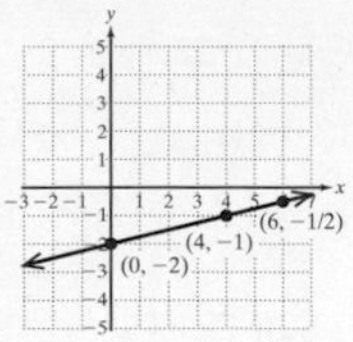

7.

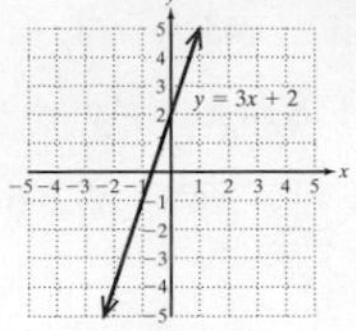

8.

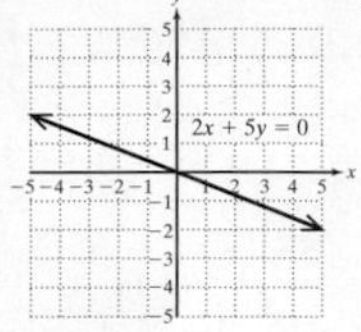

9.

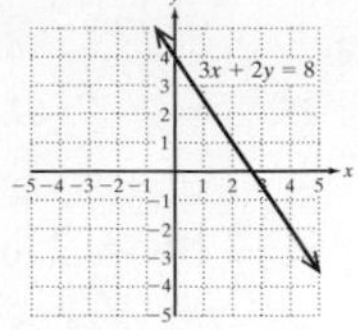

10.

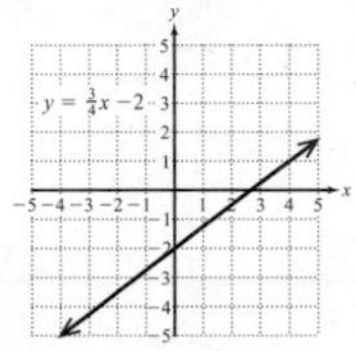

11. Horizontal

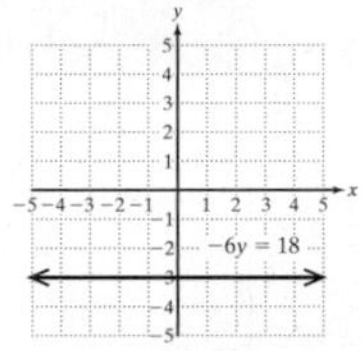

12. Vertical

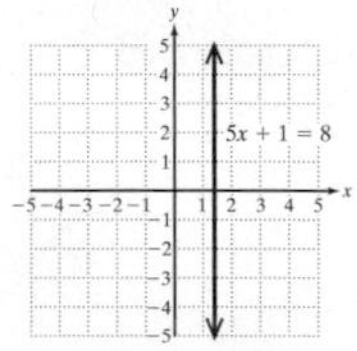

13. x-intercept: $\left(-\frac{3}{2}, 0\right)$; y-intercept: $(0, 2)$
14. x-intercept: $(0, 0)$; y-intercept: $(0, 0)$ **15.** x-intercept: $(4, 0)$; y-intercept: none **16.** x-intercept: none; y-intercept: $(0, 3)$
17. $\frac{2}{5}$ **18. a.** $\frac{1}{3}$ **b.** $\frac{4}{3}$ **19. a.** $-\frac{1}{4}$ **b.** 4
20. a. Undefined **b.** 0 **21. a.** $m = 0.6$ **b.** The cost of renting a truck increases at a rate of \$0.60 per mile. **22.** Parallel
23. Perpendicular **24.** $y = -\frac{1}{3}x + 1$ or $x + 3y = 3$
25. $y = -\frac{7}{2}x + 15$ or $7x + 2y = 30$ **26.** $y = \frac{1}{4}x + \frac{1}{2}$ or $x - 4y = -2$ **27.** $y = 3x + 8$ or $3x - y = -8$ **28.** $y = -6$
29. $y = -x - 3$ or $x + y = -3$ **30. a.** $y = 1.5x + 10$ **b.** \$25
31. a. $m = 20$; The slope indicates that there is an increase of 20 thousand medical doctors per year. **b.** $y = 20x + 414$ **c.** 1114 thousand or, equivalently, 1,114,000

Chapters 1–3 Cumulative Review Exercises, pp. 271–272

1. a. Rational **b.** Rational **c.** Irrational **d.** Rational
2. a. $\frac{2}{3}; \frac{2}{3}$ **b.** -5.3; 5.3 **3.** 69 **4.** -13 **5.** 18
6. $\frac{3}{4} \div \left(-\frac{7}{8}\right)$; $-\frac{6}{7}$ **7.** $(-2.1)(-6)$; 12.6 **8.** The associative property of addition **9.** $\{4\}$ **10.** $\{5\}$ **11.** $\left\{-\frac{9}{2}\right\}$
12. $\{-2\}$ **13.** 9241 mi^2 **14.** $a = \frac{c - b}{3}$
15.

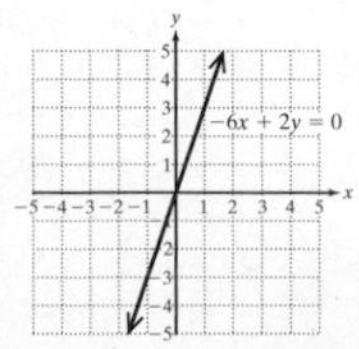

16. x-intercept: $(-2, 0)$; y-intercept: $(0, 1)$
17. $y = -\frac{3}{2}x - 6$; slope: $-\frac{3}{2}$; y-intercept: $(0, -6)$
18. $2x + 3 = 5$ can be written as $x = 1$, which represents a vertical line. A vertical line of the form $x = k$ $(k \neq 0)$ has an x-intercept of $(k, 0)$ and no y-intercept. **19.** $y = -3x + 1$ or $3x + y = 1$
20. $y = \frac{2}{3}x + 6$ or $2x - 3y = -18$

Chapter 4

Chapter Opener Puzzle

One drink costs \$3.50 and one popcorn costs \$5.00.

Section 4.1 Calculator Connections, pp. 278–279

1. $\{(2, 1)\}$

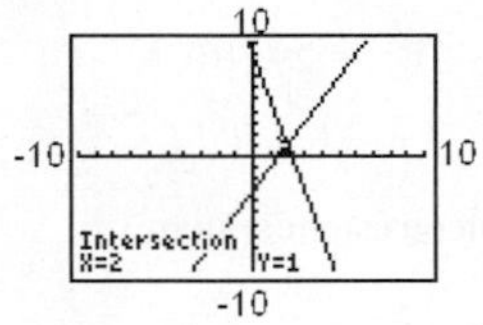

2. $\{(6, -1)\}$

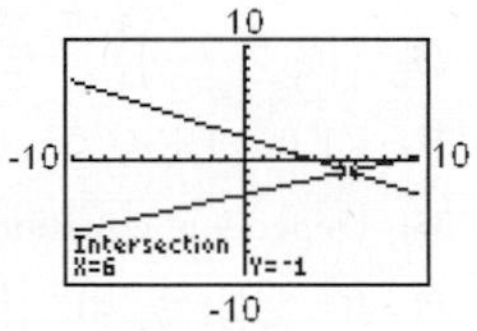

3. $\{(3, 1)\}$

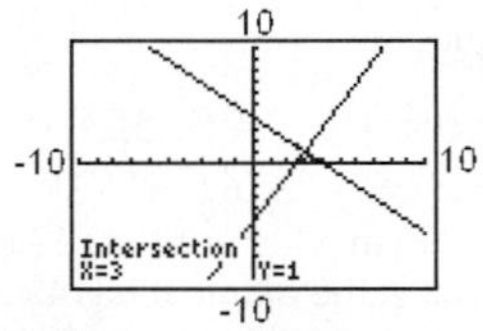

4. $\{(-2, 0)\}$

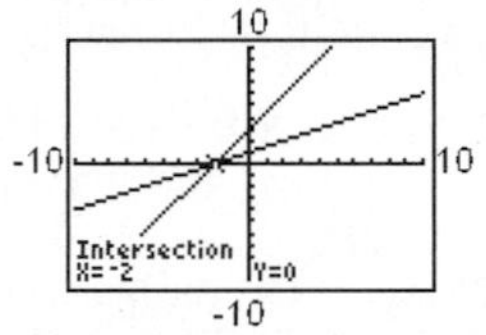

5. { }

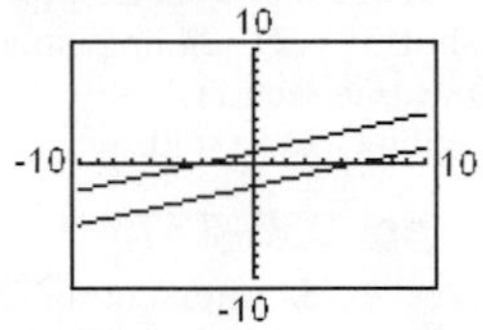

6. $\left\{(x, y) | y = -\frac{1}{4}x + 2\right\}$

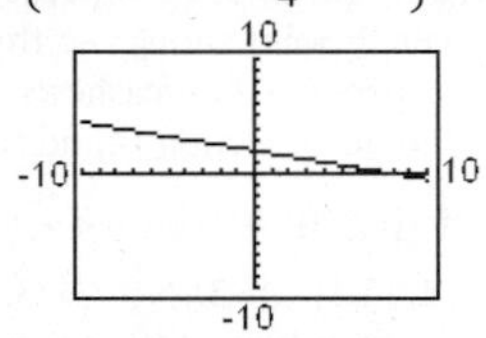

Section 4.1 Practice Exercises, pp. 279–284

1. a. system **b.** solution **c.** intersect **d.** consistent **e.** { } **f.** dependent **g.** independent **3.** Yes **5.** No **7.** Yes **9.** No **11.** b **13.** d

15. a.

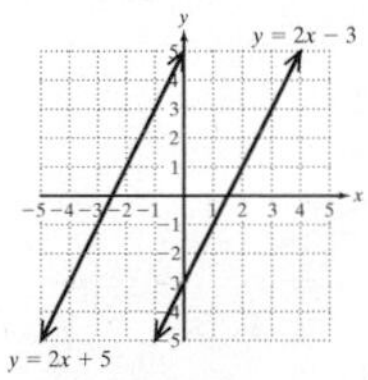

b.

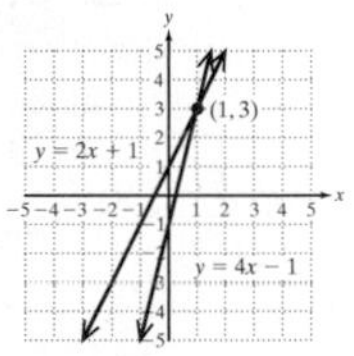

c.

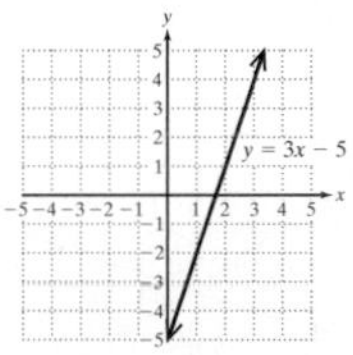

17. c **19.** a **21.** a **23.** b **25.** c

27. $\{(3, 1)\}$

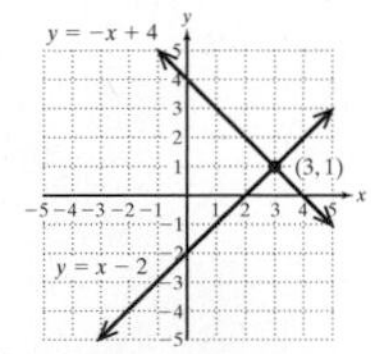

29. $\{(1, -2)\}$

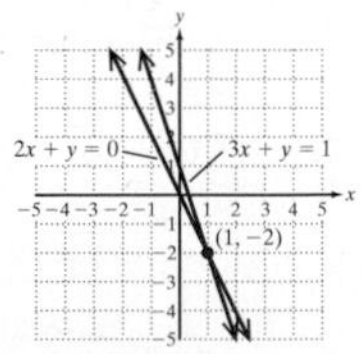

31. $\{(1, 4)\}$

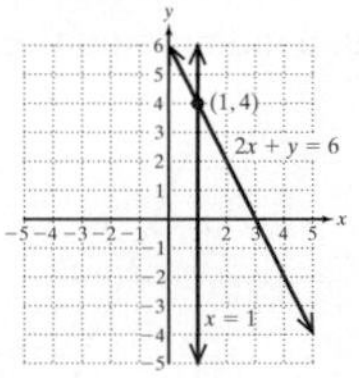

33. { }; inconsistent system

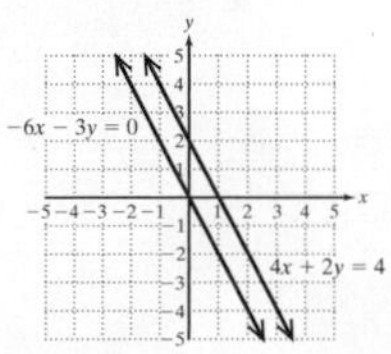

35. Infinitely many solutions; $\{(x, y) | -2x + y = 3\}$; dependent equations

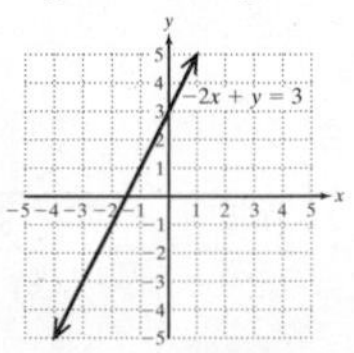

37. $\{(-3, 6)\}$

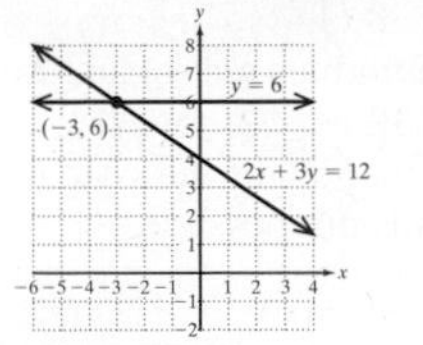

39. $\{(2, -2)\}$

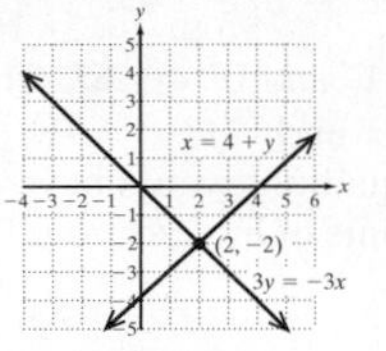

41. { }; inconsistent system

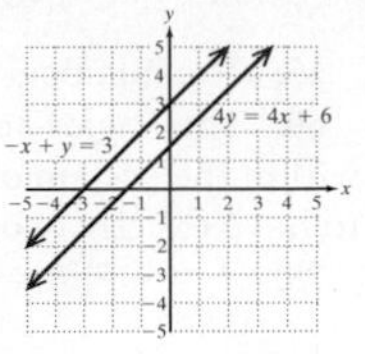

43. $\{(4, 2)\}$

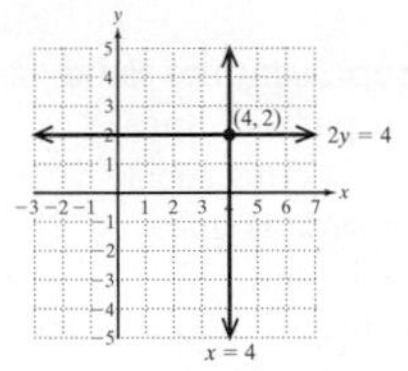

45. $\{(1, 2)\}$

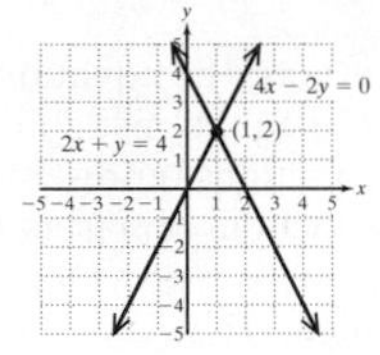

47. Infinitely many solutions; $\{(x, y) | y = 0.5x + 2\}$; dependent equations

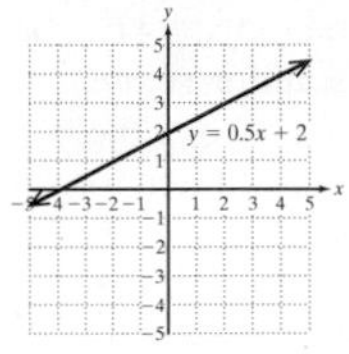

49. $\{(-3, -1)\}$

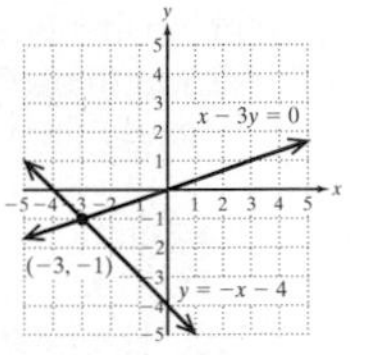

51. The same cost occurs when \$2500 of merchandise is purchased. **53.** The point of intersection is below the x-axis and cannot have a positive y-coordinate. **55.** For example: $4x + y = 9$; $-2x - y = -5$ **57.** For example: $2x + 2y = 1$

Section 4.2 Practice Exercises, pp. 292–294

1. $y = 2x - 4$; $y = 2x - 4$; coinciding lines

3. $y = -\frac{2}{3}x + 2$; $y = x - 5$; intersecting lines

5. $y = 4x - 4$; $y = 4x - 13$; parallel lines **7.** $\{(3, -6)\}$ **9.** $\{(0, 4)\}$ **11. a.** y in the second equation is easiest to isolate because its coefficient is 1. **b.** $\{(1, 5)\}$ **13.** $\{(5, 2)\}$ **15.** $\{(10, 5)\}$

17. $\left\{\left(\frac{1}{2}, 3\right)\right\}$ **19.** $\{(5, 3)\}$ **21.** $\{(1, 0)\}$ **23.** $\{(1, 4)\}$

25. { }; inconsistent system **27.** Infinitely many solutions; $\{(x, y) | 2x - 6y = -2\}$; dependent equations **29.** $\{(5, -7)\}$

31. $\left\{\left(-5, \frac{3}{2}\right)\right\}$ **33.** $\{(2, -5)\}$ **35.** $\{(-4, 6)\}$ **37.** $\{(0, 2)\}$

39. Infinitely many solutions; $\{(x, y) | y = 0.25x + 1\}$; dependent equations **41.** $\{(1, 1)\}$ **43.** { }; inconsistent system **45.** $\{(-1, 5)\}$ **47.** $\{(-6, -4)\}$ **49.** The numbers are 48 and 58. **51.** The numbers are 13 and 39. **53.** The angles are 165° and 15°. **55.** The angles are 70° and 20°. **57.** The angles are 42° and 48°. **59.** For example: (0, 3), (1, 5), (−1, 1)

Section 4.3 Practice Exercises, pp. 301–303

1. No **3.** No **5.** Yes **7. a.** True **b.** False, multiply the second equation by 5. **9. a.** x would be easier. **b.** $\{(0, -3)\}$ **11.** $\{(4, -1)\}$ **13.** $\{(4, 3)\}$ **15.** $\{(2, 3)\}$ **17.** $\{(1, -4)\}$

19. $\{(1, -1)\}$ **21.** $\{(-4, -6)\}$ **23.** $\left\{\left(\frac{7}{9}, \frac{5}{9}\right)\right\}$

25. The system will have no solution. The lines are parallel. **27.** There are infinitely many solutions. The lines coincide. **29.** The system will have one solution. The lines intersect at a point whose x-coordinate is 0. **31.** { }; inconsistent system **33.** Infinitely many solutions; $\{(x, y) | x + 2y = 2\}$; dependent equations **35.** $\{(1, 4)\}$ **37.** $\{(-1, -2)\}$ **39.** $\{(2, 1)\}$ **41.** { }; inconsistent system **43.** $\{(2, 3)\}$ **45.** $\{(3.5, 2.5)\}$

47. $\left\{\left(\frac{1}{3}, 2\right)\right\}$ **49.** $\{(-2, 5)\}$ **51.** $\left\{\left(-\frac{1}{2}, 1\right)\right\}$ **53.** $\{(0, 3)\}$

55. { } **57.** {(1, 4)} **59.** {(4, 0)} **61.** Infinitely many solutions; $\{(a, b)|9a - 2b = 8\}$ **63.** $\left\{\left(\frac{7}{16}, -\frac{7}{8}\right)\right\}$

65. The numbers are 17 and 19. **67.** The numbers are −1 and 3. **69.** The angles are 46° and 134°. **71.** {(1, 3)} **73.** One line within the system of equations would have to "bend" for the system to have exactly two points of intersection. This is not possible.
75. $A = -5, B = 2$

Chapter 4 Problem Recognition Exercises, p. 304

1. Infinitely many solutions. The equations represent the same line. **2.** No solution. The equations represent parallel lines.
3. One solution. The equations represent intersecting lines.
4. One solution. The equations represent intersecting lines.
5. No solution. The equations represent parallel lines.
6. Infinitely many solutions. The equations represent the same line.
7. The y variable will easily be eliminated by adding the equations. The solution set is {(−3, 1)}. **8.** The x variable will easily be eliminated by multiplying the second equation by 2 and then adding the equations. The solution set is {(3, 4)}. **9.** Because the variable x is already isolated in the first equation, the expression $-3y + 4$ can be easily substituted for x in the second equation. The solution set is {(−2, 2)}. **10.** Because the variable y is already isolated in the second equation, the expression $x - 8$ can be easily substituted for y in the first equation. The solution set is {(8, 0)}. **11.** {(5, 0)}
12. {(1, −7)} **13.** {(4, −5)} **14.** {(2, 3)} **15.** {(2, 0)}
16. {(8, 10)} **17.** $\left\{\left(2, -\frac{5}{7}\right)\right\}$ **18.** $\left\{\left(-\frac{14}{3}, -4\right)\right\}$
19. { }; inconsistent system **20.** { }; inconsistent system
21. {(−1, 0)} **22.** {(5, 0)} **23.** Infinitely many solutions; $\{(x, y)|y = 2x - 14\}$; dependent equations **24.** Infinitely many solutions; $\{(x, y)|x = 5y - 9\}$; dependent equations
25. {(2200, 1000)} **26.** {(3300, 1200)} **27.** {(5, −7)}
28. {(2, −1)} **29.** $\left\{\left(\frac{2}{3}, \frac{1}{2}\right)\right\}$ **30.** $\left\{\left(\frac{1}{4}, -\frac{3}{2}\right)\right\}$

Section 4.4 Practice Exercises, pp. 310–314

1. {(−1, 4)} **3.** $\left\{\left(\frac{5}{2}, 1\right)\right\}$ **5.** The numbers are 4 and 16.

7. The angles are 80° and 10°. **9.** It costs \$8.80 to rent a video game and \$5.50 to rent a DVD. **11.** Technology stock costs \$16 per share, and the mutual fund costs \$11 per share. **13.** Mylee bought forty 45 cent stamps and ten 65 cent stamps. **15.** Shanelle invested \$3500 in the 10% account and \$6500 in the 7% account.
17. \$9000 was borrowed at 6%, and \$3000 was borrowed at 9%.
19. Invest \$12,000 in the bond fund and \$18,000 in the stock fund.
21. 15 gal of the 50% mixture should be mixed with 10 gal of the 40% mixture. **23.** 12 gal of the 45% disinfectant solution should be mixed with 8 gal of the 30% disinfectant solution.
25. She should mix 20 mL of the 13% solution with 30 mL of the 18% solution. **27.** Chad needs 1 L of pure antifreeze and 5 L of the 40% solution. **29.** The speed of the boat in still water is 6 mph, and the speed of the current is 2 mph. **31.** The speed of the plane in still air is 300 mph, and the wind is 20 mph. **33.** The speed of the plane in still air is 525 mph and the speed of the wind is 75 mph. **35.** There are 17 dimes and 22 nickels. **37.** 2 qt of water should be mixed. **39. a.** 835 free throws and 1597 field goals **b.** 4029 points **c.** Approximately 50 points per game
41. The speed of the plane in still air is 160 mph, and the wind is 40 mph. **43.** \$15,000 was invested in the 5.5% account, and \$45,000 was invested in the 6.5% account. **45.** 12 lb of candy should be mixed with 8 lb of nuts. **47.** Dallas scored 30 points, and Buffalo scored 13 points. **49.** There were 300 women and 200 men in the survey.

Section 4.5 Practice Exercises, pp. 320–322

1. a. linear **b.** ordered triples **3.** { } **5.** The speeds are 65 mph and 58 mph. **7.** (4, 0, 2) is a solution.
9. (1, 1, 1) is a solution. **11.** {(1, −2, 4)}
13. {(−1, 2, 0)} **15.** {(−2, −1, −3)} **17.** {(1, −4, −2)}
19. {(1, 2, 3)} **21.** {(−6, 1, 7)} **23.** $\left\{\left(\frac{1}{2}, \frac{2}{3}, -\frac{5}{6}\right)\right\}$
25. $\left\{\left(\frac{1}{2}, 2, -\frac{1}{2}\right)\right\}$ **27.** {(6, −3, −2)} **29.** {(0, 4, −4)}
31. {(1, 0, −1)} **33.** {(−20, 8, 0)}

35. Dependent equations **37.** Inconsistent system
39. {(1, 3, 1)} **41.** $\left\{\left(-\frac{1}{2}, \frac{1}{3}, \frac{1}{6}\right)\right\}$
43. Dependent equations **45.** {(1, 0, 1)}
47. {(0, 0, 0)} **49.** Dependent equations

Section 4.6 Practice Exercises, pp. 325–327

1. {(−7, 0, 8)} **3.** Inconsistent system **5.** 67°, 82°, 31°
7. 25°, 56°, 99° **9.** 10 cm, 18 cm, 27 cm **11.** 11 in., 17 in., 26 in. **13.** The fiber supplement has 3 g; the oatmeal has 4 g; and the cereal has 1.5 g. **15.** Kyoki invested \$2000 in bonds, \$6000 in mutual funds, and \$2000 in the money market account. **17.** \$1500 at 5%, \$2000 at 5.5%, \$1000 at 4% **19.** He made six free throws, seven 2-point shots, and three 3-point shots. **21.** 24 oz peanuts, 8 oz pecans, 16 oz cashews **23.** 1500 seats in section A, 400 seats in section B, and 500 seats in section C were sold.

Chapter 4 Review Exercises, pp. 335–337

1. Yes **2.** No **3.** No **4.** Yes **5.** Intersecting lines (The lines have different slopes.) **6.** Intersecting lines (The lines have different slopes.) **7.** Parallel lines (The lines have the same slope but different y-intercepts.) **8.** Intersecting lines (The lines have different slopes.) **9.** Coinciding lines (The lines have the same slope and same y-intercept.) **10.** Intersecting lines (The lines have different slopes.)

11. {(0, −2)}

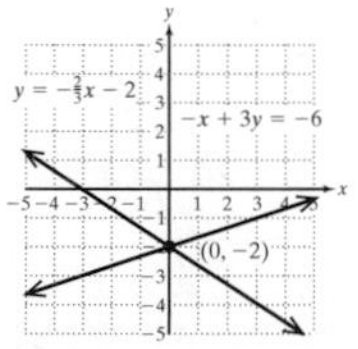

12. {(−2, 3)}

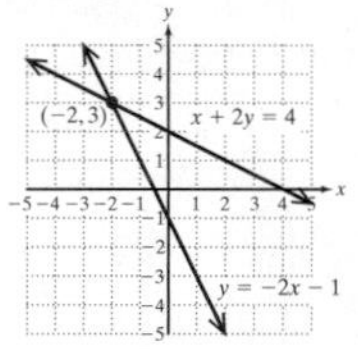

13. Infinitely many solutions; $\{(x, y)|2x + y = 5\}$; dependent equations

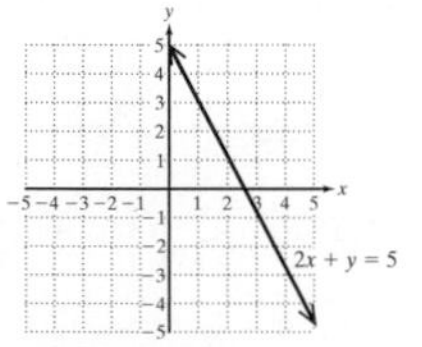

14. Infinitely many solutions; $\{(x, y)|-x + 5y = -5\}$; dependent equations

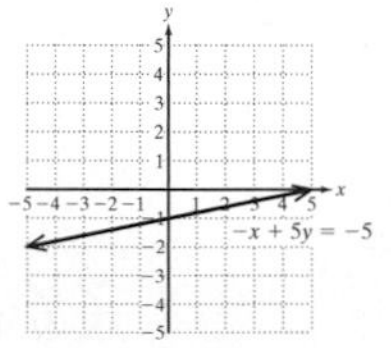

15. {(1, −1)}

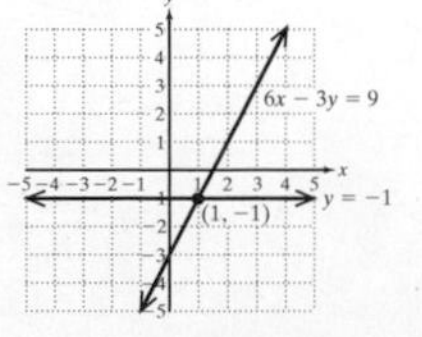

16. {(−1, 2)}

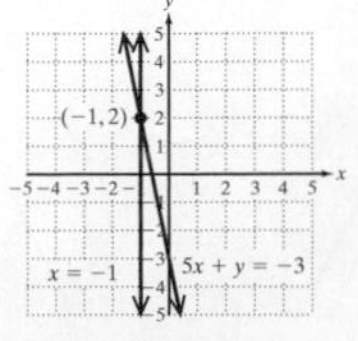

17. { }; inconsistent system

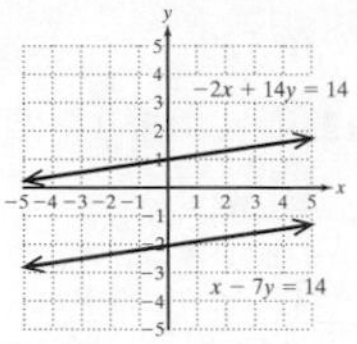

18. { }; inconsistent system

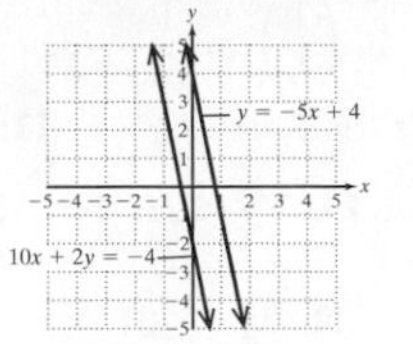

19. Using 39 minutes per month, the cost per month for each company is \$9.75. **20.** $\left\{\left(\frac{2}{3}, -2\right)\right\}$ **21.** $\{(-4, 1)\}$
22. { } **23.** Infinitely many solutions; $\{(x, y) | y = -2x + 2\}$
24. a. x in the first equation is easiest to isolate because its coefficient is 1. **b.** $\left\{\left(6, \frac{5}{2}\right)\right\}$ **25. a.** y in the second equation is easiest to isolate because its coefficient is 1. **b.** $\left\{\left(\frac{9}{2}, 3\right)\right\}$
26. $\{(5, -4)\}$ **27.** $\{(0, 4)\}$ **28.** Infinitely many solutions; $\{(x, y) | x - 3y = 9\}$ **29.** { } **30.** The numbers are 50 and 8.
31. The angles are 42° and 48°. **32.** The angles are $115\frac{1}{3}°$ and $64\frac{2}{3}°$.
33. See page 295. **34. b.** $\{(-3, -2)\}$ **35. b.** $\{(2, 2)\}$
36. $\{(2, -1)\}$ **37.** $\{(-6, 2)\}$ **38.** $\left\{\left(-\frac{1}{2}, \frac{1}{3}\right)\right\}$
39. $\left\{\left(\frac{1}{4}, -\frac{2}{5}\right)\right\}$ **40.** Infinitely many solutions; $\{(x, y) | -4x - 6y = -2\}$ **41.** { } **42.** $\{(-4, -2)\}$
43. $\{(1, 0)\}$ **44. b.** $\{(5, -3)\}$ **45. b.** $\{(-2, -1)\}$
46. There were 8 adult tickets and 52 children's tickets sold.
47. He should invest \$75,000 at 12% and \$525,000 at 4%.
48. 20 gal of whole milk should be mixed with 40 gal of low fat milk.
49. The speed of the boat is 18 mph, and that of the current is 2 mph.
50. The plane's speed in still air is 320 mph. The wind speed is 30 mph. **51.** A hot dog costs \$4.50 and a drink costs \$3.50.
52. The score was 72 on the first round and 82 on the second round.
53. $\{(2, -1, 5)\}$ **54.** Inconsistent system
55. Dependent equations **56.** $\{(-1, -2, 2)\}$
57. $\{(1, -3, -2)\}$ **58.** $\{(-1, 4, 0)\}$ **59.** 5, 12, and 13 ft
60. The pumps can drain 250, 300, and 400 gal/hr.
61. She invested \$6000 in Fund A, \$4000 in Fund B, and \$2000 in Fund C. **62.** The angles are 13°, 39°, and 128°.

Chapter 4 Test, pp. 338–339

1. $y = -\frac{5}{2}x - 3$; $y = -\frac{5}{2}x + 3$; Parallel lines
2. $\{(3, 2)\}$

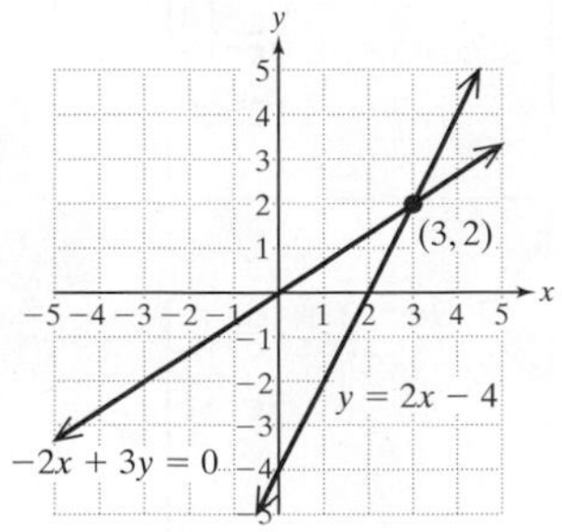

3. Infinitely many solutions; $\{(x, y) | 2x + 4y = 12\}$

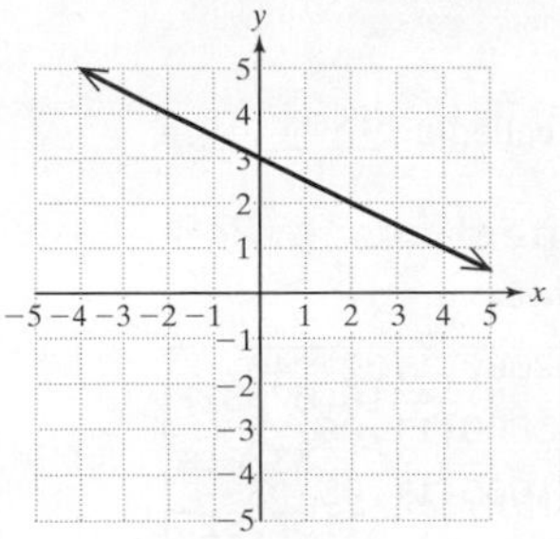

4. $\{(-2, 0)\}$ **5.** Swoopes scored 614 points and Jackson scored 597. **6.** $\left\{\left(2, -\frac{1}{3}\right)\right\}$ **7.** 12 mL of the 50% acid solution should be mixed with 24 mL of the 20% solution.
8. a. No solution **b.** Infinitely many solutions **c.** One solution
9. $\{(-5, 4)\}$ **10.** { } **11.** $\{(3, -5)\}$ **12.** $\{(-1, 2)\}$
13. Infinitely many solutions; $\{(x, y) | 10x + 2y = -8\}$
14. $\{(1, -2)\}$ **15.** CDs cost \$8 each and DVDs cost \$11 each.
16. a. \$18 was required. **b.** They used 24 quarters and 12 \$1 bills.
17. \$1200 was borrowed at 10%, and \$3800 was borrowed at 8%.
18. They would be the same cost for a distance of approximately 24 mi. **19.** The plane travels 500 mph in still air, and the wind speed is 45 mph. **20.** The cake has 340 calories, and the ice cream has 120 calories. **21.** 60 mL of 10% solution and 40 mL of 25% solution. **22.** $\{(16, -37, 9)\}$ **23.** $\{(2, -2, 5)\}$
24. { } **25.** The sides are 5 ft, 15 ft, and 23 ft
26. \$5500 was invested in Fund A. \$4000 was invested in Fund B, and \$2000 was invested in Fund C. **27.** Joanne 142 orders; Kent 162 orders; Geoff 200 orders

Chapters 1–4 Cumulative Review Exercises, pp. 339–340

1. $\frac{11}{6}$ **2.** $\left\{-\frac{21}{2}\right\}$ **3.** { } **4.** $y = \frac{3}{2}x - 3$
5. $x = 5z + m$ **6.** $\left[\frac{3}{11}, \infty\right)$

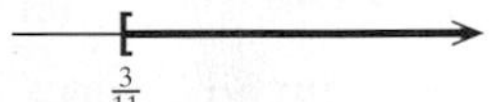

7. The angles are 37°, 33°, and 110°. **8.** The rates of the hikers are 2 mph and 4 mph. **9.** Jesse Ventura received approximately 762,200 votes. **10.** 36% of the goal has been achieved. **11.** The angles are 36.5° and 53.5°.
12. Slope: $-\frac{5}{3}$; y-intercept: $(0, -2)$
13. a. $-\frac{2}{3}$ **b.** $\frac{3}{2}$ **14.** $y = -3x + 3$
15. c. $\{(0, 2)\}$ **16.** $\{(0, 2)\}$

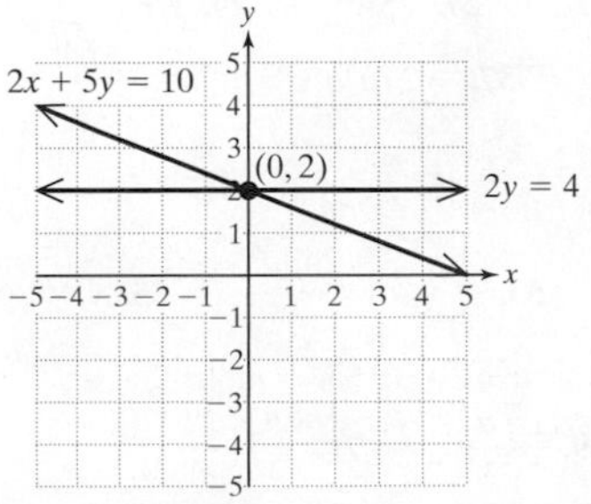

17. 20 gal of the 15% solution should be mixed with 40 gal of the 60% solution. **18.** x is 27°; y is 63° **19. a.** 1.4 **b.** Between 1920 and 1990, the winning speed in the Indianapolis 500 increased on average by 1.4 mph per year.
20. $\{(1, 0, 4)\}$

Chapter 5

Chapter Opener Puzzle

A polynomial that has two terms is called a BINOMIAL.

Section 5.1 Calculator Connections, p. 348

1.–3.

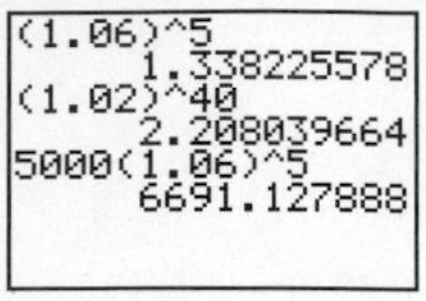

4.–6.

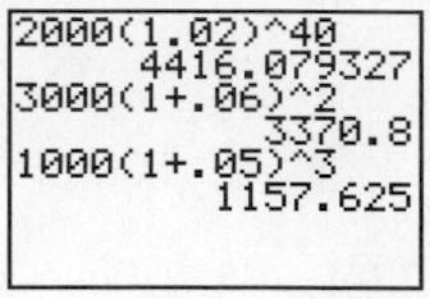

Section 5.1 Practice Exercises, pp. 349–351

1. a. exponent **b.** base; exponent **c.** 1 **d.** $I = Prt$ **e.** compound interest **3.** Base: x; exponent: 4 **5.** Base: 3; exponent: 5 **7.** Base: -1; exponent: 4 **9.** Base: 13; exponent: 1 **11.** Base: 10; exponent: 3 **13.** Base: t; exponent: 6 **15.** v **17.** 1 **19.** $(-6b)^2$ **21.** $-6b^2$ **23.** $(y+2)^4$ **25.** $\frac{-2}{t^3}$ **27.** No; $-5^2 = -25$ and $(-5)^2 = 25$ **29.** Yes; -32 **31.** Yes; $\frac{1}{8}$ **33.** Yes; -16 **35.** 16 **37.** -1 **39.** $\frac{1}{9}$ **41.** $-\frac{4}{25}$ **43.** 48 **45.** 4 **47.** 9 **49.** 50 **51.** -100 **53.** 400 **55.** 1 **57.** 1 **59.** 1000 **61.** -800 **63. a.** $(x \cdot x \cdot x \cdot x)(x \cdot x \cdot x) = x^7$ **b.** $(5 \cdot 5 \cdot 5 \cdot 5)(5 \cdot 5 \cdot 5) = 5^7$ **65.** z^8 **67.** a^9 **69.** 4^{14} **71.** $\left(\frac{2}{3}\right)^4$ **73.** c^{14} **75.** x^{18} **77. a.** $\frac{p \cdot p \cdot p \cdot p \cdot p \cdot p \cdot p \cdot p}{p \cdot p \cdot p} = p^5$ **b.** $\frac{8 \cdot 8 \cdot 8 \cdot 8 \cdot 8 \cdot 8 \cdot 8 \cdot 8}{8 \cdot 8 \cdot 8} = 8^5$ **79.** x^2 **81.** a^9 **83.** 7^7 **85.** 5^7 **87.** y **89.** h^4 **91.** 7^7 **93.** 10^9 **95.** $6x^7$ **97.** $40a^5b^5$ **99.** s^9t^{16} **101.** $-30v^8$ **103.** $16m^{20}n^{10}$ **105.** $2cd^4$ **107.** z^4 **109.** $\frac{25hjk^4}{12}$ **111.** $-8p^7q^9r^6$ **113.** $-3stu$ **115.** \$5724.50 **117.** \$4764.06 **119.** 201 in.^{2} **121.** 268 in.^{3} **123.** x^{2n+1} **125.** p^{2m+3} **127.** z **129.** r^3

Section 5.2 Practice Exercises, pp. 355–356

1. 4^9 **3.** a^{20} **5.** d^9 **7.** 7^6 **9.** When multiplying expressions with the same base, add the exponents. When raising an expression with an exponent to a power, multiply the exponents. **11.** 5^{12} **13.** 12^6 **15.** y^{14} **17.** w^{25} **19.** a^{36} **21.** y^{14} **23.** They are both equal to 2^6. **25.** $4^{3^2} = 4^9$; $(4^3)^2 = 4^6$; the expression 4^{3^2} is greater than $(4^3)^2$. **27.** $25w^2$ **29.** $s^4r^4t^4$ **31.** $\frac{16}{r^4}$ **33.** $\frac{x^5}{y^5}$ **35.** $81a^4$ **37.** $-27a^3b^3c^3$ **39.** $-\frac{64}{x^3}$ **41.** $\frac{a^2}{b^2}$ **43.** $6^3u^6v^{12}$ or $216u^6v^{12}$ **45.** $5x^8y^4$ **47.** $-h^{28}$ **49.** m^{12} **51.** $\frac{4^5}{r^5s^{20}}$ or $\frac{1024}{r^5s^{20}}$ **53.** $\frac{3^5p^5}{q^{15}}$ or $\frac{243p^5}{q^{15}}$ **55.** y^{14} **57.** x^{31} **59.** $200a^{14}b^9$ **61.** $16p^8q^{16}$ **63.** $-m^{35}n^{15}$ **65.** $25a^{18}b^6$ **67.** $\frac{4c^2d^6}{9}$ **69.** $\frac{c^{27}d^{31}}{2}$ **71.** $-\frac{27a^9b^3}{c^6}$ **73.** $16b^{26}$ **75.** x^{2m} **77.** $125a^{6n}$ **79.** $\frac{m^{2b}}{n^{3b}}$ **81.** $\frac{3^na^{3n}}{5^nb^{4n}}$

Section 5.3 Practice Exercises, pp. 364–366

1. a. 1 **b.** $\left(\frac{1}{b}\right)^n$ or $\frac{1}{b^n}$ **3.** c^9 **5.** y **7.** 3^6 or 729 **9.** $7^4w^{28}z^8$ or $2401w^{28}z^8$ **11. a.** 1 **b.** 1 **13.** 1 **15.** 1 **17.** -1 **19.** 1 **21.** 1 **23.** -7 **25. a.** $\frac{1}{t^5}$ **b.** $\frac{1}{t^5}$ **27.** $\frac{343}{8}$ **29.** 25 **31.** $\frac{1}{a^3}$ **33.** $\frac{1}{12}$ **35.** $\frac{1}{16b^2}$ **37.** $\frac{6}{x^2}$ **39.** $\frac{1}{64}$ **41.** $-\frac{3}{y^4}$ **43.** $-\frac{1}{t^3}$ **45.** a^5 **47.** $\frac{x^4}{x^{-6}} = x^{4-(-6)} = x^{10}$ **49.** $2a^{-3} = 2 \cdot \frac{1}{a^3} = \frac{2}{a^3}$ **51.** $\frac{1}{x^4}$ **53.** 1 **55.** y^4 **57.** $\frac{n^{27}}{m^{18}}$ **59.** $\frac{81k^{24}}{j^{20}}$ **61.** $\frac{1}{p^6}$ **63.** $\frac{1}{r^3}$ **65.** a^8 **67.** $\frac{1}{y^8}$ **69.** $\frac{1}{7^7}$ **71.** 1 **73.** $\frac{1}{a^4b^6}$ **75.** $\frac{1}{w^{21}}$ **77.** $\frac{1}{27}$ **79.** 1 **81.** $\frac{1}{64x^6}$ **83.** $-\frac{16y^4}{z^2}$ **85.** $-\frac{a^{12}}{6}$ **87.** $80c^{21}d^{24}$ **89.** $\frac{9y^2}{8x^5}$ **91.** $\frac{4d^{16}}{c^2}$ **93.** $\frac{9y^2}{2x}$ **95.** $\frac{9}{20}$ **97.** $\frac{9}{10}$ **99.** $\frac{5}{4}$ **101.** $\frac{10}{3}$ **103.** 2 **105.** -11

Chapter 5 Problem Recognition Exercises, p. 366

1. t^8 **2.** 2^8 or 256 **3.** y^5 **4.** p^6 **5.** r^4s^8 **6.** $a^3b^9c^6$ **7.** w^6 **8.** $\frac{1}{m^{16}}$ **9.** $\frac{x^4z^3}{y^7}$ **10.** $\frac{a^3c^8}{b^6}$ **11.** x^6 **12.** $\frac{1}{y^{10}}$ **13.** $\frac{1}{t^5}$ **14.** w^7 **15.** p^{15} **16.** p^{15} **17.** $\frac{1}{v^2}$ **18.** $c^{50}d^{40}$ **19.** 3 **20.** -4 **21.** $\frac{b^9}{2^{15}}$ **22.** $\frac{81}{y^6}$ **23.** $\frac{16y^4}{81x^4}$ **24.** $\frac{25d^6}{36c^2}$ **25.** $3a^7b^5$ **26.** $64x^7y^{11}$ **27.** $\frac{y^4}{x^8}$ **28.** $\frac{1}{a^{10}b^{10}}$ **29.** $\frac{1}{t^2}$ **30.** $\frac{1}{p^7}$ **31.** $\frac{8w^6x^9}{27}$ **32.** $\frac{25b^8}{16c^6}$ **33.** $\frac{q^3s}{r^2t^5}$ **34.** $\frac{m^2p^3q}{n^3}$ **35.** $\frac{1}{y^{13}}$ **36.** w^{10} **37.** $-\frac{1}{8a^{18}b^6}$ **38.** $\frac{4x^{18}}{9y^{10}}$ **39.** $\frac{k^8}{5h^6}$ **40.** $\frac{6n^{10}}{m^{12}}$

Section 5.4 Calculator Connections, p. 370

1.–2.

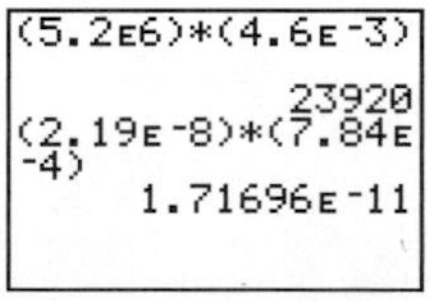

3.–4.

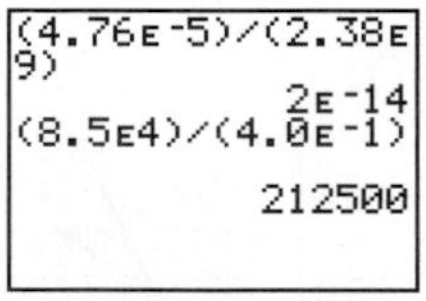

5.

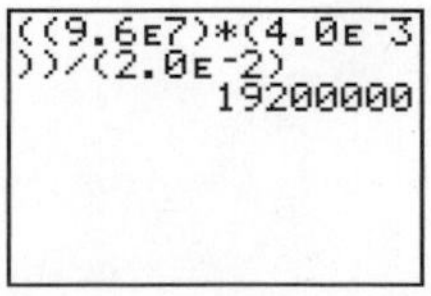

6.

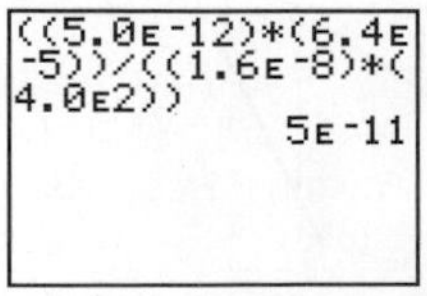

Section 5.4 Practice Exercises, pp. 371–373

1. scientific notation **3.** b^{13} **5.** 10^{13} **7.** $\frac{1}{y^5}$ **9.** $\frac{x^{20}}{y^{12}}$
11. w^4 **13.** 10^4 **15.** Move the decimal point between the 2 and 3 and multiply by 10^{-10}; 2.3×10^{-10}. **17.** 5×10^4
19. 2.08×10^5 **21.** 6.01×10^6 **23.** 8×10^{-6}
25. 1.25×10^{-4} **27.** 6.708×10^{-3} **29.** 1.7×10^{-24} g
31. $\$2.7 \times 10^{10}$ **33.** 6.8×10^7 gal; 1×10^2 miles
35. Move the decimal point nine places to the left; 0.000 000 0031.
37. 0.00005 **39.** 2800 **41.** 0.000603 **43.** 2,400,000
45. 0.019 **47.** 7032 **49.** 0.000 000 000 001 g
51. 1600 Cal and 2800 Cal **53.** 5×10^4 **55.** 3.6×10^{11}
57. 2.2×10^4 **59.** 2.25×10^{-13} **61.** 3.2×10^{14}
63. 2.432×10^{-10} **65.** 3×10^{13} **67.** 6×10^5 **69.** 1.38×10^1
71. 5×10^{-14} **73.** 3.75 in. **75.** $\$2.97 \times 10^{10}$
77. a. 6.5×10^7 **b.** 2.3725×10^{10} days **c.** 5.694×10^{11} hr **d.** 2.04984×10^{15} sec

Section 5.5 Practice Exercises, pp. 379–382

1. a. polynomial **b.** coefficient; degree **c.** 1 **d.** one **e.** binomial **f.** trinomial **g.** leading; leading coefficient **h.** greatest **i.** zero **3.** $\frac{45}{x^2}$ **5.** $\frac{2}{t^4}$ **7.** $\frac{1}{3^{12}}$ **9.** 4×10^{-2} is in scientific notation in which 10 is raised to the -2 power. 4^{-2} is not in scientific notation and 4 is being raised to the -2 power.
11. a. $-7x^5 + 7x^2 + 9x + 6$ **b.** -7 **c.** 5 **13.** Binomial; 75
15. Monomial; 54 **17.** Binomial; -12 **19.** Trinomial; 27
21. Monomial; -192 **23.** The exponents on the x-factors are different. **25.** $35x^2y$ **27.** $8b^5d^2 - 9d$ **29.** $4y^2 + y - 9$
31. $-x^3 + 5x^2 + 9x - 10$ **33.** $10.9y$ **35.** $4a - 8c$
37. $a - \frac{1}{2}b - 2$ **39.** $\frac{4}{3}z^2 - \frac{5}{3}$ **41.** $7.9t^3 - 3.4t^2 + 6t - 4.2$
43. $-4h + 5$ **45.** $2.3m^2 - 3.1m + 1.5$
47. $-3v^3 - 5v^2 - 10v - 22$ **49.** $-8a^3b^2$ **51.** $-53x^3$
53. $-5a - 3$ **55.** $16k + 9$ **57.** $2m^4 - 14m$
59. $3s^2 - 4st - 3t^2$ **61.** $-2r - 3s + 3t$ **63.** $\frac{3}{4}x + \frac{1}{3}y - \frac{3}{10}$
65. $-\frac{2}{3}h^2 + \frac{3}{5}h - \frac{5}{2}$ **67.** $2.4x^4 - 3.1x^2 - 4.4x - 7.9$
69. $4b^3 + 12b^2 - 5b - 12$ **71.** $-\frac{7}{2}x^2 + 5x - 11$
73. $4y^3 + 2y^2 + 2$ **75.** $3a^2 - 3a + 5$
77. $9ab^2 - 3ab + 16a^2b$ **79.** $4z^5 + z^4 + 9z^3 - 3z - 2$
81. $2x^4 + 11x^3 - 3x^2 + 8x - 4$ **83.** $-w^3 + 0.2w^2 + 3.7w - 0.7$
85. $-p^2q - 4pq^2 + 3pq$ **87.** 0 **89.** $-5ab + 6ab^2$
91. $11y^2 - 10y - 4$ **93.** For example: $x^3 + 6$
95. For example: $8x^5$ **97.** For example: $-6x^2 + 2x + 5$

Section 5.6 Practice Exercises, pp. 389–392

1. a. $5 - 2x$ **b.** squares; $a^2 - b^2$ **c.** perfect; $a^2 + 2ab + b^2$
3. $-2y^2$ **5.** $-8y^4$ **7.** $8uvw^2$ **9.** $7u^2v^2w^4$ **11.** $-12y$
13. $21p$ **15.** $12a^{14}b^8$ **17.** $-2c^{10}d^{12}$
19. $16p^2q^2 - 24p^2q + 40pq^2$ **21.** $-4k^3 + 52k^2 + 24k$
23. $-45p^3q - 15p^4q^3 + 30pq^2$ **25.** $y^2 + 19y + 90$
27. $m^2 - 14m + 24$ **29.** $12p^2 - 5p - 2$
31. $12w^2 - 32w + 16$ **33.** $p^2 - 14pw + 33w^2$
35. $12x^2 + 28x - 5$ **37.** $6a^2 - 21.5a + 18$
39. $9t^3 - 21t^2 + 3t - 7$ **41.** $9m^2 + 30mn + 24n^2$
43. $5s^3 + 8s^2 - 7s - 6$ **45.** $27w^3 - 8$
47. $p^4 + 5p^3 - 2p^2 - 21p + 5$ **49.** $6a^3 - 23a^2 + 38a - 45$
51. $8x^3 - 36x^2y + 54xy^2 - 27y^3$ **53.** $1.2x^2 + 7.6xy + 2.4y^2$
55. $y^2 - 36$ **57.** $9a^2 - 16b^2$ **59.** $81k^2 - 36$
61. $\frac{4}{9}t^2 - 9$ **63.** $u^6 - 25v^2$ **65.** $\frac{4}{9} - p^2$
67. $a^2 + 10a + 25$ **69.** $x^2 - 2xy + y^2$ **71.** $4c^2 + 20c + 25$
73. $9t^4 - 24st^2 + 16s^2$ **75.** $t^2 - 14t + 49$ **77.** $16q^2 + 24q + 9$
79. a. 36 **b.** 20 **c.** $(a + b)^2 \neq a^2 + b^2$ in general.
81. $4x^2 - 25$ **83.** $16p^2 + 40p + 25$
85. $27p^3 - 135p^2 + 225p - 125$ **87.** $15a^5 - 6a^2$
89. $49x^2 - y^2$ **91.** $25s^2 + 30st + 9t^2$ **93.** $21x^2 - 65xy + 24y^2$
95. $2t^2 + \frac{26}{3}t + 8$ **97.** $-30x^2 - 35x + 25$
99. $6a^3 + 11a^2 - 7a - 2$ **101.** $y^3 - 3y^2 - 6y - 20$
103. $\frac{1}{9}m^2 - \frac{2}{3}mn + n^2$ **105.** $42w^3 - 84w^2$ **107.** $16y^2 - 65.61$
109. $21c^4 + 4c^2 - 32$ **111.** $9.61x^2 + 27.9x + 20.25$
113. $k^3 - 12k^2 + 48k - 64$ **115.** $125x^3 + 225x^2 + 135x + 27$
117. $2y^4 + 3y^3 + 3y^2 + 5y + 3$ **119.** $6a^3 + 22a^2 - 40a$
121. $2x^3 - 13x^2 + 17x + 12$ **123.** $2x - 7$
125. $k = 10$ or -10 **127.** $k = 8$ or -8

Section 5.7 Practice Exercises, pp. 400–402

1. a. division; quotient; remainder **b.** Synthetic
3. a. $-4a - 11b$ **b.** $5a^2 - 49ab - 10b^2$
5. a. $7x^2 + 2$ **b.** $6x^4 - 5x^3 + x^2 - 2x$
7. For example: $(5y + 1)^2 = 25y^2 + 10y + 1$
9. $-4t^3 + t - 5$ **11.** $12 + 8y + 2y^2$
13. $x^2 + 3xy - y^2$ **15.** $2y^2 + 3y - 8$
17. $-\frac{1}{2}p^3 + p^2 - \frac{1}{3}p + \frac{1}{6}$ **19.** $a^2 + 5a + 1 - \frac{5}{a}$
21. $-3s^2t + 4s - \frac{5}{t^2}$ **23.** $8p^2q^6 - 9p^3q^5 - 11p - \frac{4}{p^2q}$
25. a. Divisor $(x - 2)$; quotient $(2x^2 - 3x - 1)$; remainder (-3) **b.** Multiply the quotient and the divisor, then add the remainder. The result should equal the dividend.
27. $x + 7 + \frac{-9}{x + 4}$ **29.** $3y^2 + 2y + 2 + \frac{9}{y - 3}$
31. $-4a + 11$ **33.** $6y - 5$ **35.** $6x^2 + 4x + 5 + \frac{22}{3x - 2}$
37. $4a^2 - 2a + 1$ **39.** $x^2 - 2x + 2$ **41.** $x^2 + 2x + 5$
43. $x^2 - 1 + \frac{8}{x^2 - 2}$ **45.** $n^3 + 2n^2 + 4n + 8$
47. $3y^2 - 3 + \frac{2y + 6}{y^2 + 1}$
49. The divisor must be of the form $x - r$.
51. No. The divisor is not of the form $x - r$.
53. a. $x - 5$ **b.** $x^2 + 3x + 11$ **c.** 58
55. $x + 6$ **57.** $t - 4$ **59.** $5y + 10 + \frac{11}{y - 1}$
61. $3y^2 - 2y + 2 + \frac{-3}{y + 3}$ **63.** $x^2 - x - 2$
65. $a^4 + 2a^3 + 4a^2 + 8a + 16$ **67.** $x^2 + 6x + 36$
69. $4w^3 + 2w^2 + 6$ **71.** $-x^2 - 4x + 13 + \frac{-54}{x + 4}$
73. $2x - 1 + \frac{3}{x}$ **75.** $4y - 3 + \frac{4y + 5}{3y^2 - 2y + 5}$
77. $2x^2 + 3x - 1$ **79.** $2k^3 - 4k^2 + 1 - \frac{5}{k^4}$
81. $x + \frac{9}{5} + \frac{2}{x}$

Chapter 5 Problem Recognition Exercises, p. 403

1. a. $8x^2$ **b.** $12x^4$ **2. a.** $9y^3$ **b.** $8y^6$ **3. a.** $16x^2 + 8xy + y^2$ **b.** $16x^2y^2$ **4. a.** $4a^2 + 4ab + b^2$ **b.** $4a^2b^2$ **5. a.** $6x + 1$ **b.** $8x^2 + 8x - 6$ **6. a.** $6m^2 + m + 1$ **b.** $5m^4 + 5m^3 + m^2 + m$
7. a. $9z^2 + 12z + 4$ **b.** $9z^2 - 4$ **8. a.** $36y^2 - 84y + 49$ **b.** $36y^2 - 49$ **9. a.** $2x^3 - 8x^2 + 14x - 12$ **b.** $x^2 - 1$
10. a. $-3y^4 - 20y^2 - 32$ **b.** $4y^2 + 12$ **11. a.** $2x$ **b.** x^2
12. a. $4c$ **b.** $4c^2$ **13.** $16x^2y^2$ **14.** $4a^2b^2$ **15.** $-x^2 - 3x + 4$
16. $5m^2 - 4m + 1$ **17.** $-7m^2 - 16m$

18. $-4n^5 + n^4 + 6n^2 - 7n + 2$ **19.** $8x^2 + 16x + 34 + \frac{74}{x - 2}$
20. $-4x^2 - 10x - 30 + \frac{-95}{x - 3}$ **21.** $6x^3 + 5x^2y - 6xy^2 + y^3$
22. $6a^3 - a^2b + 5ab^2 + 2b^3$ **23.** $x^3 + y^6$ **24.** $m^6 + 1$
25. $4b$ **26.** $-12z$ **27.** $a^6 - 4b^2$ **28.** $y^6 - 36z^2$
29. $4p + 4 + \frac{-2}{2p - 1}$ **30.** $2v - 7 + \frac{29}{2v + 3}$ **31.** $4x^2y^2$
32. $-9pq$ **33.** $\frac{9}{49}x^2 - \frac{1}{4}$ **34.** $\frac{4}{25}y^2 - \frac{16}{9}$
35. $-\frac{11}{9}x^3 + \frac{5}{9}x^2 - \frac{1}{2}x - 4$ **36.** $-\frac{13}{10}y^2 - \frac{9}{10}y + \frac{4}{15}$
37. $1.3x^2 - 0.3x - 0.5$ **38.** $5w^3 - 4.1w^2 + 2.8w - 1.2$
39. $-6x^3y^6$ **40.** $50a^4b^6$

Chapter 5 Review Exercises, pp. 408–411

1. Base: 5; exponent: 3 **2.** Base: x; exponent: 4
3. Base: -2; exponent: 0 **4.** Base: y; exponent: 1
5. a. 36 **b.** 36 **c.** -36 **6. a.** 64 **b.** -64 **c.** -64
7. 5^{13} **8.** a^{11} **9.** x^9 **10.** 6^9 **11.** 10^3 **12.** y^6
13. b^8 **14.** 7^7 **15.** k **16.** 1 **17.** 2^8 **18.** q^6
19. Exponents are added only when multiplying factors with the same base. In such a case, the base does not change.
20. Exponents are subtracted only when dividing factors with the same base. In such a case, the base does not change. **21.** \$7146.10
22. \$22,050 **23.** 7^{12} **24.** c^{12} **25.** p^{18} **26.** 9^{28}
27. $\frac{a^2}{b^2}$ **28.** $\frac{1}{3^4}$ **29.** $\frac{5^2}{c^4d^{10}}$ **30.** $-\frac{m^{10}}{4^5n^{30}}$ **31.** $2^4a^4b^8$
32. $x^{14}y^2$ **33.** $-\frac{3^3x^9}{5^3y^6z^3}$ **34.** $\frac{r^{15}}{s^{10}t^{30}}$ **35.** a^{11} **36.** 8^2
37. $4h^{14}$ **38.** $2p^{14}q^{13}$ **39.** $\frac{x^6y^2}{4}$ **40.** a^9b^6 **41.** 1
42. 1 **43.** -1 **44.** 1 **45.** 2 **46.** 1 **47.** $\frac{1}{z^5}$
48. $\frac{1}{10^4}$ **49.** $\frac{1}{36a^2}$ **50.** $\frac{6}{a^2}$ **51.** $\frac{17}{16}$ **52.** $\frac{10}{9}$
53. $\frac{1}{t^8}$ **54.** $\frac{1}{r}$ **55.** $\frac{2y^7}{x^6}$ **56.** $\frac{4a^6bc}{5}$ **57.** $\frac{n^{16}}{16m^8}$
58. $\frac{u^{15}}{27v^6}$ **59.** $\frac{k^{21}}{5}$ **60.** $\frac{h^9}{9}$ **61.** $\frac{1}{2}$ **62.** $\frac{5}{4}$
63. a. 9.74×10^7 **b.** 4.2×10^{-3} in. **64. a.** 0.000 000 0001
b. \$256,000 **65.** 9.43×10^5 **66.** 1.55×10^{10}
67. 2.5×10^8 **68.** 1.638×10^3 **69.** $\approx 9.5367 \times 10^{13}$. This number has too many digits to fit on most calculator displays.
70. $\approx 1.1529 \times 10^{-12}$. This number has too many digits to fit on most calculator displays. **71. a.** $\approx 5.84 \times 10^8$ mi
b. $\approx 6.67 \times 10^4$ mph **72. a.** $\approx 2.26 \times 10^8$ mi
b. $\approx 1.07 \times 10^5$ mph **73. a.** Trinomial **b.** 4 **c.** 7
74. a. Binomial **b.** 7 **c.** -5 **75.** $7x - 3$
76. $-y^2 - 14y - 2$ **77.** $14a^2 - 2a - 6$
78. $\frac{15}{2}x^3 + \frac{1}{4}x^2 + \frac{1}{2}x + 2$ **79.** $10w^4 + 2w^3 - 7w + 4$
80. $0.01b^5 + b^4 - 0.1b^3 + 0.3b + 0.33$ **81.** $-2x^2 - 9x - 6$
82. $-5x^2 - 9x - 12$ **83.** For example, $-5x^2 + 2x - 4$
84. For example, $6x^5 + 8$ **85.** $6w + 6$ **86.** $-75x^6y^4$
87. $18a^8b^4$ **88.** $15c^4 - 35c^2 + 25c$ **89.** $-2x^3 - 10x^2 + 6x$
90. $5k^2 + k - 4$ **91.** $20t^2 + 3t - 2$ **92.** $6q^2 + 47q - 8$
93. $2a^2 + 4a - 30$ **94.** $49a^2 + 7a + \frac{1}{4}$ **95.** $b^2 - 8b + 16$
96. $8p^3 - 27$ **97.** $-2w^3 - 5w^2 - 5w + 4$
98. $4x^3 - 8x^2 + 11x - 4$ **99.** $12a^3 + 11a^2 - 13a - 10$
100. $b^2 - 16$ **101.** $\frac{1}{9}r^8 - s^4$ **102.** $49z^4 - 84z^2 + 36$
103. $2h^5 + h^4 - h^3 + h^2 - h + 3$ **104.** $2x^2 + 3x - 20$
105. $4y^2 - 2y$ **106.** $2a^2b - a - 3b$ **107.** $-3x^2 + 2x - 1$
108. $-\frac{z^5w^3}{2} + \frac{3zw}{4} + \frac{1}{z}$ **109.** $x + 2$ **110.** $2t + 5$
111. $p - 3 + \frac{5}{2p + 7}$ **112.** $a + 6 + \frac{-4}{5a - 3}$
113. $b^2 + 5b + 25$ **114.** $z + 4$ **115.** $y^2 - 4y + 2 + \frac{9y - 4}{y^2 + 3}$
116. $t^2 - 3t + 1 + \frac{-2t - 6}{3t^2 + t + 1}$ **117.** $w^2 + w - 1$

Chapter 5 Test, pp. 411–412

1. $\frac{(3 \cdot 3 \cdot 3 \cdot 3) \cdot (3 \cdot 3 \cdot 3)}{3 \cdot 3 \cdot 3 \cdot 3 \cdot 3 \cdot 3} = 3$ **2.** 9^6 **3.** q^8 **4.** 1
5. $\frac{1}{c^3}$ **6.** $\frac{5}{4}$ **7.** $\frac{3}{2}$ **8.** $27a^6b^3$ **9.** $\frac{16x^4}{y^{12}}$ **10.** 14
11. $49s^{18}t$ **12.** $\frac{4}{b^{12}}$ **13.** $\frac{16a^{12}}{9b^6}$ **14. a.** 4.3×10^{10}
b. 0.000 0056 **15.** 8.4×10^{-9} **16.** 7.5×10^6
17. a. $2.4192 \times 10^8\ m^3$ **b.** $8.83008 \times 10^{10}\ m^3$
18. $5x^3 - 7x^2 + 4x + 11$ **a.** 3 **b.** 5
19. $5t^4 + 12t^3 + 7t - 19$ **20.** $24w^2 - 3w - 4$
21. $-10x^5 - 2x^4 + 30x^3$ **22.** $8a^2 - 10a + 3$
23. $4y^3 - 25y^2 + 37y - 15$ **24.** $4 - 9b^2$ **25.** $25z^2 - 60z + 36$
26. $15x^2 - x - 6$ **27.** $-4x^2 + 5x + 7$
28. $y^3 - 11y^2 + 32y - 12$ **29.** $15x^3 - 7x^2 - 2x + 1$
30. Perimeter: $12x - 2$; area: $5x^2 - 13x - 6$
31. $-3x^6 + \frac{x^4}{4} - 2x$ **32.** $-4a^2 + \frac{ab}{2} - 2$ **33.** $2y - 7$
34. $w^2 - 4w + 5 + \frac{-10}{2w + 3}$ **35.** $3x^2 + x - 12 + \frac{15}{x^2 + 4}$

Chapters 1–5 Cumulative Review Exercises, pp. 412–413

1. $-\frac{35}{2}$ **2.** 4 **3.** $5^2 - \sqrt{4}$; 23 **4.** $\left\{\frac{28}{3}\right\}$
5. { } **6.** Quadrant III **7.** y-axis
8. The measures are 31°, 54°, 95°. **9. a.** 12 in.
b. 19.5 in. **c.** 5.5 hr **10.** $\{(-3, 4)\}$
11. $[-5, \infty)$ 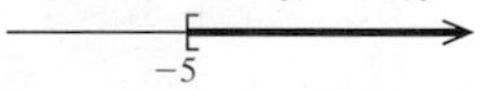
12. $5x^2 - 9x - 15$ **13.** $-2y^2 - 13yz - 15z^2$
14. $16t^2 - 24t + 9$ **15.** $\frac{4}{25}a^2 - \frac{1}{9}$
16. $-4a^3b^2 + 2ab - 1$ **17.** $4m^2 + 8m + 11 + \frac{24}{m - 2}$
18. $\frac{c^2}{16d^4}$ **19.** $\frac{2b^3}{a^2}$ **20.** 4.1×10^3

Chapter 6

Chapter Opener Puzzle

5	2	6	A 1	3	B 4
3	C 1	4	2	D 6	E 5
F 4	6	1	5	G 2	H 3
I 2	3	5	4	1	6
1	4	3	6	5	2
6	5	2	J 3	4	1

Section 6.1 Practice Exercises, pp. 423–425

1. a. product **b.** prime **c.** greatest common factor **d.** prime **e.** greatest common factor (GCF) **f.** grouping **3.** 7 **5.** 6 **7.** y **9.** $4w^2z$ **11.** $2xy^4z^2$ **13.** $(x - y)$ **15. a.** $3x - 6y$ **b.** $3(x - 2y)$ **17.** $4(p + 3)$ **19.** $5(c^2 - 2c + 3)$ **21.** $x^3(x^2 + 1)$ **23.** $t(t^3 - 4 + 8t)$ **25.** $2ab(1 + 2a^2)$ **27.** $19x^2y(2 - y^3)$ **29.** $6xy^5(x^2 - 3y^4z)$ **31.** The expression is prime because it is not factorable. **33.** $7pq^2(6p^2 + 2 - p^3q^2)$ **35.** $t^2(t^3 + 2rt - 3t^2 + 4r^2)$ **37. a.** $-2x(x^2 + 2x - 4)$ **b.** $2x(-x^2 - 2x + 4)$ **39.** $-1(8t^2 + 9t + 2)$ **41.** $-15p^2(p + 2)$ **43.** $-3mn(m^3n - 2m + 3n)$ **45.** $-1(7x + 6y + 2z)$ **47.** $(a + 6)(13 - 4b)$ **49.** $(w^2 - 2)(8v + 1)$ **51.** $7x(x + 3)^2$ **53.** $(2a - b)(4a + 3c)$ **55.** $(q + p)(3 + r)$ **57.** $(2x + 1)(3x + 2)$ **59.** $(t + 3)(2t - 1)$ **61.** $(3y - 1)(2y - 3)$ **63.** $(b + 1)(b^3 - 4)$ **65.** $(j^2 + 5)(3k + 1)$ **67.** $(2x^6 + 1)(7w^6 - 1)$ **69.** $(y + x)(a + b)$ **71.** $(vw + 1)(w - 3)$ **73.** $5x(x^2 + y^2)(3x + 2y)$ **75.** $4b(a - b)(x - 1)$ **77.** $6t(t - 3)(s - t^2)$ **79.** $P = 2(l + w)$ **81.** $S = 2\pi r(r + h)$ **83.** $\frac{1}{7}(x^2 + 3x - 5)$ **85.** $\frac{1}{4}(5w^2 + 3w + 9)$ **87.** For example: $6x^2 + 9x$ **89.** For example: $16p^4q^2 + 8p^3q - 4p^2q$

Section 6.2 Practice Exercises, pp. 430–432

1. a. positive **b.** different **c.** Both are correct. **d.** $3(x + 6)(x + 2)$ **3.** $3(t - 5)(t - 2)$ **5.** $(a + 2b)(x - 5)$ **7.** $(x + 8)(x + 2)$ **9.** $(z - 9)(z - 2)$ **11.** $(z - 6)(z + 3)$ **13.** $(p - 8)(p + 5)$ **15.** $(t + 10)(t - 4)$ **17.** Prime **19.** $(n + 4)^2$ **21.** a **23.** c **25.** They are both correct because multiplication of polynomials is a commutative operation. **27.** The expressions are equal and both are correct. **29.** It should be written in descending order. **31.** $(x - 15)(x + 2)$ **33.** $(w - 13)(w - 5)$ **35.** $(t + 18)(t + 4)$ **37.** $3(x - 12)(x + 2)$ **39.** $8p(p - 1)(p - 4)$ **41.** $y^2z^2(y - 6)(y - 6)$ or $y^2z^2(y - 6)^2$ **43.** $-(x - 4)(x - 6)$ **45.** $-5(a - 3x)(a + 2x)$ **47.** $-2(c + 2)(c + 1)$ **49.** $xy^3(x - 4)(x - 15)$ **51.** $12(p - 7)(p - 1)$ **53.** $-2(m - 10)(m - 1)$ **55.** $(c + 5d)(c + d)$ **57.** $(a - 2b)(a - 7b)$ **59.** Prime **61.** $(q - 7)(q + 9)$ **63.** $(x + 10)^2$ **65.** $(t + 20)(t - 2)$ **67.** The student forgot to factor out the GCF before factoring the trinomial further. The polynomial is not factored completely, because $(2x - 4)$ has a common factor of 2. **69.** $x^2 + 9x - 52$ **71. a.** $3x^2 + 9x - 12$ **b.** $3(x + 4)(x - 1)$ **73.** $(x^2 + 1)(x^2 + 9)$ **75.** $(w^2 + 5)(w^2 - 3)$ **77.** 7, 5, −7, −5 **79.** For example: $c = -16$

Section 6.3 Practice Exercises, pp. 439–440

1. a. Both are correct. **b.** $2(3x - 5)(x + 1)$ **3.** $(n - 1)(m - 2)$ **5.** $6(a - 7)(a + 2)$ **7.** a **9.** b **11.** $(3n + 1)(n + 4)$ **13.** $(2y + 1)(y - 2)$ **15.** $(5x + 1)(x - 3)$ **17.** $(4c + 1)(3c - 2)$ **19.** $(10w - 3)(w + 4)$ **21.** $(3q + 2)(2q - 3)$ **23.** Prime **25.** $(5m + 2)(5m - 4)$ **27.** $(6y - 5x)(y + 4x)$ **29.** $2(m + 4)(m - 10)$ **31.** $y^3(2y + 1)(y + 6)$ **33.** $-(a + 17)(a - 2)$ **35.** $-10(4m + p)(2m - 3p)$ **37.** $(x^2 + 1)(x^2 + 9)$ **39.** $(w^2 + 5)(w^2 - 3)$ **41.** $(2x^2 + 3)(x^2 - 5)$ **43.** $-2(z - 9)(z - 1)$ **45.** $(q - 7)(q - 6)$ **47.** $(2t + 3)(3t - 1)$ **49.** $(2m - 5)^2$ **51.** Prime **53.** $(2x - 5y)(3x - 2y)$ **55.** $(4m + 5n)(3m - n)$ **57.** $5(3r + 2)(2r - 1)$ **59.** Prime **61.** $(2t - 5)(5t + 1)$ **63.** $(7w - 4)(2w + 3)$ **65.** $(a - 12)(a + 2)$ **67.** $(x + 5y)(x + 4y)$ **69.** $(a + 20b)(a + b)$ **71.** $(t - 7)(t - 3)$ **73.** $d(5d^2 + 3d - 10)$ **75.** $4b(b - 5)(b + 4)$ **77.** $y^2(x - 3)(x - 10)$ **79.** $-2u(2u + 5)(3u - 2)$ **81.** $(2x^2 + 3)(4x^2 + 1)$ **83. a.** 36 ft **b.** $-4(4t + 5)(t - 2)$; Yes **85. a.** $(x - 12)(x + 2)$ **b.** $(x - 6)(x - 4)$ **87. a.** $(x - 6)(x + 1)$ **b.** $(x - 2)(x - 3)$

Section 6.4 Practice Exercises, pp. 446–447

1. a. Both are correct. **b.** $3(4x + 3)(x - 2)$ **3.** $(y + 5)(8 + 9y)$ **5.** 12, 1 **7.** −8, −1 **9.** 5, −4 **11.** 9, −2 **13.** $(x + 4)(3x + 1)$ **15.** $(w - 2)(4w - 1)$ **17.** $(x + 9)(x - 2)$ **19.** $(m + 3)(2m - 1)$ **21.** $(4k + 3)(2k - 3)$ **23.** $(2k - 5)^2$ **25.** Prime **27.** $(3z - 5)(3z - 2)$ **29.** $(6y - 5z)(2y + 3z)$ **31.** $2(7y + 4)(y + 3)$ **33.** $-(3w - 5)(5w + 1)$ **35.** $-4(x - y)(3x - 2y)$ **37.** $6y(y + 1)(3y + 7)$ **39.** $(a^2 + 2)(a^2 + 3)$ **41.** $(3x^2 - 5)(2x^2 + 3)$ **43.** $(8p^2 - 3)(p^2 + 5)$ **45.** $(5p - 1)(4p - 3)$ **47.** $(3u - 2v)(2u - 5v)$ **49.** $(4a + 5b)(3a - b)$ **51.** $(h + 7k)(3h - 2k)$ **53.** Prime **55.** $(2z - 1)(8z - 3)$ **57.** $(b - 4)^2$ **59.** $-5(x - 2)(x - 3)$ **61.** $(t - 3)(t + 2)$ **63.** Prime **65.** $2(12x - 1)(3x + 1)$ **67.** $p(p + 3)(p - 9)$ **69.** $x(3x + 7)(x + 1)$ **71.** $2p(p - 15)(p - 4)$ **73.** $x^2(y + 3)(y + 11)$ **75.** $-(k + 2)(k + 5)$ **77.** $-3(n + 6)(n - 5)$ **79.** $(x^2 - 2)(x^2 - 5)$ **81.** No. $(2x + 4)$ contains a common factor of 2. **83. a.** 128 customers **b.** $-2(x - 18)(x - 2)$; 128; Yes **85. a.** 42 **b.** $n(n + 1)$; 42; Yes

Section 6.5 Practice Exercises, pp. 453–454

1. a. difference; $(a + b)(a - b)$ **b.** sum **c.** is not **d.** square **e.** $(a + b)^2$; $(a - b)^2$ **3.** $(3x - 1)(2x - 5)$ **5.** $5xy^5(3x - 2y)$ **7.** $(x + b)(a - 6)$ **9.** $(y + 10)(y - 4)$ **11.** $x^2 - 25$ **13.** $4p^2 - 9q^2$ **15.** $(x - 6)(x + 6)$ **17.** $3(w + 10)(w - 10)$ **19.** $(2a - 11b)(2a + 11b)$ **21.** $(7m - 4n)(7m + 4n)$ **23.** Prime **25.** $(y + 2z)(y - 2z)$ **27.** $(a - b^2)(a + b^2)$ **29.** $(5pq - 1)(5pq + 1)$ **31.** $\left(c - \frac{1}{5}\right)\left(c + \frac{1}{5}\right)$ **33.** $2(5 - 4t)(5 + 4t)$ **35.** $(x + 4)(x - 4)(x^2 + 16)$ **37.** $(2 - z)(2 + z)(4 + z^2)$ **39.** $(x + 5)(x + 3)(x - 3)$ **41.** $(c - 1)(c + 5)(c - 5)$ **43.** $(x + 3)(x - 3)(2 + y)$ **45.** $(y + 3)(y - 3)(x + 2)(x - 2)$ **47.** $9x^2 + 30x + 25$ **49. a.** $x^2 + 4x + 4$ is a perfect square trinomial. **b.** $x^2 + 4x + 4 = (x + 2)^2$; $x^2 + 5x + 4 = (x + 1)(x + 4)$ **51.** $(x + 9)^2$ **53.** $(5z - 2)^2$ **55.** $(7a + 3b)^2$ **57.** $(y - 1)^2$ **59.** $5(4z + 3w)^2$ **61.** $(3y + 25)(3y + 1)$ **63.** $2(a - 5)^2$ **65.** Prime **67.** $(2x + y)^2$ **69.** $3x(x - 1)^2$ **71.** $y(y - 6)$ **73.** $(2p - 5)(2p + 7)$ **75.** $(-t + 2)(t + 6)$ or $-(t - 2)(t + 6)$ **77.** $(2a - 5 + 10b)(2a - 5 - 10b)$ **79. a.** $a^2 - b^2$ **b.** $(a - b)(a + b)$

Section 6.6 Practice Exercises, pp. 459–460

1. a. sum; cubes **b.** difference; cubes **c.** $(a - b)(a^2 + ab + b^2)$ **d.** $(a + b)(a^2 - ab + b^2)$ **3.** $5(2 - t)(2 + t)$ **5.** $(t + u)(2 + s)$ **7.** $(3v - 4)(v + 3)$ **9.** $-(c + 5)^2$ **11.** $x^3, 8, y^6, 27q^3, w^{12}, r^3s^6$ **13.** $t^3, -1, 27, a^3b^6, 125, y^6$ **15.** $(y - 2)(y^2 + 2y + 4)$ **17.** $(1 - p)(1 + p + p^2)$ **19.** $(w + 4)(w^2 - 4w + 16)$ **21.** $(x - 10y)(x^2 + 10xy + 100y^2)$ **23.** $(4t + 1)(16t^2 - 4t + 1)$ **25.** $(10a + 3)(100a^2 - 30a + 9)$ **27.** $\left(n - \frac{1}{2}\right)\left(n^2 + \frac{1}{2}n + \frac{1}{4}\right)$ **29.** $(5x + 2y)(25x^2 - 10xy + 4y^2)$ **31.** $(x^2 - 2)(x^2 + 2)$ **33.** Prime **35.** $(t + 4)(t^2 - 4t + 16)$ **37.** Prime **39.** $4(b + 3)(b^2 - 3b + 9)$ **41.** $5(p - 5)(p + 5)$ **43.** $(\frac{1}{4} - 2h)(\frac{1}{16} + \frac{1}{2}h + 4h^2)$ **45.** $(x - 2)(x + 2)(x^2 + 4)$ **47.** $\left(\frac{2}{3}x - w\right)\left(\frac{2}{3}x + w\right)$ **49.** $(q - 2)(q^2 + 2q + 4)(q + 2)(q^2 - 2q + 4)$ **51.** $(x^3 + 4y)(x^6 - 4x^3y + 16y^2)$ **53.** $(2x + 3)(x - 1)(x + 1)$ **55.** $(2x - y)(2x + y)(4x^2 + y^2)$ **57.** $(3y - 2)(3y + 2)(9y^2 + 4)$ **59.** $(a + b^2)(a^2 - ab^2 + b^4)$ **61.** $(x^2 + y^2)(x - y)(x + y)$ **63.** $(k + 4)(k - 3)(k + 3)$ **65.** $2(t - 5)(t - 1)(t + 1)$ **67.** $\left(\frac{4}{5}p - \frac{1}{2}q\right)\left(\frac{16}{25}p^2 + \frac{2}{5}pq + \frac{1}{4}q^2\right)$ **69.** $(a^4 + b^4)(a^8 - a^4b^4 + b^8)$ **71. a.** The quotient is $x^2 + 2x + 4$. **b.** $(x - 2)(x^2 + 2x + 4)$ **73.** $x^2 + 4x + 16$ **75.** $2x + 1$

Chapter 6 Problem Recognition Exercises, pp. 461–462

1. A prime polynomial cannot be factored further. **2.** Factor out the GCF. **3.** Look for a difference of

squares: $a^2 - b^2$, a difference of cubes: $a^3 - b^3$, or a sum of cubes: $a^3 + b^3$. **4.** Grouping
5. a. Difference of squares **b.** $2(a - 9)(a + 9)$
6. a. Nonperfect square trinomial **b.** $(y + 3)(y + 1)$
7. a. None of these **b.** $6w(w - 1)$
8. a. Difference of squares **b.** $(2z + 3)(2z - 3)(4z^2 + 9)$
9. a. Nonperfect square trinomial **b.** $(3t + 1)(t + 4)$
10. a. Sum of cubes **b.** $5(r + 1)(r^2 - r + 1)$
11. a. Four terms-grouping **b.** $(3c + d)(a - b)$
12. a. Difference of cubes **b.** $(x - 5)(x^2 + 5x + 25)$
13. a. Sum of cubes **b.** $(y + 2)(y^2 - 2y + 4)$
14. a. Nonperfect square trinomial **b.** $(7p - 1)(p - 4)$
15. a. Nonperfect square trinomial **b.** $3(q - 4)(q + 1)$
16. a. Perfect square trinomial **b.** $-2(x - 2)^2$
17. a. None of these **b.** $6a(3a + 2)$
18. a. Difference of cubes **b.** $2(3 - y)(9 + 3y + y^2)$
19. a. Difference of squares **b.** $4(t - 5)(t + 5)$
20. a. Nonperfect square trinomial **b.** $(4t + 1)(t - 8)$
21. a. Nonperfect square trinomial **b.** $10(c^2 + c + 1)$
22. a. Four terms-grouping **b.** $(w - 5)(2x + 3y)$
23. a. Sum of cubes **b.** $(x + 0.1)(x^2 - 0.1x + 0.01)$
24. a. Difference of squares **b.** $(2q - 3)(2q + 3)$
25. a. Perfect square trinomial **b.** $(8 + k)^2$
26. a. Four terms-grouping **b.** $(t + 6)(s^2 + 5)$
27. a. Four terms-grouping **b.** $(x + 1)(2x - y)$
28. a. Sum of cubes **b.** $(w + y)(w^2 - wy + y^2)$
29. a. Difference of cubes **b.** $(a - c)(a^2 + ac + c^2)$
30. a. Nonperfect square trinomial **b.** Prime
31. a. Nonperfect square trinomial **b.** Prime
32. a. Perfect square trinomial **b.** $(a + 1)^2$
33. a. Perfect square trinomial **b.** $(b + 5)^2$
34. a. Nonperfect square trinomial **b.** $-(t + 8)(t - 4)$
35. a. Nonperfect square trinomial **b.** $-p(p + 4)(p + 1)$
36. a. Difference of squares **b.** $(xy - 7)(xy + 7)$
37. a. Nonperfect square trinomial **b.** $3(2x + 3)(x - 5)$
38. a. Nonperfect square trinomial **b.** $2(5y - 1)(2y - 1)$
39. a. None of these **b.** $abc^2(5ac - 7)$
40. a. Difference of squares **b.** $2(2a - 5)(2a + 5)$
41. a. Nonperfect square trinomial **b.** $(t + 9)(t - 7)$
42. a. Nonperfect square trinomial **b.** $(b + 10)(b - 8)$
43. a. Four terms-grouping **b.** $(b + y)(a - b)$
44. a. None of these **b.** $3x^2y^4(2x + y)$
45. a. Nonperfect square trinomial **b.** $(7u - 2v)(2u - v)$
46. a. Nonperfect square trinomial **b.** Prime
47. a. Nonperfect square trinomial **b.** $2(2q^2 - 4q - 3)$
48. a. Nonperfect square trinomial **b.** $3(3w^2 + w - 5)$
49. a. Sum of squares **b.** Prime
50. a. Perfect square trinomial **b.** $5(b - 3)^2$
51. a. Nonperfect square trinomial **b.** $(3r + 1)(2r + 3)$
52. a. Nonperfect square trinomial **b.** $(2s - 3)(2s + 5)$
53. a. Difference of squares **b.** $(2a - 1)(2a + 1)(4a^2 + 1)$
54. a. Four terms-grouping **b.** $(p + c)(p - 3)(p + 3)$
55. a. Perfect square trinomial **b.** $(9u - 5v)^2$
56. a. Sum of squares **b.** $4(x^2 + 4)$
57. a. Nonperfect square trinomial **b.** $(x - 6)(x + 1)$
58. a. Nonperfect square trinomial **b.** Prime
59. a. Four terms-grouping **b.** $2(x - 3y)(a + 2b)$
60. a. Nonperfect square trinomial **b.** $m(4m + 1)(2m - 3)$
61. a. Nonperfect square trinomial **b.** $x^2y(3x + 5)(7x + 2)$
62. a. Difference of squares **b.** $2(m^2 - 8)(m^2 + 8)$
63. a. Four terms-grouping **b.** $(4v - 3)(2u + 3)$
64. a. Four terms-grouping **b.** $(t - 5)(4t + s)$
65. a. Perfect square trinomial **b.** $3(2x - 1)^2$
66. a. Perfect square trinomial **b.** $(p + q)^2$
67. a. Nonperfect square trinomial **b.** $n(2n - 1)(3n + 4)$
68. a. Nonperfect square trinomial **b.** $k(2k - 1)(2k + 3)$
69. a. Difference of squares **b.** $(8 - y)(8 + y)$
70. a. Difference of squares **b.** $b(6 - b)(6 + b)$
71. a. Nonperfect square trinomial **b.** Prime
72. a. Nonperfect square trinomial **b.** $(y + 4)(y + 2)$
73. a. Nonperfect square trinomial **b.** $(c^2 - 10)(c^2 - 2)$

Section 6.7 Practice Exercises, pp. 467–469

1. a. quadratic **b.** 0; 0 **3.** $4(b - 5)(b - 6)$ **5.** $(3x - 2)(x + 4)$ **7.** $4(x^2 + 4y^2)$ **9.** Neither **11.** Quadratic **13.** Linear **15.** $\{-3, 1\}$ **17.** $\left\{\frac{7}{2}, -\frac{7}{2}\right\}$ **19.** $\{-5\}$ **21.** $\left\{0, \frac{1}{5}\right\}$ **23.** The polynomial must be factored completely. **25.** $\{5, -3\}$ **27.** $\{-12, 2\}$ **29.** $\left\{4, -\frac{1}{2}\right\}$ **31.** $\left\{\frac{2}{3}, -\frac{2}{3}\right\}$ **33.** $\{6, 8\}$ **35.** $\left\{0, -\frac{3}{2}, 4\right\}$ **37.** $\left\{-\frac{1}{3}, 3, -6\right\}$ **39.** $\left\{0, 4, -\frac{3}{2}\right\}$ **41.** $\left\{0, -\frac{9}{2}, 11\right\}$ **43.** $\{0, 4, -4\}$ **45.** $\{-6, 0\}$ **47.** $\left\{\frac{3}{4}, -\frac{3}{4}\right\}$ **49.** $\{0, -5, -2\}$ **51.** $\left\{-\frac{14}{3}\right\}$ **53.** $\{5, 3\}$ **55.** $\{0, -2\}$ **57.** $\{-3\}$ **59.** $\{-3, 1\}$ **61.** $\left\{\frac{3}{2}\right\}$ **63.** $\left\{0, \frac{1}{3}\right\}$ **65.** $\{0, 2\}$ **67.** $\{3, -2, 2\}$ **69.** $\{-5, 4\}$ **71.** $\{-5, -1\}$

Chapter 6 Problem Recognition Exercises, p. 469

1. a. $(x + 7)(x - 1)$ **b.** $\{-7, 1\}$ **2. a.** $(c + 6)(c + 2)$ **b.** $\{-6, -2\}$ **3. a.** $(2y + 1)(y + 3)$ **b.** $\left\{-\frac{1}{2}, -3\right\}$ **4. a.** $(3x - 5)(x - 1)$ **b.** $\left\{\frac{5}{3}, 1\right\}$ **5. a.** $\left\{\frac{4}{5}, -1\right\}$ **b.** $(5q - 4)(q + 1)$ **6. a.** $\left\{-\frac{1}{3}, \frac{3}{2}\right\}$ **b.** $(3a + 1)(2a - 3)$ **7. a.** $\{-8, 8\}$ **b.** $(a + 8)(a - 8)$ **8. a.** $\{-10, 10\}$ **b.** $(v + 10)(v - 10)$ **9. a.** $(2b + 9)(2b - 9)$ **b.** $\left\{-\frac{9}{2}, \frac{9}{2}\right\}$ **10. a.** $(6t + 7)(6t - 7)$ **b.** $\left\{-\frac{7}{6}, \frac{7}{6}\right\}$ **11. a.** $\left\{-\frac{3}{2}, -\frac{1}{2}\right\}$ **b.** $2(2x + 3)(2x + 1)$ **12. a.** $\left\{-\frac{4}{3}, -2\right\}$ **b.** $4(3y + 4)(y + 2)$ **13. a.** $x(x - 10)(x + 2)$ **b.** $\{0, 10, -2\}$ **14. a.** $k(k + 7)(k - 2)$ **b.** $\{0, -7, 2\}$ **15. a.** $\{-1, 3, -3\}$ **b.** $(b + 1)(b - 3)(b + 3)$ **16. a.** $\{8, -2, 2\}$ **b.** $(x - 8)(x + 2)(x - 2)$ **17.** $(s - 3)(2s + r)$ **18.** $(2t + 1)(3t + 5u)$ **19.** $\left\{-\frac{1}{2}, 0, \frac{1}{2}\right\}$ **20.** $\{-5, 0, 5\}$ **21.** $\{0, 1\}$ **22.** $\{-3, 0\}$ **23.** $\left\{\frac{1}{3}\right\}$ **24.** $\left\{-\frac{7}{12}\right\}$ **25.** $(2w + 3)(4w^2 - 6w + 9)$ **26.** $(10q - 1)(100q^2 + 10q + 1)$ **27.** $\left\{-\frac{7}{5}, 1\right\}$ **28.** $\left\{-6, -\frac{1}{4}\right\}$ **29.** $\left\{-\frac{2}{3}, -5\right\}$ **30.** $\left\{-1, -\frac{1}{2}\right\}$ **31.** $\{3\}$ **32.** $\{0\}$ **33.** $\{-4, 4\}$ **34.** $\left\{-\frac{2}{3}, \frac{2}{3}\right\}$ **35.** $\{1, 6\}$ **36.** $\{-2, -12\}$

Section 6.8 Practice Exercises, pp. 474–477

1. a. $x + 1$ **b.** $x + 2$ **c.** $x + 2$ **d.** LW **e.** $\frac{1}{2}bh$ **f.** $a^2 + b^2 = c^2$ **3.** $\left\{0, -\frac{2}{3}\right\}$ **5.** $\{6, -1\}$ **7.** $\left\{-\frac{5}{6}, 2\right\}$ **9.** The numbers are 7 and −7. **11.** The numbers are 10 and −4. **13.** The numbers are −9 and −7, or 7 and 9. **15.** The numbers are 5 and 6, or −6 and −5. **17.** The height of the painting is 11 ft and the width is 9 ft. **19. a.** The slab is 7 m by 4 m. **b.** The perimeter is 22 m. **21.** The base is 7 ft and the height is 4 ft. **23.** The base is 5 cm and the height is 8 cm. **25.** The ball hits the ground in 3 sec.

27. The object is at ground level at 0 sec and 1.5 sec.
29. 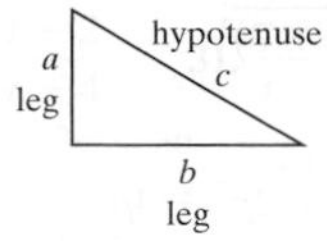

31. $c = 25$ cm **33.** $a = 15$ in.
35. The brace is 20 in. long. **37.** The kite is 19 yd high.
39. The bottom of the ladder is 8 ft from the house. The distance from the top of the ladder to the ground is 15 ft.
41. The hypotenuse is 10 m.

Chapter 6 Review Exercises, pp. 483–485

1. $3a^2b$ **2.** $x + 5$ **3.** $2c(3c - 5)$ **4.** $-2yz$ or $2yz$
5. $2x(3x + x^3 - 4)$ **6.** $11w^2y^3(w - 4y^2)$
7. $t(-t + 5)$ or $-t(t - 5)$ **8.** $u(-6u - 1)$ or $-u(6u + 1)$
9. $(b + 2)(3b - 7)$ **10.** $2(5x + 9)(1 + 4x)$
11. $(w + 2)(7w + b)$ **12.** $(b - 2)(b + y)$
13. $3(4y - 3)(5y - 1)$ **14.** $a(2 - a)(3 - b)$
15. $(x - 3)(x - 7)$ **16.** $(y - 8)(y - 11)$
17. $(z - 12)(z + 6)$ **18.** $(q - 13)(q + 3)$
19. $3w(p + 10)(p + 2)$ **20.** $2m^2(m + 8)(m + 5)$
21. $-(t - 8)(t - 2)$ **22.** $-(w - 4)(w + 5)$
23. $(a + b)(a + 11b)$ **24.** $(c - 6d)(c + 3d)$
25. Different **26.** Both negative **27.** Both positive
28. Different **29.** $(2y + 3)(y - 4)$ **30.** $(4w + 3)(w - 2)$
31. $(2z + 5)(5z + 2)$ **32.** $(4z - 3)(2z + 3)$ **33.** Prime
34. Prime **35.** $10(w - 9)(w + 3)$ **36.** $-3(y - 8)(y + 2)$
37. $(3c - 5d)^2$ **38.** $(x + 6)^2$ **39.** $(3g + 2h)(2g + h)$
40. $(6m - n)(2m - 5n)$ **41.** $(v^2 + 1)(v^2 - 3)$
42. $(x^2 + 5)(x^2 + 2)$ **43.** $5, -1$ **44.** $-3, -5$
45. $(c - 2)(3c + 1)$ **46.** $(y + 3)(4y + 1)$ **47.** $(t + 12w)(t + w)$
48. $(4x^2 - 3)(x^2 + 5)$ **49.** $(w^2 + 5)(w^2 + 2)$
50. $(p - 3q)(p - 5q)$ **51.** $-2(4v + 3)(5v - 1)$
52. $10(4s - 5)(s + 2)$ **53.** $ab(a - 6b)(a - 4b)$
54. $2z^4(z + 7)(z - 3)$ **55.** Prime **56.** Prime **57.** $(7x + 10)^2$
58. $(3w - z)^2$ **59.** $(a - b)(a + b)$ **60.** Prime
61. $(a - 7)(a + 7)$ **62.** $(d - 8)(d + 8)$ **63.** $(10 - 9t)(10 + 9t)$
64. $(2 - 5k)(2 + 5k)$ **65.** Prime **66.** Prime **67.** $(y + 6)^2$
68. $(t + 8)^2$ **69.** $(3a - 2)^2$ **70.** $(5x - 4)^2$ **71.** $-3(v + 2)^2$
72. $-2(x - 5)^2$ **73.** $2(c^2 - 3)(c^2 + 3)$ **74.** $2(6x - y)(6x + y)$
75. $(p + 3)(p - 4)(p + 4)$ **76.** $(k - 2)(2 - k)(2 + k)$ or $-1(k - 2)^2(2 + k)$ **77.** $(a + b)(a^2 - ab + b^2)$
78. $(a - b)(a^2 + ab + b^2)$ **79.** $(4 + a)(16 - 4a + a^2)$
80. $(5 - b)(25 + 5b + b^2)$ **81.** $(p^2 + 2)(p^4 - 2p^2 + 4)$
82. $\left(q^2 - \frac{1}{3}\right)\left(q^4 + \frac{1}{3}q^2 + \frac{1}{9}\right)$ **83.** $6(x - 2)(x^2 + 2x + 4)$
84. $7(y + 1)(y^2 - y + 1)$ **85.** $x(x - 6)(x + 6)$
86. $q(q - 4)(q^2 + 4q + 16)$ **87.** $4(2h^2 + 5)$ **88.** $m(m - 8)$
89. $(x + 4)(x + 1)(x - 1)$ **90.** $5q(p^2 - 2q)(p^2 + 2q)$
91. $n(2 + n)(4 - 2n + n^2)$ **92.** $14(m - 1)(m^2 + m + 1)$
93. $(x - 3)(2x + 1) = 0$ can be solved directly by the zero product rule because it is a product of factors set equal to zero.
94. $\left\{\frac{1}{4}, -\frac{2}{3}\right\}$ **95.** $\left\{9, \frac{1}{2}\right\}$ **96.** $\left\{0, -3, -\frac{2}{5}\right\}$
97. $\left\{0, 7, \frac{9}{4}\right\}$ **98.** $\left\{-\frac{5}{7}, 2\right\}$ **99.** $\left\{-\frac{1}{4}, 6\right\}$
100. $\{12, -12\}$ **101.** $\{5, -5\}$ **102.** $\left\{0, \frac{1}{5}\right\}$ **103.** $\{4, 2\}$
104. $\left\{-\frac{5}{6}\right\}$ **105.** $\left\{-\frac{2}{3}\right\}$ **106.** $\left\{\frac{2}{3}, 6\right\}$ **107.** $\left\{\frac{11}{2}, -12\right\}$
108. $\{0, 7, 2\}$ **109.** $\{0, 2, -2\}$ **110.** The height is 6 ft, and the base is 13 ft. **111.** The ball is at ground level at 0 and 1 sec.
112. The ramp is 13 ft long. **113.** The legs are 6 ft and 8 ft; the hypotenuse is 10 ft. **114.** The numbers are -8 and 8.
115. The numbers are 29 and 30, or -2 and -1.
116. The height is 4 m, and the base is 9 m.

Chapter 6 Test, p. 485

1. $3x(5x^3 - 1 + 2x^2)$ **2.** $(a - 5)(7 - a)$
3. $(6w - 1)(w - 7)$ **4.** $(13 - p)(13 + p)$
5. $(q - 8)^2$ **6.** $(2 + t)(4 - 2t + t^2)$ **7.** $(a + 4)(a + 8)$
8. $(x + 7)(x - 6)$ **9.** $(2y - 1)(y - 8)$ **10.** $(2z + 1)(3z + 8)$
11. $(3t - 10)(3t + 10)$ **12.** $(v + 9)(v - 9)$ **13.** $3(a + 6b)(a + 3b)$
14. $(c - 1)(c + 1)(c^2 + 1)$ **15.** $(y - 7)(x + 3)$ **16.** Prime
17. $-10(u - 2)(u - 1)$ **18.** $3(2t - 5)(2t + 5)$ **19.** $5(y - 5)^2$
20. $7q(3q + 2)$ **21.** $(2x + 1)(x - 2)(x + 2)$
22. $(y - 5)(y^2 + 5y + 25)$ **23.** $(mn - 9)(mn + 9)$
24. $16(a - 2b)(a + 2b)$ **25.** $(4x - 3y^2)(16x^2 + 12xy^2 + 9y^4)$
26. $3y(x - 4)(x + 2)$ **27.** $\left\{\frac{3}{2}, -5\right\}$ **28.** $\{0, 7\}$ **29.** $\{8, -2\}$
30. $\left\{\frac{1}{5}, -1\right\}$ **31.** $\{3, -3, -10\}$
32. The tennis court is 12 yd by 26 yd. **33.** The two integers are 5 and 7, or -5 and -7. **34.** The base is 12 in., and the height is 7 in. **35.** The shorter leg is 5 ft. **36.** The stone hits the ground in 2 sec.

Chapters 1–6 Cumulative Review Exercises, p. 486

1. $\frac{7}{5}$ **2.** $\{-3\}$ **3.** $y = \frac{3}{2}x - 4$
4. There are 10 quarters, and 7 dimes.
5. $[-4, \infty)$ 

6. a. Yes **b.** 1 **c.** $(0, 4)$ **d.** $(-4, 0)$ **e.**
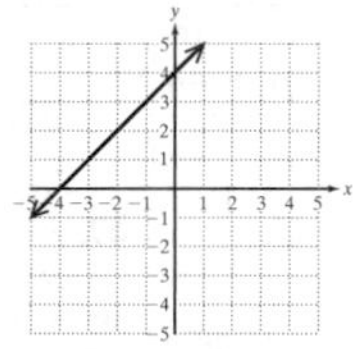

7. a. Vertical line **b.** Undefined **c.** $(5, 0)$ **d.** Does not exist
8. $\{(5, 2)\}$ **9.** $\{(0, 8, -2)\}$ **10.** $-\frac{7}{2}y^2 - 5y - 14$
11. $8p^3 - 22p^2 + 13p + 3$ **12.** $4w^2 - 28w + 49$
13. $r^3 + 5r^2 + 15r + 40 + \frac{121}{r - 3}$ **14.** c^4 **15.** $\frac{a^4}{9b^2}$
16. 1.6×10^3 **17.** $(w - 2)(w + 2)(w^2 + 4)$
18. $(a + 5b)(2x - 3y)$ **19.** $(2x - 5)(2x + 1)$
20. $\left\{0, \frac{1}{2}, -5\right\}$

Chapter 7

Chapter Opener Puzzle

p r o c r a s t i n a t i o n
4 1 2 1 5 3 5 3 2

Section 7.1 Practice Exercises, pp. 495–498

1. a. rational **b.** denominator; zero **c.** $\frac{p}{q}$ **d.** 1; -1 **3.** 0
5. $-\frac{1}{8}$ **7.** $-\frac{1}{2}$ **9.** Undefined **11. a.** $3\frac{1}{5}$ hr or 3.2 hr **b.** $1\frac{3}{4}$ hr or 1.75 hr **13.** $k = -2$ **15.** $x = \frac{5}{2}, x = -8$
17. $m = -2, m = -3$ **19.** There are no restricted values.
21. There are no restricted values. **23.** $t = 0$
25. For example: $\frac{1}{x - 2}$ **27.** For example: $\frac{1}{(x + 3)(x - 7)}$
29. a. $\frac{2}{5}$ **b.** $\frac{2}{5}$ **31. a.** Undefined **b.** Undefined
33. a. $y = -2$ **b.** $\frac{1}{2}$ **35. a.** $t = -1$ **b.** $t - 1$

12. $\left\{\frac{8}{5}\right\}$ **13.** {2} **14.** {1} **15.** { } (The value 4 does not check.) **16.** {−5} (The value 2 does not check.)
17 $r = \frac{2A}{C}$ **18.** {−8} **19.** $1\frac{1}{4}$ (1.25) cups of carrots
20. The speed of the current is 5 mph. **21.** It would take the second printer 3 hr to do the job working alone.
22. $a = 5.6$; $b = 12$

Chapters 1–7 Cumulative Review Exercises, pp. 561–562

1. 32 **2.** 7 **3.** $\left\{\frac{10}{9}\right\}$

4.

Set-Builder Notation	Graph	Interval Notation
$\{x \mid x \geq -1\}$	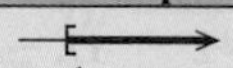 −1	$[-1, \infty)$
$\{x \mid x < 5\}$	 5	$(-\infty, 5)$

5. The width is 17 m and the length is 35 m.
6. The base is 10 in. and the height is 8 in. **7.** $\frac{x^2yz^{17}}{2}$
8. a. $6x + 4$ **b.** $2x^2 + x - 3$ **9.** $(5x - 3)^2$
10. $(2c + 1)(5d - 3)$ **11.** $x = 5, x = -\frac{1}{2}$ **12.** $\{(-3, -1, 6)\}$
13. $\frac{1}{5(x + 4)}$ **14.** −3 **15.** {1} **16.** $\left\{-\frac{7}{2}\right\}$
17. a. x-intercept: $(-4, 0)$; y-intercept: $(0, 2)$ **b.** x-intercept: $(0, 0)$; y-intercept: $(0, 0)$
18. a. $m = -\frac{7}{5}$ **b.** $m = -\frac{2}{3}$ **c.** $m = 4$ **d.** $m = -\frac{1}{4}$
19. $y = 5x - 3$ **20.** One large popcorn costs $4.50, and one drink costs $3.00.

Chapter 8

Chapter Opener Puzzle

The set of first components of a

R	E	L	A	T	I	O	N
10	4	3	13	2	14	8	1

is called the

D	O	M	A	I	N
6	5	12	11	7	9

Section 8.1 Practice Exercises, pp. 569–572

1. a. relation **b.** domain **c.** range
3. a. {(Northeast, 54.1), (Midwest, 65.6), (South, 110.7), (West, 70.7)} **b.** Domain: {Northeast, Midwest, South, West}; Range: {54.1, 65.6, 110.7, 70.7} **5. a.** {(USSR, 1961), (USA, 1962), (Poland, 1978), (Vietnam, 1980), (Cuba, 1980)} **b.** Domain: {USSR, USA, Poland, Vietnam, Cuba}; range: {1961, 1962, 1978, 1980}
7. a. {(A, 1), (A, 2), (B, 2), (C, 3), (D, 5), (E, 4)} **b.** Domain: {A, B, C, D, E}; range: {1, 2, 3, 4, 5}
9. a. {(6, A), (6, B), (6, C)} **b.** Domain: {6}; range: {A, B, C}
11. a. $\{(-4, 1), (0, 3), (1, -1), (3, 0)\}$ **b.** Domain: $\{-4, 0, 1, 3\}$; range: $\{-1, 0, 1, 3\}$
13. a. $\{(-4, 4), (1, 1), (2, 1), (3, 1), (4, -2)\}$ **b.** Domain: $\{-4, 1, 2, 3, 4\}$; range: $\{-2, 1, 4\}$
15. Domain: $[0, 4]$; range: $[-2, 2]$ **17.** Domain: $[-5, 3]$; range: $[-2.1, 2.8]$ **19.** Domain: $(-\infty, 2]$; range: $(-\infty, \infty)$
21. Domain: $(-\infty, \infty)$; range: $(-\infty, \infty)$ **23.** Domain: $\{-3\}$; range: $(-\infty, \infty)$ **25.** Domain: $(-\infty, 2)$; range: $[-1.3, \infty)$
27. Domain: $\{-3, -1, 1, 3\}$; range: $\{0, 1, 2, 3\}$
29. Domain: $[-4, 5)$; range: $\{-2, 1, 3\}$ **31. a.** 2.85 **b.** 9.33 **c.** Dec. **d.** Nov. **e.** 7.63 **f.** {Jan., Feb., Mar., Apr., May, June, July, Aug., Sept., Oct., Nov., Dec.}

33. a. 33.484 million or 33,484,000 **b.** The year 2015
35. a. For example: {(Julie, New York), (Peggy, Florida), (Stephen, Kansas), (Pat, New York)} **b.** Domain: {Julie, Peggy, Stephen, Pat}; range: {New York, Florida, Kansas}
37. $y = 2x - 1$ **39.** $y = x^2$

Section 8.2 Practice Exercises, pp. 580–584

1. a. function **b.** vertical **c.** $2x + 1$ **d.** x values **e.** y values **f.** denominator **g.** negative
3. a. $\{(-2,-4), (-1,-1), (0,0), (1,-1), (2,-4)\}$ **b.** $\{-2, -1, 0, 1, 2\}$ **c.** $\{-4, -1, 0\}$ **5.** Function
7. Not a function **9.** Function **11.** Not a function
13. Function **15.** Not a function **17.** When x is 2, the function value y is 5. **19.** $(0, 2)$ **21.** −11 **23.** 1
25. 2 **27.** $6t - 2$ **29.** 7 **31.** 4 **33.** 4
35. $6x + 4$ **37.** $-4x^2 - 8x + 1$ **39.** $-\pi^2 + 4\pi + 1$
41. 7 **43.** $-6a - 2$ **45.** $|-c - 2|$ **47.** 1 **49.** 7
51. −18.8 **53.** −7 **55.** 2π **57.** −5 **59.** 4
61. a. 3 **b.** 1 **c.** 1 **d.** $x = -3$ **e.** $x = 0, x = 2$ **f.** $(-\infty, 3]$ **g.** $(-\infty, 5]$ **63. a.** 3 **b.** $H(4)$ is not defined because 4 is not in the domain of H. **c.** 4 **d.** $x = -3$ and $x = 2$ **e.** All x on the interval $[-2, 1]$ **f.** $[-4, 4)$ **g.** $[2, 5)$
65. a. −4 **b.** 0 **c.** −3 **d.** $x = -1$ **e.** There are no such values of x. **f.** $(-\infty, \infty)$ **g.** $(-\infty, -3] \cup (-2, \infty)$
67. $\{-3, -7, -\frac{3}{2}, 1.2\}$ **69.** $\{6, 0\}$
71. $x = -3$ and $x = 1.2$ **73.** $x = 6$ and $x = 1$ **75.** −3
77. The domain is the set of all real numbers for which the denominator is not zero. Set the denominator equal to zero, and solve the resulting equation. The solution(s) to the equation must be excluded from the domain. In this case, setting $x - 2 = 0$ indicates that $x = 2$ must be excluded from the domain. The domain is $(-\infty, 2) \cup (2, \infty)$. **79.** $(-\infty, -6) \cup (-6, \infty)$
81. $(-\infty, 0) \cup (0, \infty)$ **83.** $(-\infty, \infty)$ **85.** $[-7, \infty)$
87. $[3, \infty)$ **89.** $(-\infty, \frac{1}{2}]$ **91.** $(-\infty, \infty)$ **93.** $(-\infty, \infty)$
95. a. $h(1) = 64$ and $h(1.5) = 44$ **b.** $h(1) = 64$ means that after 1 sec, the height of the ball is 64 ft. $h(1.5) = 44$ means that after 1.5 sec, the height of the ball is 44 ft. **97. a.** $d(1) = 11.5$ and $d(1.5) = 17.25$ **b.** $d(1) = 11.5$ means that after 1 hr, the distance traveled is 11.5 mi. $d(1.5) = 17.25$ means that after 1.5 hr, the distance traveled is 17.25 mi. **99.** $f(x) = 2x + 3$
101. $f(x) = |x| - 10$ **103.** $(-2, \infty)$

Section 8.2 Graphing Calculator Exercises, p. 584

105.

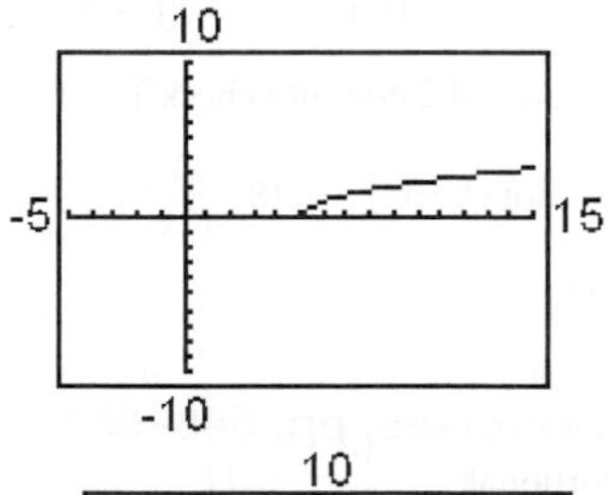

106.

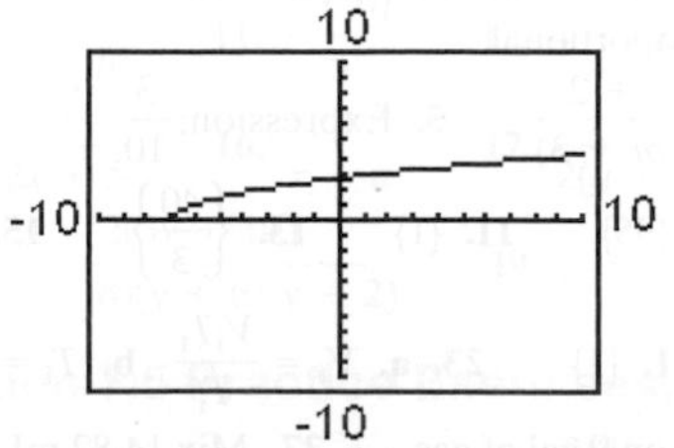

Section 8.3 Practice Exercises, pp. 592–596

1. a. linear **b.** constant **c.** quadratic **d.** parabola **e.** 0 **f.** y **3. a.** Yes **b.** $\{7, 2, -5\}$ **c.** $\{3\}$
5. $f(3) = 9$ means that 9 lb of force is required to stretch the spring 3 in. $f(10) = 30$ means that 30 lb of force is required to stretch the spring 10 in. **7.** horizontal

9. Domain $(-\infty, \infty)$; range $\{2\}$

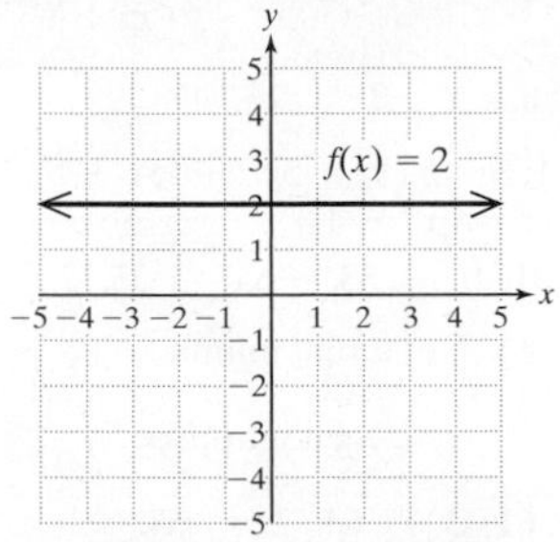

11.

x	$f(x)$	x	$f(x)$
-2	$-\frac{1}{2}$	$\frac{1}{4}$	4
-1	-1	$\frac{1}{2}$	2
$-\frac{1}{2}$	-2	1	1
$-\frac{1}{4}$	-4	2	$\frac{1}{2}$

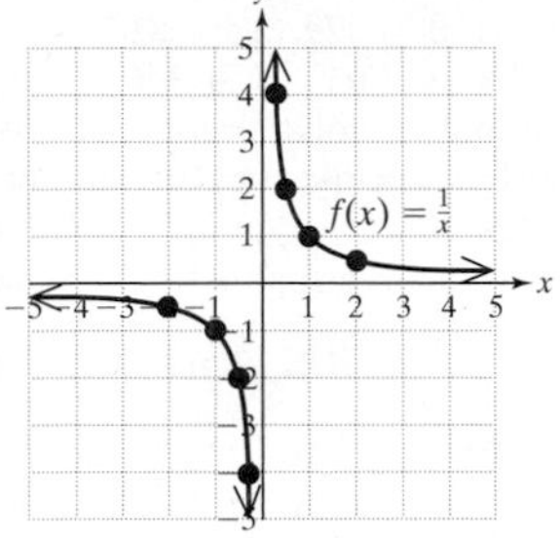

13.

x	$h(x)$
-2	-8
-1	-1
0	0
1	1
2	8

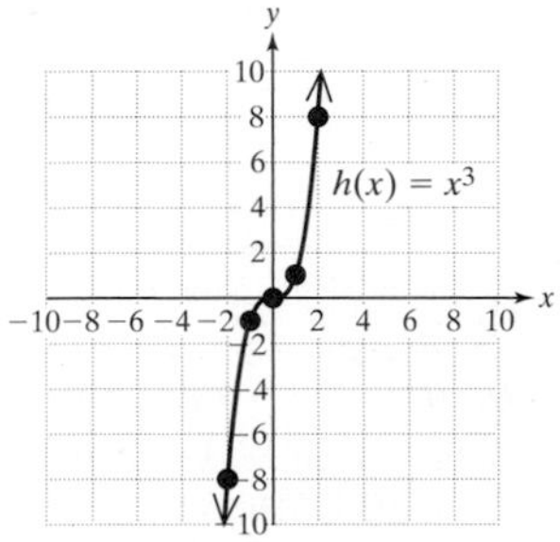

15.

x	$q(x)$
-2	4
-1	1
0	0
1	1
2	4

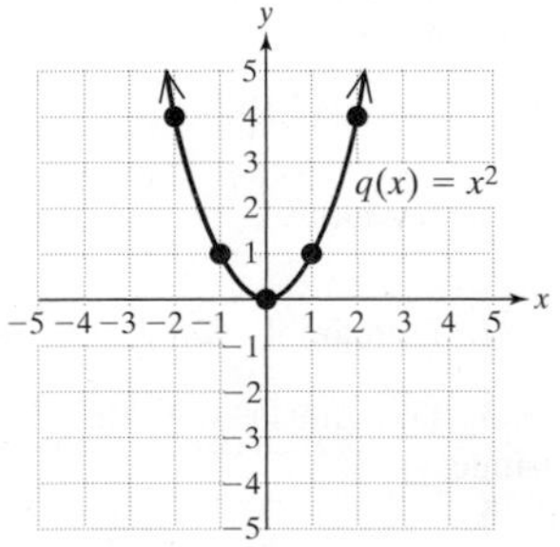

17. Quadratic **19.** Linear **21.** Constant
23. None of these **25.** Linear **27.** None of these
29. x-intercept: $(2, 0)$; y-intercept: $(0, -10)$

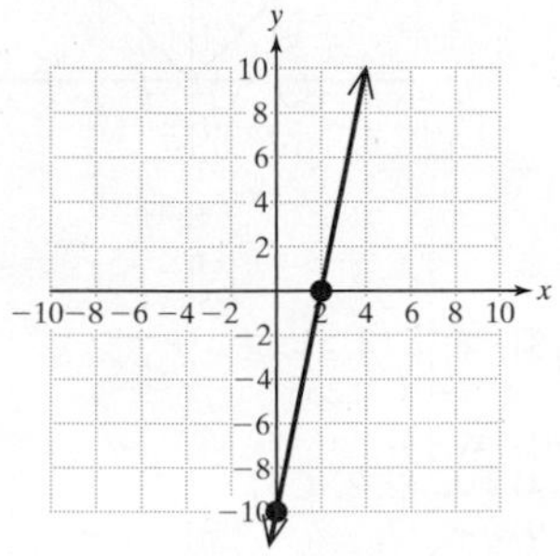

31. x-intercept: $\left(\frac{5}{6}, 0\right)$; y-intercept: $(0, 5)$

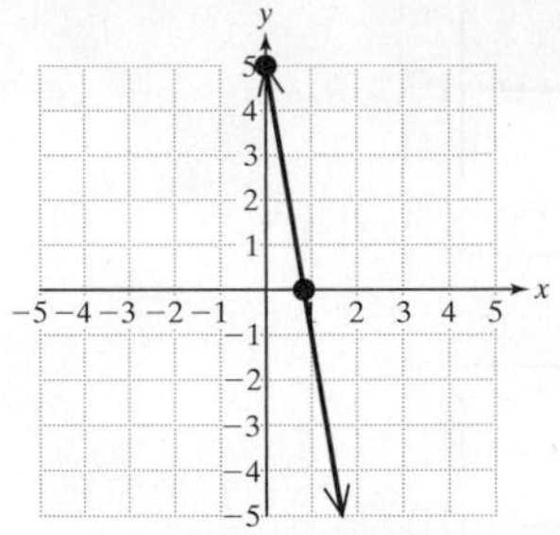

33. x-intercept: none; y-intercept: $(0, 18)$

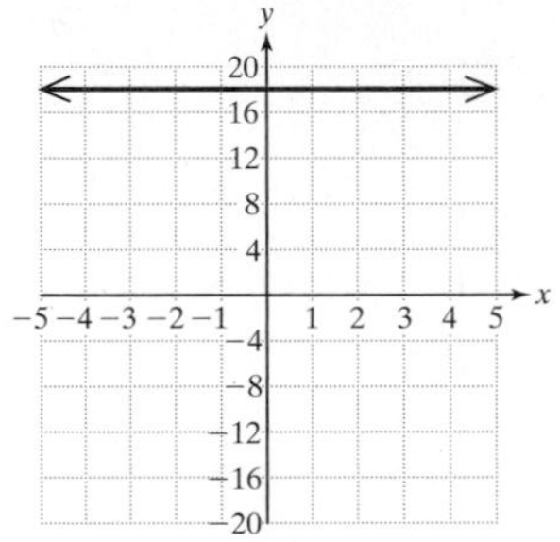

35. x-intercept: $(-3, 0)$; y-intercept: $(0, 2)$

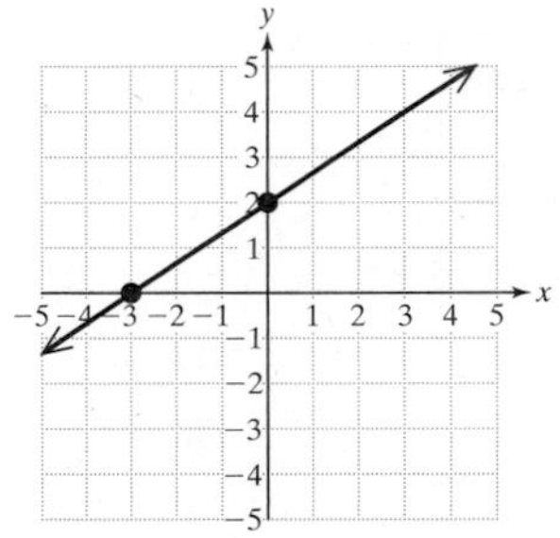

37. a. $x = -1$ **b.** $f(0) = 1$ **39. a.** $x = -2$ and $x = 2$ **b.** $f(0) = -2$ **41. a.** None **b.** $f(0) = 2$ **43. a.** $(-\infty, \infty)$ **b.** $(0, 0)$ **c.** vi **45. a.** $(-\infty, \infty)$ **b.** $(0, 1)$ **c.** viii **47. a.** $[-1, \infty)$ **b.** $(0, 1)$ **c.** vii **49. a.** $(-\infty, 3) \cup (3, \infty)$ **b.** $\left(0, -\frac{1}{3}\right)$ **c.** ii **51. a.** $(-\infty, \infty)$ **b.** $(0, 2)$ **c.** iv **53. a.** Linear **b.** $G(90) = 82.5$. This means that if the student gets a 90% score on her final exam, then her overall course average is 82.5%. **c.** $G(50) = 72.5$. This means that if the student gets a 50% score on her final exam, then her overall course average is 72.5%. **55.** $f(x) = x^2 + 2$ **57.** $f(x) = 3$ **59.** $f(x) = \frac{1}{2}x - 2$

Section 8.3 Graphing Calculator Exercises, pp. 596–597

61.

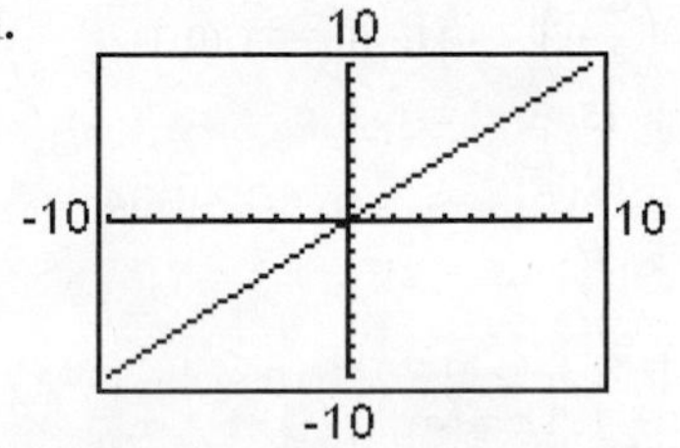

62.

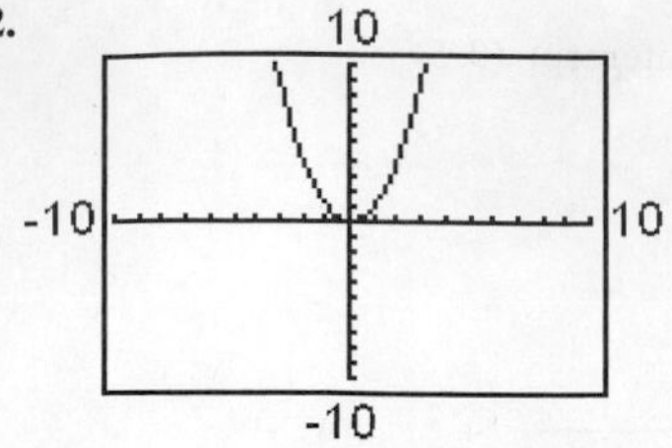

63.

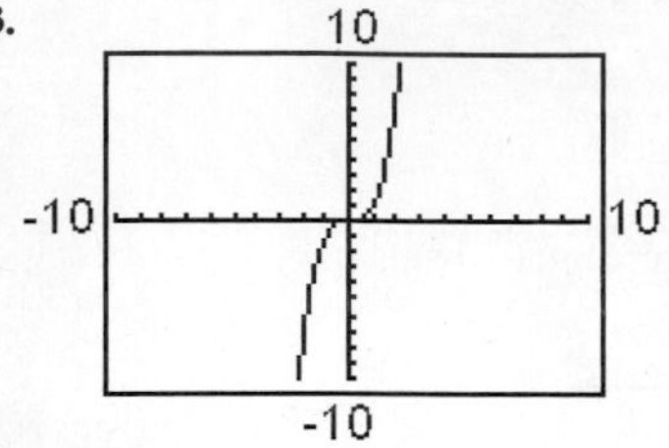

64.

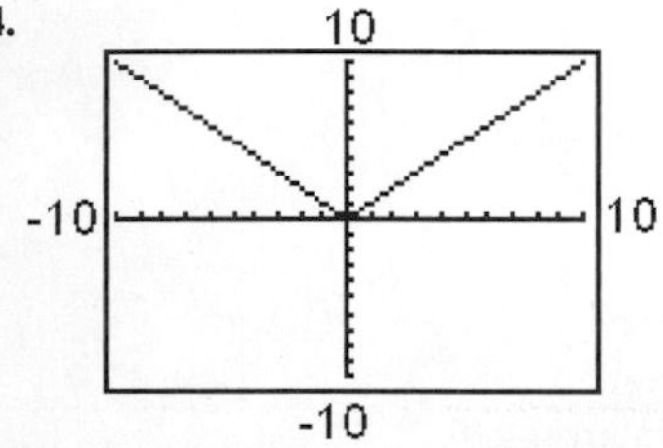

65.

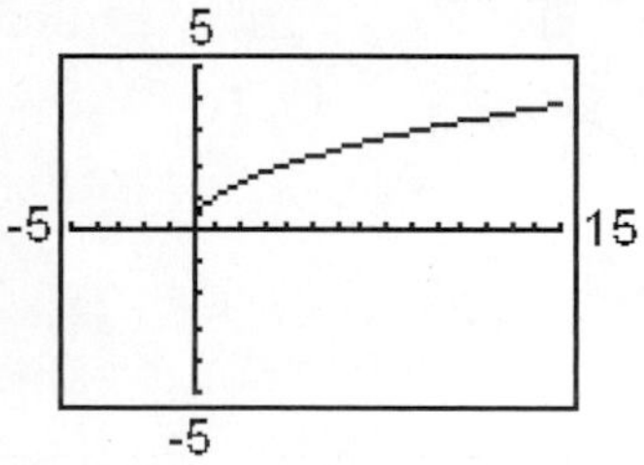

66.

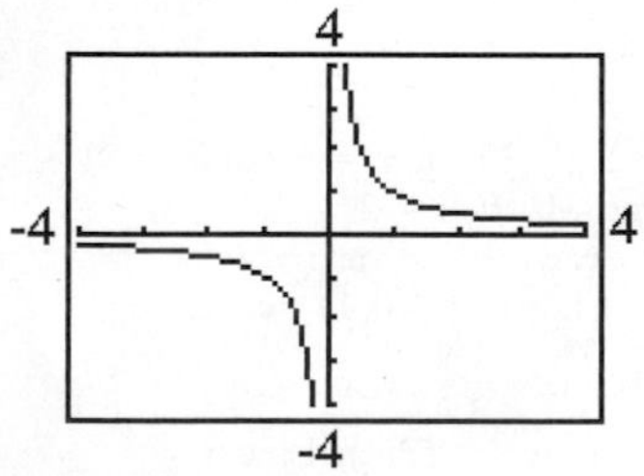

67. x-intercept: $(8, 0)$; y-intercept: $(0, 1)$ **68.** x-intercept: $(-6, 0)$; y-intercept: $(0, -3)$ **69.** x-intercept: $(-5, 0)$; y-intercept: $(0, 4)$ **70.** x-intercept: $(2, 0)$; y-intercept: $(0, -7)$

Chapter 8 Problem Recognition Exercises, p. 597

1. a, c, d, f, g **2.** a, b, d, f, h **3.** 4 **4.** 2 **5.** $\{0, 1, \frac{1}{2}, -3, 2\}$ **6.** $\{4, 3, 6, 1, 10\}$ **7.** $[-2, 4]$ **8.** $[0, \infty)$ **9.** 0 **10.** $\left(\frac{9}{5}, 0\right)$ **11.** $(0, -1), (0, 1)$ **12.** 1 **13.** c **14.** d **15.** 3

Section 8.4 Practice Exercises, pp. 602–604

1. a. $f(x)$; $g(x)$ **b.** $g(x)$ **c.** $f(g(x))$
3. $(f + g)(x) = 2x^2 + 5x + 4$
5. $(g - f)(x) = 2x^2 + 3x - 4$
7. $(f \cdot h)(x) = x^3 + 4x^2 + x + 4$
9. $(g \cdot f)(x) = 2x^3 + 12x^2 + 16x$
11. $\left(\frac{h}{f}\right)(x) = \frac{x^2 + 1}{x + 4}, x \neq -4$
13. $\left(\frac{f}{g}\right)(x) = \frac{x + 4}{2x^2 + 4x}, x \neq 0, x \neq -2$
15. $(f \circ g)(x) = 2x^2 + 4x + 4$
17. $(g \circ f)(x) = 2x^2 + 20x + 48$ **19.** $(k \circ h)(x) = \frac{1}{x^2 + 1}$
21. $(k \circ g)(x) = \frac{1}{2x^2 + 4x}, x \neq 0, x \neq -2$ **23.** No
25. $(f \circ g)(x) = 25x^2 - 15x + 1$; $(g \circ f)(x) = 5x^2 - 15x + 5$
27. $(f \circ g)(x) = |x^3 - 1|$; $(g \circ f)(x) = |x|^3 - 1$
29. $(h \circ h)(x) = 25x - 24$ **31.** 0 **33.** -64 **35.** 2
37. 1 **39.** $\frac{1}{64}$ **41.** 0 **43.** Not a real number
45. $\frac{4}{9}$ **47.** -2 **49.** 2 **51.** 0 **53.** 1 **55.** 0
57. Undefined **59.** -1 **61.** 2 **63.** 2 **65.** -1
67. -2 **69.** 3 **71.** -6 **73.** -1 **75.** 4
77. 0 **79.** 2 **81. a.** $P(x) = 3.78x - 1$ **b.** $188
83. a. $F(t) = 0.2t + 6.4$; F represents the amount of child support (in billion dollars) not paid. **b.** $F(4) = 7.2$ means that in 2004, $7.2 billion of child support was not paid.
85. a. $(D \circ r)(t) = 560t$; This function represents the total distance Joe travels as a function of time that he rides. **b.** 5600 ft

Section 8.5 Practice Exercises, pp. 610–613

1. a. kx **b.** $\frac{k}{x}$ **c.** kxw **3.** $x^2 - 4x + 4$ **5.** $x^2 - 2$
7. -1 **9.** Inversely **11.** $T = kq$ **13.** $b = \frac{k}{c}$
15. $Q = \frac{kx}{y}$ **17.** $c = kst$ **19.** $L = kw\sqrt{v}$ **21.** $x = \frac{ky^2}{z}$
23. $k = \frac{9}{2}$ **25.** $k = 512$ **27.** $k = 1.75$ **29.** $x = 70$
31. $b = 6$ **33.** $Z = 56$ **35.** $Q = 9$ **37.** $L = 9$
39. $B = \frac{15}{2}$ **41. a.** The heart weighs 0.92 lb. **b.** Answers will vary. **43. a.** 3.6 g **b.** 4.5 g **c.** 2.4 g
45. a. $0.40 **b.** $0.30 **c.** $1.00 **47.** 355,000 tons
49. 42.6 ft **51.** 300 W **53.** 18.5 A **55.** 20 lb.
57. $3500

Chapter 8 Review Exercises, pp. 618–621

1. Domain; $\left\{\frac{1}{3}, 6, \frac{1}{4}, 7\right\}$; range; $\left\{10, -\frac{1}{2}, 4, \frac{2}{5}\right\}$
2. Domain; $\{-3, -1, 0, 2, 3\}$; range; $\left\{-2, 0, 1, \frac{5}{2}\right\}$
3. Domain; $[-3, 9]$; range; $[0, 60]$ **4.** Domain; $[-4, 4]$; range; $[1, 3]$

5.

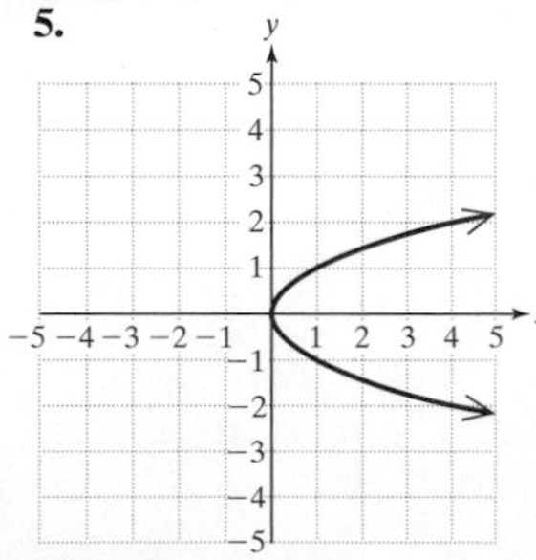

6.

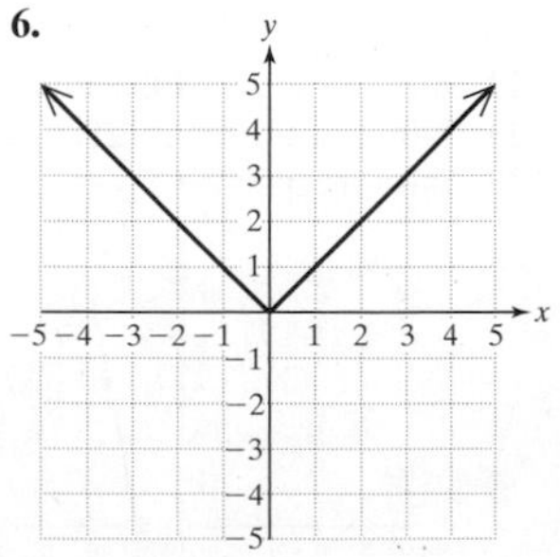

7. a. Not a function **b.** $[1, 3]$ **c.** $[-4, 4]$
8. a. Function **b.** $(-\infty, \infty)$ **c.** $(-\infty, 0.35]$
9. a. Function **b.** $\{1, 2, 3, 4\}$ **c.** $\{3\}$
10. a. Not a function **b.** $\{0, 4\}$ **c.** $\{2, 3, 4, 5\}$
11. a. Not a function **b.** $\{4, 9\}$ **c.** $\{2, -2, 3, -3\}$
12. a. Function **b.** $\{6, 7, 8, 9\}$ **c.** $\{9, 10, 11, 12\}$
13. -4 **14.** 2 **15.** 2 **16.** $6t^2 - 4$ **17.** $6b^2 - 4$
18. $6\pi^2 - 4$ **19.** $6a^2 - 4$ **20.** 20 **21.** $(-\infty, \infty)$
22. $(-\infty, 11) \cup (11, \infty)$ **23.** $[8, \infty)$ **24.** $[-2, \infty)$
25. a. $98 **b.** $123 **c.** $148

26.

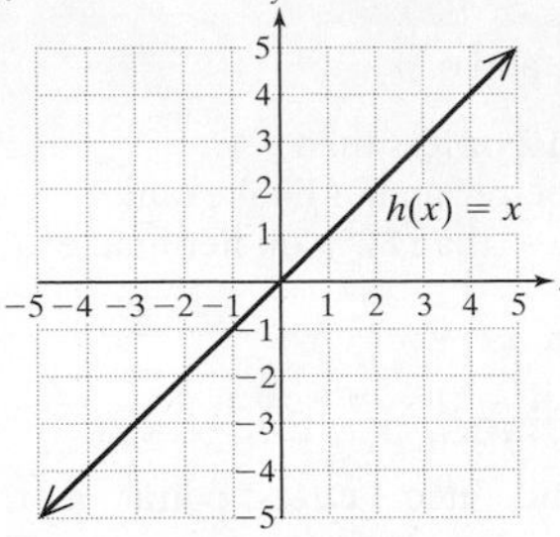

27.

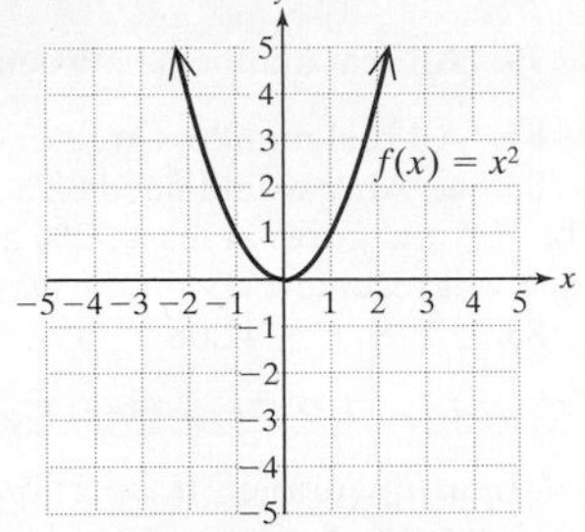

28.

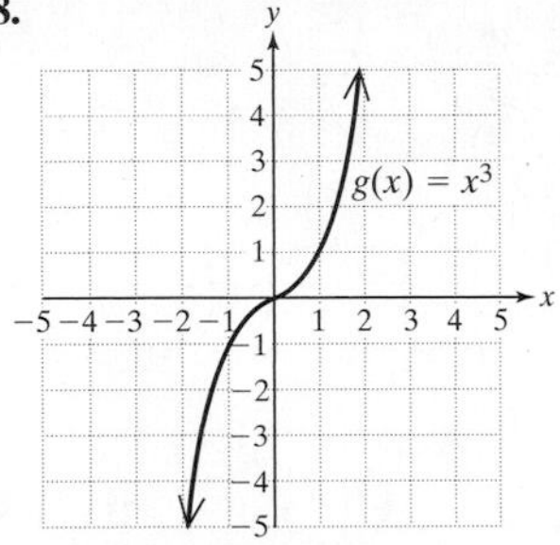

29.

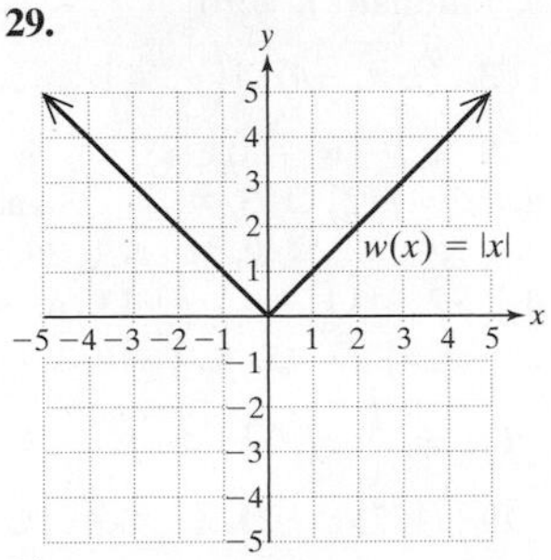

30.

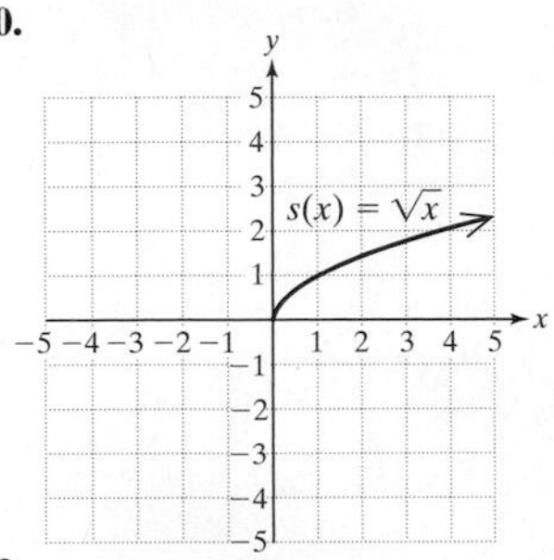

31.

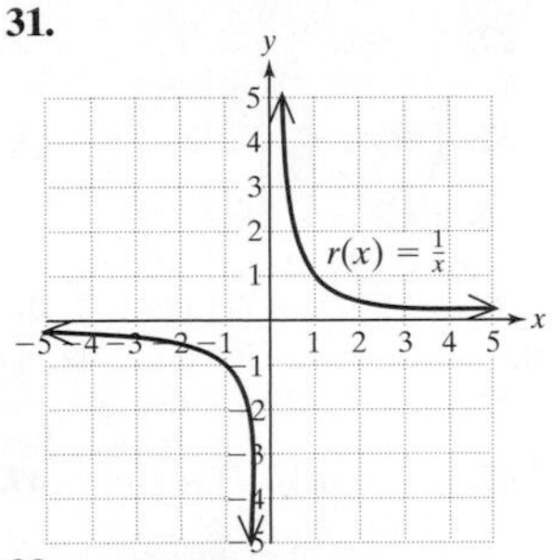

32.

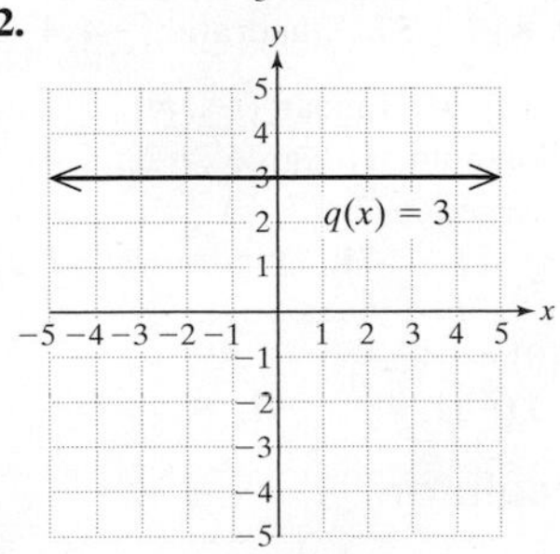

33.

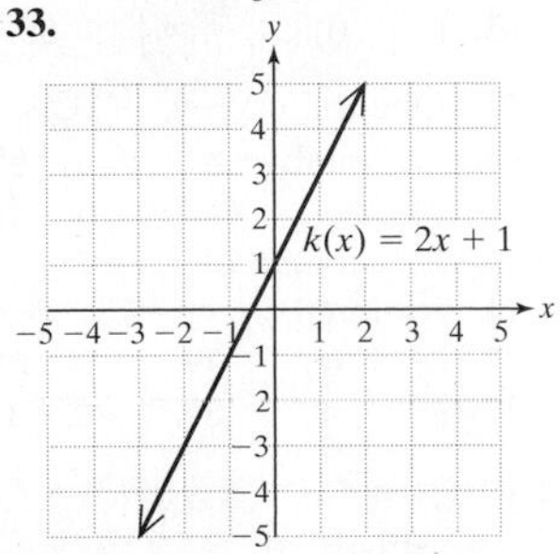

34. a. $s(4) = 4, s(-3) = 25, s(2) = 0, s(1) = 1, s(0) = 4$ **b.** $(-\infty, \infty)$ **35. a.** $r(2)$ is not a real number, $r(4) = 0, r(5) = 2, r(8) = 4$ **b.** $[4, \infty)$

36. a. $h(-3) = -\dfrac{1}{2}, h(0) = -1, h(2) = -3, h(5) = \dfrac{3}{2}$ **b.** $(-\infty, 3) \cup (3, \infty)$

37. a. $k(-5) = -2, k(-4) = -1, k(-3) = 0,$ $k(2) = -5$ **b.** $(-\infty, \infty)$ **38.** x-intercept: $\left(\dfrac{7}{4}, 0\right)$; y-intercept: $(0, -7)$

39. x-intercept: $\left(\dfrac{9}{2}, 0\right)$; y-intercept: $(0, 9)$

40. a. $b(0) = 4.5$. In 1985 consumption was 4.5 gal of bottled water per capita. $b(7) = 9.4$. In 1992 consumption was 9.4 gal of bottled water per capita. **b.** $m = 0.7$. Consumption increased at a rate of 0.7 gal/year.
41. -1 **42.** 0 **43.** $x = 0$ and $x = 4$
44. There are no values of x for which $g(x) = 4$.
45. $(-4, \infty)$ **46.** $(-\infty, 1]$ **47.** $(f - g)(x) = 2x^3 + 9x - 7$

48. $(f + g)(x) = -2x^3 - 7x - 7$ **49.** $(f \cdot n)(x) = \dfrac{x - 7}{x - 2}, x \neq 2$

50. $(f \cdot m)(x) = x^3 - 7x^2$ **51.** $\left(\dfrac{f}{g}\right)(x) = \dfrac{x - 7}{-2x^3 - 8x}; x \neq 0$

52. $\left(\dfrac{g}{f}\right)(x) = \dfrac{-2x^3 - 8x}{x - 7}, x \neq 7$
53. $(m \circ f)(x) = (x - 7)^2$ or $x^2 - 14x + 49$

54. $(n \circ f)(x) = \dfrac{1}{x - 9}, x \neq 9$ **55.** 100 **56.** $\dfrac{1}{8}$

57. -167 **58.** -10 **59. a.** $(2x + 1)^2$ or $4x^2 + 4x + 1$ **b.** $2x^2 + 1$ **c.** No, $f \circ g \neq g \circ f$ **60.** $\dfrac{1}{4}$ **61.** -3

62. 0 **63.** -1 **64.** 4 **65.** 1 **66. a.** $F = kd$ **b.** $k = 3$ **c.** 12.6 lb **67.** $y = \dfrac{8}{3}$ **68.** $y = 12$ **69.** 48 km

Chapter 8 Test, pp. 621–622

1. a. Not a function **b.** $\{-3, -1, 1, 3\}$ **c.** $\{-2, -1, 1, 3\}$ **2. a.** Function **b.** $(-\infty, \infty)$ **c.** $(-\infty, 0]$ **3.** To find the x-intercept(s), solve for the real solutions of the equation $f(x) = 0$. To find the y-intercept, find $f(0)$.

4.

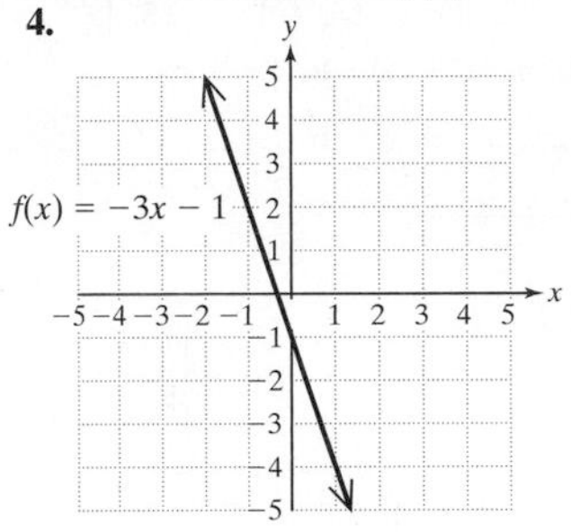

5.

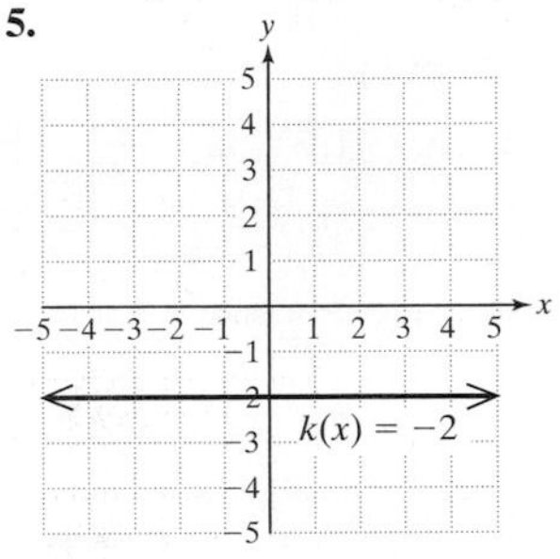

6.

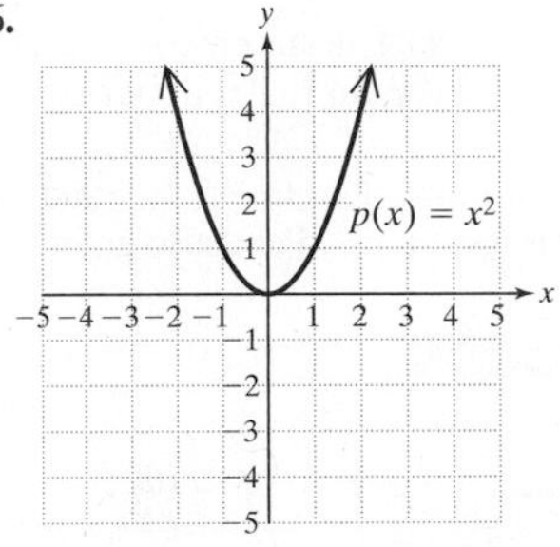

7.

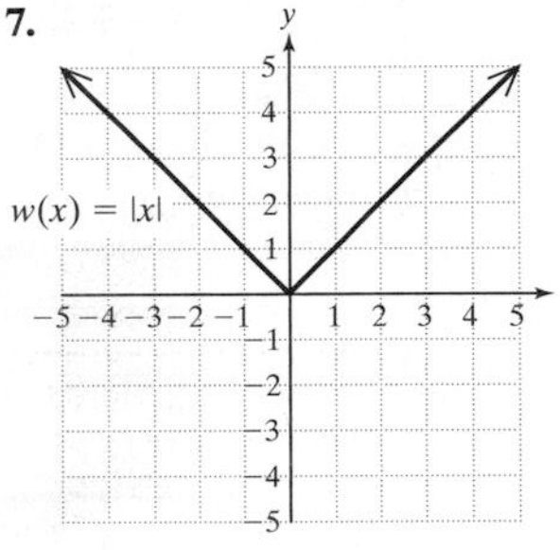

8. $(-\infty, -7) \cup (-7, \infty)$ **9.** $[-7, \infty)$ **10.** $(-\infty, \infty)$
11. a. $r(-2) = 9, r(0) = 1, r(3) = 4$ **b.** $(-\infty, \infty)$
12. $s(0) = 67$. In 2000 the per capita consumption was 67 L. $s(7) = 109$. In 2007 the per capita consumption was 109 L.
13. 1 **14.** 2 **15.** $(-1, 7]$ **16.** $[-1, 4)$
17. False **18.** (6, 0) **19.** $x = 6$ **20.** All x in the interval $[1, 3]$ and $x = 5$ **21.** Quadratic **22.** Linear
23. Constant **24.** None of these
25. x-intercept: $(-12, 0)$; y-intercept: $(0, 9)$

26. $\left(\dfrac{f}{g}\right)(x) = \dfrac{x - 4}{x^2 + 2}$ **27.** $(h \cdot g)(x) = \dfrac{x^2 + 2}{x}, x \neq 0$

28. $(g \circ f)(x) = x^2 - 8x + 18$ **29.** $(h \circ f)(x) = \dfrac{1}{x - 4}, x \neq 4$

30. -48 **31.** $-\dfrac{3}{2}$ **32.** $\dfrac{1}{18}$ **33.** 18

34. $\left(\dfrac{g}{f}\right)(x) = \dfrac{x^2 + 2}{x - 4}, x \neq 4$ **35.** 8.25 mL
36. 200 drinks are sold.

Chapters 1–8 Cumulative Review Exercises, p. 623

1. -1 **2.** $21x - 62y + 12$ **3.** $\{-15\}$ **4.** $\{\ \}$

5. $[-3, \infty)$ **6.** x-intercept: $\left(\dfrac{10}{3}, 0\right)$ y-intercept: $(0, -2)$

7. $m = -\dfrac{1}{5}$ **8.** $m = \dfrac{5}{2}$ **9.** $\{(2, -1)\}$ **10.** $\{(-4, 0, 5)\}$

11. $\frac{9x^2}{y^6}$ **12.** $5x^2 - 8x + 7$ **13.** $-10x^3 + 47x^2 - 42x$

14. $(2x + 1)(x + 3)$ **15.** $5(x - 4)(x + 4)$ **16.** $\frac{x^2+5}{(x-5)(x+1)}$

17. $\frac{x+2}{x^2}$ **18.** Domain: $\{2, -1, 9, -6\}$ Range: $\{4, 2, 8\}$

19. $(-\infty, 0) \cup (0, \infty)$ **20.** $(f \circ g)(x) = x^2 + 2x - 5$

Chapter 9

Chapter Opener Puzzle

1. b **2.** g **3.** f **4.** a **5.** e **6.** c **7.** d **8.** h

Section 9.1 Practice Exercises, pp. 634–638

1. a. union; $A \cup B$ **b.** intersection; $A \cap B$ **c.** intersection **d.** $a < x < b$ **e.** union **3.** $(-\infty, 2]$ **5.** $(-\infty, 15)$

7. a. $\{-3, -1\}$ **b.** $\{-4, -3, -2, -1, 0, 1, 3, 5\}$

9. $[-7, -4)$ **11.** $(-\infty, -4) \cup (2, \infty)$ **13.** { } **15.** $[-7, \infty)$

17. $[0, 5)$ **19.** $[-7, \infty)$ **21. a.** $[-1, 5)$ **b.** $(-2, \infty)$

23. a. $(-1, 3)$ **b.** $\left(-\frac{5}{2}, \frac{9}{2}\right)$ **25. a.** $(0, 2]$ **b.** $(-4, 5]$

27. $[-2, 3]$ 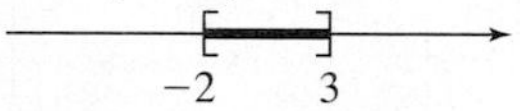

29. $(3, 6)$ 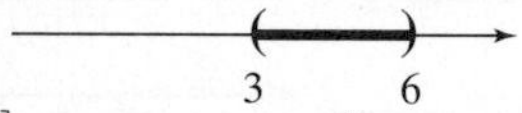

31. $(-\infty, 2]$ 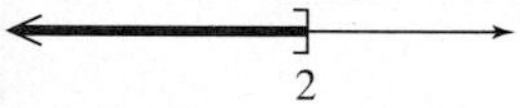

33. $[8, \infty)$ 

35. { } **37.** $-4 \le t$ and $t < \frac{3}{4}$ **39.** The statement $6 < x < 2$ is equivalent to $6 < x$ and $x < 2$. However, no real number is greater than 6 and also less than 2.

41. The statement $-5 > y > -2$ is equivalent to $-5 > y$ and $y > -2$. However, no real number is less than -5 and also greater than -2.

43. $\left[\frac{5}{2}, 7\right)$ 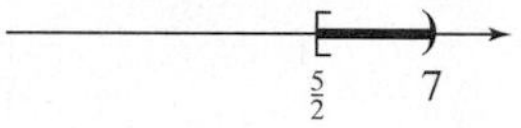

45. $(-6, 6]$ 

47. $(2, 8)$ 

49. $\left[-\frac{10}{3}, -\frac{7}{3}\right]$ 

51. $\left[-\frac{1}{2}, \frac{3}{2}\right)$ 

53. $(-0.4, 0.2)$ 

55. $(-\infty, -2) \cup [2, \infty)$ 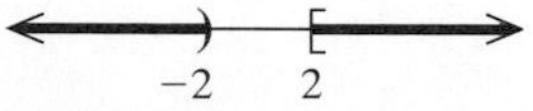

57. $(-\infty, 2]$ 

59. $[-6, \infty)$ 

61. $(-\infty, \infty)$ 

63. $(-\infty, -4] \cup (4.5, \infty)$ 

65. a. $(-10, 8)$ **b.** $(-\infty, \infty)$

67. a. $(-\infty, -8] \cup [1.3, \infty)$ **b.** { }

69. $\left(-\frac{11}{2}, \frac{7}{2}\right]$ **71.** $\left(-\frac{13}{2}, \infty\right)$ **73.** $(-\infty, 1) \cup (5, \infty)$

75. a. $4800 \le x \le 10{,}800$ **b.** $x < 4800$ or $x > 10{,}800$

77. a. $44\% < x < 48\%$ **b.** $x \le 44\%$ or $x \ge 48\%$

79. All real numbers between $-\frac{3}{2}$ and 6

81. All real numbers greater than 2 or less than -1

83. a. Amy would need 82% or better on her final exam. **b.** If Amy scores at least 32% and less than 82% on her final exam she will receive a "B" in the class.

85. $32° \le F \le 42.08°$

Section 9.2 Practice Exercises, pp. 645–648

1. a. quadratic **b.** solutions; undefined **c.** test point **d.** true **e.** rational **f.** zero

3. $(-\infty, -4) \cup \left(\frac{1}{3}, \infty\right)$ **5.** $\left[3, \frac{16}{5}\right]$ **7.** $[-1, 3]$

9. a. $(-\infty, -2) \cup (3, \infty)$ **b.** $(-2, 3)$ **c.** $[-2, 3]$ **d.** $(-\infty, -2] \cup [3, \infty)$ **11. a.** $(-2, 0) \cup (3, \infty)$ **b.** $(-\infty, -2) \cup (0, 3)$ **c.** $(-\infty, -2] \cup [0, 3]$ **d.** $[-2, 0] \cup [3, \infty)$ **13. a.** $\{4, -\frac{1}{2}\}$ **b.** $(-\infty, -\frac{1}{2}) \cup (4, \infty)$ **c.** $(-\frac{1}{2}, 4)$ **15. a.** $\{-10, 3\}$ **b.** $(-10, 3)$ **c.** $(-\infty, -10) \cup (3, \infty)$

17. a. $\left\{-\frac{1}{2}, 3\right\}$ **b.** $\left[-\frac{1}{2}, 3\right]$ **c.** $\left(-\infty, -\frac{1}{2}\right] \cup [3, \infty)$

19. $(1, 7)$ **21.** $(-\infty, -2) \cup (5, \infty)$ **23.** $[-5, 0]$ **25.** $[4, 8]$

27. $\left(-\infty, -\frac{1}{5}\right) \cup (1, \infty)$ **29.** $(-11, 11)$

31. $\left(-\infty, -\frac{1}{3}\right] \cup [3, \infty)$ **33.** $(-\infty, -3] \cup [0, 4]$

35. $(-2, -1) \cup (2, \infty)$ **37. a.** $(-1, 1]$ **b.** $(-\infty, -1) \cup [1, \infty)$ **c.** $(-\infty, -1) \cup (1, \infty)$ **d.** $(-1, 1)$

39. a. $(-\infty, -1) \cup (2, \infty)$ **b.** $(-1, 2)$ **c.** $[-1, 2)$ **d.** $(-\infty, -1] \cup (2, \infty)$ **41. a.** $\{7\}$ **b.** $(-\infty, 5) \cup (7, \infty)$ **c.** $(5, 7)$

43. a. $\{4\}$ **b.** $[4, 6)$ **c.** $(-\infty, 4] \cup (6, \infty)$ **45.** $(1, \infty)$

47. $(-\infty, -4) \cup (4, \infty)$ **49.** $\left(2, \frac{7}{2}\right)$ **51.** $(5, 7]$

53. $(-\infty, 0) \cup \left[\frac{1}{2}, \infty\right)$ **55.** $(0, \infty)$ **57.** Quadratic; $[-4, 4]$

59. Quadratic; $(-\infty, -\frac{4}{5}) \cup (0, \infty)$ **61.** Linear; $(-\frac{5}{2}, \infty)$

63. Rational; $(-\infty, -1)$ **65.** Polynomial (degree > 2); $(0, 5) \cup (5, \infty)$ **67.** Polynomial (degree > 2); $(2, \infty)$

69. Polynomial (degree > 2); $(-\infty, 5]$ **71.** Quadratic; $(-2, 2)$

73. Rational; $(-\infty, -2] \cup (5, \infty)$ **75.** Linear; $(-\infty, 5]$

77. $(-\infty, \infty)$ **79.** { } **81.** $\{0\}$ **83.** { } **85.** { }

87. $(-\infty, \infty)$ **89.** $(-\infty, -11) \cup (-11, \infty)$ **91.** $\{\frac{3}{2}\}$

Section 9.2 Graphing Calculator Exercises, p. 648

93. $(-\infty, 0) \cup (2, \infty)$

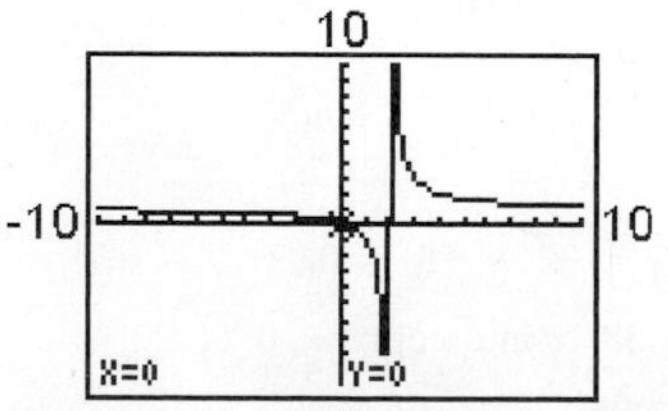

94. $(0, 2)$

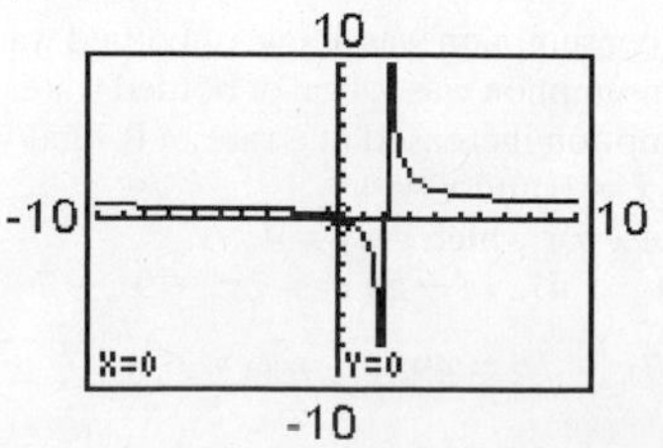

95. $(-1, 1)$

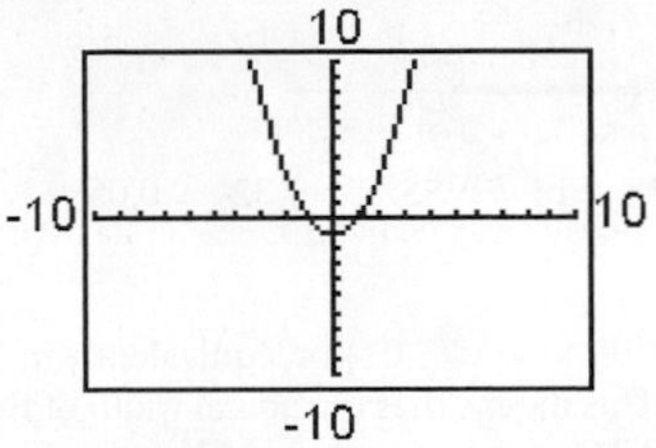

96. $(-\infty, -1) \cup (1, \infty)$

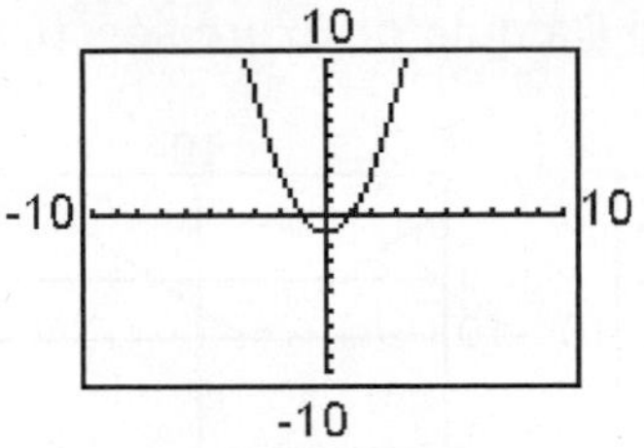

97. $\{-5\}$

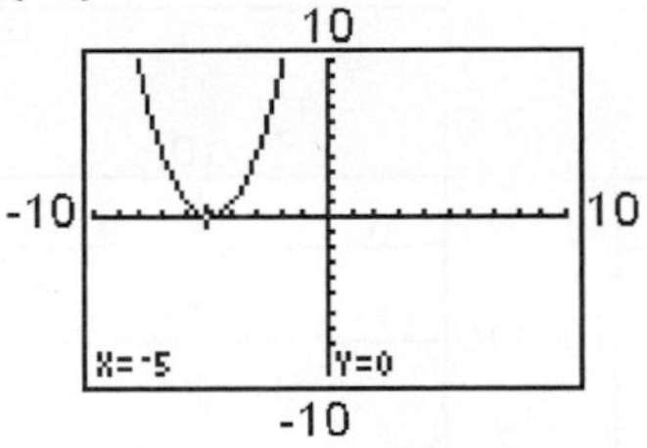

98. $\{5\}$

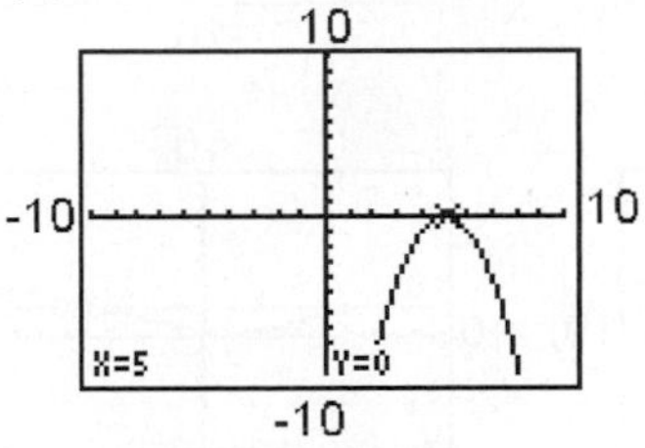

99. $\{\ \}$

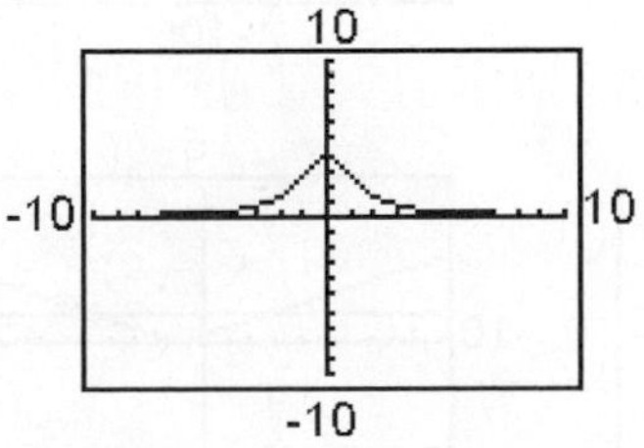

100. $\{\ \}$

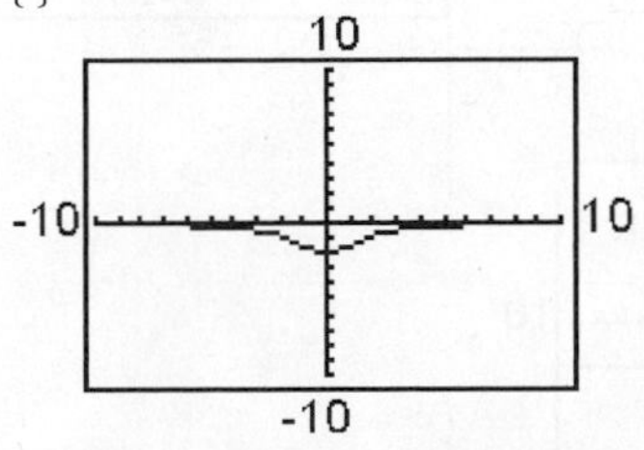

Section 9.3 Practice Exercises, pp. 654–655

1. a. absolute; $\{a, -a\}$ **b.** Subtract 5 from both sides. **c.** y; $-y$ **d.** $\{\ \}$; $\{-4\}$

3. $(-\infty, -1] \cup [1, \infty)$ **5.** $(-\infty, -1) \cup \left[\frac{1}{2}, \infty\right)$

7. $\{7, -7\}$ **9.** $\{6, -6\}$ **11.** $\{\ \}$ **13.** $\{-2, 2\}$

15. $\{0\}$ **17.** $\left\{4, -\frac{4}{3}\right\}$ **19.** $\left\{\frac{9}{2}, -\frac{1}{2}\right\}$ **21.** $\left\{\frac{10}{7}, -\frac{8}{7}\right\}$

23. $\{\ \}$ **25.** $\{-12, 28\}$ **27.** $\left\{\frac{5}{2}, -\frac{7}{2}\right\}$ **29.** $\left\{\frac{7}{3}\right\}$

31. $\{\ \}$ **33.** $\left\{\frac{3}{2}\right\}$ **35.** $\left\{-4, \frac{16}{5}\right\}$ **37.** $\left\{-\frac{1}{2}, \frac{7}{6}\right\}$

39. $\left\{\frac{5}{2}, -\frac{3}{2}\right\}$ **41.** $\left\{-4, \frac{1}{3}\right\}$ **43.** $\left\{\frac{1}{2}\right\}$ **45.** $\left\{-\frac{1}{16}\right\}$

47. $\left\{\frac{1}{4}\right\}$ **49.** $\{-1.44, -0.4\}$ **51.** $\{\ \}$

53. $\{w \mid w \text{ is a real number}\}$ **55.** $\{\ \}$ **57.** $|x| = 6$

59. $|x| = \frac{4}{3}$

Section 9.3 Graphing Calculator Exercises, p. 655

61. $\left\{2, -\frac{1}{2}\right\}$

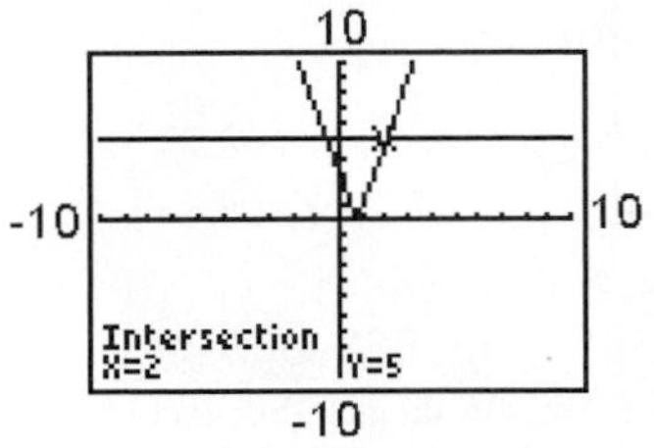

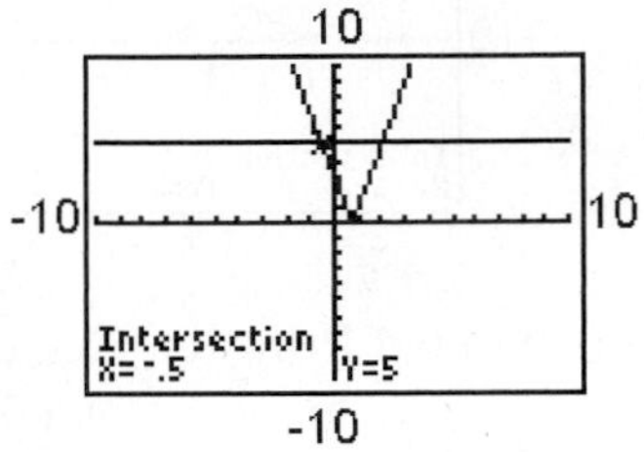

62. $\{7, 1\}$

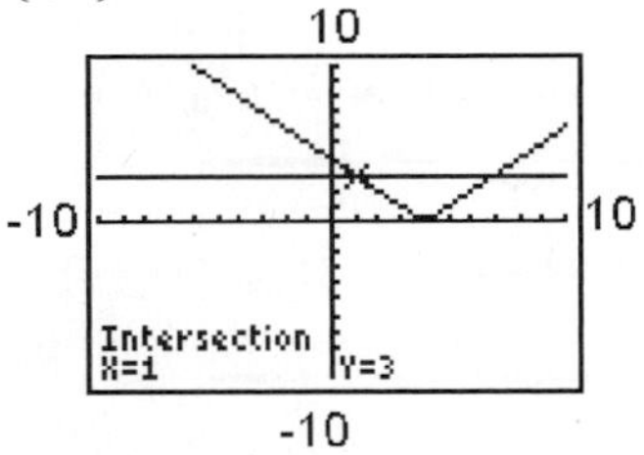

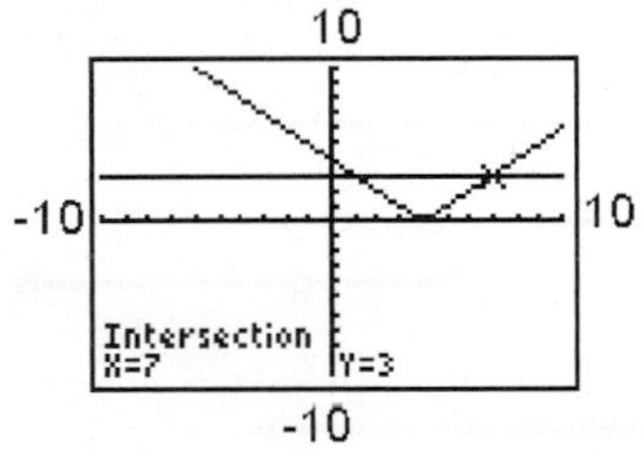

63. $\{\ \}$

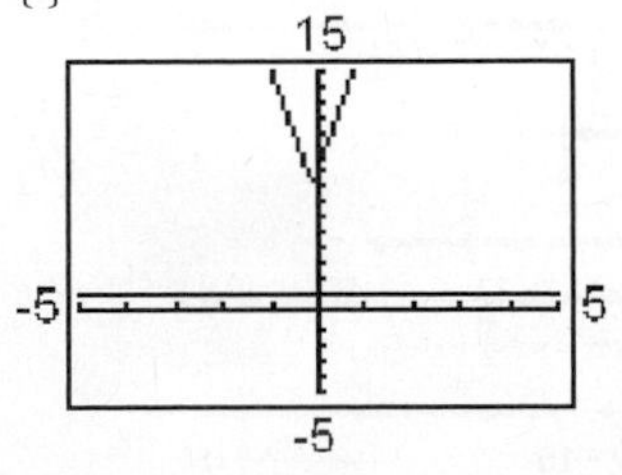

64. $\{\ \}$

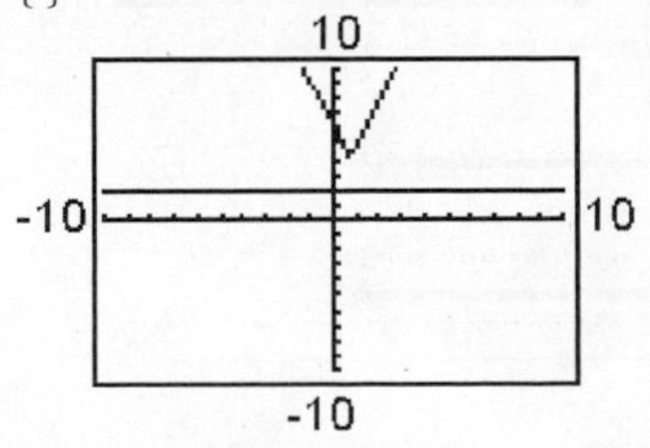

65. $\left\{\frac{1}{2}\right\}$

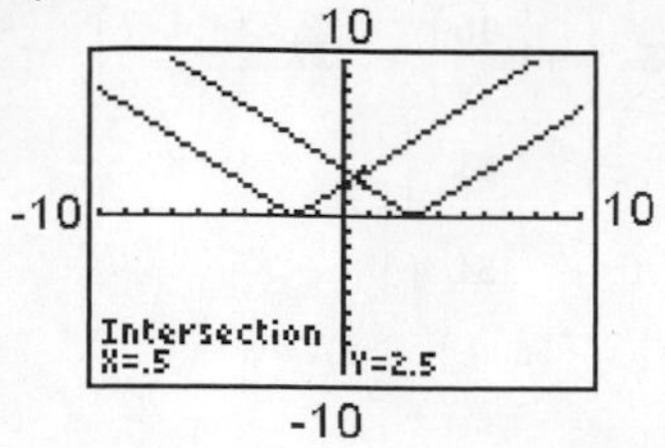

66. $\{-1\}$

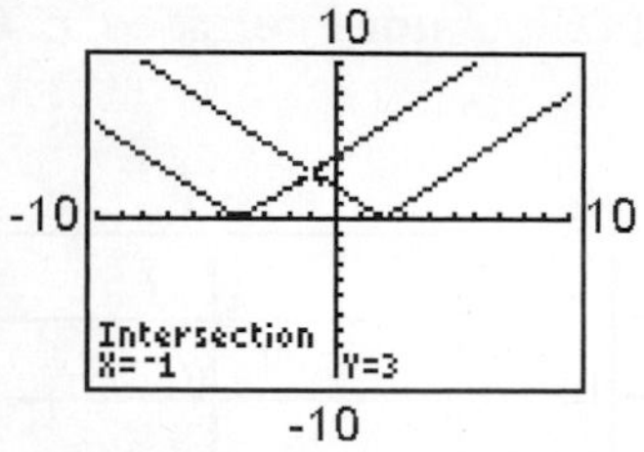

Section 9.4 Practice Exercises, pp. 663–665

1. a. $-a$; a **b.** $-a$; $>$ **c.** $\{\ \}$; $(-\infty, \infty)$ **d.** includes; excludes

3. $\left\{\frac{4}{7}, \frac{6}{7}\right\}$ **5.** $(-3, -1]$

7. $(-\infty, \infty)$

9. a. $\{-5, 5\}$

b. $(-\infty, -5) \cup (5, \infty)$

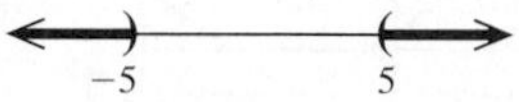

c. $(-5, 5)$

11. a. $\{10, -4\}$

b. $(-\infty, -4) \cup (10, \infty)$

c. $(-4, 10)$

13. a. $\{\ \}$ **b.** $(-\infty, \infty)$

c. $\{\ \}$ **15. a.** $\{\ \}$

b. $(-\infty, \infty)$

c. $\{\ \}$

17. a. $\{0\}$ **b.** $(-\infty, 0) \cup (0, \infty)$

c. $\{\ \}$ **19. a.** $\{7\}$

b. $(-\infty, 7) \cup (7, \infty)$

c. $\{\ \}$

21. $(-\infty, -6) \cup (6, \infty)$

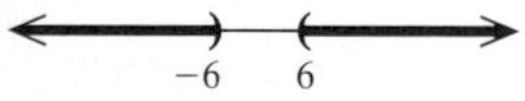

23. $[-3, 3]$

25. $(-\infty, \infty)$

27. $(-\infty, -2] \cup [3, \infty)$

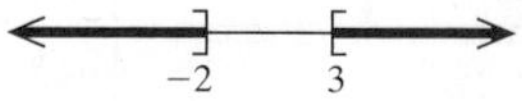

29. $\{\ \}$ **31.** $[-10, 14]$

33. $\left(-\infty, -\frac{5}{4}\right] \cup \left[\frac{23}{4}, \infty\right)$

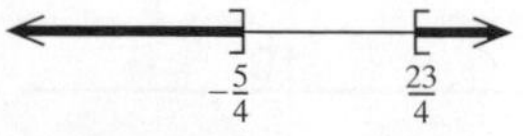

35. $\left(-\frac{21}{2}, \frac{19}{2}\right)$

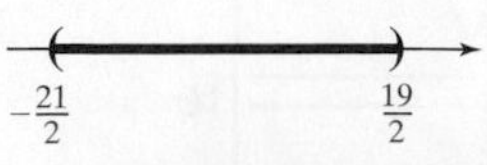

37. $(-\infty, \infty)$

39. $\{\ \}$ **41.** $\{-5\}$

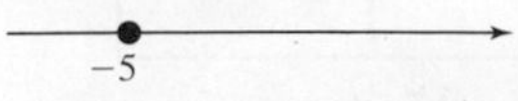

43. $(-\infty, 6) \cup (6, \infty)$

45. $(-\infty, 2] \cup [4, \infty)$

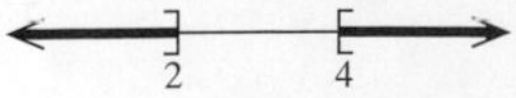

47. $(4, 8)$

49. $(-10.5, 4.5)$

51. $|x| > 7$ **53.** $|x - 2| \leq 13$ **55.** $|x - 32| \leq 0.05$

57. $\left|x - 6\frac{3}{4}\right| \leq \frac{1}{8}$

59. The solution set is $\{w \mid 1.99 \leq w \leq 2.01\}$ or, equivalently in interval notation, $[1.99, 2.01]$. This means that the actual width of the bolt could be between 1.99 cm and 2.01 cm, inclusive. **61.** b **63.** a

Section 9.4 Graphing Calculator Exercises, p. 666

65. $(-\infty, -6) \cup (2, \infty)$

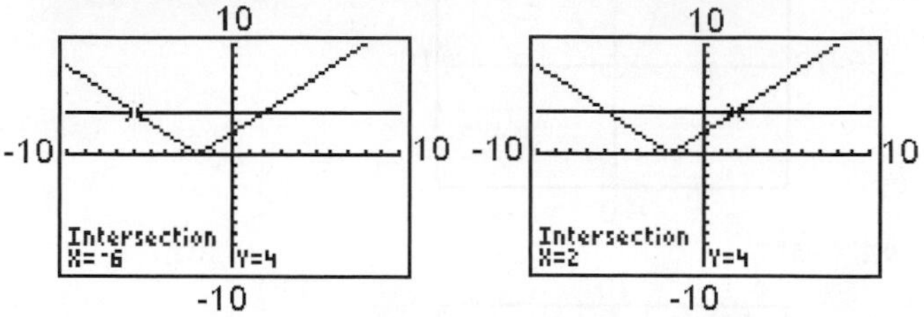

66. $(-\infty, -3) \cup (9, \infty)$

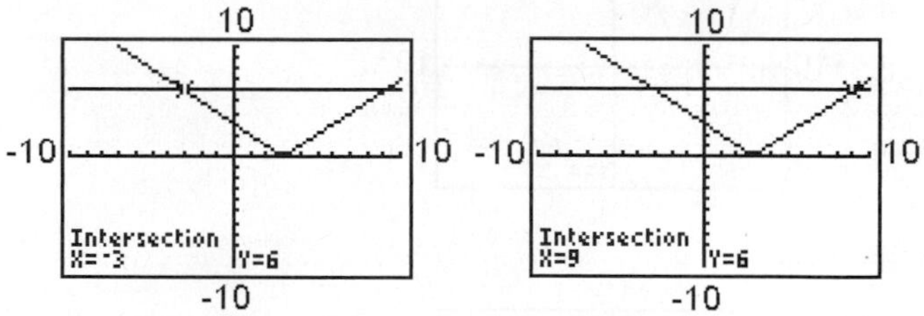

67. $(-7, 5)$

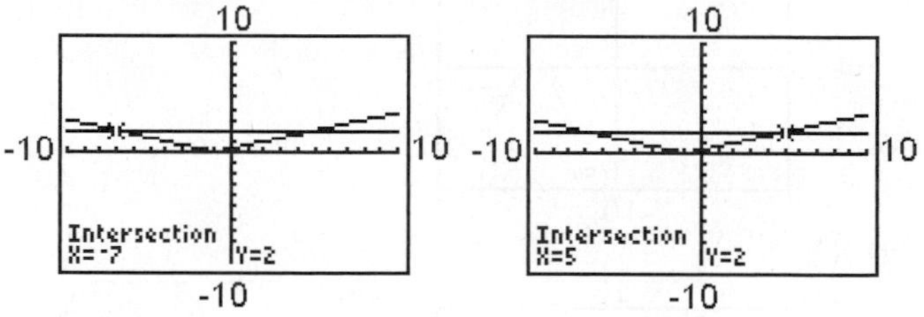

68. $(-3, 5)$

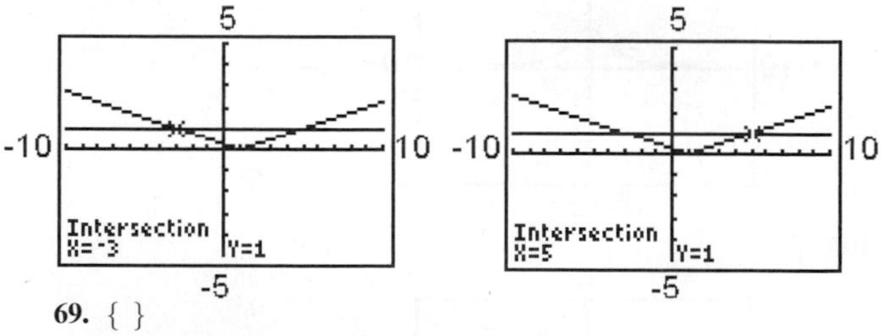

69. $\{\ \}$

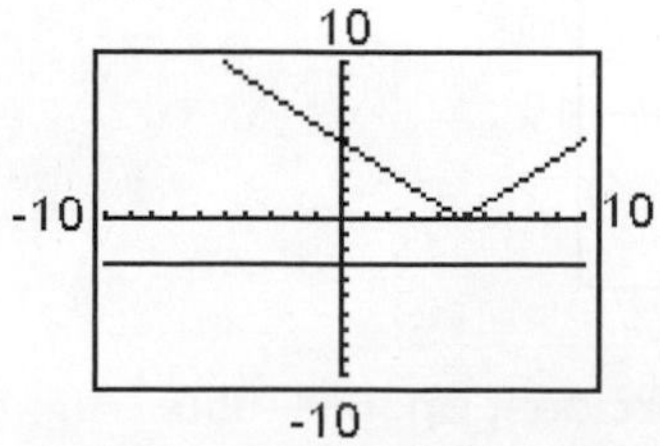

70. { }

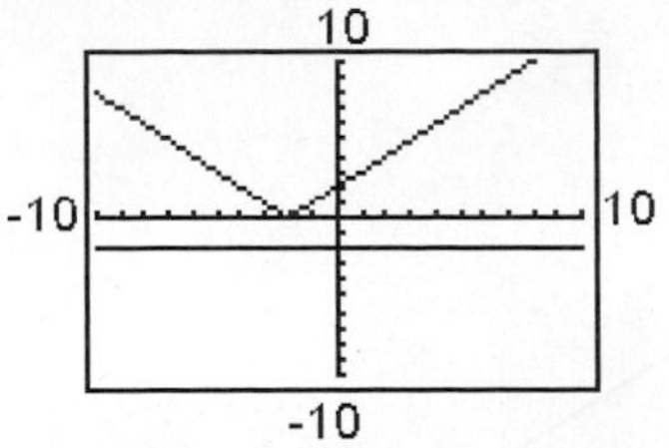

71. $(-\infty, \infty)$

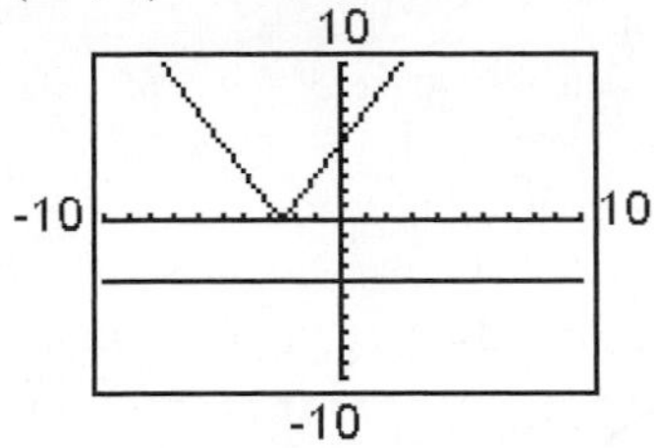

72. $(-\infty, \infty)$

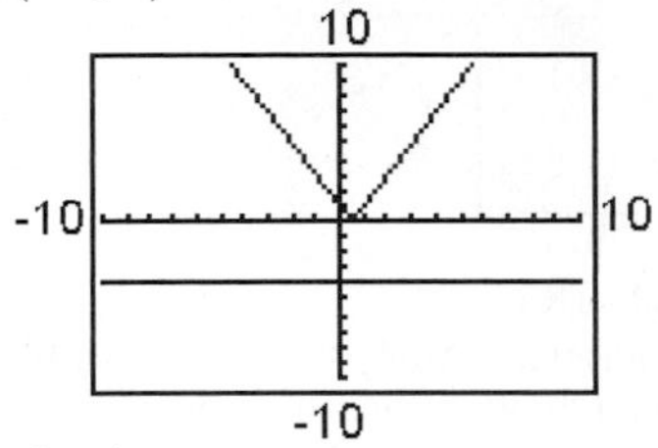

73. $\left\{-\frac{1}{6}\right\}$

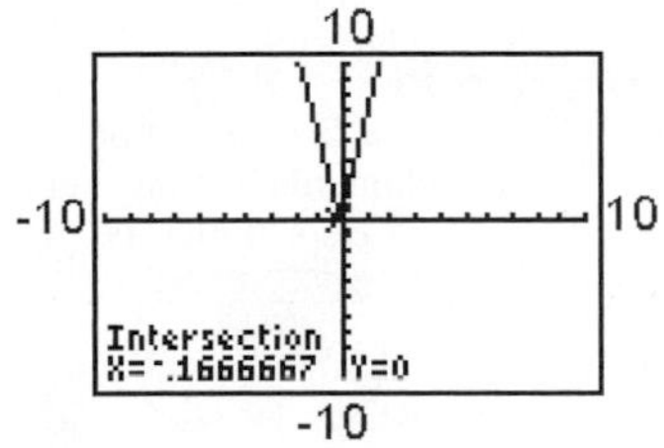

74. $\left\{\frac{4}{3}\right\}$

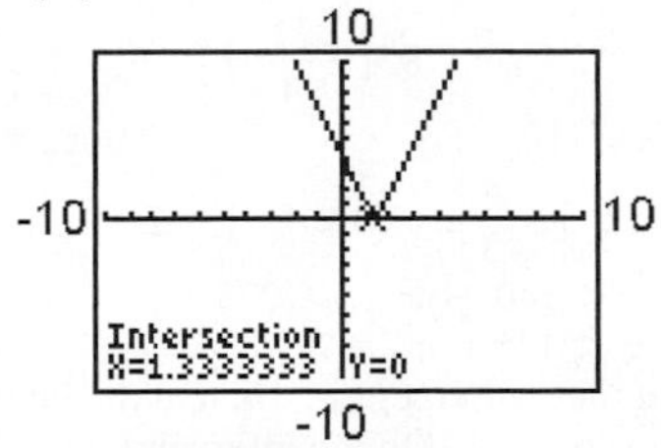

Chapter 9 Problem Recognition Exercises, p. 666

1. Quadratic; $(-\infty, -9) \cup (-1, \infty)$ **2.** Linear; $\{-26\}$
3. Rational; $[-8, -2)$ **4.** Quadratic; $\{-\frac{1}{4}, 2\}$
5. Absolute value; $(-\frac{1}{3}, 1)$ **6.** Quadratic; { }
7. Linear; $(-\infty, -10)$ **8.** Quadratic; $[-4, 1]$
9. Quadratic; $(-\infty, -1] \cup [\frac{2}{3}, \infty)$ **10.** Rational; $\{-\frac{11}{3}\}$
11. Linear; $\left[\frac{16}{7}, \infty\right)$ **12.** Absolute value; { }
13. Polynomial; $[-5, -\frac{1}{2}] \cup [3, \infty)$ **14.** Quadratic; $(-\infty, \infty)$
15. Rational; $(-\infty, -1) \cup (2, \infty)$ **16.** Quadratic; $\{-1, 5\}$
17. Absolute value; $(-\infty, -8) \cup (-8, \infty)$
18. Quadratic; $(-6, 6)$ **19.** Polynomial; $\{2, -2, -\frac{5}{3}\}$
20. Absolute value; $\{12, -4\}$ **21.** Linear; $\{0\}$
22. Rational; $(-\infty, 0] \cup (5, \infty)$ **23.** Absolute value; $\{-\frac{1}{2}\}$
24. Polynomial; $(-\frac{3}{2}, 0)$

Section 9.5 Practice Exercises, pp. 674–679

1. a. linear **b.** is not; is **c.** dashed; is not **d.** solid; is
3. $[1, 3)$ **5.** $(-\infty, -4] \cup (-2, \infty)$ **7. a.** No **b.** No **c.** Yes **d.** Yes **9. a.** No **b.** Yes **c.** Yes **d.** No
11. $>$ **13.** $\geq$ **15.** $\geq, \leq$

17.

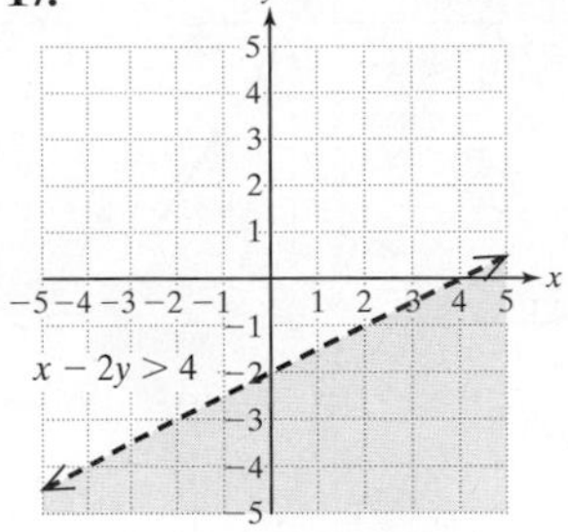

19.

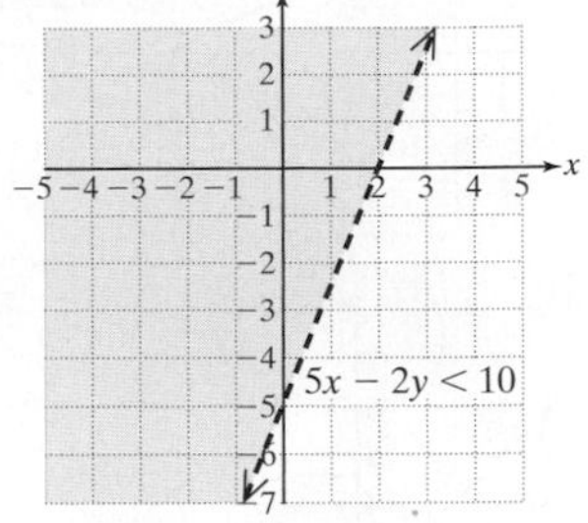

21.

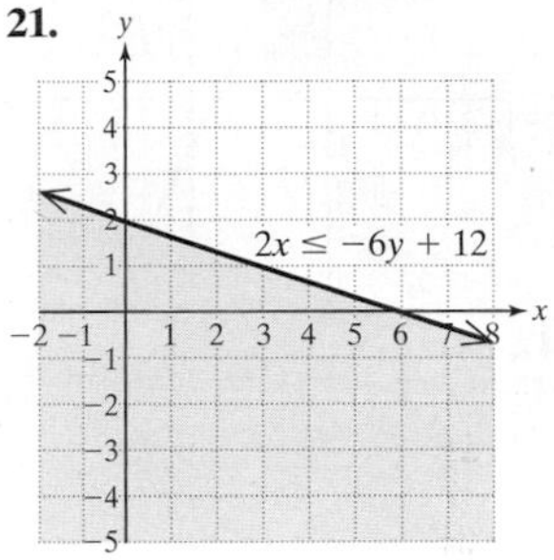

23.

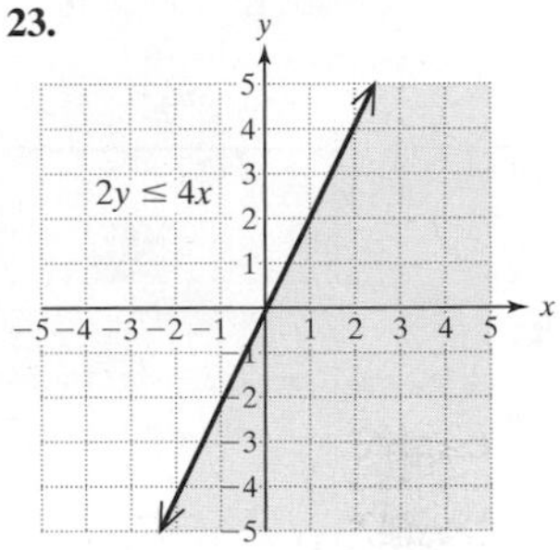

25.

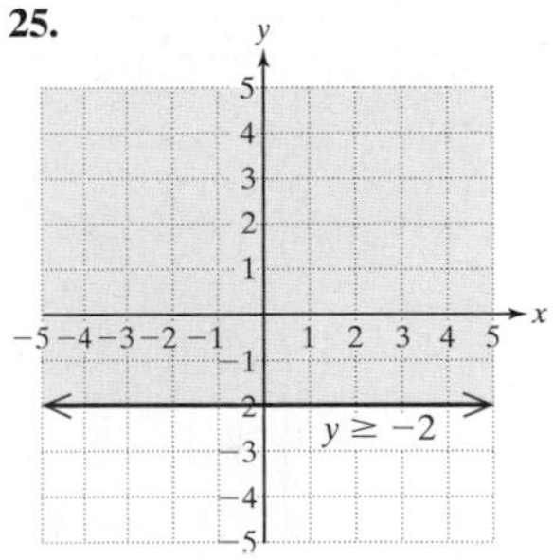

27.

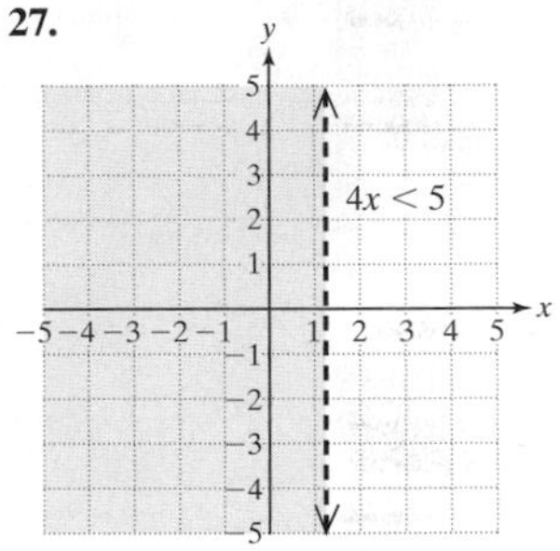

29.

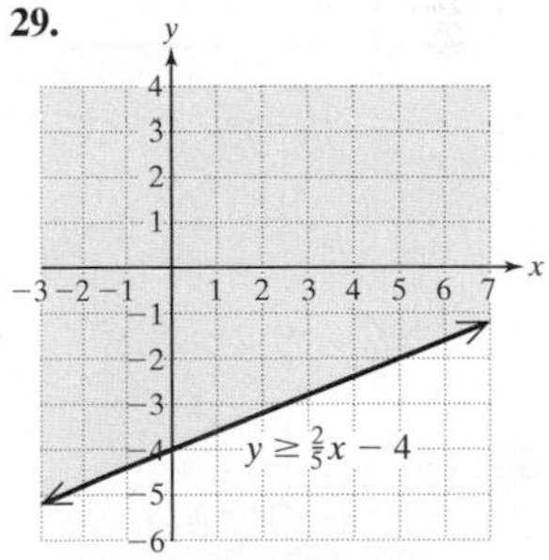

31.

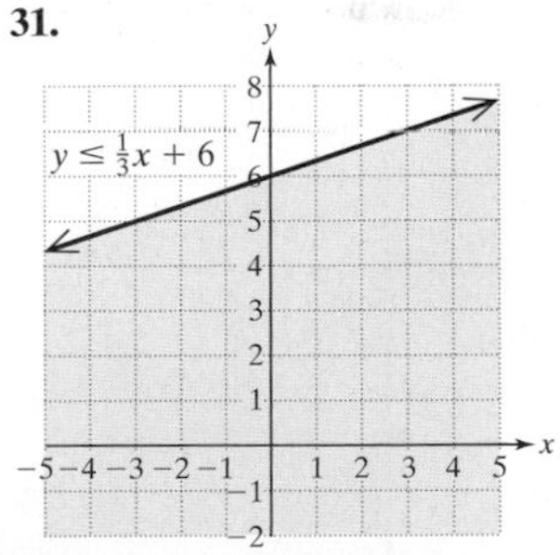

33.

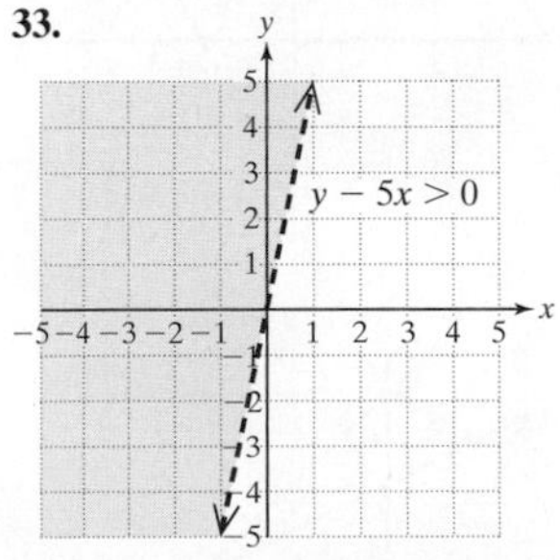

35.

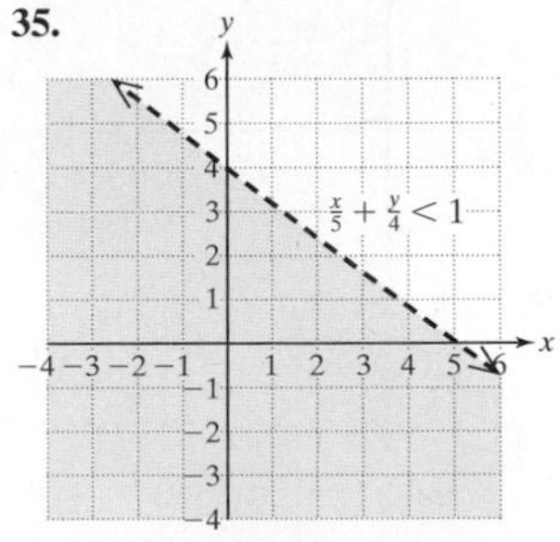

37.
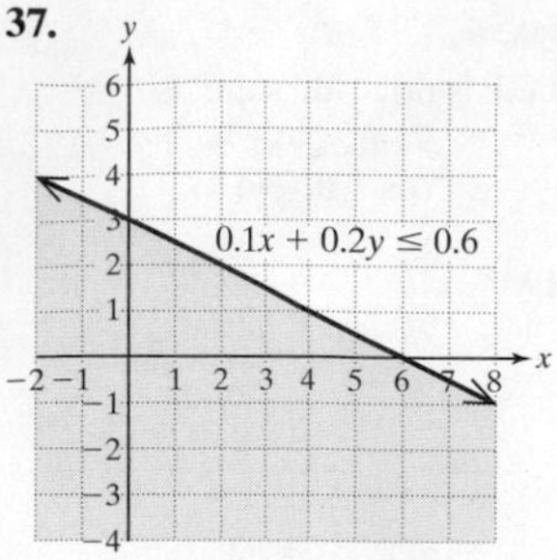

39.
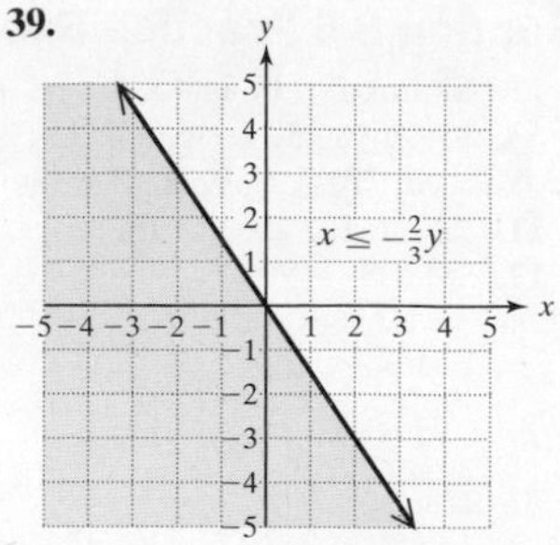

41.
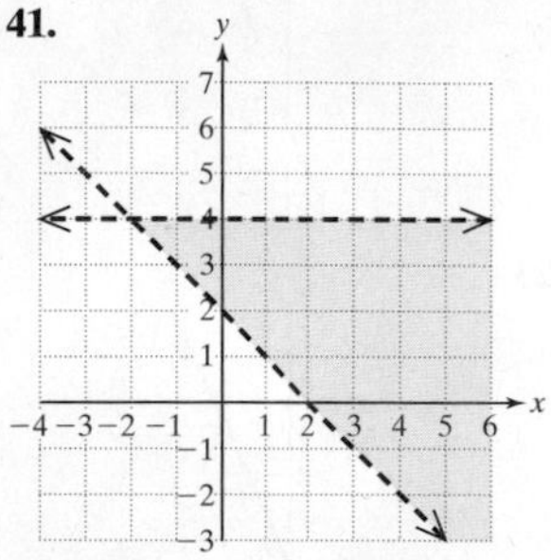

43.
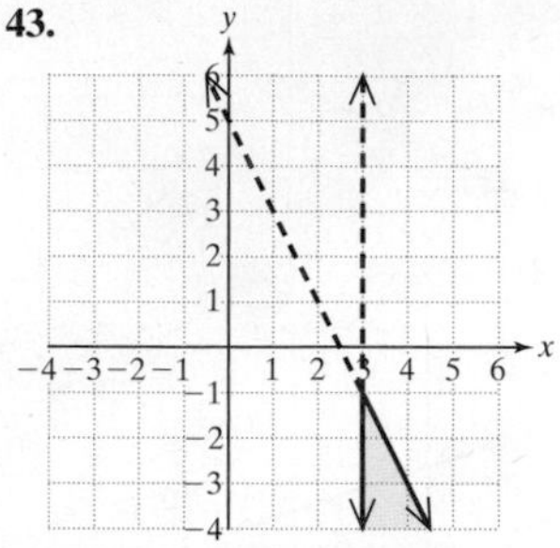

45.
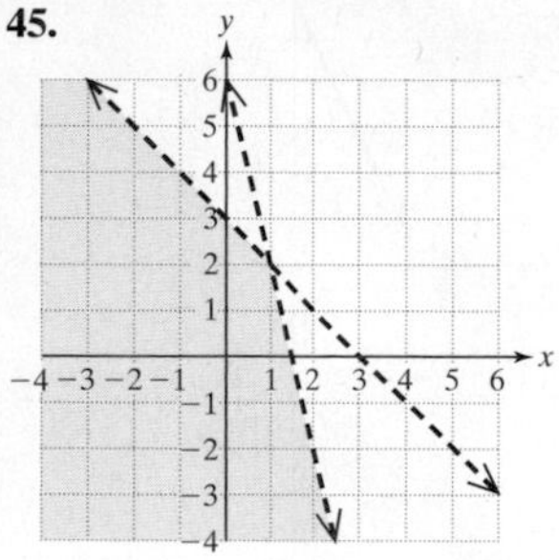

47.
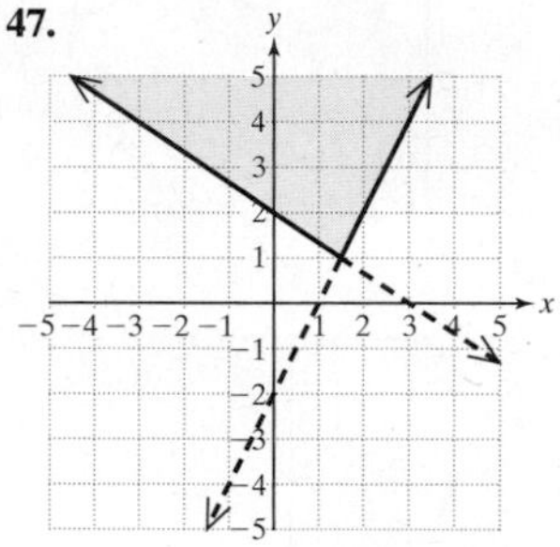

49.
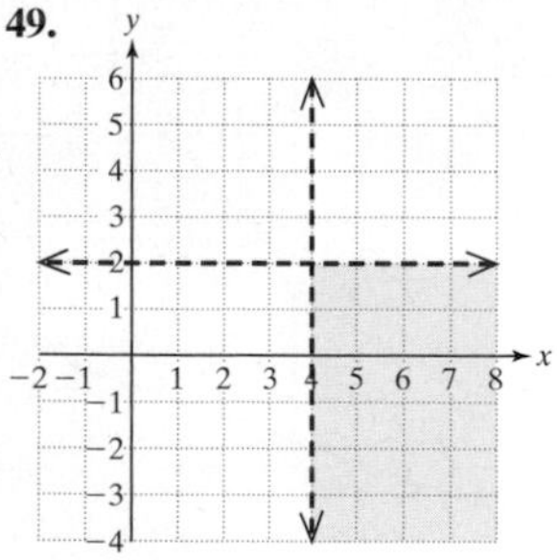

51.
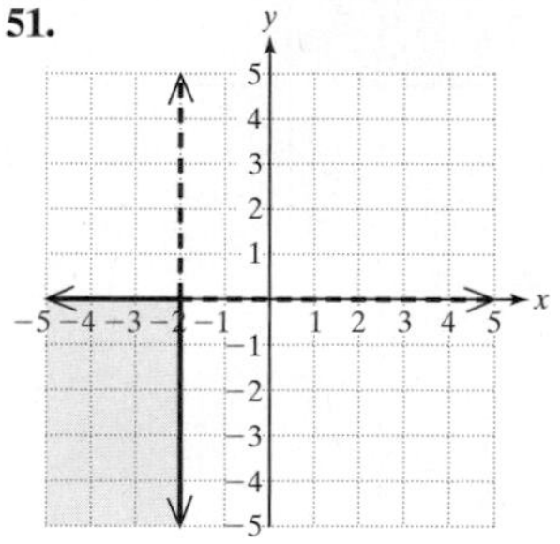

53.
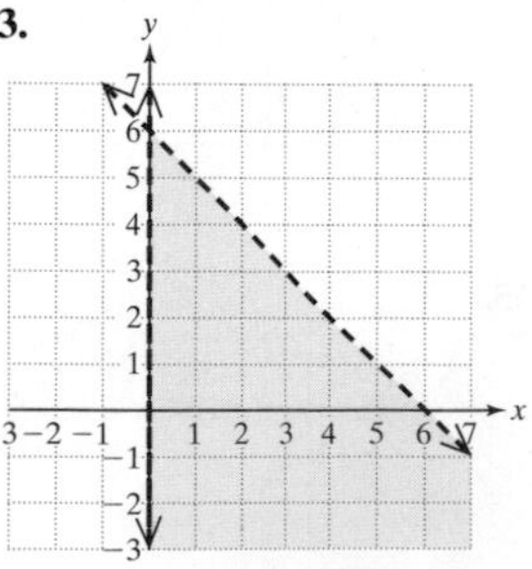

55.
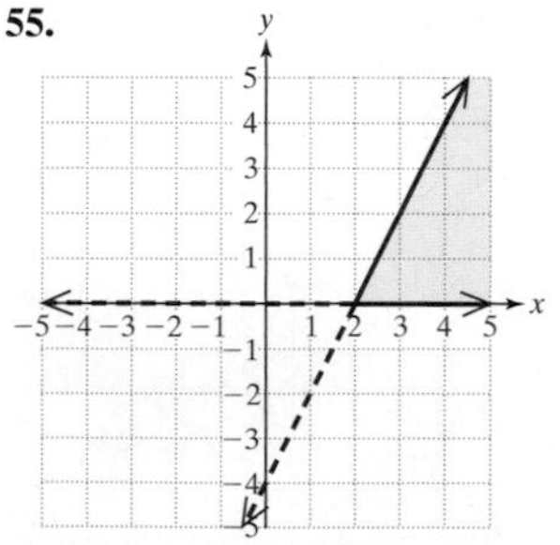

57.
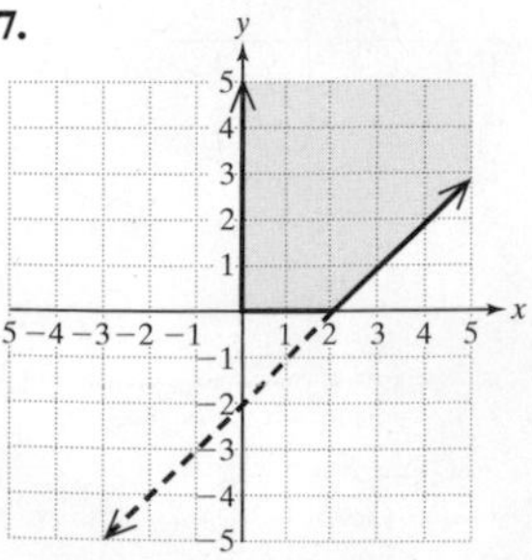

59.
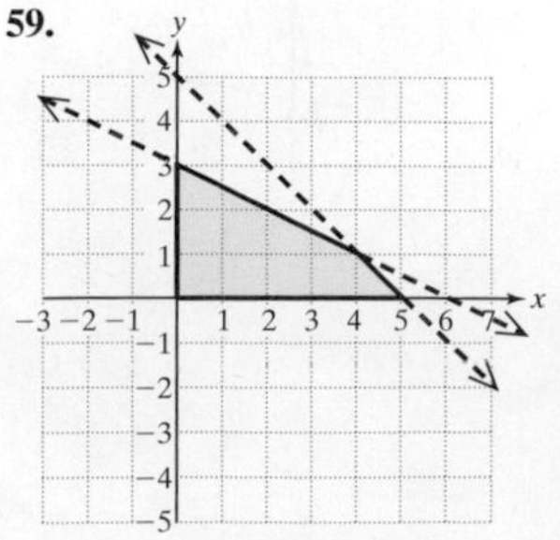

61. a. $2x + 2y \le 40$
b.
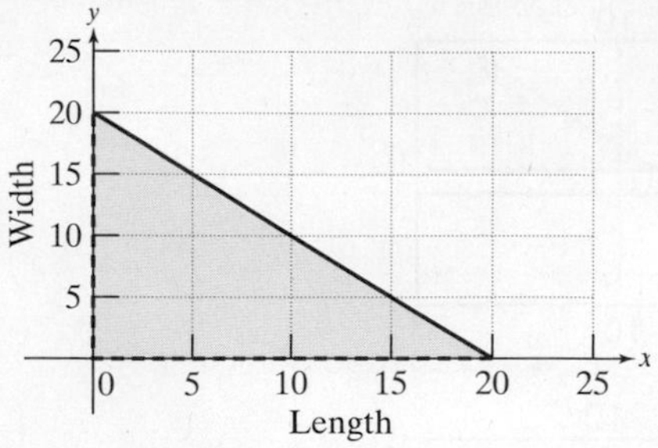

63. a. $x \ge 0, y \ge 0$ **b.** $x \le 40, y \le 40$ **c.** $x + y \ge 65$
d.
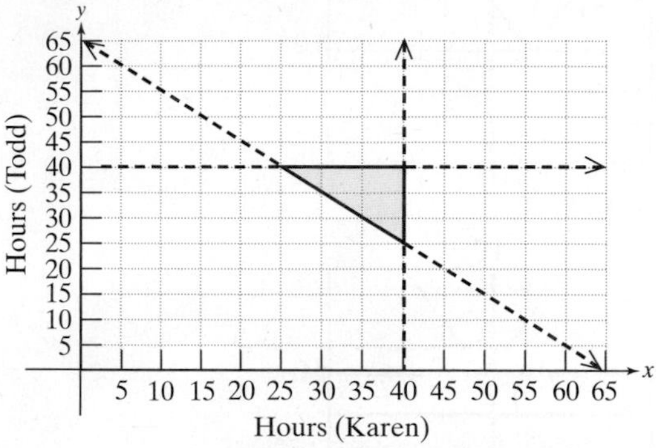

e. Yes; The point (35, 40) means that Karen works 35 hr and Todd works 40 hr. **f.** No; The point (20, 40) means that Karen works 20 hr and Todd works 40 hr. This does not satisfy the constraint that there must be at least 65 hr total.

Chapter 9 Review Exercises, pp. 686–689

1. $C \cap D$ is the set of elements common to both sets C and D.
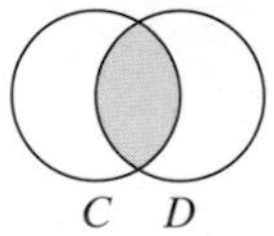

$C \cup D$ is the set of elements in either set C, set D, or both sets.
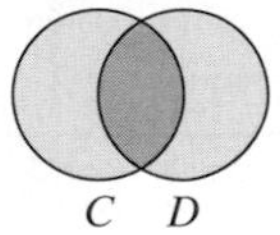

2. $[-10, 1)$ **3.** $(-\infty, \infty)$ **4.** $(-\infty, \infty)$ **5.** $(-1, 1)$
6. $(-\infty, -3] \cup (-1, \infty)$ **7.** { } **8.** $\left(-\frac{11}{4}, 4\right]$
9. $[-5, 2)$ **10.** $(-\infty, 6] \cup (12, \infty)$
11. $(-\infty, -2) \cup [2, \infty)$ **12.** $\left[0, \frac{4}{3}\right]$ **13.** $[-7, -2)$
14. a. $140 \le x \le 225$ **b.** $x < 140$ or $x > 225$
15. a. $125 \le x \le 200$ **b.** $x < 125$ or $x > 200$
16. a. $(-2, 0)$ and $(2, 0)$ are the x-intercepts. **b.** On the interval $(-2, 2)$ the graph is below the x-axis. **c.** On the intervals $(-\infty, -2)$ and $(2, \infty)$ the graph is above the x-axis.
17. a. $x = 0$; $(0, 0)$ is the x-intercept. **b.** $x = 2$ is the vertical asymptote. **c.** On the intervals $(-\infty, 0]$ and $(2, \infty)$ the graph is on or above the x-axis. **d.** On the interval $[0, 2)$ the graph is on or below the x-axis. **18.** $(-2, 6)$ **19.** $(-\infty, \infty)$ **20.** $(-\infty, -2) \cup [0, \infty)$
21. $(-\infty, -1] \cup (1, \infty)$ **22.** $(-2, 0) \cup (5, \infty)$
23. $(-2, 0) \cup \left(\frac{5}{2}, \infty\right)$ **24.** $[-3, -1]$
25. $(-\infty, -5) \cup (1, \infty)$ **26.** $(3, \infty)$ **27.** $(-3, \infty)$
28. $\{-5\}$ **29.** $(-\infty, -2) \cup (-2, \infty)$ **30.** $\{10, -10\}$
31. $\{17, -17\}$ **32.** $\{1.3, 7.4\}$ **33.** $\{-0.44, 2.54\}$
34. $\{5, -9\}$ **35.** $\{3, 1\}$ **36.** { }
37. { } **38.** $\left\{\frac{3}{7}\right\}$ **39.** $\left\{-\frac{5}{4}\right\}$ **40.** $\left\{6, \frac{4}{5}\right\}$

41. $\left\{-\frac{1}{2}\right\}$ **42.** Both expressions give the distance between 3 and −2. **43.** $|x| > 5$ **44.** $|x| < 4$
45. $|x| < 6$ **46.** $|x| > \frac{2}{3}$
47. $(-\infty, -14] \cup [2, \infty)$ 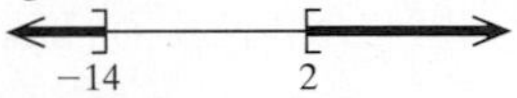

48. $[-11, -5]$ 

49. $\left(-\infty, \frac{1}{7}\right) \cup \left(\frac{1}{7}, \infty\right)$ 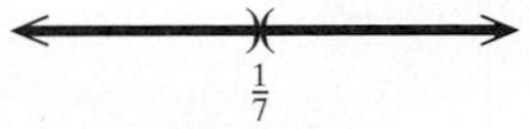

50. $\left(-\infty, -\frac{1}{5}\right) \cup \left(-\frac{1}{5}, \infty\right)$ 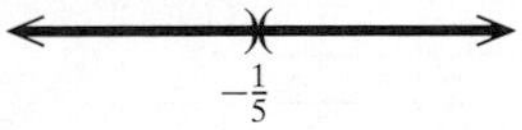

51. $\left[-2, -\frac{2}{3}\right]$ 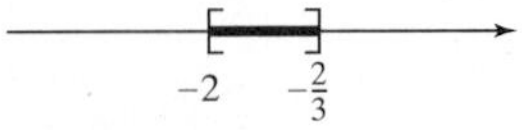

52. $\left[0, \frac{6}{5}\right]$ 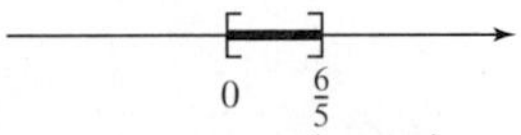

53. $(2, 22)$ 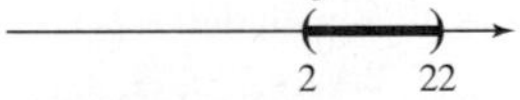

54. $(-12, 0)$ 

55. $(-\infty, \infty)$ 
56. $(-\infty, \infty)$ 
57. $(-\infty, \infty)$ 
58. $(-\infty, \infty)$
59. { } **60.** { } **61.** If an absolute value is less than a negative number, there will be no solution. **62.** If an absolute value is greater than a negative number, then all real numbers are solutions. **63.** $0.17 \le p \le 0.23$ or, equivalently in interval notation, $[0.17, 0.23]$. This means that the actual percentage of viewers is estimated to be between 17% and 23%, inclusive.
64. $3\frac{1}{8} \le L \le 3\frac{5}{8}$ or, equivalently in interval notation, $[3\frac{1}{8}, 3\frac{5}{8}]$. This means that the actual length of the screw may be between $3\frac{1}{8}$ in. and $3\frac{5}{8}$, inclusive.

65.
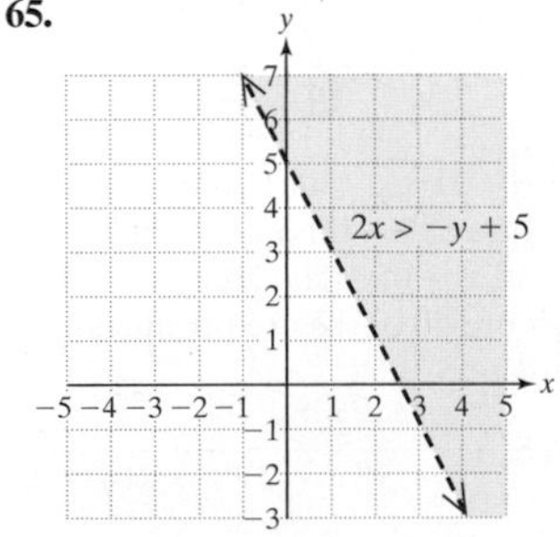

66.
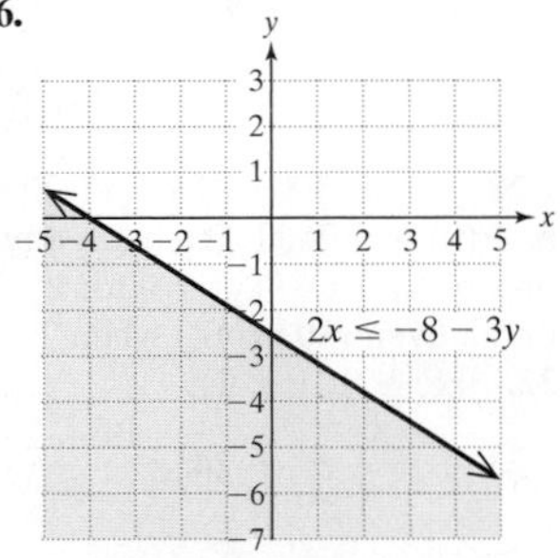

67.
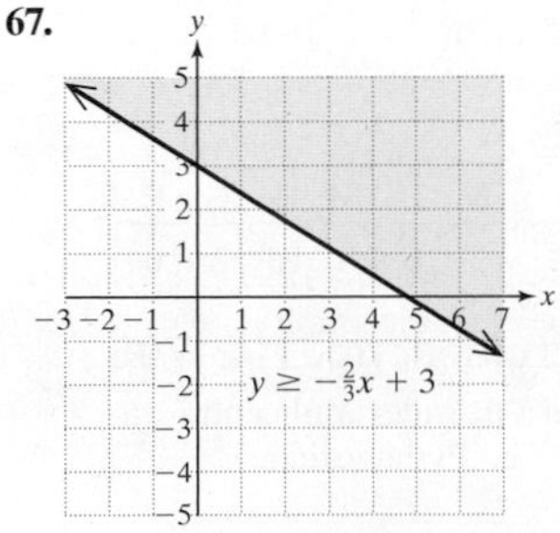

68.
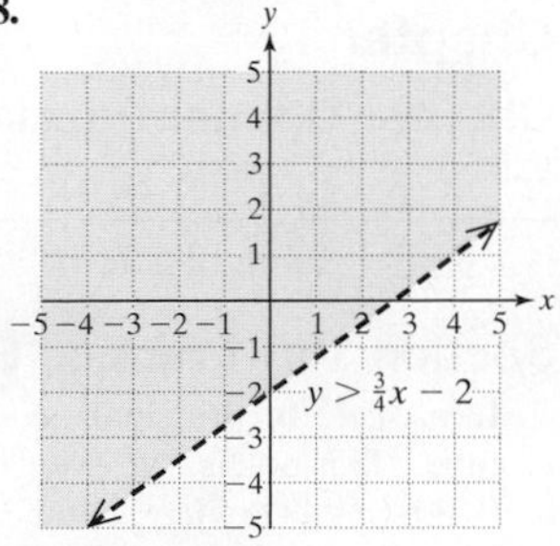

69.
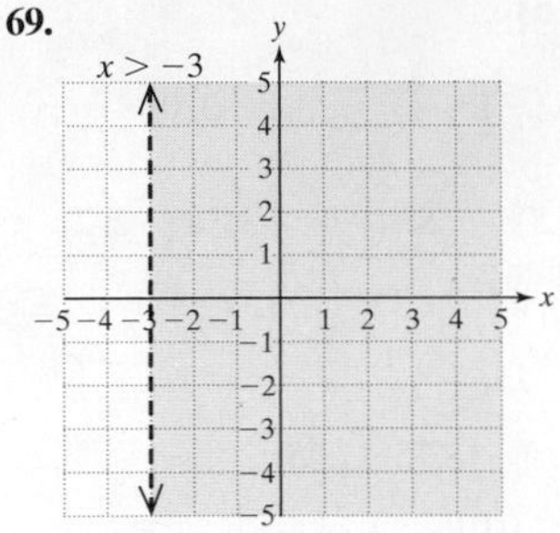

70.
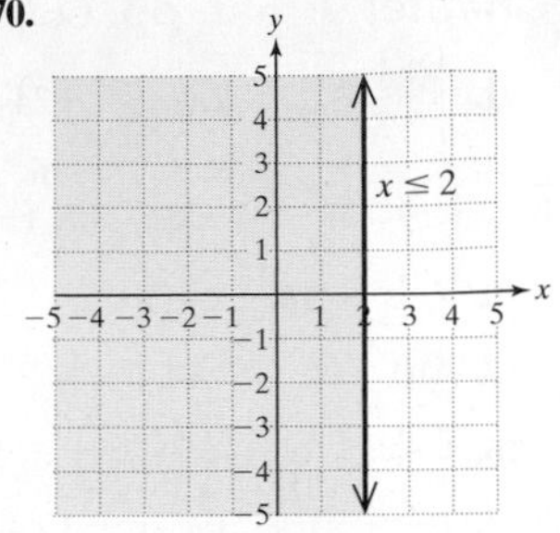

71.
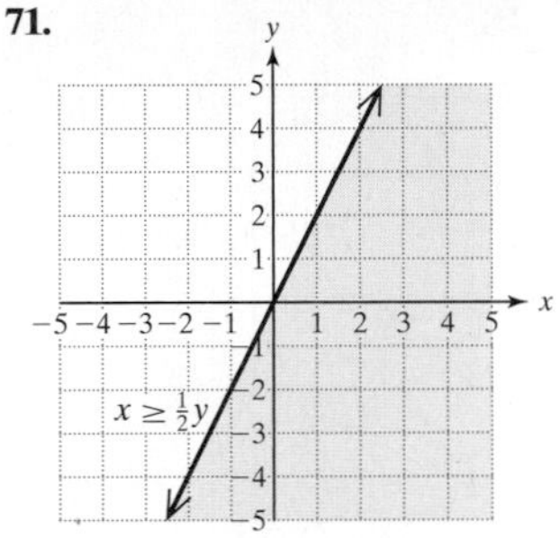

72.
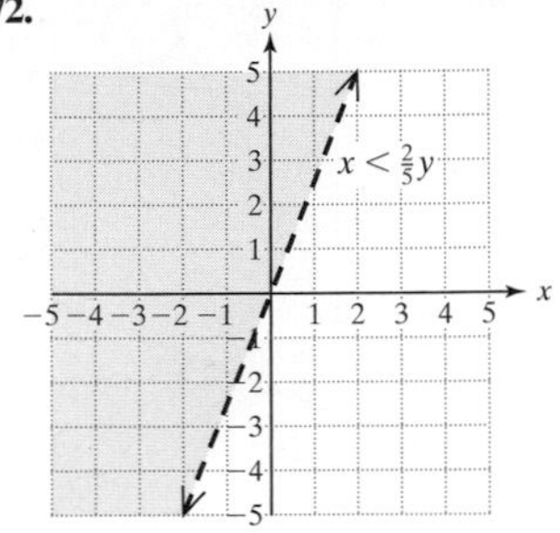

73.
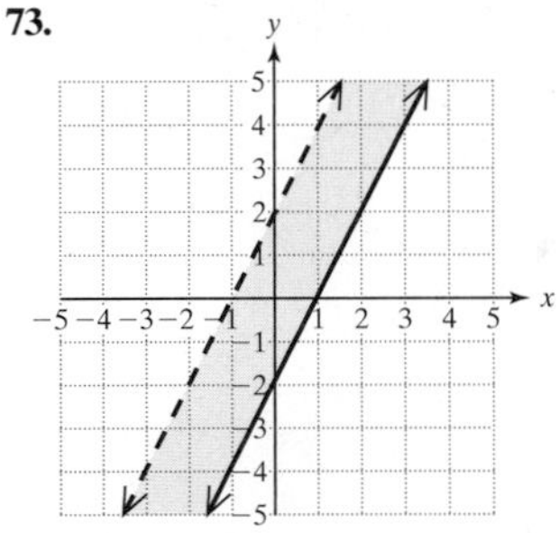

74.
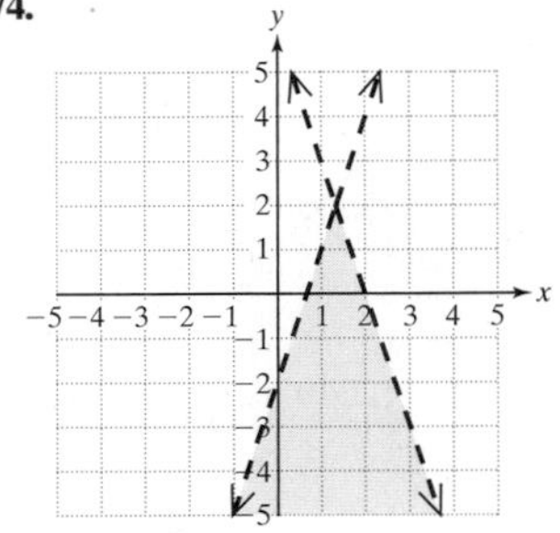

75.
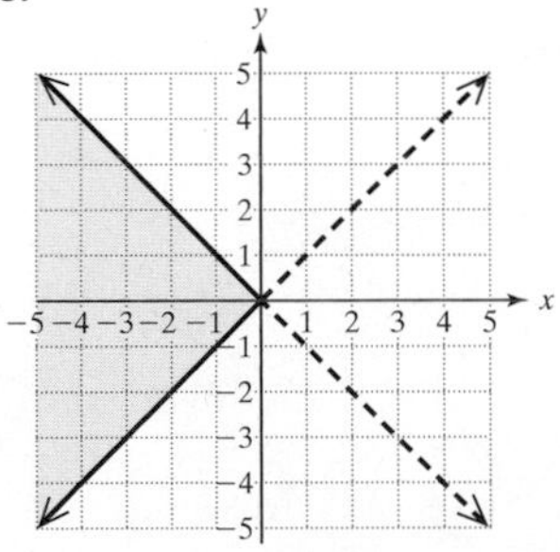

76.
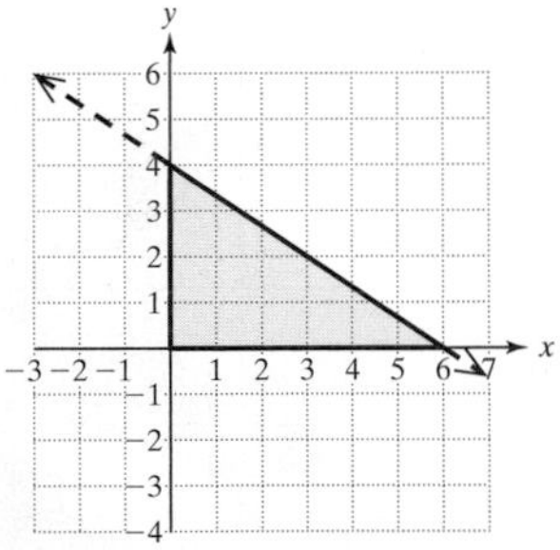

77. **a.** $x \ge 0, y \ge 0$ **b.** $x + y \le 100$ **c.** $x \ge 4y$
d.
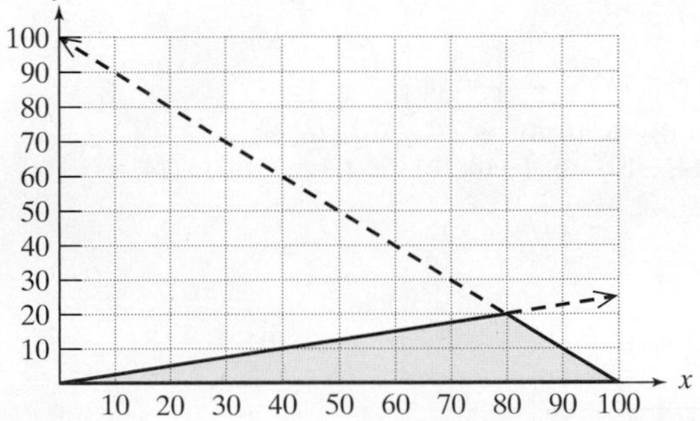

Chapter 9 Test, pp. 689–690

1. $\left[-\frac{1}{3}, 2\right]$ **2.** $(-\infty, -24] \cup [-15, \infty)$ **3.** $[-3, 0)$
4. $(-\infty, \infty)$ **5.** { } **6. a.** $9 \le x \le 33$
b. $x < 9$ or $x > 33$ **7.** $(-5, 5)$ **8.** $(-\infty, -3) \cup (-2, 2)$
9. { } **10.** $\{-11\}$ **11.** $\left[\frac{1}{2}, 6\right)$ **12.** $\left(-3, -\frac{3}{2}\right)$
13. $\{10, -22\}$ **14.** $\{-8, 2\}$ **15.** { }
16. $\left(-\infty, -\frac{1}{3}\right) \cup \left(\frac{17}{3}, \infty\right)$ **17.** $(-18.75, 17.25)$
18. $(-\infty, \infty)$ **19.** $|x - 15.41| \le 0.01$
20.

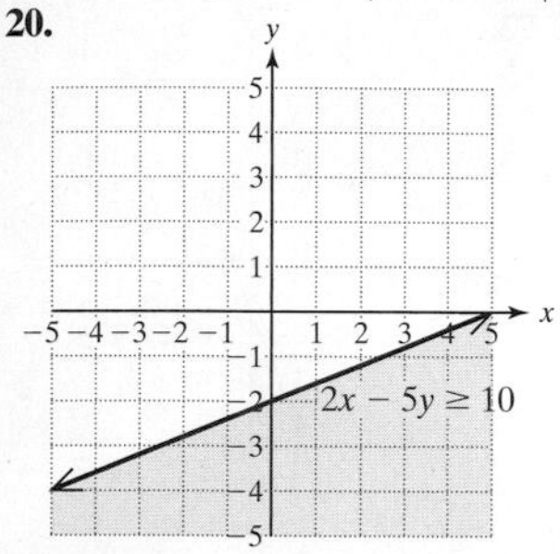

21.

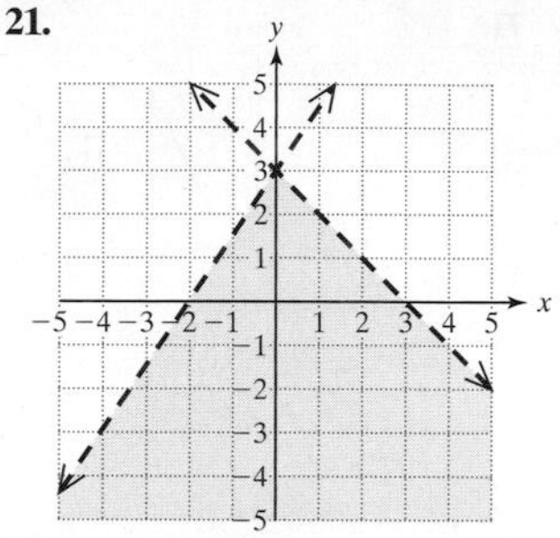

22.

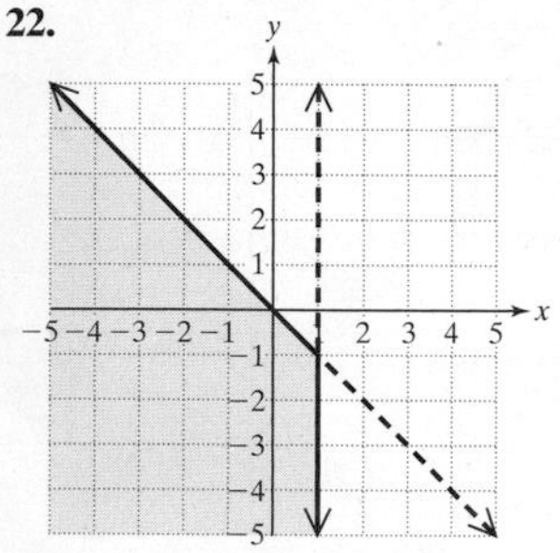

23. a. $x \ge 0, y \ge 0$ **b.** $300x + 400y \ge 1200$
c.

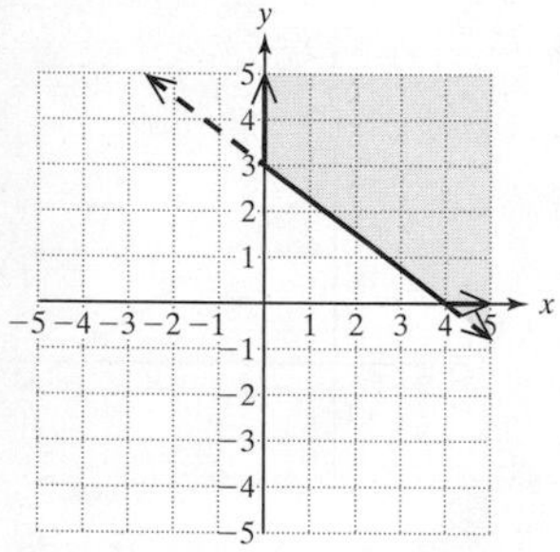

Chapters 1–9 Cumulative Review Exercises, pp. 690–692

1. $x^2 - x - 13$ **2.** $\left\{-\frac{3}{2}, 1\right\}$
3. a. $\{0, 6\}$ **b.** $(0, 6)$ **c.** $(-\infty, 0) \cup (6, \infty)$
4. a. $\{14, -10\}$ **b.** $(-10, 14)$ **c.** $(-\infty, -10) \cup (14, \infty)$
5.

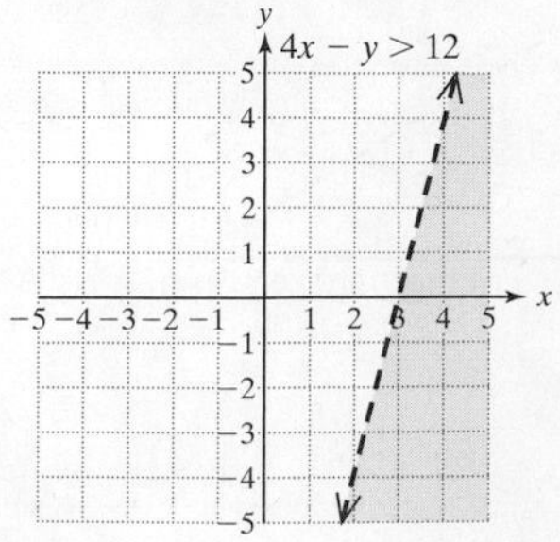

6. a. $t(1) = 9$. After one trial the rat requires 9 min to complete the maze. $t(50) = 3.24$. After 50 trials the rat requires 3.24 min to complete the maze. $t(500) = 3.02$. After 500 trials the rat requires 3.02 min to complete the maze. **b.** The limiting time is 3 min. **c.** More than 5 trials
7. a. $\left(-\infty, -\frac{5}{2}\right] \cup [2, \infty)$ **b.** On these intervals the graph is on or above the x-axis.
8.

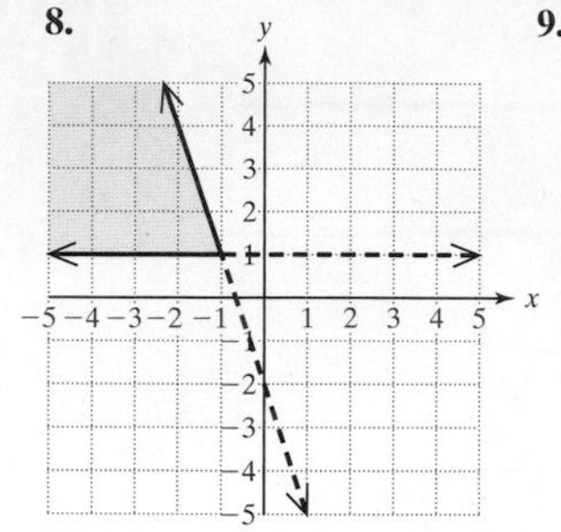

9. $-7x + 13$
10. a. Quotient: $2x^2 - 5x + 12$; remainder: $-24x + 5$
11. a. $b_1 = \dfrac{2A - hb_2}{h}$ or $b_1 = \dfrac{2A}{h} - b_2$ **b.** 10 cm
12. 75 mph **13.** 57°, 123° **14.** \$8000 in the 6.5% account; \$5000 in the 5% account **15.** Neither
16. a. x-intercept $(1, 0)$; no y-intercept; undefined slope **b.** x-intercept $(8, 0)$; y-intercept $(0, 4)$; slope $-\frac{1}{2}$

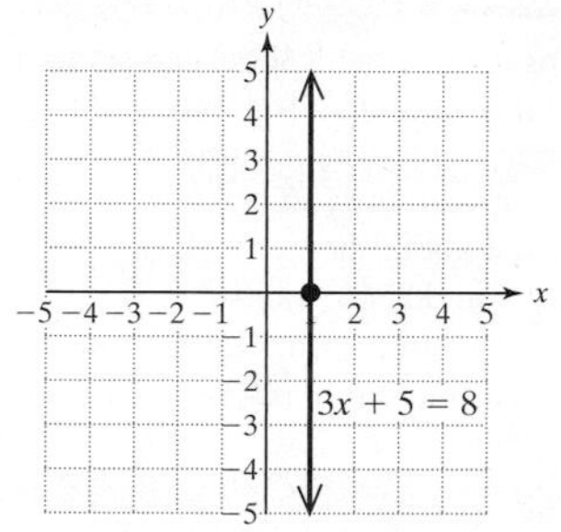

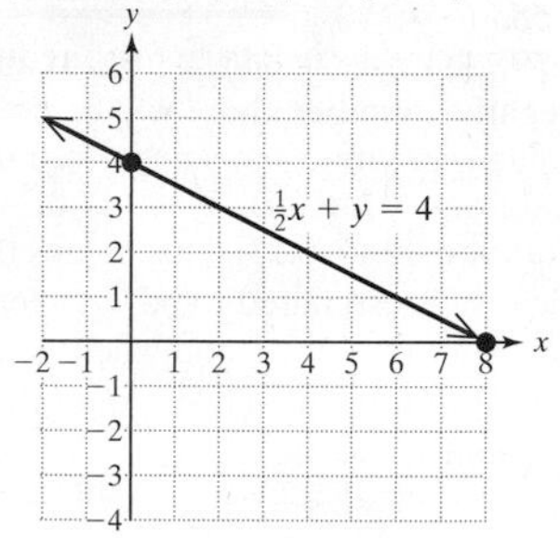

17. $y = -\frac{2}{3}x - \frac{13}{3}$ **18.** $\{(-1, 3, -2)\}$ **19.** $\dfrac{6}{x^4y^5}$
20. Plane: 500 mph; wind: 20 mph **21. a.** Quadratic **b.** $P(0) = -2600$. The company will lose \$2600 if no desks are produced. **c.** $P(x) = 0$ for $x = 20$ and $x = 650$. The company will break even (\$0 profit) when 20 desks or 650 desks are produced.
22. $3(x - 2)^2(x + 2)$
23. $-\dfrac{xy}{x + y}$ **24.** $-\dfrac{a + 1}{a}$ **25.** $\dfrac{2x + 5}{(x - 5)(x - 2)(x + 10)}$

Chapter 10

Chapter Opener Puzzle

I	M	A	G	I	N	A	R	Y		N	U	M	B	E	R
4	8	7	1	4	3	7	6	9		3	5	8	10	2	6

Section 10.1 Practice Exercises, pp. 702–705

1. a. b; a **b.** principal **c.** b^n; a **d.** index; radicand **e.** cube **f.** is not; is **g.** even; odd **h.** Pythagorean; c^2 **i.** $[0, \infty)$; $(-\infty, \infty)$ **j.** -5 and -4
3. a. 8, -8 **b.** 8 **c.** There are two square roots for every positive number. $\sqrt{64}$ identifies the positive square root.
5. a. 9 **b.** -9 **7.** There is no real number b such that $b^2 = -36$. **9.** 7 **11.** -7 **13.** Not a real number
15. $\frac{8}{3}$ **17.** 0.9 **19.** -0.4 **21. a.** 8 **b.** 4 **c.** -8 **d.** -4 **e.** Not a real number **f.** -4

23. -3 **25.** $\frac{1}{2}$ **27.** 2 **29.** $-\frac{5}{4}$ **31.** Not a real number **33.** 10 **35.** -0.2 **37.** 0.5 **39.** $|a|$ **41.** a **43.** $|a|$ **45.** $|x+1|$ **47.** $|x|y^2$ **49.** $-\frac{x}{y}$ **51.** $\frac{2}{|x|}$ **53.** -92 **55.** 2 **57.** -923 **59.** y^4 **61.** $\frac{a^3}{b}$ **63.** $-\frac{5}{q}$ **65.** $3xy^2z$ **67.** $\frac{hk^2}{4}$ **69.** $-\frac{t}{3}$ **71.** $2y^2$ **73.** $2p^2q^3$ **75.** 9 cm **77.** 13 ft **79.** They were 5 mi apart. **81.** They are 25 mi apart. **83. a.** Not a real number **b.** Not a real number **c.** 0 **d.** 1 **e.** 2 Domain: $[2, \infty)$ **85. a.** -2 **b.** -1 **c.** 0 **d.** 1 Domain: $(-\infty, \infty)$ **87.** $\left(-\infty, \frac{5}{2}\right]$ **89.** $(-\infty, \infty)$ **91.** $[5, \infty)$ **93.** $(-\infty, \infty)$

95. a. $(-\infty, 1]$
b.

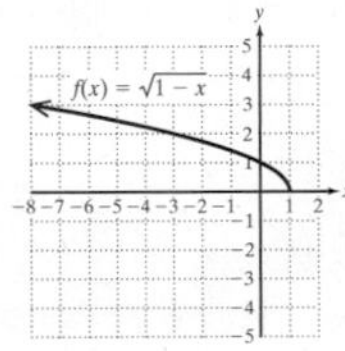

97. a. $[-3, \infty)$
b.

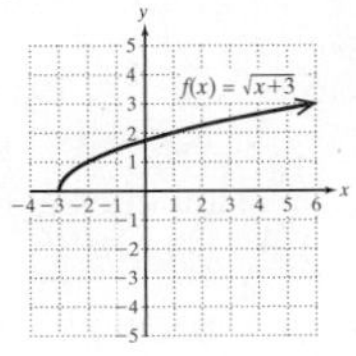

99. a. $[0, \infty)$
b.

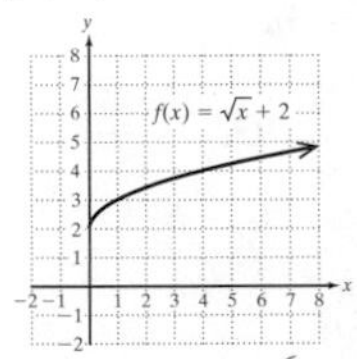

101. a. $(-\infty, \infty)$
b.

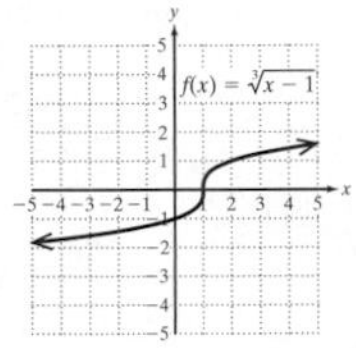

103. $q + p^2$ **105.** $\frac{6}{\sqrt[3]{x}}$ **107.** 8 in.

Section 10.1 Graphing Calculator Exercises, p. 705

109. 8.3066 **110.** 76.1446 **111.** 3.7100 **112.** -0.5566 **113.** 15.6525 **114.** -6.2403 **115.** -0.1235 **116.** 1.0622

117.

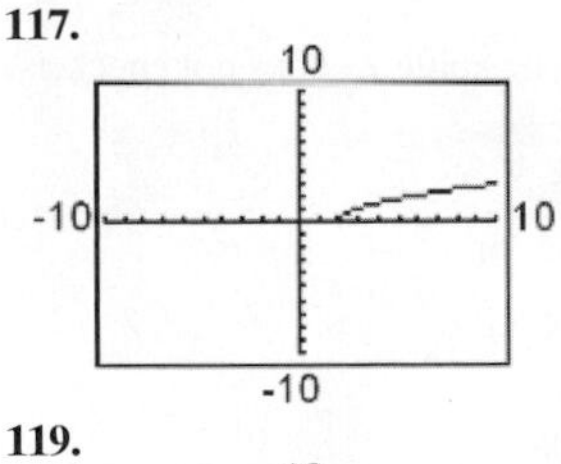

118.

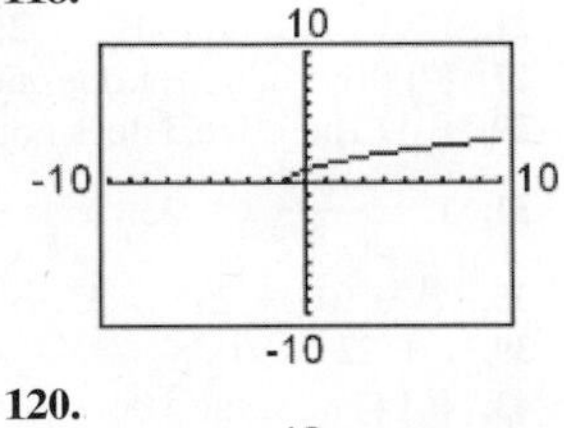

119.

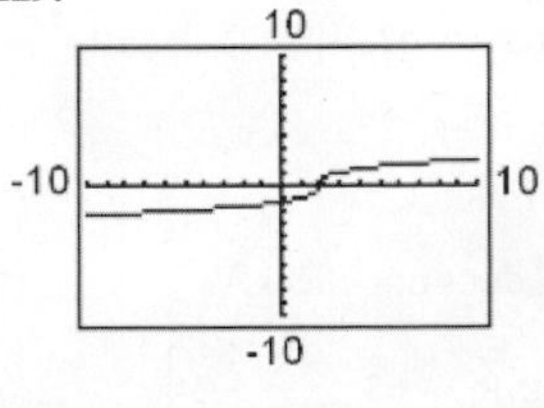

120.

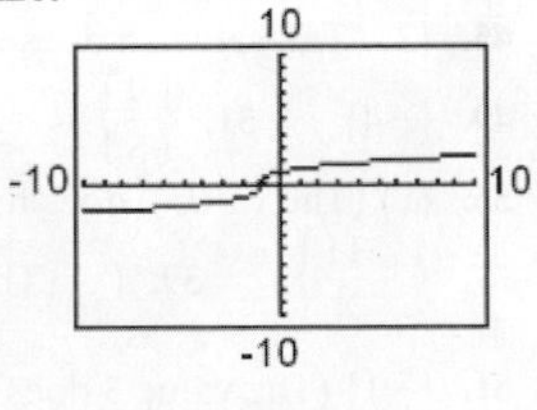

Section 10.2 Practice Exercises, pp. 710–713

1. a. $\sqrt[n]{a}$ **b.** $(\sqrt[n]{a})^m$ or $\sqrt[n]{a^m}$ **c.** $\frac{1}{\sqrt{x}}$ **d.** 2; $\frac{1}{2}$ **3.** 5 **5.** 3 **7.** 12 **9.** -12 **11.** Not a real number **13.** -4 **15.** $\frac{1}{5}$ **17.** $-\frac{1}{7}$ **19.** $a^{m/n} = \sqrt[n]{a^m}$; The numerator of the exponent represents the power of the base. The denominator of the exponent represents the index of the radical. **21. a.** 8 **b.** -8 **c.** Not a real number **d.** $\frac{1}{8}$ **e.** $-\frac{1}{8}$ **f.** Not a real number **23. a.** 125 **b.** -125 **c.** Not a real number **d.** $\frac{1}{125}$ **e.** $-\frac{1}{125}$ **f.** Not a real number **25.** $\frac{1}{512}$ **27.** 27 **29.** $-\frac{1}{81}$ **31.** $\frac{27}{1000}$ **33.** Not a real number **35.** -2 **37.** -2 **39.** 6 **41.** 10 **43.** $\frac{3}{4}$ **45.** 1 **47.** $\frac{9}{2}$ **49.** $\sqrt[3]{q^2}$ **51.** $6\sqrt[4]{y^3}$ **53.** $\sqrt[3]{x^2y}$ **55.** $\frac{6}{\sqrt[5]{r^2}}$ **57.** $x^{1/3}$ **59.** $10b^{1/2}$ **61.** $y^{2/3}$ **63.** $(a^2b^3)^{1/4}$ **65.** $\frac{1}{x}$ **67.** p **69.** y^2 **71.** $6^{2/5}$ **73.** $\frac{4}{t^{5/3}}$ **75.** a^7 **77.** $\frac{25a^4d}{c}$ **79.** $\frac{y^9}{x^8}$ **81.** $\frac{2z^3}{w}$ **83.** $5xy^2z^3$ **85.** $x^{13}z^{4/3}$ **87.** $\frac{x^3y^2}{z^5}$ **89. a.** 10.9% **b.** 8.8% **c.** The account in part (a). **91.** 2.7 in. **93.** $\sqrt{y}$ **95.** $\sqrt[4]{z}$ **97.** $\sqrt[3]{x^2}$ **99.** $y\sqrt{x}$ **101.** $4x^4y^3$ **103.** $2x\sqrt[3]{y^2z}$ **105.** $\sqrt[6]{x}$ **107.** $\sqrt[15]{w}$ **109.** 3 **111.** 0.3761 **113.** 2.9240 **115.** 31.6228

Section 10.3 Practice Exercises, pp. 718–720

1. a. $\sqrt[n]{a}$; $\sqrt[n]{b}$ **b.** The exponent within the radicand is greater than the index. **c.** is not **d.** 3 **e.** t^{12} **f.** No. $\sqrt{2}$ is an irrational number and the decimal form is a nonterminating, nonrepeating decimal. **3.** $\frac{p}{q^5}$ **5.** $\sqrt[7]{x^4}$ **7.** $y^{9/2}$ **9.** $x^2\sqrt{x}$ **11.** $q^2\sqrt[3]{q}$ **13.** $a^2b^2\sqrt{a}$ **15.** $-x^2y^3\sqrt[4]{y}$ **17.** $2\sqrt{7}$ **19.** $2\sqrt{5}$ **21.** $15\sqrt{2}$ **23.** $3\sqrt[3]{2}$ **25.** $5b\sqrt{ab}$ **27.** $2x^2\sqrt[3]{5x}$ **29.** $-2x^2z\sqrt[3]{2y}$ **31.** $2wz\sqrt[4]{5z^3}$ **33.** x **35.** p^2 **37.** 5 **39.** $\frac{1}{2}$ **41.** $\frac{5\sqrt[3]{2}}{3}$ **43.** $\frac{5\sqrt[3]{9}}{6}$ **45.** $4\sqrt{5}$ **47.** $-30\sqrt{3}$ **49.** $5x^2y\sqrt{y}$ **51.** $3yz\sqrt[3]{x^2z}$ **53.** $2w^2$ **55.** $\frac{1}{10y^6}$ **57.** $\frac{2}{b}$ **59.** $2a^7b^4c^{15}d^{11}\sqrt{2c}$ **61.** $3a^2b\sqrt[3]{2b}$ **63.** $-10a^2b^2\sqrt{3ac}$ **65.** $x\sqrt[4]{7xy}$ **67.** $3a^2b\sqrt{6}$ **69.** $2\sqrt{3}$ **71.** $\frac{3\sqrt{5}}{4}$ **73.** $\frac{1}{\sqrt[3]{w^6}}$ simplifies to $\frac{1}{w^2}$ **75.** $\sqrt{k^3}$ simplifies to $k\sqrt{k}$ **77.** $2\sqrt{41}$ ft **79.** $6\sqrt{5}$ m **81.** The distance is $90\sqrt{2}$ ft or approximately 127.3 ft. **83.** The path from A to B and B to C is faster.

Section 10.4 Practice Exercises, pp. 723–725

1. a. index; radicand **b.** $2\sqrt{3x}$ **c.** cannot; can **d.** $4\sqrt{2}$ **3.** $-xy\sqrt[4]{x^3}$ **5.** $\frac{b^2}{2}$ **7.** $(x^3y)^{1/4}$ **9.** $y^{11/12}$ **11. a.** Not *like* radicals **b.** *Like* radicals **c.** Not *like* radicals **13. a.** Both expressions can be simplified by using the distributive property. **b.** Neither expression can be simplified because the terms do not contain *like* radicals or *like* terms. **15.** $9\sqrt{5}$ **17.** $2\sqrt[3]{tw}$ **19.** $5\sqrt{10}$ **21.** $8\sqrt[4]{3} - \sqrt[4]{14}$ **23.** $2\sqrt{x} + 2\sqrt{y}$ **25.** Cannot be simplified further **27.** Cannot be simplified further **29.** $\frac{29}{18}z\sqrt[3]{6}$ **31.** $0.7x\sqrt{y}$ **33.** Simplify each radical: $3\sqrt{2} + 35\sqrt{2}$. Then add *like* radicals: $38\sqrt{2}$ **35.** 15 **37.** $8\sqrt{3}$ **39.** $3\sqrt{7}$ **41.** $-5\sqrt{2} + 3\sqrt{3}$ **43.** $\sqrt[3]{3}$ **45.** $-5\sqrt{2a}$

47. $8s^2t^2\sqrt[3]{s^2}$ **49.** $6x\sqrt[3]{x}$ **51.** $14p^2\sqrt{5}$
53. $-\sqrt[3]{a^2b}$ **55.** $(5x + 6)\sqrt{x}$ **57.** $(5x - 6)\sqrt{2}$
59. $33d\sqrt[3]{2c}$ **61.** $2a^2b\sqrt{6a}$ **63.** $5x\sqrt[3]{2} - 6\sqrt[3]{x}$
65. False; $\sqrt{9} + \sqrt{16} \neq \sqrt{9 + 16}$; $7 \neq 5$ **67.** True
69. False; $\sqrt{y} + \sqrt{y} = 2\sqrt{y} \neq \sqrt{2y}$
71. False; $2w\sqrt{5} + 4w\sqrt{5} = 6w\sqrt{5} \neq 6w^2\sqrt{5}$
73. $\sqrt{48} + \sqrt{12}$ simplifies to $6\sqrt{3}$
75. $5\sqrt[3]{x^6} - x^2$ simplifies to $4x^2$ **77.** The difference of the principal square root of 18 and the square of 5
79. The sum of the principal fourth root of x and the cube of y
81. $9\sqrt{6}$ cm $\approx$ 22.0 cm **83.** $x = 2\sqrt{2}$ ft
85. **a.** $10\sqrt{5}$ yd **b.** 22.36 yd **c.** \$105.95

Section 10.5 Practice Exercises, pp. 731–733

1. **a.** $\sqrt[n]{ab}$ **b.** x **c.** a **d.** conjugates **e.** $m - n$
f. $c + 8\sqrt{c} + 16$ **3.** $-2ab\sqrt{5bc}$ **5.** $x^{1/6}y^{7/12}$ **7.** $2\sqrt[3]{7}$
9. $\sqrt[3]{21}$ **11.** $2\sqrt{5}$ **13.** $4\sqrt[4]{4}$ **15.** $8\sqrt[3]{20}$
17. $-24ab\sqrt{a}$ **19.** $6\sqrt{10}$ **21.** $6x\sqrt{2}$ **23.** $10a^3b^2\sqrt{b}$
25. $-24x^2y^2\sqrt{2y}$ **27.** $6ab\sqrt[3]{2a^2b^2}$ **29.** $12 - 6\sqrt{3}$
31. $2\sqrt{3} - \sqrt{6}$ **33.** $-2x - \frac{7}{3}\sqrt{x}$ **35.** $-8 + 7\sqrt{30}$
37. $x - 5\sqrt{x} - 36$ **39.** $\sqrt[3]{y^2} - \sqrt[3]{y} - 6$
41. $9a - 28\sqrt{ab} + 3b$ **43.** $8\sqrt{p} + 3p + 5\sqrt{pq} + 16\sqrt{q} - 2q$
45. 15 **47.** $3y$ **49.** 6 **51.** 709 **53.** **a.** $x^2 - y^2$
b. $x^2 - 25$ **55.** $29 + 8\sqrt{13}$ **57.** $p - 2\sqrt{7p} + 7$
59. $2a - 6\sqrt{2ab} + 9b$ **61.** $3 - x^2$ **63.** 4
65. $\frac{4}{9}x - \frac{1}{4}y$ **67.** **a.** $3 - x$ **b.** $3 + 2\sqrt{3x} + x$
c. $3 - 2\sqrt{3x} + x$ **69.** True **71.** False; $(x - \sqrt{5})^2 = x^2 - 2x\sqrt{5} + 5$ **73.** False; 5 is multiplied by 3 only.
75. True **77.** $6x$ **79.** $3x + 1$
81. $x + 19 - 8\sqrt{x + 3}$ **83.** $2t + 10\sqrt{2t - 3} + 22$
85. $12\sqrt{5}$ ft² **87.** $18\sqrt{15}$ in.² **89.** $\sqrt[4]{x^3}$
91. $\sqrt[15]{(2z)^8}$ **93.** $p^2\sqrt[6]{p}$ **95.** $u\sqrt[6]{u}$
97. $\sqrt[6]{x^2y}$ **99.** $\sqrt[4]{2^3 \cdot 3^2}$ or $\sqrt[4]{72}$ **101.** $\sqrt[12]{2^4 5^3 x^7 y^7}$
103. $2m\sqrt[6]{3^3 2mn^5}$ **105.** $a + b$

Chapter 10 Problem Recognition Exercises, p. 734

1. **a.** $2\sqrt{6}$ **b.** $2\sqrt[3]{3}$ **2.** **a.** $3\sqrt{6}$ **b.** $3\sqrt[3]{2}$
3. **a.** $10y^3\sqrt{2}$ **b.** $2y^2\sqrt[3]{25}$ **4.** **a.** $4z^7\sqrt{2z}$ **b.** $2z^5\sqrt[3]{4}$
5. **a.** $4\sqrt{5}$ **b.** $2\sqrt[3]{10}$ **c.** $2\sqrt[4]{5}$ **6.** **a.** $4\sqrt{3}$ **b.** $2\sqrt[3]{6}$ **c.** $2\sqrt[4]{3}$
7. **a.** $x^2y^3\sqrt{x}$ **b.** $xy^2\sqrt[3]{x^2}$ **c.** $xy\sqrt[4]{xy^2}$
8. **a.** $a^5b^4\sqrt{b}$ **b.** $a^3b^3\sqrt[3]{a}$ **c.** $a^2b^2\sqrt[4]{a^2b}$ **9.** **a.** $2st^2\sqrt[3]{4s^2}$
b. $2st\sqrt[4]{2st^2}$ **c.** $2st\sqrt[5]{t}$ **10.** **a.** $2v^2w^6\sqrt[3]{12vw^2}$
b. $2vw^5\sqrt[4]{6v^3}$ **c.** $2vw^4\sqrt[5]{3v^2}$ **11.** **a.** $2\sqrt{5}$ **b.** 5
12. **a.** $2\sqrt{10}$ **b.** 10 **13.** **a.** $-3\sqrt{6}$ **b.** 60
14. **a.** $-7\sqrt{7}$ **b.** 210 **15.** **a.** $3\sqrt{2}$ **b.** 4
16. **a.** $3\sqrt{3}$ **b.** 6 **17.** **a.** $7\sqrt{2}$ **b.** 240
18. **a.** $-\sqrt{2}$ **b.** 60 **19.** **a.** $14\sqrt[3]{3}$ **b.** $48\sqrt[3]{9}$
20. **a.** $\sqrt[3]{2}$ **b.** $30\sqrt[3]{4}$

Section 10.6 Practice Exercises, pp. 741–744

1. **a.** radical **b.** $\frac{\sqrt[n]{a}}{\sqrt[n]{b}}$ **c.** $\frac{4}{x^2}$ **d.** rationalizing **e.** is; is not
f. denominator **3.** $12y\sqrt{5}$ **5.** $-18y + 3\sqrt{y} + 3$
7. $64 - 16\sqrt{t} + t$ **9.** -5 **11.** $\frac{7x^2}{y^3}$ **13.** $\frac{2a\sqrt{2}}{x^3}$
15. $\frac{-2j\sqrt[3]{2}}{k}$ **17.** $3b^2$ **19.** $\frac{1}{2b^2}$ **21.** $\frac{z\sqrt{3y}}{w^2}$ **23.** $\frac{\sqrt{5}}{\sqrt{5}}$
25. $\frac{\sqrt[3]{x^2}}{\sqrt[3]{x^2}}$ **27.** $\frac{\sqrt{3z}}{\sqrt{3z}}$ **29.** $\frac{\sqrt[4]{2a^2}}{\sqrt[4]{2a^2}}$ **31.** $\frac{\sqrt{3}}{3}$
33. $\frac{\sqrt{x}}{x}$ **35.** $\frac{3\sqrt{2y}}{y}$ **37.** $\frac{a\sqrt{2a}}{2}$ **39.** $\frac{3\sqrt{2}}{2}$
41. $\frac{3\sqrt[3]{4}}{2}$ **43.** $\frac{-6\sqrt[4]{x^3}}{x}$ **45.** $\frac{7\sqrt[3]{2}}{2}$ **47.** $\frac{\sqrt[3]{4w}}{w}$
49. $\frac{2\sqrt[4]{27}}{3}$ **51.** $\frac{\sqrt[3]{2x}}{x}$ **53.** $\frac{2\sqrt{6}}{21}$ **55.** $\frac{\sqrt{x}}{x^4}$
57. $\frac{\sqrt{2x}}{2x^3}$ **59.** $\sqrt{2} + \sqrt{6}$ **61.** $\sqrt{x} - 23$
63. $\frac{4\sqrt{2} - 12}{-7}$ or $\frac{-4\sqrt{2} + 12}{7}$ **65.** $4\sqrt{6} + 8$
67. $-\sqrt{21} + 2\sqrt{7}$ **69.** $\frac{-\sqrt{p} + \sqrt{q}}{p - q}$ **71.** $\sqrt{x} - \sqrt{5}$
73. $\frac{w + 11\sqrt{w} + 18}{81 - w}$ **75.** $\frac{4\sqrt{xy} - 3x - y}{y - x}$
77. $5 - \sqrt{10}$ **79.** $\frac{5 + \sqrt{21}}{4}$ **81.** $-6\sqrt{5} - 13$
83. $\frac{16}{\sqrt[3]{4}}$ simplifies to $8\sqrt[3]{2}$
85. $\frac{4}{x - \sqrt{2}}$ simplifies to $\frac{4x + 4\sqrt{2}}{x^2 - 2}$
87. $\frac{\pi\sqrt{2}}{4}$ sec $\approx$ 1.11 sec **89.** **a.** $\frac{\sqrt{2}}{2}$ **b.** $\frac{\sqrt[3]{4}}{2}$
91. **a.** $\frac{\sqrt{5a}}{5a}$ **b.** $\frac{\sqrt{5} - a}{5 - a^2}$ **93.** $\frac{2\sqrt{6}}{3}$ **95.** $\frac{17\sqrt{15}}{15}$
97. $\frac{8\sqrt[3]{25}}{5}$ **99.** $\frac{-33}{2\sqrt{3} - 12}$ **101.** $\frac{a - b}{a + 2\sqrt{ab} + b}$
103. $\frac{3}{\sqrt{5 + 3h} + \sqrt{5}}$ **105.** $\frac{5}{\sqrt{4 + 5h} + 2}$

Section 10.7 Practice Exercises, pp. 751–754

1. **a.** radical **b.** isolate; 7 **c.** extraneous **d.** third
3. $\frac{3w\sqrt{w}}{4}$ **5.** $3c\sqrt[3]{2c}$ **7.** $4x - 6$ **9.** $9p + 7$
11. {100} **13.** {4} **15.** {3} **17.** {42} **19.** {2}
21. {29} **23.** {140} **25.** { } (The value 25 does not check.)
27. {7} (The value −1 does not check.)
29. { } (The value 3 does not check.)
31. $V = \frac{4\pi r^3}{3}$ **33.** $h^2 = \frac{r^2 - \pi^2 r^2}{\pi^2}$ or $h^2 = \frac{r^2}{\pi^2} - r^2$
35. $a^2 + 10a + 25$ **37.** $5a - 6\sqrt{5a} + 9$
39. $r + 22 + 10\sqrt{r - 3}$ **41.** {−3}
43. { } (The value $\frac{1}{2}$ does not check.)
45. {2} (The value 18 does not check.) **47.** {9}
49. {−4} **51.** $\left\{\frac{9}{5}\right\}$ **53.** {2}
55. { } (The value 9 does not check.)
57. $\left\{-\frac{11}{4}\right\}$ **59.** { } (The value $\frac{8}{3}$ does not check.)
61. {−1} (The value 3 does not check.) **63.** $\left\{\frac{1}{3}, -1\right\}$
65. { } (The values 3 and 23 do not check.)
67. {6} **69.** {2} (The value 18 does not check.)
71. **a.** 30.25 ft **b.** 34.5 m **73.** **a.** \$2 million
b. \$1.2 million **c.** 50,000 passengers **75.** **a.** 12 lb
b. $t(18) = 5.1$. An 18-lb turkey will take about 5.1 hr to cook.
77. $b = \sqrt{25 - h^2}$ **79.** $a = \sqrt{k^2 - 196}$

Section 10.7 Graphing Calculator Exercises, p. 754

80. The x-coordinate of the point of intersection is the solution to the equation.

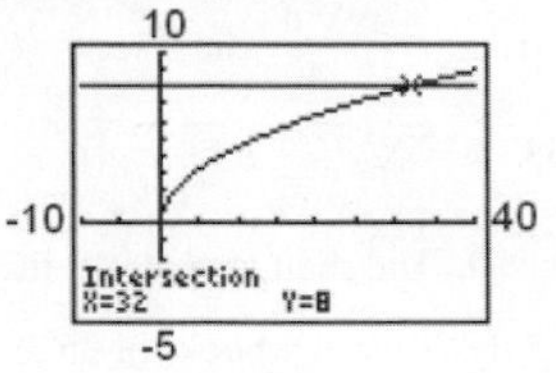

81. The x-coordinate of the point of intersection is the solution to the equation.

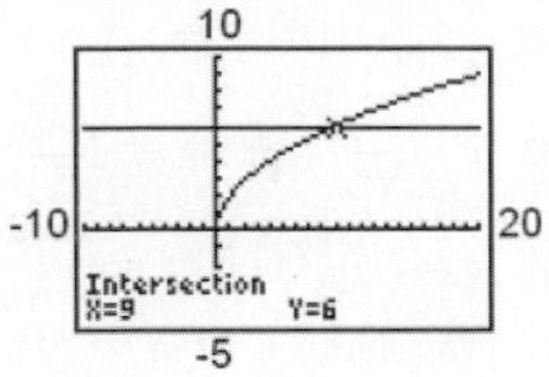

82.

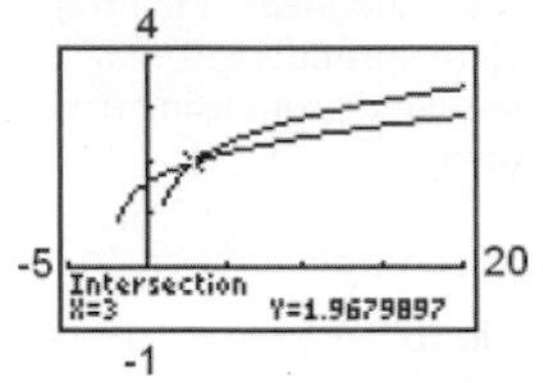

83.

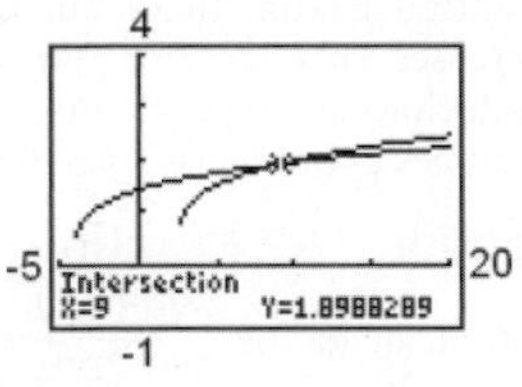

Section 10.8 Practice Exercises, pp. 762–764

1. a. imaginary **b.** $\sqrt{-1}$; -1 **c.** $i\sqrt{b}$ **d.** $a + bi$; $\sqrt{-1}$ **e.** real; b **f.** $a + bi$ **g.** True **h.** True
3. $9 - x$ **5.** $\{-8\}$ **7.** $\left\{\frac{1}{25}\right\}$ **9.** $\sqrt{-1} = i$ and $-\sqrt{1} = -1$ **11.** $12i$ **13.** $i\sqrt{3}$ **15.** $-2i\sqrt{5}$
17. -60 **19.** $13i\sqrt{7}$ **21.** -7 **23.** -12
25. $-3\sqrt{10}$ **27.** $i\sqrt{2}$ **29.** 3 **31.** $-i$ **33.** 1
35. i **37.** 1 **39.** $-i$ **41.** -1 **43.** $a - bi$
45. Real: -5; imaginary: 12 **47.** Real: 0; imaginary: -6
49. Real: 35; imaginary: 0 **51.** Real: $\frac{3}{5}$; imaginary: 1
53. $7 + 6i$ **55.** $\frac{3}{10} + \frac{3}{2}i$ **57.** $5i\sqrt{2}$
59. $-1 + 10i$ **61.** $-24 + 0i$ **63.** $18 + 6i$
65. $26 - 26i$ **67.** $-29 + 0i$ **69.** $-9 + 40i$
71. $35 + 20i$ **73.** $-20 + 48i$ **75.** $\frac{13}{16} + 0i$
77. $\frac{1}{5} - \frac{3}{5}i$ **79.** $\frac{3}{25} - \frac{4}{25}i$ **81.** $\frac{21}{29} + \frac{20}{29}i$
83. $-\frac{17}{10} - \frac{1}{10}i$ **85.** $-\frac{1}{2} - \frac{5}{2}i$ **87.** $\frac{1}{2} - \frac{1}{3}i$
89. $1 + 10i$ **91.** $\frac{1}{4} + \frac{1}{2}i$ **93.** $-1 + i\sqrt{2}$
95. $-2 - i\sqrt{3}$ **97.** $-\frac{1}{2} + \frac{\sqrt{2}}{2}i$ **99.** Yes **101.** Yes

Chapter 10 Review Exercises, pp. 772–774

1. a. False; $\sqrt{0} = 0$ is not positive. **b.** False; $\sqrt[3]{-8} = -2$
2. $\sqrt{(-3)^2} = \sqrt{9} = 3$ **3. a.** False **b.** True
4. $\frac{5}{4}$ **5.** 5 **6.** 6 **7. a.** 3 **b.** 0 **c.** $\sqrt{7}$ **d.** $[1, \infty)$ **8. a.** 0 **b.** 1 **c.** 3 **d.** $[-5, \infty)$
9. $\frac{\sqrt[3]{2x}}{\sqrt[4]{2x}} + 4$ **10. a.** $|x|$ **b.** x **c.** $|x|$ **d.** $x + 1$
11. a. $2|y|$ **b.** $3y$ **c.** $|y|$ **d.** y **12.** 8 cm
13. Yes, provided the expressions are defined. For example: $x^5 \cdot x^3 = x^8$ and $x^{1/5} \cdot x^{2/5} = x^{3/5}$ **14.** n represents the root.
15. Take the reciprocal of the base and change the exponent to positive. **16.** -5 **17.** $\frac{1}{2}$ **18.** 4
19. b^{10} **20.** $\frac{16y^{12}}{xz^9}$ **21.** $\frac{a^3c}{b^2}$ **22.** $x^{3/4}$
23. $(2y^2)^{1/3}$ **24.** 2.1544 **25.** 6.8173 **26.** 54.1819
27. See page 714. **28.** $6\sqrt{3}$ **29.** $xz\sqrt[4]{xy}$
30. $-10ab^3\sqrt[3]{2b}$ **31.** $-\frac{2a}{b}$
32. a. The principal square root of the quotient of 2 and x **b.** The cube of the sum of x and 1 **33.** 31 ft
34. they are *like* radicals. **35.** Cannot be combined; the indices are different. **36.** Cannot be combined; one term has a radical, but the other does not. **37.** Can be combined: $3\sqrt[4]{3xy}$ **38.** Can be added after simplifying: $19\sqrt{2}$
39. $5\sqrt{7}$ **40.** $9\sqrt[3]{2} - 8$ **41.** $10\sqrt{2}$ **42.** $13x\sqrt[3]{2x^2}$
43. False; 5 and $3\sqrt{x}$ are not *like* radicals.
44. False; $\sqrt{y} + \sqrt{y} = 2\sqrt{y}$ (add the coefficients).
45. 6 **46.** $2\sqrt[4]{2}$ **47.** $-2\sqrt{21} + 6\sqrt{33}$
48. $-6\sqrt{15} + 15$ **49.** $4x - 9$ **50.** $y - 16$
51. $7y - 2\sqrt{21xy} + 3x$ **52.** $12w + 20\sqrt{3w} + 25$
53. $-2z - 9\sqrt{6z} - 42$ **54.** $3a + 5\sqrt{5a} - 10$
55. $u^2\sqrt[6]{u^5}$ **56.** $\sqrt[4]{4w^3}$ **57.** $\frac{y^2\sqrt{3y}}{5x^3}$
58. $\frac{-2x^2y^2\sqrt[3]{2x}}{z^3}$ **59.** $9w^2$ **60.** $\frac{t^4}{4}$ **61.** $\frac{\sqrt{14y}}{2y}$
62. $\frac{\sqrt{15w}}{3w}$ **63.** $\frac{4\sqrt[3]{3p}}{3p}$ **64.** $-\frac{\sqrt[3]{4x^2}}{x}$
65. $\sqrt{10} - \sqrt{15}$ **66.** $3\sqrt{5} - 3\sqrt{7}$ **67.** $\sqrt{t} + \sqrt{3}$
68. $\sqrt{w} + \sqrt{7}$ **69.** The quotient of the principal square root of 2 and the square of x
70. $\left\{\frac{49}{2}\right\}$ **71.** $\{31\}$ **72.** $\{-12\}$ **73.** $\{7\}$
74. $\{9\}$ **75.** $\{\ \}$ (The value -2 does not check.)
76. $\left\{\frac{1}{2}, 4\right\}$ **77.** $\{-2\}$ (The value 2 does not check.)
78. $6\sqrt{5}$ m $\approx$ 13.4 m **79. a.** $v(20) \approx 25.3$ ft/sec. When the water depth is 20 ft, a wave travels about 25.3 ft/sec. **b.** 8 ft **80.** $a + bi$, where a and b are real numbers and $i = \sqrt{-1}$
81. $a + bi$, where $b \neq 0$
82. Multiply the numerator and denominator by $4 - 6i$, which is the complex conjugate of the denominator.
83. $4i$ **84.** $-i\sqrt{5}$ **85.** -15 **86.** $-2i$ **87.** -1
88. i **89.** $-i$ **90.** 0 **91.** $-5 + 5i$ **92.** $9 + 17i$
93. $25 + 0i$ **94.** $24 - 10i$
95. $-\frac{17}{4} + i$; real part: $-\frac{17}{4}$; imaginary part: 1
96. $-2 - i$; real part: -2; imaginary part: -1
97. $\frac{4}{13} - \frac{7}{13}i$ **98.** $3 + 4i$ **99.** $-\frac{3}{2} + \frac{5}{2}i$
100. $-\frac{4}{17} + \frac{16}{17}i$ **101.** $-\frac{2}{3} + \frac{\sqrt{10}}{6}i$ **102.** $2 - 4i$

Chapter 10 Test, pp. 775–776

1. a. 6 **b.** -6 **2. a.** Real **b.** Not real **c.** Real **d.** Real **3. a.** y **b.** $|y|$ **4.** 3 **5.** $\frac{4}{3}$ **6.** $2\sqrt[3]{4}$
7. $a^2bc^2\sqrt{bc}$ **8.** $3x^2yz^2\sqrt{2xy}$ **9.** $4w^2\sqrt{w}$ **10.** $\frac{x^2}{5y}$
11. $\frac{3\sqrt{2}}{2}$ **12. a.** $f(-8) = 2\sqrt{3}$; $f(-6) = 2\sqrt{2}$; $f(-4) = 2$; $f(-2) = 0$ **b.** $(-\infty, -2]$ **13.** -0.3080
14. -3 **15.** $\frac{20x^2y^3}{z}$ **16.** $\sqrt[6]{7y^3}$ **17.** $\sqrt[12]{10}$
18. $3\sqrt{5}$ **19.** $3\sqrt{2x} - 3\sqrt{5x}$ **20.** $40 - 10\sqrt{5x} - 3x$
21. $\frac{-2\sqrt[3]{x^2}}{x}$ **22.** $\frac{x + 6 + 5\sqrt{x}}{9 - x}$ **23. a.** $2i\sqrt{2}$ **b.** $8i$ **c.** $\frac{1}{2} + \frac{\sqrt{2}}{2}i$ **24.** $1 - 11i$ **25.** $30 + 16i$ **26.** -28

27. $-33 - 56i$ **28.** 104 **29.** $\frac{17}{25} + \frac{6}{25}i$

30. $-\frac{15}{17} + \frac{9}{17}i$ **31.** $r(10) \approx 1.34$; the radius of a sphere of volume 10 cubic units is approximately 1.34 units.

32. 21 ft **33.** $\{-16\}$ **34.** $\left\{\frac{17}{5}\right\}$

35. $\{2\}$ (The value 42 does not check.)

Chapters 1–10 Cumulative Review Exercises, pp. 776–777

1. 54 **2.** $15x - 5y - 5$ **3.** $\{-3\}$ **4.** $(-\infty, -5)$
5. $[-9, -3)$ **6.** $\{\ \}$ **7.** $y = -2x + 5$ **8.** $x = -5$
9. $\left\{\left(\frac{1}{2}, \frac{1}{3}\right)\right\}$ **10.** $\left(2, -2, \frac{1}{2}\right)$ is not a solution.
11. Together it will take them $1\frac{7}{8}$ hr.
12. a. $f(-2) = -10$; $f(0) = -2$; $f(4) = 14$; $f\left(\frac{1}{2}\right) = 0$
b. $(-2, -10), (0, -2), (4, 14), \left(\frac{1}{2}, 0\right)$
c.

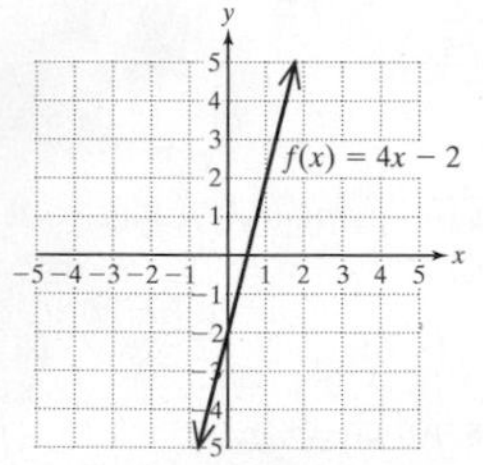

13. $a^6b^{12}c^4$ **14. a.** 1.4×10^{-4} **b.** 3.14×10^9
15. $2x^2 - x - 15$; 2nd degree **16.** $\sqrt{15} + 3\sqrt{2} + 3$
17. $x - 4$ **18.** $-\frac{1}{6}$ **19.** $\frac{3c\sqrt[3]{2}}{d}$ **20.** $32b\sqrt{5b}$
21. $2 + 3i$ **22.** $\{10\}$ **23.** $\frac{x - 15}{x(x + 5)(x - 5)}$
24. $\frac{-1}{(2a + 1)(a + 2)}$ **25.** $-14x^2 + 26x - 17$
26. $2\sqrt{3} + 2\sqrt{5}$ **27.** $\frac{6}{17} + \frac{10}{17}i$ **28.** $\left\{\frac{7}{6}, -\frac{3}{2}\right\}$
29. $(x + 3 - y)(x + 3 + y)$ **30.** $(x^2 + 2)(x^4 - 2x^2 + 4)$

Chapter 11

Chapter Opener Puzzle

Q	U	A	D	R	A	T	I	C
2	1	6	5	8	6	4	7	3

Section 11.1 Practice Exercises, pp. 786–789

1. a. 0; 0 **b.** 0 **c.** $\sqrt{k}$; $-\sqrt{k}$ **d.** 2; $\{3, -3\}$ **e.** completing **f.** 100 **g.** 4; 1 **h.** 8
3. $\{\pm 2\}$ **5.** $\{\pm\sqrt{7}\}$ **7.** $\left\{\frac{11}{6}, -\frac{11}{6}\right\}$ **9.** $\{\pm 5i\}$
11. $\{-1, -5\}$ **13.** $\left\{\frac{-3 \pm \sqrt{7}}{2}\right\}$ **15.** $\{-5 \pm 3i\sqrt{2}\}$
17. $\left\{\pm\frac{\sqrt{33}}{3}\right\}$ **19.** $\left\{-\frac{4}{5} \pm \frac{\sqrt{3}}{5}i\right\}$ **21.** $\{4i, -4i\}$
23. 1. Factoring and applying the zero product rule. 2. Applying the square root property. $\{\pm 6\}$ **25. a.** $\{16\}$ **b.** $\{2, -2\}$
27. $n = 9$; $(x - 3)^2$ **29.** $n = 16$; $(t + 4)^2$
31. $n = \frac{1}{4}$; $\left(c - \frac{1}{2}\right)^2$ **33.** $n = \frac{25}{4}$; $\left(y + \frac{5}{2}\right)^2$
35. $n = \frac{1}{25}$; $\left(b + \frac{1}{5}\right)^2$ **37.** $n = \frac{1}{9}$; $\left(p - \frac{1}{3}\right)^2$
39. See page 783. **41.** $\{-3, -5\}$ **43.** $\{-3 \pm i\sqrt{7}\}$
45. $\{-2 \pm i\sqrt{2}\}$ **47.** $\{5, -2\}$ **49.** $\left\{-1 \pm \frac{\sqrt{6}}{2}i\right\}$
51. $\left\{2 \pm \frac{2}{3}i\right\}$ **53.** $\left\{\frac{1}{5} \pm \frac{\sqrt{3}}{5}\right\}$ **55.** $\left\{-\frac{3}{4} \pm \frac{\sqrt{65}}{4}\right\}$
57. $\{2 \pm \sqrt{11}\}$ **59.** $\{1, -7\}$ **61. a.** $t = \frac{\sqrt{d}}{4}$ **b.** 8 sec
63. $r = \sqrt{\frac{A}{\pi}}$ or $r = \frac{\sqrt{A\pi}}{\pi}$ **65.** $a = \sqrt{d^2 - b^2 - c^2}$
67. $r = \sqrt{\frac{3V}{\pi h}}$ or $r = \frac{\sqrt{3V\pi h}}{\pi h}$ **69.** The shelf extends 4.2 ft.
71. The sides are 7.1 in. **73. a.** 4.5 thousand textbooks or 35.5 thousand textbooks **b.** Profit increases to a point as more books are produced. Beyond that point, the market is "flooded," and profit decreases. There are two points at which the profit is \$20,000. Producing 4.5 thousand books makes the same profit using fewer resources as producing 35.5 thousand books.

Section 11.2 Practice Exercises, pp. 800–803

1. a. quadratic; $\frac{-b \pm \sqrt{b^2 - 4ac}}{2a}$ **b.** $ax^2 + bx + c = 0$ **c.** 8; −42; −27 **d.** 7; 97 **e.** $b^2 - 4ac$; discriminant **f.** imaginary **g.** real **h.** less than
3. $4 - 2\sqrt{5}$ **5.** $2 - i\sqrt{3}$ **7.** linear **9.** $\{-12, 1\}$
11. $\left\{\frac{1}{9} \pm \frac{2\sqrt{11}}{9}i\right\}$ **13.** $\left\{\frac{1}{6} \pm \frac{\sqrt{14}}{6}i\right\}$ **15.** $\{7, -5\}$
17. $\left\{\frac{-3 \pm \sqrt{41}}{2}\right\}$ **19.** $\left\{\frac{2}{5}\right\}$ **21.** $\{3 \pm i\sqrt{5}\}$
23. $\left\{\frac{1 \pm \sqrt{29}}{2}\right\}$ **25.** $\left\{\frac{-1 \pm \sqrt{13}}{4}\right\}$
27. $\left\{-\frac{2}{3} \pm \frac{2\sqrt{2}}{3}i\right\}$ **29.** $\left\{\frac{-5 \pm \sqrt{13}}{2}\right\}$
31. $\{-2, -4\}$ **33.** $\left\{\frac{-7 \pm \sqrt{109}}{6}\right\}$
35. a. $(x - 3)(x^2 + 3x + 9)$ **b.** $\left\{3, -\frac{3}{2} \pm \frac{3\sqrt{3}}{2}i\right\}$
37. a. $3x(x^2 - 2x + 2)$ **b.** $\{0, 1 \pm i\}$ **39.** The length of each side is 3 ft. **41.** The legs are approximately 1.6 in. and 3.6 in.
43. The legs are approximately 8.2 m and 6.1 m.
45. a. Approximately 4.5 fatalities per 100 million miles driven
b. Approximately 1 fatality per 100 million miles driven
c. Approximately 4.2 fatalities per 100 million miles driven
d. For drivers 26 yr old and 71 yr old
47. The times are $\frac{3 + \sqrt{5}}{2}$ sec $\approx$ 2.62 sec or $\frac{3 - \sqrt{5}}{2}$ sec $\approx$ 0.38 sec. **49. a.** $x^2 + 2x + 1 = 0$ **b.** 0 **c.** 1 rational solution **51. a.** $19m^2 - 8m + 0 = 0$ **b.** 64 **c.** 2 rational solutions **53. a.** $5p^2 + 0p - 21 = 0$ **b.** 420 **c.** 2 irrational solutions **55. a.** $n^2 + 3n + 4 = 0$ **b.** −7 **c.** 2 imaginary solutions **57.** Discriminant: 16; two x-intercepts
59. Discriminant: 0; one x-intercept
61. Discriminant: −39; no x-intercepts
63. x-intercepts: $\left(\frac{5 + \sqrt{13}}{2}, 0\right), \left(\frac{5 - \sqrt{13}}{2}, 0\right)$; y-intercept: $(0, 3)$ **65.** x-intercepts: none; y-intercept: $(0, -1)$
67. x-intercepts: $\left(\frac{-5 - \sqrt{41}}{4}, 0\right), \left(\frac{-5 + \sqrt{41}}{4}, 0\right)$; y-intercept: $(0, -2)$ **69.** $\{-1 \pm 3i\}$
71. $\left\{-\frac{1}{3}, 6\right\}$ **73.** $\left\{\frac{5}{2} \pm \frac{3\sqrt{2}}{2}i\right\}$ **75.** $\left\{-\frac{1}{2} \pm 2i\right\}$
77. $\left\{\frac{3 \pm \sqrt{7}}{2}\right\}$ **79.** $\{1 \pm 3i\sqrt{2}\}$ **81.** $\{2 + \sqrt{2}\}$
83. $\left\{-\frac{1}{8}, \frac{3}{4}\right\}$ **85.** $\left\{\pm\frac{\sqrt{21}}{2}\right\}$
87. a. $\{-3 \pm \sqrt{14}\}$ **b.** $\{-3 \pm \sqrt{14}\}$ **c.** Answers will vary

Section 11.2 Graphing Calculator Exercises, p. 803

89.

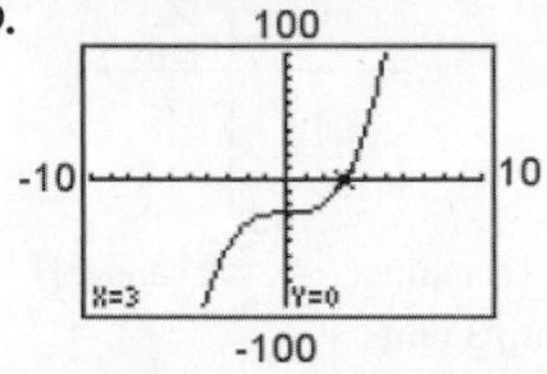

90.

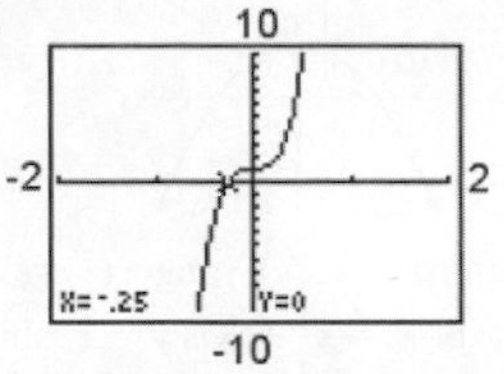

91.

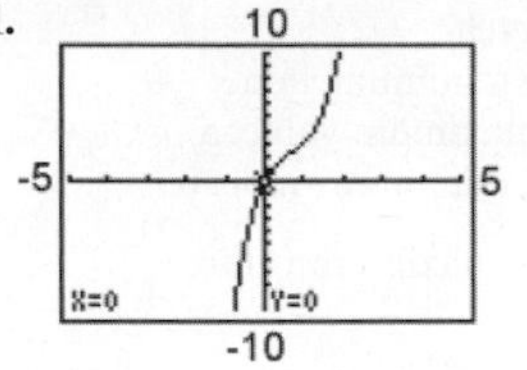

92.

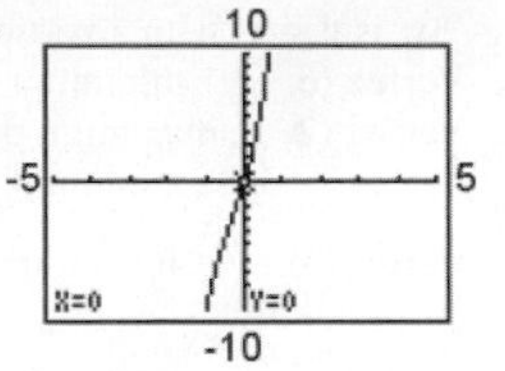

Section 11.3 Practice Exercises, pp. 807–809

1. a. quadratic **b.** $3x - 1$ **c.** $p^{1/3}$
3. $\left\{\frac{3}{2} \pm \frac{\sqrt{7}}{2}\right\}$ **5.** $\{-4\}$ **7.** $\{2 \pm \sqrt{26}\}$
9. a. $\{-4, -6\}$ **b.** $\{-4, -1, -2, -3\}$
11. $\{1 \pm i\sqrt{2}, 1 \pm \sqrt{2}\}$ **13.** $\{5, -1, 2\}$ **15.** $\{27, -8\}$
17. $\left\{-\frac{1}{32}, -243\right\}$ **19.** $\{4\}$ (The value 64 does not check.)
21. $\left\{\frac{1}{4}\right\}$ (The value 4 does not check.)
23. $\{-7\}$ **25.** $\{16\}$; yes **27.** $\{\pm 3i, \pm\sqrt{5}\}$
29. $\left\{\pm\frac{\sqrt{3}}{2}, \pm i\sqrt{5}\right\}$ **31.** $\left\{\frac{-5 \pm \sqrt{13}}{2}\right\}$
33. $\left\{\frac{9 \pm \sqrt{73}}{4}\right\}$ **35.** $\{2 \pm \sqrt{3}\}$ **37.** $\{\pm 2, \pm 2i\}$
39. $\left\{-\frac{7}{4}, -\frac{3}{2}\right\}$ **41.** $\left\{\frac{1}{2}, -\frac{1}{2}, \sqrt{2}, -\sqrt{2}\right\}$
43. $\left\{2, 1, -1 \pm i\sqrt{3}, -\frac{1}{2} \pm \frac{\sqrt{3}}{2}i\right\}$ **45.** $\{5, 4\}$ **47.** $\{0, 2\}$
49. $\left\{1, \frac{17}{2}\right\}$ **51.** $\{64, -125\}$ **53.** $\{\pm\sqrt{2}, \pm 2i\}$
55. $\{\pm 4i, 1\}$ **57.** $\{4, \pm i\sqrt{5}\}$ **59.** $\left\{\frac{8}{3}, 2\right\}$

Section 11.3 Graphing Calculator Exercises, p. 809

61. a. $\{\pm i\sqrt{2}\}$ **b.** Two imaginary solutions; no real solutions
c. No x-intercepts
d.

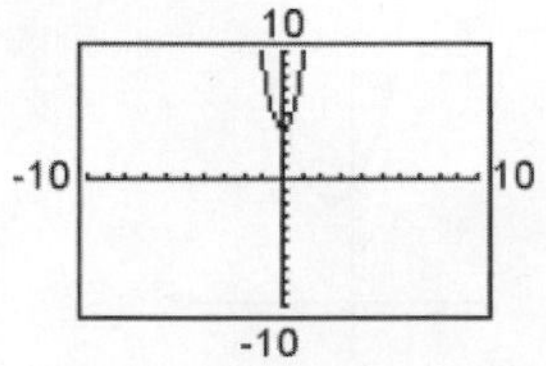

62. a. $\{1, -1\}$ **b.** Two real solutions; no imaginary solutions
c. Two x-intercepts
d.

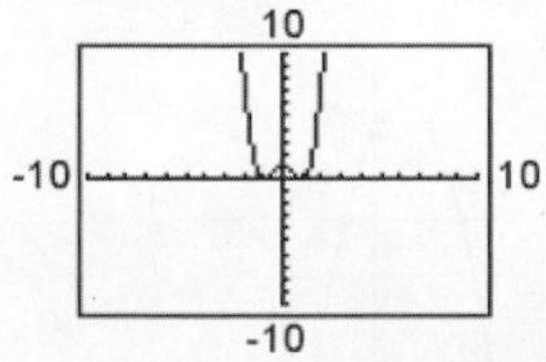

63. a. $\{0, 3, -2\}$ **b.** Three real solutions; no imaginary solutions
c. Three x-intercepts
d.

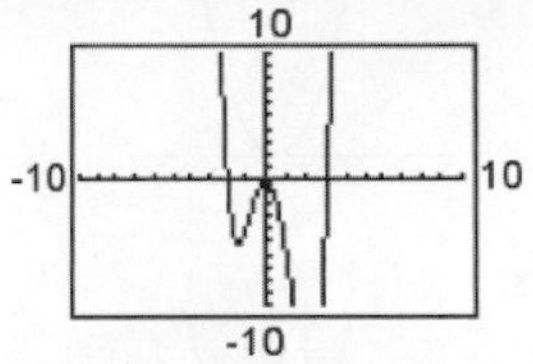

64. a. $\{\pm 1, \pm 3\}$ **b.** Four real solutions; no imaginary solutions
c. Four x-intercepts
d.

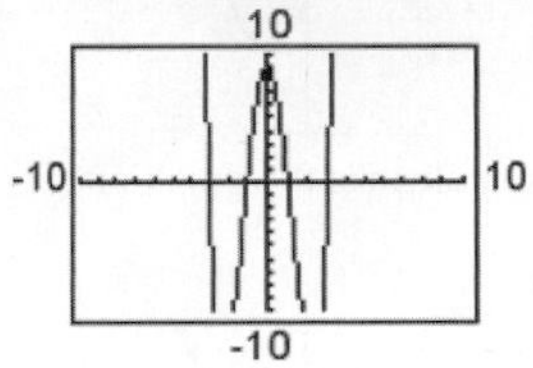

Chapter 11 Problem Recognition Exercises, pp. 809–810

1. $\{-5 \pm \sqrt{22}\}$ **2.** $\{8 \pm \sqrt{59}\}$ **3.** $\left\{-\frac{1}{6} \pm \frac{\sqrt{47}}{6}i\right\}$
4. $\left\{-\frac{3}{8} \pm \frac{\sqrt{71}}{8}i\right\}$ **5. a.** Quadratic **b.** $\{2, -7\}$
6. a. Quadratic **b.** $\{4, 5\}$ **7. a.** Quadratic form **b.** $\{-3, -1, 1, 3\}$ **8. a.** Quadratic form **b.** $\{2, -2, i, -i\}$
9. a. Quadratic form (or radical) **b.** $\{16\}$ (The value 1 does not check.) **10. a.** Quadratic **b.** $\left\{\frac{9 \pm \sqrt{89}}{2}\right\}$
11. a. Linear **b.** $\{4\}$ **12. a.** Linear **b.** $\{-1\}$
13. a. Quadratic **b.** $\{\pm i\sqrt{2}\}$ **14. a.** Quadratic **b.** $\{\pm i\sqrt{6}\}$ **15. a.** Rational **b.** $\{2, -1\}$
16. a. Rational **b.** $\{-2, 4\}$
17. a. Quadratic **b.** $\{10 \pm \sqrt{101}\}$
18. a. Quadratic **b.** $\{-9 \pm \sqrt{77}\}$
19. a. Quadratic **b.** $\left\{\frac{1 \pm \sqrt{17}}{2}\right\}$
20. a. Quadratic **b.** $\left\{\frac{1 \pm \sqrt{13}}{2}\right\}$
21. a. Radical **b.** $\{3\}$ (The value -1 does not check.)
22. a. Radical **b.** $\{6\}$ (The value -1 does not check.)
23. a. Quadratic form (or radical) **b.** $\{-125, 27\}$
24. a. Quadratic form (or radical) **b.** $\{-64, -1\}$

Section 11.4 Practice Exercises, pp. 819–823

1. a. parabola **b.** $>$; $<$ **c.** lowest; highest **d.** (h, k); upward; downward **e.** vertex; $x = h$
3. $\{3 \pm 2i\}$ **5.** $\left\{\frac{5 \pm \sqrt{10}}{5}\right\}$ **7.** $\{-27, -8\}$
9. The value of k shifts the graph of $f(x) = x^2$ vertically.

11.

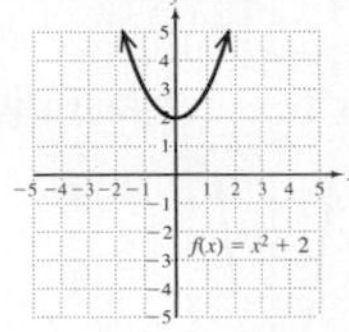

13.

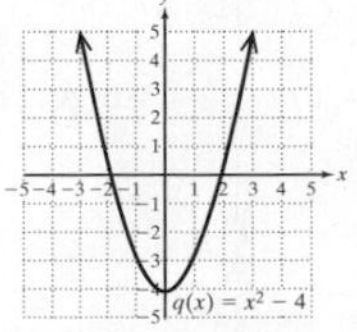

15.

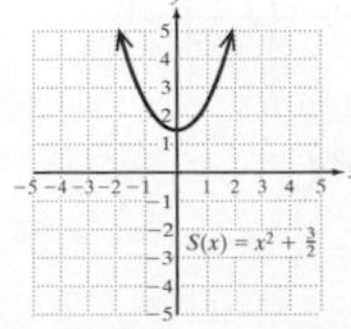

17.

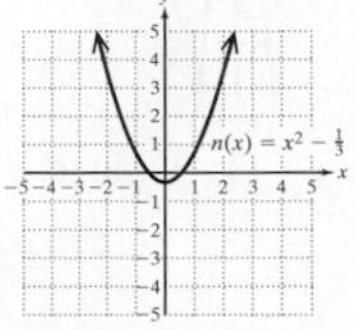

19.

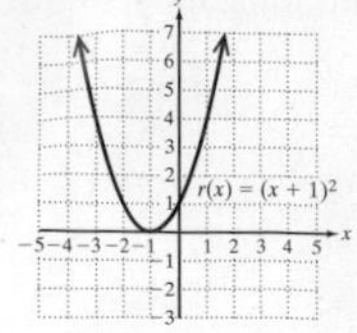

21.

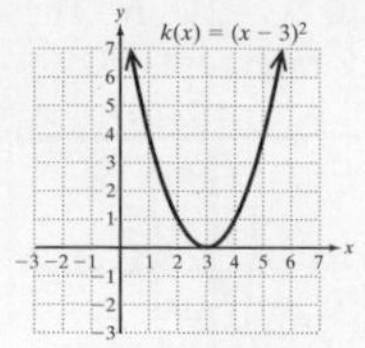

23.

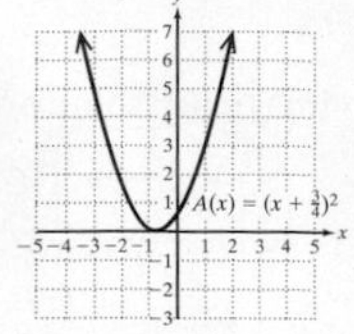

25.

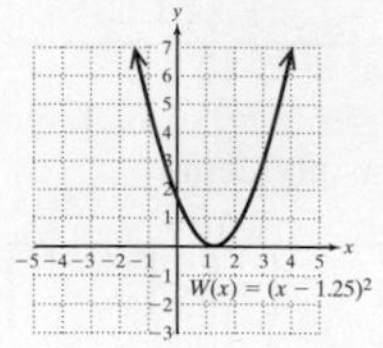

27. The value of a vertically stretches or shrinks the graph of $f(x) = x^2$.

29.

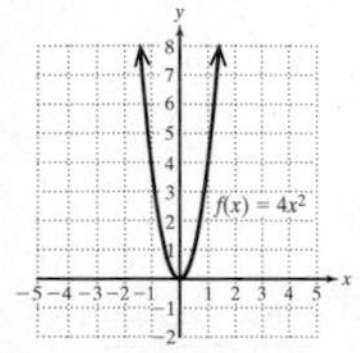

31.

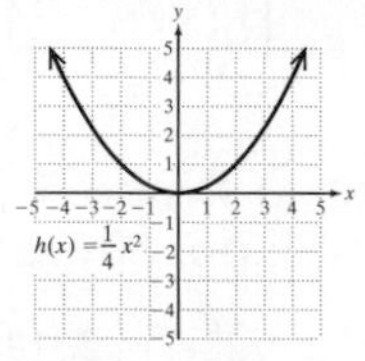

33.

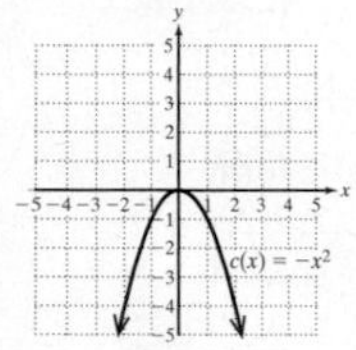

35.

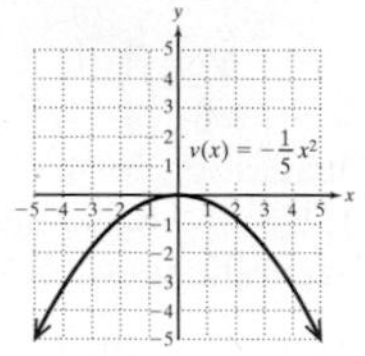

37. d **39.** g **41.** a **43.** e

45.

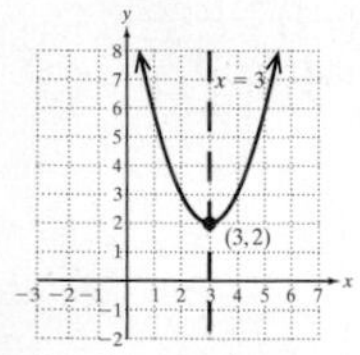

Domain: $(-\infty, \infty)$; range: $[2, \infty)$

47.

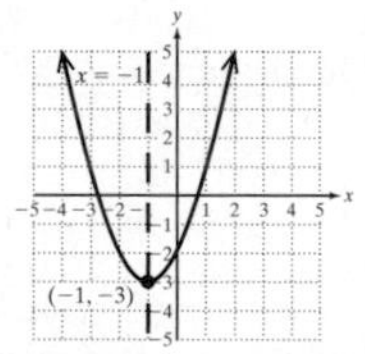

Domain: $(-\infty, \infty)$; range: $[-3, \infty)$

49.

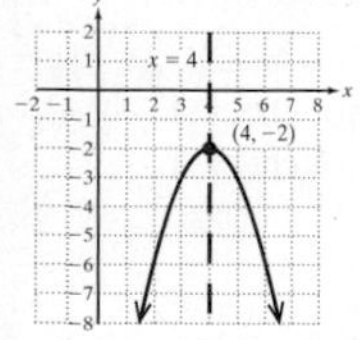

Domain: $(-\infty, \infty)$; range: $(-\infty, -2]$

51.

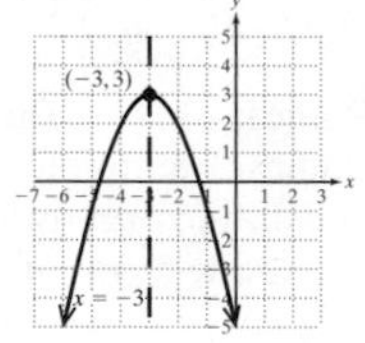

Domain: $(-\infty, \infty)$; range: $(-\infty, 3]$

53.

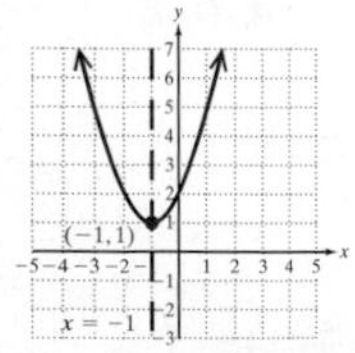

Domain: $(-\infty, \infty)$; range: $[1, \infty)$

55.

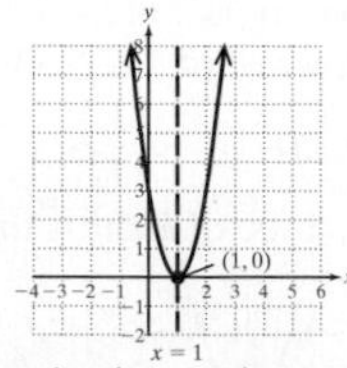

Domain: $(-\infty, \infty)$; range: $[0, \infty)$

57.

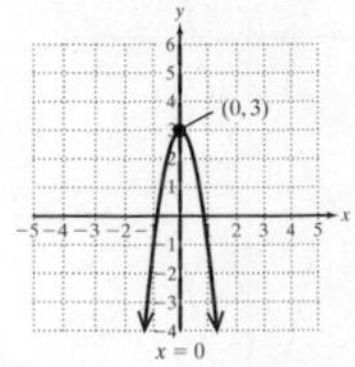

Domain: $(-\infty, \infty)$; range: $(-\infty, 3]$

59.

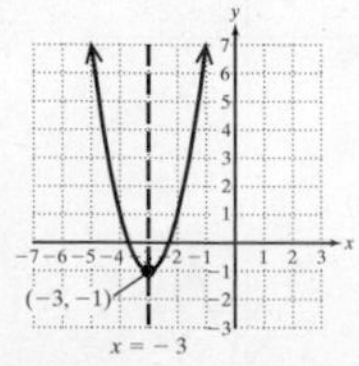

Domain: $(-\infty, \infty)$; range: $[-1, \infty)$

61.

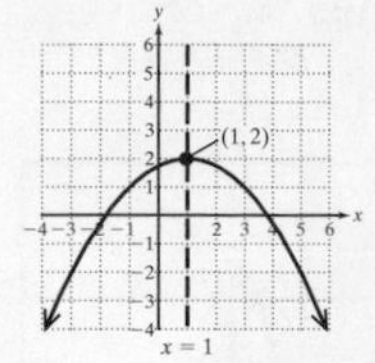

Domain: $(-\infty, \infty)$; range: $(-\infty, 2]$

63.

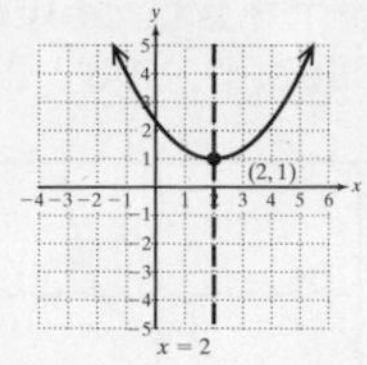

Domain: $(-\infty, \infty)$; range: $[1, \infty)$

65. a. $y = x^2 + 3$ is $y = x^2$ shifted up 3 units.
b. $y = (x + 3)^2$ is $y = x^2$ shifted left 3 units.
c. $y = 3x^2$ is $y = x^2$ with a vertical stretch.
67. Vertex $(6, -9)$; minimum point; minimum value: -9
69. Vertex $(2, 5)$; maximum point; maximum value: 5
71. Vertex $(-8, 0)$; minimum point; minimum value: 0
73. Vertex $\left(0, \frac{21}{4}\right)$; maximum point; maximum value: $\frac{21}{4}$
75. Vertex $\left(7, -\frac{3}{2}\right)$; minimum point; minimum value: $-\frac{3}{2}$
77. Vertex $(0, 0)$; minimum point; minimum value: 0
79. True **81.** False **83. a.** $(60, 30)$ **b.** 30 ft **c.** 70 ft
85. a. The fireworks will explode at a height of 150 ft.
b. Yes, because the ordered pair $(3, 150)$ is the vertex.

Section 11.5 Practice Exercises, pp. 830–834

1. a. $\frac{-b}{2a}; \frac{-b}{2a}$ **b.** True **c.** True **d.** True **e.** False
3. The graph of p is the graph of $y = x^2$ shrunk vertically by a factor of $\frac{1}{4}$.
5. The graph of r is the graph of $y = x^2$ shifted up 7 units.
7. The graph of t is the graph of $y = x^2$ shifted to the left 10 units. **9.** $16; (x - 4)^2$ **11.** $\frac{49}{4}; \left(y + \frac{7}{2}\right)^2$
13. $\frac{1}{81}; \left(b + \frac{1}{9}\right)^2$ **15.** $\frac{1}{36}; \left(t - \frac{1}{6}\right)^2$
17. $g(x) = (x - 4)^2 - 11; (4, -11)$
19. $n(x) = 2(x + 3)^2 - 5; (-3, -5)$
21. $p(x) = -3(x - 1)^2 - 2; (1, -2)$
23. $k(x) = \left(x + \frac{7}{2}\right)^2 - \frac{89}{4}; \left(-\frac{7}{2}, -\frac{89}{4}\right)$
25. $F(x) = 5(x + 1)^2 - 4; (-1, -4)$
27. $P(x) = -2\left(x - \frac{1}{4}\right)^2 + \frac{1}{8}; \left(\frac{1}{4}, \frac{1}{8}\right)$ **29.** $(2, 3)$
31. $(-1, -2)$ **33.** $(-4, -15)$ **35.** $(-1, 2)$ **37.** $(1, 3)$
39. $\left(\frac{3}{2}, \frac{3}{4}\right)$ **41.** $(-4, -15)$ **43.** $(-1, 4)$
45. a. $(-1, -4)$ **b.** $(0, -3)$
c. $(1, 0), (-3, 0)$
d.

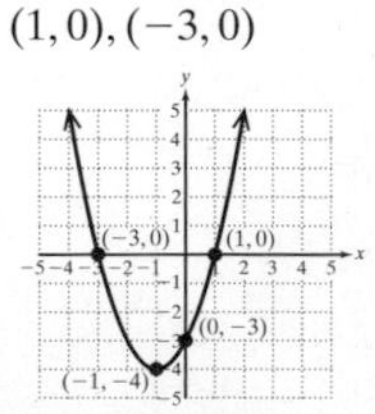

47. a. $(\frac{1}{2}, \frac{7}{2})$ **b.** $(0, 4)$
c. No x-intercepts
d.

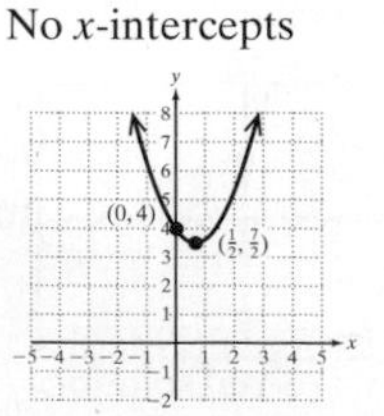

49. a. $(\frac{3}{2}, 0)$ **b.** $(0, -\frac{9}{4})$
c. $(\frac{3}{2}, 0)$
d.

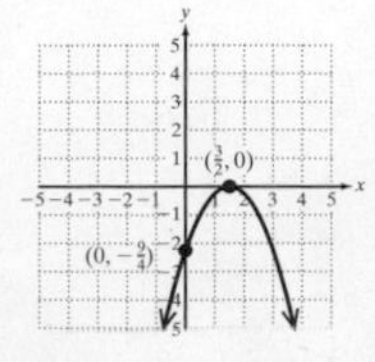

51. a. $(-1, 4)$ **b.** $(0, 3)$
c. $(1, 0), (-3, 0)$
d.

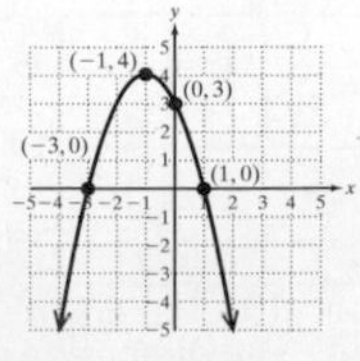

53. Mia must package 10 MP3 players. **55. a.** 164.25 ft **b.** 3.125 sec **57. a.** 45 mph **b.** 32 mpg **59. a.** 48 hr **b.** 2 g **61.** $a = -9, b = 5, c = 4; y = -9x^2 + 5x + 4$
63. $a = 2, b = -1, c = -5; y = 2x^2 - x - 5$
65. $a = -3, b = 4, c = 0; y = -3x^2 + 4x$
67. a. The sum of the sides must equal the total amount of fencing. **b.** $A = x(200 - 2x)$ **c.** 50 ft by 100 ft

Section 11.5 Graphing Calculator Exercises, p. 834

69.

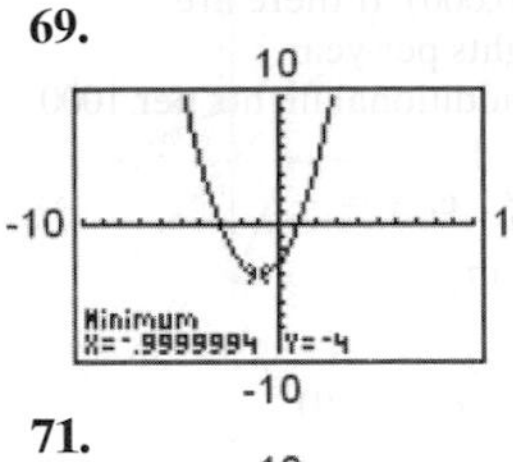

70.

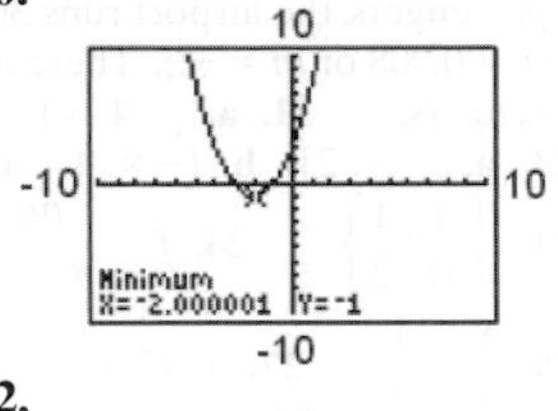

71.

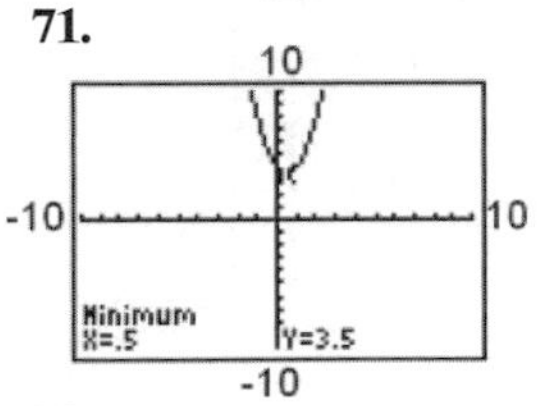

72.

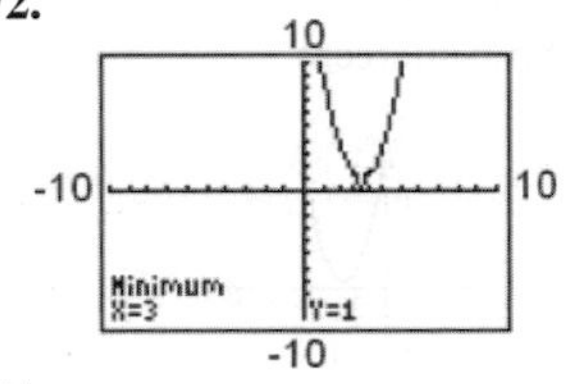

73.

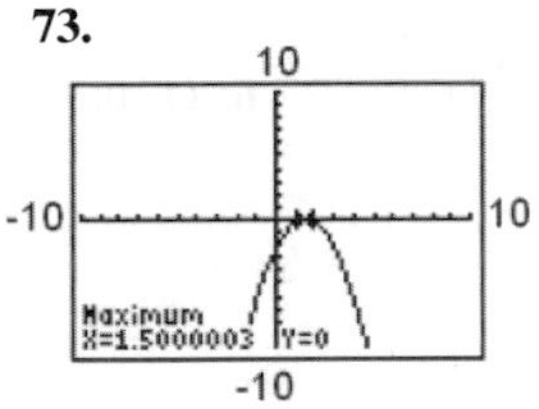

74.

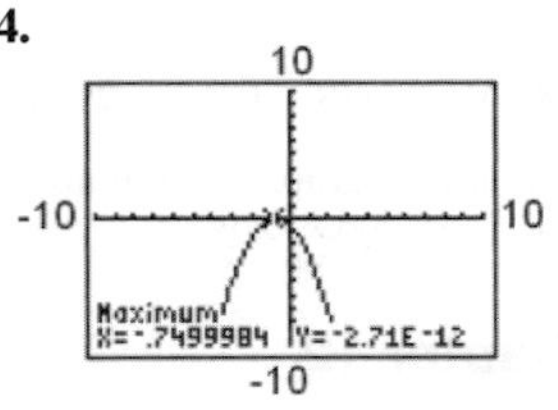

Chapter 11 Review Exercises, pp. 840–843

1. $\{\pm\sqrt{5}\}$ **2.** $\{\pm 2i\}$ **3.** $\{\pm 9\}$ **4.** $\left\{\pm\frac{\sqrt{57}}{3}i\right\}$
5. $\{2 \pm 6\sqrt{2}\}$ **6.** $\left\{\frac{5}{2} \pm \frac{3}{2}i\right\}$ **7.** $\left\{\frac{1 \pm \sqrt{3}}{3}\right\}$
8. $\{4 \pm \sqrt{5}\}$ **9.** $5\sqrt{3}$ in. ≈ 8.7 in. **10.** 9 in.
11. $5\sqrt{6}$ in. ≈ 12.2 in. **12.** $n = 64; (x + 8)^2$
13. $n = \frac{81}{4}; \left(x - \frac{9}{2}\right)^2$ **14.** $n = \frac{1}{16}; \left(y + \frac{1}{4}\right)^2$
15. $n = \frac{1}{25}; \left(z - \frac{1}{5}\right)^2$ **16.** $\{-2 \pm 3i\}$ **17.** $\{1 \pm \sqrt{6}\}$
18. $\{3 \pm 2\sqrt{3}\}$ **19.** $\{4 \pm 3i\}$ **20.** $\left\{\frac{1}{3}, -1\right\}$
21. $\left\{\frac{1}{2}, -4\right\}$ **22.** $r = \sqrt{\frac{V}{\pi h}}$ or $r = \frac{\sqrt{V\pi h}}{\pi h}$
23. $s = \sqrt{\frac{A}{6}}$ or $s = \frac{\sqrt{6A}}{6}$ **24.** See page 794.
25. Two rational solutions **26.** Two rational solutions
27. Two irrational solutions **28.** Two imaginary solutions
29. One rational solution **30.** Two imaginary solutions
31. $\{2 \pm \sqrt{3}\}$ **32.** $\left\{\frac{5}{2} \pm \frac{5\sqrt{3}}{2}i\right\}$ **33.** $\left\{2, -\frac{5}{6}\right\}$
34. $\left\{2, \frac{4}{3}\right\}$ **35.** $\left\{\frac{4}{5}, -\frac{1}{5}\right\}$ **36.** $\left\{\frac{1}{10}, -\frac{1}{2}\right\}$
37. $\{2 \pm 2i\sqrt{7}\}$ **38.** $\{4 \pm \sqrt{6}\}$ **39.** $\left\{\frac{2 \pm \sqrt{22}}{3}\right\}$
40. $\{8, -2\}$ **41.** $\{-7 \pm \sqrt{3}\}$ **42.** $\{-1 \pm \sqrt{11}\}$
43. a. 1822 ft **b.** 115 ft/s **44. a.** $\approx$ 53,939 thousand **b.** 2021 **45.** The dimensions are approximately 3.1 ft by 7.2 ft. **46.** The distance between Lincoln and Omaha is approximately 50 mi. **47.** $\{49\}$ (The value 9 does not check.)

48. $\{4, 16\}$ **49.** $\{\pm 3, \pm\sqrt{2}\}$ **50.** $\left\{\pm\frac{\sqrt{6}}{2}, \pm i\right\}$
51. $\{-243, 32\}$ **52.** $\{32, 1\}$ **53.** $\{3 \pm \sqrt{10}\}$
54. $\left\{\frac{1 \pm \sqrt{181}}{6}\right\}$ **55.** $\{\pm 3i, \pm i\sqrt{3}\}$ **56.** $\{\pm\sqrt{7}, \pm 2\}$

57.

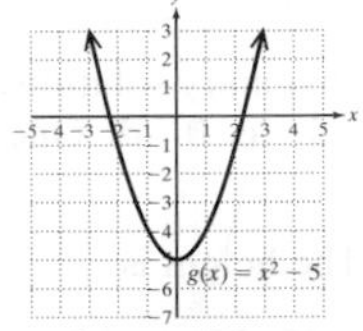

Domain: $(-\infty, \infty)$; range: $[-5, \infty)$

58.

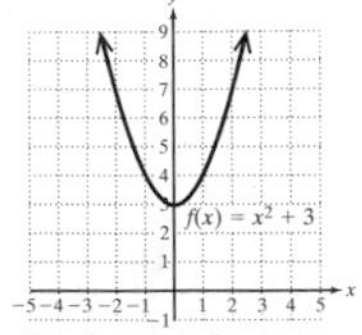

Domain: $(-\infty, \infty)$; range: $[3, \infty)$

59.

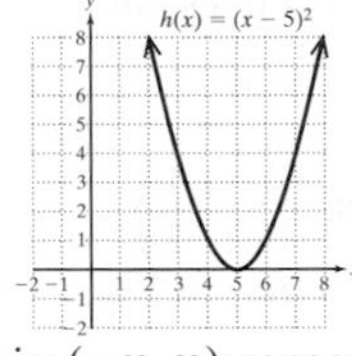

Domain: $(-\infty, \infty)$; range: $[0, \infty)$

60.

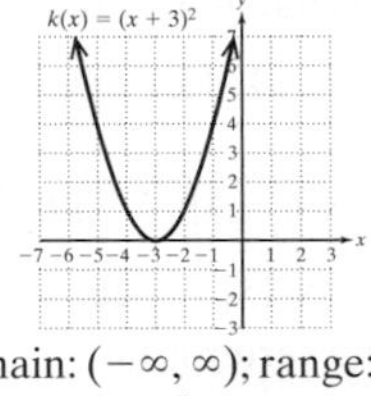

Domain: $(-\infty, \infty)$; range: $[0, \infty)$

61.

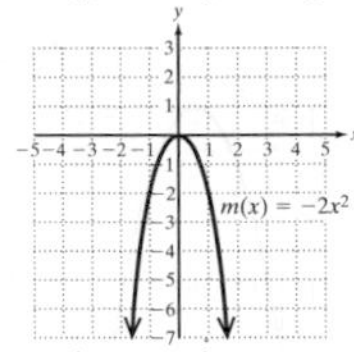

Domain: $(-\infty, \infty)$; range: $(-\infty, 0]$

62.

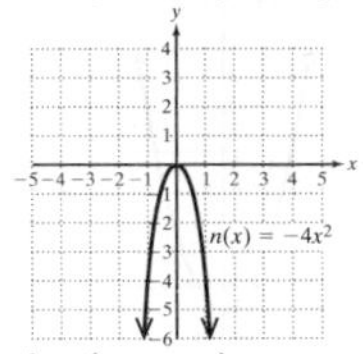

Domain: $(-\infty, \infty)$; range: $(-\infty, 0]$

63.

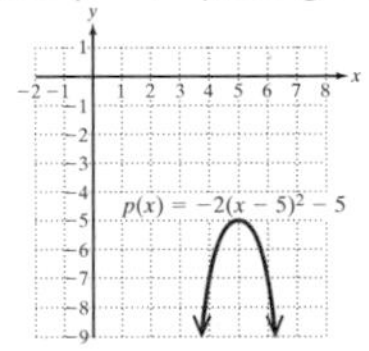

Domain: $(-\infty, \infty)$; range: $(-\infty, -5]$

64.

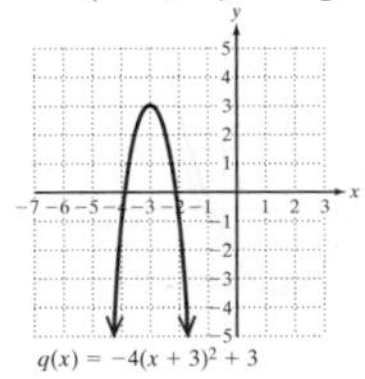

Domain: $(-\infty, \infty)$; range: $(-\infty, 3]$

65. $\left(4, \frac{5}{3}\right)$ is the minimum point. The minimum value is $\frac{5}{3}$.
66. $\left(1, -\frac{1}{7}\right)$ is the maximum point. The maximum value is $-\frac{1}{7}$. **67.** $x = -\frac{2}{11}$ **68.** $x = \frac{3}{16}$
69. $z(x) = (x - 3)^2 - 2; (3, -2)$
70. $b(x) = (x - 2)^2 - 48; (2, -48)$
71. $p(x) = -5(x + 1)^2 - 8; (-1, -8)$
72. $q(x) = -3(x + 4)^2 - 6; (-4, -6)$ **73.** $(1, -15)$
74. $(-1, 7)$ **75.** $\left(\frac{1}{2}, \frac{41}{4}\right)$ **76.** $\left(-\frac{1}{3}, -\frac{22}{3}\right)$
77. a. $(2, -3)$ **b.** $(0, 0), (4, 0)$
c.

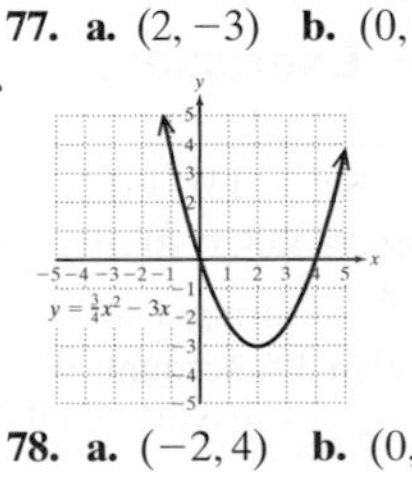

78. a. $(-2, 4)$ **b.** $(0, 0)$ $(-4, 0)$
c.

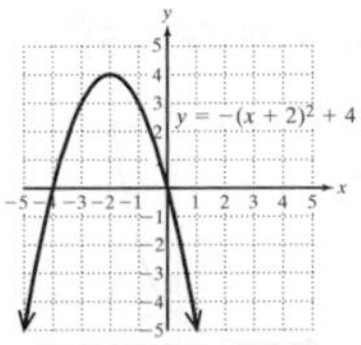

79. a. 3 sec **b.** 144 ft **80. a.** 150 meals **b.** \$1200
81. $a = 1, b = 4, c = -1; y = x^2 + 4x - 1$
82. $a = 1, b = -1, c = 6; y = x^2 - x + 6$

7. $g(-2) = \frac{1}{9}, g(-1) = \frac{1}{3}, g(0) = 1, g(1) = 3, g(2) = 9$
9. $b^y = x$ **11.** $5^4 = 625$ **13.** $10^{-4} = 0.0001$ **15.** $6^2 = 36$
17. $b^x = 15$ **19.** $3^x = 5$ **21.** $\left(\frac{1}{4}\right)^{10} = x$ **23.** $\log_3 81 = x$
25. $\log_5 25 = 2$ **27.** $\log_7\left(\frac{1}{7}\right) = -1$ **29.** $\log_b y = x$
31. $\log_e y = x$ **33.** $\log_{1/3} 9 = -2$ **35.** 2 **37.** -1 **39.** $\frac{1}{2}$
41. 0 **43.** 5 **45.** 1 **47.** 3 **49.** $\frac{1}{2}$ **51.** 1 **53.** 3
55. 6 **57.** -2 **59.** 0.7782 **61.** 0.4971 **63.** -1.5051
65. -2.2676 **67.** 5.5315 **69.** -7.4202
71. a. Slightly less than 2 **b.** Slightly more than 1
c. $\log 93 \approx 1.9685, \log 12 \approx 1.0792$
73. a. $f\left(\frac{1}{64}\right) = -3, f\left(\frac{1}{16}\right) = -2, f\left(\frac{1}{4}\right) = -1, f(1) = 0,$
$f(4) = 1, f(16) = 2, f(64) = 3$
b.

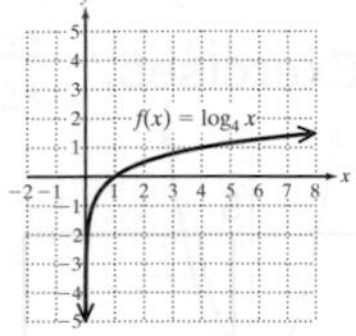

75. $3^y = x$

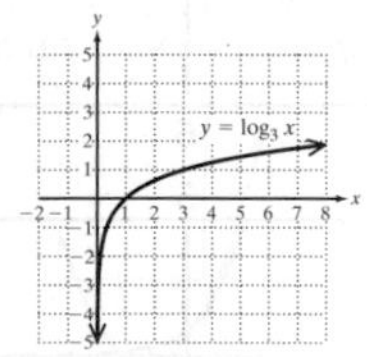

x	y
$\frac{1}{9}$	-2
$\frac{1}{3}$	-1
1	0
3	1
9	2

77. $\left(\frac{1}{2}\right)^y = x$

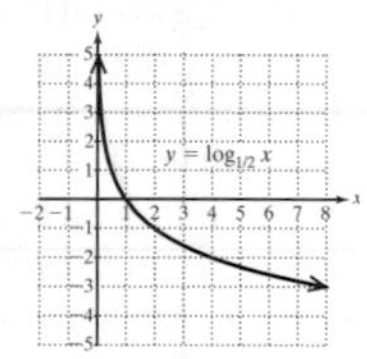

x	y
4	-2
2	-1
1	0
$\frac{1}{2}$	1
$\frac{1}{4}$	2

79. $(5, \infty)$ **81.** $(-\infty, 2)$ **83.** $\left(\frac{1}{3}, \infty\right)$ **85.** $(-1.2, \infty)$
87. $(-\infty, 2)$ **89.** $(-\infty, 0) \cup (0, \infty)$ **91.** ≈ 7.35
93. a.

t (months)	0	1	2	6	12	24
$S_1(t)$	91	82.0	76.7	65.6	57.6	49.1
$S_2(t)$	88	83.5	80.8	75.3	71.3	67.0

b. Group 1: 91; Group 2: 88 **c.** Method II

Section 12.3 Graphing Calculator Exercises, p. 879

95. Domain: $(-6, \infty)$; asymptote: $x = -6$

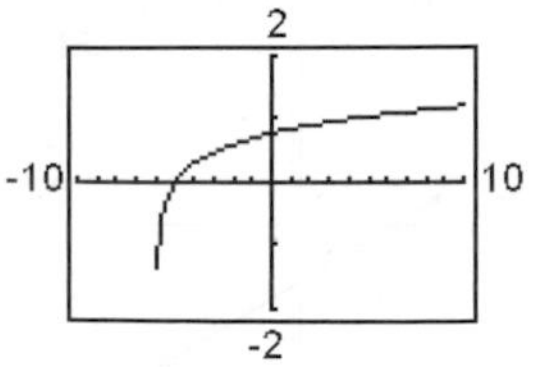

96. Domain: $(-2, \infty)$; asymptote: $x = -2$

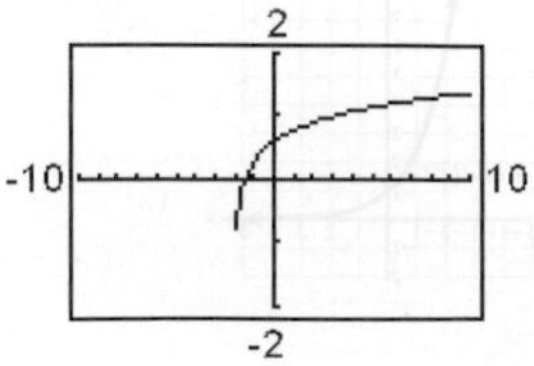

97. Domain: $(2, \infty)$; asymptote: $x = 2$

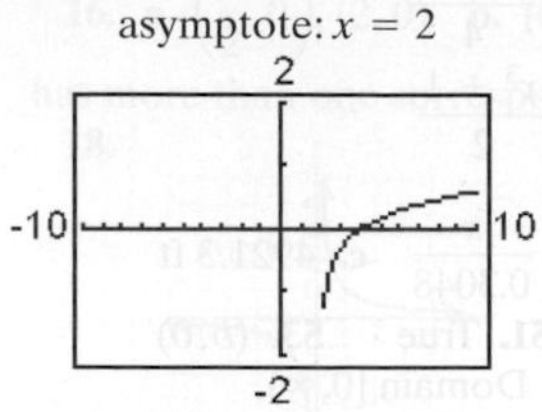

98. Domain: $(-8, \infty)$; asymptote: $x = -8$

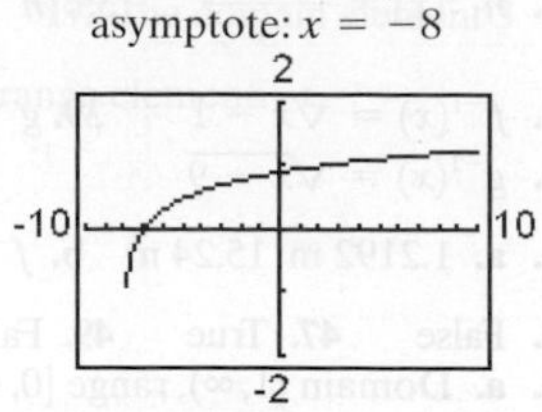

99. Domain: $(-\infty, 2)$; asymptote: $x = 2$

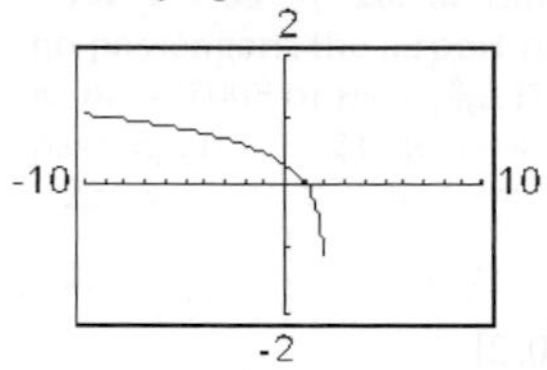

100. Domain: $(-\infty, 3)$; asymptote: $x = 3$

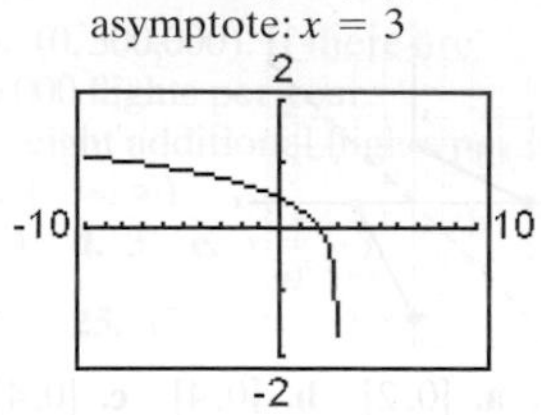

Chapter 12 Problem Recognition Exercises, p. 880

1. e **2.** l **3.** j **4.** g **5.** c **6.** a
7. k **8.** b **9.** i **10.** h **11.** f **12.** d

Section 12.4 Practice Exercises, pp. 886–889

1. a. $1; 0; x; x$ **b.** $\log_b x + \log_b y; \log_b x - \log_b y$ **c.** $p \log_b x$
d. False **e.** False **f.** False
3. 4 **5.** $\frac{1}{6}$ **7.** 0.9031 **9.** 5.0475 **11.** a **13.** c
15. a, b, c **17.** 1 **19.** 4 **21.** 11 **23.** 3 **25.** 0
27. 9 **29.** 0 **31.** 3 **33.** 1 **35.** $2x$ **37.** 4 **39.** 0
41. Expressions a and c are equivalent.
43. Expressions a and c are equivalent.
45. $\log_3 x - \log_3 5$ **47.** $\log 2 + \log x$ **49.** $4 \log_5 x$
51. $\log_4 a + \log_4 b - \log_4 c$
53. $\frac{1}{2}\log_b x + \log_b y - 3 \log_b z - \log_b w$
55. $\log_2(x + 1) - 2 \log_2 y - \frac{1}{2}\log_2 z$
57. $\frac{1}{3}\log a + \frac{2}{3}\log b - \frac{1}{3}\log c$ **59.** $-5 \log w$
61. $\frac{1}{2}\log_b a - 3 - \log_b c$ **63.** 3 **65.** 2 **67.** $\log_3\left(\frac{x^2 z}{y^3}\right)$
69. $\log_3\left(\frac{a^2 c}{\sqrt[4]{b}}\right)$ **71.** $\log_b x^2$ **73.** $\log_8(8a^5)$ or $\log_8 a^5 + 1$
75. $\log\left[\frac{(x + 6)^2\sqrt[3]{y}}{z^5}\right]$ **77.** $\log_b\left(\frac{1}{x - 1}\right)$ **79.** 1.792
81. 2.485 **83.** 4.396 **85.** 0.916 **87.** 13.812 **89.** 16.09
91. a. $B = 10 \log I - 10 \log I_0$ **b.** $10 \log I + 160$

Section 12.4 Graphing Calculator Exercises, p. 889

93. a. Domain: $(-\infty, 0) \cup (0, \infty)$ **b.** Domain: $(0, \infty)$

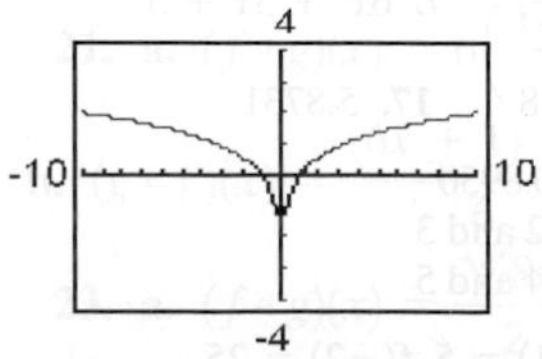

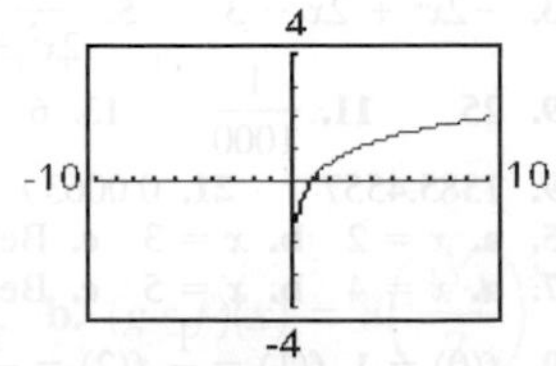

c. They are equivalent for all x in the intersection of their domains, $(0, \infty)$.

94. a. Domain: $(-\infty, 1) \cup (1, \infty)$ **b.** Domain: $(1, \infty)$

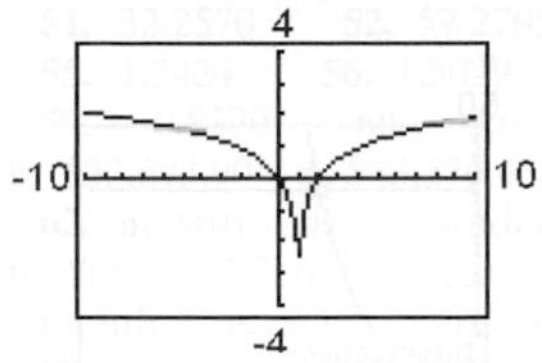

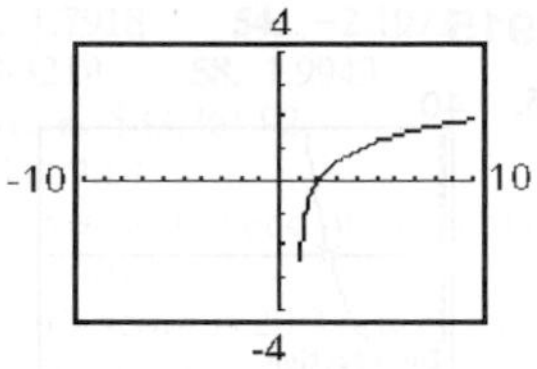

c. They are equivalent for all x in the intersection of their domains, $(1, \infty)$.

Section 12.5 Practice Exercises, pp. 897–901

1. a. e **b.** e **c.** natural; $\ln x$ **d.** 0; 1; p, x **e.** $\ln x + \ln y$; $\ln x - \ln y$ **f.** $p \ln x$ **g.** $\log_a b$

3. $\log_3\left(\frac{a\sqrt{d}}{c^5}\right)$ **5.** $\frac{1}{4}\log_6 x + \frac{1}{2}\log_6 y - \frac{3}{4}\log_6 z$

7.

x	y
−4	0.05
−3	0.14
−2	0.37
−1	1
0	2.72
1	7.39

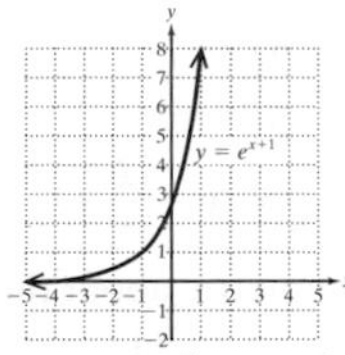

Domain: $(-\infty, \infty)$

9.

x	y
−2	2.14
−1	2.37
0	3
1	4.72
2	9.39
3	22.09

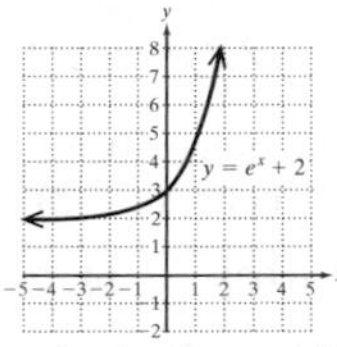

Domain: $(-\infty, \infty)$

11. a. \$12,209.97 **b.** \$13,488.50 **c.** \$14,898.46 **d.** \$16,050.09 An investment grows more rapidly at higher interest rates.
13. a. \$12,423.76 **b.** \$12,515.01 **c.** \$12,535.94 **d.** \$12,546.15 **e.** \$12,546.50 More money is earned at a greater number of compound periods per year. **15. a.** \$6920.15 **b.** \$9577.70 **c.** \$13,255.84 **d.** \$18,346.48 **e.** \$35,143.44 More money is earned over a longer period of time.

17.

x	y
2.25	−1.39
2.50	−0.69
2.75	−0.29
3	0
4	0.69
5	1.10
6	1.39

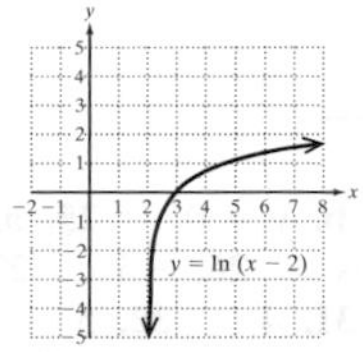

Domain: $(2, \infty)$

19.

x	y
0.25	−2.39
0.5	−1.69
0.75	−1.29
1	−1.00
2	−0.31
3	0.10
4	0.39

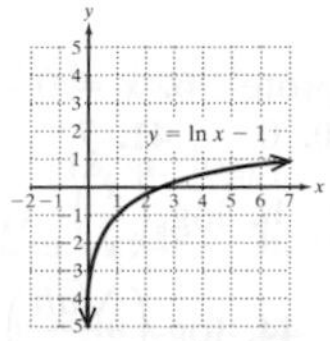

Domain: $(0, \infty)$

21. a.

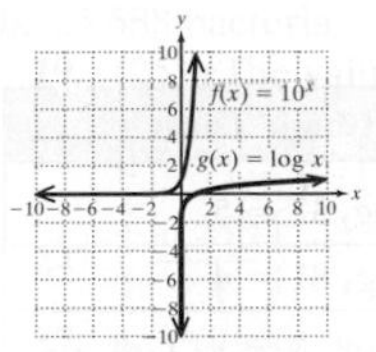

b. Domain: $(-\infty, \infty)$; range: $(0, \infty)$
c. Domain: $(0, \infty)$; range: $(-\infty, \infty)$

23. 1 **25.** 0 **27.** −6 **29.** $2x + 3$ **31.** $\ln(p^6\sqrt[3]{q})$
33. $\ln\sqrt{\frac{x}{y^3}}$ **35.** $\ln\left(\frac{a^2}{b\sqrt[3]{c}}\right)$ **37.** $\ln\left(\frac{x^4}{y^3 z}\right)$
39. $2\ln a - 2\ln b$ **41.** $2\ln b + 1$ **43.** $4\ln a + \frac{1}{2}\ln b - \ln c$
45. $\frac{1}{5}\ln a + \frac{1}{5}\ln b - \frac{2}{5}\ln c$ **47. a.** 2.9570 **b.** 2.9570 **c.** They are the same. **49.** 2.8074 **51.** 1.5283 **53.** −2.1269 **55.** 0 **57.** −3.3219 **59.** −3.8124 **61. a.** 15.4 yr **b.** 6.9 yr **c.** 13.8 yr **63. a.** 19.8 yr **b.** 13.9 yr **c.** 27.8 yr

Section 12.5 Graphing Calculator Exercises, pp. 901–902

65. a–b

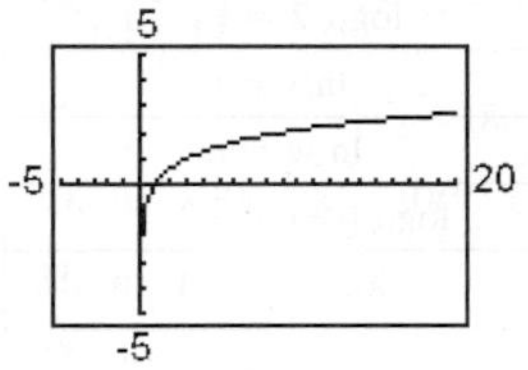

c. They appear to be the same.

66. a–b

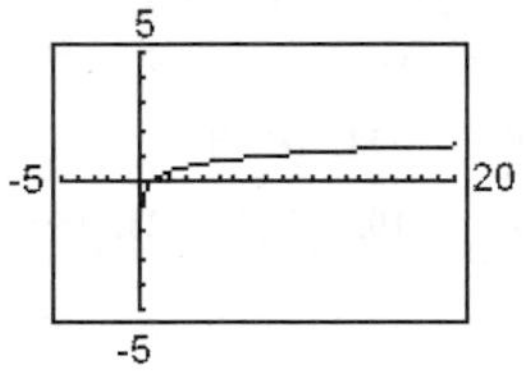

c. They appear to be the same.

67.

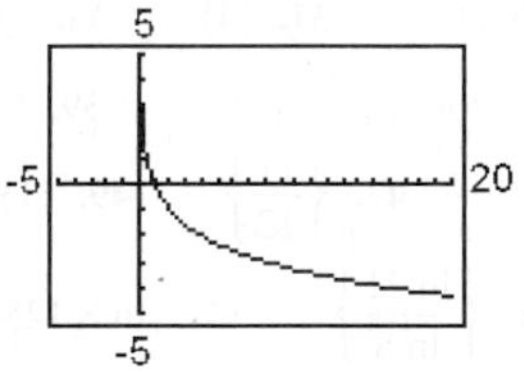

68.

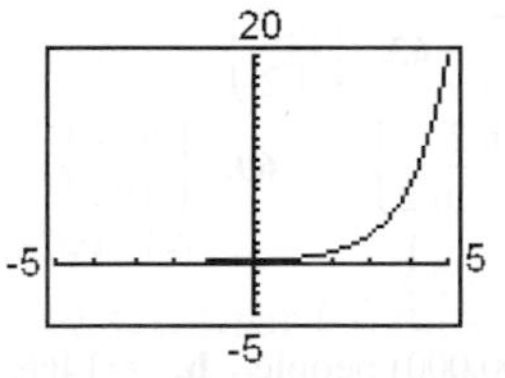

69.

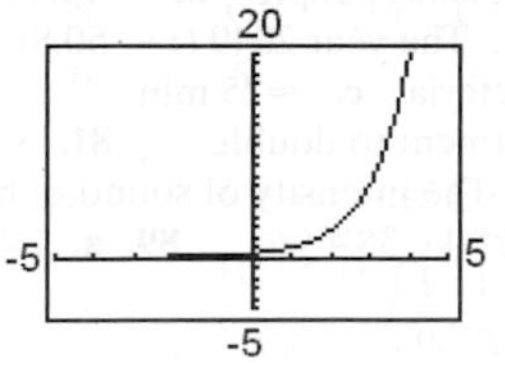

27. Center $(4, -2)$; $r = 3$

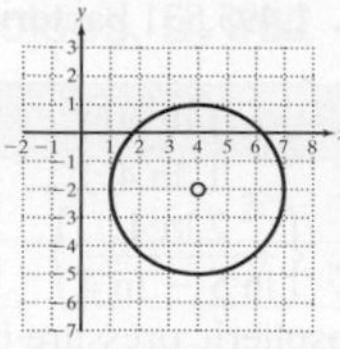

29. Center $(-1, -1)$; $r = 1$

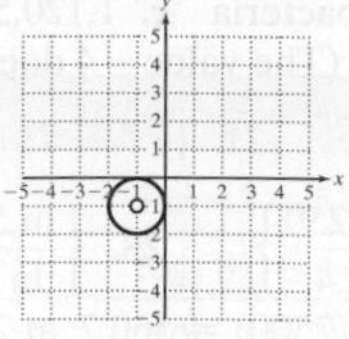

31. Center $(0, 2)$; $r = 2$

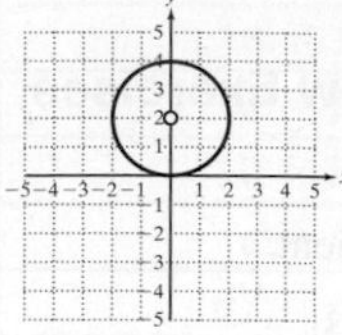

33. Center $(3, 0)$; $r = 2\sqrt{2}$

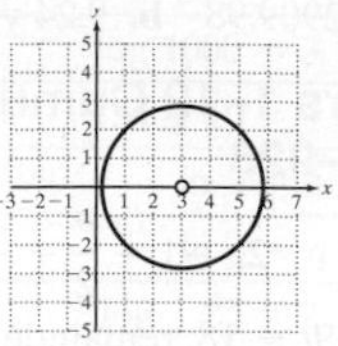

35. Center $(0, 0)$; $r = \sqrt{6}$

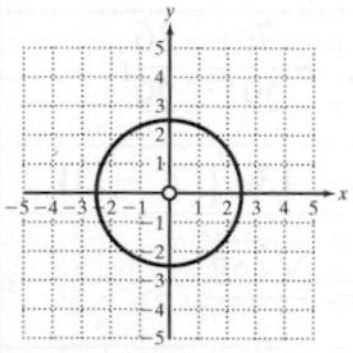

37. Center $\left(-\frac{4}{5}, 0\right)$; $r = \frac{8}{5}$

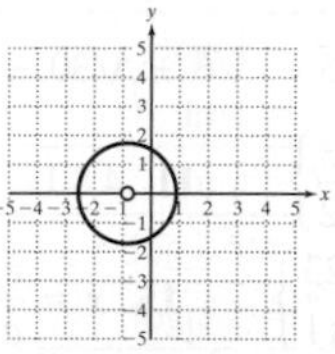

39. Center $(1, 3)$; $r = 6$

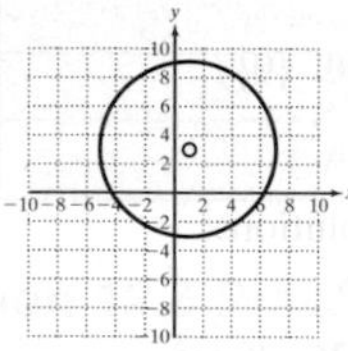

41. Center: $(0, 3)$; $r = 2$

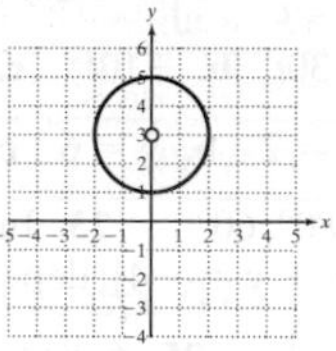

43. Center $(0, -3)$; $r = \frac{4}{3}$

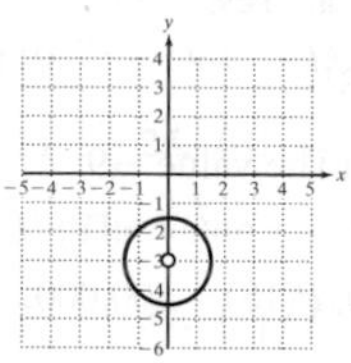

45. Center: $(-1, -2)$; $r = 3$

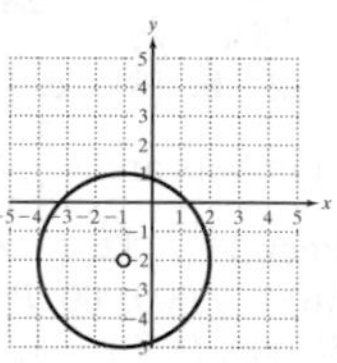

47. Center $(0, 0)$; $r = 1$

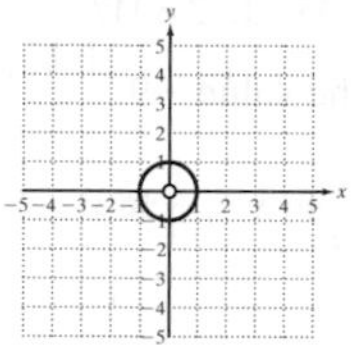

49. $x^2 + y^2 = 4$ **51.** $x^2 + (y - 2)^2 = 4$
53. $(x + 2)^2 + (y - 2)^2 = 9$ **55.** $x^2 + y^2 = 49$
57. $(x + 3)^2 + (y + 4)^2 = 36$ **59.** $(x - 5)^2 + (y - 3)^2 = 2.25$
61. $(1, 2)$ **63.** $(-1, 0)$ **65.** $(-1, 6)$
67. $(0, 3)$ **69.** $\left(-\frac{1}{2}, \frac{3}{2}\right)$ **71.** $(-0.4, -1)$
73. $(40, 7\frac{1}{2})$; they should meet 40 mi east, $7\frac{1}{2}$ mi north of the warehouse. **75. a.** $(1, 3)$ **b.** $(x - 1)^2 + (y - 3)^2 = 5$
77. a. $(0, 3)$ **b.** $x^2 + (y - 3)^2 = 4$
79. $(x - 4)^2 + (y - 4)^2 = 16$

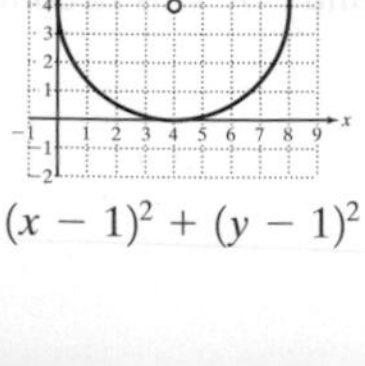

81. $(x - 1)^2 + (y - 1)^2 = 29$

Section 13.1 Graphing Calculator Exercises, p. 940

83.

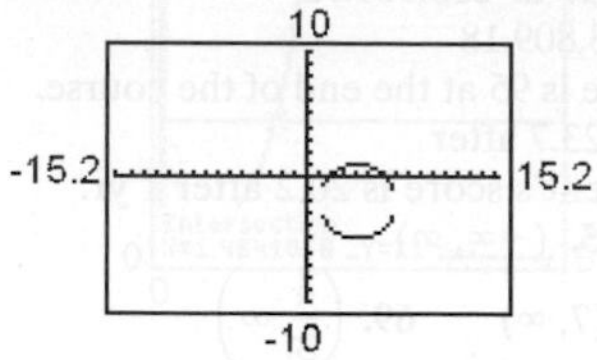

84.

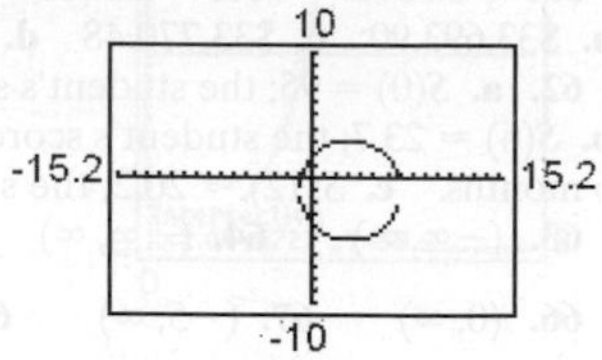

85.

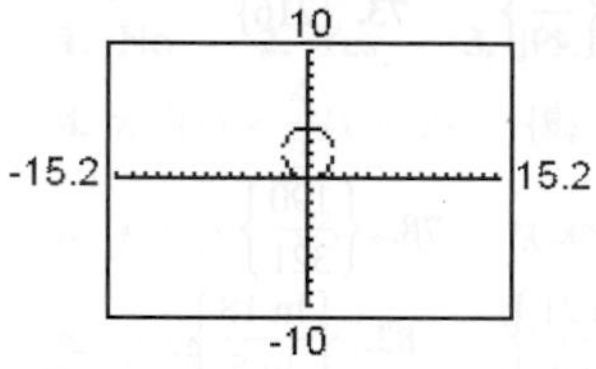

86.

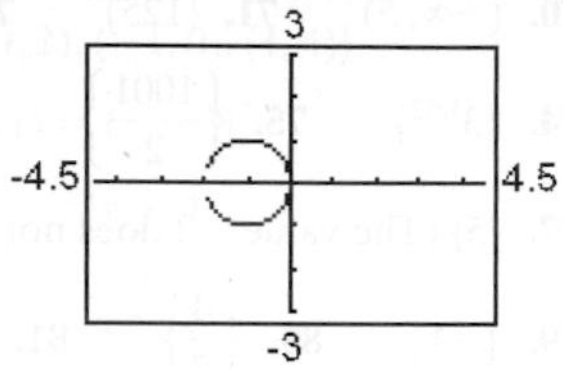

87.

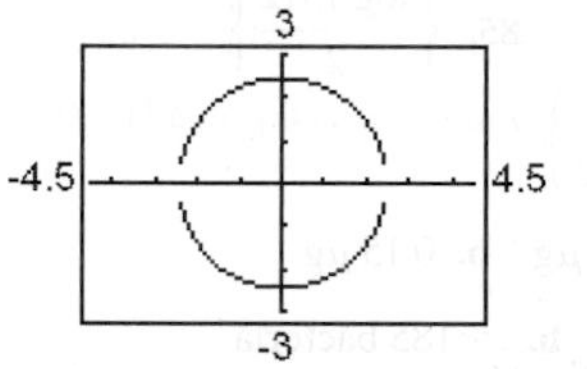

88.

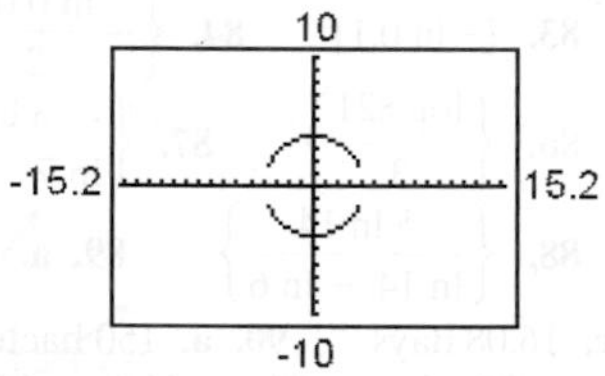

Section 13.2 Practice Exercises, pp. 947–950

1. a. conic; plane **b.** parabola; directrix; focus **c.** vertex; symmetry **d.** $y = k$ **3.** 5
5. Center: $(0, -1)$; radius: 4

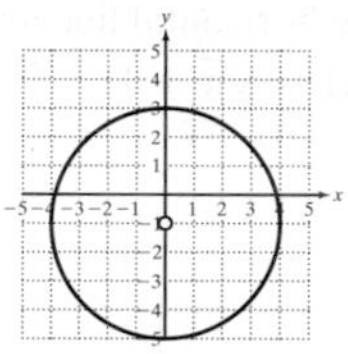

7. $\left(\frac{11}{2}, 1\right)$

9.

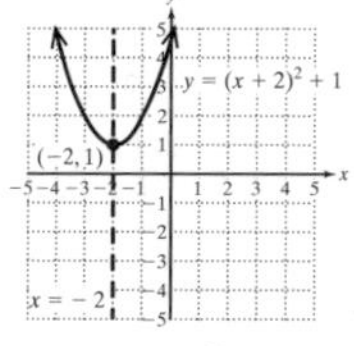

11.

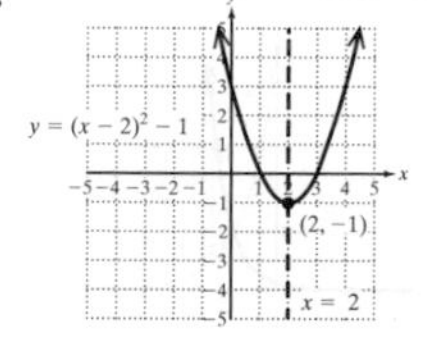

13.

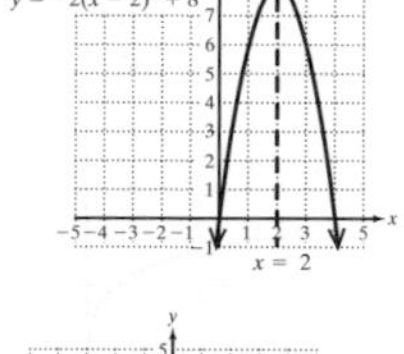

15.

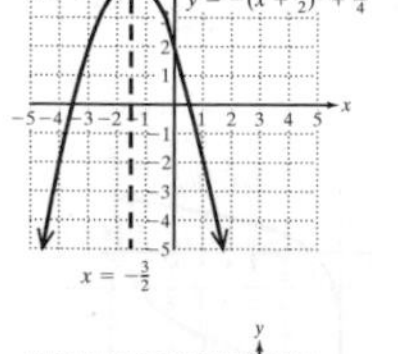

17.

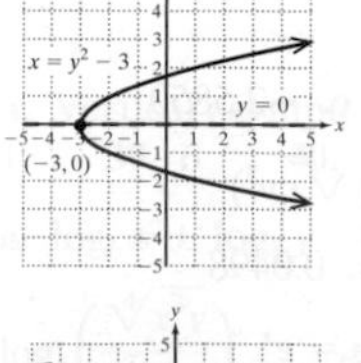

19.

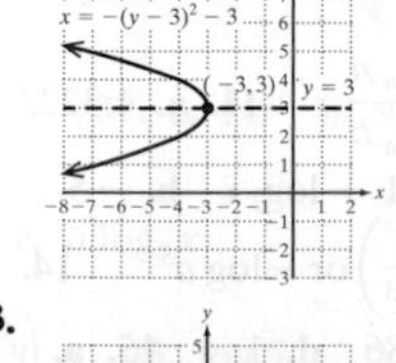

21.

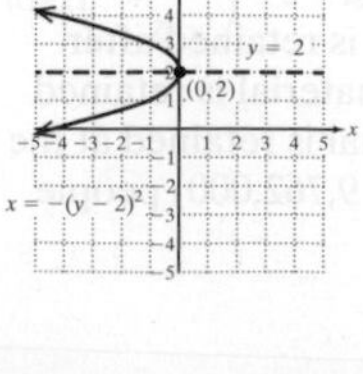

23.

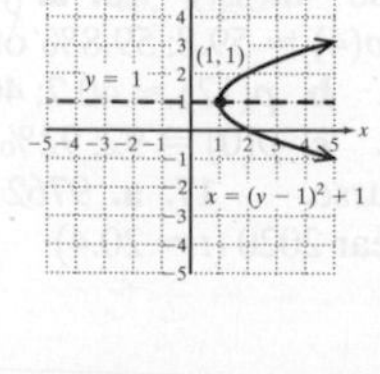

25. $(2, -1)$ **27.** $(5, -1)$ **29.** $\left(2, \frac{7}{4}\right)$ **31.** $\left(\frac{3}{2}, -\frac{1}{4}\right)$

33. $(10, -1)$ **35.** The maximum height of the water is 22 ft.

37. A parabola whose equation is in the form $y = a(x - h)^2 + k$ has a vertical axis of symmetry. A parabola whose equation is in the form $x = a(y - k)^2 + h$ has a horizontal axis of symmetry.

39. Vertical axis of symmetry; opens upward

41. Vertical axis of symmetry; opens downward

43. Horizontal axis of symmetry; opens right

45. Horizontal axis of symmetry; opens left

47. Vertical axis of symmetry; opens downward

49. Horizontal axis of symmetry; opens right

Section 13.3 Practice Exercises, pp. 955–959

1. a. ellipse; foci **b.** ellipse **c.** hyperbola; foci **d.** transverse

e. $\frac{x^2}{a^2} - \frac{y^2}{b^2} = 1$ **f.** $\frac{y^2}{b^2} - \frac{x^2}{a^2} = 1$

3. Center: $(8, -6)$; radius: 10

5. Vertex: $(-3, -1)$; $x = -3$

7. $\left(x - \frac{1}{2}\right)^2 + \left(y - \frac{5}{2}\right)^2 = \frac{1}{4}$

9.

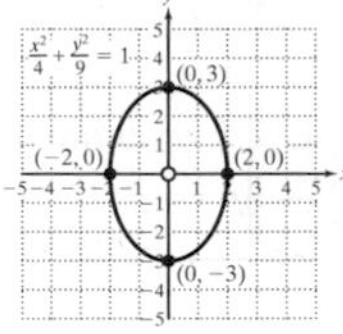

11.

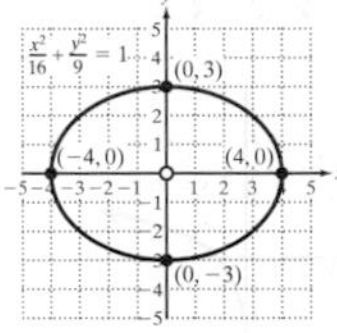

13.

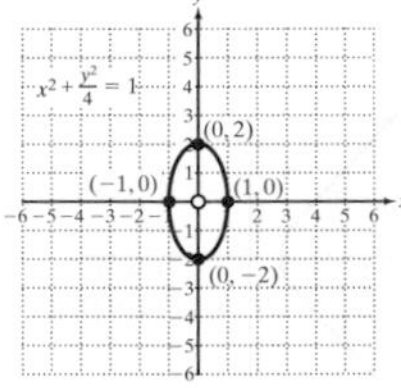

15.

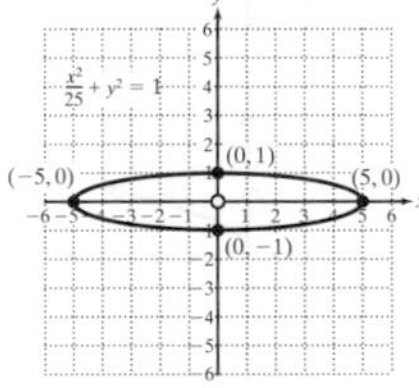

17. Center: $(4, 5)$

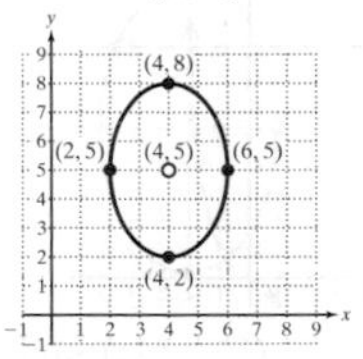

19. Center: $(-1, 2)$

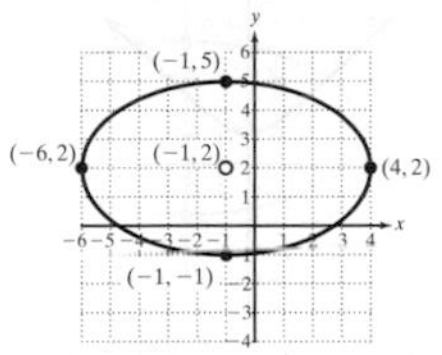

21. Center: $(2, -3)$

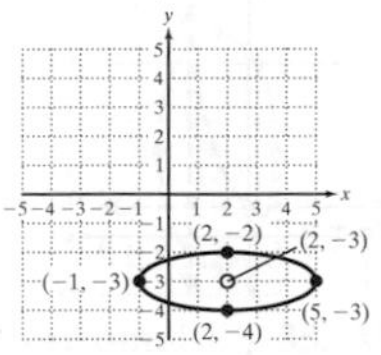

23. Center: $(0, 1)$

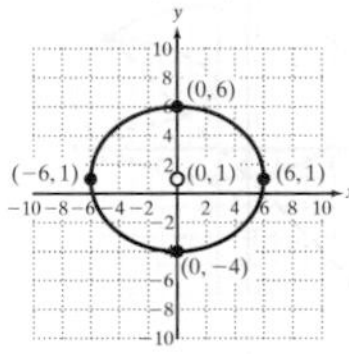

25. Vertical **27.** Horizontal **29.** Horizontal

31. Vertical

33.

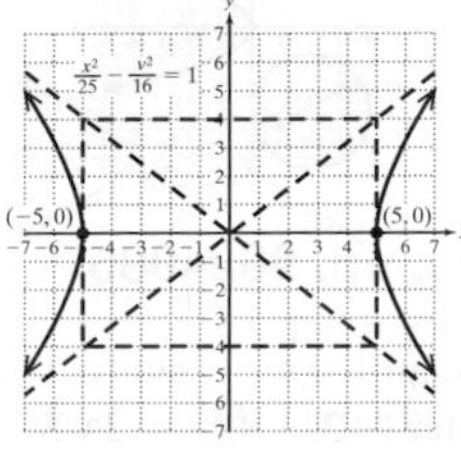

35.

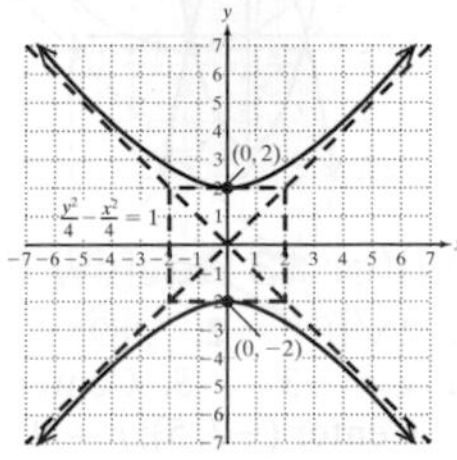

37.

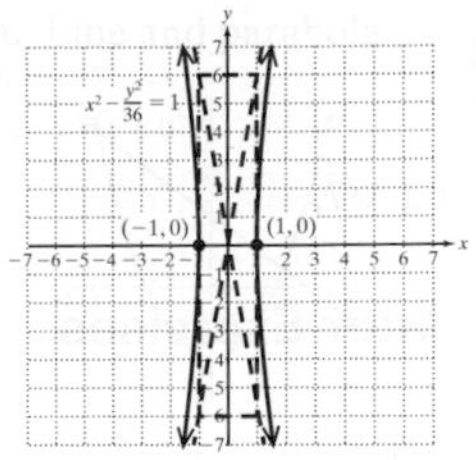

39.

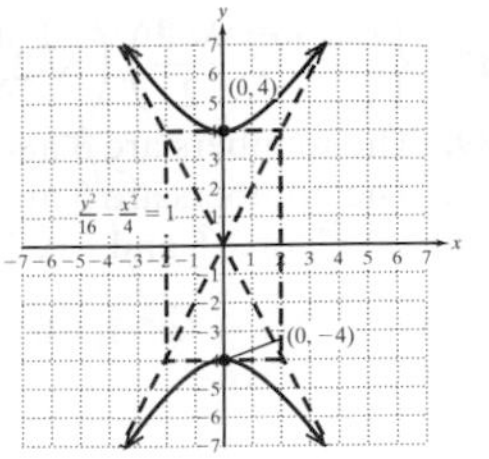

41. Hyperbola **43.** Ellipse

45. Ellipse **47.** Hyperbola

49. Ellipse **51.** Hyperbola

53. The height 10 ft from the center is approximately 49 ft.

55.

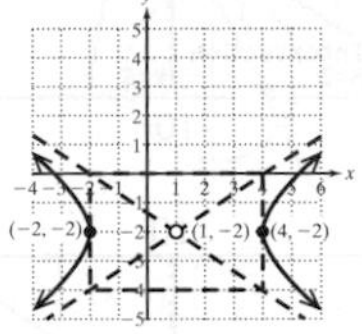

57.

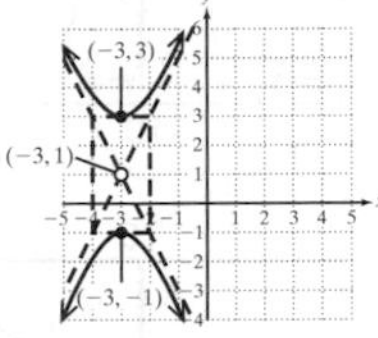

Section 13.3 Problem Recognition Exercises, pp. 959–960

1. Standard equation of a circle **2.** Ellipse centered at the origin **3.** Distance between two points

4. Midpoint between two points **5.** Parabola with vertical axis of symmetry **6.** Hyperbola with horizontal transverse axis

7. Hyperbola with vertical transverse axis

8. Parabola with horizontal axis of symmetry

9. Parabola **10.** Hyperbola **11.** Circle **12.** Circle

13. Hyperbola **14.** Ellipse **15.** None of the above

16. Circle **17.** Parabola **18.** Hyperbola **19.** Parabola

20. Circle **21.** None of the above **22.** Parabola

23. Ellipse **24.** Circle **25.** Parabola **26.** Ellipse

27. Hyperbola **28.** Circle **29.** Ellipse **30.** Parabola

Section 13.4 Practice Exercises, pp. 964–967

1. a. nonlinear **b.** intersection

3. $7\sqrt{2}$ **5.** $(x + 5)^2 + (y - 3)^2 = 64$ **7.** $\left(-\frac{1}{2}, -\frac{7}{2}\right)$

9. Zero, one, or two **11.** Zero, one, or two

13. Zero, one, two, three, or four **15.** Zero, one, two, three, or four

17. $\{(-3, 0), (2, 5)\}$

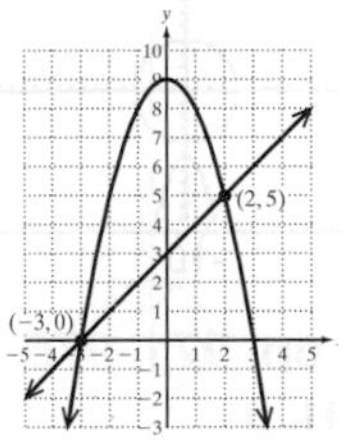

19. $\{(0, 1), (-1, 0)\}$

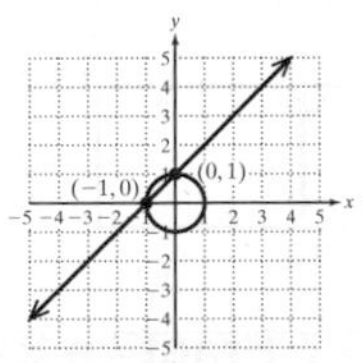

21. $\{(\sqrt{2}, 2), (-\sqrt{2}, 2)\}$

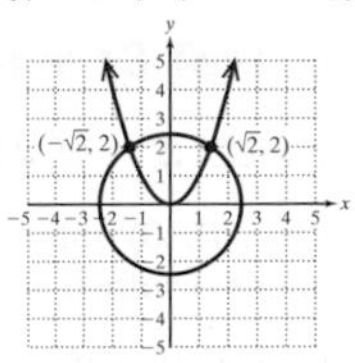

23. $\{(1, 1)\}$ **25.** $\{(0, 0)\}$ **27.** $\left\{\left(\frac{3}{2}, \frac{9}{4}\right)\right\}$

29. $\{(0, 0), (-2, -8)\}$ **31.** $\{(1, 4)\}$

33. $\{(1, 0), (-1, 0)\}$ **35.** $\{(2, 0), (-2, 0)\}$

37. $\{(3, 2), (-3, 2), (3, -2), (-3, -2)\}$

39. $\{(8, 6), (-8, -6)\}$ **41.** $\{(0, -2), (0, 2)\}$

43. $\{(2, 0), (0, 1)\}$ **45.** $\{(4, 5), (-4, -5)\}$

8.

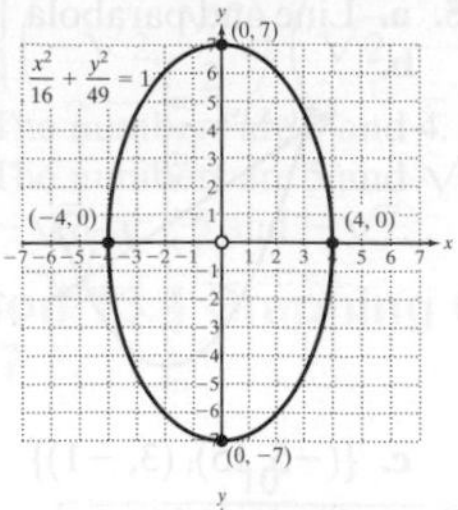

9.

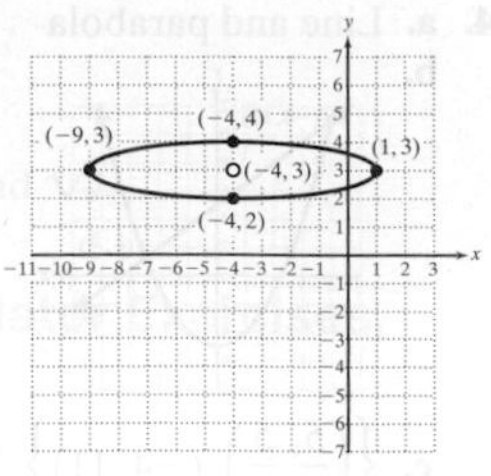

10.

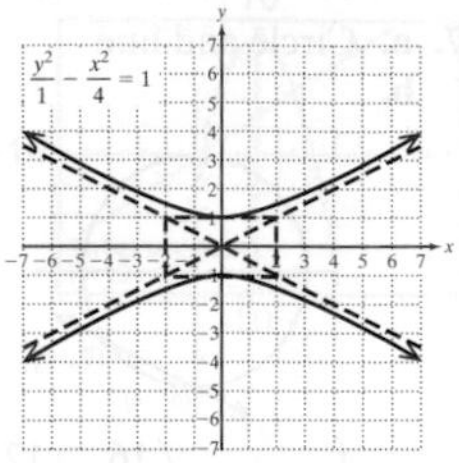

11. $\{(-3, 0), (0, 4)\}$; graph b **12.** { }; graph a
13. The addition method can be used if the equations have corresponding *like* terms. **14.** $\{(2, 0), (-2, 0)\}$

15.

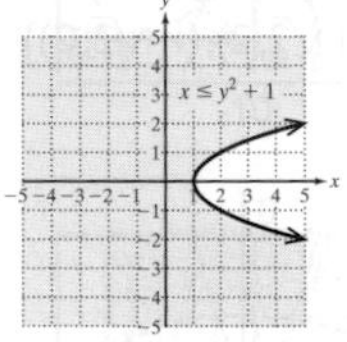

16.

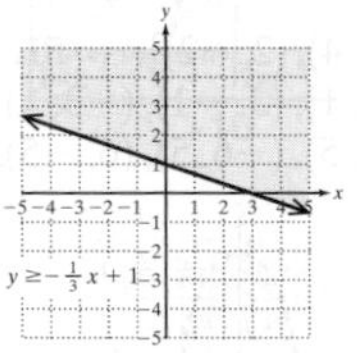

17.

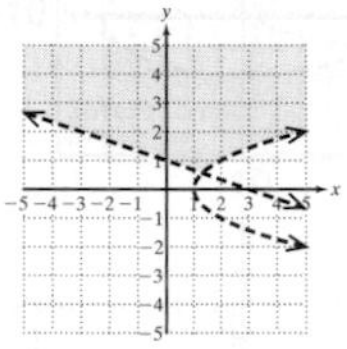

18.

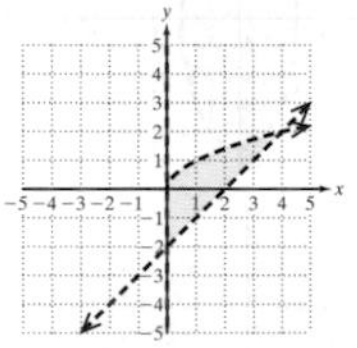

Chapters 1–13 Cumulative Review Exercises, pp. 987–988

1. $\{x \mid x \text{ is a real number}\}$
2. $\left(\frac{10}{3}, \infty\right)$

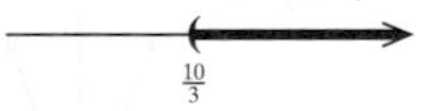

3. The integers are 10 and 15. **4. a.** $(-5, 0), (0, 3)$ **b.** $m = \frac{3}{5}$
c.

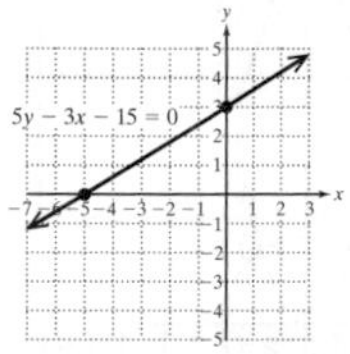

5. slope: $\frac{3}{4}$; y-intercept: $\left(0, -\frac{3}{2}\right)$
6. There are 12 dimes and 5 quarters.
7. $\{(2, -3, 1)\}$ **8.** $\left\{\left(\frac{5}{2}, \frac{3}{2}\right)\right\}$ **9.** $\{(6, 3)\}$
10. $f(0) = -12; f(-1) = -16; f(2) = -10; f(4) = -16$
11. $(-4, -2)$ **12.** $z = 32$ **13.** $(g \circ f)(x) = x + 7$; $x \ge -1$ **14. a.** -5 **b.** $(x + 1)(x^2 + 1)$; -5
c. They are the same. **15.** $(x + y)(x - y - 6)$
16. $x^3 - 2x^2 - 7x - 4$ **17.** $\left\{6, \frac{3}{2}\right\}$ **18.** $\frac{a - 1}{a + 2}$
19. $\frac{-x^2 - x - 4}{(x + 3)(x - 2)}$ **20.** $\{0, -1\}$ **21. a.** { }
b. $\{-11\}$ **22.** $-30 + 24i$ **23.** $\frac{12}{41} + \frac{15}{41}i$
24. $2\sqrt{7}$ m **25. a.** 17.6 ft; 39.6 ft; 70.4 ft **b.** 8 sec

26. $\left\{-\frac{1}{5}, \frac{1}{10} \pm \frac{\sqrt{3}}{10}i\right\}$ **27.** $\{2 \pm \sqrt{11}\}$
28. $(-5, -36)$
29. a. $(-3, 0), (1, 0)$ **b.** $(0, 3)$ **c** $(-1, 4)$

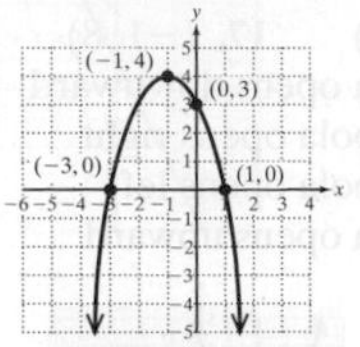

30. $(-1, 19)$ **31.** $\left(-\infty, \frac{1}{2}\right] \cup \left[\frac{9}{2}, \infty\right)$ **32.** $\log_8 32 = \frac{5}{3}$
33. $\left\{\frac{2}{3}\right\}$ **34.** $h^{-1}(x) = \sqrt[3]{x + 1}$
35. $x^2 + (y - 5)^2 = 16$
36.

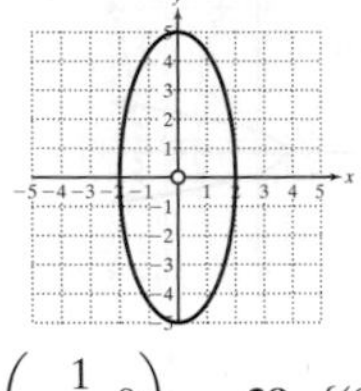

37. $\left(-\frac{1}{2}, 0\right)$ **38.** $\{(0, -4)\}$

39.

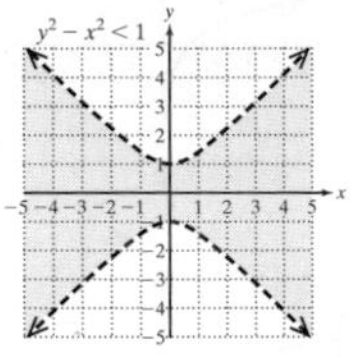

40.

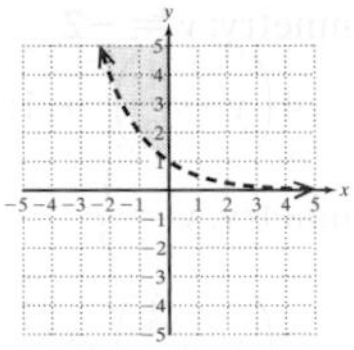

Chapter 14

Chapter Opener Puzzle

1. 13, 16, 19 **2.** −26, −34, −42 **3.** 48, 96, 192
4. $\frac{1}{9}, \frac{1}{27}, \frac{1}{81}$ **5.** 25, 36, 49 **6.** −324, 972, −2916
7. x^3y^4, x^2y^5, xy^6 **8.** a^2b^7, ab^8, b^9 **9.** $a^2 + 2ab + b^2$
10. $a^3 + 3a^2b + 3ab^2 + b^3$ **11.** $n + 1$

Section 14.1 Practice Exercises, pp. 995–996

1. a. $a^2 + 2ab + b^2$; $a^3 + 3a^2b + 3ab^2 + b^3$; binomial
b. $n(n - 1)(n - 2) \cdots (2)(1)$; factorial **c.** 6; 2; 1; 1
d. binomial **e.** Pascal's **3.** $a^3 + 3a^2b + 3ab^2 + b^3$
5. $1 + 4g + 6g^2 + 4g^3 + g^4$
7. $p^7 + 7p^6q^2 + 21p^5q^4 + 35p^4q^6 + 35p^3q^8 + 21p^2q^{10} + 7pq^{12} + q^{14}$
9. $s^5 - 5s^4t + 10s^3t^2 - 10s^2t^3 + 5st^4 - t^5$
11. $625 - 500u^3 + 150u^6 - 20u^9 + u^{12}$
13. $x^6 - 12x^4 + 48x^2 - 64$ **15.** 120 **17.** 1 **19.** False
21. True **23.** $6! = 6 \cdot (5 \cdot 4 \cdot 3 \cdot 2 \cdot 1) = 6 \cdot 5!$ **25.** 1680
27. 6 **29.** 56 **31.** 1 **33.** $m^{11} + 11m^{10}n + 55m^9n^2$
35. $u^{24} - 12u^{22}v + 66u^{20}v^2$ **37.** 9 terms
39. $s^6 + 6s^5t + 15s^4t^2 + 20s^3t^3 + 15s^2t^4 + 6st^5 + t^6$
41. $b^3 - 9b^2 + 27b - 27$ **43.** $16x^4 + 32x^3y + 24x^2y^2 + 8xy^3 + y^4$ **45.** $c^{14} - 7c^{12}d + 21c^{10}d^2 - 35c^8d^3 + 35c^6d^4 - 21c^4d^5 + 7c^2d^6 - d^7$
47. $\frac{1}{32}a^5 - \frac{5}{16}a^4b + \frac{5}{4}a^3b^2 - \frac{5}{2}a^2b^3 + \frac{5}{2}ab^4 - b^5$
49. $x^4 + 16x^3y + 96x^2y^2 + 256xy^3 + 256y^4$
51. $-462m^6n^5$ **53.** $495u^{16}v^4$ **55.** g^9

Section 14.2 Practice Exercises, pp. 1002–1004

1. a. infinite; finite **b.** terms; nth **c.** alternating **d.** series
e. summation **f.** index; $(3)^2 + (4)^2 + (5)^2$
3. 28 **5.** $16x^4 + 32x^3z + 24x^2z^2 + 8xz^3 + z^4$

7. 4, 7, 10, 13, 16 **9.** $\sqrt{3}, 2, \sqrt{5}, \sqrt{6}$ **11.** $-\frac{2}{3}, \frac{3}{4}, -\frac{4}{5}, \frac{5}{6}$
13. 0, −3, 8 **15.** 0, 2, 6, 12, 20, 30 **17.** −3, 9, −27, 81
19. When n is odd, the term is negative. When n is even, the term is positive. **21.** $a_n = 2n$ **23.** $a_n = 2n - 1$
25. $a_n = \frac{1}{n^2}$ **27.** $a_n = (-1)^{n+1}$ **29.** $a_n = (-1)^n 2^n$
31. $a_n = \frac{3}{5^n}$ **33.** \$60, \$58.80, \$57.62, \$56.47
35. 25,000; 50,000; 100,000; 200,000; 400,000; 800,000; 1,600,000
37. A sequence is an ordered list of terms. A series is the sum of the terms of a sequence.
39. 90 **41.** $\frac{31}{16}$ **43.** 30 **45.** 10 **47.** $\frac{73}{12}$ **49.** 38
51. −1 **53.** 55 **55.** $\sum_{n=1}^{6} n$ **57.** $\sum_{i=1}^{5} 4$ **59.** $\sum_{j=1}^{5} 4j$
61. $\sum_{k=1}^{4} (-1)^{k+1} \frac{1}{3^k}$ **63.** $\sum_{i=1}^{6} \frac{i+4}{11i}$ **65.** $\sum_{n=1}^{5} x^n$
67. −3, 2, 7, 12, 17 **69.** 5, 21, 85, 341, 1365
71. 1, 1, 2, 3, 5, 8, 13, 21, 34, 55

Section 14.3 Practice Exercises, pp. 1009–1010

1. a. arithmetic **b.** difference **c.** $a_1 + (n-1)d$; d
d. series **e.** $\frac{n}{2}(a_1 + a_n)$
3. −1, 1, −1, 1 **5.** −55 **7.** 3, 11, 19, 27, 35
9. 80, 60, 40, 20, 0 **11.** $3, \frac{15}{4}, \frac{9}{2}, \frac{21}{4}, 6$ **13.** 2 **15.** −3
17. −2 **19.** 3, 8, 13, 18, 23 **21.** $2, \frac{5}{2}, 3, \frac{7}{2}, 4$
23. 2, −2, −6, −10, −14 **25.** $a_n = -5 + 5n$
27. $a_n = -2n$ **29.** $a_n = \frac{3}{2} + \frac{1}{2}n$ **31.** $a_n = 25 - 4n$
33. $a_n = -14 + 6n$ **35.** $a_6 = 17$ **37.** $a_9 = 47$
39. $a_7 = -30$ **41.** $a_{11} = -48$ **43.** 19 **45.** 22
47. 23 **49.** 11 **51.** $a_1 = -2, a_2 = -5$ **53.** 670
55. 290 **57.** −15 **59.** 95 **61.** 924 **63.** 300
65. −210 **67.** 5050 **69.** 980 seats; \$14,700

Section 14.4 Practice Exercises, pp. 1016–1019

1. a. geometric **b.** ratio **c.** $a_1 r^{n-1}$ **d.** $\frac{a_1(1-r^n)}{1-r}$
e. $\frac{a_1}{1-r}$; 1 **3.** $a_n = 4n - 8$ **5.** 25 **7.** 1, 10, 100, 1000
9. 64, 32, 16, 8 **11.** $8, -2, \frac{1}{2}, -\frac{1}{8}$ **13.** 2 **15.** $-\frac{1}{4}$
17. −2 **19.** −3, 6, −12, 24, −48 **21.** $6, 3, \frac{3}{2}, \frac{3}{4}, \frac{3}{8}$
23. −1, −6, −36, −216, −1296 **25.** $a_n = 3(4)^{n-1}$
27. $a_n = -5(-3)^{n-1}$ **29.** $a_n = \frac{1}{2}(4)^{n-1}$ **31.** $\frac{1}{64}$
33. $-\frac{243}{8}$ **35.** −48 **37.** −9 **39.** $\frac{1}{8}$ **41.** 4
43. A geometric sequence is an ordered list of numbers in which the ratio between each term and its predecessor is constant. A geometric series is the sum of the terms of such a sequence.
45. a. 3 + 12 + 48 + 192 **b.** 255
47. $\frac{1562}{125}$ **49.** $-\frac{11}{8}$ **51.** $\frac{3124}{27}$ **53.** $\frac{665}{243}$
55. −172 **57. a.** \$1050.00, \$1102.50, \$1157.63, \$1215.51
b. a_{10} = \$1628.89; a_{20} = \$2653.30; a_{40} = \$7039.99
59. $r = \frac{1}{6}$; sum is $\frac{6}{5}$ **61.** $r = -\frac{1}{4}$; sum is $\frac{4}{5}$
63. $r = -\frac{3}{2}$; sum does not exist **65.** The sum is \$800 million.
67. The total vertical distance traveled is 28 ft.
69. a. $\frac{7}{10}$ **b.** $\frac{1}{10}$ **c.** $\frac{7}{9}$ **71. a.** \$1,429,348
b. \$1,505,828 **c.** \$76,480

Chapter 14 Problem Recognition Exercises, p. 1019

1. Geometric, $r = -\frac{1}{2}$ **2.** Arithmetic, $d = \frac{1}{2}$
3. Geometric, $r = 2$ **4.** Neither **5.** Arithmetic, $d = \frac{2}{3}$
6. Geometric, $r = -\frac{3}{2}$ **7.** Neither **8.** Geometric, $r = -1$
9. Arithmetic, $d = -2$ **10.** Neither **11.** Neither
12. Arithmetic, $d = 4$ **13.** Arithmetic, $d = \frac{1}{4}\pi$
14. Geometric, $r = -1$ **15.** Neither
16. Arithmetic, $d = \frac{1}{3}e$ **17.** Neither **18.** Geometric, $r = 3$

Chapter 14 Review Exercises, pp. 1024–1025

1. 40,320 **2.** 120 **3.** 66 **4.** 84
5. $x^{10} + 20x^8 + 160x^6 + 640x^4 + 1280x^2 + 1024$
6. $c^4 - 12c^3d + 54c^2d^2 - 108cd^3 + 81d^4$
7. $a^{11} - 22a^{10}b + 220a^9b^2$ **8.** $1512x^{10}y^3$
9. $-15{,}000x^3y^{21}$ **10.** $160a^3b^3$ **11.** 1, −2, −5, −8, −11
12. −2, −16, −54 **13.** $\frac{1}{3}, -\frac{1}{2}, \frac{3}{5}, -\frac{2}{3}$ **14.** $-\frac{2}{3}, \frac{4}{9}, -\frac{8}{27}, \frac{16}{81}$
15. $a_n = \frac{n}{n+1}$ **16.** $a_n = (-1)^n \cdot \frac{3}{2^n}$ **17.** k **18.** 5
19. 5 **20.** −22 **21.** $\sum_{i=1}^{7} \frac{3+i}{i}$ **22.** $a_n = n^2 + \left(\frac{n}{2}\right)h$
23. −12, −10.5, −9, −7.5, −6 **24.** $\frac{2}{3}, 1, \frac{4}{3}, \frac{5}{3}, 2$
25. $a_n = 10n - 9$ **26.** $a_n = -14n + 20$ **27.** $a_{17} = \frac{9}{2}$
28. $a_{25} = -155$ **29.** 24 terms **30.** 19 terms
31. $d = 10$ **32.** $a_n = -5n + 19$ **33.** −620
34. 92.5 **35.** 294 **36.** 5989 **37.** $r = 3$
38. $r = 1.2$ **39.** $-1, \frac{1}{4}, -\frac{1}{16}, \frac{1}{64}$ **40.** 10, 20, 40, 80
41. $a_n = -4(2)^{n-1}$ **42.** $a_n = 6\left(-\frac{1}{3}\right)^{n-1}$ **43.** $a_6 = \frac{128}{243}$
44. $a_4 = 270$ **45.** $a_1 = 4$ **46.** $a_1 = 1$ **47.** 1275
48. $-\frac{182}{3}$ **49.** 18 **50.** $\frac{25}{2}$
51. a. \$10,700, \$11,449, \$12,250.43 **b.** The account is worth \$12,250.43 after 3 yr. **c.** \$19,671.51

Chapter 14 Test, pp. 1025–1026

1. 1 **2.** 210 **3.** $a^4 + 4a^3b + 6a^2b^2 + 4ab^3 + b^4$
4. $81y^4 - 216y^3x^2 + 216y^2x^4 - 96yx^6 + 16x^8$
5. $-56a^3c^{15}$ **6.** $-1, -\frac{3}{4}, -\frac{3}{5}, -\frac{1}{2}$ **7.** 65
8. a. 8, 9.5, 11, 12.5, 14 **b.** $a_n = 1.5n + 6.5$ **9.** $\sum_{n=1}^{4} x^{3n}$
10. $d = \frac{1}{4}$ **11.** $r = \frac{1}{3}$ **12. a.** −15, −18, −21, −24
b. $a_n = -3n - 12$ **c.** $a_{40} = -132$ **13. a.** 4, −8, 16, −32
b. $a_n = 4(-2)^{n-1}$ **c.** −2048 **14.** $a_n = \frac{3}{5} \cdot \left(\frac{1}{2}\right)^{n-1}$
15. $a_n = -2n + 22$ **16.** 31 terms **17.** 7 terms
18. 10,900 **19.** $\frac{1023}{64}$ **20.** 8 **21.** $a_1 = \frac{1}{27}$
22. $a_{18} = -202$ **23. a.** \$1095 **b.** \$1160.70
c. \$5933.13 **d.** \$86,568.71

87. Isosceles 89. True

91. No; a 90° angle plus an angle greater than 90° would make the sum of the angles greater than 180°. 93. 40°

97. $m(\angle a) = 80°$, $m(\angle b) = 80°$, $m(\angle c) = 100°$, $m(\angle d) = 100°$, $m(\angle e) = 65°$, $m(\angle f) = 115°$, $m(\angle g) = 115°$, $m(\angle h) = 35°$, $m(\angle i) = 145°$, $m(\angle j) = 145°$

99. $m(\angle a) = 70°$, $m(\angle b) = 65°$, $m(\angle c) = 65°$, $m(\angle d) = 110°$, $m(\angle e) = 70°$, $m(\angle f) = 110°$, $m(\angle g) = 115°$, $m(\angle h) = 115°$, $m(\angle i) = 65°$, $m(\angle j) = 70°$, $m(\angle k) = 65°$

101. 82 ft **103.** 36 in.^{2} **105.** 15.2464 cm^2

21. $(x - 5 - y)(x - 5 + y)$ 25. $(5a + 2b - 10c)$

27. $(8w - 3t + 4p)(8w + 3t - 4p)$

31. $(w + 2)(w^2 - 2w + 4)(w - 1)$

33. $(y - 4)(x + 2z - 2)$ 35. $(x - y)$

39. $(n - 4)(n^2 + 4n + 16)(n + 1)(n^2 - n + 1)$

41. $2x(2x - 5)(x + 3)(x - 3)$

45. $(x - y)(x + y)^2$

49. $18(3x + 5)^2(4x + 5)$

53. $5x^3(5x^2 - 6)$

Application Index

Biology/Health/Life Sciences

Adenosine levels, 689
Age and heart rate, 571
Bacteria culture maximum yield, 833
Bacterial growth rate, 913, 924–925, 1003
Bacteria population rate of decrease, 866, 927
Bamboo plant height per day, 269
Body mass index computing, 180–181
Calcium levels needed by women, 690
Calorie intake at meals, 32
Calories burned by walking, 32
Cancer cases by type, 144
Child weight fluctuations, 73
Cholera deaths in London, 901
Cholesterol levels normal for certain age range, 686
Daily growth height of tomato seedling, 1025
Dinosaur extinction, 373
Dosage amount, 145
Drug prescription increases, 269
Heart rate by age, 22
Height for boys based on age, 258
Height for girls based on age, 268
Height of woman with certain femur length, 568
Height vs. arm length of humans, 258, 260
Hemoglobin levels for adult males, 637
Length of human pregnancy, 633
Length of ulna and gender of human, 260
Lyme disease cases by year, 241
Medication mixture for injured bird, 163
Medicine prescribed according to weight of patient, 612, 622
pH levels in selected substances, 873–874, 878, 923
Pulse rate per minute of humans, 549
Salt solution for patients, 312
Systolic blood pressure and age in women, 202
Tetanus toxin maximum yield, 833
Thyroid-stimulating hormone levels, 633
Tiger population in India, 251–252
Time for rat to run a maze, 691, 1028
Waistline increase/decrease, 20, 21, 73
Weight fluctuation of humans, 53
Weight of human heart and person's weight, 612
Weight of newborn infants, 50
Weights of animals examined by veterinarians, 256
White blood cell numbers, 637

Business

Acres available for orange and grapefruit trees, 689
Advertising expenditures, 879
Airline cost for certain number of passengers, 753
Amazon.com and eBay sales, 137
Average production cost per item, 496
Babysitting hours needed for profit, 180
Booth rental at market/art show, 259
Bottled water consumption in U.S., 620, 622
Cell phone plans, 180
Commission earnings, 146
Cost, 305–306, 311
Cost before tax, 145, 185, 191–192
Cost with sales tax, 144, 145
Debt-to-income ratio, 44
Delivery scheduling, 679
Depreciation, 924
Discount amount, 145, 179–180, 189
Downloading from iTunes, 32
Employees working together, 339, 557, 776
Gas mileage, 32, 549, 568, 833
House appreciation, 1018
Hybrid car monthly sales, 253
Income after discount pricing, 447
Job earnings plans, 857–858, 1019
Landscaping service profits, 180
Markup, 145
Maximizing profit, 842
Membership fees, 146
Minimizing average cost, 832
Minimum hourly wage in U.S., 256
Money earned, 138
Monthly mortgage payments, 552
Monthly paycheck, 141
New car sales, 267
Number of containers filled, 19
Number of pages printed, 19
Number of passengers flying given total cost of flight, 753
Number of tables and customers in restaurant, 447
Original cost/price, 142–143, 145, 146, 188
Popcorn sales and movie attendance, 201
Prices of individual items, 327, 338
Pricing, 612, 622
Profit, 604, 692, 753, 789, 842
Profit/loss, 53, 145, 146
Quota of ads sold for newspaper, 73
Rent, 19
Revenue, 1010
Revenue from movies, 134
Revenue respending rates, 1018
Sale price, 145
Sales figures for each employee, 325
Sales tax computation, 139–140, 145
Savings account, 19, 162
Servings contained in box, 19
Small cleaning company costs, 269
Small moving company charges, 252
Soft drink sales at stadium, 254
Storage rental cost, 284
Taxable income, 144
Telephone charges, 335
Theater company advertising costs, 254
Tickets of each type sold, 157, 162
Time needed to manufacture an item, 679
Tipping computation, 22
Tips earned by waitress, 619
Truck rental cost, 270, 339
Tutoring earnings, 180
Unit cost of production, 612
Water purification company charges, 269
Weekly salary, 135
Wholesale club memberships, 283
Work rates for two persons/machines together, 339, 547–548, 551, 557, 776

Chemistry

Acid mixture, 163
Acid solution, 308, 338
Alcohol mixture, 926
Alcohol/water mixture, 165
Antifreeze mixture, 158, 163
Antifreeze solution, 312, 340
Bleach mixture, 158
Chlorine mixture, 165
Disinfectant mixture, 186
Disinfectant solution, 307–308, 312
Ethanol mixture, 163
Measurement of compound on a scale, 663
Medication mixture, 163
Pesticide mixture, 163
pH levels in selected substances, 873–874, 878, 923
Plant food mixturc, 549
Saline mixture, 163
Salt solution, 312
Soldering compound mixture, 189
Sugar solution, 165
Vinegar solution, 313

Construction

Board length, 21
Buckingham Fountain dimensions, 155
Dimensions of fenced area to give maximum area, 833–834, 844
Dimensions of kitchen island, 841
Hammer strikes to drive nail, 19
Height of bridge supporting cable, 823
Height of bulge in bridge, 773
Height of semielliptical arch, 959
Height of towers of suspension bridge, 823
Measurement error of length of board, 665
Parking lot dimensions, 153
Pieces cut from a length, 19, 21, 133–134, 137, 138
Pool dimensions, 153
Pumps working together to drain water, 337
Pyramid of Khufu dimensions, 155
Radius of circular garden, 151

Kinetic energy, 609–610
Length of pendulum given time for one swing, 753
Light intensity, 613
Loudness of sound, 608–609, 914
Mass of piece of metal, 690
Pendulum swing lengths after first, 1000
Period of a pendulum, 743, 753
Power in electric circuit, 613
Velocity of ocean wave, 774
Volume of a gas, 927
Weight of medicine ball, 613

Politics

Democrats and Republicans in U.S. House, 137
Men and women in U.S. Senate, 137
Number of representatives in U.S. House, 542, 855
Votes received by governor, 340
Voting estimates for a candidate, 637, 665

School

Exam scores and time spent studying, 584
Faculty members needed in a university, 542
How many questions on a test, 141
Males/females completing 4 or more years of college, 203
Mean test scores, A-7, A-8
Memory retention after finishing a course, 874–875, 923, 925
Number of students in math class, A-10
Pages printed for report, 19
Scores needed on tests, 175, 179
Students passing test, 19
Students receiving "A" and "B" grades, 135
Study times for each subject, 672–673
Test grades needed for final "A," 638
Vocabulary teaching techniques, 878–879
Weighted mean to computer GPA, A-5 – A-6
Women and men in a class, 135

Sports

Average speed in car race, 340
Baseball minimum salary, 188
Basketball field goals, 313
Basketball free throws, 326
Basketball points scored per game, 313, 326, 338
Bungee jumping distance traveled after each rope stretch, 1018
Distance between home plate and second base, 720
Exercise routine and waist measurements, 73
Football points scored by each team, 314
Football yards gained, 97
Golf scores, 33, 53, 337
Goofie Golf par types, 327
Height of players in NBA teams, A-7
Intramural sports preferred, 140
Mean golf scores, A-8
Slope of treadmill, 226
Soccer field dimensions, 155, 191
Volleyball court dimensions, 155
Women's track and field records, 572

Statistics/Demographic

Amazon.com and eBay sales, 137
Annual income for males in U.S., 224–225
Bottled water consumption in U.S., 620, 622
Child support due and paid in U.S., 604
Cholera deaths in London, 901
Drug-related arrests for small city, 264
Earnings for males ages 25 to 34 with high school diploma, 229
Episodes of TV series produced, 138
Facebook and Twitter users, 135
Faculty members needed in a university, 542
Female inmates in prisons, 229
Male inmates in prisons, 229
Males/females completing 4 or more years of college, 203
Men and women at motorcycle rally, 135
Men and women using Facebook, 135
Minimum hourly wage in U.S., 256
Number of medical doctors in U.S., 271
Number of people in survey, 144
Numbers of men and women in survey, 314
Population growth, 225
Population growth prediction, 571, 841, 844, 863, 866, 909–910, 913, 915–916, 925
Population of selected states, 188
Rural and urban populations in the South, U.S., 604
Space shuttle launches for selected years, 265
Survey results and margin of error, 764–765
Television commercials of selected lengths, 314
Television program viewers, 137
Total number of flights at airport, 845
Vehicle fatality rates by age, 802
Wind energy consumption in U.S., 258

Subject Index

Absolute value
of real numbers, 29–30, 90, 658
solving equations containing two, 653–654
Absolute value equations
explanation of, 649, 683
on graphing calculators, 651, 654
method to solve, 649–654, 656, 683
Absolute value expressions, 662–663
Absolute value functions, 585, 588
Absolute value inequalities
explanation of, 656, 684
to express distance, 662
on graphing calculators, 657–659
method to solve, 656–659
test point method to solve, 660–662, 684
AC-method to factor trinomials, 441–445, 479
Acute angles, A–16
Acute triangles, A–18
Addition
commutative property of, 75–76
of complex numbers, 759
distributive property of multiplication over, 79–80, 93
of fractions, 12–15
of functions, 598–599
identity property of, 78
of *like* terms, 82, 375–377, 721
of polynomials, 375–376, 407
of radicals, 720–723, 768
of rational expressions, 511–517, 555
of real numbers, 45–50, 91
symbol for, 21, 39
Addition method
explanation of, 294
to solve nonlinear systems of equations, 963–964
to solve systems of linear equations, 294–300, 331
Addition property
of equality, 101–103, 107, 181
of inequality, 169–171
Additive identity, 77
Additive inverse, 78
Algebraic expressions
evaluation of, 21–23, 69
explanation of, 21, 81–84
writing English phrases as, 39–41
Alternate exterior angles, A–17
Alternate interior angles, A–17
Alternating sequences, 998–999
Angles
complementary, 149, 150
facts about, 149
method to find unknown, A–18
properties of, A–17
supplementary, 149
within triangles, 149–151
types of, A–16 – A–18
vertical, 149
Applications. *See also* Applications Index
addition of real numbers in, 50
binomial theorem in, 993–994
compound inequalities in, 633–634
consecutive integers in, 132–133
cost in, 156–157, 305
discount and markup in, 142–143
distance, rate, and time in, 159–161, 309–310, 545–547
exponential equations in, 910–911
exponential functions in, 861–863, 909–910
exponents in, 347–348
geometric series in, 1015
geometry, 146–151, 185, 291–292, 323–325, 378–379, 388, 749–750
linear equations in, 133–135, 184, 264
linear inequalities in, 174–175
mixtures in, 156–161, 186, 307–308, 324–325
natural logarithmic functions in, 895–896
percents in, 139–143, 185
plotting and identifying points in, 197–198
principal and interest in, 306–307, 890–891
proportions in, 542–544
Pythagorean theorem in, 472–473, 700
quadratic equations in, 470–474, 482
quadratic formula in, 792–794
quadratic functions in, 828–829
radical equations in, 749–750
radical functions in, 750–751
rate of change in, 224–225, 254
rational equations in, 541–548, 557
rational exponents in, 710
relations in, 568
sequences in, 1000
similar triangles in, 542–544
simple interest in, 141–142, 185, 306–307, 347
slope in, 219, 224–225
strategies to solve, 128–129
substitution method in, 290–292
subtraction of real numbers in, 56–57
systems of linear equations in three variables in, 323–325, 334
systems of linear equations in two variables in, 305–310, 332
variation in, 607–610
work, 547–548
"approximately equal to," 31
Approximation
of exponential expressions, 858–859
of irrational numbers, 30–31
Area
of circle, 786
formulas for, A–12 – A–13
units for, A–12
Argument, of logarithmic expressions, 867
Arithmetic sequences
explanation of, 1005
finding number of terms in, 1006–1007
finding specified term of, 1006
*n*th term of, 1005–1006
Arithmetic series
explanation of, 1007–1008, 1023
sum of, 1008
Associative properties of real numbers, 76–77, 93, 346
Asymptotes
explanation of, 953
horizontal, 587
vertical, 587
Augmented matrix, A–27 – A–28, A–30
Axis of symmetry, of parabolas, 810, 941–944, 978

b^0, 357–358, 406
Base
explanation of, 342
of logarithmic expressions, 867
multiplying and dividing expressions with common, 344–346, 405
Bimodal data, A–5
Binomial expansions
binomial theorem for, 992–994, 1021
explanation of, 990–991, 1021
factorial notation to find coefficients of, 991–992
finding specific term in, 994–995
Pascal's triangle and, 991, 1021
Binomial factors
determining signs within, 428
factoring higher degree trinomial into, 438
factoring out, 420–421
Binomials. *See also* Polynomials
explanation of, 373
factoring, 417, 418, 420–421, 426, 428, 449–450, 456–459
FOIL and, 384
square of, 387, 407, 990
Binomial theorem
applications of, 993–994
explanation of, 992–993, 1021
b^{-n}, 358–360, 406
Body mass index (BMI), 180
Boundary points, 640–642
Braces, 36
Brackets, 36, 168

Calculator features. *See* Graphing calculator features
Calculators. *See* Graphing calculators
Center, of circle, 931, 933
Change-of-base formula, 894–895, 920

Graphing calculators–(*continued*)
logarithms on, 870, 873, 892
matrices on, A–32
minimum and maximum values on, 818
nonlinear functions on, 587
nonlinear systems of equations on, 962
*n*th roots on, 697
operations with signed numbers on, 59
parabolas on, 812, 945
pi (π) key on, 152
polynomial inequalities on, 642
radical expressions on, 707, 716
radical functions on, 701
scientific notation on, 370
sequences on, 998, 1001
square roots on, 695
systems of linear equations in two variables on, 278–279
x- and *y*-intercepts of functions on, 591
Graphs
of circles, 931–933
of ellipse, 951–952, 979
of exponential functions, 859–861, 872
of feasible region, 672–673
finding function values from, 578
of functions, 585–588, 601, 616
of horizontal lines, 210
of hyperbolas, 953–955, 968–969
interpretation of, 194–195
of linear equations in two variables, 203–211, 251–252
of linear inequalities, 166–167, 667–669, 685
of lines using slope-intercept form, 233–234
of logarithmic functions, 870–873, 892, 895
of nonlinear inequalities in two variables, 968–969
of nonlinear systems of equations, 961, 962
of nonlinear systems of inequalities, 969–970
of parabolas, 810–818, 838, 942–946
plotting points on, 195–198
of quadratic functions, 810–818
of radical functions, 701–702
to solve quadratic inequalities, 639–640
to solve systems of linear equations, 275–279, 329
of systems of linear inequalities in two variables, 669–671
of vertical lines, 210–211
Greatest common factor (GCF)
binomials and, 417, 418
explanation of, 9, 416, 478
factoring out, 418–419
identification of, 416–418
Grouping, factoring by, 421–423
Grouping symbols, 36–37

Horizontal asymptotes, 587
Horizontal lines
equations of, 209–211, 246, 261
explanation of, 209
graphs of, 210
slope of, 222
Horizontal line test, 848–849
Horizontal transverse axis, of hyperbola, 953, 979
Hyperbolas
explanation of, 953, 979
focus of, 953, 979
graphs of, 953–955, 968–969
standard form of equation of, 953, 968, 979
vertex of, 953

Identities
additive, 77
explanation of, 117, 182
identification of, 117–118
multiplicative, 78
Identity functions, 585, 588
Identity property, 77–78, 493
Imaginary numbers *(i)*
explanation of, 754
powers of, 756–757
simplifying expressions in terms of, 755–756
Improper fractions
explanation of, 6, 7
mixed numbers as, 15, 16
Inconsistent systems of linear equations
addition method to solve, 299
explanation of, 275, 329
Gauss-Jordan method to solve, A–32
graphs of, 277
in three variables, 315, 320
in two variables, 299, 330
Independent systems of linear equations
in three variables, 275
in two variables, 275
Index of radical, 696, 730–731
Index of summation, 1001, 1008
Inequalities. *See also* specific types of inequalities
absolute value, 656–662, 684
addition and subtraction properties of, 169–171
applications of, 174–175
boundary points of, 640–642
compound, 167, 174, 626–634, 681
explanation of, 26–27, 186
graphs of, 166–167
methods to solve, 170–174
multiplication and division properties of, 171–173
nonlinear, 967–969
polynomial, 641–642, 682
quadratic, 638–641
rational, 642–645, 682
solution set of, 166–167
symbols for, 26, 27
test point method to solve, 640–645
Infinite sequences, 997, 1022
Infinite series, 1001, 1014–1015
Integer exponents, 360–363
Integers
explanation of, 90
set of, 24
subtraction of, 54
word problems with consecutive, 131–133
Interest
applications of, 890–891
compound, 347, 348, 890–891
compounded continuously, 891
simple, 141–142, 185, 306–307, 347
Intersect (graphing calculator feature), 278, 279
Intersection
of sets, 626–627, 681
of two intervals, 627–628
Interval notation
explanation of, 168, 186
union and intersection in, 627–628
use of, 168–169, 172
Inverse, 78
Inverse functions
explanation of, 617, 848, 850, 851, 917
finding equation of, 851–853, 917
one-to-one, 848–849
property of, 850, 917
Inverse of *f*, 848
Inverse property of real numbers, 78, 93
Inverse variation
applications involving, 608–609
explanation of, 605, 606
Irrational number *e*, 889–890, 920
Irrational numbers
on calculators, 30–31
explanation of, 25, 90
Isolating the variable, 101, 107, 112, 114
Isosceles triangle, A–18 – A–19

Joint variation
applications involving, 609–610
explanation of, 606, 618

Leading coefficient
explanation of, 373
factoring trinomials with, 426–429
Leading term, of polynomial, 373
Least common denominator (LCD)
of complex fractions, 523–527
explanation of, 14, 505
method to find, 14, 15, 123, 124
of rational expressions, 505–509, 554
Least common multiple (LCM), 13, 122
Like radicals, 720, 721
Like terms
addition and subtraction of, 82, 375–378, 721
combining, 82–84
explanation of, 81, 93
Linear, 205
Linear equations
applications of, 133–135, 184, 264
on calculators, 211
clearing fractions to solve, 121–124, 183
with decimals, 124–125
explanation of, 101, 203, 530
interpretation of, 251–252
methods to solve, 112–118
modeling, 253–254, 259–260, 264
procedure to solve, 114–116, 122–125, 182
summary of forms of, 246, 263
translations to, 108–109, 129–131

Linear equations in two variables. *See also* Systems of linear equations in two variables
explanation of, 203–204, 261
on graphing calculators, 211
graphs of, 203–211, 251–252, 667–669
horizontal and vertical lines in graphs of, 209–211
interpretation of, 251–252
plotting points in graphs of, 204–207
slope-intercept form of, 232–237, 263
summary of forms of, 246, 263
x-intercepts and y-intercepts in graphs of, 207–209
Linear functions, 585, 616
Linear inequalities. *See also* Systems of linear inequalities in two variables
addition and subtraction properties of, 169–171
applications of, 174–175
graphs of, 166–167, 667–669, 685
methods to solve, 170–174
multiplication and division properties of, 171–173
in one variable, 165–166, 186
solution set of, 166–167
in two variables, 667–669, 685
Linear models
examples of, 253–254, 259–260, 264
method to create, 327–328
Lines
finding x- and y-intercepts of, 207–209
horizontal, 209–211
parallel, 223–224, A–17
perpendicular, 223–224
slope-intercept form of, 232–237
slope of, 218–225
vertical, 209–211
Literal equations, 146–148, 185, 786. *See also* Quadratic formula
Logarithmic equations
explanation of, 903, 920
method to solve, 903–906, 920–921
Logarithmic expressions
equivalence of, 905
evaluation of, 868–869
in expanded form, 883–885, 894
as single logarithm, 885–886
Logarithmic form, converted to exponential form, 867–868
Logarithmic functions
applications of, 873–874
common, 869–870, 873–874
conversions to exponential form, 867–868
domain of, 870, 872–873
explanation of, 867, 918
graphs of, 870–873, 895
natural, 891–894
Logarithms
on calculators, 870, 873, 892
change-of-base formula and, 894–895
explanation of, 867
power property of, 882, 883, 886, 892
product property of, 881–883, 892
properties of, 919
quotient property of, 882, 883, 892
sum or difference of logarithms as single, 885–886
Long division
of polynomials, 393–397
synthetic division vs., 399
when to use, 397
Lowest terms, 8–9, 490

Matrices
augmented, A–27 – A–28, A–30
coefficient, A–27
column, A–27
determinants of, A–36
elementary row operations and, A–28
explanation of, A–26
on graphing calculators, A–32
order of, A–26
reduced row echelon form of, A–29, A–30
row, A–27
square, A–27
3×3, A–37 – A–39
2×2, A–36
Maximum (calculator feature), 818
Maximum value, 817
Mean
explanation of, A–1 – A–2
weighted, A–5 – A–6
Median
explanation of, A–2 – A–3
mode vs., A–5
Midpoint formula, 934–935, 977
Minimum (calculator feature), 818
Minimum value, 817
Minor, of element of matrix, A–37 – A–38
Mixed numbers
explanation of, 6, 7
operations on, 15–17
shortcut to writing, 15
Mixture applications, 156–161, 186, 307–308, 324–325
Mode
explanation of, A–3 – A–5
median vs., A–5
Modeling, linear equations, 253–254, 259–260, 264
Monomials. *See also* Polynomials
division by, 392–393
explanation of, 373
multiplication of, 382–383, 407
Mortgage payments, 552
Multiplication
associative property of, 77
to check division problems, 67
commutative property of, 75, 76
of complex numbers, 760
of conjugates, 386–387
of expressions with *like* bases, 344, 405
of fractions, 9–10, 498
of functions, 598–599
identity property of, 78, 493
of polynomials, 382–388, 407, 427
of radicals, 726–731, 768
of rational expressions, 498–500, 502–503, 553
of real numbers, 63–64, 92
in scientific notation, 369
symbol for, 21, 39
Multiplication property
to clear fractions, 121
of equality, 103–107, 121, 181
of inequality, 171–173
of radicals, 714–716, 726–728
Multiplicative identity, 78

Natural logarithmic functions
applications of, 895–896
in expanded form, 894
explanation of, 891
graphs of, 892
properties of, 892
simplifying expressions with, 893
writing sum or difference of, 893
Natural numbers
explanation of, 6, 24, 90
as product of prime factors, 7
set of, 24
Negative exponents, 358–360
Negative factors, factoring out, 420
Nonlinear functions, on graphing calculators, 587
Nonlinear inequalities
graphs of, 968–969, 981
systems of, 969–970
test point method for, 967, 968, 981
in two variables, 967–969
Nonlinear systems of equations
addition method to solve, 963–964
on calculators, 962
explanation of, 960, 980
graphs of, 961, 962
substitution method to solve, 960–963, 980
Nonlinear systems of inequalities
explanation of, 969
graphs of, 969–970, 981
Notation/symbols
factorial, 991–992
function, 575–576, 585, 616
pi (π), A–11
radical, 694, 708
scientific, 367–370, 406
summation, 1001–1002
nth roots
on calculators, 697
explanation of, 696–697, 766
identification of, 697
method to simplify, 697, 699
of real numbers, 697
of variable expressions, 697–699
nth term of sequence
on calculators, 998
explanation of, 997
method to find, 999–1000
Number line
addition of real numbers and, 45–47
domain of function and, 579
explanation of, 23, 26
graphs of individual sets on, 627–631
inequalities on, 166
plotting points on, 23–24
Numbers. *See also* Complex numbers; Integers; Real numbers
composite, 7
imaginary, 754–757
irrational, 25, 30–31, 90

Numbers—(*continued*)
mixed, 6, 7, 15–17
natural, 6, 7, 24, 90
rational, 24–25
reciprocal of, 11
sets of, 23–26
whole, 6, 24, 90
Numerators
of complex fractions, 522–527
explanation of, 6

Obtuse angles, A–16
Obtuse triangles, A–18
One-to-one functions
explanation of, 848–849
inverse of, 851–853
Opposites
explanation of, 28, 90
factors as, 493
of real numbers, 28
Ordered pairs
explanation of, 196, 260
functions and, 573
relation as set of, 564–566
as solution to linear equation in two variables, 204
Ordered triples, 314–315, 333
Order of operations
application of, 37–39, 57–58, 68–69
explanation of, 36–37, 91
to simplify radicals, 716–717
Origin, 195, 260

Parabolas
axis of symmetry of, 810, 941–944, 978
on calculators, 812, 945
directrix of, 941
explanation of, 616, 810, 941, 978
focus of, 941
graphs of, 589, 810–818, 838, 942–946
standard form of equation of, 942, 944, 978
vertex of, 810, 826–827, 839, 941, 942, 946–947, 978
Parallel lines
explanation of, 223, A–17
point-slope formula and, 245
slope-intercept form and, 234–236
slope of, 223, 224, 262
Parallelograms, A–12
Parentheses
avoiding mistakes involving, 131
clearing, 83–84, 123
as grouping symbols, 36–37, 513
in interval notation, 168
Pascal, Blaise, 991
Pascal's triangle, 991, 994, 1021
Percents
applications of, 139–143, 185
explanation of, 139
Perfect cubes, 455, 456, 697, 698
Perfect fifth powers, 697
Perfect fourth powers, 697
Perfect squares, 448, 695, 698
Perfect square trinomials
checking for, 451
explanation of, 386, 407
factoring, 450–452

Perimeter
explanation of, A–10 – A–11
solving application involving, 149
of triangles, 146
Perpendicular lines
explanation of, 223
point-slope formula and, 246
slope-intercept form and, 235–236
slope of, 223, 224, 262
Pi (π), 25, 152, A–11
Plotting points
applications of, 197–198
in linear equations in two variables, 204–207
on real number line, 23–24
in rectangular coordinate system, 195–198
Point-slope formula
explanation of, 243, 246, 263
writing equation of line using, 243–246
Polynomial equations
first-degree, 462
higher-degree, 466–467
second-degree, 462
Polynomial inequalities
explanation of, 682
on graphing calculator, 642
test point method to solve, 641–642, 682
Polynomials. *See also* Binomials; Factors/factoring; Monomials; Trinomials
addition of, 375–376, 407
degree of, 373, 374
in descending order, 373
division of, 392–400, 408
explanation of, 373
geometry applications of, 378–379
identifying parts of, 374
leading coefficient of, 373
leading term of, 373
long division to divide, 393–397
multiplication of, 382–388, 407, 427
prime, 419, 433, 437, 441, 445
special case products of, 386–388
subtraction of, 376–379, 407
synthetic division to divide, 398–400
Population models, 915–916
Power of product, 353, 405
Power of quotient, 353, 405
Power property of logarithms, 882, 883, 886, 892
Power rule for exponents
explanation of, 352, 405
use of, 354
Powers, of quotient, 353
Prime factorization, 7, 416
Prime polynomials, 419, 433, 437, 441, 445
Principal and interest problems, 890–891
Principal square root, 36
Principal square roots, 694, 766
Problem-solving strategies, 128–129
Product property of logarithms, 881–883, 892
Products
of conjugates, 386–387, 407
explanation of, 7, 39
power of, 353
special case, 386–388, 407
Proper fractions, 6, 7

Proportions
applications of, 542–544
explanation of, 541, 557
methods to solve, 541, 557
Pythagorean theorem
applications of, 472–473, 700
explanation of, 472, 699, 766
geometric "proof" of, 404

Quadrants, 195, 260
Quadratic equations. *See also* Parabolas
applications of, 470–474, 482
completing the square to solve, 783–785
discriminant and, 794–797
explanation of, 462–463, 530
factoring to solve, 464–467
methods to solve, 797–800, 837
quadratic formula to solve, 791–792
square root property to solve, 780–781
zero product rule to solve, 463–464, 481
Quadratic formula
applications using, 792–794
derivation of, 790
explanation of, 790, 837
to solve quadratic equations, 791–792, 797
Quadratic functions
analysis of, 793–794, 825
applications of, 828–829
explanation of, 585, 588–589, 616
in form $f(x) = a(x - h)^2 + k$, 824–825
graphs of, 810–818, 838 (*See also* Parabolas)
Quadratic inequalities
explanation of, 638
graphs to solve, 639–640
test point method to solve, 640–641
Quadratic in form, equations, 804–807
Quadratic models
method to create, 834–835
method to write, 829–830
Quotient property of logarithms, 882, 883, 892
Quotients
explanation of, 39
power of, 353
of real numbers, 105

Radical equations
applications of, 749–751
explanation of, 744
method to solve, 744–749, 770
Radical expressions
addition of, 720–723, 768
on calculators, 707, 716
conjugate, 729–730
division property of, 735–736, 769
like, 720, 721
method to simplify, 695–696, 698, 713–717, 728, 735–736, 767
multiplication of, 726–731, 768
multiplication property of, 713–716, 726–728
order of operations to simplify, 716–717
rationalizing the denominator of, 736–741, 769

simplified form of, 714, 734–735
special case products and, 729–730
subtraction of, 720–723, 768
Radical functions
applications, 750–751
on calculators, 701
domain of, 700
explanation of, 700–701
graphs of, 701–702
Radical notation, 694, 708
Radical sign, 36
Radicand, 696
Radius, of circle, 931, 933
Range
of functions, 578
of relations, 564–567, 615
Rate of change
applications of, 224–225, 254
explanation of, 254
Rational equations
applications of, 541–548, 557
containing fractions, 530
explanation of, 530, 556
method to solve, 531–534, 556
solving formulas involving, 535–537
translation to, 535
Rational exponents
applications of, 710
converting between radical notation and, 708–709
evaluating expressions with, 706–707
explanation of, 706–707, 767
properties of, 709
Rational expressions
addition and subtraction of, 511–517
addition of, 511–517, 555
division of, 500–503, 554
evaluation of, 488
explanation of, 488, 553
fundamental principle of, 491
least common denominator of, 505–509, 554
method to simplify, 490–495, 553
method to write, 494
multiplication of, 498–500, 502–503, 553
restricted values of, 489–490, 553
subtraction of, 511–517, 555
in translations, 517
Rational inequalities
explanation of, 642, 682
test point method to solve, 643–645, 682
Rationalizing the denominator
explanation of, 736–737
one term, 738–739, 769
two terms, 739–741, 769
Rational numbers
explanation of, 24, 90
identification of, 24–25
Ratios
common, 1011
explanation of, 541
of -1, 493–495
Real number line. *See also* Number line
explanation of, 23, 26
plotting points on, 23–24
Real numbers
absolute value of, 29–30
addition of, 45–50, 91
associative properties of, 76–77, 93
commutative properties of, 75–76, 93
distributive property of multiplication over addition and, 79–80, 93
division of, 65–68, 92
explanation of, 23, 90
identity properties of, 77–78, 93
inverse properties of, 78, 93
multiplication of, 63–64, 92
opposite of, 28
ordering of, 27–28
reciprocal of, 65
set of, 23–26, 90
subtraction of, 54–58, 92, 130
summary of properties of, 93
Reciprocal functions, 585, 588
Reciprocals
explanation of, 11, 65
product of number and, 104
Rectangles, A–12
Rectangular coordinate system
explanation of, 195–196, 260
plotting points in, 196–198
Rectangular solids, A–14
Reduced row echelon form, A–29, A–30
Relations
applications involving, 568
domain and range of, 564–567, 615
explanation of, 564, 615
functions vs., 573, 574
as set of ordered pairs, 564–566
Restricted values, of rational expressions, 489–490, 553
Right angles, A–16
Right circular cones, A–14
Right circular cylinders, A–14
Right triangles, 699, 700
Roots. *See also* Cube roots; *n*th roots; Square roots
*n*th, 696–697
square, 694–696
of variable expressions, 697–699
Row matrix, A–27

Sales tax, 139–140
Sample mean, 1020
Sample standard deviation, 1020
Scalene triangle, A–18 – A–19
Scientific notation
on calculator, 370
explanation of, 367, 406
multiplying and dividing numbers in, 369
writing numbers in, 367–368
Second-degree polynomial equations, 462
Seq (calculator feature), 998
Sequences
alternating, 998–999
in applications, 1000
arithmetic, 1005–1007, 1022
on calculators, 998, 1001
explanation of, 996–997, 1022
finite, 997
geometric, 1011–1012, 1023
infinite, 997, 1022
*n*th term of, 999
terms of, 997–1000
Series
arithmetic, 1007–1008, 1023
explanation of, 1000–1002, 1022
finite, 1001
geometric, 1013–1015, 1023
infinite, 1001
Set-builder notation, 168, 169, 172, 186
Sets
classifying numbers by, 26
explanation of, 24
of integers, 24
of natural numbers, 24
of real numbers, 23–26
Signed numbers
addition of, 46–49
on calculators, 59
division of, 66–67
factoring out and, 429
multiplication of, 63–64
Sign rules, for trial-and-error method, 434
Similar triangles
applications of, 542–544
explanation of, 542
Simple interest
application involving, 141–142, 185, 306–307, 347
explanation of, 141
formula for, 141, 185
Simplification
of complex fractions, 522–527
of complex numbers, 761
of expressions in terms of *i*, 755–756
of expressions with exponents, 346–347, 353–355, 357–368
of fractions, 8–9, 490
of natural logarithms, 893
of *n*th roots, 697, 699
of radical expressions, 695–696, 698, 713–717, 728, 734–736, 767
of rational exponents, 709
of rational expressions, 490–495, 553
Slope
applications of, 219, 224–225
explanation of, 218–219, 262
graphing line by using *y*-intercept and, 233–234
method to find, 220–222, 232, 233
of parallel lines, 223, 224, 262
of perpendicular lines, 223, 224, 262
Slope formula, 219–221, 243
Slope-intercept form
explanation of, 232–233, 246, 263
graphs of, 233–234
parallel and perpendicular lines and, 234–236
systems of linear equations and, 276, 277, 290
to write equation of line, 236–237, 247
Solutions
to equations, 100
extraneous, 744
to systems of linear equations, 274–275
Solution set
explanation of, 101
of inequalities, 166–167
Special case product formulas, 386

Special case products, 729–730
explanation of, 386–387, 407
in geometry application, 388
Square brackets, 168
Square matrix, A–27
Square root functions, 585, 588
Square root property
explanation of, 780, 836
to solve quadratic equations, 780–781, 783–785
Square roots
evaluation of, 36
explanation of, 36, 694
identification of, 694
method to simplify, 695–696
positive and negative, 694
principal, 36, 694, 766
Squares. *See also* Completing the square
area of, A–12
of binomials, 387, 407, 990
difference of, 386, 407, 448–450, 480
perfect, 448, 695, 698
sum of, 449
Standard deviation, 1020
Standard form
of ellipse equation, 951, 979
of equation of circle, 931
of equation of line, 232, 246
of hyperbola equation, 953, 968
of parabola equation, 942, 944, 978
writing numbers in, 368
Straight angles, A–16
Study tips, 1–2
Subscripts, 219
Subsets, 24
Substitution method
applications of, 290–292
to solve nonlinear systems of equations, 960–963, 980
to solve systems of linear equations, 289–290, 300
Subtraction
of complex numbers, 759
of fractions, 12–15
of functions, 598–599
of *like* terms, 82, 377–378, 721
of polynomials, 377–379, 407
of radicals, 720–723, 768
of rational expressions, 511–517, 555
of real numbers, 54–58, 92, 130
symbol for, 21, 39
Subtraction property
of equality, 101–103, 107, 181
of inequality, 169–171
Sum
of cubes, 454–457
explanation of, 39
of squares, 449
Sum formula, 1008
Summation notation, 1001–1002
Supplementary angles, 149, A–17
Symbols. *See* Notation/symbols
Symbols and notation
addition, 21, 39
approximately equal to, 31
braces, 36
brackets, 36, 168
division, 21, 39
grouping, 36–37
inequality, 26, 27
interval, 168–169, 172, 186
multiplication, 21, 39
parentheses, 36–37, 168
pi (π), 25, 152
radical, 36
set-builder, 168, 169, 172, 186
slope, 219
subtraction, 21, 39
Synthetic division
to divide polynomials, 398–400
explanation of, 397
long division vs., 399
Systems of dependent equations
addition method to solve, 300
analysis of, A–43
explanation of, 275
Gauss-Jordan method to solve, A–31
graphs of, 278
substitution method to solve, 289–290, 330
in three variables, 319
Systems of linear equations in three variables
applications of, 323–325, 334
consistent, 315
dependent, 315, 319
explanation of, 314, 333
inconsistent, 315, 320
independent, 315
methods to solve, 316–320
solutions to, 314–315
Systems of linear equations in two variables
addition method to solve, 294–300, 331
applications of, 305–310, 332
consistent, 275, 329
Cramer's rule to solve, A–40 – A–44
dependent equations in, 275, 278, 329
explanation of, 274
Gauss-Jordan method to solve, A–29 – A–32
graphing to solve, 275–279, 329
inconsistent, 275, 277, 299, 329, 330
independent equations in, 275, 329
solutions to, 274–275, 290, 329
substitution method to solve, 284–290, 300, 330
Systems of linear inequalities in two variables
feasible regions and, 671–673
graphs of, 669–671, 685
Systems of nonlinear equations. *See* Nonlinear systems of equations

Terminating decimals, rational numbers represented by, 30–31
Terms
constant, 81
explanation of, 81, 93
like, 81, 82, 93
of sequences, 997–1000
unlike, 81
variable, 81
Test point method
for absolute value inequalities, 660–662, 684
for nonlinear inequalities, 967, 968
for polynomial inequalities, 641–642, 682
for rational inequalities, 643–645, 682
Test points, 171
3×3 matrix, A–37 – A–39
Trace (graphing calculator feature), 278, 279
Translations
of English form to algebraic form, 39–41
of expressions involving addition, 49–50
of expressions involving subtraction, 55–56
of inequalities, 175
of linear equations, 108–109, 129–131
of quadratic equations, 470
of rational equations, 535
of rational expressions, 517
for variation, 605–606
Transverse axis, of hyperbola, 953, 979
Trapezoids, A–12, A–13
Trial-and-error method, 432–438, 479
Triangles
area of, A–12
finding measure of angles in, 323–324
Pascal's, 991, 994, 1021
perimeter of, 146, 378
right, A–18
similar, 542–544
sum of angles in, 149–151, A–19
types of, A–18 – A–19
Trinomials. *See also* Polynomials
AC-method to factor, 441–445, 479
of form $x^2 + bx + c$, 426–429
with leading coefficient of 1, 426–429, 478
perfect square, 386, 407, 450–452
procedure to factor, 426–429
trial-and-error method to factor, 432–438, 479
2×2 matrix, A–36

Union, of sets, 626–628, 681
Unlike terms, 81

Value (graphing calculator feature), 577
Variable expressions, 697–699
Variables
explanation of, 21–22, 90
isolation of, 101, 107, 112, 114
solving equations for indicated, 147–148
Variable terms, 81
Variation
applications of, 607–610
constant of, 605
direct, 605, 606, 617
inverse, 605, 606, 617
joint, 606, 618
translations involving, 605–606
Vertex
of hyperbola, 953
of parabola, 810, 826–827, 839, 941, 942, 946–947, 978
of quadratic function, 827–828
Vertex formula, 826–827, 839, 946, 947
Vertical angles, 149, A–17
Vertical asymptotes, 587

Vertical lines
  equations of, 209–211, 246, 261
  explanation of, 209
  graphs of, 210–211
  slope of, 222
Vertical line test, 574–575, 615
Vertical transverse axis, of hyperbola, 953, 979
Volume, A–14 – A–16

Weighted mean, A–5 – A–6
Whole numbers
  explanation of, 6, 90
  set of, 24
Word problems
  checking answers in, 132
  problem-solving strategies for, 128–129
Work applications, 547–548

x-axis, 195, 218, 260
x-coordinates, 196, 207, 848
x-intercepts
  explanation of, 207, 261
  of functions, 590–592
  method to find, 207–209
  of quadratic functions, 796–797

y-axis, 195, 218, 260
y-coordinates, 196, 207, 848
y-intercepts
  explanation of, 207, 261
  of functions, 590, 591
  graphing line by using slope and, 233–234
  method to find, 207–209, 232, 233
  of quadratic functions, 796–797

Zero, division involving, 67, 68
Zero exponents, 357–368
Zero product rule
  explanation of, 463, 780
  to solve quadratic equations, 463–464, 481, 797

Section B.4 Review of the Set of Real Numbers

Concepts

1. Sets of Real Numbers
2. Symbols and Mathematical Language
3. Operations on Real Numbers
4. Exponents and Square Roots
5. Order of Operations
6. Properties of Real Numbers
7. Simplifying Expressions

1. Sets of Real Numbers

The numbers we are familiar with in everyday life comprise the **set of real numbers**. Every real number corresponds to a unique point on a number line.

For example:

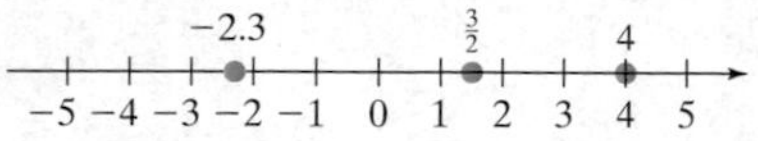

Several subsets of the real numbers are given in Table B-1. We use the symbols { } to enclose the elements of a set.

Table B-1

Set	Definition
Natural numbers	$\{1, 2, 3, \ldots\}$
Whole numbers	$\{0, 1, 2, 3, \ldots\}$
Integers	$\{\ldots, -3, -2, -1, 0, 1, 2, 3, \ldots\}$
Rational numbers	the set of numbers of the form $\frac{p}{q}$ where p and q are integers and $q \neq 0$.
Irrational numbers	the set of real numbers that are not rational

Rational numbers can be written as a ratio of two integers such as $\frac{1}{3}$ or $\frac{3}{4}$. When expressed in decimal form a rational number is either a repeating decimal or a terminating decimal such as $0.\overline{3}$ or 0.75. The decimal form of an irrational number is non-repeating and non-terminating. Examples of irrational numbers are π and $\sqrt{2}$.

2. Symbols and Mathematical Language

In mathematics, the symbol $<$ (meaning "is less than") and the symbol $>$ (meaning "is greater than") are used to express inequalities. These and other inequality symbols are summarized in Table B-2.

Table B-2

Inequality	In Words	Example
$a < b$	a is less than b	$5 < 7$
$a > b$	a is greater than b	$8 > 3$
$a \leq b$	a is less than or equal to b	$8 \leq 9$
$a \geq b$	a is greater than or equal to b	$3 \geq 3$
$a < x < b$	x is between a and b	$3 < 4 < 5$
$a \neq b$	a is not equal to b	$4 \neq 6$

The operations of addition, subtraction, multiplication, and division can be denoted several ways. These along with other common operations on real numbers are summarized in (Table B-3).

Table B-3

Operation	Symbols	Translation/Example
Addition	$a + b$	"the **sum** of a and b" "the sum of 8 and −4" $\Rightarrow 8 + (-4)$
Subtraction	$a - b$	"the **difference** of a and b" "the difference of −8 and 2" $\Rightarrow -8 - 2$
Multiplication	$a \times b, a \cdot b, a(b),$ $(a)b, (a)(b), ab$	"the **product** of a and b" "the product of 3 and −2" $\Rightarrow 3(-2)$
Division	$a \div b, \frac{a}{b}, a/b, b\overline{)a}$	"the **quotient** of a and b" "the quotient of 10 and 5" $\Rightarrow \frac{10}{5}$
Absolute value	$\|a\|$	"the **absolute value** of a" "the absolute value of −3" $\Rightarrow \|-3\|$
Opposite	$-a$	"the **opposite** of a" "the opposite of 7" $\Rightarrow -(7)$
Reciprocal	$\frac{1}{a}\ (a \neq 0)$	"the **reciprocal** of a" "the reciprocal of 5" $\Rightarrow \frac{1}{5}$
Square root	$\sqrt{a}$	"the **square root** of a" "the square root of 64" $\Rightarrow \sqrt{64}$

3. Operations on Real Numbers

The **absolute value** of a real number, a, denoted $|a|$, is its distance from 0 on the number line. Two numbers that are the same distance from 0 but on opposite sides of the number line are called **opposites**. The opposite of a is denoted $-a$.

Example 1 Finding Opposites and Absolute Value

a. Find the opposite of 5.

b. Find the opposite of $-\frac{1}{2}$.

c. Evaluate $|-6|$.

d. Evaluate $|2.7|$.

e. Evaluate $-|-8|$.

Solution:

a. The opposite of 5 is −5.

b. The opposite of $-\frac{1}{2}$ is $\frac{1}{2}$.

c. $|-6| = 6$

d. $|2.7| = 2.7$

e. $-|-8| = -8$ Take the opposite of the absolute value of −8.

The rules for adding, subtracting, multiplying, and dividing real numbers are given as follows.

Addition of Two Real Numbers

• To add two numbers with the *same sign:* Add the absolute values of the numbers and apply the common sign to the sum.	example: $-3 + (-7) = -(3 + 7) = -10$
• To add two numbers with *unlike signs:* Subtract the smaller absolute value from the larger absolute value. Then apply the sign of the number having the larger absolute value.	examples: $10 + (-4) = 10 - 4 = 6$ $-8 + 5 = -(8 - 5) = -3$

Subtraction of Two Real Numbers

Add the opposite of the second number to the first number. In symbols: $a - b = a + (-b)$	examples: $8 - (-4) = 8 + (4) = 12$ $-3 - 6 = -3 + (-6) = -9$

Multiplication and Division of Two Real Numbers

• The product or quotient of two real numbers with the *same* sign is positive.	example: $-20 \cdot (-4) = 80$
• The product or quotient of two real numbers with *unlike* signs is negative.	example: $\frac{30}{-2} = -15$
Notes: • The product of any real number and 0 is 0.	example: $5 \cdot 0 = 0$
• The quotient of 0 and any nonzero real number is 0.	example: $0 \div 6 = 0$
• The quotient of a real number and 0 is undefined.	example: $6 \div 0$ is undefined

4. Exponents and Square Roots

We can use **exponents** to represent repeated multiplication. For example, the product

$$3 \cdot 3 \cdot 3 \cdot 3 \cdot 3 \quad \text{can be written as} \quad 3^5.$$

(exponent: 5; base: 3)

The expression 3^5 is written in exponential form. The exponent (or **power**) is 5 and represents the number of times the **base**, 3, is used as a factor. The expression 3^5 is read as "three to the fifth power." In general,

$$x^n = \underbrace{x \cdot x \cdot x \cdot \cdots \cdot x}_{\text{the factor } x \text{ occurs } n \text{ times}}$$

The number b is a **square root** of a if $b^2 = a$. A **radical sign**, $\sqrt{\ }$, is used to denote the principle (or positive) square root of a nonnegative real number.

Example 2 Evaluating Expressions Containing Exponents and Square Roots

Evaluate. **a.** 2^4 **b.** $\sqrt{36}$

Solution:

a. $2^4 = 2 \cdot 2 \cdot 2 \cdot 2 = 16$

b. $\sqrt{36} = 6$ because $6^2 = 36$.

5. Order of Operations

Algebraic expressions often have more than one operation. In such a case, it is important to follow the order of operations.

Order of Operations

Step 1 Simplify expressions within parentheses and other grouping symbols first. These include absolute value bars, fraction bars, and radicals. If imbedded parentheses are present, start with the innermost parentheses.

Step 2 Evaluate expressions involving exponents, radicals, and absolute value.

Step 3 Perform multiplication or division in the order that they occur from left to right.

Step 4 Perform addition or subtraction in the order that they occur from left to right.

Example 3 **Applying the Order of Operations**

Simplify. $50 \div [15 - 2(4 + 6) + 15] \cdot 2^3$

Solution:

$50 \div [15 - 2(4 + 6) + 15] \cdot 2^3$

$= 50 \div [15 - 2(10) + 15] \cdot 2^3$	Simplify inside the inner parentheses.
$= 50 \div [15 - 20 + 15] \cdot 2^3$	Simplify inside [ ]. Within [ ], we perform multiplication before addition or subtraction.
$= 50 \div [-5 + 15] \cdot 2^3$	Within [ ], subtract and add from left to right.
$= 50 \div [10] \cdot 2^3$	Simplify within [ ].
$= 50 \div [10] \cdot 8$	Evaluate the exponential expressions.
$= 5 \cdot 8$	Divide and multiply from left to right.
$= 40$	Multiply.

Example 4 **Applying the Order of Operations within a Formula**

Given $x = -3$, evaluate the expressions. **a.** x^2 **b.** $-x^2$

Solution:

a. x^2

$= (\ \ )^2$	Use parentheses in place of the variable.
$= (-3)^2$	Substitute -3 for x.
$= 9$	Evaluate expressions with exponents.

b. $-x^2$

$= -(\ \ )^2$	Use parentheses in place of the variable.
$= -(-3)^2$	Substitute -3 for x.
$= -(9)$	Simplify $(-3)^2$ first. Note that $(-3)^2 = 9$.
$= -9$	Now take the opposite of 9.

TIP: The expression $-(-3)^2$ is equivalent to $-1(-3)^2$. The order of operations indicates that we should square -3 first, and then multiply the result by -1.

6. Properties of Real Numbers

Several properties of real numbers are reviewed in Table B-4.

Table B-4

Property Name	Algebraic Representation	Example	Description/Notes
Commutative property of addition	$a + b = b + a$	$5 + 3 = 3 + 5$	The order in which two real numbers are added or multiplied does not affect the result.
Commutative property of multiplication	$a \cdot b = b \cdot a$	$(5)(3) = (3)(5)$	
Associative property of addition	$(a + b) + c = a + (b + c)$	$(2 + 3) + 7 = 2 + (3 + 7)$	The manner in which two real numbers are grouped under addition or multiplication does not affect the result.
Associative property of multiplication	$(a \cdot b)c = a(b \cdot c)$	$(2 \cdot 3)7 = 2(3 \cdot 7)$	
Distributive property of multiplication over addition	$a(b + c) = ab + ac$	$3(5 + 2) = 3 \cdot 5 + 3 \cdot 2$	A factor outside the parentheses is multiplied by each term inside the parentheses.
Identity property of addition	0 is the identity element for addition because $a + 0 = 0 + a = a$	$5 + 0 = 0 + 5 = 5$	Any number added to the identity element, 0, will remain unchanged.
Identity property of multiplication	1 is the identity element for multiplication because $a \cdot 1 = 1 \cdot a = a$	$5 \cdot 1 = 1 \cdot 5 = 5$	Any number multiplied by the identity element, 1, will remain unchanged.
Inverse property of addition	a and $(-a)$ are additive inverses because $a + (-a) = 0$ and $(-a) + a = 0$	$3 + (-3) = 0$	The sum of a number and its additive inverse (**opposite**) is the identity element, 0.
Inverse property of multiplication	a and $\frac{1}{a}$ are multiplicative inverses because $a \cdot \frac{1}{a} = 1$ and $\frac{1}{a} \cdot a = 1$ (provided $a \neq 0$)	$5 \cdot \frac{1}{5} = 1$	The product of a number and its multiplicative inverse (**reciprocal**) is the identity element, 1.

7. Simplifying Expressions

We can simplify expressions containing variables by adding or subtracting *like* terms. Recall that *like* terms have the same variables and the corresponding variables are raised to the same powers. To combine *like* terms, we use the distributive property. The same result may also be obtained by adding or subtracting the coefficients of each term and leaving the variable factors unchanged.

$$5x + 2x - 3x = 4x$$

Example 5 **Simplifying Expressions**

Simplify. $4x - 3(2x - 8) - 1 + 5x$

Solution:

$4x - 3(2x - 8) - 1 + 5x$

$= 4x - 6x + 24 - 1 + 5x$ Apply the distributive property.

$= 4x - 6x + 5x + 24 - 1$ Arrange *like* terms together.

$= 3x + 23$ Combine *like* terms.

Section B.4 Practice Exercises

For Exercises 1–8, refer to sets

$A = \{-6, -\sqrt{5}, -\frac{7}{8}, -0.\overline{3}, 0, \frac{4}{9}, \pi, 7, 10.4\}$ and $B = \{-2, -\pi, -\frac{1}{2}, 0, 1, \sqrt{3}, \frac{5}{4}, 8\}$

1. List all rational numbers in set *A*. $\left\{-6, -\frac{7}{8}, -0.\overline{3}, 0, \frac{4}{9}, 7, 10.4\right\}$

2. List all irrational numbers in set *A*. $\{-\sqrt{5}, \pi\}$

3. List all integers in set *A*. $\{-6, 0, 7\}$

4. List all whole numbers in set *A*. $\{0, 7\}$

5. List all natural numbers in set *B*. $\{1, 8\}$

6. List all integers in set *B*. $\{-2, 0, 1, 8\}$

7. List all irrational numbers in set *B*. $\{-\pi, \sqrt{3}\}$

8. List all rational numbers in set *B*. $\left\{-2, -\frac{1}{2}, 0, 1, \frac{5}{4}, 8\right\}$

9. Find the opposite of -9. 9

10. Find the opposite of -13. 13

11. Find the opposite of $\frac{2}{3}$. $-\frac{2}{3}$

12. Find the opposite of $\frac{1}{4}$. $-\frac{1}{4}$

For Exercises 13–20, evaluate the expression.

13. $|-4|$ 4

14. $|-12.6|$ 12.6

15. $|8.5|$ 8.5

16. $|3|$ 3

17. $-|22|$ -22

18. $-|8|$ -8

19. $-|-13|$ -13

20. $-|-7|$ -7

For Exercises 21–28, write the expression in words.

21. $5 > -2$
5 is greater than -2

22. $8 \leq 9$
8 is less than or equal to 9

23. $-3 \geq -4$
-3 is greater than or equal to -4

24. $\frac{1}{2} > -\frac{1}{2}$
$\frac{1}{2}$ is greater than $-\frac{1}{2}$

25. $6 < 10 < 12$
10 is between 6 and 12

26. $-1 < 0 < 1$
0 is between -1 and 1

27. $2 \neq -5$
2 is not equal to -5

28. $\frac{2}{3} \neq -\frac{2}{3}$
$\frac{2}{3}$ is not equal to $-\frac{2}{3}$

For Exercises 29–38, write the English phrase as an algebraic expression.

29. The product of 6 and 3 $6 \cdot 3$

30. The difference of 7 and 4 $7 - 4$

31. The quotient of 20 and 5 $20 \div 5$

32. The sum of 2 and 12 $2 + 12$

33. The absolute value of -5 $|-5|$

34. The absolute value of -13 $|-13|$

35. The sum of 2 and the absolute value of -8. $2 + |-8|$

36. The difference of 10 and the absolute value of -1 $10 - |-1|$

37. The product of 4 and the reciprocal of 3 $4 \cdot \frac{1}{3}$

38. The quotient of 8 and the square root of 16 $8 \div \sqrt{16}$

For Exercises 39–58, add or subtract as indicated.

39. $8 + (-10)$ -2

40. $23 + (-9)$ 14

41. $51 - 32$ 19

42. $12 - 15$ -3

43. $0 + 16$ 16

44. $26 + 0$ 26

45. $-13 - 20$ -33

46. $-5 - 30$ -35

47. $-2.1 + (-2.2)$ -4.3

48. $-4.0 + (-0.5)$ -4.5

49. $-19 - (-3)$ -16

50. $-7 - (-28)$ 21

51. $0 - 19$ -19

52. $0 - 41$ -41

53. $5.2 - (-0.4)$ 5.6

54. $0.03 - (-1.2)$ 1.23

55. $-\frac{3}{4} - \frac{3}{8}$ $-\frac{9}{8}$

56. $-\frac{5}{2} - \frac{1}{6}$ $-\frac{8}{3}$

57. $-\frac{7}{3} - \left(-\frac{1}{9}\right)$ $-\frac{20}{9}$

58. $-\frac{7}{10} - \left(-\frac{4}{5}\right)$ $\frac{1}{10}$

For Exercises 59–78, multiply or divide as indicated.

59. $3(-9)$ -27

60. $(-8)(2)$ -16

61. $(-5)(-7)$ 35

62. $(-11)(-3)$ 33

63. $0 \cdot 32$ 0

64. $0 \cdot (-12)$ 0

65. $(2.05)(-4.2)$ -8.61

66. $(-10.7)(3.4)$ -36.38

67. $\left(-\frac{5}{9}\right) \cdot \left(-\frac{3}{2}\right)$ $\frac{5}{6}$

68. $\left(-\frac{1}{6}\right) \cdot \left(-\frac{12}{7}\right)$ $\frac{2}{7}$

69. $-56 \div (-8)$ 7

70. $-51 \div (-3)$ 17

71. $-78 \div 13$ -6

72. $112 \div (-16)$ -7

73. $0 \div (-5)$ 0

74. $0 \div 12$ 0

75. $3.1 \div 0$ Undefined

76. $-1.4 \div 0$ Undefined

77. $\left(-\frac{7}{8}\right) \div \left(-\frac{7}{4}\right)$ $\frac{1}{2}$

78. $\left(-\frac{3}{11}\right) \div \left(\frac{21}{22}\right)$ $-\frac{2}{7}$

For Exercises 79–92, simplify using the order of operations.

79. $|-14| - |-5|$ 9

80. $\sqrt{81} - |-4|$ 5

81. $10 \div 5 \cdot 4$ 8

82. $12 \div 2 - 3$ 3

83. $6 + 42 \div 7 - 10$ 2

84. $21 - 3 \cdot 5 + 6$ 12

85. $(8 - 5)^2 - (2 + 3)^2$ -16

86. $16 - (10 - 3)^2 + 2 \cdot 7$ -19

87. $3^3 - 2 + 5(3 - 7)$ 5

88. $6 - 4^2 + (8 \div 4 + 5)$ -3

89. $12 - \sqrt{25} + 4^2 \div 2$ 15

90. $\sqrt{81} - \sqrt{16} \div 4 + 18$ 26

91. $\dfrac{6 + 8 - (-2)}{-40 \div 8 - 1}$ $-\frac{8}{3}$

92. $\dfrac{\sqrt{32 \div 2} + 7}{-52 + (7 \cdot 4 + 2)}$ $-\frac{1}{2}$

For Exercises 93–96, evaluate the expressions given $a = 3$, $b = -5$, $c = 9$, and $d = -2$.

93. $a^2 - b^2$ -16

94. $c \div a - b$ 8

95. $b + \sqrt{c} \cdot d$ -11

96. $-a^2 + c$ 0

97. The area of a trapezoid is given by the formula $A = \frac{1}{2}(b_1 + b_2)h$. Find the area of the given trapezoid.

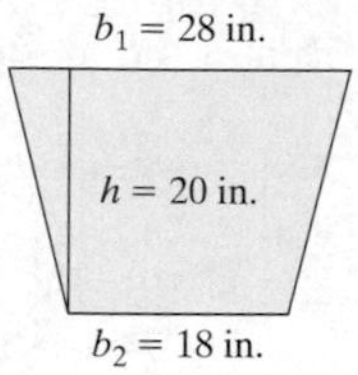

460 in.^{2}

98. The surface area of a rectangular solid with a square base is given by $S = 4ab + 2a^2$. Find the surface area of the given rectangular solid.

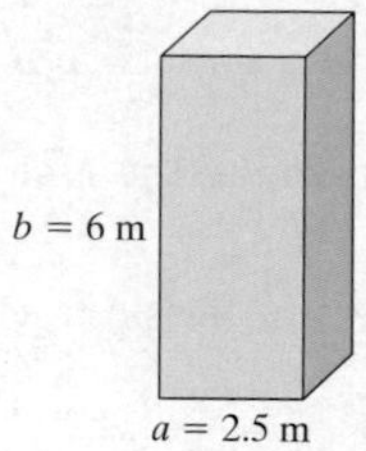

72.5 m^2

For Exercises 99–104, identify the property that is shown. Choose from the commutative property of addition, commutative property of multiplication, associative property of addition, associative property of multiplication, or distributive property of multiplication over addition.

99. $4(8 \cdot 14) = (4 \cdot 8)(14)$ Associative property of multiplication

100. $(7 + 4) + 6 = 7 + (4 + 6)$ Associative property of addition

101. $-6(3 + 9) = -6(3) + -6(9)$ Distributive property of multiplication over addition

102. $9 \cdot 2 = 2 \cdot 9$ Commutative property of multiplication

103. $5 + 15 = 15 + 5$ Commutative property of addition

104. $9(11 + 4) = 9(11) + 9(4)$ Distributive property of multiplication over addition

105. What is the identity element for multiplication? Use it in an example. 1; for example $1(3) = 3$

106. What is the identity element for addition? Use it in an example. 0; for example $0 + 8 = 8$

107. **a.** What is another name for multiplicative inverse? reciprocal

b. Write the multiplicative inverse of 4. $\frac{1}{4}$

108. **a.** What is another name for the additive inverse? opposite

b. Write the additive inverse of 6. -6

For Exercises 109–116, simplify the expression by applying the distributive property.

109. $5(a + 9)$ $5a + 45$

110. $3(x + 12)$ $3x + 36$

111. $-7(y - z)$ $-7y + 7z$

112. $-2(a - b)$ $-2a + 2b$

113. $\frac{1}{3}(6b + 9c - 15)$ $2b + 3c - 5$

114. $\frac{1}{5}(10h - 20k - 5)$ $2h - 4k - 1$

115. $-(2x - 3y + 8)$ $-2x + 3y - 8$

116. $-(-3p - q + 9)$ $3p + q - 9$

For Exercises 117–124, simplify the expression by clearing parentheses and combining like terms.

117. $5a + 2(a + 7)$ $7a + 14$

118. $6b - 3(b + 4)$ $3b - 12$

119. $8y - 3(y + 2) - 19$ $5y - 25$

120. $9k - 3(k - 4) + 8$ $6k + 20$

121. $4w + 9u - (5w - 3u)$ $-w + 12u$

122. $-5m + 2(m + 4n) - 7n$ $-3m + n$

123. $2g - 4[2 - 3(g - 4h) - 2]$ $14g - 48h$

124. $3p + 8[q - (p - 4) - 3p]$ $-29p + 8q + 32$

Review of Linear Equations and Linear Inequalities

Section B.5

Concepts

1. Solving Linear Equations in One Variable
2. Problem Solving
3. Linear Inequalities

1. Solving Linear Equations in One Variable

An equation that can be written in the form $ax + b = c$, where $a \neq 0$, is called a **linear equation in one variable**. The steps for solving a linear equation in one variable are given next.

Solving a Linear Equation in One Variable

Step 1 Simplify both sides of the equation.
- Clear parentheses
- Consider clearing fractions or decimals (if any are present) by multiplying both sides of the equation by a common denominator of all terms.
- Combine *like* terms

Step 2 Use the addition or subtraction property of equality to collect the variable terms on one side of the equation.

Step 3 Use the addition or subtraction property of equality to collect the constant terms on the other side of the equation.

Step 4 Use the multiplication or division property of equality to make the coefficient of the variable term equal to 1.

Step 5 Check your answer.

Example 1 Solving Linear Equations in One Variable

Solve. $\frac{1}{3}x + \frac{1}{4}x = x + 5$

Solution:

$\frac{1}{3}x + \frac{1}{4}x = x + 5$	The LCD (least common denominator) is 12.
$12\left(\frac{1}{3}x + \frac{1}{4}x\right) = 12(x + 5)$	Multiply both sides by 12.
$\frac{12}{1}\left(\frac{1}{3}x\right) + \frac{12}{1}\left(\frac{1}{4}x\right) = \frac{12}{1}(x) + \frac{12}{1}(5)$	Apply the distributive property.
$4x + 3x = 12x + 60$	
$7x = 12x + 60$	Combine *like* terms.
$-5x = 60$	Subtract $12x$ from both sides.
$x = -12$	Divide both sides by -5.

The answer can be checked by substituting $x = -12$ back into the original equation and verifying that the left-hand side equals the right-hand side.

The solution set is $\{-12\}$.

2. Problem Solving

Solving word problems in mathematics takes practice and often a little patience. We also offer the following guidelines for problem solving.

Problem-Solving Guidelines

Step 1 Read the problem carefully.
Step 2 Assign labels to unknown quantities.
Step 3 Write a verbal model.
Step 4 Write a mathematical equation.
Step 5 Solve the equation.
Step 6 Interpret the results and write the answer in words.

Example 2 Solving an Application Involving Principal and Interest

Kadriana took out two student loans for a total of \$8500. One loan was for 5% simple interest and the other was for 8% simple interest. If the total interest after one year was \$530, find the amount borrowed at each rate.

Solution:

We have two unknown values. We arbitrarily let x represent the amount borrowed at 5%. Then the remaining principal, $8500 - x$, is the amount borrowed at 8%.

Step 1: Read the problem.

	5% Loan	8% Loan	Total
Principal	x	$8500 - x$	
Interest	$0.05x$	$0.08(8500 - x)$	530

Step 2: Label the variables. A chart may help to organize the information given in the problem.

$$\begin{pmatrix}\text{Interest from}\\ \text{5\% loan}\end{pmatrix} + \begin{pmatrix}\text{Interest from}\\ \text{8\% loan}\end{pmatrix} = \begin{pmatrix}\text{Total}\\ \text{interest}\end{pmatrix}$$

Step 3: Verbal model.

$$0.05x + 0.08(8500 - x) = 530$$

Step 4: Mathematical equation.

$$0.05x + 680 - 0.08x = 530$$
$$-0.03x + 680 = 530$$

Step 5: Solve the equation. Combine *like* terms.

$$-0.03x = -150$$

Subtract 680 from both sides.

$$\frac{-0.03x}{-0.03} = \frac{-150}{-0.03}$$

Divide both sides by -0.03.

$$x = 5000$$

Step 6: Write the answer in words.

The amount borrowed at 5% is \$5000. The amount borrowed at 8% is given by $8500 - x = 8500 - 5000 = 3500$. Thus, \$3500 was borrowed at 8%.

Example 3 **Solving an Application Involving Distance, Rate, and Time**

Two cars leave a rest area at 12:00 P.M. One car travels north on Interstate 25 through Colorado and the other travels south. The southbound car travels 10 mph slower than the northbound car. After 2 hours, the cars are 260 miles apart. How fast is the northbound car traveling?

Solution:

Step 1: Read the problem.

Let x represent the speed of the northbound car. **Step 2:** Label the variables.

	Distance	Rate	Time
Northbound Car	$2(x)$	x	2
Southbound Car	$2(x - 10)$	$x - 10$	2

$d = rt$ distance = (rate)(time)

$$\left(\begin{array}{c}\text{Distance by}\\ \text{northbound car}\end{array}\right) + \left(\begin{array}{c}\text{distance by}\\ \text{southbound car}\end{array}\right) = \left(\begin{array}{c}\text{total}\\ \text{distance}\end{array}\right)$$ **Step 3:** Verbal model.

$$2x + 2(x - 10) = 260$$ **Step 4:** Mathematical equation.

$$2x + 2x - 20 = 260$$ **Step 5:** Solve the equation.

$$4x - 20 = 260$$

$$4x = 280$$

$$x = 70$$

The northbound car travels at 70 mph. **Step 6:** Interpret the answer.

3. Linear Inequalities

A linear inequality is a mathematical sentence written with one of the symbols, $<, >, \leq,$ or $\geq$. The solution to an inequality can be visualized graphically on a number line or can be written in interval notation. For any real numbers a and b, Table B-5 summarizes the solution sets for five general inequalities.

Table B-5

Inequality	Graph	Interval Notation
$x > a$	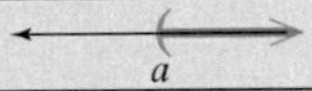	(a, ∞)
$x \geq a$	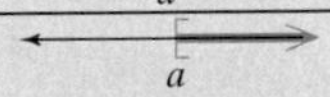	$[a, \infty)$
$x < a$	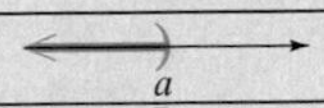	$(-\infty, a)$
$x \leq a$	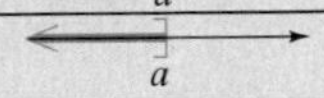	$(-\infty, a]$
$a < x < b$	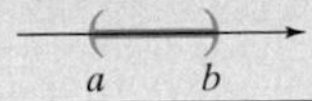	(a, b)

The use of a parenthesis (or) indicates that an endpoint is not included in the solution. The use of a square bracket [or] indicates that an endpoint *is* included in the solution. Note that a parenthesis is always used for infinity.

The steps to solve a linear inequality mirror those to solve a linear equation. **However, if an inequality is multiplied or divided by a negative number, then the direction of the inequality sign must be reversed.** This is demonstrated in Example 4.

Example 4 Solving a Linear Inequality

Solve the inequality. Graph the solution and write the solution in interval notation.

$$-4(x-3)+1 \le x+23$$

Solution:

$-4(x-3)+1 \le x+23$

$-4x+12+1 \le x+23$ Apply the distributive property.

$-4x+13 \le x+23$ Combine *like* terms.

$-4x-x+13 \le x-x+23$ Subtract x from both sides.

$-5x+13 \le 23$

$-5x+13-13 \le 23-13$ Subtract 13 from both sides.

$-5x \le 10$

$\dfrac{-5x}{-5} \ge \dfrac{10}{-5}$ Divide both sides by -5. Reverse the direction of the inequality sign.

$x \ge -2$

Graph: 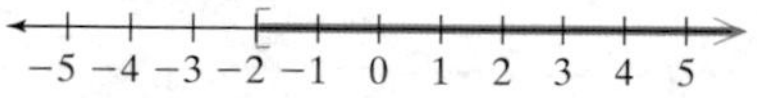

Interval notation: $[-2, \infty)$

Section B.5 Practice Exercises

For Exercises 1–30, solve the equation.

1. $4x = -84$ $\{-21\}$
2. $-3y = 72$ $\{-24\}$
3. $\dfrac{t}{5} = 12$ $\{60\}$
4. $\dfrac{r}{3} = 13$ $\{39\}$
5. $6 + p = -14$ $\{-20\}$
6. $-5 + q = -23$ $\{-18\}$
7. $7x + 12 = 33$ $\{3\}$
8. $-3x - 4 = -1$ $\{-1\}$
9. $4(x + 5) = 14$ $\left\{-\frac{3}{2}\right\}$
10. $5(y - 2) = -22$ $\left\{-\frac{12}{5}\right\}$
11. $3b + 25 = 5b - 21$ $\{23\}$
12. $4c - 9 = 6c + 17$ $\{-13\}$

13. $3w + 2(w - 7) = 7(w - 1)$ $\left\{-\frac{7}{2}\right\}$

14. $x + 5(x - 4) = 3(x - 8) - 5$ $\{-3\}$

15. $\frac{1}{5}y - \frac{3}{10}y = y - \frac{2}{5}y + 1$ $\left\{-\frac{10}{7}\right\}$

16. $\frac{2}{3}q + 2 - \frac{1}{9}q = \frac{5}{9}q + \frac{4}{3}q$ $\left\{\frac{3}{2}\right\}$

17. $\frac{5}{6}(x + 2) = \frac{1}{3}x - \frac{3}{2}$ $\left\{-\frac{19}{3}\right\}$

18. $\frac{1}{4}(6 - p) = \frac{3}{8}(2 + 3p)$ $\left\{\frac{6}{11}\right\}$

19. $0.2a + 6 = 1.8a - 2.8$ $\{5.5\}$

20. $0.3(v - 3) = 1.4v - 3.1$ $\{2\}$

21. $0.72t - 1.18 = 0.28(4 - t)$ $\{2.3\}$

22. $0.08(100 - 73x) = 1.2(1 - 5x)$ $\{-42.5\}$

23. $-4(x + 1) - 2x = -2(3x + 2) - x$ $\{0\}$

24. $5(z + 3) - 2z + 6(1 - z) = 4 - 2(1 + z)$ $\{19\}$

25. $11 - 5(y + 3) = -2[2y - 3(1 - y)]$ $\{2\}$

26. $-4p + 2[p - 4(2 - p)] = 4(p - 5)$ $\{-2\}$

27. $-8m - 2[4 - 3(m + 1)] = 4(3 - m) + 4$ $\{9\}$

28. $10x - 5[1 + 3(1 - 2x)] = [4(x - 3) + 27] + x$ $\{1\}$

29. $4 - 6[2y - 2(y + 3)] = 7 - y$ $\{-33\}$

30. $-3(x + 4) + 2x + 12 = -6(x - 5)$ $\{6\}$

For Exercises 31–40, solve.

31. Five times the product of 8 and a number is 20. What is the number? $\frac{1}{2}$

32. One half of the total of 6 times a number and 20 is 4. What is the number? -2

33. The sum of three consecutive integers is -57. Find the integers. $-20, -19, -18$

34. The sum of three consecutive odd integers is 111. Find the integers. 35, 37, 39

35. If Casey invested \$2500 in an account and earned \$112.50 in interest the first year, what was the simple interest rate? 4.5%

36. Roberto deposited \$4050 in an account that made \$202.50 simple interest the first year. Find the simple interest rate. 5%

37. Ketul made a total investment of \$3500 into two accounts earning 4.2% simple interest and 3.8% simple interest. If his total interest after 1 year was \$141.40, how much was invested in each account?
\$2100 in the 4.2% account, \$1400 in the 3.8% account

38. Kaitlin borrowed \$1800, part from her parents and part from a bank. The bank charged 8% interest but her parents only charged 2%. If she paid off the loan in 1 year and paid a total of \$102 interest, how much did she borrow from her parents? \$700

39. A car and a truck leave home at the same time traveling in opposite directions. The truck travels 4 mph slower than the car. If the distance between the two vehicles is 372 mi after 3 hr, find the speed of each vehicle. Car: 64 mph; truck: 60 mph

40. Juan and Peter both leave a shopping center at the same time going in opposite directions. Juan is on his bike and travels 3 mph faster than Peter who is on his skateboard. After 1.5 hr they are 19.5 mi apart. How fast does Peter travel. 5 mph

For Exercises 41–56, solve the inequality. Graph the solution set and write the set in interval notation.

41. $3 - x > 5$ $(-\infty, -2)$

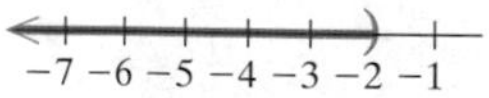

42. $4 - 2d < 6$ $(-1, \infty)$

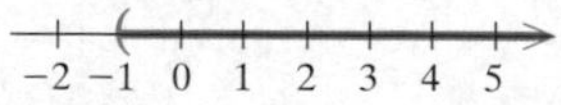

43. $4y + 6 \geq -18$ $[-6, \infty)$

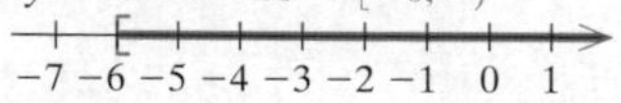

44. $3r - 13 \leq 27$ $\left(-\infty, \frac{40}{3}\right]$

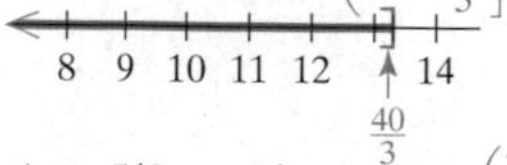

45. $8m - 15 < 9m - 13$ $(-2, \infty)$

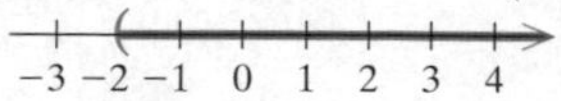

46. $6n + 23 > -3n - 13$ $(-4, \infty)$

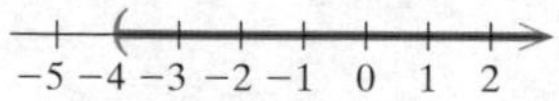

47. $1 - 5(2t - 7) < 38t$ $\left(\frac{3}{4}, \infty\right)$

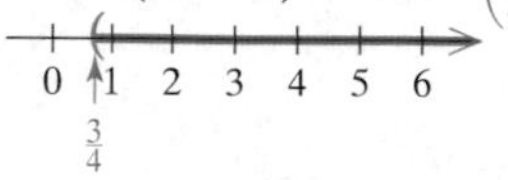

48. $9r + 3(r - 14) \geq 6$ $[4, \infty)$

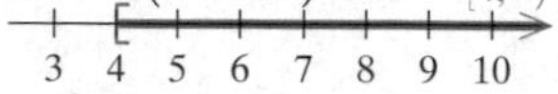

49. $-5 < 4p + 2 \leq 6$ $\left(-\frac{7}{4}, 1\right]$

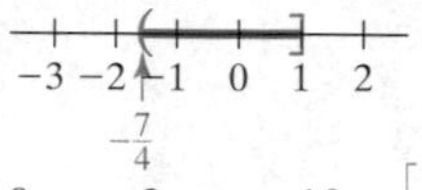

50. $-8 \leq 7 + 5k \leq 17$ $[-3, 2]$

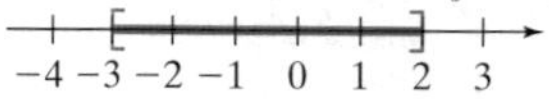

51. $2 > -y + 1 > -6$ $(-1, 7)$

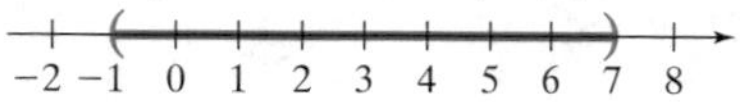

52. $0 \geq -3x \geq -10$ $\left[0, \frac{10}{3}\right]$

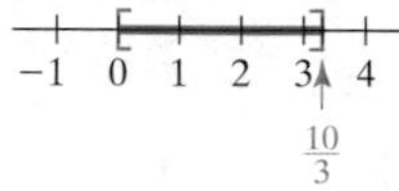

53. $\frac{1}{7}h + 2 > \frac{5}{14}h - \frac{1}{2}$ $\left(-\infty, \frac{35}{3}\right)$

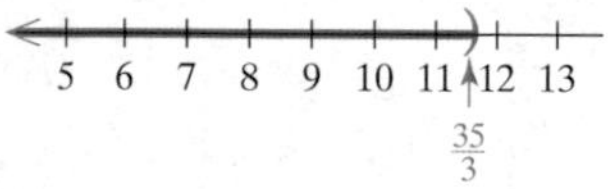

54. $\frac{2}{3}b - \frac{1}{6} \leq 3b + \frac{5}{6}$ $\left[-\frac{3}{7}, \infty\right)$

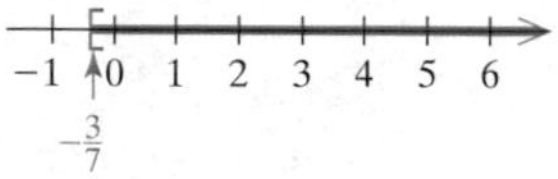

55. $0.4w + 3.1(w - 1) \leq -3.8$ $(-\infty, -0.2]$

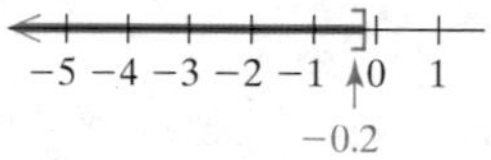

56. $2.1x - 2(x + 5.1) > -8.2$ $(20, \infty)$

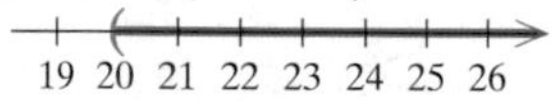

Section B.6 Review of Graphing

Concepts

1. Plotting Ordered Pairs
2. Graphing Linear Equations in Two Variables
3. x- and y-Intercepts
4. Horizontal and Vertical Lines
5. Slope of a Line
6. Slope-Intercept Form
7. Point-Slope Formula

1. Plotting Ordered Pairs

In Figure B-10, we review some important features of a rectangular coordinate system. The x- and y-axes are perpendicular lines that cross at a common point called the **origin**. The arrows indicate the positive direction for the x- and y-axes. The four regions in the graph are called **quadrants**. Each point in a rectangular coordinate system is represented by an **ordered pair**. Figure B-11 shows the location of the following ordered pairs: (4, 1), (−2, 5), (5, −2), (−2, 1), (0, 4), and $(-\frac{7}{2}, -2)$. For example, to plot the point represented by (−2, 5) move −2 units in the x-direction (left) and 5 units in the y-direction (up) and draw a dot.

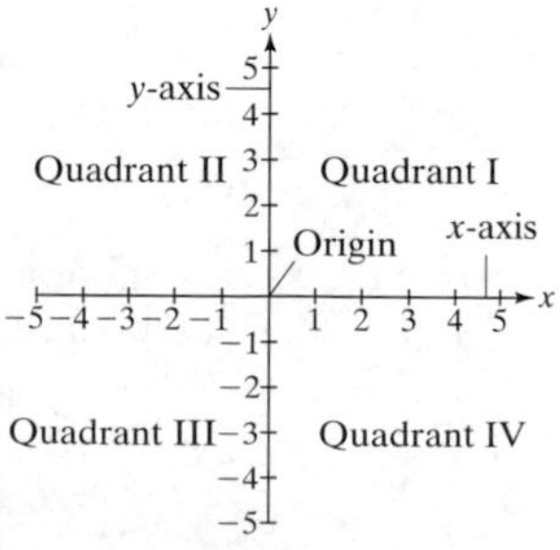

Figure B-10

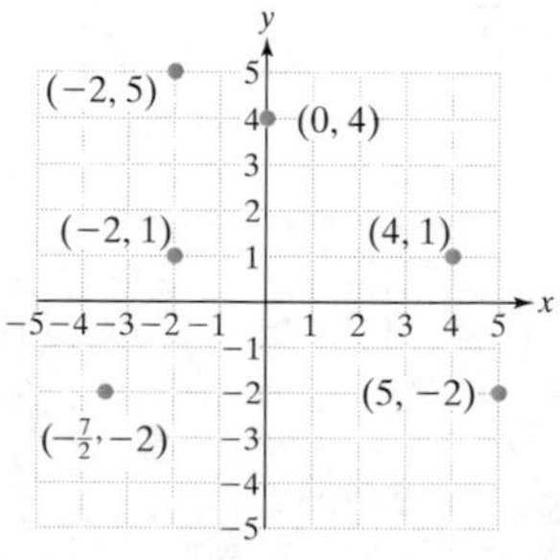

Figure B-11

2. Graphing Linear Equations in Two Variables

An equation that can be written in the form $Ax + By = C$ (where A and B are not both 0) is called a linear equation in two variables. The equation $3x + y = 5$ is a linear equation in two variables. A solution to such an equation is an ordered pair (x, y) that when substituted into the equation makes the equation a true statement. For example, the ordered pair $(-1, 8)$ is a solution to the equation $3x + y = 5$ because $3(-1) + 8 = 5$. A linear equation in two variables has infinitely many solutions that when plotted form a line in a rectangular coordinate system. To find a solution to a linear equation in two variables, we substitute any real number for one of the variables in the equation and then solve for the other variable.

Example 1 **Graphing a Linear Equation in Two Variables**

Complete the ordered pairs to form solutions to the equation $3x + y = 5$. Then graph the equation.

$(1, \ )$ $(\ , -4)$ $(0, \ )$ $(\ , 0)$

Solution:

The ordered pairs can also be represented in tabular form as follows.

x	y		$3x + y = 5$		x	y	Ordered pair
1		→	$3(1) + y = 5$	→	1	2	$(1, 2)$
	−4	→	$3x + (-4) = 5$	→	3	−4	$(3, -4)$
0		→	$3(0) + y = 5$	→	0	5	$(0, 5)$
	0	→	$3x + (0) = 5$	→	$\frac{5}{3}$	0	$(\frac{5}{3}, 0)$

The ordered pairs are graphed in Figure B-12. Notice that the points all "line up." The line drawn through the points represents all solutions to the equation. Therefore, we say the line represents a graph of the equation.

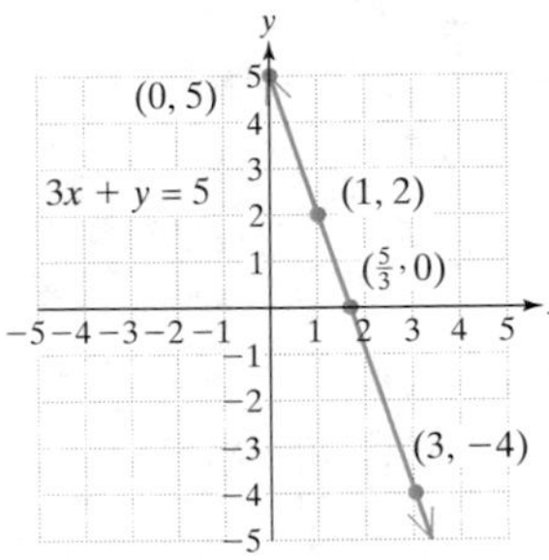

Figure B-12

3. x- and y-Intercepts

In Example 1, the points $(\frac{5}{3}, 0)$ and $(0, 5)$ lie on the x-axis and y-axis, respectively. The point $(\frac{5}{3}, 0)$ is called an x-intercept and the point $(0, 5)$ is called a y-intercept. In general, the x- and y-intercepts of a graph are points where the graph intersects the x- and y-axes, respectively. Notice that the x-intercept $(\frac{5}{3}, 0)$ has a y-coordinate of 0. The y-intercept $(0, 5)$ has an x-coordinate of 0.

Finding x- and y-Intercepts

Step 1 Find the x-intercept(s) by substituting $y = 0$ into the equation and solving for x.

Step 2 Find the y-intercept(s) by substituting $x = 0$ into the equation and solving for y.

Example 2 Finding *x*- and *y*-Intercepts

Given $7x - 3y = 6$, find the *x*- and *y*-intercepts.

Solution:

To find the *x*-intercept, substitute zero for *y*:

$$7x - 3(0) = 6$$
$$7x = 6$$
$$x = \frac{6}{7}$$

To find the *y*-intercept, substitute zero for *x*:

$$7(0) - 3y = 6$$
$$-3y = 6$$
$$y = -2$$

The *x*-intercept is $(\frac{6}{7}, 0)$ and the *y*-intercept is $(0, -2)$.

4. Horizontal and Vertical Lines

An equation of the form $x = k$ is a vertical line in a rectangular coordinate system. An equation of the form $y = k$ is a horizontal line.

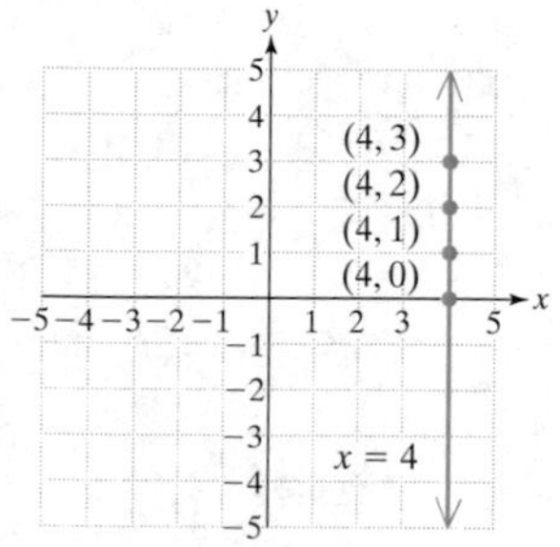

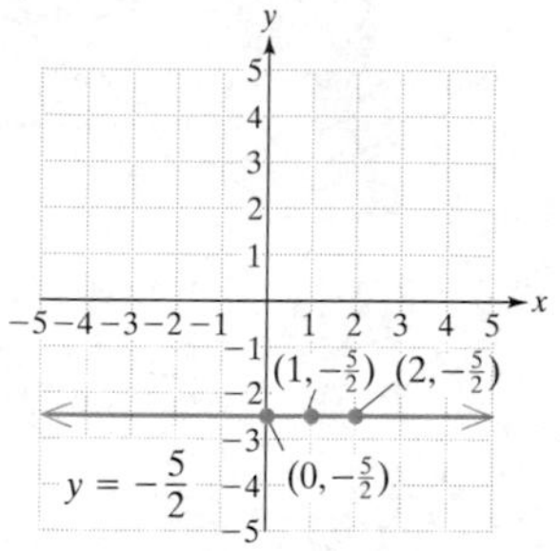

Example 3 Graphing Horizontal and Vertical Lines

Graph the lines. **a.** $x = 4$ **b.** $-2y = 5$

Solution:

a. The equation $x = 4$ is in the form $x = k$. Therefore, the graph of the equation is a vertical line that passes through the *x*-axis at 4.

The solutions to the equation $x = 4$ are ordered pairs whose *x*-coordinate is 4 and whose *y*-coordinate has no restriction. Several such solutions are $(4, 0)$, $(4, 1)$, $(4, 2)$, $(4, 3)$, and so on.

b. The equation $-2y = 5$ is equivalent to $y = -\frac{5}{2}$. The equation is in the form $y = k$. Therefore, the graph of the equation is a horizontal line passing through the *y*-axis at $-\frac{5}{2}$.

The solutions to the equation $y = -\frac{5}{2}$ are ordered pairs whose *y*-coordinate is $-\frac{5}{2}$ and whose *x*-coordinate has no restriction. Several such solutions are $(0, -\frac{5}{2})$, $(1, -\frac{5}{2})$, $(2, -\frac{5}{2})$, and so on.

5. Slope of a Line

The slope of a line (often denoted by m) is a measure of the line's "steepness." It measures the ratio of an incremental change in y to an incremental change in x between two points on the line.

The slope is $\frac{3}{2}$.

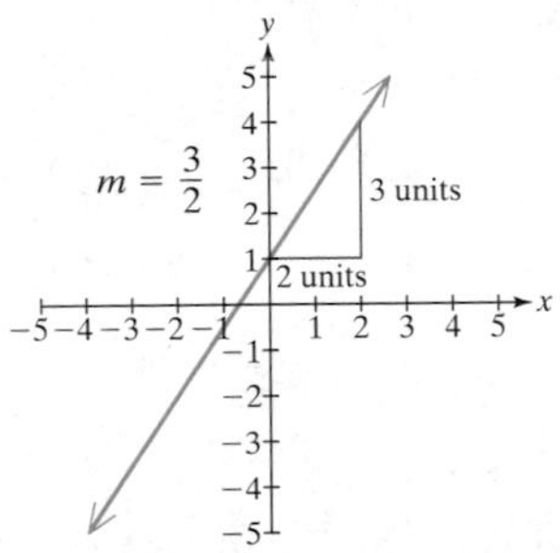

The slope is 4.

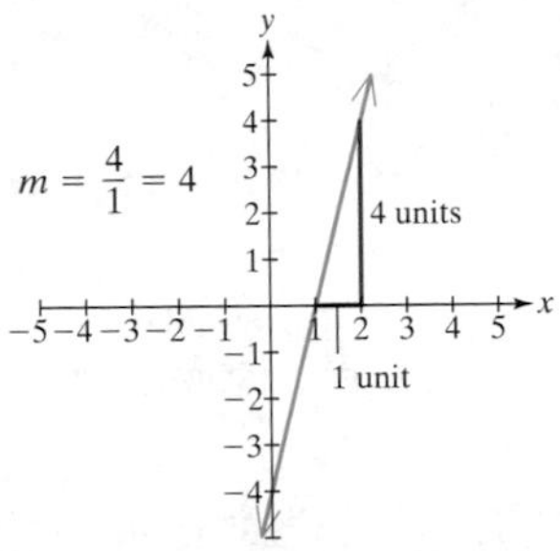

The slope of a line may be positive, negative, zero, or undefined.

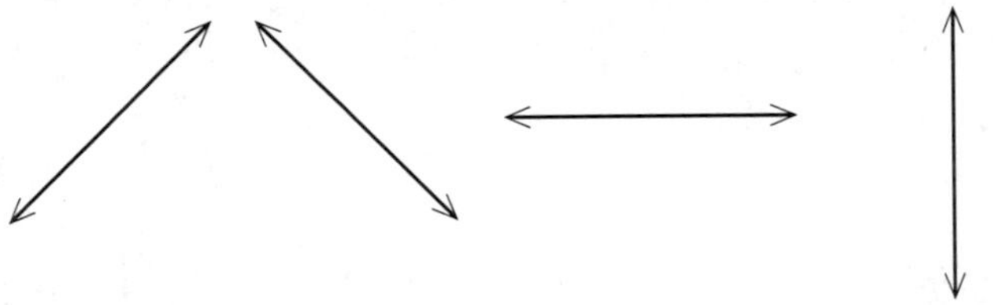

To find the slope of a line given two points, (x_1, y_1) and (x_2, y_2), we use the slope formula.

Slope Formula

The slope of a line passing through the distinct points (x_1, y_1) and (x_2, y_2) is

$$m = \frac{y_2 - y_1}{x_2 - x_1} \text{ provided } x_2 - x_1 \neq 0.$$

Example 4 **Finding the Slope Given Two Points on a Line**

Find the slope of the line between $(-3, -4)$ and $(7, -1)$.

Solution:

(x_1, y_1) (x_2, y_2)

$(-3, -4)$ $(7, -1)$ Label the points.

$$m = \frac{y_2 - y_1}{x_2 - x_1} = \frac{-1 - (-4)}{7 - (-3)} = \frac{3}{10}$$ The slope is $\frac{3}{10}$.

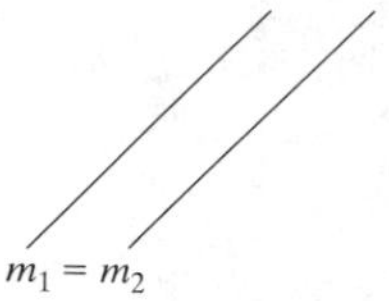

$m_1 = m_2$

$m_1 = -\frac{1}{m_2}$

The slopes of two lines can be used to determine whether the lines are parallel or perpendicular.

- Two lines that are parallel have the same slope. That is, $m_1 = m_2$.
- The slopes of perpendicular lines are related such that one slope is the opposite of the reciprocal of the other.

  That is, $m_1 = -\frac{1}{m_2}$.

6. Slope-Intercept Form

A linear equation in two variables written in the form $y = mx + b$ is said to be in slope-intercept form. In such a case, m is the slope, and $(0, b)$ is the y-intercept. To write a linear equation in slope-intercept form, solve the equation for y.

Example 5 Writing an Equation in Slope-Intercept Form

Given $2x + 5y = 20$,

a. Write the equation in slope-intercept form.

b. Identify the slope and y-intercept.

c. Graph the line using the slope and y-intercept.

Solution:

a. $2x + 5y = 20$ — To write in the form $y = mx + b$, solve for y.

$5y = -2x + 20$ — Subtract $2x$ from both sides.

$\frac{5y}{5} = \frac{-2x}{5} + \frac{20}{5}$ — Divide by 5.

$y = -\frac{2}{5}x + 4$ — The equation is in slope-intercept form.

b. The slope is $-\frac{2}{5}$ and the y-intercept is $(0, 4)$.

c. To graph the line using the slope and y-intercept, first plot the y-intercept. Then we can use the slope to find a second point on the line. For example,

The slope can be interpreted as $\frac{-2}{5}$, which indicates that we move two units in the negative y-direction (down) and 5 units in the positive x-direction (right).

The slope can also be interpreted as $\frac{2}{-5}$ which indicates that we move two units in the positive y direction (up) and 5 units in the negative x-direction (left). See Figure B-13.

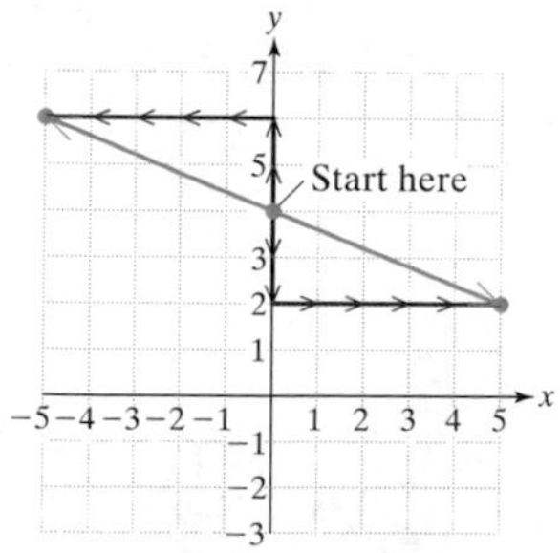

Figure B-13

Example 6 Determining Whether Lines are Parallel, Perpendicular, or Neither

Determine whether the lines l_1 and l_2 are parallel, perpendicular, or neither.

l_1: $2x - 3y = 12$ $\qquad$ l_2: $6x + 4y = 4$

Solution:

Write each line in slope-intercept form and compare the slopes.

l_1: $2x - 3y = 12$

$$-3y = -2x + 12$$

$$\frac{-3y}{-3} = \frac{-2x}{-3} + \frac{12}{-3}$$

$$y = \frac{2}{3}x - 4$$

The slope of l_1 is $\frac{2}{3}$.

l_2: $6x + 4y = 4$

$$4y = -6x + 4$$

$$\frac{4y}{4} = \frac{-6x}{4} + \frac{4}{4}$$

$$y = -\frac{3}{2}x + 1$$

The slope of l_2 is $-\frac{3}{2}$.

The slope of l_1 is the opposite of the reciprocal of the slope of l_2. Therefore, the lines are perpendicular.

7. Point-Slope Formula

The point-slope formula is a useful tool to find an equation of a line given a point on the line and the slope of the line.

Point-Slope Formula

The **point-slope formula** is given by

$$y - y_1 = m(x - x_1)$$

where m is the slope of the line and (x_1, y_1) is a known point on the line.

Example 7 Writing an Equation of a Line Given Two Points

Write an equation of the line passing through the points $(-2, -1)$ and $(-4, 5)$. Write the final answer in slope-intercept form and in standard form.

Solution:

We can find the slope of the line by using the slope formula. Once the slope is known, we can apply the point-slope formula using the slope and either given point.

$(-2, -1)$ and $(-4, 5)$

(x_1, y_1) and (x_2, y_2) — Label the points.

$$m = \frac{y_2 - y_1}{x_2 - x_1} = \frac{5 - (-1)}{-4 - (-2)} = \frac{6}{-2} = -3$$ Apply the slope formula.

$$y - y_1 = m(x - x_1)$$

$$y - (-1) = -3[(x - (-2))]$$ Apply the point-slope formula.

$$y + 1 = -3(x + 2)$$

$$y + 1 = -3x - 6$$

$$y = -3x - 7 \text{ (slope-intercept form)}$$ Solve for y.

or

$$3x + y = -7 \text{ (standard form)}$$ Write in the form $Ax + By = C$.

Section B.6 Practice Exercises

For Exercises 1–8, plot the points on a rectangular coordinate system.

1. $(2, 4)$ **2.** $(4, 2)$ **3.** $(4, -3)$

4. $(0, 2)$ **5.** $(-3, 0)$ **6.** $(0, 0)$

7. $\left(-\frac{3}{2}, -2\right)$ **8.** $(-1, 3)$

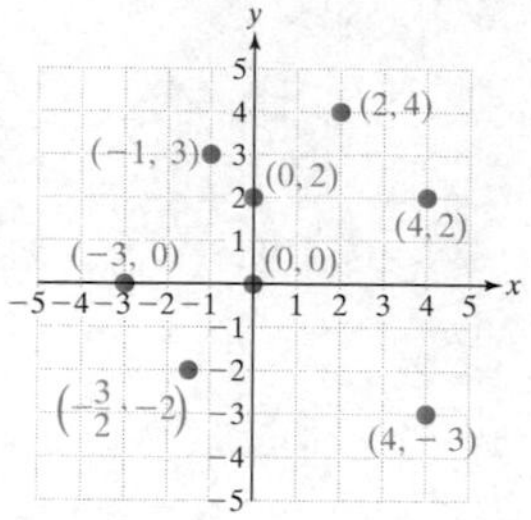

For Exercises 9–16, identify the quadrant in which each point is located.

9. $(20, -6)$ IV **10.** $(-3, -3)$ III **11.** $\left(-13, -\frac{7}{8}\right)$ III **12.** $\left(\frac{12}{7}, 5\right)$ I

13. $(\pi, 14)$ I **14.** $(7.8, -42)$ IV **15.** $(-3.8, 6.2)$ II **16.** $(-7.8, 42)$ II

For Exercises 17–22, complete the table and graph the line.

17. $x + y = 4$

x	y
3	1
5	−1
0	4

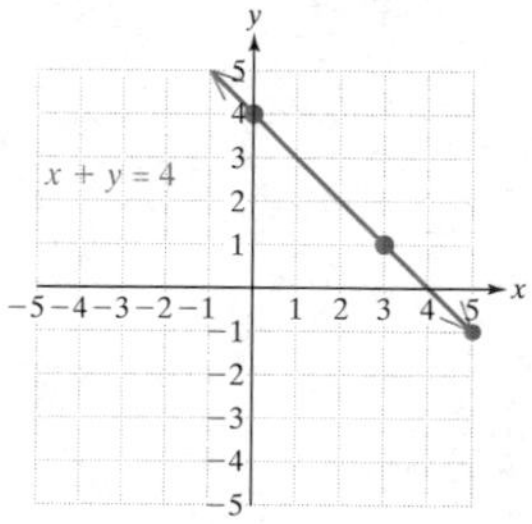

18. $3x - y = 6$

x	y
2	0
7/3	1
1	−3

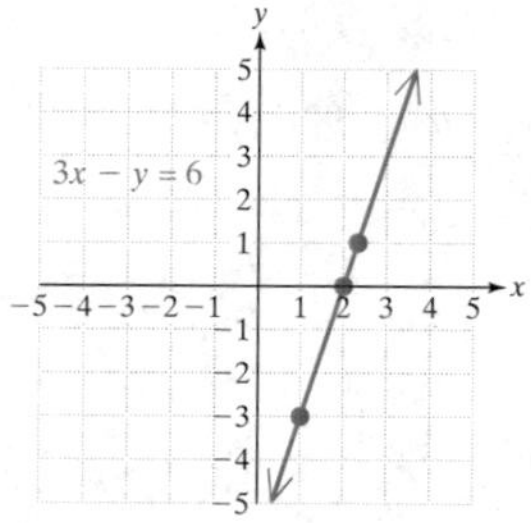

19. $y = 5x$

x	y
0	0
$\frac{2}{5}$	2
−1	−5

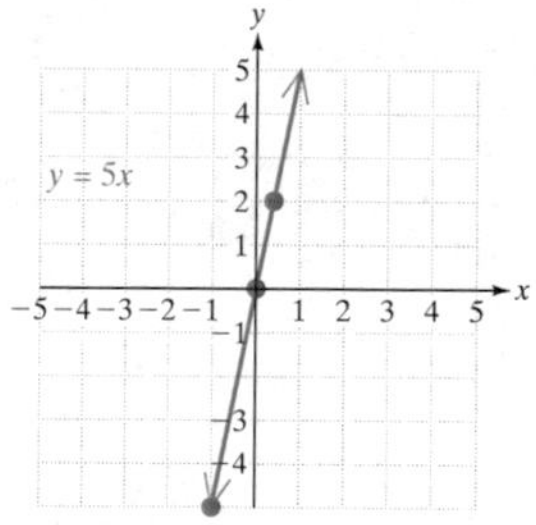

20. $y = -2x + 3$

x	y
1	1
$\frac{1}{2}$	2
−1	5

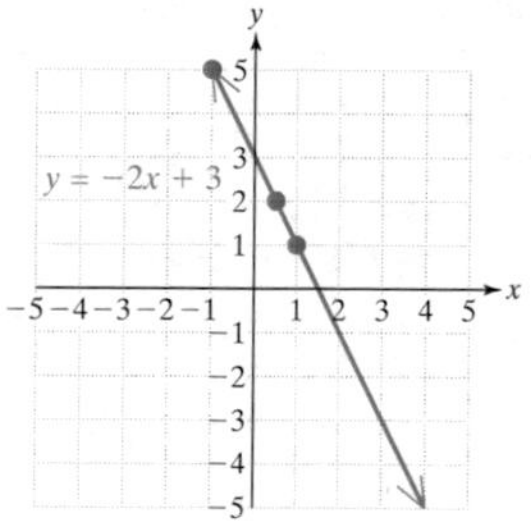

21. $y = \frac{2}{3}x + 1$

x	y
3	3
−3	−1
0	1

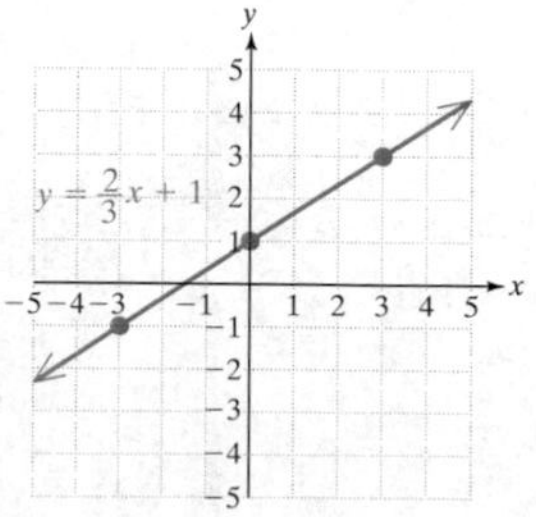

22. $y = -\frac{4}{3}x + 2$

x	y
3	−2
0	2
−1	10/3

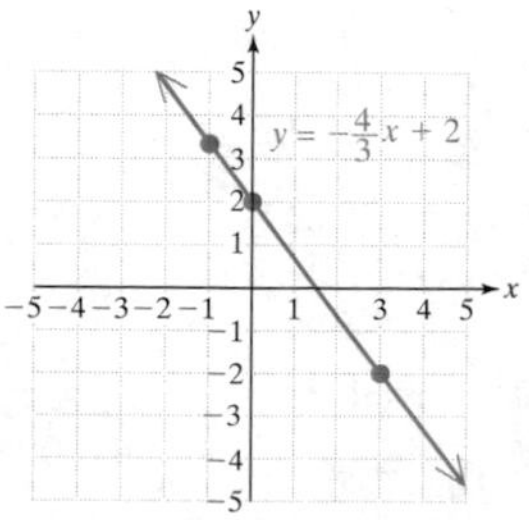

For Exercises 23–34, find the x- and y-intercepts.

23. $3x - 2y = 18$
x-intercept $(6, 0)$; y-intercept $(0, -9)$

24. $x - 4y = 16$
x-intercept $(16, 0)$; y-intercept $(0, -4)$

25. $5x + y = -15$
x-intercept $(-3, 0)$; y-intercept $(0, -15)$

26. $-6x - y = 6$
x-intercept $(-1, 0)$; y-intercept $(0, -6)$

27. $\frac{1}{2}x + y = 2$
x-intercept $(4, 0)$; y-intercept $(0, 2)$

28. $x - \frac{1}{3}y = -4$
x-intercept $(-4, 0)$; y-intercept $(0, 12)$

29. $-3x + 4y = 0$
x-intercept $(0, 0)$; y-intercept $(0, 0)$

30. $6x - 5y = 0$
x-intercept $(0, 0)$; y-intercept $(0, 0)$

31. $y = -\frac{2}{3}x - 3$
x-intercept $\left(-\frac{9}{2}, 0\right)$; y-intercept $(0, -3)$

32. $y = \frac{3}{5}x + 1$
x-intercept $\left(-\frac{5}{3}, 0\right)$; y-intercept $(0, 1)$

33. $y = 6x - 5$
x-intercept $\left(\frac{5}{6}, 0\right)$; y-intercept $(0, -5)$

34. $y = -2x - 3$
x-intercept $\left(-\frac{3}{2}, 0\right)$; y-intercept $(0, -3)$

For Exercises 35–40, write the equation in the form $x = k$ or $y = k$ and identify the line as horizontal or vertical.

35. $2x = 6$ $x = 3$; vertical

36. $5y = 10$ $y = 2$; horizontal

37. $-3y + 1 = 2$ $y = -\frac{1}{3}$; horizontal

38. $7x - 1 = 3$ $x = \frac{4}{7}$; vertical

39. $5x = 0$ $x = 0$; vertical

40. $\frac{2}{3}y = 0$ $y = 0$; horizontal

For Exercises 41–46, determine the slope of the line passing through the given points.

41. $(3, -4)$ and $(5, 0)$ 2

42. $(-7, 4)$ and $(-14, -3)$ 1

43. $(-2, -2)$ and $(-5, -10)$ $\frac{8}{3}$

44. $(6, 1)$ and $(0, -2)$ $\frac{1}{2}$

45. $(5, -12)$ and $(2, 1)$ $-\frac{13}{3}$

46. $(0, 4)$ and $(9, 0)$ $-\frac{4}{9}$

For Exercises 47–56, write the equation in slope-intercept form (if possible). Then identify the slope and the y-intercept (if they exist).

47. $4x - 5y = 6$
$y = \frac{4}{5}x - \frac{6}{5}$; slope is $\frac{4}{5}$; y-intercept $\left(0, -\frac{6}{5}\right)$

48. $2x - 5y = 11$
$y = \frac{2}{5}x - \frac{11}{5}$; slope is $\frac{2}{5}$; y-intercept $\left(0, -\frac{11}{5}\right)$

49. $-6x + 2y = 3$
$y = 3x + \frac{3}{2}$; slope is 3; y-intercept $\left(0, \frac{3}{2}\right)$

50. $-x + 3y = 4$
$y = \frac{1}{3}x + \frac{4}{3}$; slope is $\frac{1}{3}$; y-intercept $\left(0, \frac{4}{3}\right)$

51. $5x - 1 = 4$
$x = 1$; undefined slope; no y-intercept

52. $2y - 3 = 0$
$y = \frac{3}{2}$; slope is 0; y-intercept $\left(0, \frac{3}{2}\right)$

53. $x + 4y = 0$
$y = -\frac{1}{4}x$; slope is $-\frac{1}{4}$; y-intercept $(0, 0)$

54. $8x + 2y = 0$
$y = -4x$; slope is -4; y-intercept $(0, 0)$

55. $y + 4 = 8$
$y = 4$; slope is 0; y-intercept is $(0, 4)$

56. $x - 3 = 5$
$x = 8$; undefined slope; no y-intercept

For Exercises 57–62, graph the line given the slope and y-intercept.

57. Slope is $\frac{1}{2}$, y-intercept is $(0, -2)$

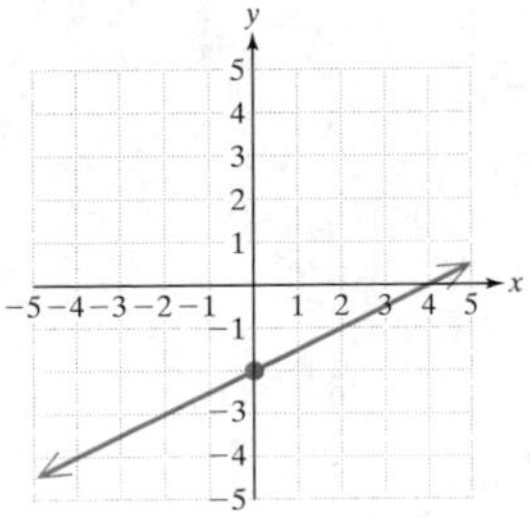

58. Slope is -3, y-intercept is $(0, 1)$

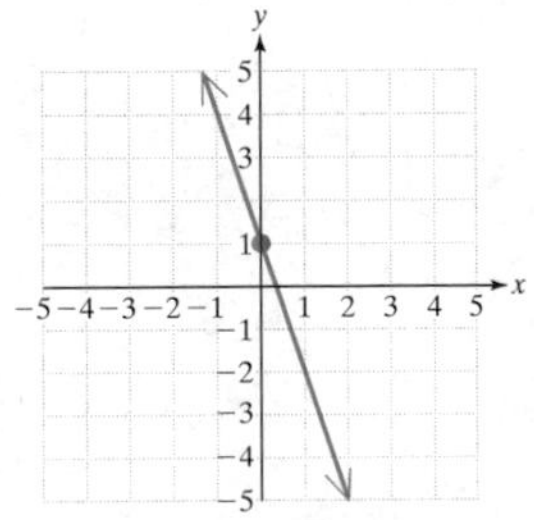

59. Slope is $-\frac{3}{2}$, y-intercept is $(0, 3)$

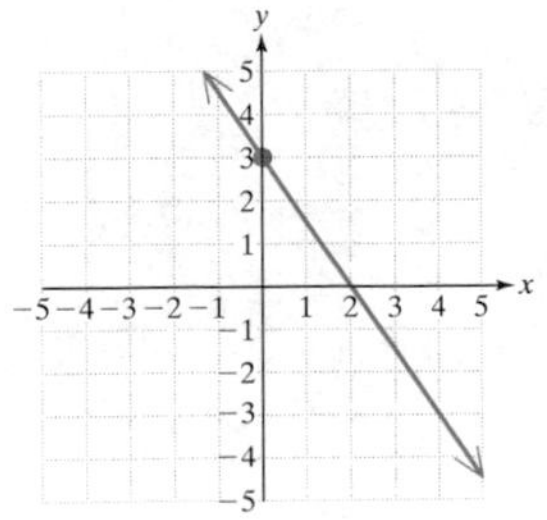

60. Slope is $\frac{5}{3}$, y-intercept is $(0, -1)$

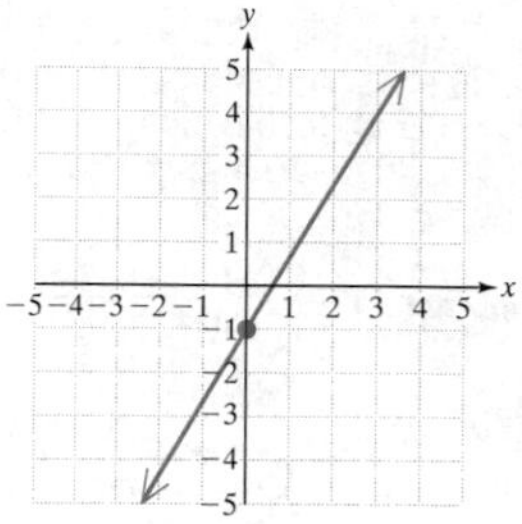

61. Slope is 4, y-intercept is $(0, -2)$

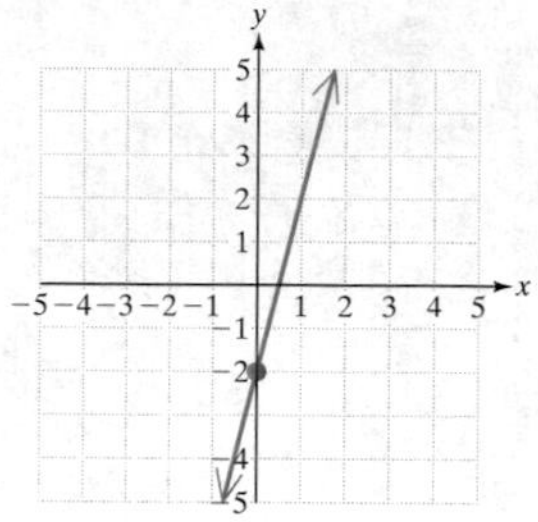

62. Slope is 2, y-intercept is $(0, -3)$

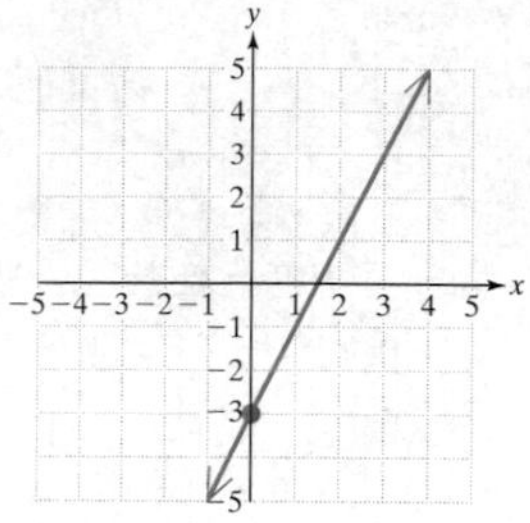

For Exercises 63–74, graph the line.

63. $2x - 3y = 12$

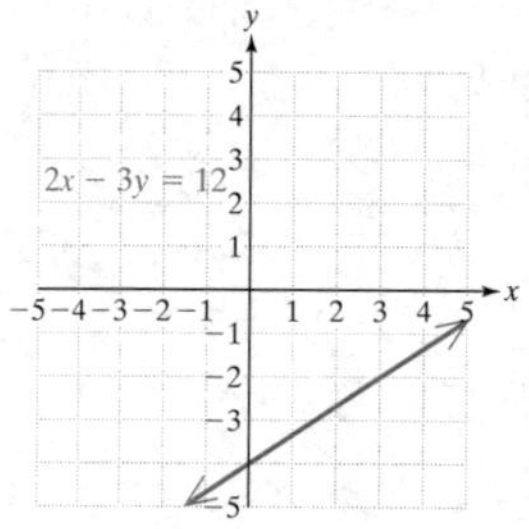

64. $2x + 4y = -8$

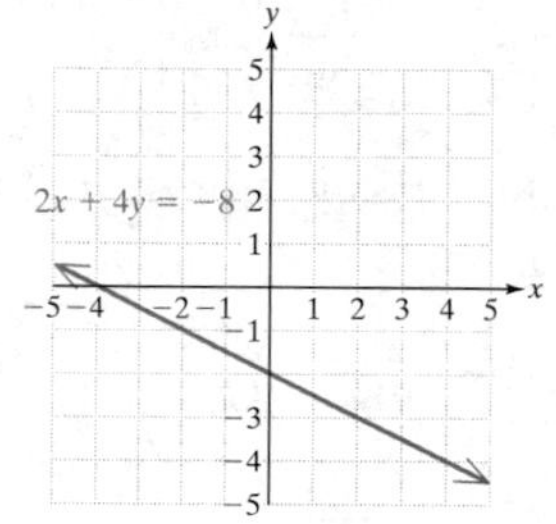

65. $x - 2y = -4$

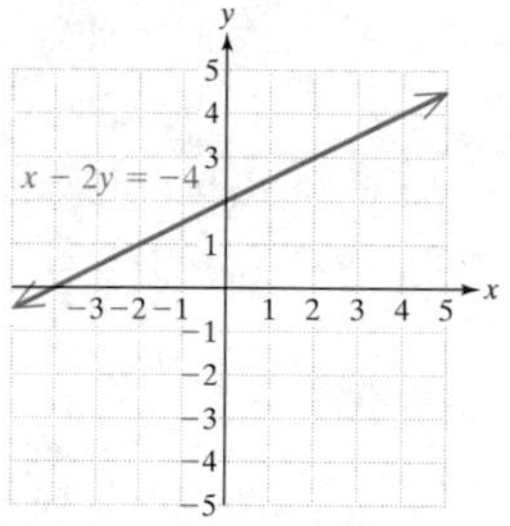

66. $6x - y = 4$

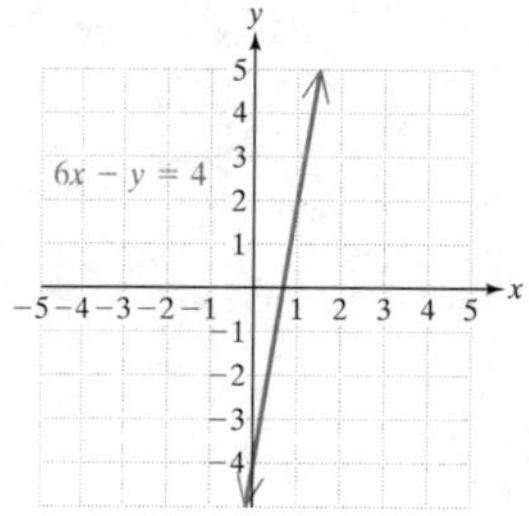

67. $4x + y = 0$

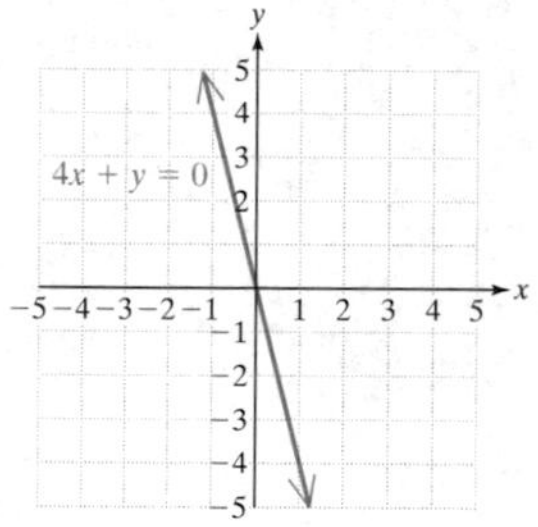

68. $-x - 3y = 0$

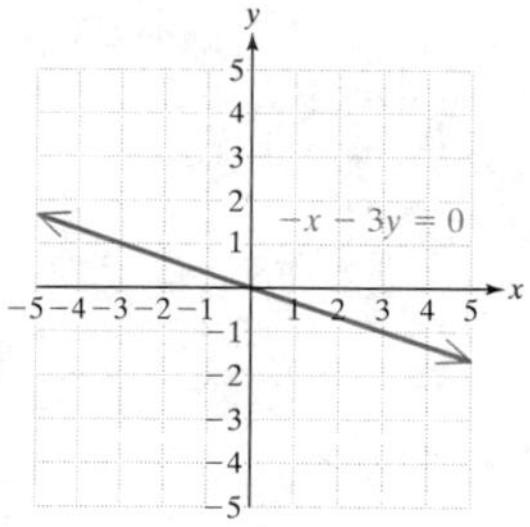

69. $y = -\frac{2}{3}x + 1$

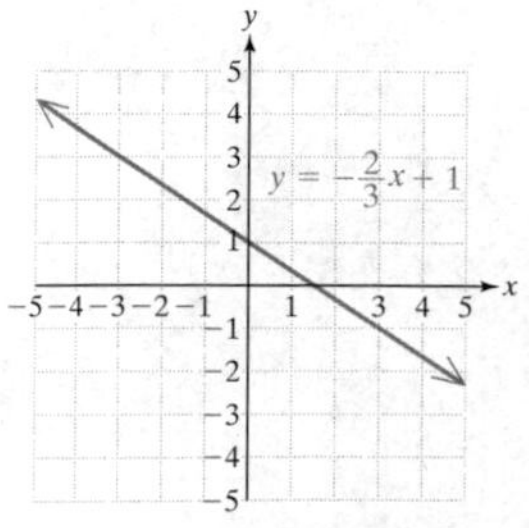

70. $y = \frac{1}{4}x - 1$

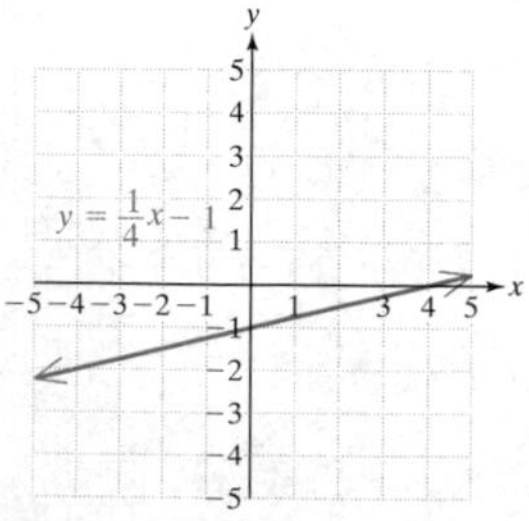

71. $-2x + 1 = 5$

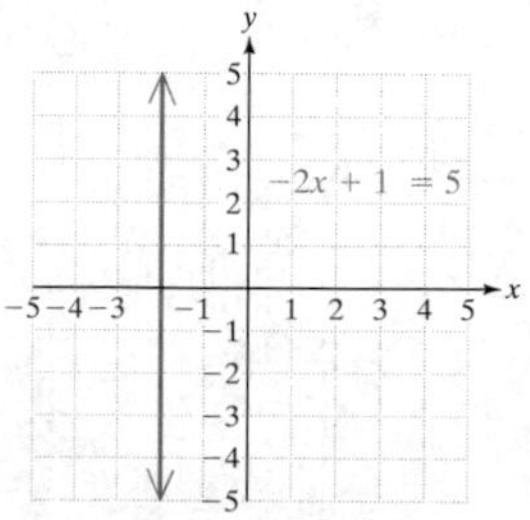

72. $4y - 2 = 6$

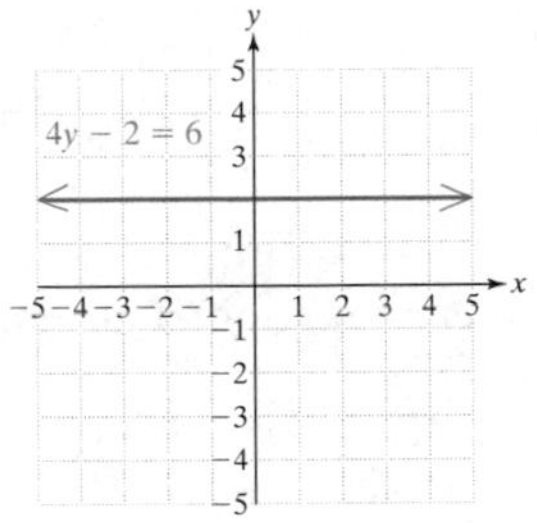

73. $y = 3x - 3$

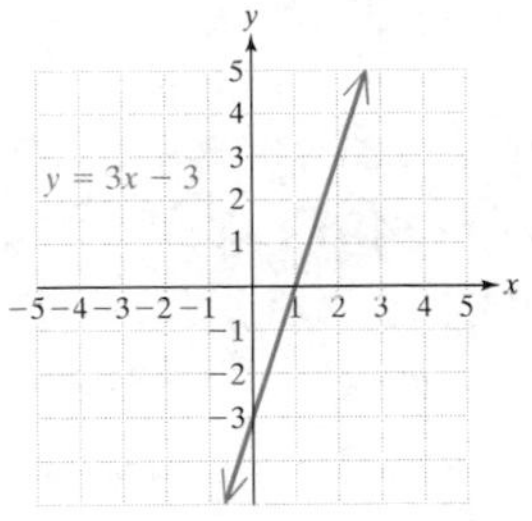

74. $y = -4x - 4$

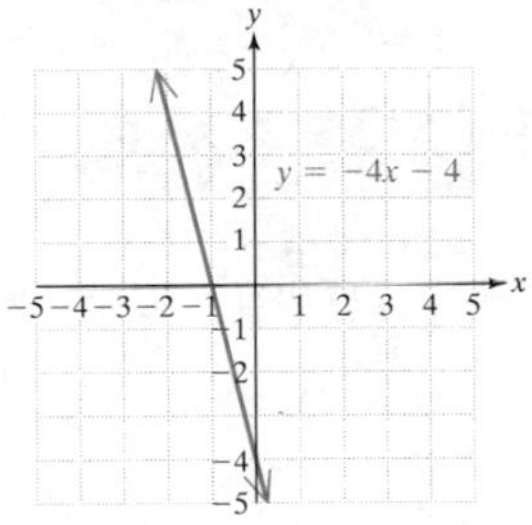

For Exercises 75–82, determine if the lines are parallel, perpendicular, or neither.

75. l_1: $-2x + y = 1$
l_2: $2x - y = 3$
Parallel

76. l_1: $y = 3x + 6$
l_2: $-x + 3y = -3$
Neither

77. l_1: $-2x + 5y = 5$
l_2: $5x - 2y = -2$
Neither

78. l_1: $-7x + y = 1$
l_2: $-7x = 0$
Neither

79. l_1: $x + y = 7$
l_2: $x - y = -2$
Perpendicular

80. l_1: $y = -\frac{1}{4}x + 2$
l_2: $2x + 8y = 24$
Parallel

81. l_1: $y = 6$
l_2: $y = -2$
Parallel

82. l_1: $x = 3$
l_2: $y = 0$
Perpendicular

For Exercises 83–92, find an equation of the line given the following information. Write the final answer in slope-intercept form and in standard form.

83. The slope is -3 and the line passes through $(-5, -2)$. $y = -3x - 17$; $3x + y = -17$

84. The slope is $\frac{1}{2}$ and the line passes through $(5, 0)$. $y = \frac{1}{2}x - \frac{5}{2}$; $x - 2y = 5$

85. The line passes through $(-3, -4)$ and $(-1, 4)$. $y = 4x + 8$; $4x - y = -8$

86. The line passes through $(-1, 7)$ and $(4, -3)$. $y = -2x + 5$; $2x + y = 5$

87. The linc passes through $(4, 2)$ and is parallel to the line defined by $3y = 6x - 1$. $y = 2x - 6$; $2x - y = 6$

88. The line passes through $(-5, 6)$ and is parallel to the line defined by $4x = y - 3$. $y = 4x + 26$; $4x - y = -26$

89. The line passes through $(1, -2)$ and is perpendicular to the line defined by $-2x + 4y = 5$. $y = -2x$; $2x + y = 0$

90. The line passes through $(3, 0)$ and is perpendicular to the line defined by $3x + 9y = 1$. $y = 3x - 9$; $3x - y = 9$

91. The line passes through $(4, -9)$ and is parallel to the line $x = 3$. $x = 4$

92. The line passes through $(-7, 2)$ and is perpendicular to the line $2y = 8$. $x = -7$

Section B.7 Review of Systems of Linear Equations in Two Variables

Concepts

1. Solving Systems of Equations by the Graphing Method
2. Solving Systems of Equations by the Substitution Method
3. Solving Systems of Equations by the Addition Method
4. Applications of Systems of Equations

1. Solving Systems of Equations by the Graphing Method

Two or more linear equations can form a system of linear equations. For example, the following is a system of linear equations.

$$2x + y = 5$$
$$-x + y = 2$$

A solution to a system of equations is an ordered pair that satisfies both equations. Graphically, a solution to a system of linear equations is a point of intersection of the two lines.

Example 1 Solving a System of Linear Equations by Graphing

Solve by graphing. $2x + y = 5$

$-x + y = 2$

Solution:

First, graph the line defined by each equation. To graph the lines, we will use the slope-intercept form of each equation.

$$2x + y = 5 \xrightarrow{\text{slope-intercept form}} y = -2x + 5$$
$$-x + y = 2 \longrightarrow y = x + 2$$

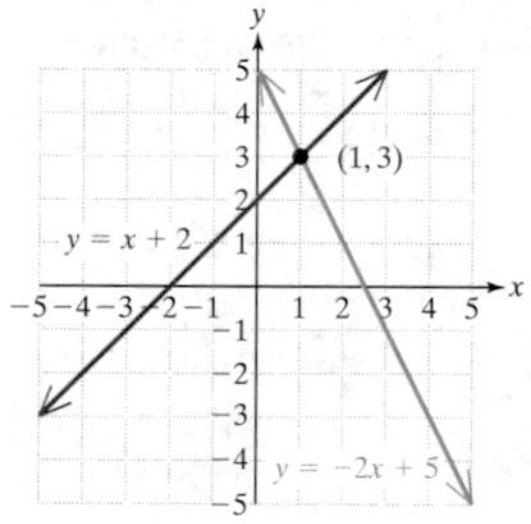

From the graph, we estimate the point of intersection to be (1, 3). The solution must be checked in each original equation.

$$2x + y = 5 \longrightarrow 2(1) + (3) \stackrel{?}{=} 5 \longrightarrow 5 = 5 \checkmark \text{ True}$$
$$-x + y = 2 \longrightarrow -(1) + (3) \stackrel{?}{=} 2 \longrightarrow 2 = 2 \checkmark \text{ True}$$

The solution set is $\{(1, 3)\}$.

2. Solving Systems of Equations by the Substitution Method

The graphing method to solve a system of linear equations can be cumbersome because of the limited accuracy of the graph. We will review two algebraic methods to solve systems of linear equations. The first is called the substitution method.

Example 2 **Solving a System of Linear Equations by Using the Substitution Method**

Solve by using the substitution method: $3x - y = 6$
$2x + 5y = 4$

Solution:

The first step in the substitution method is to isolate one of the variables in one of the equations. It is generally easiest to solve for a variable whose coefficient is 1 or -1. Therefore, we will isolate y in the first equation.

First equation: $3x - y = 6$

$$-y = -3x + 6$$
$$y = 3x - 6$$

Second equation: $2x + 5y = 4$ — Now substitute the quantity $(3x - 6)$ for y in the other equation.

$$2x + 5(3x - 6) = 4$$
$$2x + 15x - 30 = 4$$
$$17x - 30 = 4$$
$$17x = 34$$
$$x = 2$$

We can find the value of y by substituting $x = 2$ into either of the two equations. However, we will use the equation $y = 3x - 6$ because y is already isolated.

$y = 3x - 6$ First equation

$y = 3(2) - 6$ Substitute $x = 2$.

$y = 0$

The solution set is $\{(2, 0)\}$. The check is left to the reader.

3. Solving Systems of Equations by the Addition Method

A second method to solve a system of linear equations is called the addition method (also called the elimination method). The basis of this method is to eliminate one of the variables by adding two equations that have opposite coefficients for that variable.

Example 3 **Solving a System of Linear Equations by Using the Addition Method**

Solve by using the addition method. $2x = 5y - 4$
$3(x + y) = y + 13$

Solution:

To use the addition method, first write each equation in standard form $Ax + By = C$.

$$2x = 5y - 4 \xrightarrow{\text{subtract } 5y} 2x - 5y = -4 \longrightarrow 2x - 5y = -4$$
$$3(x + y) = y + 13 \xrightarrow[\text{clear parentheses}]{} 3x + 3y = y + 13 \xrightarrow[\text{subtract } y]{} 3x + 2y = 13$$

We will now eliminate one of the variables by multiplying one or both equations by appropriate constants to create opposite coefficients on that variable. Suppose we want to eliminate the x-variable. To do so, we want the coefficients on x to be 6 and -6 (the number 6 is the LCM of the original coefficients 2 and 3).

$2x - 5y = -4$ → (To create an x-coefficient of 6, multiply both sides by 3.) → $6x - 15y = -12$

$3x + 2y = 13$ → (To create an x-coefficient of -6, multiply both sides by -2.) → $-6x - 4y = -26$

$-19y = -38$ — Add the equations.

$y = 2$ — With the x-variable eliminated, solve for y.

Substitute $y = 2$ back into either of the original equations. We will use the first.

$2x = 5y - 4$

$2x = 5(2) - 4$ Substitute $y = 2$ into the first equation.

$2x = 10 - 4$ Solve for x.

$2x = 6$

$x = 3$

The solution set is $\{(3, 2)\}$. The check is left for the reader.

Two linear equations in a system may represent parallel lines. In such a case, the system has no solution because there is no point of intersection. A system of equations that has no solution is called an **inconsistent system**.

Example 4 Identifying an Inconsistent System

Solve the system of linear equations.

$$2x + y = 4$$
$$4x + 2y = 0$$

Solution:

Using the addition method we have

$2x + y = 4$ → (multiply by -2) → $-4x - 2y = -8$

$4x + 2y = 0$ → $4x + 2y = 0$

$0 = -8$ (contradiction)

This system has no solution { }. The system is inconsistent.

Graphing the linear equations in Example 4, we see that the lines are indeed parallel and that there is no point of intersection (Figure B-14). In general if a system of equations results in a contradiction (such as $0 = -8$), then there is no solution.

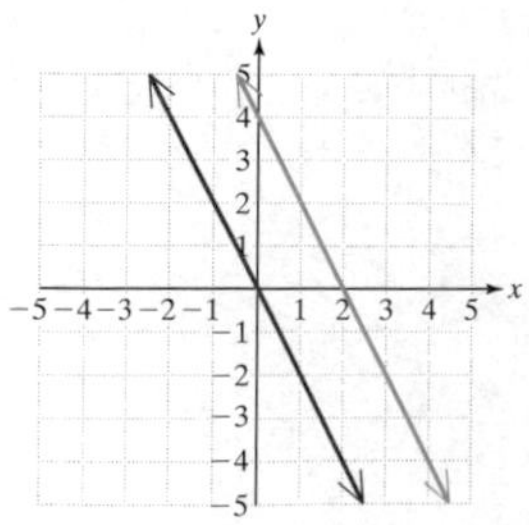

Figure B-14

Two linear equations may represent the same line. In such a case, all points on the common line are solutions to the system. That is, there are infinitely many solutions, and the equations are **dependent**.

Example 5 Solving a System of Dependent Equations

Solve the system. $6x - 9y = 18$

$$\frac{1}{2}x - \frac{3}{4}y = \frac{3}{2}$$

Solution:

First note that we can clear fractions in the second equation by multiplying by the LCD of all fractions in the equation.

$$6x - 9y = 18 \longrightarrow 6x - 9y = 18 \longrightarrow 6x - 9y = 18$$

$$\frac{1}{2}x - \frac{3}{4}y = \frac{3}{2} \xrightarrow{\text{multiply by 4}} 2x - 3y = 6 \xrightarrow{\text{multiply by } -3} \underline{-6x + 9y = -18}$$

$$0 = 0$$

The system reduces to the identity, $0 = 0$. This tells us that the equations have the same (identical) solution set, and that the equations are dependent.

Both equations can be written in slope-intercept form as $y = \frac{2}{3}x - 2$. All points on this line are solutions to the system. Therefore, we can write the solution set as $\{(x, y) \mid y = \frac{2}{3}x - 2\}$.

4. Applications of Systems of Equations

A system of equations is often useful to solve application problems where there are two unknown quantities.

Example 6 Solving an Application Using a System of Linear Equations

Ashlee invested a total of \$6000 in two accounts, a money market account and a certificate of deposit (CD). The money market pays 3.5% simple interest, and the CD pays 5% simple interest. At the end of one year, she earned \$276 in interest. Find the amount invested in each account.

Solution:

Let x represent the amount invested at 3.5%.
Let y represent the amount invested at 5%.

We have two variables, and therefore, we need two independent equations relating the variables. One equation relates the amount invested (principal), the second equation relates the amount of interest earned.

$$\begin{pmatrix}\text{Principal}\\\text{invested at 3.5\%}\end{pmatrix} + \begin{pmatrix}\text{Principal}\\\text{invested at 5\%}\end{pmatrix} = \begin{pmatrix}\text{Total}\\\text{invested}\end{pmatrix} \qquad x + y = 6000$$

$$\begin{pmatrix}\text{Interest}\\\text{earned at 3.5\%}\end{pmatrix} + \begin{pmatrix}\text{Interest}\\\text{earned at 5\%}\end{pmatrix} = \begin{pmatrix}\text{Total}\\\text{interest}\end{pmatrix} \qquad 0.035x + 0.05y = 276$$

$$x + y = 6000 \xrightarrow{\text{multiply by } -35} -35x - 35y = -210{,}000$$
$$0.035x + 0.05y = 276 \xrightarrow[\text{multiply by 1000}]{} 35x + 50y = 276{,}000$$
$$15y = 66{,}000$$
$$y = 4400$$

$$x + y = 6000$$
$$x + 4400 = 6000 \qquad \text{Substitute } y = 4400 \text{ back into the first equation.}$$
$$x = 1600$$

Interpret the results: $x = 1600$ means that \$1600 was invested at 3.5%.
$y = 4400$ means that \$4400 was invested at 5%.

Section B.7 Practice Exercises

For Exercises 1–4, solve the system by graphing.

1. $3x + y = 1$
$-2x + 2y = -6$
$\{(1, -2)\}$

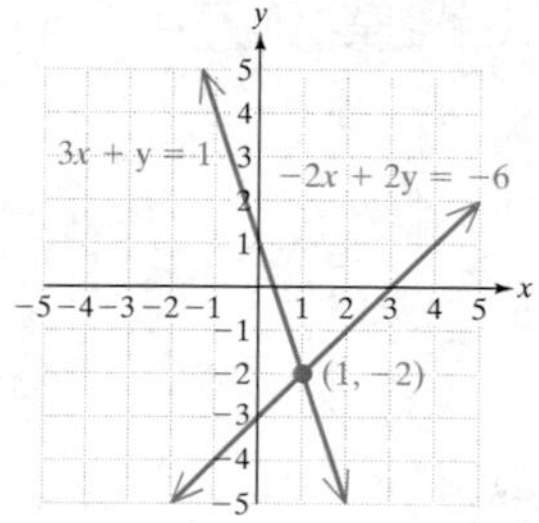

2. $3x - 2y = -6$
$4x + y = 3$
$\{(0, 3)\}$

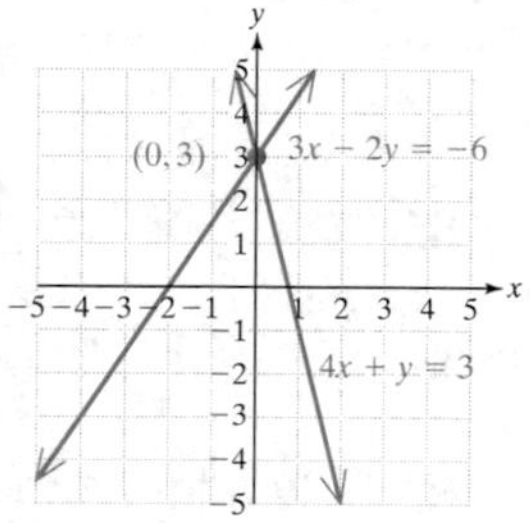

3. $2x = 8$
$-3x + 5y = -2$
$\{(4, 2)\}$

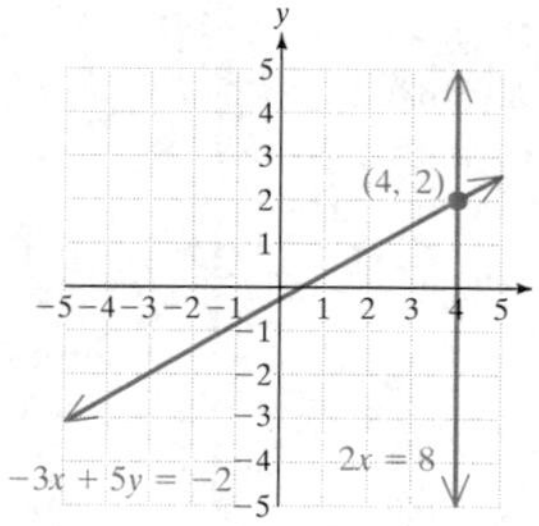

4. $y + 3 = 1$
$x - 2y = 3$
$\{(-1, -2)\}$

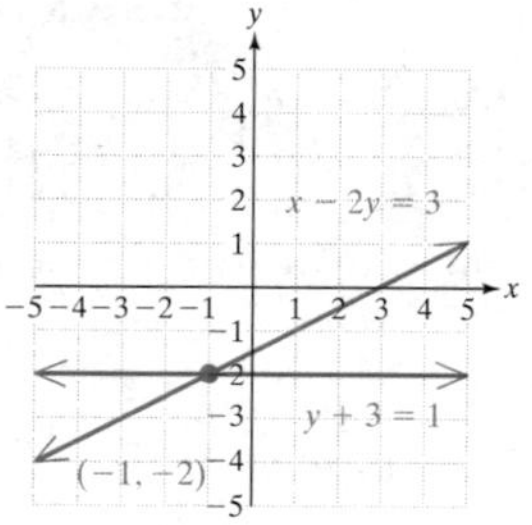

For Exercises 5–8, solve the systems by using the substitution method.

5. $y = 3x - 4$ $\{(1, -1)\}$
$-2x + 5y = -7$

6. $x = 4y + 1$ $\{(25, 6)\}$
$-2x + 5y = -20$

7. $9x - 4y = 9$ $\{(1, 0)\}$
$x + 6y = 1$

8. $-4x - 2y = -14$ $\{(2, 3)\}$
$3x + y = 9$

For Exercises 9–12, solve the systems by using the addition method.

9. $2x + y = -5$ $\{(1, -7)\}$
$-3x + 4y = -31$

10. $-6x + 5y = 1$ $\{(4, 5)\}$
$x - 3y = -11$

11. $5x - 6y = 16$ $\{(2, -1)\}$
$3x - 4y = 10$

12. $7x + 2y = 19$ $\{(3, -1)\}$
$5x + 3y = 12$

Writing Translating Expression Geometry Scientific Calculator Video

Mixed Exercises

For Exercises 13–24, solve the systems using any method. For systems that do not have one unique solution, also state the number of solutions and whether the system is inconsistent or the equations are dependent.

13. $5x + 2y = 10$

$-10x - 4y = 20$

{ } inconsistent system

14. $-3x + y = 6$

$9x - 3y = 0$

{ } inconsistent system

15. $3x + y - 7 = x - 4$

$3x + 4y + 4 = -6y + 5$

$\{(5, -7)\}$

16. $7y - 8y - 3 = -3x + 4$ $\{(2, -1)\}$

$5(2x - y) - 12 = 13$

17. $-2x = -y - 14$ Infinitely many solutions; $\{(x, y) \mid y = 2x - 14\}$; dependent equations

$4x - 2y = 28$

18. $y = 0.4x - 0.3$

$\frac{2}{5}x - y = \frac{3}{10}$

Infinitely many solutions; $\{(x, y) \mid y = 0.4x - 0.3\}$; dependent equations

19. $x + y = 3200$ $\{(2200, 1000)\}$

$0.06x + 0.04y = 172$

20. $x + y = 4500$ $\{(3300, 1200)\}$

$0.07x + 0.05y = 291$

21. $\frac{1}{3}x + \frac{1}{2}y = \frac{2}{3}$ $\{(2, 0)\}$

$y = \frac{2}{3}x - \frac{4}{3}$

22. $-y = \frac{1}{8}x - \frac{1}{8}$ $\left\{\left(-5, \frac{3}{4}\right)\right\}$

$-\frac{1}{4}x + \frac{1}{2}y = \frac{13}{8}$

23. $u - v = 3$ $\left\{\left(\frac{1}{2}, -\frac{5}{2}\right)\right\}$

$6u - 4v = 13$

24. $5v + 6w = -11$ $\{(-1, -1)\}$

$3v + w = -4$

25. Lynn has \$10,000 to invest. In one account he earns 6% simple interest and in the other he earns 4.5% simple interest. How much did he invest in each account if he makes \$570 in interest after 1 year?
He invested \$8000 at 6% interest and \$2000 at 4.5% interest.

26. Greg has \$8500 to invest. In a CD (certificate of deposit) he earns 5.5% simple interest. In a money market account he earns 4% simple interest. How much did he invest in each account if he made \$415 in interest in one year?
Greg invested \$5000 at 5.5% interest and \$3500 at 4% interest.

27. Two angles are complementary (the sum of their measures is 90°). The difference in the measures of the larger angle and the smaller angle is 14°. Find the measure of each angle.
The angles are 52° and 38°.

28. Two angles are supplementary (the sum of their measures is 180°). The measure of one angle is 11 times the measure of the other angle. Find the measure of each angle. The angles are 165° and 15°.

29. The sum of Denisha's age and her sister's age is 48. If Denisha is 4 years older than her sister, find each of their ages. Denisha is 26 and her sister is 22.

30. In a right triangle, one acute angle measures 10° less than 4 times the measure of the other acute angle. Find the measure of each acute angle. The angles are 70° and 20°.

Section B.8 Review of Polynomials and Properties of Exponents

Concepts

1. Properties of Exponents
2. Scientific Notation
3. Addition and Subtraction of Polynomials
4. Multiplication of Polynomials
5. Division of Polynomials

1. Properties of Exponents

Recall that expressions with exponents can be simplified using the following definitions and properties.

Properties and Definitions Involving Exponents

Assume that a and b are real numbers such that $a \neq 0, b \neq 0$ and m and n are integers.

Property/Definition		Example
Multiplication of like bases:	$b^m b^n = b^{m+n}$	$x^3x^5 = x^{3+5} = x^8$
Division of like bases:	$\frac{b^m}{b^n} = b^{m-n}$	$\frac{y^7}{y^3} = y^{7-3} = y^4$
The power rule:	$(b^m)^n = b^{m \cdot n}$	$(5^4)^2 = 5^{4 \cdot 2} = 5^8$
Power of a product:	$(ab)^m = a^m b^m$	$(5x)^2 = 5^2x^2 = 25x^2$
Power of a quotient:	$\left(\frac{a}{b}\right)^m = \frac{a^m}{b^m}$	$\left(\frac{x}{4}\right)^3 = \frac{x^3}{4^3} = \frac{x^3}{64}$
Definition of b^0:	$b^0 = 1$	$5^0 = 1$
Definition of b^{-n}:	$b^{-n} = \left(\frac{1}{b}\right)^n = \frac{1}{b^n}$	$x^{-6} = \left(\frac{1}{x}\right)^6 = \frac{1}{x^6}$

These properties and definitions may be combined to simplify exponential expressions.

Example 1 Simplifying Exponential Expressions

Simplify. **a.** $\frac{x^4x^6}{x^3}$ **b.** $(2y^3)^4$ **c.** $\left(\frac{pw^2}{2z^5}\right)^3$

d. $\frac{4x^6z^{-3}}{y^{-2}}$ **e.** $\left(\frac{1}{2}\right)^{-3} + \left(\frac{1}{4}\right)^0$

Solution:

a. $\frac{x^4x^6}{x^3} = \frac{x^{4+6}}{x^3} = \frac{x^{10}}{x^3} = x^{10-3} = x^7$

b. $(2y^3)^4 = 2^4(y^3)^4 = 2^4y^{3 \cdot 4} = 16y^{12}$

c. $\left(\frac{pw^2}{2z^5}\right)^3 = \frac{p^3w^6}{2^3\,z^{15}} = \frac{p^3w^6}{8z^{15}}$

d. $\frac{4x^6z^{-3}}{y^{-2}} = \frac{4x^6y^2}{z^3}$

e. $\left(\frac{1}{2}\right)^{-3} + \left(\frac{1}{4}\right)^0 = \left(\frac{2}{1}\right)^3 + 1 = 8 + 1 = 9$

2. Scientific Notation

Recall that scientific notation is a convenient method to write very large or very small numbers. A positive number is in scientific notation if it is written in the form $a \times 10^n$, where $1 \le a < 10$ and n is an integer. See Table B-6.

Table B-6

Number	Equivalent Form	Scientific Notation
4200	4.2×1000	4.2×10^3
0.008	$8 \times 0.001 = 8 \times \frac{1}{1000} = 8 \times \frac{1}{10^3}$	8×10^{-3}

Writing a number in scientific notation can be done easily by moving the decimal point to the left or right and then multiplying the resulting number by the appropriate power of 10.

$730{,}000 = 7.3 \times 10^5$ $\qquad$ $0.000046 = 4.6 \times 10^{-5}$

Example 2 Multiplying and Dividing Numbers in Scientific Notation

Perform the indicated operations and write the answer in scientific notation.

$$\frac{(6 \times 10^3)(9 \times 10^5)}{2 \times 10^{-2}}$$

Solution:

$$\frac{(6 \times 10^3)(9 \times 10^5)}{2 \times 10^{-2}} = \frac{(6)(9) \times 10^3 10^5}{2 \times 10^{-2}}$$ Multiply the numerators.

$$= \frac{54 \times 10^8}{2 \times 10^{-2}}$$ Simplify.

$$= \left(\frac{54}{2}\right) \times \frac{10^8}{10^{-2}}$$ Divide.

$$= 27 \times 10^{8-(-2)}$$ Simplify.

$$= 27 \times 10^{10}$$ This number is not in proper scientific notation.

$$= (2.7 \times 10^1) \times 10^{10}$$ Write 27.0 as $= 2.7 \times 10^1$.

$$= 2.7 \times 10^{11}$$

3. Addition and Subtraction of Polynomials

To add or subtract polynomials, we add or subtract *like* terms.

Example 3 Adding and Subtracting Polynomials

Perform the indicated operations.

$$\left(2x^4 - 5x^2 - \frac{3}{4}x\right) + (7x^2 + 13) - \left(8x^4 + x^3 + \frac{1}{4}x\right)$$

Solution:

$\left(2x^4 - 5x^2 - \frac{3}{4}x\right) + (7x^2 + 13) - \left(8x^4 + x^3 + \frac{1}{4}x\right)$

$= 2x^4 - 5x^2 - \frac{3}{4}x + 7x^2 + 13 - 8x^4 - x^3 - \frac{1}{4}x$ Apply the distributive property.

$= 2x^4 - 8x^4 - x^3 - 5x^2 + 7x^2 - \frac{3}{4}x - \frac{1}{4}x + 13$ Collect *like* terms together.

$= -6x^4 - x^3 + 2x^2 - \frac{4}{4}x + 13$ Add *like* terms.

$= -6x^4 - x^3 + 2x^2 - x + 13$ Simplify.

4. Multiplication of Polynomials

To multiply polynomials, multiply each term in the first polynomial by each term in the second and combine *like* terms.

Example 4 Multiplying Polynomials

Multiply. **a.** $(2y + 5)(6y^2 - 4y + 3)$ **b.** $(2x - 3y)(5x + 7y)$

Solution:

a. $(2y + 5)(6y^2 - 4y + 3)$

$= 2y(6y^2) + 2y(-4y) + 2y(3) + 5(6y^2) + 5(-4y) + 5(3)$ Multiply.

$= 12y^3 - 8y^2 + 6y + 30y^2 - 20y + 15$ Simplify.

$= 12y^3 + 22y^2 - 14y + 15$ Combine *like* terms.

b. $(2x - 3y)(5x + 7y)$

$= 2x(5x) + 2x(7y) + (-3y)(5x) + (-3y)(7y)$ Multiply.

$= 10x^2 + 14xy - 15xy - 21y^2$ Simplify.

$= 10x^2 - xy - 21y^2$ Combine *like* terms.

When squaring a binomial such as $(a + b)^2$, we can write the expression as $(a + b)(a + b)$. Proceeding as in Example 4, we have $(a + b)(a + b) = a^2 + ab + ab + b^2 = a^2 + 2ab + b^2$. The resulting trinomial is a **perfect square trinomial**.

To multiply the product of conjugates such as $(a + b)(a - b)$, we have $a^2 - ab + ab - b^2 = a^2 - b^2$. This result is called a **difference of squares**.

These general results are summarized in Table B-7.

Table B-7

Product	Example
The square of a binomial results in a perfect square trinomial.	
1. $(a + b)^2 = a^2 + 2ab + b^2$	1. $(2x + 5y)^2 = (2x)^2 + 2(2x)(5y) + (5y)^2$ $= 4x^2 + 20xy + 25y^2$
2. $(a - b)^2 = a^2 - 2ab + b^2$	2. $(4m - 3n)^2 = (4m)^2 - 2(4m)(3n) + (3n)^2$ $= 16m^2 - 24mn + 9n^2$
The product of conjugate factors results in a difference of squares.	
3. $(a + b)(a - b) = a^2 - b^2$	3. $(7w + 3)(7w - 3) = (7w)^2 - (3)^2$ $= 49w^2 - 9$

5. Division of Polynomials

Division of polynomials is presented in two separate cases.

1. To divide a polynomial by a monomial divisor (that is, when the divisor has only one term), we use the properties:

$$\frac{a + b}{c} = \frac{a}{c} + \frac{b}{c} \quad \text{and} \quad \frac{a - b}{c} = \frac{a}{c} - \frac{b}{c}.$$

2. If the divisor has more than one term, we use long division.

Example 5 Dividing a Polynomial by a Monomial

Divide. $(15xy^2 - 5x^2y^3 + 10x^3y^6) \div (5x^2y^2)$

Solution:

We can write the expression as $\dfrac{15xy^2 - 5x^2y^3 + 10x^3y^6}{5x^2y^2}$

$= \dfrac{15xy^2}{5x^2y^2} - \dfrac{5x^2y^3}{5x^2y^2} + \dfrac{10x^3y^6}{5x^2y^2}$ Divide each term in the numerator by $5x^2y^2$.

$= \dfrac{3}{x} - y + 2xy^4$ Simplify each term.

Example 6 Using Long Division to Divide Polynomials

Divide. $(8x^3 + 14x^2 - 7) \div (x + 3)$

Solution:

Write the polynomials in long division format. The term $0x$ is inserted in the dividend as a place holder for the missing power of x.

$$\begin{array}{r|l} & 8x^2 \\ \hline x+3 & 8x^3 + 14x^2 + 0x - 7 \end{array}$$

Divide the leading term of the dividend by the leading term of the divisor $(8x^3/x)$. The result, $8x^2$, is the first term in the quotient.

$$\begin{array}{r|l} & 8x^2 \\ \hline x+3 & 8x^3 + 14x^2 + 0x - 7 \\ & -(8x^3 + 24x^2) \end{array}$$

Multiply $8x^2$ by the divisor and subtract the result.

$$\begin{array}{r|l} & 8x^2 \\ \hline x+3 & 8x^3 + 14x^2 + 0x - 7 \\ & -8x^3 - 24x^2 \quad \downarrow \\ & \quad -10x^2 + 0x \end{array}$$

Subtract the quantity $8x^3 + 24x^2$. To do this we can add the opposite.

Bring down the next column and repeat the process.

$$\begin{array}{r|l} & 8x^2 - 10x \\ \hline x+3 & 8x^3 + 14x^2 + 0x - 7 \\ & -8x^3 - 24x^2 \\ & \quad -10x^2 + 0x \\ & \quad -(-10x - 30x) \end{array}$$

$$\begin{array}{r|l} & 8x^2 - 10x + 30 \\ \hline x+3 & 8x^3 + 14x^2 + 0x - 7 \\ & -8x^3 - 24x^2 \\ & \quad -10x^2 + 0x \\ & \quad 10x + 30x \quad \downarrow \\ & \qquad 30x - 7 \\ & \qquad -(30x + 90) \end{array}$$

$$\begin{array}{r|l} & 8x^2 - 10x + 30 \\ \hline x+3 & 8x^3 + 14x^2 + 0x - 7 \\ & -8x^3 - 24x^2 \\ & \quad -10x^2 + 0x \\ & \quad 10x + 30x \\ & \qquad 30x - 7 \\ & \qquad -30x - 90 \\ & \qquad\quad -97 \end{array}$$

Therefore, $(8x^3 + 14x^2 - 7) \div (x + 3) = 8x^2 - 10x + 30 + \dfrac{-97}{x + 3}$.

Section B.8 Practice Exercises

Assume that all variables represent positive numbers.

For Exercises 1–8, simplify and state the property used. Choose from multiplication of like bases, division of like bases, power rule, power of a product, or power of a quotient.

1. $6^2 \cdot 6^5$
6^7; multiplication of like bases

2. $(x^3)^4$
x^{12}; power rule

3. $\dfrac{y^{10}}{y^7}$
y^3, division of like bases

4. $(10p)^5$
10^5p^5; power of a product

5. $\left(\dfrac{w}{4}\right)^4$
$\dfrac{w^4}{256}$; power of a quotient

6. $x^{10} \cdot x^3 \cdot x$
x^{14}; multiplication of like bases

7. $(q^5)^6$
q^{30}; power rule

8. $\dfrac{z^4}{z^4}$
1; division of like bases

For Exercises 9–28, simplify. Write the answers with positive exponents.

9. 3^0 1

10. 5^{-1} $\frac{1}{5}$

11. $\left(\dfrac{1}{2}\right)^{-1}$ 2

12. $(-6)^0$ 1

13. $(-5)^{-2}$ $\frac{1}{25}$

14. $\left(\dfrac{2}{3}\right)^{-2}$ $\frac{9}{4}$

15. $6^{-1} + (-4)^0$ $\frac{7}{6}$

16. $(-2)^{-2} + 8^{-1}$ $\frac{3}{8}$

17. $\dfrac{r^2 \cdot r^6}{r^{10}}$ $\frac{1}{r^2}$

18. $\dfrac{t^3 \cdot t^7}{t^{13}}$ $\frac{1}{t^3}$

19. $\dfrac{b^3}{b^4 \cdot b^{-3}}$ b^2

20. $\dfrac{c^{-2}}{c^{-5} \cdot c^2}$ c

21. $(3x^2)^3$ $27x^6$

22. $(-7y^4)^2$ $49y^8$

23. $\dfrac{6w^2z}{2z^{-1}}$ $3w^2z^2$

24. $\dfrac{-8m^4n^{-2}}{4n^3}$ $\frac{-2m^4}{n^5}$

25. $\left(\dfrac{a^2b^{-1}}{c^3d^{-4}}\right)^{-2}$ $\frac{b^2c^6}{a^4d^8}$

26. $\left(\dfrac{p^{-3}q}{r^2s^{-1}}\right)^{-3}$ $\frac{p^9r^6}{q^3s^3}$

27. $(5^0w^2z) \cdot (w^{-3}z^{-4})$ $\frac{1}{wz^3}$

28. $(4p^{-3}q) \cdot (p^{-2}q^4)$ $\frac{4q^5}{p^5}$

For Exercises 29–36, write the number in scientific notation.

29. 3,050,000
3.05×10^6

30. 82,500,000
8.25×10^7

31. 0.0000251
2.51×10^{-5}

32. 0.0038
3.8×10^{-3}

33. There were 89,600,000 people who watched the Super Bowl. 8.96×10^7

34. Mont Blanc, a mountain in the Alps, is about 15,800 ft high. 1.58×10^4

35. A single blood cell is approximately 0.00039 in. long. 3.9×10^{-4}

36. The shortest flash of light recorded was 0.000 000 000 000 000 69 seconds. 6.9×10^{-16}

For Exercises 37–44, perform the operation. Write the answer in scientific notation.

37. $(2.4 \times 10^1)(1.5 \times 10^3)$
3.6×10^4

38. $(8 \times 10^{-5})(1.2 \times 10^9)$
9.6×10^4

39. $\dfrac{6.3 \times 10^{14}}{3 \times 10^{-2}}$
2.1×10^{16}

40. $\dfrac{9.6 \times 10^{-12}}{4 \times 10^3}$
2.4×10^{-15}

41. $(3 \times 10^{-5})(7.3 \times 10^2)$
2.19×10^{-2}

42. $(2.1 \times 10^{13})(5 \times 10^{-2})$
1.05×10^{12}

43. $\dfrac{(4 \times 10^3)(1.2 \times 10^{-4})}{(6 \times 10^{10})}$ 8×10^{-12}

44. $\dfrac{(2.8 \times 10^2)(4 \times 10^4)}{(7 \times 10^{-6})}$ 1.6×10^{12}

For Exercises 45–50, add or subtract as indicated.

45. $(5p^3 + 2p - 3) + (8p^3 - 4p^2 + 14)$
$13p^3 - 4p^2 + 2p + 11$

46. $(2m^2 - 3m + 9) - (-3m^2 + 2m - 8)$
$5m^2 - 5m + 17$

47. $\left(10n^2 - \frac{3}{8}n + 2\right) - \left(11n^2 + \frac{5}{8}n - 6\right)$
$-n^2 - n + 8$

48. $(a^2 - 5a + 10) + \left(-3a^3 + \frac{1}{2}a^2 - 13\right)$
$-3a^3 + \frac{3}{2}a^2 - 5a - 3$

49. $(-u^2v + 6u^2 - 2uv^2) + (11u^2 + 7uv^2) - (9u^2v + u^2 + 3uv^2)$ $-10u^2v + 16u^2 + 2uv^2$

50. $(8a^2b - 5ab + 12ab^2) - (4a^2b - 6ab - ab^2) + (10a^2b + 3ab^2)$ $14a^2b + ab + 16ab^2$

For Exercises 51–66, multiply the polynomials.

51. $4p(p^3 - 5p^2 + 2p + 8)$
$4p^4 - 20p^3 + 8p^2 + 32p$

52. $5mn(-3m^2 + 6mn + n^2)$
$-15m^3n + 30m^2n^2 + 5mn^3$

53. $(3x + y)(-2x - 5y)$
$-6x^2 - 17xy - 5y^2$

54. $(4u - 7v)(3u - v)$
$12u^2 - 25uv + 7v^2$

55. $(8b + 4)(2b - 3)$
$16b^2 - 16b - 12$

56. $(-5a + 2)(5a - 3)$
$-25a^2 + 25a - 6$

57. $(x - 3y)(x^2 - 3xy + 5y^2)$
$x^3 - 6x^2y + 14xy^2 - 15y^3$

58. $(3p - 5q)(p - 2pq + q)$
$3p^2 - 6p^2q - 2pq + 10pq^2 - 5q^2$

59. $(3h - 8)(3h + 8)$
$9h^2 - 64$

60. $(k - 5)(k + 5)$
$k^2 - 25$

61. $(4x - 5)^2$
$16x^2 - 40x + 25$

62. $(3y + 8)^2$
$9y^2 + 48y + 64$

63. $\left(\frac{1}{3}t^2 - 9\right)\left(\frac{1}{3}t^2 + 9\right)$ $\frac{1}{9}t^4 - 81$

64. $\left(ab - \frac{3}{4}\right)\left(ab + \frac{3}{4}\right)$
$a^2b^2 - \frac{9}{16}$

65. $(0.2x^2 - 3)^2$
$0.04x^4 - 1.2x^2 + 9$

66. $(1.2y^2 + 4)^2$
$1.44y^4 + 9.6y^2 + 16$

For Exercises 67–76, divide the polynomials.

67. $(6a^3b^2 - 18a^2b^2 + 3ab^2 - 9ab) \div (3ab)$
$2a^2b - 6ab + b - 3$

68. $(8x^4y^4 + 4x^3y^2 - 12x^2y^4 + 4x^2y^2) \div (4x^2y^2)$
$2x^2y^2 + x - 3y^2 + 1$

69. $(x^3 - 2x^2 - 4x + 33) \div (x + 3)$
$x^2 - 5x + 11$

70. $(2y^3 - 7y^2 + y + 10) \div (y - 2)$
$2y^2 - 3y - 5$

71. $(2p^3 - 17p^2 + 39p - 10) \div (p - 5)$
$2p^2 - 7p + 4 + \dfrac{10}{p - 5}$

72. $(t^3 - t^2 - 10t + 4) \div (t + 3)$
$t^2 - 4t + 2 + \dfrac{-2}{t + 3}$

73. $(10m^5 - 16m^4 + 8m^3 + 8m^2 - 2m) \div (-2m)$
$-5m^4 + 8m^3 - 4m^2 - 4m + 1$

74. $(-25b^5 + 10b^4 - 5b^3 - 35b^2) \div (-5b^2)$
$5b^3 - 2b^2 + b + 7$

75. $(8a^3 - 9) \div (2a - 3)$
$4a^2 + 6a + 9 + \dfrac{18}{2a - 3}$

76. $(32k^3 + 5) \div (2k - 1)$
$16k^2 + 8k + 4 + \dfrac{9}{2k - 1}$

Review of Factoring Polynomials and Solving Quadratic Equations

Section B.9

Concepts

1. Factoring Polynomials
2. Solving Quadratic Equations Using the Zero Product Rule

1. Factoring Polynomials

Factoring Strategy

Step 1 Factor out the GCF.

Step 2 Identify whether the polynomial has two terms, three terms, or more than three terms.

Step 3 If the polynomial has more than three terms, try factoring by grouping.

Step 4 If the polynomial has three terms, check first for a perfect square trinomial. Otherwise, factor the trinomial with the trial-and-error method or the ac-method.

Step 5 If the polynomial has two terms, determine if it fits the pattern for

- A difference of squares: $a^2 - b^2 = (a - b)(a + b)$
- A sum of squares: $a^2 + b^2$ prime
- A difference of cubes: $a^3 - b^3 = (a - b)(a^2 + ab + b^2)$
- A sum of cubes: $a^3 + b^3 = (a + b)(a^2 - ab + b^2)$

Step 6 Be sure to factor the polynomial completely.

Step 7 Check by multiplying.

Example 1 Factoring Binomials

Factor completely. **a.** $81w^4 - 1$ **b.** $2y^3 + 128$

Solution:

When factoring a binomial, determine if it fits any of the following patterns.

$a^2 - b^2 = (a + b)(a - b)$ Difference of squares (Section 6.5)

$a^3 - b^3 = (a - b)(a^2 + ab + b^2)$ Difference of cubes (Section 6.6)

$a^3 + b^3 = (a + b)(a^2 - ab + b^2)$ Sum of cubes (Section 6.6)

a. $81w^4 - 1$ The GCF is 1.

$= (9x^2)^2 - (1)^2$ This is a difference of squares, $a^2 - b^2$, where $a = 9x^2$ and $b = 1$.

$= (9x^2 + 1)(9x^2 - 1)$ Apply the formula $a^2 - b^2 = (a + b)(a - b)$.

$= (9x^2 + 1)(3x + 1)(3x - 1)$ The factor $9x^2 - 1$ factors further as a difference of squares. $9x^2 - 1 = (3x + 1)(3x - 1)$.

b. $2y^3 + 128$ The GCF is 2.

$= 2(y^3 + 64)$ Factor out 2.

$= 2[(y)^3 + (4)^3]$ The resulting binomial is a sum of cubes, $a^3 + b^3$, where $a = y$ and $b = 4$.

$= 2(y + 4)(y^2 - 4y + 16)$ Apply the formula $a^3 + b^3 = (a + b)(a^2 - ab + b^2)$

Avoiding Mistakes

The binomial $9x^2 - 1$ is a difference of squares and may be factored as $(3x + 1)(3x - 1)$. However, the binomial $9x^2 + 1$ is a sum of squares and may not be factored over the real numbers.

TIP: Recall that a factoring problem may be checked by multiplication.

$$2(y + 4)(y^2 - 4y + 16) = (2y + 8)(y^2 - 4y + 16)$$
$$= 2y(y^2) + 2y(-4y) + 2y(16) + 8(y^2) + 8(-4y) + 8(16)$$
$$= 2y^3 - 8y^2 + 32y + 8y^2 - 32y + 128$$
$$= 2y^3 + 128$$

In Examples 2 and 3, we review factoring quadratic trinomials. Example 2 demonstrates the ac-method.

Example 2 Factoring a Trinomial by Using the ac-Method

Factor completely. $-10x + 60x^2 - 120$

Solution:

$-10x + 60x^2 - 120$

$= 60x^2 - 10x - 120$ — Write the trinomial in descending order.

$= 10(6x^2 - x - 12)$ — Factor out the greatest common factor, 10. The trinomial is in the form $ax^2 + bx + c$ where $a = 6$, $b = -1$, and $c = -12$.

Find the product $ac = 6(-12) = -72$.

Find two numbers whose product is -72 and whose sum is -1. The numbers are -9 and 8.

$= 10(6x^2 - 9x + 8x - 12)$ — Write the middle term of the trinomial as the sum of two terms whose coefficients are -9 and 8.

$= 10[3x(2x - 3) + 4(2x - 3)]$ — Factor the four-term polynomial by grouping.

$= 10[(2x - 3)(3x + 4)]$ — Factor out the common binomial $(2x - 3)$ from each term.

$= 10(2x - 3)(3x + 4)$

In Example 3, we revisit the trial-and-error technique to factor a trinomial, and the patterns associated with perfect square trinomials.

Example 3 Factoring Trinomials

Factor completely. **a.** $49w^2 - 28w + 4$ **b.** $5x^4y - 8x^3y + 3x^2y$

Solution:

Check first to see if the trinomial is a perfect square trinomial, in which case factor as the square of a binomial.

Perfect square trinomials $\begin{cases} a^2 + 2ab + b^2 = (a + b)^2 \\ a^2 - 2ab + b^2 = (a - b)^2 \end{cases}$

Otherwise factor the trinomial using the trial-and-error method or the ac-method.

a. $49w^2 - 28w + 4$	The GCF is 1.
$= (7w)^2 - 2(7w)(2) + (2)^2$	The polynomial is a perfect square trinomial, $a^2 - 2ab + b^2$ where $a = 7w$ and $b = 2$.
$= (7w - 2)^2$	Apply the formula $a^2 - 2ab + b^2 = (a - b)^2$.
b. $5x^4y - 8x^3y + 3x^2y$	The GCF is x^2y.
$= x^2y(5x^2 - 8x + 3)$	Factor out x^2y. The factored form of $5x^2 - 8x + 3$ must be a product of binomials of the form:

factors of 5

$(\square x - \square)(\square x - \square)$

factors of 3

The signs within parentheses must both be negative for a product of 3 and a sum of $-8x$.

Trying all possible combinations we have:

$(5x - 1)(x - 3) = 5x^2 - 15x - x + 3$	
$= 5x^2 - 16x + 3$	Wrong middle term.
$(5x - 3)(x - 1) = 5x^2 - 5x - 3x + 3$	
$= 5x^2 - 8x + 3$	Correct!
$= x^2y(5x - 3)(x - 1)$	Factored completely.

Example 4 Factoring a Four-Term Polynomial

Factor completely. $6ab + 8ax + 15bx + 20x^2$

Solution:

This polynomial has 4 terms. Therefore, try factoring by grouping.

$6ab + 8ax + 15bx + 20x^2$	The GCF is 1.
$= 6ab + 8ax \;\vdots\; + 15bx + 20x^2$	Group the first pair of terms and the second pair of terms.
$= 2a(3b + 4x) + 5x(3b + 4x)$	Factor out the GCF from each pair. Note that the two resulting terms share a common binomial factor.
$= (3b + 4x)(2a + 5x)$	Factor out the common binomial factor.

2. Solving Quadratic Equations Using the Zero Product Rule

A quadratic equation is an equation of the form $ax^2 + bx + c = 0$, where $a \neq 0$. To solve a quadratic equation in this form, we factor the expression $ax^2 + bx + c$ and set each factor equal to zero.

Example 5 Solving Quadratic Equations

Solve. **a.** $(2x - 1)(x - 3) = 0$ **b.** $10x^2 + 50x = 140$

Solution:

a. $(2x - 1)(x - 3) = 0$ The equation is already in factored form and set equal to zero.

$2x - 1 = 0$ or $x - 3 = 0$ Set each factor equal to zero.

$2x = 1$ or $x = 3$ Solve each equation.

$x = \frac{1}{2}$ or $x = 3$

The solution set is $\left\{\frac{1}{2}, 3\right\}$.

b. $10x^2 + 50x = 140$

$10x^2 + 50x - 140 = 0$ Write the equation in the form $ax^2 + bx + c = 0$.

$10(x^2 + 5x - 14) = 0$ Factor out the GCF.

$10(x - 2)(x + 7) = 0$ Factor the trinomial.

$10 \neq 0$ or $x - 2 = 0$ or $x + 7 = 0$ Set each factor equal to zero.

$x = 2$ or $x = -7$

The solution set is $\{2, -7\}$.

Section B.9 Practice Exercises

1. Write the formula to factor the difference of squares, $a^2 - b^2$. $a^2 - b^2 = (a + b)(a - b)$

2. Write the formula to factor the difference of cubes, $a^3 - b^3$. $a^3 - b^3 = (a - b)(a^2 + ab + b^2)$

3. Write the formula to factor the sum of cubes, $a^3 + b^3$. $a^3 + b^3 = (a + b)(a^2 - ab + b^2)$

4. Is it possible to factor the sum of squares $a^2 + b^2$ over the real numbers? No

For Exercises 5–50,

a. Identify the category in which the polynomial best fits. Choose from

- difference of squares
- sum of squares
- difference of cubes
- sum of cubes
- trinomial (perfect square trinomial)
- trinomial (nonperfect square trinomial)
- four terms—grouping
- none of these

(*Hint:* You may have to factor out the greatest common factor first to categorize the polynomial.)

b. Factor the polynomial completely.

5. $t^2 - 100$ a. Difference of squares b. $(t - 10)(t + 10)$

6. $4m^2 - 49n^2$ a. Difference of squares b. $(2m - 7n)(2m + 7n)$

7. $y^3 + 27$ a. Sum of cubes b. $(y + 3)(y^2 - 3y + 9)$

8. $x^3 + 1$ a. Sum of cubes b. $(x + 1)(x^2 - x + 1)$

9. $d^2 + 3d - 28$ a. Trinomial (nonperfect square trinomial) b. $(d - 4)(d + 7)$

10. $c^2 + 5c - 24$ a. Trinomial (nonperfect square trinomial) b. $(c + 8)(c - 3)$

11. $x^2 - 12x + 36$ a. Trinomial (perfect square trinomial) b. $(x - 6)^2$

12. $p^2 + 16p + 64$ a. Trinomial (perfect square trinomial) b. $(p + 8)^2$

13. $2ax^2 - 5ax + 2bx - 5b$ a. Four terms—grouping b. $(ax + b)(2x - 5)$

14. $8x^2 - 4bx + 2ax - ab$ a. Four terms—grouping b. $(4x + a)(2x - b)$

15. $10y^2 + 3y - 4$ a. Trinomial (nonperfect square trinomial) b. $(2y - 1)(5y + 4)$

16. $12z^2 + 11z + 2$ a. Trinomial (nonperfect square trinomial) b. $(3z + 2)(4z + 1)$

17. $10p^2 - 640$ a. Difference of squares b. $10(p - 8)(p + 8)$

18. $50a^2 - 72$ a. Difference of squares b. $2(5a - 6)(5a + 6)$

19. $z^4 - 64z$ a. Difference of cubes b. $z(z - 4)(z^2 + 4z + 16)$

20. $t^4 - 8t$ a. Difference of cubes b. $t(t - 2)(t^2 + 2t + 4)$

21. $b^3 - 4b^2 - 45b$ a. Trinomial (nonperfect square trinomial) b. $b(b + 5)(b - 9)$

22. $y^3 - 14y^2 + 40y$ a. Trinomial (nonperfect square trinomial) b. $y(y - 4)(y - 10)$

23. $9w^2 + 24wx + 16x^2$ a. Trinomial (perfect square trinomial) b. $(3w + 4x)^2$

24. $4k^2 - 20kp + 25p^2$ a. Trinomial (perfect square trinomial) b. $(2k - 5p)^2$

25. $60x^2 - 20x + 30ax - 10a$ a. Four terms—grouping b. $10(2x + a)(3x - 1)$

26. $50x^2 - 200x + 10cx - 40c$ a. Four terms—grouping b. $10(5x + c)(x - 4)$

27. $x^3 + 4x^2 - 9x - 36$ a. Four terms—grouping b. $(x - 3)(x + 3)(x + 4)$

28. $m^3 + 5m^2 - 4m - 20$ a. Four terms—grouping b. $(m + 5)(m - 2)(m + 2)$

29. $w^4 - 16$ a. Difference of squares b. $(w^2 + 4)(w - 2)(w + 2)$

30. $k^4 - 81$ a. Difference of squares b. $(k^2 + 9)(k - 3)(k + 3)$

31. $t^6 - 8$ a. Difference of cubes b. $(t^2 - 2)(t^4 + 2t^2 + 4)$

32. $p^6 + 27$ a. Sum of cubes b. $(p^2 + 3)(p^4 - 3p^2 + 9)$

33. $8p^2 - 22p + 5$ a. Trinomial (nonperfect square trinomial) b. $(4p - 1)(2p - 5)$

34. $9m^2 - 3m - 20$ a. Trinomial (nonperfect square trinomial) b. $(3m + 4)(3m - 5)$

35. $36y^2 - 12y + 1$ a. Trinomial (perfect square trinomial) b. $(6y - 1)^2$

36. $9a^2 + 42a + 49$ a. Trinomial (perfect square trinomial) b. $(3a + 7)^2$

37. $x^2 + 4x - xy - 4y$ a. Four terms—grouping b. $(x + 4)(x - y)$

38. $m^2 - 6m + mn - 6n$ a. Four terms—grouping b. $(m - 6)(m + n)$

39. $2x^2 + 50$ a. Sum of squares b. $2(x^2 + 25)$

40. $4y^2 + 64$ a. Sum of squares b. $4(y^2 + 16)$

41. $12r^2s^2 + 7rs^2 - 10s^2$ a. Trinomial (nonperfect square trinomial) b. $s^2(3r - 2)(4r + 5)$

42. $7z^2w^2 - 10zw^2 - 8w^2$ a. Trinomial (nonperfect square trinomial) b. $w^2(7z + 4)(z - 2)$

43. $x^2 + 8xy - 33y^2$ a. Trinomial (nonperfect square trinomial) b. $(x - 3y)(x + 11y)$

44. $s^2 - 9st - 36t^2$ a. Trinomial (nonperfect square trinomial) b. $(s + 3t)(s - 12t)$

45. $m^6 + n^3$ a. Sum of cubes b. $(m^2 + n)(m^4 - m^2n + n^2)$

46. $a^3 - b^6$ a. Difference of cubes b. $(a - b^2)(a^2 + ab^2 + b^4)$

47. $x^2(a + b) - x(a + b) - 12(a + b)$ a. Trinomial (nonperfect square trinomial) b. $(a + b)(x - 4)(x + 3)$

48. $y^2(y + 2) + 10y(y + 2) + 9(y + 2)$ a. Trinomial (nonperfect square trinomial) b. $(y + 2)(y + 1)(y + 9)$

49. $x^2 - 4x$ a. None of these b. $x(x - 4)$

50. $y^2 - 9y$ a. None of these b. $y(y - 9)$

For Exercises 51–64, solve the equation.

51. $(2x + 5)(x - 3) = 0$ $\left\{-\frac{5}{2}, 3\right\}$

52. $(4x - 1)(x + 6) = 0$ $\left\{\frac{1}{4}, -6\right\}$

53. $x(x - 5) = 0$ $\{0, 5\}$

54. $y(y + 7) = 0$ $\{0, -7\}$

55. $5(w + 3) = 0$ $\{-3\}$

56. $-2(t - 10) = 0$ $\{10\}$

57. $z^2 - 2z - 8 = 0$ $\{4, -2\}$

58. $p^2 - 15p - 16 = 0$ $\{16, -1\}$

59. $6x^2 - 7x = 5$ $\left\{\frac{5}{3}, -\frac{1}{2}\right\}$

60. $4x^2 = x + 14$ $\left\{-\frac{7}{4}, 2\right\}$

61. $2x(x - 10) = -9x - 12$ $\left\{\frac{3}{2}, 4\right\}$

62. $x(x - 12) + 5 = -30$ $\{5, 7\}$

63. $w^3 - w^2 - w + 1 = 0$ $\{1, -1\}$

64. $z^3 - 4z^2 - 16z + 64 = 0$ $\{4, -4\}$

Section B.10 Review of Rational Expressions

Concepts

1. Definition of a Rational Expression
2. Simplifying Rational Expressions
3. Multiplying and Dividing Rational Expressions
4. Adding and Subtracting Rational Expressions
5. Simplifying Complex Fractions
6. Solving Rational Equations

1. Definition of a Rational Expression

A rational expression is an expression of the form $\frac{p}{q}$, where p and q are polynomials. The following are rational expressions.

$$\frac{x^2 + x - 4}{x - 2}, \quad \frac{1}{x^3}, \quad \frac{2}{5}$$

A rational expression is defined for all real numbers except those that make the denominator equal to zero. For example,

$\frac{x^2 + x - 4}{x - 2}$ The expression is defined for all real numbers except 2. We say that 2 is a restricted value in the expression.

$\frac{1}{x^3}$ The expression is defined for all real numbers except 0. We say that 0 is a restricted value in the expression.

$\frac{2}{5}$ The expression is defined for all real numbers with no restrictions.

2. Simplifying Rational Expressions

The expressions $\frac{6}{12}$, $\frac{2}{4}$, and $\frac{1}{2}$ are all equivalent. However, the value $\frac{1}{2}$ is in lowest terms. To simplify a rational expression to lowest terms, first factor the numerator and denominator. Then reduce the common factors that form a ratio of 1.

Example 1 Simplifying a Rational Expression to Lowest Terms

Simplify to lowest terms. $\frac{x^2 + 10x + 9}{x^2 - 1}$

Solution:

$$\frac{x^2 + 10x + 9}{x^2 - 1} = \frac{(x + 1)(x + 9)}{(x + 1)(x - 1)} \quad \text{Factor numerator and denominator.}$$

$$= \frac{\overset{1}{\cancel{(x + 1)}}(x + 9)}{\cancel{(x + 1)}(x - 1)} \quad \text{Simplify } (x + 1)/(x + 1) \text{ to 1.}$$

$$= \frac{x + 9}{x - 1} \text{ (where } x \neq 1 \text{ and } x \neq -1)$$

In Example 1, it is important to realize that the original restrictions on the variable $x \neq 1$ and $x \neq -1$, are still in effect even after the expression is simplified. That is,

$$\frac{x^2 + 10x + 9}{x^2 - 1} = \frac{x + 9}{x - 1} \quad \text{for } x \neq 1 \text{ and } x \neq -1.$$

3. Multiplying and Dividing Rational Expressions

To multiply two rational expressions, factor the numerator and denominator of both expressions. Then simplify common factors that form a ratio of 1.

Example 2 **Multiplying Rational Expressions**

Multiply and simplify the result. $\dfrac{2x-4}{4x+4}\cdot\dfrac{2x^2-7x-4}{x^2-6x+8}$

Solution:

$$\frac{2x-4}{4x+4}\cdot\frac{2x^2-7x-4}{x^2-6x+8}=\frac{2(x-2)}{4(x+1)}\cdot\frac{(2x+1)(x-4)}{(x-4)(x-2)}$$ Factor.

$$=\frac{\overset{1}{\cancel{2}}\overset{1}{\cancel{(x-2)}}}{\cancel{2}\cdot 2(x+1)}\cdot\frac{(2x+1)\overset{1}{\cancel{(x-4)}}}{\cancel{(x-4)}\cancel{(x-2)}}$$ Simplify ratios of 1.

$$=\frac{2x+1}{2(x+1)}$$

TIP: In the expression $\dfrac{2x+1}{2(x+1)}$, do not try to "cancel" the 2's. The 2 in the numerator is not a factor of the numerator.

To divide two rational expressions, multiply the first expression by the reciprocal of the second expression.

Example 3 **Dividing Rational Expressions**

Divide and simplify. $\dfrac{-x^2+x}{-x^2}\div\dfrac{3x^2+2x-5}{5x}$

Solution:

$$\frac{-x^2+x}{-x^2}\div\frac{3x^2+2x-5}{5x}=\frac{-x^2+x}{-x^2}\cdot\frac{5x}{3x^2+2x-5}$$ Multiply the first expression by the reciprocal of the second.

$$=\frac{-x(x-1)}{-x\cdot x}\cdot\frac{5x}{(3x+5)(x-1)}$$ Factor.

$$=\frac{\overset{1}{\cancel{(-x)}}\overset{1}{\cancel{(x-1)}}}{\cancel{(-x)}\cdot \cancel{x}}\cdot\frac{5\overset{1}{\cancel{x}}}{(3x+5)\cancel{(x-1)}}$$ Simplify ratios of 1.

$$=\frac{5}{3x+5}$$

4. Adding and Subtracting Rational Expressions

To add or subtract a rational expression it is necessary that the expressions have a common denominator. To add or subtract expressions with a common denominator add or subtract the terms in the numerators and write the result over the common denominator. Then simplify the expression to lowest terms if possible.

Example 4 Subtracting Rational Expressions with a Common Denominator

Subtract. $\frac{x^2 - 2x}{x - 5} - \frac{8x - 25}{x - 5}$

Solution:

$$\frac{x^2 - 2x}{x - 5} - \frac{8x - 25}{x - 5} = \frac{x^2 - 2x - (8x - 25)}{x - 5}$$

Subtract terms in the numerator. Use parentheses to help you remember to subtract both terms in the numerator of the second expression.

$$= \frac{x^2 - 2x - 8x + 25}{x - 5}$$

Apply the distributive property.

$$= \frac{x^2 - 10x + 25}{x - 5}$$

Combine *like* terms.

$$= \frac{\cancel{(x - 5)}(x - 5)}{\cancel{x - 5}}$$

Factor and simplify.

$$= x - 5$$

To add or subtract two rational expressions that do not have a common denominator, it is necessary to convert each expression to an equivalent rational expression with a common denominator. The steps below outline the process to find the least common denominator of two or more rational expressions.

Finding the LCD of Two or More Rational Expressions

Step 1 Factor all denominators completely.

Step 2 The LCD is the product of unique factors from the denominators, where each factor is raised to the highest power to which it appears in any denominator.

For example, the LCD of the expressions $\frac{2}{5x^2y^4}$ and $\frac{1}{7x^3y}$ is given by the product: $5^1 \cdot 7^1 \cdot x^3 \cdot y^4 = 35x^3y^4$.

To convert a rational expression to an equivalent expression with a common denominator, we multiply the numerator and denominator by the factors in the LCD that are missing from the denominator of the original expression. This is mathematically feasible because we are multiplying the original expression by 1. For example, we convert $\frac{2}{5x^2y^4}$ and $\frac{1}{7x^3y}$ to equivalent expressions with a denominator of $35x^3y^4$ as follows.

$$\frac{2}{5x^2y^4} = \frac{2 \cdot 7x}{5x^2y^4 \cdot 7x} = \frac{14x}{35x^3y^4} \qquad \text{Note that } \frac{7x}{7x} = 1.$$

$$\frac{1}{7x^3y} = \frac{1 \cdot 5y^3}{7x^3y \cdot 5y^3} = \frac{5y^3}{35x^3y^4} \qquad \text{Note that } \frac{5y^3}{5y^3} = 1.$$

Example 5 **Subtracting Two Rational Expressions with Different Denominators**

Subtract the rational expressions. $\dfrac{3x}{x^2 + 7x + 10} - \dfrac{2x}{x^2 + 6x + 8}$

Solution:

$$\frac{3x}{x^2 + 7x + 10} - \frac{2x}{x^2 + 6x + 8}$$

$$= \frac{3x}{(x + 2)(x + 5)} - \frac{2x}{(x + 4)(x + 2)}$$

Factor the denominators. The LCD is $(x + 2)(x + 5)(x + 4)$.

$$= \frac{3x(x + 4)}{(x + 2)(x + 5)(x + 4)} - \frac{2x(x + 5)}{(x + 4)(x + 2)(x + 5)}$$

Convert each expression to an equivalent expression with the LCD.

$$= \frac{3x(x + 4) - 2x(x + 5)}{(x + 2)(x + 5)(x + 4)}$$

Subtract the numerators.

$$= \frac{3x^2 + 12x - 2x^2 - 10x}{(x + 2)(x + 5)(x + 4)}$$

Apply the distributive property.

$$= \frac{x^2 + 2x}{(x + 2)(x + 5)(x + 4)}$$

Combine *like* terms.

$$= \frac{x\overset{1}{\cancel{(x + 2)}}}{\cancel{(x + 2)}(x + 5)(x + 4)}$$

Factor and simplify.

$$= \frac{x}{(x + 5)(x + 4)}$$

5. Simplifying Complex Fractions

A complex fraction is a fraction whose numerator or denominator contains one or more rational expressions. For example:

$$\frac{1 - \dfrac{4}{3y}}{y - \dfrac{16}{9y}}$$

One method to simplify such an expression is to multiply the numerator and denominator of the complex fraction by the LCD of all four individual fractions. This is demonstrated in Example 6.

Example 6 Simplifying a Complex Fraction

Simplify. $\dfrac{1 - \dfrac{4}{3y}}{y - \dfrac{16}{9y}}$

Solution:

$\dfrac{1 - \dfrac{4}{3y}}{y - \dfrac{16}{9y}}$ The LCD of the expressions $\dfrac{1}{1}, \dfrac{4}{3y}, \dfrac{y}{1}$, and $\dfrac{16}{9y}$ is $9y$.

$$\frac{1 - \dfrac{4}{3y}}{y - \dfrac{16}{9y}} = \frac{9y\left(1 - \dfrac{4}{3y}\right)}{9y\left(y - \dfrac{16}{9y}\right)} = \frac{(9y)\cdot 1 - (9y)\cdot \dfrac{4}{3y}}{(9y)\cdot y - (9y)\cdot \dfrac{16}{9y}}$$ Apply the distributive property.

$$= \frac{9y - 12}{9y^2 - 16}$$ Simplify.

$$= \frac{3\overset{1}{\cancel{(3y - 4)}}}{\cancel{(3y - 4)}(3y + 4)}$$ Factor and reduce to lowest terms.

$$= \frac{3}{3y + 4}$$

The expression in Example 6 could also have been simplified by using the order of operations to combine the expressions in the numerator and denominator separately and then dividing the resulting expressions.

6. Solving Rational Equations

An equation with one or more rational expressions is called a rational equation. To solve a rational equation, we offer the following steps.

Solving a Rational Equation

Step 1 Factor the denominators of all rational expressions. Identify the restricted values.

Step 2 Identify the LCD of all expressions in the equation.

Step 3 Multiply both sides of the equation by the LCD.

Step 4 Solve the resulting equation.

Step 5 Check potential solutions in the original equation.

Example 7 **Solving a Rational Equation**

Solve. $\dfrac{4}{y-4} + \dfrac{y}{2} = \dfrac{y}{y-4}$

Solution:

$$\frac{4}{y-4} + \frac{y}{2} = \frac{y}{y-4}$$

Step 1: The denominators are already factored. Note that $y \neq 4$.

$$2(y-4)\left(\frac{4}{y-4} + \frac{y}{2}\right) = 2(y-4)\left(\frac{y}{y-4}\right)$$

Step 2: The LCD is $2(y - 4)$.

Step 3: Multiply by the LCD.

$$\frac{2(y-4)}{1} \cdot \left(\frac{4}{y-4}\right) + \frac{2(y-4)}{1} \cdot \frac{y}{2} = \frac{2(y-4)}{1} \cdot \left(\frac{y}{y-4}\right)$$

Apply the distributive property.

$$2 \cdot 4 + (y-4) \cdot y = 2 \cdot y$$

Step 4: Solve the resulting equation.

$$8 + y^2 - 4y = 2y$$

Apply the distributive property to clear parentheses.

$$y^2 - 4y - 2y + 8 = 0$$

The equation is quadratic. Set the equation equal to zero.

$$y^2 - 6y + 8 = 0$$

$$(y-4)(y-2) = 0$$

Factor.

$$y - 4 = 0 \quad \text{or} \quad y - 2 = 0$$

Set each factor equal to zero.

$$y = 4 \quad \text{or} \quad y = 2$$

Step 5: Check each potential solution.

Check $y = 4$:

$$\frac{4}{(4)-4} + \frac{(4)}{2} \stackrel{?}{=} \frac{(4)}{(4)-4}$$

$$\frac{4}{0} + \frac{4}{2} \stackrel{?}{=} \frac{4}{0} \text{ (Undefined)}$$

Check $y = 2$:

$$\frac{4}{(2)-4} + \frac{(2)}{2} \stackrel{?}{=} \frac{(2)}{(2)-4}$$

$$\frac{4}{-2} + 1 \stackrel{?}{=} \frac{2}{-2}$$

$$-2 + 1 = -1 \checkmark$$

The solution set is {2}. The value $y = 4$ does not check because it makes the denominator zero in one or more of the rational expressions.

TIP: Before solving a rational equation you might consider noting any values of the variable for which the equation is undefined. In Example 7, the equation $\dfrac{4}{y-4} + \dfrac{y}{2} = \dfrac{y}{y-4}$ is not defined for $y = 4$ because this value makes the denominator zero in the first and third rational expressions. If one of your potential solutions matches a restricted value, then you automatically know that this value cannot be a solution to the original equation.

Section B.10 Practice Exercises

For Exercises 1–6, determine the restricted values of the expression.

1. $\dfrac{x+2}{x+4}$ $x \neq -4$

2. $\dfrac{x-5}{x-1}$ $x \neq 1$

3. $\dfrac{2x}{25x^2 - 9}$ $x \neq \frac{3}{5}$ and $x \neq -\frac{3}{5}$

4. $\dfrac{5y}{4y^2 - 49}$ $y \neq \frac{7}{2}$ and $y \neq -\frac{7}{2}$

5. $\dfrac{t-7}{8}$ There are no restricted values.

6. $\dfrac{x+2}{5}$ There are no restricted values.

Writing ↔ Translating Expression Geometry Scientific Calculator Video

For Exercises 7–12, simplify the expression to lowest terms.

7. $\dfrac{3x^4y^7}{12xy^8}$ $\quad \dfrac{x^3}{4y}$

8. $\dfrac{21ab^5}{7a^3b^4}$ $\quad \dfrac{3b}{a^2}$

9. $\dfrac{t^2 - 4}{2t - 4}$ $\quad \dfrac{t + 2}{2}$

10. $\dfrac{m^2 - 9}{3m - 9}$ $\quad \dfrac{m + 3}{3}$

11. $\dfrac{2y^2 + 5y - 12}{2y^2 + y - 6}$ $\quad \dfrac{y + 4}{y + 2}$

12. $\dfrac{2x^2 + 20x + 48}{4x^2 - 144}$ $\quad \dfrac{x + 4}{2(x - 6)}$

For Exercises 13–22, multiply or divide as indicated and simplify.

13. $\dfrac{2x}{15y^2} \cdot \dfrac{3y^5}{4x^2}$ $\quad \dfrac{y^3}{10x}$

14. $\dfrac{4s^2t}{8t^3} \cdot \dfrac{2t^5}{6s^4}$ $\quad \dfrac{t^3}{6s^2}$

15. $\dfrac{5y - 15}{10y + 40} \cdot \dfrac{2y^2 + y - 28}{2y^2 - 13y + 21}$ $\quad \dfrac{1}{2}$

16. $\dfrac{x^2 - 36}{x^2 - 4x - 12} \cdot \dfrac{4x + 8}{4x - 24}$ $\quad \dfrac{x + 6}{x - 6}$

17. $\dfrac{a^2b^3}{5c^2} \div \dfrac{ab}{15c^3}$ $\quad 3ab^2c$

18. $\dfrac{m^3}{14n^5} \div \dfrac{m^7}{21n}$ $\quad \dfrac{3}{2m^4n^4}$

19. $\dfrac{p^2 - 36}{2p - 4} \div \dfrac{2p + 12}{p^2 - 2p}$ $\quad \dfrac{p(p - 6)}{4}$

20. $\dfrac{y^2 + y}{y^2 - y - 12} \div \dfrac{5y + 5}{y^2 - 5y + 4}$ $\quad \dfrac{y(y - 1)}{5(y + 3)}$

21. $\dfrac{t^2 + 7t}{3 - t} \div \dfrac{t^2 - 49}{t^2 - 3t}$ $\quad -\dfrac{t^2}{t - 7}$

22. $\dfrac{x^2 - 2x}{2 - x} \div \dfrac{x^2 + 5x}{x^2 - 25}$ $\quad -(x - 5)$

For Exercises 23–26, find the LCD for each pair of expressions.

23. $\dfrac{1}{4x^3y^7}, \dfrac{1}{8xy^{10}}$ $\quad 8x^3y^{10}$

24. $\dfrac{1}{16ab^4}, \dfrac{1}{24a^2b^2}$ $\quad 48a^2b^4$

25. $\dfrac{1}{x^2 - x - 12}, \dfrac{1}{x^2 - 9}$ $\quad (x - 4)(x + 3)(x - 3)$

26. $\dfrac{1}{x^2 + 10x + 9}, \dfrac{1}{x^2 - 81}$ $\quad (x + 1)(x + 9)(x - 9)$

For Exercises 27–40, add or subtract as indicated.

27. $\dfrac{1}{2x} - \dfrac{5}{6x}$ $\quad -\dfrac{1}{3x}$

28. $\dfrac{7}{15t} - \dfrac{4}{5t}$ $\quad -\dfrac{1}{3t}$

29. $\dfrac{1}{2x^3y} + \dfrac{5}{4xy^2}$ $\quad \dfrac{5x^2 + 2y}{4x^3y^2}$

30. $\dfrac{1}{3a^2b^4} + \dfrac{7}{9a^2b}$ $\quad \dfrac{7b^3 + 3}{9a^2b^4}$

31. $\dfrac{x^2}{x - 7} - \dfrac{14x - 49}{x - 7}$ $\quad x - 7$

32. $\dfrac{z^2}{z - 10} - \dfrac{20z - 100}{z - 10}$ $\quad z - 10$

33. $\dfrac{7x}{4x - 2} + \dfrac{5x}{2x - 1}$ $\quad \dfrac{17x}{2(2x - 1)}$

34. $\dfrac{-8}{5x + 4} + \dfrac{7}{10x + 8}$ $\quad \dfrac{-9}{2(5x + 4)}$

35. $\dfrac{x}{x^2 + x - 12} - \dfrac{2}{x^2 + 3x - 4}$ $\quad \dfrac{x^2 - 3x + 6}{(x + 4)(x - 3)(x - 1)}$

36. $\dfrac{4y}{y^2 - 4y + 4} + \dfrac{3}{y^2 - 7y + 10}$ $\quad \dfrac{4y^2 - 17y - 6}{(y - 2)^2(y - 5)}$

37. $\dfrac{-3}{y - 2} + \dfrac{2y + 11}{y^2 + y - 6} - \dfrac{2}{y + 3}$ $\quad \dfrac{-3}{y + 3}$

38. $\dfrac{-2}{x + 2} + \dfrac{x}{x - 1} + \dfrac{3x - 6}{x^2 + x - 2}$ $\quad \dfrac{x + 4}{x + 2}$

39. $\dfrac{5}{x - 3} - \dfrac{x + 2}{x - 3}$ $\quad -1$

40. $\dfrac{3x}{x + 2} - \dfrac{4x + 2}{x + 2}$ $\quad -1$

For Exercises 41–48, simplify the complex fractions.

41. $\dfrac{\frac{3}{a}+\frac{4}{b}}{\frac{7}{a}-\frac{1}{b}}$ $\frac{3b+4a}{7b-a}$

42. $\dfrac{\frac{2}{p}-\frac{4}{q}}{\frac{2}{p}+\frac{1}{q}}$ $\frac{2(q-2p)}{2q+p}$

43. $\dfrac{8x-\frac{1}{2x}}{1-\frac{1}{4x}}$ $2(4x+1)$

44. $\dfrac{\frac{1}{2}-\frac{1}{2t}}{1-\frac{1}{t^2}}$ $\frac{t}{2(t+1)}$

45. $\dfrac{\frac{u^2-v^2}{uv}}{\frac{u+v}{uv}}$ $u-v$

46. $\dfrac{\frac{a^2-b^2}{ab}}{\frac{2a-2b}{ab}}$ $\frac{a+b}{2}$

47. $\dfrac{\frac{1}{y-5}}{\frac{2}{y+5}+\frac{1}{y^2-25}}$ $\frac{y+5}{2y-9}$

48. $\dfrac{\frac{3}{x+1}}{\frac{2}{x^2-1}+\frac{1}{x-1}}$ $\frac{3(x-1)}{x+3}$

For Exercises 49–56, solve the equation.

49. $\frac{1}{8}-\frac{3}{4x}=\frac{1}{2x}$ $\{10\}$

50. $\frac{3}{10}-\frac{4}{5x}=\frac{1}{x}$ $\{6\}$

51. $\frac{5}{x-3}=\frac{2}{x-3}$ $\{\ \}$

52. $\frac{6}{x+2}=\frac{4}{x+2}$ $\{\ \}$

53. $1+\frac{6}{x}=-\frac{8}{x^2}$ $\{-2,-4\}$

54. $1=\frac{8}{x}-\frac{15}{x^2}$ $\{3,5\}$

55. $\frac{4x+11}{x^2-4}-\frac{5}{x+2}=\frac{2x}{x^2-4}$ $\{7\}$

56. $\frac{3x}{x+1}-2=\frac{12}{x^2-1}$ $\{5,-2\}$

Perimeter and Circumference

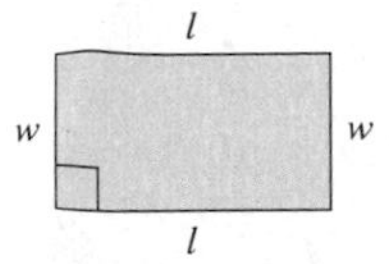

Rectangle

$P = 2l + 2w$

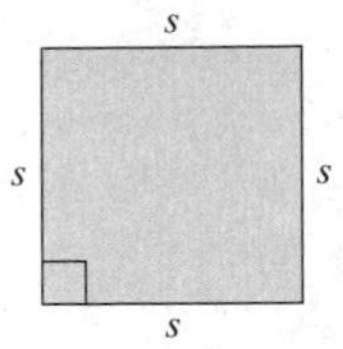

Square

$P = 4s$

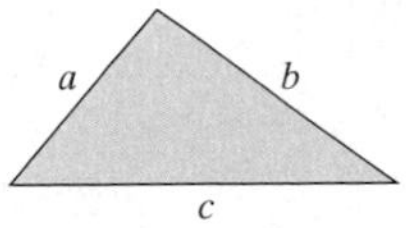

Triangle

$P = a + b + c$

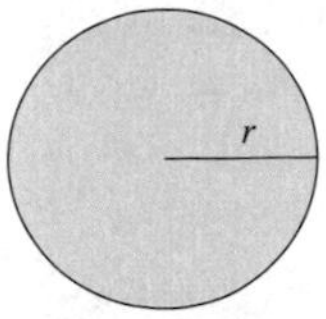

Circle

Circumference: $C = 2\pi r$

Area

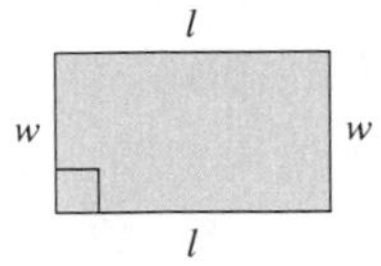

Rectangle

$A = lw$

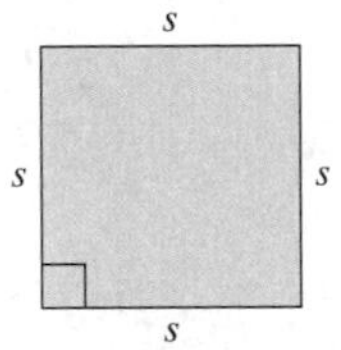

Square

$A = s^2$

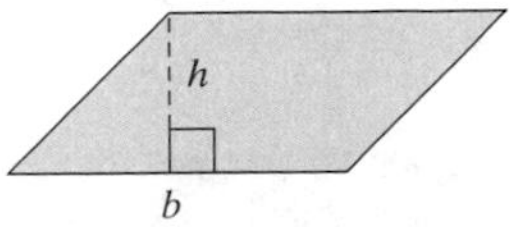

Parallelogram

$A = bh$

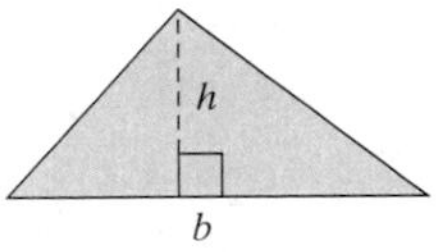

Triangle

$A = \frac{1}{2}bh$

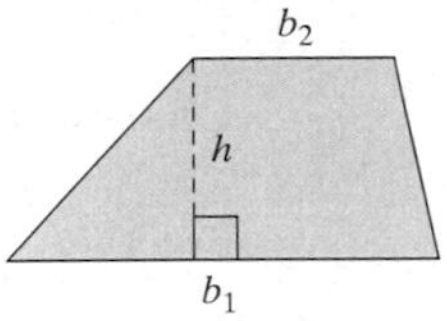

Trapezoid

$A = \frac{1}{2}(b_1 + b_2)h$

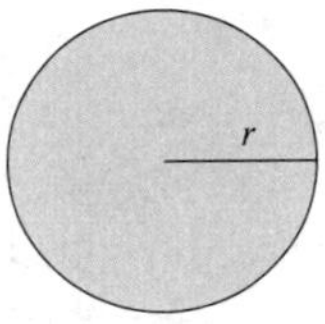

Circle

$A = \pi r^2$

Volume

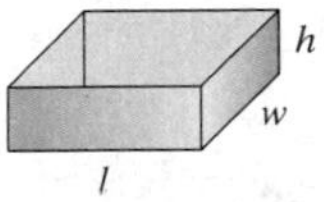

Rectangular Solid

$V = lwh$

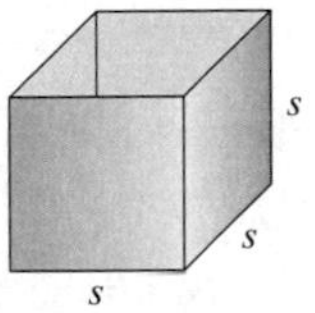

Cube

$V = s^3$

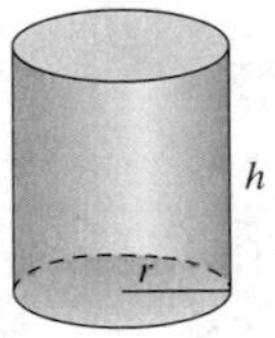

Right Circular Cylinder

$V = \pi r^2 h$

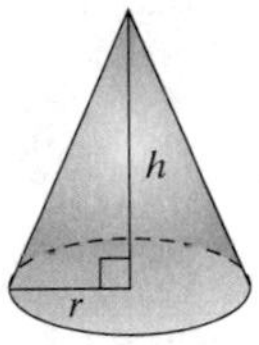

Right Circular Cone

$V = \frac{1}{3}\pi r^2 h$

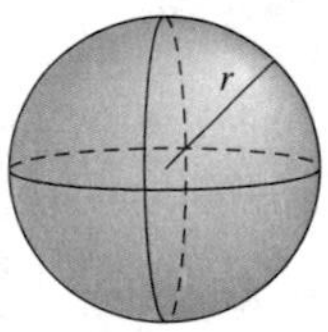

Sphere

$V = \frac{4}{3}\pi r^3$

Angles

- Two angles are **complementary** if the sum of their measures is 90°.

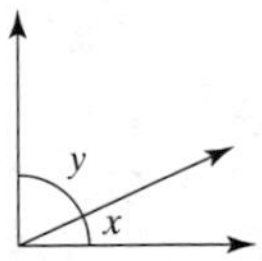

- Two angles are **supplementary** if the sum of their measures is 180°.

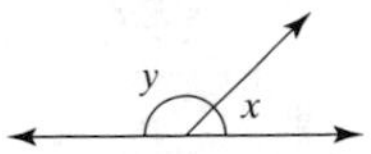

- $\angle a$ and $\angle c$ are vertical angles, and $\angle b$ and $\angle d$ are vertical angles. The measures of vertical angles are equal.

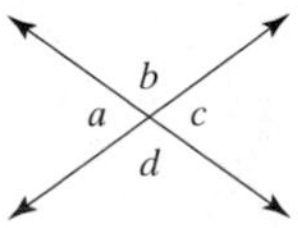

- The sum of the measures of the angles of a triangle is 180°.

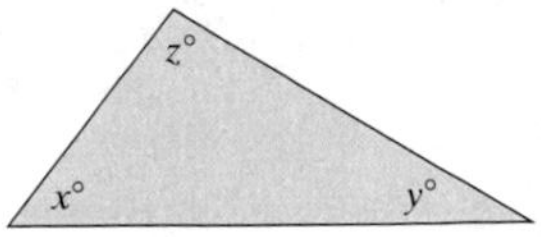

$x° + y° + z° = 180°$

Linear Equations and Slope

The slope, m, of a line between two distinct points (x_1, y_1) and (x_2, y_2):

$$m = \frac{y_2 - y_1}{x_2 - x_1}, \quad x_2 - x_1 \neq 0$$

Standard form: $Ax + By = C$, (A and B are not both zero.)

Horizontal line: $y = k$

Vertical line: $x = k$

Slope intercept form: $y = mx + b$

Point-slope formula: $y - y_1 = m(x - x_1)$

Midpoint Formula

Given two points (x_1, y_1) and (x_2, y_2), the midpoint is

$$\left(\frac{x_1 + x_2}{2}, \frac{y_1 + y_2}{2}\right)$$

Properties and Definitions of Exponents

Let a and b $(b \neq 0)$ represent real numbers and m and n represent positive integers.

$$b^m b^n = b^{m+n}; \qquad \frac{b^m}{b^n} = b^{m-n}; \qquad (b^m)^n = b^{mn};$$

$$(ab)^m = a^m b^m; \qquad \left(\frac{a}{b}\right)^m = \frac{a^m}{b^m}; \qquad b^0 = 1; \qquad b^{-n} = \left(\frac{1}{b}\right)^n$$

The Quadratic Formula

The solutions to $ax^2 + bx + c = 0$ $(a \neq 0)$ are given by

$$x = \frac{-b \pm \sqrt{b^2 - 4ac}}{2a}$$

The Vertex Formula

For $f(x) = ax^2 + bx + c$ $(a \neq 0)$, the vertex is

$$\left(\frac{-b}{2a}, \frac{4ac - b^2}{4a}\right) \quad \text{or} \quad \left(\frac{-b}{2a}, f\left(\frac{-b}{2a}\right)\right)$$

The Distance Formula

The distance between two points (x_1, y_1) and (x_2, y_2) is
$d = \sqrt{(x_2 - x_1)^2 + (y_2 - y_1)^2}$

The Standard Form of a Circle

$(x - h)^2 + (y - k)^2 = r^2$ with center (h, k) and radius r

Properties of Logarithms

Let b, x, and y be positive real numbers where $b \neq 1$, and let p be a real number. Then the following properties are true.

1. $\log_b 1 = 0$
2. $\log_b b = 1$
3. $\log_b(b^p) = p$
4. $b^{\log_b(x)} = x$
5. $\log_b(xy) = \log_b x + \log_b y$
6. $\log_b\left(\frac{x}{y}\right) = \log_b x - \log_b y$
7. $\log_b(x^p) = p \log_b x$

Change-of-Base Formula:

$$\log_b x = \frac{\log_a x}{\log_a b} \quad a > 0, a \neq 1, b > 0, b \neq 1$$

Properties and Definitions of Radicals

Let a be a real number and n be an integer such that $n > 1$. If $\sqrt[n]{a}$ exists, then

$$a^{1/n} = \sqrt[n]{a}; \qquad a^{m/n} = (\sqrt[n]{a})^m = \sqrt[n]{a^m}$$

Let a and b represent real numbers such that $\sqrt[n]{a}$ and $\sqrt[n]{b}$ are both real. Then

$\sqrt[n]{ab} = \sqrt[n]{a} \cdot \sqrt[n]{b}$ Multiplication property

$\sqrt[n]{\frac{a}{b}} = \frac{\sqrt[n]{a}}{\sqrt[n]{b}}$ Division property

The Pythagorean Theorem:

$a^2 + b^2 = c^2$

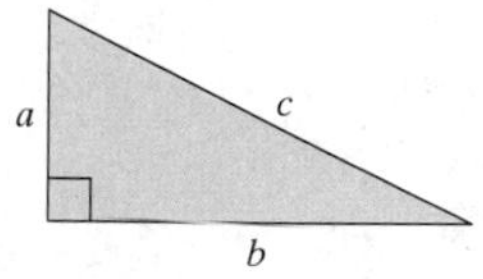